Nuclear Interactions

Nuclear Interactions

SERGIO DeBENEDETTI

Professor of Physics, Carnegie Institute of Technology

John Wiley & Sons, Inc., New York · London · Sydney

Library of Congress Catalog Card Number: 64-13215
Printed in the United States of America

PREFACE

It is customary to start the preface of a book with a statement of purpose. Why was the book written and for whom?

If I want to be honest about these matters I must confess that the present book has had a selfish motivation. I have written it exclusively for my own benefit. If a book like this had existed, I should have been very glad to read it and I should have been saved the bother of writing it myself.

The book I wanted to read was one on nuclear interactions (not on nuclear physics) containing a description of the basic facts and a clear presentation of the theory in sufficient detail to be understandable to the experimentalist.

But I came to realize that, with a few exceptions, books on nuclear physics and on elementary particles were written either by experimentalists for experimentalists or by theoreticians for theoreticians for the purpose of teaching techniques rather than facts.

It is indeed natural that theoretical books should be devoted to the foundation of the theories and the technical developments of the formalisms. Consequently, they often fail to give a coherent account of the experimental results and of the physical laws. The derivation of the formulas which are directly comparable to observation is often left as an exercise for the reader. The implication is that the reader should have all the time at his disposal for this purpose: in other words, that he should not be busy designing or running experiments.

That is why I decided to write the book myself. If I had to interrupt my own work, I should at least save others the same trouble.

My aim has been to be as clear and simple as possible without leaving out any of the essential parts of the subject matter and its interpretation. I found that in order to fulfill this unusual purpose the treatment had to be complete and consistent. I had to start from a review of the basic principles, introducing my notation unambiguously. As a result, I have been led to include sections and chapters that are not usually found in a book on nuclear interactions but that were needed as references for the main part of the treatment. I have chosen to be complete in the explanation of selected material rather than to attempt a systematic coverage of the literature. References are included only for the purpose of illustration and clarification and are not complete. I know that this is bound to displease many, and I appeal for forgiveness to the authors whose names have been left out.

I have tried to report all the logical links: no postulate is introduced without presenting the experimental evidence from which it originated and no formula is written without proof. In the derivations I have chosen to exaggerate algebraic detail rather than to fall into the usual sin of leaving too much to the reader. Thus the forbidding aspect of some pages full of formulas actually testifies that the book is elementary and easy to read. Those who do not like to follow the algebraic details can skip them and read only the intuitive discussions that always explain the meaning of the formalism.

Despite my selfish motivation, I hope that my work may be interesting and helpful to others. I am sure that there are many professional nuclear experimentalists who may appreciate a source of more complete and more accessible presentation of the theory.

And, of course, I hope that the book may be useful to students. In the form of notes it has been used for several years in my graduate class, and the subject matter has been selected to fit the particular needs of our Institution: my students have already had several courses in quantum mechanics, and they are preparing themselves for research work in low- and high-energy physics, either as experimentalists or as theoreticians. It is my opinion that a serious discussion of nuclear interactions will be more useful to them than a specialized course in any one of the fields to which they will devote themselves. After this course they should be prepared to read without excessive effort the literature of the physics of nuclei and of elementary particles.

Having been written by an experimentalist, the theoretical discussions initially contained more than the average number of errors. An honest and not indifferent amount of work has gone into the correction of the manuscript, and the number of mistakes found has decreased exponentially with time. Given infinite time, it can probably be reduced to zero.

Though I must assume responsibility for the errors that are left, it is my pleasure to acknowledge with gratitude the advice and constructive criticism that I have received from many of my friends. To make a partial list of them, I can mention J. Ashkin, M. Baranger, R. E. Cutkosky, Ugo Fano, V. Gillet, P. K. Kabir, G. Lang, J. Langer, R. Sorensen, and L. Wolfenstein.

I am grateful to the students of my graduate classes who have seen this treatment grow, year after year, from a set of embryonic notes to the present form and who have suffered in the first stages from the many imperfections of the presentation. Their help in checking and proofreading the manuscript is recognized; in particular, I want to express my thanks to M. Victor Namias, Ingénieur de l'Ecole Polytechnique de Bruxelles, who has gone over much of the algebra with admirable thoroughness and patience.

I also want to acknowledge the help of many of the secretaries of our Physics Department who have assisted in many ways in the preparation of the manuscript. In particular, in the last stages, the work of Mrs. L. Horton, who, besides doing much of the typing, has taken care of editing the figures and footnotes, has been very valuable. I would also like to extend my thanks to the staff of John Wiley & Sons for their competent help in the preparation of the manuscript for the printer.

Finally, I want to mention that during the years of studying and writing that have preceded the completion of this book I have been awarded research grants and contracts from the National Science Foundation, the Office of Naval Research, and the U. S. Air Force. Despite the fact that a large part of my time was devoted to the book, I have maintained a constant and active interest in the research done under the sponsorship of these agencies and have spent a good deal of time in advising and administering in connection with it. The experimental work has been carried on under the immediate supervision of my collaborators, such as Dr. S. Jha, and of my younger colleagues, Dr. Lang, Dr. Ingalls, and Dr. Barros, whose competent attention has resulted in excellent progress. However, my participation in the research has been less direct than it would have been otherwise, and my name has not appeared in many of the publications of the results. I trust that the sponsoring agencies will share my opinion that the writing of this book has been a worthwhile activity that, in the long run, will contribute to their aims of scientific advancement more effectively than any other use of my time and efforts. With this in mind, I wish to express my gratitude to these agencies for their generosity and understanding.

S. DEBENEDETTI

Pittsburgh, Pennsylvania
March 1964

CONTENTS

CHAPTER 6 RELATIVISTIC INTERACTION BETWEEN FERMIONS AND RADIATION, 360

ONE

General Properties of Nuclear Forces

1.1 Nonrelativistic Conservation Laws and the Symmetries of Space and Time

1.11 Introduction

a. The Problem of Nuclear Interactions. Though nuclear effects are not readily apparent in our immediate surroundings, they have been of essential importance in determining the basic nature of the world in which we live. The formation and the abundance of the atomic species, the evolution of the universe, the energy liberated in the stars, the temperature of the earth, and many other such fundamental questions are directly related to nuclear phenomena. We can therefore say that an understanding of nuclear physics is necessary to our understanding of nature.

The nucleus, however, is remote. It is hidden in the center of the atom, protected—so to say—by the electronic shells, and considerable energy is required to probe its behavior. This is the reason why natural nuclear phenomena at present do not play a significant role on the surface of our planet and have not influenced the lives of primitive men. Therefore our intuition cannot be applied to nuclear physics. Both the subject and the methods of this discipline do not belong naturally to man and to the earth, but rather to what the ancients called the heavens. The fascination of probing such profound and recondite matters has led to the formation of a hieratic class and of a hieroglyphic script which is difficult to vulgarize for the use of the layman. The secrecy, however, is not intentional and the knowledge of any one person is limited only by his own desire and capacity to learn. The purpose of the present treatment is to help the willing student along the arduous path toward our very partial knowledge of nuclear matter and of nuclear matters.

The first nuclear effect to be discovered by man on earth (the man was Becquerel, the time 1896) was natural radioactivity, a weak remainder of the times when the world was being formed. In the years after this discovery progress in the understanding of nuclear processes was slow, compared with the advances in our knowledge of the atomic system, whose problems were effectively solved in the first half of the twentieth century.

But the development of atomic physics was essential to open the possibility for a study of nuclear structure. This was not only because of the position occupied by the nucleus at the center of the atom, but—more basically important—because in atomic physics we have developed a method of thinking and a mathematical apparatus—the formalism of quantum mechanics—which is surely necessary, and we hope sufficient, for an understanding of the nucleus. In other words, we can say that atomic physics has provided us with the logical tools to proceed in a field in which our intuition is of no help.

But the physicist who studies the structure of the nucleus faces a problem that is in a sense quite different from the classical problem of atomic physics. At the beginning of the study of the atom we already knew the forces acting within the atomic system: essentially electromagnetic and almost exclusively electrostatic forces. What was not known were the laws of mechanics needed to treat such forces on a microscopic scale.

In nuclear physics, instead, the situation is reversed: we may know the laws of mechanics—relativistic quantum mechanics—but we are ignorant of the forces. The fundamental problem of nuclear physics is to find the forces between the nuclear particles, and this book is mainly a description of our limited successes in their investigation.

Keeping this purpose in mind, we shall gloss over the modelistic in nuclear structure (Chapter 2) and in nuclear reactions (Chapter 5) and concentrate our attention on nuclear interactions which are the basic problem of nature.

b. The Laws of Force and the Conservation Principles. Nuclear interactions seem to be complex. Though this impression may be due to our limited understanding, it is certain that they exhibit many different features, such as spin dependence, tensor character, and exchange nature. Our investigation of nuclear forces has led to so many surprises that we might have the feeling that "anything can happen." It is therefore useful to limit the number of things that "may happen" according to some general principles. These principles are the conservation laws, or the equivalent invariances and symmetries of space time.

For historical as well as for didactical reasons we concern ourselves in the first part of this book with "low-energy" nuclear physics. Relativistic effects are not important in the low energy range and enter at most as a small correction. We shall therefore discuss at this point the conservation principles in a nonrelativistic manner. The subject of conservation principles and of space-time symmetries is considered relativistically in the second part of the book.

I.12 Conservation of Energy and Momentum and the Homogeneity of Space Time

a. Conservation of Energy. Classically, the law of conservation of energy states that *the total energy E of an isolated system is constant in time:*

$$\frac{dE}{dt} = 0. \tag{1}$$

In quantum mechanics the time derivative of an operator $\mathcal{O}$ can be expressed by using the commutator with the Hamiltonian $\mathcal{H}$ of the system

$$\frac{d\mathcal{O}}{dt} = \frac{1}{i\hbar}(\mathcal{O}\mathcal{H} - \mathcal{H}\mathcal{O}) + \frac{\partial \mathcal{O}}{\partial t}, \tag{2}$$

where i is the imaginary unit and $\hbar$ is Planck's constant divided by 2π. Since the energy E corresponds to the operator $i\hbar\,(\partial/\partial t)$,

$$E \to i\hbar \frac{\partial}{\partial t}, \tag{3}$$

which does not contain the time explicitly, (1) can be written as

$$\frac{\partial}{\partial t}\mathcal{H} - \mathcal{H}\frac{\partial}{\partial t} = 0. \tag{4}$$

Thus the law of conservation of energy is equivalent to the statement that *the Hamiltonian of an isolated system must not contain the time variable explicitly.*

This is equivalent to saying that *the laws of motion and of interaction do not depend on time* or that *an experiment performed in an isolated laboratory at a given time gives the same result as the same experiment performed in the same laboratory at a different time.*

Conservation of energy can be regarded as a property of space time: *the laws of physics are invariant under translations along the time axis.*

b. Conservation of Momentum. Classically, the conservation of the momentum vector refers to particles and to systems of particles to which no external force is applied. For the derivation of the law from the equations of motion we make use of Newton's third law, the principle of action and reaction, which is assumed to hold for each pair of interacting particles.

As a result of these assumptions, it is reasonable to expect that the location of the system does not affect its behavior and that the conservation of momentum corresponds to the fact that *the laws of physics are invariant under translations in space.*

This is immediately apparent for a single free particle, using quantum mechanical formalism.

Momentum is a vector **p** and its cartesian components are individually conserved: *the total momentum* **p** *of a system not subject to external forces is constant in time*

$$\frac{dp_i}{dt} = 0 \qquad p_i = p_x, p_y, p_z. \tag{5}$$

Transition to quantum mechanics is accomplished by writing (5) as

$$\frac{1}{i\hbar}(p_i\mathcal{H} - \mathcal{H}p_i) + \frac{\partial p_i}{\partial t} = 0 \tag{6}$$

and using

$$p_i \rightarrow -i\hbar\frac{\partial}{\partial x_i} \qquad x_i = x, y, z \tag{7}$$

so that (5) becomes

$$\frac{\partial}{\partial x_i}\mathcal{H} - \mathcal{H}\frac{\partial}{\partial x_i} = 0. \tag{8}$$

This is equivalent to saying that *the Hamiltonian of a free particle must not contain explicitly the position coordinates* or that we have *invariance under translation.*

Let us consider next the case of two interacting particles 1 and 2. Then we have, in absence of external forces,

$$\frac{d(p_{i1} + p_{i2})}{dt} = 0, \tag{9}$$

which, going over to quantum mechanics, leads to

$$\left(\frac{\partial}{\partial x_{i1}} + \frac{\partial}{\partial x_{i2}}\right)\mathcal{H} - \mathcal{H}\left(\frac{\partial}{\partial x_{i1}} + \frac{\partial}{\partial x_{i2}}\right) = 0. \tag{10}$$

This relation is satisfied if the classical Hamiltonian satisfies the differential equation

$$\left(\frac{\partial}{\partial x_{i1}} + \frac{\partial}{\partial x_{i2}}\right)\mathcal{H}(x_{i1}, x_{i2}, p_{i1}, p_{i2}) = 0, \tag{11}$$

or if $\mathcal{H}$ depends on the space variables through a potential

$$U = U(x_{i1} - x_{i2}). \tag{12}$$

Conservation of parity (see 1.15) further restricts (12) to

$$U = U\,(|x_{i1} - x_{i2}|). \tag{13}$$

This expression may be considered as a formulation of the third law of Newton. Though (12) and (13) contain the coordinates of the particles, they are invariant under translation of both particles, confirming that conservation of momentum corresponds to translational invariance.

c. Conservation of Mass and of Number of Particles. In a nonrelativistic theory the law of conservation of mass holds separately from the law of conservation of energy, and there is no mechanism to provide for creation and annihilation of particles.

Even in a nonrelativistic treatment[1] of nuclear physics, however, we must consider two exceptions to the conservation of mass and of particles. The first concerns the mass defects due to the binding energy of the particles within a nucleus. The second has to do with the nonconservation of the number of photons; these particles, which travel at the speed of light, are always "extremely relativistic" and must be allowed to appear and disappear even in a nonrelativistic treatment of their source.

1.13 Conservation of Orbital Angular Momentum and the Isotropy of Space

a. Conservation of Orbital Angular Momentum. In classical mechanics the orbital angular momentum of a particle is defined as[2]

$$\mathbf{L} = \mathbf{r} \times \mathbf{p} \tag{1a}$$

or

$$L_k = r_i p_j - r_j p_i \tag{1b}$$

(i, j, k is a cyclic permutation of 1, 2, 3).

The orbital angular momentum of a particle or of a system of particles is conserved if the forces are central: typically, this happens in planetary motion if we neglect the interaction between the magnetic moments of the celestial bodies as well as the quadrupole effects resulting from the polar flattening of the planets.

[1] By nonrelativistic treatment we mean one that does not make use of relativistic quantum mechanics, though we may occasionally use relativistic kinematics.

[2] Vector products are defined with the right-hand rule. The components are referred to a right-handed system of coordinates (x, y, z, x_1, x_2, x_3, or 1, 2, 3; see Fig. 1.13-1).

The situation is similar in quantum mechanics in which the orbital angular momentum

(2*a*) $$\mathbf{L} = -i\hbar\mathbf{r} \times \boldsymbol{\nabla}$$

or

(2*b*) $$L_k = -i\hbar\left(x_i\frac{\partial}{\partial x_j} - x_j\frac{\partial}{\partial x_i}\right)$$

is conserved for central potentials; typically, for particles with no intrinsic

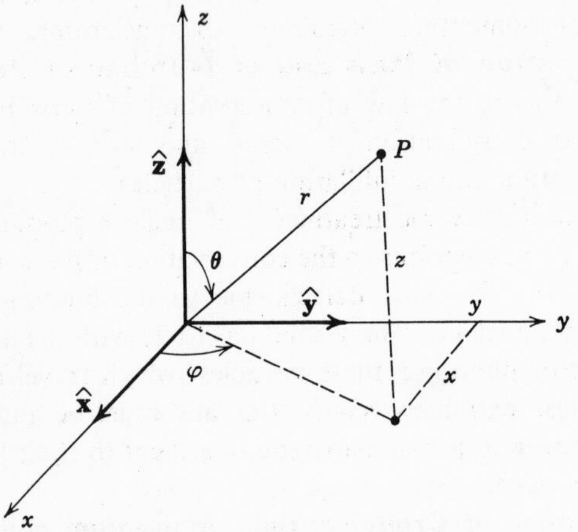

Fig. 1.13-1. Definition of cartesian and polar coordinates of a point P: $\hat{\mathbf{x}}$, $\hat{\mathbf{y}}$, and $\hat{\mathbf{z}}$ are unit vectors in the direction of the right-handed cartesian axes.

spins or, a little more formally, if the wave function of the particle is a scalar (one-valued) function of position.

Let us fix our attention on a component of the vector operator (2), say the z component, and introduce a system of polar coordinates (Fig. 1.13-1) with polar axis in the z direction. Then we have

(3) $$L_z = -i\hbar\frac{\partial}{\partial\varphi},$$

and conservation of angular momentum requires that

(4) $$\left(\frac{\partial}{\partial\varphi}\mathcal{H} - \mathcal{H}\frac{\partial}{\partial\varphi}\right) = 0,$$

which means that the Hamiltonian must be invariant under rotation.

Thus the *laws of motion do not depend on the orientation in space*, and *an experiment performed in an isolated laboratory yields the same result as the same experiment performed after a rotation of the laboratory.*

In other words, *space is isotropic*, besides being homogeneous, as required for the conservation of momentum.

b. Orbital Angular Momentum and Rotation Operators. In order to make the connection between angular momentum and rotations more precise, let us define an operator $R_A(\theta)$ which, when applied to any object, rotates the object through an angle θ around the axis A. (The sign of θ is positive if the rotation is right-handed around the positive direction of A; see Fig. 1.13-2).

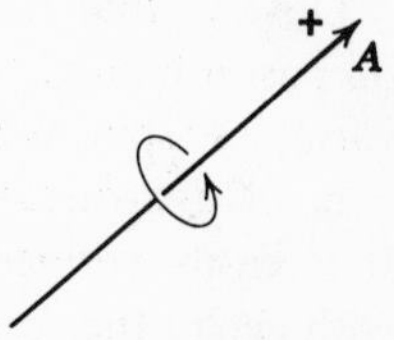

Fig. 1.13-2. Definition of the positive (right-handed) direction of rotation.

If the rotation is small, through an infinitesimal angle ε, the operator $R_A(\varepsilon)$ will be very close to the identity operator; furthermore, $R_A(\varepsilon) - 1$ will be proportional to ε. Thus we can define a differential operator J_A, which does not depend on the magnitude of ε, by the relation

$$R_A(\varepsilon) = 1 - \frac{i}{\hbar} J_A \varepsilon. \tag{5}$$

The factor $-i/\hbar$ is introduced to conform with (3). The operator J_A can be called the *differential rotation operator around the axis A*.

The rotation operator for a finite angle $\theta = N\varepsilon$ (N large), can be obtained by repeated application of $R_A(\varepsilon)$; thus

$$\begin{aligned} R_A(\theta) &= \left(1 - \frac{iJ_A}{\hbar}\varepsilon\right)^N = \left(1 - \frac{iJ_A}{\hbar}\varepsilon\right)^{\theta/\varepsilon} \\ \to \exp\left(-\frac{iJ_A}{\hbar}\theta\right) &= 1 - i\theta\frac{J_A}{\hbar} - \frac{\theta^2}{2}\frac{J_A{}^2}{\hbar^2} + i\frac{\theta^3}{3!}\frac{J_A{}^3}{\hbar^3} + \cdots . \end{aligned} \tag{6}$$

If we rotate through an angle ε, around the z axis, a system described by a (scalar) wave function $\psi(\mathbf{r}) = \psi(r, \theta, \varphi)$, we replace $\psi(r, \theta, \varphi)$ by $\psi(r, \theta, \varphi - \varepsilon)$; thus we can write

$$\psi(r, \theta, \varphi - \varepsilon) = R_z(\varepsilon)\, \psi(r, \theta, \varphi) = \left(1 - i\frac{J_z}{\hbar}\varepsilon\right) \psi(r, \theta, \varphi).$$

But, on the other hand, remembering (3),

$$\begin{aligned} \psi(r, \theta, \varphi - \varepsilon) &= \psi(r, \theta, \varphi) - \varepsilon\frac{\partial\psi(r, \theta, \varphi)}{\partial\varphi} \\ &= \left(1 - i\frac{L_z}{\hbar}\varepsilon\right) \psi(r, \theta, \varphi). \end{aligned}$$

By equating the right-hand sides of the last two expressions, we obtain the relation between angular momentum and rotation operators, which is simply

$$L_z = J_z. \tag{7}$$

Observe that (7) has been proved for scalar wave functions, depending on position only. The case of a wave function depending on other internal variables (spin) is treated later.

c. Commutation Rules of Angular Momenta and of Rotation. It is easily verified that the differential operators (2*b*) do not commute with each other but satisfy the relation

$$L_i L_j - L_j L_i = i\hbar L_k \tag{8}$$

(i, j, k cyclic permutation of 1, 2, 3).

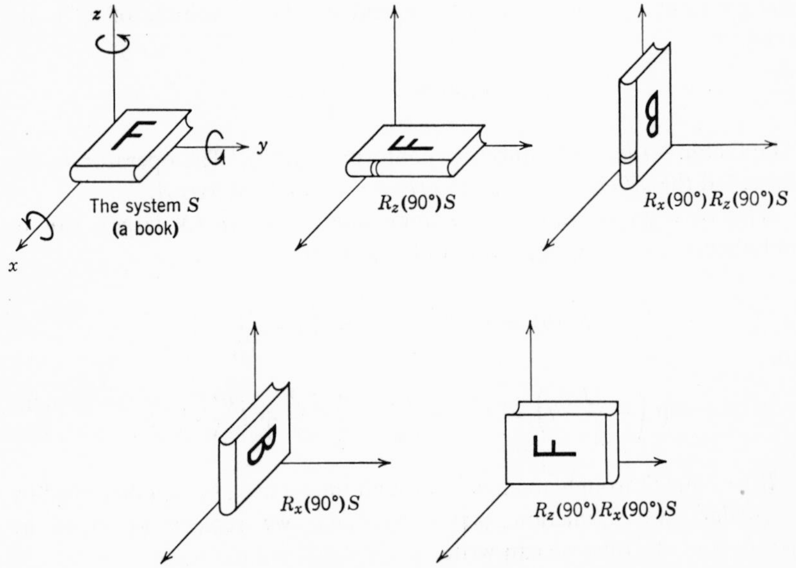

Fig. 1.13-3. Successive 90° rotations of a book S, showing that rotations do not commute: F is the front, B the back of the book.

Though it is evident that the same commutation rules must apply to the operators J_i, it is of some pedagogical interest to derive the commutation rules of the J_i's directly from purely geometrical considerations.

That rotations about different axes are not commutative can be most clearly illustrated by Fig. 1.13-3, which shows the effect of 90° rotations around the coordinate axes [$R_x(90°)$, $R_y(90°)$, $R_z(90°)$] on a system S, a book having a front F and a back B.

Let us now follow what happens to particular points of the system when infinitesimal rotations $R_y(\eta)$, $R_x(\varepsilon)$, $R_y(-\eta)$, $R_x(-\varepsilon)$ are successively applied.

A point P initially on the z axis of the unit sphere goes back to P after having occupied the positions P', P'', P''' (Fig. 1.13-4). But if we start from a point Q along the y axis the situation is different. $R_y(\eta)$ leaves us in Q,

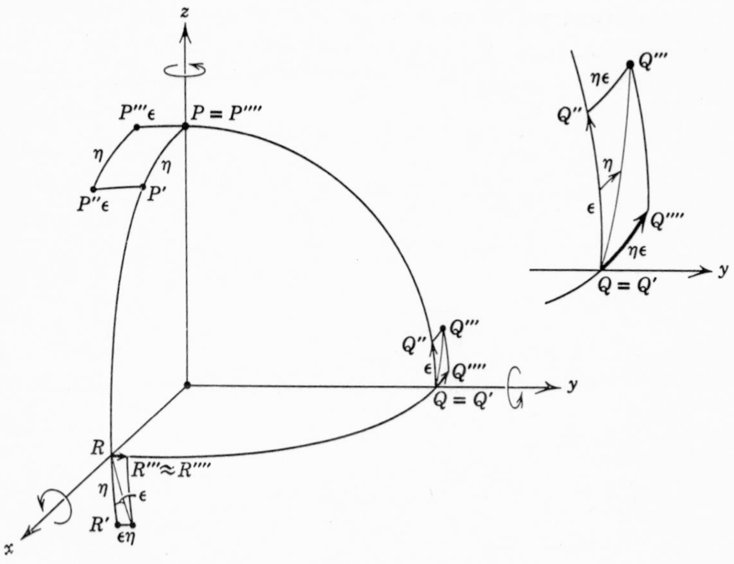

Fig. 1.13-4. Successive application of infinitesimal rotations.

and, after the four rotations are applied, we end up in Q'''', on the xy plane, at a distance $\varepsilon\eta$ in the direction of a positive rotation around the z axis. A point R on the x axis moves similarly to R''''.

Thus we can write

$$R_x(-\varepsilon)\, R_y(-\eta)\, R_x(\varepsilon)\, R_y(\eta) = R_z(\varepsilon\eta).$$

Expressing this relation in terms of J_x, J_y, J_z and using (6), we have

$$\left(1 + i\varepsilon\frac{J_x}{\hbar} - \frac{\varepsilon^2}{2}\frac{J_x{}^2}{\hbar^2} + \cdots\right)\left(1 + i\eta\frac{J_y}{\hbar} - \frac{\eta^2}{2}\frac{J_y{}^2}{\hbar^2} + \cdots\right)$$
$$\times\left(1 - i\varepsilon\frac{J_x}{\hbar} - \frac{\varepsilon^2}{2}\frac{J_x{}^2}{\hbar^2} + \cdots\right)\left(1 - i\eta\frac{J_y}{\hbar} - \frac{\eta^2}{2}\frac{J_y{}^2}{\hbar^2} + \cdots\right)$$
$$= \left(1 - i\varepsilon\eta\frac{J_z}{\hbar} - \cdots\right).$$

By keeping terms up to second order we obtain

$$J_xJ_y - J_yJ_x = i\hbar J_z \tag{9}$$

in agreement with (8).

d. Orbital Angular Momentum Eigenfunctions.[1] It is first observed that the operator $L^2 = L_x^2 + L_y^2 + L_z^2$ commutes with any of the L_i's, whereas according to (8) the L_i's do not commute with one another. Thus the operator L^2 can be diagonalized simultaneously with any one of the L_i's, say L_z, and we can find functions that are simultaneous eigenfunctions of L^2 and L_z. Such functions are the well-known spherical harmonics[2] defined, for l, m integers and for $0 \leq m \leq l$, from

$$\begin{aligned} Y_l^m(\theta, \varphi) &= (-1)^m(Y_l^{-m})^* \\ &= \frac{(-1)^{l+m}}{(2l)!!}\left[\frac{(2l+1)}{4\pi}\frac{(l-m)!}{(l+m)!}\right]^{1/2}(\sin\theta)^m \\ &\quad \times \frac{d^{l+m}}{(d\cos\theta)^{l+m}}(\sin\theta)^{2l}e^{im\varphi}, \end{aligned} \tag{10}$$

and corresponding to eigenvalues $l(l+1)\hbar^2$ for L^2 and to eigenvalues $m\hbar$ ($|m| \leq l$) for L_z. Some particular cases follow:

(11)

$l = 0$ (S states): $$Y_0 = \frac{1}{\sqrt{4\pi}}$$

$l = 1$ (P states): $$\begin{cases} Y_1^1 = -(Y_1^{-1})^* = -\sqrt{\dfrac{3}{8\pi}}\sin\theta e^{i\varphi}, \\ Y_1^0 = \sqrt{\dfrac{3}{4\pi}}\cos\theta. \end{cases}$$

$l = 2$ (D states): $$\begin{cases} Y_2^2 = +(Y_2^{-2})^* = \sqrt{\dfrac{15}{32\pi}}\sin^2\theta e^{2i\varphi}, \\ Y_2^1 = -(Y_2^{-1})^* = -\sqrt{\dfrac{15}{8\pi}}\sin\theta\cos\theta e^{i\varphi}, \\ Y_2^0 = \sqrt{\dfrac{5}{16\pi}}(3\cos^2\theta - 1). \end{cases}$$

[1] Subsections (d) and (e) are inserted for future reference and can be omitted without prejudice to the logical sequence of the treatment.

[2] There is some arbitrariness in the choice of signs. The present choice is known as the Condon and Shortley phase convention and is used almost exclusively in the extensive literature dealing with the algebra of angular momentum. (The book by Schiff is an exception.) The symbol double factorial has the meaning: $n!! = n(n-2)(n-4)\cdots$, the last factor being 1 or 2.

The spherical harmonics, as we have written them, are orthonormal upon integration over the whole solid angle:

$$\int (Y_l^m)^* Y_{l'}^{m'}\, d\Omega = \delta_{mm'}\, \delta_{ll'}. \tag{12}$$

The Y_l^0's are simply related to Legendre polynomials $P_l(\cos\theta)$:

$$P_l(\cos\theta) = \sqrt{\frac{4\pi}{2l+1}}\, Y_l^0(\theta), \tag{13}$$

whose normalization is expressed by

$$\int P_l P_{l'}\, d\Omega = \frac{4\pi}{2l+1}\, \delta_{ll'}. \tag{14}$$

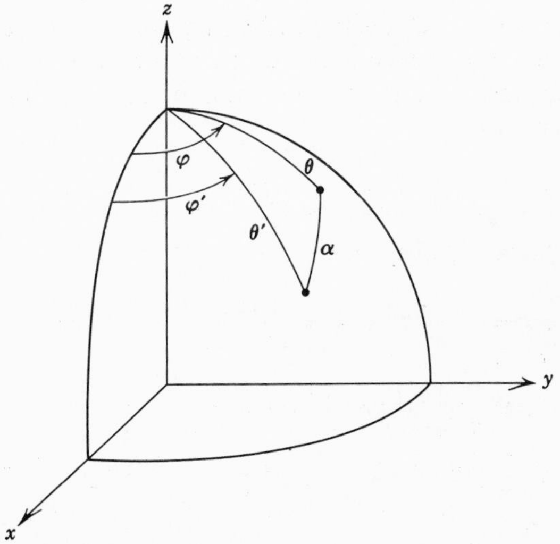

Fig. 1.13-5. Definition of the angles entering in the addition theorem.

We will have occasion to use the "addition theorem" of the $Y_l^m(\cos\theta)$, which states the following equality:

$$\begin{aligned} Y_l^0(\alpha) &= \sqrt{\frac{4\pi}{2l+1}} \sum_{m=-l}^{+l} (Y_l^m(\theta, \varphi))^* Y_l^m\ (\theta', \varphi') \\ &= \sqrt{\frac{4\pi}{2l+1}}\, [Y_l^0(\theta, \varphi) Y_l^0(\theta', \varphi') \\ &\qquad + \text{terms containing a factor } \cos m(\varphi - \varphi')], \end{aligned} \tag{15a}$$

where the angles α, θ, φ, θ', φ' are geometrically related, as shown in Fig. 1.13-5. For $l = 1$, (15a) reduces to the well-known relation of spherical trigonometry:

(15b) $$\cos \alpha = \cos \theta \cos \theta' + \sin \theta \sin \theta' \cos (\varphi - \varphi').$$

The spherical harmonics can be multiplied by an arbitrary function of r to obtain three-dimensional eigenfunctions of L^2 and L_z. It is useful, however, to study the r dependence of the eigenfunctions corresponding to a free particle of mass m and definite kinetic energy

$$T = \frac{p^2}{2m} = \frac{\hbar^2 k^2}{2m},$$

where k is the momentum divided by $\hbar$ or the inverse deBroglie wavelength $\lambda\!\!\!^{-}$ ($k = 1/\lambda\!\!\!^{-} = 2\pi/\lambda$).

For each k and each value of l there are two independent radial solutions of the free-particle wave equation: the $j_l(kr)$, which are regular at the origin, and the $n_l(kr)$, which are not. These are called spherical Bessel functions and can be expressed in terms of conventional Bessel and Neumann functions:

(16) $$j_l(kr) = \sqrt{\frac{\pi}{2kr}}\, J_{l+\frac{1}{2}}(kr); \qquad n_l(kr) = -\sqrt{\frac{\pi}{2kr}}\, N_{l+\frac{1}{2}}(kr).$$

Particular cases for small l:

(17)
$$j_0 = \frac{\sin kr}{kr}; \qquad j_1 = \frac{1}{kr}\left(\frac{\sin kr}{kr} - \cos kr\right);$$
$$j_2 = \frac{1}{kr}\left\{\left[\frac{3}{(kr)^2} - 1\right]\sin kr - \frac{3}{kr}\cos kr\right\};$$
$$n_0 = \frac{\cos kr}{kr}; \qquad n_1 = \frac{1}{kr}\left(\sin kr + \frac{\cos kr}{kr}\right);$$
$$n_2 = \frac{1}{kr}\left\{\frac{3}{kr}\sin kr + \left[\frac{3}{(kr)^2} - 1\right]\cos kr\right\}.$$

The following approximate formulas hold for all l:

(18)
$$\text{for } kr \ll l, \quad j_l(kr) \cong \frac{(kr)^l}{(2l+1)!!};$$
$$\text{for } kr \gg l, \quad j_l(kr) \cong \frac{\sin [kr - l(\pi/2)]}{kr};$$
$$\text{for } kr \ll l, \quad n_l(kr) \cong \frac{(2l-1)!!}{(kr)^{l+1}};$$
$$\text{for } kr \gg l, \quad n_l(kr) \cong \frac{\cos [kr - l(\pi/2)]}{kr}.$$

The functions rj_l and rn_l have a first point of inflection at $kr = \sqrt{l(l+1)}$; this value of kr separates the region in which the spherical Bessel functions behave like a power of r from the region in which they have an oscillatory character.

It is useful to construct, by means of the j's and the n's, radial functions that, away from the origin, correspond to incoming or outgoing traveling spherical waves. These are the functions,

$$\begin{aligned} j_l^+(kr) &= n_l(kr) + ij_l(kr), \\ j_l^-(kr) &= [j_l^+(kr)]^*, \end{aligned} \tag{19}$$

for which we can write the following approximate expressions:

$$\begin{aligned} &\text{for } kr \ll l, \quad j_l^\pm(kr) \cong \frac{(2l-1)!!}{(kr)^{l+1}}\ ; \\ &\text{for } kr \gg l, \quad j_l^\pm(kr) \cong \frac{1}{kr}\exp\left[\pm i\left(kr - l\frac{\pi}{2}\right)\right]. \end{aligned} \tag{20}$$

e. Use of Cartesian Rotational Coordinates. Some of the expressions involving angular momenta assume a more direct geometrical meaning if, instead of using the conventional system of cartesian coordinates defined by the unit vectors $\hat{\mathbf{x}}$, $\hat{\mathbf{y}}$, $\hat{\mathbf{z}}$, we introduce a system of complex "rotational" axes corresponding to the basic vectors

$$\begin{aligned} \hat{\mathbf{e}}_+ &= -\frac{1}{\sqrt{2}}(\hat{\mathbf{x}} + i\hat{\mathbf{y}}), \\ \hat{\mathbf{e}}_- &= \frac{1}{\sqrt{2}}(\hat{\mathbf{x}} - i\hat{\mathbf{y}}), \\ \hat{\mathbf{e}}_0 &= \hat{\mathbf{z}}. \end{aligned} \tag{21a}$$

These, when solved for $\hat{\mathbf{x}}$, $\hat{\mathbf{y}}$, $\hat{\mathbf{z}}$, become

$$\begin{aligned} \hat{\mathbf{x}} &= \frac{1}{\sqrt{2}}(-\hat{\mathbf{e}}_+ + \hat{\mathbf{e}}_-) \\ \hat{\mathbf{y}} &= \frac{i}{\sqrt{2}}(\hat{\mathbf{e}}_+ + \hat{\mathbf{e}}_-) \\ \hat{\mathbf{z}} &= \hat{\mathbf{e}}_0. \end{aligned} \tag{21b}$$

If we use the conventional formula for the (noncommutative) dot product of complex vectors,

$$\mathbf{u} \cdot \mathbf{v} = u_x^* v_x + u_y^* v_y + u_z^* v_z, \tag{22}$$

it is immediately verified that the basic vectors (21a) are orthonormal.

It is convenient to define the rotational "components" of an arbitrary complex vector $\mathbf{v}$ as[1]

$$v_+ = -\hat{\mathbf{e}}_- \cdot \mathbf{v} = -\frac{1}{\sqrt{2}}(v_x + iv_y)$$

$$v_- = -\hat{\mathbf{e}}_+ \cdot \mathbf{v} = \frac{1}{\sqrt{2}}(v_x - iv_y) \tag{23}$$

$$v_0 = \hat{\mathbf{e}}_0 \cdot \mathbf{v} = v_z.$$

Then we can easily verify that

$$\mathbf{v} = v_x\hat{\mathbf{x}} + v_y\hat{\mathbf{y}} + v_z\hat{\mathbf{z}} = -v_-\hat{\mathbf{e}}_+ - v_+\hat{\mathbf{e}}_- + v_0\hat{\mathbf{e}}_0 \tag{24}$$

and

$$\mathbf{u} \cdot \mathbf{v} = u_+{}^*v_+ + u_-{}^*v_- + u_0{}^*v_0. \tag{25a}$$

In particular, if u is real, $u_+{}^* = -u_-$, $u_-{}^* = -u_+$, and we can write

$$\mathbf{u} \cdot \mathbf{v} = -u_-v_+ - u_+v_- + u_0v_0. \tag{25b}$$

We recognize immediately that the spherical harmonics $Y_1{}^m(\theta, \varphi)$ are proportional to the rotational coordinates of a unit vector $\hat{\mathbf{r}}$ in the direction $\theta\varphi$:

$$r_+ = -\frac{1}{\sqrt{2}}\sin\theta(\cos\varphi + i\sin\varphi) = -\frac{1}{\sqrt{2}}\sin\theta e^{i\varphi} = \sqrt{\frac{4\pi}{3}}\,Y_1{}^1,$$

$$r_- = \frac{1}{\sqrt{2}}\sin\theta(\cos\varphi - i\sin\varphi) = \frac{1}{\sqrt{2}}\sin\theta e^{-i\varphi} = \sqrt{\frac{4\pi}{3}}\,Y_1{}^{-1}, \tag{26}$$

$$r_0 = \cos\theta = \sqrt{\frac{4\pi}{3}}\,Y_1{}^0.$$

Similarly, we can show that spherical harmonics of higher order are related to higher rank tensors (FR-59).

The + and − components of the angular momentum operators are the well known step-up and step-down operators for which one can prove the following relations:

$$L_+Y_l{}^m = -\frac{1}{\sqrt{2}}(L_x + iL_y)Y_l^m = -\hbar\sqrt{\tfrac{1}{2}(l-m)(l+m+1)}\,Y_l^{m+1}$$

$$L_-Y_l{}^m = \frac{1}{\sqrt{2}}(L_x - iL_y)Y_l^m = \hbar\sqrt{\tfrac{1}{2}(l+m)(l-m+1)}\,Y_l^{m-1} \tag{27}$$

$$L_0Y_l{}^m = \hbar m Y_l{}^m.$$

[1] The definitions in (23) seem awkward from the geometrical point of view, but, as we shall see, they are useful for the discussion of angular momentum, since both $\hat{\mathbf{e}}_+$ and $\mathbf{v}_+$ are eigenfunctions of angular momentum for $J = 1$, $M = +1$, etc. For $\mathbf{v}$ real we have simply $\mathbf{v}_+ = \mathbf{v} \cdot \mathbf{e}_+$, etc.

1.14 Conservation of Total Angular Momentum: Spin $\frac{1}{2}$ and 1

a. Decomposition of Infinitesimal Rotations into Orbital and Intrinsic Parts. Let us suppose now that the interacting particles are not mere points but that the description of their state requires some information concerning the orientation of an internal axis. Under such conditions orbital angular momentum is not necessarily conserved.

In the classical example of planetary motion the privileged axes may be those of revolution or the magnetic axes of the planet and the sun. Then, because of dipole and quadrupole coupling, the axis of the planet precesses, and this precession must be compensated by a corresponding change of orbital angular momentum. Kepler's law of areas does not apply and must be replaced by the more general law of conservation of total angular momentum.

In the mechanics of elementary particles the privileged axis is defined by the spin. In the presence of spin **S** the orbital angular momentum may not be conserved. But, *in accordance with a postulated isotropy of space, we assume that rotational invariance still holds.* It will be found that this assumption corresponds, both mathematically and intuitively, to the conservation of total angular momentum.

In the presence of spin the wave function $\psi(\mathbf{r}, \mathbf{S})$ depends on both space and spin coordinates. If space and spin dependence can be separated,[1] $\psi(\mathbf{r}, \mathbf{S}) = \psi(\mathbf{r})\zeta(\mathbf{S})$, the rotation operator R_z can be decomposed as the product of two operators:

(1) $$R_z(\theta) = R_z^{(i)}(\theta)\, R_z^{(o)}(\theta).$$

One of these, $R_z^{(o)}$ rotates the space-dependent part of the wave function and is connected as before to *orbital angular momentum:*

(2) $$R_z^{(o)}(\varepsilon) = 1 - \frac{i}{\hbar} L_z\varepsilon = 1 - \varepsilon \frac{\partial}{\partial \varphi} .$$

The other $R_z^{(i)}(\theta)$, rotates the part of the wave function that depends on the spin[2] and is related to the "*intrinsic*," or "*spin*," angular momentum **S**, whose z component is defined by

(3) $$R_z^{(i)}(\varepsilon) = 1 - i\frac{S_z}{\hbar}\varepsilon.$$

From (1), (2), and (3), keeping only the first power of ε, we obtain

(4) $$R_z(\varepsilon) = 1 - \frac{i}{\hbar}(L_z + S_z)\varepsilon.$$

[1] Space and spin dependence can be separated for $J = L + S$ (see later).

[2] The examples in (b) and (c) will make clear the significance of applying rotational operators to the spin part of a wave function.

Finally, defining

(5) $$J_z = L_z + S_z,$$

we see that the over-all rotation corresponds to the total angular momentum **J**, which is the sum of an intrinsic and an orbital part.

The assumption of space isotropy means now that the Hamiltonian commutes with the differential rotation operators J, which describe the rotational behavior of the whole state:

(6)
$$\begin{aligned} J_z\mathcal{H} - \mathcal{H}J_z &= 0, \\ J^2\mathcal{H} - \mathcal{H}J^2 &= 0. \end{aligned}$$

The operators J^2 and J_z have eigenvalues $J^2 = j(j+1)\hbar^2$ (j integer or half integer) and $J_z = m_j\hbar$ ($m_j = J, J-1, \cdots -J$), which are good quantum numbers. The same cannot be said in general of the eigenvalues of S_z, S^2, L_z, and L^2.

If the space and spin dependence of the state cannot be separated, the decomposition (1) of the rotation operator is justified only for infinitesimal rotations [see (16), (29)] but definitions (2), (3), and (5) in terms of differential rotation operators remain valid.

b. The Pauli Formalism for Two-Component Wave Functions (Spin $\frac{1}{2}$). Let us consider the case in which the spin variable can assume only two values. Here the wave function has two scalar components and the operators S_i can be expressed as 2 × 2 matrices.

Following Pauli, we introduce a vector operator

(7) $$\boldsymbol{\sigma} = \sigma_x\hat{\mathbf{x}} + \sigma_y\hat{\mathbf{y}} + \sigma_z\hat{\mathbf{z}} = \begin{pmatrix} 0 & 1 \\ 1 & 0 \end{pmatrix}\hat{\mathbf{x}} + \begin{pmatrix} 0 & -i \\ i & 0 \end{pmatrix}\hat{\mathbf{y}} + \begin{pmatrix} 1 & 0 \\ 0 & -1 \end{pmatrix}\hat{\mathbf{z}},$$

whose components are hermitian and satisfy the relations

(8)
$$\begin{aligned} \sigma_i^2 &= 1, & |\boldsymbol{\sigma}|^2 &= \sigma_x^2 + \sigma_y^2 + \sigma_z^2 = 3, \\ \sigma_i\sigma_j - \sigma_j\sigma_i &= 2i\sigma_k, & \sigma_i\sigma_j &= -\sigma_j\sigma_i = i\sigma_k \end{aligned}$$

(ijk cyclic permutation of 1, 2, 3).

The projection of $\boldsymbol{\sigma}$ in an arbitrary direction specified by a unit vector $\hat{\mathbf{s}}$ or by polar angles θ_s and φ_s is

(9) $$\boldsymbol{\sigma}\cdot\hat{\mathbf{s}} = \begin{pmatrix} \cos\theta_s & \sin\theta_s \exp(-i\varphi_s) \\ \sin\theta_s \exp(i\varphi_s) & -\cos\theta_s \end{pmatrix}.$$

Since $|\boldsymbol{\sigma}\cdot\hat{\mathbf{s}}|^2 = 1$, the operator (9) has eigenvalues ± 1. The eigenstate $\zeta_{\hat{\mathbf{s}}}$ corresponding to the eigenvalue $+1$ satisfies the relation

(10) $$(\boldsymbol{\sigma}\cdot\hat{\mathbf{s}})\zeta_{\hat{\mathbf{s}}} = \zeta_{\hat{\mathbf{s}}}$$

and corresponds to the Pauli spin pointing in the $\hat{\mathbf{s}}$ direction. The equation for the eigenfunction $\zeta_{\hat{s}} = \begin{pmatrix} f \\ g \end{pmatrix}$ can be obtained by introducing (9) in (10):

$$f \cos \theta_s + g \sin \theta_s \exp(-i\varphi_s) = f,$$
$$f \sin \theta_s \exp(i\varphi_s) - g \cos \theta_s = g,$$

from which,

$$\frac{f}{g} = \frac{\sin \theta_s \exp(-i\varphi_s)}{1 - \cos \theta_s} = \frac{\cos(\frac{1}{2}\theta_s) \exp(-\frac{1}{2}i\varphi_s)}{\sin(\frac{1}{2}\theta_s) \exp(\frac{1}{2}i\varphi_s)}$$

and, introducing the normalization $f^2 + g^2 = 1$:

$$\zeta_{\hat{s}} = \begin{pmatrix} \cos(\frac{1}{2}\theta_s) \exp(-\frac{1}{2}i\varphi_s) \\ \sin(\frac{1}{2}\theta_s) \exp(\frac{1}{2}i\varphi_s) \end{pmatrix} \tag{11}$$

for spin in direction θ_s, φ_s. The angles appearing in (11) do not express the dependence of $\zeta_{\hat{s}}$ on position but refer to the orientation of the spin. The dependence of the wave function on the space coordinates may be spherically symmetrical, but the state still is not rotationally invariant.

If we assume that the spin orientation does not vary with position (θ_s and φ_s independent of $\mathbf{r}$), we can easily prove with rotational arguments that (11) corresponds to spin $S = \hbar/2$. Applying to (11) the operator $R_z^{(i)}(\varepsilon)$ we obtain

$$R_z^{(i)}(\varepsilon)\zeta_{\hat{s}} = \left(1 - i\frac{S_z}{\hbar}\varepsilon\right)\zeta_{\hat{s}}$$

$$= \begin{pmatrix} \cos(\frac{1}{2}\theta_s) \exp[-\frac{1}{2}i(\varphi_s + \varepsilon)] \\ \sin(\frac{1}{2}\theta_s) \exp[\frac{1}{2}i(\varphi_s + \varepsilon)] \end{pmatrix} \approx \begin{pmatrix} (1 - \frac{1}{2}i\varepsilon) \cos(\frac{1}{2}\theta_s) \exp(-\frac{1}{2}i\varphi_s) \\ (1 + \frac{1}{2}i\varepsilon) \sin(\frac{1}{2}\theta_s) \exp(\frac{1}{2}i\varphi_s) \end{pmatrix}$$

and thus

$$S_z\zeta_{\hat{s}} = \frac{\hbar}{2}\begin{pmatrix} \cos(\frac{1}{2}\theta_s) \exp(-\frac{1}{2}i\varphi_s) \\ -\sin(\frac{1}{2}\theta_s) \exp(\frac{1}{2}i\varphi_s) \end{pmatrix}. \tag{12}$$

This relation shows that $\zeta_{\hat{s}}$ is not in general an eigenfunction of S_z, since this operator changes the sign of the lower component. It is immediately seen, however, that it is an eigenfunction of S_z^2, corresponding to eigenvalue $\hbar^2/4$. Thus the possible eigenvalues of S_z are

$$S_z = \pm \frac{1}{2}\hbar. \tag{13}$$

In particular, if $\theta_s = 0$ or π ($\hat{\mathbf{s}} = \pm\hat{\mathbf{z}}$), $\zeta_{\hat{s}}$ becomes an eigenstate of S_z

corresponding to the eigenvalue $\pm\hbar/2$. The eigenstates can be written

$$(14)\qquad \zeta_{\hat{z}} = \zeta_{1/2}^{1/2} \equiv \begin{pmatrix}1\\0\end{pmatrix} \equiv \alpha; \qquad \zeta_{-\hat{z}} = \zeta_{1/2}^{-1/2} \equiv \begin{pmatrix}0\\1\end{pmatrix} \equiv \beta.$$

These are the well-known Pauli eigenstates.

Referred to these states, the matrix S_z is diagonal and equal to $\frac{1}{2}\hbar\sigma_z$, with σ_z defined in (7). This proves the equivalence between the Pauli treatment and the introduction of the spin through rotation operators. For any two-component wave function, which can always be expressed as a linear combination of α and β states, we can write

$$(15)\qquad \mathbf{S} = \frac{\hbar}{2}\,\boldsymbol{\sigma}.$$

If θ_s and φ_s depend on r, θ, φ, the situation is somewhat more complicated; the rotation $R_z(\varepsilon)$, besides affecting the spin orientation, rotates the whole system through an angle φ, and we have

$$(16)\qquad R_z(\varepsilon)\zeta_{\hat{s}} = \begin{pmatrix}\cos[\frac{1}{2}\theta_s(r, \theta, \varphi - \varepsilon)]\exp\{-\frac{1}{2}i[\varphi_s(r, \theta, \varphi - \varepsilon) + \varepsilon]\}\\ \sin[\frac{1}{2}\theta_s(r, \theta, \varphi - \varepsilon)]\exp\{\frac{1}{2}i[\varphi_s(r, \theta, \varphi - \varepsilon) + \varepsilon]\}\end{pmatrix}$$
$$\approx \begin{pmatrix}(1 - \frac{1}{2}i\varepsilon)[1 - \varepsilon(\partial/\partial\varphi)]\cos(\frac{1}{2}\theta_s)\exp(-\frac{1}{2}i\varphi_s)\\ (1 + \frac{1}{2}i\varepsilon)[1 - \varepsilon(\partial/\partial\varphi)]\sin(\frac{1}{2}\theta_s)\exp(\frac{1}{2}i\varphi_s)\end{pmatrix}.$$

From this it is seen, again neglecting ε^2, that the total differential rotation $J_z/\hbar$ decomposes into the sum of $S_z/\hbar$ and $L_z/\hbar$, even when the radial and spin dependence of the wave function are not separable.

For future reference we introduce at this point the operators

$$(17)\qquad \Lambda_+ = \tfrac{1}{2}(1 + \sigma_z) = \begin{pmatrix}1 & 0\\0 & 0\end{pmatrix}; \quad \Lambda_- = \tfrac{1}{2}(1 - \sigma_z) = \begin{pmatrix}0 & 0\\0 & 1\end{pmatrix},$$

which may be called the *spin-up* and *spin-down projection operators,* since

$$(18)\qquad \begin{aligned} \Lambda_+\zeta_{1/2}^{1/2} &= \zeta_{1/2}^{1/2}, & \Lambda_+\zeta_{1/2}^{-1/2} &= 0,\\ \Lambda_-\zeta_{1/2}^{1/2} &= 0, & \Lambda_-\zeta_{1/2}^{-1/2} &= \zeta_{1/2}^{-1/2}. \end{aligned}$$

We also need the *spin step-up* and *spin step-down* operators,

$$(19)\qquad \begin{aligned} \sigma^+ &= \tfrac{1}{2}(\sigma_x + i\sigma_y) = -\frac{1}{\sqrt{2}}\sigma_+ = \begin{pmatrix}0 & 1\\0 & 0\end{pmatrix}\\ \sigma^- &= \tfrac{1}{2}(\sigma_x - i\sigma_y) = \frac{1}{\sqrt{2}}\sigma_- = \begin{pmatrix}0 & 0\\1 & 0\end{pmatrix} \end{aligned}$$

which satisfy the relations

$$\begin{aligned} \sigma^+\zeta_{1/2}^{\ 1/2} &= 0, & \sigma^+\zeta_{1/2}^{\ -1/2} &= \zeta_{1/2}^{\ 1/2}, \\ \sigma^-\zeta_{1/2}^{\ 1/2} &= \zeta_{1/2}^{\ -1/2}, & \sigma^-\zeta_{1/2}^{\ -1/2} &= 0. \end{aligned} \tag{20}$$

c. Vector Wave Functions (Spin 1). Another interesting case—particularly for the treatment of the electromagnetic field—is that of a three-component wave function which transforms like a vector.

Let us consider a vector field $\mathbf{V}$ of components

$$V_x = V \sin\theta_s \cos\varphi_s, \quad V_y = V \sin\theta_s \sin\varphi_s, \quad V_z = V\cos\theta_s$$

and assume, for the moment, that $\mathbf{V}$ does not depend on $\mathbf{r}$. If we apply the infinitesimal rotation operator around the z axis, we obtain

$$R_z^{(i)}(\varepsilon)\mathbf{V} = \left(1 - i\varepsilon\frac{S_z}{\hbar}\right)\begin{pmatrix} V\sin\theta_s\cos\varphi_s \\ V\sin\theta_s\sin\varphi_s \\ V\cos\theta_s \end{pmatrix} = \begin{pmatrix} V\sin\theta_s\cos(\varphi_s+\varepsilon) \\ V\sin\theta_s\sin(\varphi_s+\varepsilon) \\ V\cos\theta_s \end{pmatrix} \tag{21}$$

$$\approx \begin{pmatrix} V\sin\theta_s\cos\varphi_s - V\varepsilon\sin\theta_s\sin\varphi_s \\ V\sin\theta_s\sin\varphi_s + V\varepsilon\sin\theta_s\cos\varphi_s \\ V\cos\theta_s \end{pmatrix} = \begin{pmatrix} V_x - \varepsilon V_y \\ V_y + \varepsilon V_x \\ V_z \end{pmatrix}.$$

Thus

$$\frac{S_z}{\hbar}\begin{pmatrix} V_x \\ V_y \\ V_z \end{pmatrix} = \begin{pmatrix} -iV_y \\ +iV_x \\ 0 \end{pmatrix}. \tag{22}$$

Clearly, a vector pointing in an arbitrary direction is not an eigenstate of $S_z/\hbar$. It is easily verified, however, that it is an eigenstate of

$$(S_z/\hbar)[(S_z^2/\hbar^2) - 1]$$

corresponding to eigenvalue 0:

$$\frac{S_z}{\hbar}\left(\frac{S_z^{\ 2}}{\hbar^2} - 1\right)\begin{pmatrix} V_x \\ V_y \\ V_z \end{pmatrix} = 0. \tag{23}$$

This means that for any vector wave function the eigenvalues of S_z are

$$S_z = +\hbar, 0, -\hbar. \tag{24}$$

It is immediately verified that the corresponding normalized eigenvectors are the unit vectors 1.13 (21a). Thus both the vectors

$$\hat{\mathbf{e}}_+ = -\frac{1}{\sqrt{2}}\begin{pmatrix}1\\ i\\ 0\end{pmatrix};\quad \hat{\mathbf{e}}_- = \frac{1}{\sqrt{2}}\begin{pmatrix}1\\ -i\\ 0\end{pmatrix};\quad \hat{\mathbf{e}}_0 = \begin{pmatrix}0\\ 0\\ 1\end{pmatrix}, \tag{25}$$

and the scalar functions Y_1^1, Y_1^{-1}, Y_1^0 are eigenstates for angular momentum 1.

We can represent the operators S_x, S_y, S_z to be applied to a vector wave function by means of 3×3 matrices. Let us first observe that an infinitesimal rotation through an angle ε about the i axis corresponds to the addition of a vector $\varepsilon\hat{\mathbf{x}}_i \times \mathbf{V}$ to the original vector $\mathbf{V}$. Thus

$$\frac{S_x}{\hbar}\mathbf{V} = i\hat{\mathbf{x}} \times \mathbf{V};\quad \frac{S_y}{\hbar}\mathbf{V} = i\hat{\mathbf{y}} \times \mathbf{V};\quad \frac{S_z}{\hbar}\mathbf{V} = i\hat{\mathbf{z}} \times \mathbf{V}. \tag{26}$$

From this we obtain the matrix representation

$$S_x = \hbar\begin{pmatrix}0 & 0 & 0\\ 0 & 0 & -i\\ 0 & i & 0\end{pmatrix};\quad S_y = \hbar\begin{pmatrix}0 & 0 & i\\ 0 & 0 & 0\\ -i & 0 & 0\end{pmatrix};\quad S_z = \hbar\begin{pmatrix}0 & -i & 0\\ i & 0 & 0\\ 0 & 0 & 0\end{pmatrix}. \tag{27}$$

It is easily verified that these matrices are hermitian and that they satisfy angular momentum commutation rules. Passing to a representation with S_z diagonal, we obtain

$$S_x = \frac{\hbar}{\sqrt{2}}\begin{pmatrix}0 & 1 & 0\\ 1 & 0 & 1\\ 0 & 1 & 0\end{pmatrix};\quad S_y = \frac{\hbar}{\sqrt{2}}\begin{pmatrix}0 & -i & 0\\ i & 0 & -i\\ 0 & i & 0\end{pmatrix};\quad S_z = \hbar\begin{pmatrix}1 & 0 & 0\\ 0 & 0 & 0\\ 0 & 0 & -1\end{pmatrix}. \tag{28}$$

Finally, we must consider the case of nonseparable radial and spin dependence of a vector $\mathbf{V}$ whose direction depends on position. We must prove that the behavior of the vector field under rotation corresponds to orbital angular momentum and to one unit of intrinsic spin.

Let us show how this happens for the x component. $V_x(x, y, z)$ changes, under rotation, for two reasons: because it is the component of a vector that transforms into $V_x \cos\varepsilon - V_y \sin\varepsilon \approx V_x - \varepsilon V_y$ and because the point x, y, z must be changed into $x\cos\varepsilon + y\sin\varepsilon \approx x + \varepsilon y$, $y\cos\varepsilon - x\sin\varepsilon \approx y - \varepsilon x$, z. Thus, in first order in ε,

$$\begin{aligned} R_z(\varepsilon)\, V_x(x, y, z) &= V_x(x + \varepsilon y, y - \varepsilon x, z) - \varepsilon V_y(x + \varepsilon y, y - \varepsilon x, z) \\ &= V_x(x, y, z) + \varepsilon y \frac{\partial}{\partial x} V_x - \varepsilon x \frac{\partial}{\partial y} V_x - \varepsilon V_y \\ &= V_x - \varepsilon V_y - \varepsilon(\mathbf{r} \times \nabla V_x)_z. \end{aligned} \tag{29}$$

The addition of $-\varepsilon V_y$ is contributed by the intrinsic spin [see (21)] and the term $\varepsilon(\mathbf{r} \times \nabla V_x)_z$ by the orbital angular momentum [see 1.13 (2)].

d. Total Angular Momentum Eigenfunctions and Vector Addition of Angular Momenta.[1] Let **j** and **j**′ be two commuting angular momentum operators, which may be either "orbital" or "intrinsic," or may even represent the sum of an orbital and intrinsic part. Let $\mathcal{Y}_j^m(1)$ and $\mathcal{Y}_{j'}^{m'}(2)$ be eigenfunctions of **j** and **j**′ corresponding to eigenvalues j, j', m, m' [short for eigenvalue $j(j+1)\hbar^2$ for j^2, $m\hbar$ for j_z etc.]. $\mathcal{Y}_j^m$ is a spherical harmonic if **j** is purely orbital, a spin function if **j** is purely intrinsic, and may have a more complicated structure in the general case. The variables (1) and (2) stand either for angular or spin variables or for both spin and angular variables.

When the vector operators **j** and **j**′ are added to give

$$\mathbf{J} = \mathbf{j} + \mathbf{j}',$$

we obtain a new angular momentum vector which has eigenvalues J^2 and M [short for $J(J+1)\hbar^2$ and $M\hbar$]. We have the problem of finding the eigenfunctions corresponding to these eigenvalues.

Obviously the product $\mathcal{Y}_j^m(1)\,\mathcal{Y}_{j'}^{m'}(2)$ is an eigenstate of J_z for $M = m + m'$. It can be proved quite generally, using group theoretical methods, that the orthonormal eigenfunctions of J^2 and J_z are a linear combination of $\mathcal{Y}_j^m\mathcal{Y}_{j'}^{m'}$ of the form

$$(30) \qquad \mathcal{Y}_{Jjj'}^M(1, 2) = \sum_{m'=-j'}^{j'} C(jj'J; mm')\,\mathcal{Y}_j^m(1)\,\mathcal{Y}_{j'}^{m'}(2),$$

where the C are numerical coefficients called the "*Clebsch-Gordan*" or "*vector addition*" coefficients and $m = M - m'$ in each term of the sum.

Conversely, we can write the product $\mathcal{Y}_j^m(1)\,\mathcal{Y}_{j'}^{m'}(2)$ as a linear combination of $\mathcal{Y}_{Jjj'}^M(1, 2)$ as follows:

$$(31) \qquad \mathcal{Y}_j^m(1)\,\mathcal{Y}_{j'}^{m'}(2) = \sum_{J=j-j'}^{j+j'} C(jj'J; mm')\,\mathcal{Y}_{Jjj'}^M(1, 2),$$

where $M = m + m'$ in each term of the sum.

The expression in (30) can be used to find the spin-angle functions corresponding to a given total angular momentum for each particle and also the general angular momentum eigenfunctions of a system of many particles.

A formula similar to (31) holds for spherical functions of the same variable

$$(32) \quad Y_l^m(1)\,Y_{l'}^{m'}(1) = \sum_L \left[\frac{(2l+1)(2l'+1)}{4\pi(2L+1)}\right]^{1/2} C(ll'L; mm')C(ll'L; 00)Y_L^{m+m'}(1).$$

[1] For future reference.

Note that the coefficients of this sum differ from those of (31) only by factors which do not involve m and m'.

Making use of (32) and of the orthonormality of the spherical harmonics we obtain the integral relation

$$(33)\quad \int (Y_{l'}^{m'})^* Y_L^M Y_l^m \, d\Omega = \left[\frac{(2L+1)(2l+1)}{4\pi(2l'+1)}\right]^{1/2} C(lLl'; mM)C(lLl'; 00).$$

This relation enables us to compute the matrix elements of a spherical harmonic for eigenstates of orbital angular momentum.

An important generalization of (33) is given by the Wigner-Eckart theorem which can be stated as follows: the matrix elements of a (irreducible) tensor operator T_J^M for eigenstates of angular momentum depend on the quantum numbers m and m' in a way which is completely described by the Clebsch-Gordan coefficients:

$$(34)\qquad \langle j'm'|\, T_J^M \,|jm\rangle = C(jJj';\ mM)\, \langle j'|\, T_J \,|j\rangle.$$

It follows that the matrix elements of T_J^M are nonzero only for $|j - j'| \leqslant J \leqslant j + j'$ and $M = m' - m$.

For proofs and for the properties of the vector addition coefficients we refer to specialized books (CS-57; Wi-31; Wi-59; Ro-57; Ed-57).

In our treatment we are particularly interested in the addition of angular momenta in which one of the addends is $\frac{1}{2}$ or 1. Tables of vector addition coefficients for these values of j' follow. Tables for $j' = \frac{3}{2}$ and 2 are given in Condon and Shortley (CS-57).

Table I.14-1: $j' = \frac{1}{2}$

$C(j\frac{1}{2}J;\ mm')$	$m' = \frac{1}{2}$	$m' = -\frac{1}{2}$
$J = j + \frac{1}{2}$	$\left(\frac{j + M + \frac{1}{2}}{2j+1}\right)^{1/2}$	$\left(\frac{j - M + \frac{1}{2}}{2j+1}\right)^{1/2}$
$J = j - \frac{1}{2}$	$-\left(\frac{j - M + \frac{1}{2}}{2j+1}\right)^{1/2}$	$\left(\frac{j + M + \frac{1}{2}}{2j+1}\right)^{1/2}$

Table I.14-2: $j' = j = \frac{1}{2}$

	$C(\frac{1}{2}\frac{1}{2}J;\ mm')$	$m' = \frac{1}{2}$	$m' = -\frac{1}{2}$
	$M = 1$	1	0
$J = 1$	$M = 0$	$\sqrt{1/2}$	$\sqrt{1/2}$
	$M = -1$	0	1
$J = 0$		$-\sqrt{1/2}$	$\sqrt{1/2}$

Table I.14-3: $j' = 1,\ j = \frac{1}{2}$

$C(1\frac{1}{2}J;\ mm')$		$m' = \frac{1}{2}$	$m' = -\frac{1}{2}$
$J = \frac{3}{2}$	$M = \frac{3}{2}$	1	0
	$M = \frac{1}{2}$	$\sqrt{2/3}$	$\sqrt{1/3}$
	$M = -\frac{1}{2}$	$\sqrt{1/3}$	$\sqrt{2/3}$
	$M = -\frac{3}{2}$	0	1
$J = \frac{1}{2}$	$M = \frac{1}{2}$	$-\sqrt{1/3}$	$\sqrt{2/3}$
	$M = -\frac{1}{2}$	$-\sqrt{2/3}$	$\sqrt{1/3}$

Of particular importance are the spin states of two particles of spin $\frac{1}{2}$. These consist of the singlet state

(35*s*) $$\zeta_0^{\ 0} = \frac{1}{\sqrt{2}}\,[\alpha(1)\beta(2) - \beta(1)\alpha(2)],$$

which is odd under spin exchange, and of the triplet states

(35*t*) $$\begin{aligned} \zeta_1^{\ 1} &= \alpha(1)\alpha(2), \\ \zeta_1^{\ 0} &= \frac{1}{\sqrt{2}}\,[\alpha(1)\beta(2) + \beta(1)\alpha(2)], \\ \zeta_1^{-1} &= \beta(1)\beta(2), \end{aligned}$$

which are even.

It is useful to consider the dot product of the spin vector operators of two particles:

(36) $$\boldsymbol{\sigma}_1 \cdot \boldsymbol{\sigma}_2 \text{ whose eigenvalues are } \begin{cases} -3 \text{ in singlet states,} \\ \ \ 1 \text{ in triplet states.} \end{cases}$$ [1]

From this operator we can construct the *singlet* and *triplet projection operators*

(37) $$\Lambda_s = \tfrac{1}{4}(1 - \boldsymbol{\sigma}_1 \cdot \boldsymbol{\sigma}_2), \qquad \Lambda_t = \tfrac{1}{4}(3 + \boldsymbol{\sigma}_1 \cdot \boldsymbol{\sigma}_2),$$

and the *spin exchange operator*

(38) $$\mathcal{T}_\sigma = \tfrac{1}{2}(1 + \boldsymbol{\sigma}_1 \cdot \boldsymbol{\sigma}_2),$$

which, when applied to the states (35) has eigenvalues -1 and $+1$ and thus effectively exchanges the spins of the two particles (1) and (2).

[1] Formula (36) is most readily proved by writing $\boldsymbol{\sigma}_1 \cdot \boldsymbol{\sigma}_2 = \frac{1}{2}(-\boldsymbol{\sigma}_1^{\,2} - \boldsymbol{\sigma}_2^{\,2} + 4\mathbf{S}^2)$, where $\mathbf{S} = \frac{1}{2}(\boldsymbol{\sigma}_1 + \boldsymbol{\sigma}_2)$, and observing that the eigenvalues of $\boldsymbol{\sigma}_1^{\,2}$ and $\boldsymbol{\sigma}_2^{\,2}$ are 3 and those of $\mathbf{S}^2$ are $S(S + 1)$, or 0 for the singlet and 2 for the triplet.

Table I.14-4: $j' = 1$

$C(j1J;\ mm')$	$m' = 1$	$m' = 0$	$m' = -1$
$J = j + 1$	$\left[\dfrac{(j+M)(j+M+1)}{(2j+1)(2j+2)}\right]^{1/2}$	$\left[\dfrac{(j-M+1)(j+M+1)}{(2j+1)(j+1)}\right]^{1/2}$	$\left[\dfrac{(j-M)(j-M+1)}{(2j+1)(2j+2)}\right]^{1/2}$
$J = j$	$-\left[\dfrac{(j+M)(j-M+1)}{2j(j+1)}\right]^{1/2}$	$\dfrac{M}{[j(j+1)]^{1/2}}$	$\left[\dfrac{(j-M)(j+M+1)}{2j(j+1)}\right]^{1/2}$
$J = j - 1$	$\left[\dfrac{(j-M)(j-M+1)}{2j(2j+1)}\right]^{1/2}$	$-\left[\dfrac{(j-M)(j+M)}{j(2j+1)}\right]^{1/2}$	$\left[\dfrac{(j+M+1)(j+M)}{2j(2j+1)}\right]^{1/2}$

Table I. 14-5: j′ = j = 1

	$C(11J;\ mm')$	$m' = 1$	$m' = 0$	$m' = -1$
	$M = 2$	1	0	0
	1	$\sqrt{1/2}$	$\sqrt{1/2}$	0
$J = 2$	0	$\sqrt{1/6}$	$\sqrt{2/3}$	$\sqrt{1/6}$
	-1	0	$\sqrt{1/2}$	$\sqrt{1/2}$
	-2	0	0	1
	$M = 1$	$-\sqrt{1/2}$	$\sqrt{1/2}$	0
$J = 1$	0	$-\sqrt{1/2}$	0	$\sqrt{1/2}$
	-1	0	$-\sqrt{1/2}$	$\sqrt{1/2}$
$J = 0$	$M = 0$	$\sqrt{1/3}$	$-\sqrt{1/3}$	$\sqrt{1/3}$

1.15 Invariance under Space Inversion and Conservation of Parity

a. The Parity Operator. After having examined the invariances under space and time translations and under space rotations, we proceed to study the invariance under inversion of space-time axes. We shall consider in this section the inversion of space coordinates and in 1.17 the reversal of time. Four dimensional rotations (Lorentz transformations) and inversions are treated later (Chapters 6, 7, 8).

The three-dimensional rotations of orthogonal cartesian coordinate axes correspond to the group of transformations

(1) $$x_i' = \sum a_{ij}x_j,$$

with the conditions

(2) $$\sum_j a_{ji}a_{jk} = \delta_{ik},$$
$$\det a_{ij} = 1,$$

which are needed in order to prevent changes in scale and to maintain invariant the element of volume $dx\, dy\, dz$. As we have seen, [1.13 (5)], the rotations can be obtained by continuous variations from the identity transformation.

The rotations described by (1) and (2) include reflection of two space axes $[R_z(\pi)\{\hat{\mathbf{x}}, \hat{\mathbf{y}}, \hat{\mathbf{z}}\} = \{-\hat{\mathbf{x}}, -\hat{\mathbf{y}}, \hat{\mathbf{z}}\}]$ but do not include reflections of an odd number of axes. The latter correspond to linear transformation of the form (1) but with

(3) $$\det a_{ij} = -1.$$

Let us define the *parity operator* P_r as one that inverts the direction of the three coordinates axes

(4) $$P_r\{\hat{\mathbf{x}}, \hat{\mathbf{y}}, \hat{\mathbf{z}}\} = \{-\hat{\mathbf{x}}, -\hat{\mathbf{y}}, -\hat{\mathbf{z}}\}.$$

Reflection of any one axis P_i can be described as a product of P_r and of a rotation

(5) $$P_z\{\hat{\mathbf{x}}, \hat{\mathbf{y}}, \hat{\mathbf{z}}\} = \{\hat{\mathbf{x}}, \hat{\mathbf{y}}, -\hat{\mathbf{z}}\},$$
$$P_z = P_r R_z(\pi).$$

The operators P_r and P_i transform a right-handed system of coordinates into a left-handed one; they cannot be obtained by continuous variation from the identity transformation. The negative determinant (3) inverts the sign of the element of volume $dx\, dy\, dz = d\mathbf{x} \times d\mathbf{y} \cdot d\mathbf{z}$, as well as that of all other triple products.

b. Invariance under Reflection in Classical Physics. Non-quantum physical theories are always invariant under reflection of coordinates. This principle of invariance is seldom mentioned, since it is an obvious result of daily observation whose consequences are trivially true.

In order to facilitate the understanding of the meaning of parity in quantum mechanics, we nevertheless start with a classical discussion.

Classical quantities can be divided into even and odd according to whether they maintain or change their sign under the parity operator.

Mass, temperature, and energy are one-component even quantities, or *scalars*.

Momentum, force, and electric field are three-component *odd* quantities, or *vectors*. (This generally accepted notation identifies the vector with its three components, which are odd, rather than with a geometrical "arrow," which remains unchanged under transformation of coordinates.) Vectors are more or less directly related to translations.

Angular momentum, magnetic field, etc., are three-component *even* quantities; they are called *pseudovectors* or *axial vectors*. (Here the components do not change sign, whereas the "arrow" does.) Pseudovectors are connected with rotations.

Odd one-component quantities are called *pseudoscalars*. Examples are the triple product of three vectors or the scalar product of a vector and a pseudovector. Pseudoscalars involve both translations and rotations. A typical pseudoscalar is the *helicity* (or chirality) χ of a screw defined as

$$\chi = \frac{\mathbf{v} \cdot \boldsymbol{\omega}}{v\omega}. \tag{6}$$

χ is ± 1 according to whether the velocity $\mathbf{v}$ with which the screw advances is parallel or antiparallel to its angular velocity vector $\boldsymbol{\omega}$ or, more simply, whether the screw is right- or left-handed. Another interesting pseudoscalar is the potential of a pseudodipole, such as the magnetostatic potential, whose transformation properties are the same as those of the mesic field (see Chapter 7).

Tensors of an order higher than vectors can also be divided into even or odd according to the behavior of their components.

Invariance under rotation means that *all terms of an equation must behave in the same manner under rotation:* thus they must be tensors of the same order.

Similarly, invariance under reflection requires that *all terms of an equation must have the same behavior* (*even or odd*) *under reflection.* This is what is meant, in classical terms, by conservation of parity: scalars and pseudoscalars, vectors and pseudovectors, etc., cannot be added together. Reflection invariance and parity conservation would be violated if the force exerted by a right-handed spring were different from that of an identical but left-handed spring, since in this case the potential energy (scalar) would involve the helicity (pseudoscalar). Reflection invariance would be violated if the force between two coils depended on the sense of rotation of the current traversing them (rather than on the relative sense).

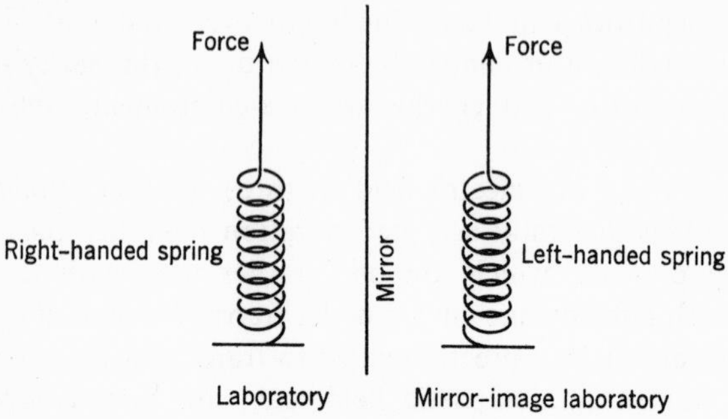

Fig. 1.15-1. It follows from reflection invariance that the force exerted by identical springs wound in opposite directions must be the same.

Invariance under reflection can also be stated in a more graphic manner: *If a certain experiment, carried on in a certain laboratory, gives a certain result, the mirror-image experiment, carried on in the mirror-image laboratory, must give the mirror-image result.* Figures 1.15-1 and 1.15-2 show

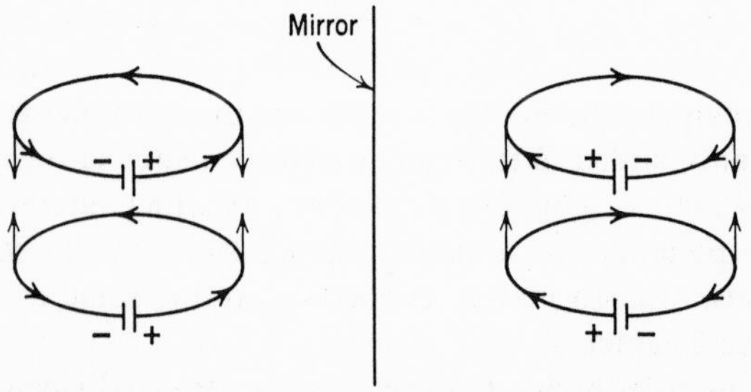

Fig. 1.15-2. It follows from reflection invariance that, if coils traversed by right-handed (relative to $+z$) currents attract, coils traversed by left-handed currents must also attract.

that if parity is conserved right- or left-handed springs must give the same force and two right- or two left-handed coils must both attract or both repel each other.

c. Conservation of Parity in Quantum Mechanics. Conservation of parity in quantum mechanics requires that the Hamiltonian of a free system commute with the parity operator

$$(P_r\mathcal{H} - \mathcal{H}P_r) = 0. \tag{7}$$

This relation is always satisfied for strong and electromagnetic forces; its violation in the case of weak interactions is discussed at an appropriate time (Chapter 8).

Equation (7) requires that $\mathcal{H}$ contain only even terms. Since the Hamiltonian is a one-component quantity, it must be scalar. The energy cannot depend on right- and left-handedness.

If (7) is satisfied, the eigenvalues of the parity operator are good quantum numbers: since $P_r^2 = 1$, parity can have only the two eigenvalues ± 1, and the states of a system can be divided into even and odd, according to whether

$$P_r\psi = \pm\psi. \tag{8}$$

d. Orbital, Intrinsic, and Total Parity. We must now introduce the concept of *intrinsic parity*, which is not usually considered in atomic physics.

We have seen that the wave function of a particle is not necessarily scalar and have already considered wave functions with 1, 2, and 3 components corresponding to spin 0, $\frac{1}{2}$, and 1, respectively. Now we want to focus our attention on the fact that the wave function of a particle is *not necessarily intrinsically even.* In other words, there may be particles whose states are odd for l even and vice versa. The pion (Chapter 7) is the most important example of an odd particle.

The intrinsic parity of a complex wave function (charged particle) cannot be measured directly, and we can arbitrarily assign positive intrinsic parity to protons, neutrons, and electrons. We shall see, however, that the relative intrinsic parity of particles produced or destroyed in parity conserving reactions (5.16c; 7.13e) can be determined experimentally.

Because it has to do with the creation and annihilation of particles, the idea of intrinsic parity properly belongs to the relativistic theory of quantized fields. However, the production and absorption of photons must be considered in the most elementary form of atomic physics and may properly be discussed at this point. The case of electromagnetism is particularly clear, since the fields are real and their parity directly measurable.[1]

We have already observed that **E** and **A** are vectors (*intrinsically odd*) and that **H** is a pseudovector (*intrinsically even*). Apart from its intrinsic parity, an electric or magnetic field may be "*orbitally*" even or odd according to whether $E_i(x, y, z)$ and $H_i(x, y, z)$ are even or odd functions of position.

[1] It follows from conservation of parity that the parity of *neutral* particles which decay into photons is directly measurable in the same sense. Examples are the neutral π meson (7.13e) and the atom of positronium (6.27d).

We now define *total parity* as the *product of intrinsic* and orbital parity:

(9) $$P_r = P_r^{(i)} P_r^{(o)}.$$

In order to clarify the concept of intrinsic parity, let us consider (Fig. 1.15-3) a wave function $\psi_i(xyz)$ (where the subscript i is a spin or tensor

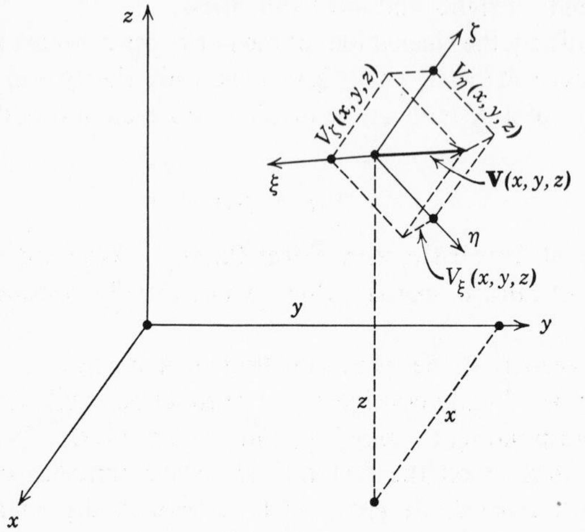

Fig. 1.15-3. Showing a vector field of components $V_\xi(x, y, z)$, $V_\eta(x, y, z)$, $V_\zeta(x, y, z)$.

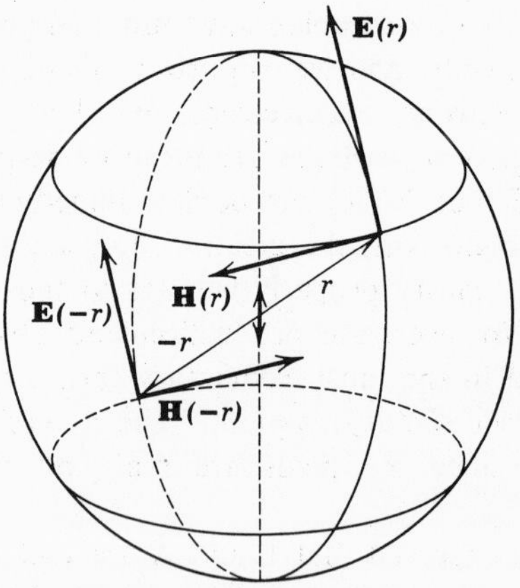

Fig. 1.15-4. Showing the "orbital" parity of the electric and magnetic fields for dipole radiation. The "total" parity is odd for both fields.

index which assumes 1, 2, 3, · · · values for spin 0, $\frac{1}{2}$, 1, · · ·) and imagine that the components of the wave function are projected on a system of axes ξ, η, ζ which may be different from the axes xyz used to express its functional dependence on position. Then the *intrinsic parity operator*

$P_r^{(i)}$ inverts the axes ξ, η, ζ, the *orbital parity operator* $P_r^{(o)}$ inverts the axes x, y, z, and the *total parity operator* P_r inverts both systems of axes. For instance, for the ξ component,

$$\begin{aligned} P_r^{(i)}\psi_\xi(x, y, z) &= \psi_{-\xi}(x, y, z), \\ P_r^{(o)}\psi_\xi(x, y, z) &= \psi_\xi(-x, -y, -z), \\ P_r\psi_\xi(x, y, z) &= P_r^{(i)}P_r^{(o)}\,\psi_\xi(x, y, z) = \psi_{-\xi}(-x, -y, -z). \end{aligned}$$

In order to show that total parity is a useful concept, let us apply it to the emission of electric dipole radiation. The electric dipole radiation field has odd total parity, since its electric field is intrinsically odd and orbitally even, whereas its magnetic field is intrinsically even and orbitally odd (Fig. 1.15-4). Thus the assumption of *conservation of parity in electromagnetic processes* requires that the source change parity in the emission of a quantum of electric dipole radiation in accordance with a well-known selection rule.

1.16 Highest Order of Static Electric and Magnetic Multipoles

a. Definition of the Multipoles. An arbitrary distribution of electric charge and current, such as a nucleus, may possess electric and magnetic multipole moments whose components, in the language of Racah, can be expressed as "irreducible tensors."

Given the charge distribution $\rho(r)$, the mth component of the 2^l-pole electric moment is (Ra-56):

(1) $$\mathcal{E}_l^{\,m} = \sqrt{\frac{4\pi}{2l+1}} \int \rho(r) r^l\, Y_l^{\,m}(\theta, \varphi)\, d\mathbf{r}.$$

Thus the 2^0-pole is the electric charge

$$\mathcal{E}_0 = q = \int \rho\, d\mathbf{r};$$

the components of the 2^1-pole are the projections of the electric dipole moment vector $\mathbf{d}$ on the axes $\hat{\mathbf{e}}_+$, $\hat{\mathbf{e}}_-$, $\hat{\mathbf{e}}_0$ [1.13 (23)]:

$$\begin{aligned} \mathcal{E}_1^{\,0} &= \int \rho(r) r \cos\theta\, d\mathbf{r} = d_z \\ \mathcal{E}_1^{\,\pm 1} &= \mp\frac{1}{\sqrt{2}} \int \rho(r)(x \pm iy)\, d\mathbf{r} = \mp\frac{1}{\sqrt{2}}(d_x \pm i d_y); \end{aligned}$$

the components of the 2^2-pole (quadrupole) form a second-order tensor, etc.

The components of the magnetic multipole moments $\mathcal{M}_l^{\,m}$ are obtained from (1) by replacing the scalar electric charge density ρ with the pseudoscalar "magnetic charge density" $-\nabla \cdot \mathbf{m}$, where $\mathbf{m}$ is the density of magnetic moment, related to the density of electric current $\mathbf{j}_e$ by

$$\mathbf{curl}\ \mathbf{m} = \frac{1}{c}\mathbf{j}_e.$$

Thus electric and magnetic multipoles of the same order have opposite parity. We can write the general expression

$$\mathcal{M}_l^m = -\sqrt{\frac{4\pi}{2l+1}}\int(\nabla\cdot\mathbf{m})r^l\,Y_l^m(\theta,\varphi)\,d\mathbf{r}. \tag{2a}$$

It can be shown[1] that this is equivalent to

$$\mathcal{M}_l^m = -\sqrt{\frac{-4\pi}{2l+1}}\frac{1}{l+1}\int r^l Y_l^m\,\nabla\cdot\frac{\mathbf{r}\times\mathbf{j}_e}{c}d\mathbf{r}. \tag{2b}$$

Since the vector $\mathbf{m}$ vanishes over a surface surrounding the volume of integration, we have

$$\mathcal{M}_0 = 0,$$

as we expect from the absence of separated magnetic charges. For $l = 1$ (2) yields the components of the magnetic dipole moment. In vector form we have the familiar expression[1,2]

$$\boldsymbol{\mu} = \int\mathbf{m}\,d\mathbf{r} = \frac{1}{2c}\int\mathbf{r}\times\mathbf{j}_e\,d\mathbf{r}. \tag{3}$$

Let us now consider the nucleus as a quantum mechanical system composed of many particles of masses m_α, charges e_α, coordinates $\mathbf{r}_\alpha$, and spins $\mathbf{S}_\alpha$. Then, the steady-state electric moments are the expectation values of the operators

$$\sqrt{\frac{4\pi}{2l+1}}\sum_\alpha e_\alpha r_\alpha{}^l\,Y_l^m(\theta_\alpha,\varphi_\alpha), \tag{4}$$

and the steady state magnetic moments are the expectation values of

$$-\sqrt{\frac{4\pi}{2l+1}}\sum_\alpha r_\alpha{}^l\,Y_l^m(\theta_\alpha,\varphi_\alpha)\frac{1}{\hbar}\nabla_\alpha\cdot\left[\frac{2g_{\alpha L}}{l+1}\mathbf{L}_\alpha + g_{\alpha S}\mathbf{S}_\alpha\right], \tag{5}$$

[1] Use the integral relation (which can be proved with successive integrations by parts)

$$\int r^l Y_l^m\,\nabla\cdot(\mathbf{r}\times\mathbf{curl}\,\mathbf{V})\,d\mathbf{r} = \int[(1+\mathbf{r}\cdot\nabla)r^l Y_l^m]\,\nabla\cdot\mathbf{V}\,d\mathbf{r}$$
$$= (l+1)\int r^l Y_l^m\,\nabla\cdot\mathbf{V}\,d\mathbf{r}\quad.$$

[2] For $l = 1$ the three components of $\mathcal{M}_1^m$ contain integrals of the form $\int(\nabla\cdot\mathbf{m})x_i\,dr$. But $x_i(\nabla\cdot\mathbf{m}) = \nabla\cdot(x_i\mathbf{m}) - \mathbf{m}\cdot\nabla x_i = \nabla\cdot(x_i\mathbf{m}) - m_i$. Since the integral of $\nabla\cdot(x_i\mathbf{m})$ is a flux which can be made to vanish if the volume of integration is sufficiently large, $\int(\nabla\cdot\mathbf{m})x_i\,dr = -\int m_i\,dr$.

where $g_{\alpha L} = e_\alpha \hbar/2m_\alpha c$ and $g_{\alpha S}$ are the orbital and intrinsic gyromagnetic ratios of the αth particle.

In particular, the magnetic dipole moment operator is

(6) $$\mu_{\text{op}} = \sum_\alpha (g_{\alpha L}\mathbf{L}_\alpha + g_{\alpha S}\mathbf{S}_\alpha),$$

as can be seen with an integration by parts.

The electric multipole operators (4) are tensor components whose parity is $(-1)^l$. They have an angular dependence characteristic of angular momentum eigenfunctions for eigenvalues l and m.

The magnetic multipole operators contain, besides the Y_l^m's the operators $\boldsymbol{\nabla} \cdot \mathbf{L}$ and $\boldsymbol{\nabla} \cdot \mathbf{S}$, which change the orbital parity of the wave function to which they are applied ($\boldsymbol{\nabla}$ is odd and $\boldsymbol{\nabla} \cdot \mathbf{L}$ contains three odd operators, $\boldsymbol{\nabla}$, $\mathbf{r}$, $\boldsymbol{\nabla}$) without changing its angular momentum eigenvalues ($\boldsymbol{\nabla} \cdot \mathbf{L}$ and $\boldsymbol{\nabla} \cdot \mathbf{S}$ are rotationally invariant). Thus their parity is $(-1)^{l+1}$.

b. Restrictions Due to Parity Conservation. If parity is conserved, it follows from the definitions of the multipole operators that, for all quantum mechanical states that are nondegenerate in parity

(7) *all odd electric multipoles vanish*

and

(8) *all even magnetic multipoles vanish.*

The proof is immediate if we consider that the eigenfunction ψ of the state in which the expectation value has to be found is either even or odd. Thus $\psi^*\psi$ is necessarily even and

(9) $$\int \psi^* \mathcal{O} \psi$$

vanishes if $\mathcal{O}$ is an odd function, as for the odd electric moments, or an odd operator as for the even magnetic moments.

The restriction of nondegeneracy is essential to the proof and is satisfied in all cases of interest for nuclei referred to their own center of mass.

However, in atomic and molecular physics we find numerous examples of systems with nonvanishing electric dipole moments. Among these the simplest is the excited hydrogen atom, whose dipole moment is caused by the accidental degeneracy of coulomb wave functions with different orbital angular momenta (Sc-55).

It is important to note that a plane wave of definite linear momentum can be decomposed in a sum of degenerate even and odd angular momentum states [see 3.12(1)] and is not an eigenstate of parity. The same can be said about localized wave packets, obtained by superimposing many waves. This explains how macroscopic classical bodies can have electric dipole moments without contradicting (7).

c. Restrictions Due to Conservation of Angular Momentum. As a consequence of the law of vector addition of angular momentum, which expresses the conservation of this quantity, we can prove that

(10) *for a state of total angular momentum J, the expectation value of all moments of order $l > 2J$ is zero.*

For the proof we note that the spin-angle part of the expectation value has the form

$$\langle JM | T_l^m | JM \rangle; \tag{11a}$$

it then follows from the Wigner-Eckart theorem 1.14(34) that nonvanishing contributions are obtained only for $0 \leqslant l \leqslant 2J$ and $m = 0$; this proves quite generally the statement (10).

A less general proof can be obtained if we neglect spin effects and assume that the states are eigenstates of orbital angular momentum. In this case (11a) is replaced by

$$\int (Y_J^M)^* Y_l^m Y_J^M \, d\Omega; \tag{11b}$$

but using 1.14 (32) the product $(Y_J^M)^* Y_J^M = (-1)^M Y_J^{-M} Y_J^M$ can be written as the sum of $2J + 1$ terms, each containing a factor $Y_{J'}^0$ with $0 \leqslant J' \leqslant 2J$; then, (10) follows from the orthogonality of the spherical harmonics.

The nonvanishing moments are listed in the following table:

Nuclear Spin J	Multipole Order l			
	$l = 0$	$l = 1$	$l = 2$	$l = 3$
0	Electric charge	—	—	—
$\frac{1}{2}$	Electric charge	magnetic dipole	—	—
1	Electric charge	magnetic dipole	electric quadrupole	—
$\frac{3}{2}$	Electric charge	magnetic dipole	electric quadrupole	magnetic octupole
...	...	...	...	...

The $m = 0$ component of each multipole may have $2J + 1$ nonvanishing expectation values, one for each value of M. The quantity of physical interest is the expectation value in the state with $M = J$, that is, in the state in which the spin is directed along the z axis.

The magnetic moment that we find tabulated in nuclear physics tables is

$$\mu = \sum_\alpha \langle g_{\alpha L} L_{\alpha z} + g_{\alpha S} S_{\alpha z} \rangle_{JJ}. \tag{12}$$

It is usually expressed in units of nuclear magnetons

$$\mu_N = \frac{e\hbar}{2M_p c} = 5.0504 \times 10^{-24} \text{ erg gauss}^{-1} \tag{13}$$

(M_p is the mass of the proton). The tabulated quadrupole moments Q are given in cm². They are *twice* the expectation value of the $m = 0$ component of the quadrupole moment operator, divided by the elementary charge e:

$$Q = \frac{2}{e}\sum_\alpha e_\alpha \left\langle \frac{1}{2}(3\cos^2\theta_\alpha - 1)r_\alpha^2 \right\rangle_{JJ}.$$

An excellent description of the methods used for the measurement of μ and Q can be found in Ramsey (Ra-53, Ra-56).[1]

The absence of the electric dipole moment confirms our assumption of parity conservation. A special experiment performed on the neutron (S-57) showed that the electric dipole moment of this particle is smaller than 10^{-20} cm $\times\ e$; this upper limit is indeed small if we consider that nuclear sizes are of the order of 10^{-13} cm.

The observations on higher multipoles are very difficult, and only one case of detection of a nuclear magnetic octupole has been reported (J-54).

I.17 Time Reversal Invariance

a. Behavior of Schrödinger's States. The operation of time reversal consists in the inversion of the direction of all motions. Under this operation displacements, accelerations, and electric fields remain invariant but momenta, angular momenta, and magnetic fields (due to motion of charges) invert their signs.

In simple words, invariance under time reversal means that if we take a moving picture of a certain phenomenon and project it backward the projection still satisfies the equations of motion. This invariance holds for frictionless motions in gravitational and electrostatic fields [the case of magnetic fields is discussed in (b)].

More formally we can say that time reversal invariance is valid if for each solution of the equation of motion of a point $\mathbf{x} = \mathbf{x}(t)$ there is another solution $\mathbf{x} = \mathbf{x}(-t)$.

The assumption of invariance under time reversal cannot be treated quantum mechanically along the lines followed for the conservation principles discussed up to this point. Even when the Hamiltonian is time independent, the time variable remains in the Schrödinger equation, where it appears in the energy operator $i\hbar(\partial/\partial t)$. Formally, the inversion

[1] For a discussion of quadrupole effects in the solid state see C-57.

of the sign of time results in an inversion of the sign of energy, leading to negative energies that are meaningless, at least nonrelativistically; more conveniently, we can say that the inversion of time is equivalent to a change in the sign of the imaginary unit i, leaving the energy unchanged and interchanging the wave function with its complex conjugate. This is made clear in what follows.

In order to give a nonrelativistic quantum mechanical meaning to time reversal invariance we shall say that *time reversal invariance is satisfied if, under the transformation* $t' \to -t$, *the solution of the Schrödinger equation transforms in such a way that* $|\psi'(t')|^2 = |\psi(t)|^2$.

We now prove that

(1) *time reversal invariance is satisfied in quantum mechanics if the Hamiltonian is real:* $\mathcal{H} = \mathcal{H}^*$; *in this case the time inverted state of* ψ *is* ψ^*.

In effect, if ψ is an eigenfunction of $\mathcal{H}$, it satisfies Schrödinger's equation:

$$\mathcal{H}\psi = i\hbar \frac{\partial \psi}{\partial t};$$

taking the complex conjugate, we have

$$\mathcal{H}^*\psi^* = -i\hbar \frac{\partial \psi^*}{\partial t}, \tag{2}$$

which, if $\mathcal{H} = \mathcal{H}^*$, can be written

$$\mathcal{H}\psi^* = i\hbar \frac{\partial \psi^*}{\partial(-t)},$$

proving that ψ^* satisfies the time-inverted equation for the original Hamiltonian.

This is easily understood intuitively because the operation of complex conjugation inverts the eigenvalues of momentum,

$$\exp(i\mathbf{k}\cdot\mathbf{r})^* = \exp[i(-\mathbf{k})\cdot\mathbf{r}]$$

and thus the direction of the motion.

We introduce the special symbol K for the *operator of complex conjugation*, defined from the relation

$$K\psi = \psi^* K, \tag{3}$$

or simply at the end of an expression, $K\psi = \psi^*$. Then (1) can be reworded by saying that if K commutes with the Hamiltonian it can be identified with the operator of time reversal T for Schrödinger states.

From this formulation we may be led to believe that K corresponds to some observable dynamical variable and that its eigenvalues may be good quantum numbers.

This, however, is not the case. The operator K does not possess the properties of quantum mechanical operators corresponding to dynamical variables. First of all, it is not a linear operator, since

$$K(a_1\psi_1 + a_2\psi_2) = a_1{}^*\psi_1{}^* + a_2{}^*\psi_2{}^* \neq a_1K\psi_1 + a_2K\psi_2;$$

and we must also exercise some care in using the associative property in expressions involving K:

$$(K\psi_1)\psi_2 = \psi_1{}^*\psi_2 \neq \psi_1{}^*\psi_2{}^* = K(\psi_1\psi_2).$$

b. Time Reversal in the Electromagnetic Field. The motion of a particle in an external fixed magnetic field is not invariant under the inversion of time. This is so because the Lorentz force changes sign when the velocity is inverted. A well-known consequence of this lack of invariance is the possibility of distinguishing the direction of motion of a particle of known sign in a cloud chamber with applied magnetic field.

This classical fact is not in disagreement with the theorem proved in (a): the Hamiltonian in the presence of a magnetic potential vector is obtained by replacing the kinetic energy term $(1/2m)(-i\hbar\,\nabla)^2$ with $(1/2m)[-i\hbar\,\nabla - (e/c)\mathbf{A}]^2$, and this last expression is complex.

But the difficulty is only apparent: it is due to the fact that we have inverted the motion of the particle under observation, but we have not inverted the motion of the particles that produce the magnetic field. If the time reversal operator is applied to the whole system (particle in the chamber and magnetic coils), the particle goes back on its own track and time reversal invariance holds.

Formally, the Schrödinger equation does not contain terms corresponding to the current of the coil, but only the magnetic field $\mathbf{H}$, or the vector potential $\mathbf{A}$, which they produce. In this formulation the operation of time reversal T consists of two different transformations: $t \to -t$ and $\mathbf{A} \to -\mathbf{A}$.

We can then proceed as in (a) to prove that the time reversed state of ψ is ψ^*, provided the Hamiltonian is invariant under the simultaneous transformations

$$\mathcal{H} \to K\mathcal{H} \quad \text{and} \quad \mathbf{A} \to -\mathbf{A}.$$

This invariance holds for the Hamiltonian of a particle in a magnetic field.

In a relativistic treatment of time reversal we must take into account that the inversion of time axis inverts the sign of the electrostatic potential, which is the time component of a four vector. Time reversal invariance for electrons and mesons is discussed relativistically in 6.21e and 7.31d.

c. Behavior of Pauli States. It is clear that the time reversed state ψ^* has inverted orbital angular momenta, and we may ask whether the time reversal operation also inverts the intrinsic spins. Since the spin often appears in a real term of the Hamiltonian, dotted with a magnetic field ($\boldsymbol{\sigma} \cdot \mathbf{H}$), we expect that the spin must be inverted with the magnetic field in order to keep the Hamiltonian invariant.

Let us now study the behavior of the spin under time reversal when the magnetic field does not appear explicitly. For conservation of parity and angular momentum, a spin must enter in the Hamiltonian always dotted with another pseudovector. If the coupling is between two intrinsic spins $\boldsymbol{\sigma}_1 \cdot \boldsymbol{\sigma}_2$, there is no problem, since the Hamiltonian remains the same with or without spin inversion. In the interesting case of coupling to the motion of particles (spin-orbit coupling)

$$\boldsymbol{\sigma} \cdot \mathbf{L} = \boldsymbol{\sigma} \cdot \mathbf{r} \times \mathbf{p} = -i\hbar\boldsymbol{\sigma} \cdot \mathbf{r} \times \boldsymbol{\nabla},$$

the Hamiltonian contains the operator $\boldsymbol{\sigma}$ and the imaginary unit; the theorem in (1) is not applicable.

But we can readily extend (1) in a way that is applicable to the case of spin-orbit coupling.

(4) *If there exists a unitary transformation U such that $\mathcal{H} = U\mathcal{H}^*U^{-1}$, time reversal invariance is satisfied and the time inverted state of ψ is $UK\psi = U\psi^*$.*

This is easily proved, since (2) can be written

$$(U\mathcal{H}^*U^{-1})(U\psi^*) = i\hbar\,\frac{\partial(U\psi^*)}{\partial(-t)}\,.$$

We can also prove that the transformation U appropriate to the spin-orbit coupling Hamiltonian $\boldsymbol{\sigma} \cdot \mathbf{L}$, [with $\boldsymbol{\sigma}$ defined by 1.14(7)], is expressed by the Pauli spin operator σ_y.

The proof is immediate if we take into account that $L_i^* = -L_i$, $\sigma_x^* = \sigma_x$, $\sigma_y^* = -\sigma_y$, $\sigma_z^* = \sigma_z$ and remember the commutation rules in 1.14(8):

$$\begin{aligned}\sigma_y(\sigma_x^*L_x^* + \sigma_y^*L_y^* + \sigma_z^*L_z^*)\sigma_y &= \sigma_y(-\sigma_xL_x + \sigma_yL_y - \sigma_zL_z)\sigma_y \\ &= \sigma_xL_x + \sigma_yL_y + \sigma_zL_z.\end{aligned}$$

Thus the operator of time reversal for particles with spin $\frac{1}{2}$ is σ_yK. It is easily seen that this operator inverts the spin direction:

$$(5)\qquad \begin{aligned}\sigma_yK\begin{pmatrix}1\\0\end{pmatrix} &= \begin{pmatrix}0 & -i\\ i & 0\end{pmatrix}\begin{pmatrix}1\\0\end{pmatrix} = \begin{pmatrix}0\\i\end{pmatrix} = i\begin{pmatrix}0\\1\end{pmatrix},\\ \sigma_yK\begin{pmatrix}0\\1\end{pmatrix} &= \begin{pmatrix}0 & -i\\ i & 0\end{pmatrix}\begin{pmatrix}0\\1\end{pmatrix} = \begin{pmatrix}-i\\0\end{pmatrix} = -i\begin{pmatrix}1\\0\end{pmatrix}.\end{aligned}$$

We now note that (5) can be written

$$(6a)\qquad T\zeta_{1/2}^{\pm 1/2} = (-1)^{\pm 1/2}\zeta_{1/2}^{\mp 1/2}$$

and that a similar relation holds for the eigenstates of orbital angular momentum as a consequence of the Condon-Shortley phase convention:

(6b) $$TY_l^m = (Y_l^m)^* = (-1)^m Y_l^{-m}.$$

However, considering that the usual Clebsch-Gordan coefficients have the property

(7) $$C(jj'J; mm') = (-1)^{j+j'-J} C(jj'J; -m-m'),$$

the spin-angle functions $\mathcal{Y}_J^M$ defined in 1.14 (30) behave in a different manner:

$$T\mathcal{Y}_J^M = (-1)^{l+\frac{1}{2}-J}(-1)^M \mathcal{Y}_J^{-M}.$$

In order to eliminate the cumbersome phase factors $(-1)^{l+1/2-J}$ in this last equation, an extra phase factor $(i)^{l+1/2-J}$ could be introduced in the definition of the vector addition coefficients.

1.2 The Neutron-Proton Force and the Deuteron

1.21 Properties of the Nucleons and of the Deuteron

a. The Proton and the Neutron. Around 1930 it became apparent that nuclei could not contain electrons because of their size, spins, statistics, and magnetic moments. This observation was followed by the discovery of the neutron (Chadwick, 1932), and it was then universally recognized that nuclei are composed of *protons* and *neutrons*. These two particles have been given the comprehensive name *nucleon*. The properties of the nucleons are listed in Table 1.21-1.

Table 1.21-1

	Proton	Neutron
Charge	$+e$	0
Mass (in MU)*	1.008144†	1.008984
Spin	$\frac{1}{2}$	$\frac{1}{2}$
Statistics	Fermi	Fermi
Magnetic moment (in nuclear magnetons)	2.79270	−1.91316
Decay reaction	stable	$n \rightarrow p + e + \bar{\nu}$
Decay energy	—	0.782 MeV
Mean life	∞	12/ln 2 min

* A physical mass unit is $\frac{1}{16}$ of the mass of O^{16}:

$$1 \text{ MU} = 931.16 \text{ MeV} = 1.65985 \times 10^{-24} \text{ g}$$

(but the physical MU has recently been redefined as $\frac{1}{12}$ of the mass of C^{12}).

† The value tabulated is the mass of the hydrogen atom, as it is customary to report atomic, rather than nuclear, masses.

The mass of the hydrogen atom is known from chemical and mass spectroscopic determinations. That of the neutron is obtained from the energy balance of one of the reactions

(1) $\mathrm{n} + \mathrm{p} \leftrightarrows \mathrm{D} + \gamma$ (+2.22 MeV) (B-50),

(2) $\mathrm{n} \rightarrow \mathrm{p} + e + \bar{\nu}$ (+0.782 MeV) (R-51; R-55)[1].

The proton's spin is determined from spectroscopic studies. In order to account for the spins of complex nuclei, we must assign to the neutron a half integer spin. The value $\frac{1}{2}$ is obtained as a result of scattering experiments (see 3.17).

It is found from the spectra of homonuclear molecules that nuclei containing an odd number of nucleons obey Fermi statistics, whereas nuclei with an even number of nucleons follow the statistics of Bose. From this observation it is determined that the nucleons are fermions.

The magnetic moments of the nucleons are obtained with great precision by means of magnetic resonance experiments on molecular beams (Rabi) and on condensed materials (Bloch and Purcell). The description of these elegant experiments is found in the books by Ramsey. We shall discuss in due time (3.31) how the required beams of polarized neutrons are produced.

The neutron mean life and decay energy have been measured directly (R-51; R-55) by counting the decay electrons and protons from a slow neutron beam of known neutron density.

Though the nucleons are elementary particles, they are not point particles. They possess a structure that is revealed in scattering experiments, chiefly at high energy (see 3.33). In meson theories this structure is interpreted as a "meson cloud" which surrounds a "bare nucleon core" and which accounts for the nuclear forces. The fact that the magnetic moments are "anomalous," that is, different from $e\hbar/2Mc$, is attributed to the presence of currents in the meson cloud. We are not concerned with these questions at present and postpone their study to an appropriate time (Chapter 7).

b. Properties of Nuclei with Two Nucleons. There are three possible nuclei with two nucleons; their properties are given in Table 1.21-2.

The binding energy B is the energy liberated in the reaction of formation of the deuteron from its elementary constituents. It may be directly measured as the energy of the γ rays of reaction (1) (γ rays of capture).

[1] $\bar{\nu}$ stands for antineutrino; see Chapter 8.

Table 1.21-2

	Di-Neutron n-n	Deuteron n-p	Di-Proton p-p
Mass	Unbound	2.014741	Unbound
B		2.22 MeV	
Spin		1	
μ		0.857393	
Q		2.73×10^{-27} cm^2	
Mean life		Stable	

1.22 General Discussion of the Force between Neutron and Proton

a. Qualitative Properties of the Neutron-Proton Forces. From the inspection of the data on the deuteron and on the other (non-existing) nuclei with $A = 2$ we can reach a number of qualitative conclusions concerning the properties of nuclear forces. Let us discuss the deuteron data first.

The magnetic moment of the deuteron is close to the sum of the magnetic moments of the neutron and proton ($\mu_p + \mu_n = 0.87975$); we can therefore picture the deuteron in a first approximation as a body in which the nucleons are in a $^3S_1$ state and whose magnetic moment is almost totally contributed by the magnetic moments associated with the parallel spins of the elementary particles. No contribution from orbital angular momentum is required to explain the value of the magnetic moment to a first approximation.

This view is corroborated by the smallness of the quadrupole moment. The value $Q = 2.74 \times 10^{-27}$ cm^2 must be compared with πR^2, where R is some sort of deuteron radius. We note in 1.23a that $R = 4.31 \times 10^{-13}$ cm and thus $\pi R^2 = 600 \times 10^{-27}$ cm$^2 \gg Q$. The deuteron is almost spherically symmetrical.

We conclude that

(1) the deuteron is predominantly a $^3S_1$ state;

(2) $L = 0$ is almost a good quantum number for the deuteron;

(3) the properties of the deuteron are almost explained by central forces alone.

However, since $\mu_D \neq \mu_p + \mu_n$ [1], and $Q_D \neq 0$, we can also say that

(4) there is evidence for the presence of *noncentral forces.*

[1] The computation of the magnetic moment of the deuteron is a complex problem and the inequality $\mu_D \neq \mu_p + \mu_n$ could have other interpretations beside the one indicated here.

Because of conservation of total angular momentum, J is a good quantum number, and the fact that the deuteron has $J = 1$ is true in an exact sense. Furthermore, since the deuteron is predominantly an S state, it follows from parity conservation that it must be exactly even.

Thus only a D-state admixture is compatible with the conservation principles; since singlet S has $J = 0$ and singlet D has $J = 2$, the deuteron must be a pure triplet state (parallel spins). We can finally conclude that

(5) the deuteron is an admixture of ${}^3S_1$ and ${}^3D_1$.

Not only is the ground state of the deuteron a triplet, but there are no bound excited states of the deuteron of 0 angular momentum. Thus

(6) the forces between neutron and proton are different in the singlet and triplet state: *nuclear forces are spin-dependent.*

Let us observe at once that the spin dependence of nuclear forces is of many orders of magnitude larger than that expected from the interaction between the magnetic moments of the nucleons.

Let us also make clear that spin dependence does not imply that the forces are not central, as in dipole-dipole forces. It simply means that the usual central scalar potential is different according to the relative orientation of the spins, a situation that has no direct analogy either in electromagnetism or in atomic physics.

b. Formulation of n-p Interaction. The Hamiltonian describing the interaction between a neutron and a proton must contain at least three terms.

(i) An ordinary central force term.
(ii) A spin-dependent central force term.
(iii) A noncentral force term.

The first term can be expressed by an ordinary, or Wigner, potential, a function of the distance between the nucleons:

(7) $$V_W(r),$$

where

$$r = |\mathbf{r}_\mathrm{p} - \mathbf{r}_\mathrm{n}|.$$

The second term may be formulated with the help of the spin-exchange operator $\mathfrak{T}_\sigma$ [see 1.14(38)], which has eigenvalues $+1$ for parallel spins (triplets) and -1 for antiparallel spins (singlets).

The spin dependent part of the potential can then be written as

(8) $$V_\sigma(r)\,\mathfrak{T}_\sigma = V_\sigma(r)\tfrac{1}{2}(1 + \boldsymbol{\sigma}_\mathrm{p} \cdot \boldsymbol{\sigma}_\mathrm{n}),$$

where $V_\sigma(r)$ expresses an appropriate dependence on distance.

Finally we must discuss the noncentral force term. In writing down this term, we are guided by the fact that *the nucleons have spin* $\frac{1}{2}$ and cannot possess moments of any kind higher than dipoles. This means that the potential between two nucleons can, at most, have spin angular dependence characteristic of dipole-dipole interaction.

We recall from electromagnetism that the potential energy of an electric dipole $\mathbf{d}_1$ in the field of another dipole $\mathbf{d}_2$ at distance $\mathbf{r}$ is

$$-\frac{1}{r^3}[3(\mathbf{d}_1 \cdot \hat{\mathbf{r}})(\mathbf{d}_2 \cdot \hat{\mathbf{r}}) - \mathbf{d}_1 \cdot \mathbf{d}_2]. \tag{9}$$

In this formula the radial dependence r^{-3} arises from the fact that electric charges interact with a potential going as r^{-1}.

In order to extend the dipole interaction formula to nucleons, we must keep in mind that we do not know the r dependence of the potential acting between the "mesic charges" which may be thought of as the sources of nuclear force fields. Thus the r^{-3} dependence must be replaced by an arbitrary function of r, and we write, for the noncentral or "tensor" forces, the expression

$$V_T(r)S_{\text{pn}}, \tag{10}$$

where the *tensor-force operator* S_{pn} is defined as

$$S_{\text{pn}} = 3(\boldsymbol{\sigma}_{\text{p}} \cdot \hat{\mathbf{r}})(\boldsymbol{\sigma}_{\text{n}} \cdot \hat{\mathbf{r}}) - \boldsymbol{\sigma}_{\text{p}} \cdot \boldsymbol{\sigma}_{\text{n}}. \tag{11}$$

This operator, like the dipole-dipole potential, averages to zero over the solid angle.

Thus the analytical expression corresponding to the qualitative properties discussed in (a) is obtained by adding (7), (8), and (10). We obtain the interaction Hamiltonian

$$V_W(r) + V_\sigma(r)\mathcal{T}_\sigma + V_T(r)S_{\text{pn}}. \tag{12}$$

Since it is easily verified that the contribution of the tensor-force operator vanishes in the singlet state, there is no need to consider an additional spin dependence of the tensor force.

c. Most General Form of Velocity Independent Hamiltonian between Two Particles of Spin $\frac{1}{2}$. We now wish to prove that the expression in (12) is indeed the most general form of Hamiltonian between neutron and proton if we exclude velocity dependent forces.

For the proof we follow the lines of a classical paper by Eisenbud and Wigner (E-41).

The Hamiltonian expressing the interaction between proton and neutron involves their space and spin coordinates $\mathbf{r}_{\text{p}}$, $\mathbf{r}_{\text{n}}$, $\boldsymbol{\sigma}_{\text{p}}$, $\boldsymbol{\sigma}_{\text{n}}$. The conservation principles in 1.1 require that the Hamiltonian be a scalar.

The number of scalar expressions we can form from $\mathbf{r}_p$, $\mathbf{r}_n$, $\boldsymbol{\sigma}_p$, $\boldsymbol{\sigma}_n$ is limited because the number of independent operators containing the spins is finite. Two particles of spin $\frac{1}{2}$ may be found in four different spin states. Thus any operator involving their spins is a 4×4 matrix. Obviously there are 16 and only 16 linearly independent matrices.

We can select a set of 16 independent 4×4 matrices as follows:

(13*a*) 1 scalar matrix 1,

(13*b*) 1 scalar matrix $\frac{1}{2}(1 + \boldsymbol{\sigma}_p \cdot \boldsymbol{\sigma}_n)$,

(13*c*) 3 components of the pseudovector matrix $\boldsymbol{\sigma}_p + \boldsymbol{\sigma}_n$,

(13*d*) 3 components of the pseudovector matrix $\boldsymbol{\sigma}_p - \boldsymbol{\sigma}_n$,

(13*e*) 3 components of the pseudovector matrix $\boldsymbol{\sigma}_p \times \boldsymbol{\sigma}_n$,

(13*f*) 5 components of the symmetric tensor matrix with zero trace[1] $T_{ij} = \frac{1}{2}(\sigma_{pi}\sigma_{nj} + \sigma_{pj}\sigma_{ni}) - \frac{1}{3}\delta_{ij}\boldsymbol{\sigma}_p \cdot \boldsymbol{\sigma}_n$.

These matrices are certainly independent because linear combinations cannot change tensor behavior.

On the other hand, the vectors $\mathbf{r}_p$ and $\mathbf{r}_n$ must enter only in the combination $\mathbf{r} = \mathbf{r}_p - \mathbf{r}_n$ for conservation of momentum. From the radius vector $\mathbf{r}$ and from its absolute value r we can form

(14*a*) scalar functions $f(r)$,

(14*b*) 1 vector $\mathbf{r}$,

(14*c*) 1 tensor $r_i r_j$.

We can obtain scalar expressions saturating the indices of the tensors in (13) with those of the tensors in (14). The simplest way is to choose scalars from both sides. By multiplying (13*a* and *b*), by scalar functions of r (14*a*) we obtain the first and second terms of (12). The only other possibility is to dot the tensor (13*f*) with the tensor (14*c*) and multiply the result by a scalar function of r (14*a*). But it is soon recognized that the result is equivalent to the third term of (12); the origin of the name "tensor force" is also made clear.

Thus we have proven that (12) is the most general expression for the neutron-proton interaction Hamiltonian consistent with the conservation principles and with the value of the spin.

[1] The nine components of the tensor $\sigma_{pi}\sigma_{nj}$ are linearly related to the antisymmetric components of $\boldsymbol{\sigma}_p \times \boldsymbol{\sigma}_n$ (three relations) and to $\boldsymbol{\sigma}_1 \cdot \boldsymbol{\sigma}_2$ (one relation). Thus only the five components of (13*f*) are independent of tensors already taken into account.

d. Velocity-Dependent Forces. Though velocity-dependent forces are not needed in the discussion of the deuteron we are considering here, for the sake of completeness, the form of possible velocity-dependent terms.

Such terms are obtained if we include the vectors $\mathbf{p}_p$ and $\mathbf{p}_n$ in the nuclear force Hamiltonian. However, because of Galilean invariance, only the difference between these vectors $\mathbf{p} = \mathbf{p}_p - \mathbf{p}_n$ can appear.[1]

We can form three scalars from $\mathbf{p}$ and $\mathbf{r}$

$$p^2, \quad r^2, \quad \mathbf{p} \cdot \mathbf{r}.$$

Thus the function $f(r)$ in (14*a*) can be replaced by

$$f(p^2, r^2, \mathbf{p} \cdot \mathbf{r}), \tag{15}$$

with the restriction that f must be an even function of $\mathbf{p} \cdot \mathbf{r}$ if time reversal invariance is assumed.

We can also form the pseudovector $\mathbf{p} \times \mathbf{r}$, which can be dotted with any of the pseudovectors in (13*c*, *d*, *e*) to give a scalar, time-reversal-invariant quantity. The term derived from (13*c*)

$$V_{\text{S}\cdot\text{L}}(r)(\boldsymbol{\sigma}_p + \boldsymbol{\sigma}_n) \cdot \mathbf{p} \times \mathbf{r} \tag{16}$$

[more generally we could write $V_{\text{S}\cdot\text{L}}(r, p, \mathbf{r} \cdot \mathbf{p})$ instead of $V_{\text{S}\cdot\text{L}}(r)$] is perfectly acceptable and corresponds to *spin-orbit coupling*.

At this point we introduce another restriction: in accordance with the assumption of charge independence of nuclear forces (discussed in 1.31), we require that the *interaction be symmetrical with respect to the exchange of the nucleons.*

Thus the terms obtained from (13*d* and *e*), which change in sign upon interchange of the particles, must be discarded and the spin-orbit coupling is the only velocity dependent term in the first power of p.

Finally, we have the tensors formed from the products $p_i p_j$ and $r_i p_j$, which can be dotted with the spin tensor T_{ij} (13*f*). These are acceptable but seldom used. In order to ensure time-reversal invariance, the dot product of the tensors $p_i p_j$ and T_{ij} must be multiplied by a function that is even in $\mathbf{p} \cdot \mathbf{r}$; the dot product of $r_i p_j$ and T_{ij} must be multiplied by an odd function of $\mathbf{p} \cdot \mathbf{r}$.

1.23 The Deuteron as a Pure S State

a. The Wave Equation for Central Forces. If we assume that nuclear forces are central and that the neutron-proton triplet interaction

[1] In the approximation of equal nucleon masses $\mathbf{p}_p - \mathbf{p}_n$ is proportional to the relative velocity.

is expressed by the central potential $V_C(r) = V_W(r) + V_\sigma(r)$, the Schrödinger equation for the nucleons of the deuteron is, in the center of mass system,

(1) $$\left[-\frac{\hbar^2}{M}\nabla^2 + V_C(r)\right]\psi = E\psi,$$

where r is the relative coordinate and $M/2$ has been used for the reduced mass in the approximation $M = M_n = M_p$.[1] This equation, for a pure S state, $l = 0$, reduces to

(2) $$\frac{d^2u}{dr^2} + k^2(r)u = 0, \qquad u = r\psi$$

with

(3) $$k = \frac{1}{\lambda} = \frac{p}{\hbar} = \frac{1}{\hbar}\sqrt{2\frac{M}{2}T} = \frac{1}{\hbar}\sqrt{M(E - V_C)}.$$

The energy eigenvalue is known from experiment:

(4) $$E = -B = -2.22 \text{ MeV}.$$

E is negative. Since $V_C(r)$ must be attractive, the sign of V_C is also negative, at least for certain values of r.

For constant V_C the solutions of (2) are of the form

(5) $$u = e^{\pm ikr}.$$

If k is real (real momentum, $E > V_C$), u has a sinusoidal behavior, whereas the behavior of u is exponential if k is imaginary (imaginary momentum, $E < V_C$).

In particular, if the force has a finite range ($V_C = 0$ for $r > r_0$), the function u behaves exponentially outside the range. Only exponentials decreasing with r are acceptable in this region, since u must go to zero at infinity, and we can write

(6) $$u = e^{-ik_{\text{out}}r} = e^{-r/R} \quad \text{for } r > r_0,$$

where

(7) $$R = \frac{1}{ik_{\text{out}}} = \frac{\hbar}{i\sqrt{ME}} = \frac{\hbar}{\sqrt{MB}} = 4.31 \times 10^{-13} \text{ cm}$$

is a real quantity which is called the "*radius*" of the deuteron.

[1] If $r_p, r_n, p_p, p_n, T_p, T_n$ are the coordinates, momenta, and kinetic energies of proton and neutron in the center of mass system, the following relations hold for $l = 0$:

$$|r_p| = |r_n| = \frac{r}{2}; \quad |p_p| = |p_n| = M\frac{\dot{r}}{2} = \mu\dot{r} = p; \quad T = 2T_n = 2T_p = \frac{2|p_p|^2}{2M} = \frac{p^2}{M} = \frac{p^2}{2\mu}$$

where r and p are the coordinate and momentum of the relative motion used in the text.

Let us assume that the potential corresponds to some kind of well-behaved, more or less square well. Then the function u starts about linearly, like a sine function, at the origin. Since it describes a ground state, it cannot have nodes and its general appearance is as shown in Fig. 1.23-1.

In the "zero range" approximation the potential acts within a short distance and must be deep to account for the observed binding; the function u is everywhere an exponential. As the range of the force becomes larger, compared to the deuteron radius, the depth of the potential decreases and the sinusoidal part of the wave function becomes more and more prominent.

We shall find from an analysis of the scattering data [3.19(16)] that the range of triplet nuclear forces is around 1.7×10^{-13} cm. Thus

(8) the nuclear forces can be said to be "short-range" in the sense that $r_0 < R$.

It will be useful for what follows to write down a form of the deuteron wave function, which has simple analytic properties and which closely approximates the square well solution. This is the so-called *Hulthén* wave function, which is written, with the proper normalization factor,

$$U(r) = \left[2\pi\left(R + \rho - \frac{4R\rho}{R + \rho}\right)\right]^{-\frac{1}{2}} (e^{-r/R} - e^{-r/\rho}). \tag{9}$$

This function starts from zero at the origin, goes through a maximum, and, for $\rho < R$, decays as $e^{-r/R}$ for large r. Certain experiments (2.24c) indicate that $\rho/R \approx \frac{1}{7}$.

It is believed at present that the nuclear-force potential might consist of a central repulsive core, surrounded by a region of attraction. Assuming that the repulsive core is impenetrable ($V_C = +\infty$ for $r < r_c$), the potential can be schematically represented as in Fig. 1.23-2. The function u is the same as in Fig. 1.23-1, apart from a shift r_c away from the origin.

b. Relation between Range and Depth of Potential. If we assume a square well potential of range r_0 and depth V_0, the function u has the form

$$u_{\text{in}} = C \sin |k_{\text{in}}|\, r \quad \text{for } r < r_0, \tag{10a}$$

with

$$|k_{\text{in}}| = \frac{1}{\hbar}\sqrt{M(|V_0| - B)}$$

and

$$u_{\text{out}} = C' e^{-r/R} \quad \text{for } r > r_0, \tag{10b}$$

where C and C' are two arbitrary constants.

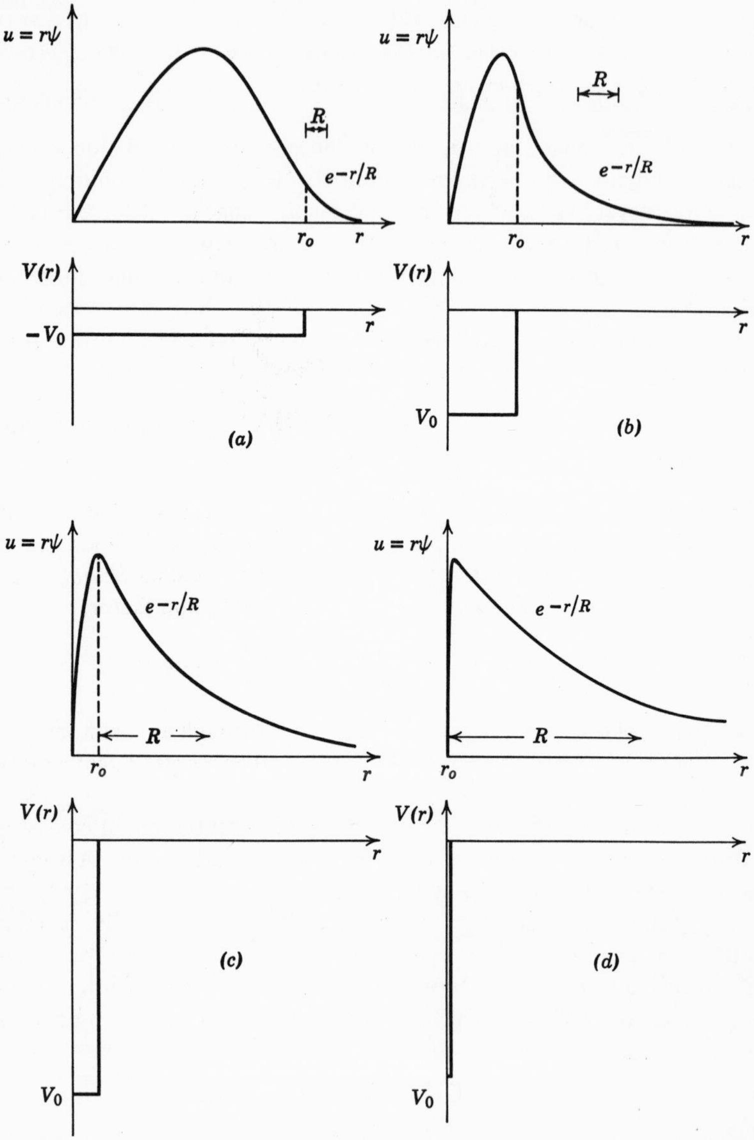

Fig. 1.23-1. Qualitative behavior of the deuteron wave function for four typical cases: (*a*) $r_0 \gg R$ (long-range potential); (*b*) $r_0 \approx R$ (medium-range); (*c*) $r_0 \ll R$ (short-range); (*d*) $r_0 = 0$ (zero-range). Observe that $R = 4.3 \times 10^{-13}$ in all cases: the scale of the abscissa is not the same in the four figures.

The continuity of the logarithmic derivative $1/u\,(du/dr)$ at $r = r_0$ yields

(11) $$|k_{\text{in}}| \cot |k_{\text{in}}|\, r_0 = -\frac{1}{R}.$$

When k_{in} is expressed as a function of V_0, as in (10), equation (11) is a relation between r_0 and V_0.

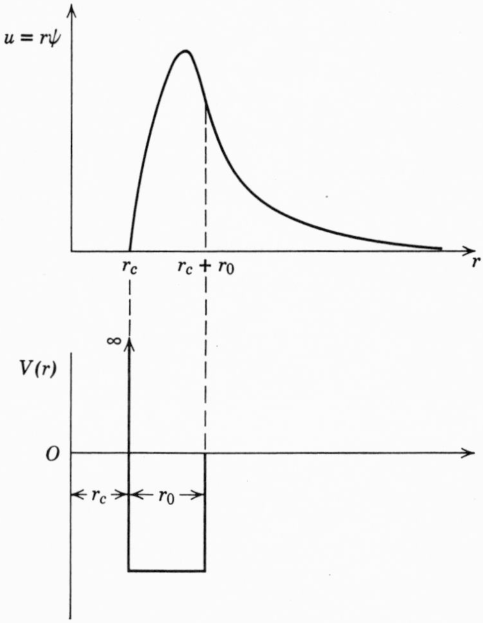

Fig. 1.23-2. Qualitative behavior of the deuteron wave function with repulsive core potential.

In order to obtain a simple expression from which a rough computation of V_0 may be made, let us assume $r_0 \ll R$. Then the function u has its maximum near r_0. This means that we can write approximately

$$k_{\text{in}} r_0 = \frac{\pi}{2}$$

or

(12) $$\frac{1}{\hbar}\sqrt{M(|V_0| - B)}\,r_0 = \frac{\pi}{2};$$

but in the short range approximation $|V_0| \gg B$, and thus we obtain the following simple relation:

(13) $$|V_0|\, r_0^{\,2} = \frac{\pi^2}{4}\frac{\hbar^2}{M} = 1.02 \times 10^{-24} \text{ MeV cm}^2.$$

For $r_0 = 1.4 \times 10^{-13}$ cm (Compton wavelength of π meson) we obtain $|V_0| \approx 50$ MeV.

The finite range of the forces may be taken into account a little more carefully by expanding the cotangent in (11) around $\pi/2$ to first order: $\cot k_{in}r = (\pi/2) - k_{in}r$. Then, solving for k_{in} and using (10), we obtain instead of (12)

$$(14) \qquad \frac{1}{\hbar}\sqrt{M(|V_0| - B)}r_0 = \frac{\pi}{4}\left(1 + \sqrt{1 + \frac{16}{\pi^2}\frac{r_0}{R}}\right).$$

By squaring, keeping only first-order terms in r_0/R, and using (7), we have

$$(15) \qquad |V_0| = \frac{\pi^2\hbar^2}{4Mr_0^{\,2}} + B\left(1 + \frac{2R}{r_0}\right).$$

Again, for $r_0 = 1.4 \times 10^{-13}$ cm, this formula gives

$$|V_0| \approx (50 + 13)\text{MeV}.$$

Similar considerations for other potential shapes are found in the old literature (B-36), where one considers the following potentials: Exponential

$$V = -|V_0|\, e^{-r/r_0},$$

Gaussian

$$V = -|V_0|\, e^{-r^2/r_0^2},$$

and Yukawa

$$V = -|V_0|\,\frac{r_0}{r}\, e^{-r/r_0}.$$

These computations are not reported here.

I.24 The Deuteron as a Mixture of S and D States

a. Admixtures in the Deuteron Wave Function. As we saw in 1.22(5), the deuteron may consist of a superimposition of $^3S_1$ and $^3D_1$ states. Thus its wave function can be written

$$(1) \qquad \psi = \phi_S + \phi_D.$$

Without losing generality, we can take the z axis in the direction of the spin and introduce two radial functions $v(r)$ and $w(r)$ such that

$$(2) \quad \phi_S = \frac{v(r)}{r}\,\mathcal{Y}^1_{101} = \frac{v(r)}{r}\,Y_0^{\,0}\zeta_1^{\,1} = \frac{1}{\sqrt{4\pi}}\frac{v(r)}{r}\,\zeta_1^{\,1},$$

$$(3) \quad \phi_D = \frac{w(r)}{r}\,\mathcal{Y}^1_{121} = \frac{w(r)}{r}\left(\sqrt{\tfrac{6}{10}}\, Y_2^{\,2}\zeta_1^{\,-1} - \sqrt{\tfrac{3}{10}}\, Y_2^{\,1}\zeta_1^{\,0} + \sqrt{\tfrac{1}{10}}\, Y_2^{\,0}\zeta_1^{\,1}\right).$$

The rules for the addition of angular momentum described in 1.14 have been used to obtain (2) and (3).

If ψ is normalized to unity, the functions v and w are not so separately normalized. We can write

$$(4)\quad \begin{aligned} 1 &= \int \psi^* \psi \, d\mathbf{r} = \int (\phi_S^* + \phi_D^*)(\phi_S + \phi_D) \, d\mathbf{r} \\ &= \int (\phi_S^* \phi_S + \phi_D^* \phi_D) \, d\mathbf{r} = \int (v^2(r) + w^2(r)) \, dr. \end{aligned}$$

Then

$$(5)\quad \begin{aligned} P_S &= \int v^2(r) \, dr \\ P_D &= \int w^2(r) \, dr \end{aligned}$$

are the probability of finding the deuteron in the S or D state, respectively.

b. The Magnetic Moment of the Deuteron and the Value of P_D. We now proceed to an unsophisticated computation of the magnetic moment of the deuteron, starting from 1.16(12). Let us first remark that when the expectation value is computed for the states described by (1), (2), and (3) the mixed term $\int \phi_S^* \mu_z \phi_D \, d\tau$ vanishes because of the law of addition and of the orthogonality of angular momentum states.

Thus we can write

$$(6)\quad \mu = \langle \phi_S | \mu_z | \phi_S \rangle + \langle \phi_D | \mu_z | \phi_D \rangle,$$

where μ_z is the operator,[1]

$$(7)\quad \mu_z = g_{\mathrm{p}L} L_{\mathrm{p}z} + g_{\mathrm{n}L} L_{\mathrm{n}z} + g_{\mathrm{p}s} s_{\mathrm{p}z} + g_{\mathrm{n}s} s_{\mathrm{n}z},$$

and the states ϕ_S and ϕ_D correspond to $m_J = J = 1$, as shown in (2) and (3). By introducing the values appropriate to our case we have

$$(8)\quad \mu_z = \tfrac{1}{2} L_z + 2\mu_{\mathrm{p}} s_{\mathrm{p}z} + 2\mu_{\mathrm{n}} s_{\mathrm{n}z}.$$

For the ^3S state we obtain, as expected,

$$(9)\quad \langle \phi_S | \mu_z | \phi_S \rangle = (\mu_{\mathrm{p}} + \mu_{\mathrm{n}}) P_S.$$

The calculation for the ^3D state is slightly more complicated, since L_z, $s_{\mathrm{p}z}$, and $s_{\mathrm{n}z}$ are not good quantum numbers and it becomes useful to express μ_z in terms of the operators J^2, J_z, L^2, S^2, whose eigenvalues are easily computed.

For this purpose (8) can be rewritten in the form

$$(10a)\quad \tfrac{1}{2} L_z + (\mu_{\mathrm{p}} + \mu_{\mathrm{n}})(s_{\mathrm{p}z} + s_{\mathrm{n}z}) + (\mu_{\mathrm{p}} - \mu_{\mathrm{n}})(s_{\mathrm{p}z} - s_{\mathrm{n}z}).$$

[1] The subscripts p and n stand for proton and neutron.

We observe now that the last term has zero expectation value in the triplet, and we may transform the first two terms into

(10*b*) $$(\tfrac{1}{2} - \mu_p - \mu_n)L_z + (\mu_p + \mu_n)J_z.$$

Since the expectation value of J_z is 1 and that of L_z is $\frac{3}{2}$ [1], we obtain

(11) $$\langle \phi_D | \mu_z | \phi_D \rangle = \left(\frac{3}{4} - \frac{\mu_p + \mu_n}{2}\right) P_D.$$

Finally, considering that $P_S + P_D = 1$,

(12) $$\mu = (\mu_p + \mu_n)P_S + \left(\frac{3}{4} - \frac{\mu_p + \mu_n}{2}\right) P_D$$
$$= (\mu_p + \mu_n) - \tfrac{3}{2}(\mu_p + \mu_n - \tfrac{1}{2})P_D.$$

The only unknown in this equation is the amount of *D*-state admixture P_D. By substituting the experimental values of the moments we obtain $P_D = 0.04$.

However, we cannot expect the present computation to be accurate to the order of a few percent. For this accuracy we should introduce relativistic corrections, which are difficult to calculate and remain unknown, both in magnitude and sign, despite the work of several authors. Furthermore, we must keep in mind that the anomalous part of the magnetic moments of the neutron and proton is due to currents in the "meson cloud": these clouds may be distorted when the two nucleons are close to each other in the deuteron and will produce a change in the values of μ_p and μ_n to be used in (12).

Thus the conclusions that can be derived from (12) must be stated in a conservative manner, and we report without further comment the following estimated result, which is found in the literature:

(13) $$0.02 \leq P_D \leq 0.08.$$

c. The Quadrupole Moment. For the calculation of the quadrupole moment we must compute the expectation value

(14) $$\langle Q_{0p} \rangle_{JJ} = \langle \tfrac{1}{4}(3\cos^2\theta - 1)r^2 \rangle_{JJ}.$$

The factor $\frac{1}{4}$ arises from the fact that only the proton contributes to the electric properties and that its distance from the center of mass of the deuteron is $r/2$.

Since Q_{0p} has the angular dependence of Y_2^0, it gives a vanishing contribution in the *S* state but it mixes *S* and *D* states. The expectation value consists of two terms,

(15) $$2\langle \phi_S | Q | \phi_D \rangle_{JJ} + \langle \phi_D | Q | \phi_D \rangle_{JJ},$$

[1] Write as usual $L_z = [(\mathbf{L} \cdot \mathbf{J})/J^2]J_z = [(J^2 + L^2 - S^2)/2J^2]J_z$ and substitute $J^2 \to J(J+1) = 2$, $L^2 \to L(L+1) = 6$, $S^2 \to S(S+1) = 2$, $J_z \to 1$.

which lead to (BW-52)

$$(16) \qquad Q = \frac{1}{\sqrt{50}} \int_0^\infty r^2 vw \, dr - \frac{1}{20} \int_0^\infty r^2 w^2 \, dr.$$

It is seen that Q depends not only on P_S and P_D but also on the radial functions $v(r)$ and $w(r)$. The factor r^2 in the integrand shows that the behavior of these functions away from the origin is important. Since $v \gg w$, the first term of (16) predominates, and both v and w are needed to compute Q in a first approximation; these, in turn, depend on the radial functions entering in the potential 1.22(12), as discussed in the next section.

1.25 Differential Equations for the Radial Functions v(r) and w(r)

a. The Equations of Rarita and Schwinger. The most general velocity-independent potential operator for neutron and proton in the triplet state is of the form[1]

$$(1) \qquad V_C(r) + V_T(r) S_{\text{pn}}.$$

On the other hand, the wave function of the deuteron is of the type described in 1.24(1), (2), and (3).

Thus the Schrödinger equation for the deuteron can be written

$$(2) \quad \left[\frac{\hbar^2}{M}\left(-\frac{1}{r}\frac{d^2}{dr^2}r + \frac{L^2}{r^2}\right) + V_C(r) + V_T(r)S_{\text{pn}}\right]\left[\frac{v(r)}{r}\,\mathcal{Y}^1_{101} + \frac{w(r)}{r}\,\mathcal{Y}^1_{121}\right]$$
$$= E\left[\frac{v(r)}{r}\,\mathcal{Y}^1_{101} + \frac{w(r)}{r}\,\mathcal{Y}^1_{121}\right].$$

In this equation we have used $J_z = 1$, which is equivalent to choosing the z axis in the direction of the spin. We also know that

$$L^2\mathcal{Y}^1_{1l1} = l(l+1)\mathcal{Y}^1_{1l1}.$$

We must now compute $S_{\text{pn}}\mathcal{Y}^1_{101}$ and $S_{\text{pn}}\mathcal{Y}^1_{121}$. For this we follow a short-cut method in Blatt and Weisskopf (BW-52, p. 101).

The operator S_{pn} is scalar, and symmetrical in the exchange of proton and neutron. Thus it can mix only states of the same J, S, and parity, and we can write

$$S_{\text{pn}}\mathcal{Y}^1_{101} = a\mathcal{Y}^1_{101} + b\mathcal{Y}^1_{121}.$$

where a and b are constants to be determined. If we integrate this equation over 4π, the left-hand side yields 0, since S_{pn} averages to zero and $\mathcal{Y}^1_{101}$ does not depend on direction. Since $\mathcal{Y}^1_{121}$ also integrates to zero and $\mathcal{Y}^1_{101}$ is spherically symmetrical, we must have $a = 0$.

[1] As in 1.23, the central force $V_C(r)$ is the sum of $V_W(r)$ and $V_\sigma(r)$ from 1.22(12).

In order to evaluate b, we can take advantage of the simplifications for $\theta = 0$:

$$(S_{pn}\mathcal{Y}^1_{101})_{\theta=0} = b(\mathcal{Y}^1_{121})_{\theta=0}.$$

On the left-hand side we must substitute $\hat{\mathbf{z}}$ in place of $\hat{\mathbf{r}}$ in the S_{pn} operator 1.22(11). Then, using 1.24(2) and(3), we obtain

$$(3\sigma_{pz}\sigma_{nz} - \boldsymbol{\sigma}_p \cdot \boldsymbol{\sigma}_n)\frac{1}{\sqrt{4\pi}}\alpha_p\alpha_n = b\sqrt{\frac{1}{10}}\sqrt{\frac{5}{16\pi}}\,2\alpha_p\alpha_n.$$

Carrying on the operations indicated on the left-hand side, we obtain $b = \sqrt{8}$ and we conclude

(3) $$S_{pn}\mathcal{Y}^1_{101} = \sqrt{8}\,\mathcal{Y}^1_{121}.$$

Starting now with

$$S_{pn}\mathcal{Y}^1_{121} = b\mathcal{Y}^1_{101} + c\mathcal{Y}^1_{121}$$

($b = \sqrt{8}$ here also because S_{12} is hermitian), we can compute at $\theta = 0$, as previously indicated, with the result $c = -2$. Thus

(4) $$S_{pn}\mathcal{Y}^1_{121} = \sqrt{8}\,\mathcal{Y}^1_{101} - 2\mathcal{Y}^1_{121}.$$

We can now substitute (3) and (4) into (2). Equating to zero the coefficients of $\mathcal{Y}^1_{101}$ and $\mathcal{Y}^1_{121}$ in the resulting equation, we obtain for v and w a system of coupled differential equations

(5a) $$-\frac{\hbar^2}{M}\frac{d^2v}{dr^2} + V_C(r)v - Ev = -\sqrt{8}\,V_T(r)w,$$

(5b) $$-\frac{\hbar^2}{M}\left(\frac{d^2w}{dr^2} - \frac{6w}{r^2}\right) + [V_C(r) - 2V_T(r)]w - Ew = -\sqrt{8}\,V_T(r)v.$$

These equations were first obtained by Rarita and Schwinger (R-41). Their solution can be obtained numerically for any given set of potentials $V_C(r)$ and $V_T(r)$. Thus (5) is useful for the comparison of the potentials obtained from meson theories or from high-energy scattering experiments with the properties of the deuteron.

b. Example of Modern Solutions. As a typical example of a more modern approach to the deuteron problem, we report briefly a discussion (G-55) based on a potential obtained from a particular approximate form of meson theory (see 7.18 and 7.26a). Such a potential for the triplet S state is graphically shown in Fig. 1.25-1. The form of the potential is completely determined by the theory and by the method of approximation. The theory contains two arbitrary parameters (the nucleon-meson coupling constant f^2 and a cutoff energy ω_{max}), which are, in principle, determined from meson-proton scattering ($f^2 \approx 0.08$, $\omega_{max} \approx 6m_\pi c^2$, where m_π is the π meson mass) but which are somewhat adjusted to obtain the correct binding energy for the deuteron ($f^2 = 0.089$, $\omega_{max} = 6m_\pi c^2$).

The potential shape is quite different from the simple square well with which we started! The central forces show a repulsive core, whereas the tensor forces do not, but even these go to zero at the origin. The function $V_T(r)$ is much larger than $V_C(r)$.

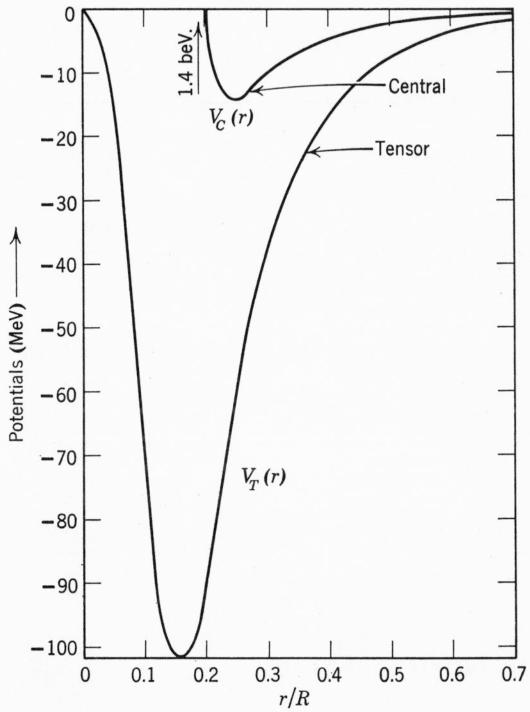

Fig. 1.25-1. The Gartenhaus potential for triplet states and even l. Abscissa is in units of $R = 4.315 \times 10^{-13}$ cm [from S. Gartenhaus, *Phys. Rev.*, **100**, 903 (1955)].

The functions $v(r)$ and $w(r)$ of Fig. 1.25-2 are found by using the potential of Fig. 1.25-1. With these we can compute in turn the constants entering in the deuteron and in low energy n-p scattering with the results in Table 1.25-1.

The agreement is rather encouraging; but we should not be misled into believing that the final word has been said or that we have a satisfactory theory of nuclear forces! The approximation chosen is not unique, and its validity is still a subject for discussion. On the other hand, it cannot be denied that there is something true in interactions of the form presented in Fig. 1.25-1, as we shall see in connection with high-energy nucleon-nucleon scattering (3.58).

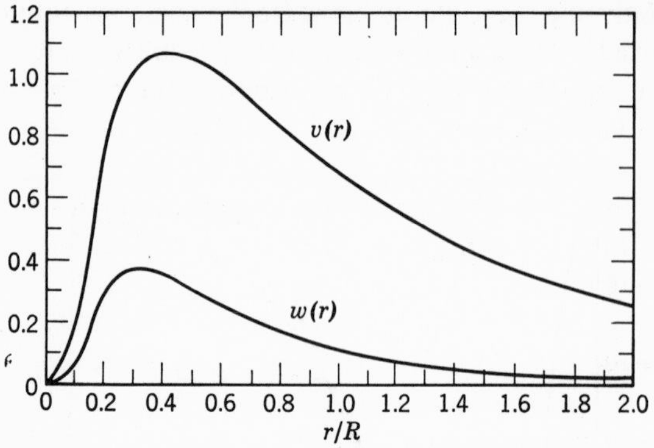

Fig. 1.25-2. The radial functions $v(r)$ and $w(r)$ from the potential of Fig. 1.25-1. The units are the same [from S. Gartenhaus, *Phys. Rev.*, **100**, 904 (1955)].

Table I.25-I *

	Theory	Experiment
	$(f^2 = 0.089, \omega_{max} = 6m_\pi c^2)$	
P_D	6.80%	2 to 8% [1.24(13)]
Q	2.90×10^{-27} cm^2	2.73×10^{-27} cm^2 (1.21b)
r_{e_t}	1.75×10^{-13} cm	1.70×10^{-13} cm [3.19(16)]
a_t	5.42×10^{-13} cm	5.41×10^{-13} cm [3.19(14)]

* See Chapter 3 for the meaning of r_{e_t} and a_t.

I.3 Nucleon-Nucleon Forces

I.31 The Assumption of Charge Independence

So far we have discussed the properties of the force between neutron and proton (n-p). Now we must consider the forces between neutron and neutron (n-n) and between proton and proton (p-p).

An inspection of the data on heavy nuclei, and particularly the behavior of the so-called "mirror nuclei" (see 2.14a), will convince us that the n-n and p-p nuclear forces are equal. By this it is meant that the total n-n and p-p forces differ only because of electromagnetic effects—mainly the electrostatic repulsion between protons—which are small, at short distances, compared with nuclear forces proper.

The equality of the forces acting between like nucleons

$$\text{(n-n)} = \text{(p-p)} \tag{1}$$

has been given the name of *charge symmetry of nuclear forces.*

In order to compare the forces between like nucleons with those acting in the n-p case, let us go back to Table 2 in 1.21b. The data concerning the di-proton and the di-neutron are simply stated: these nuclei are unbound, they do not exist in nature and they cannot be produced as radioactive isotopes.

From this observation we would be inclined to think at first sight that n-p forces must be different from p-p and n-n forces. This, however, is not necessarily true.

Even if the nuclear forces were the same for all nucleon pairs, the di-proton and the di-neutron would be unbound. This is because the exclusion principle prevents like nucleons from being in a ^3S state. The forces acting in the S state of the di-neutron and di-proton cannot be compared with the forces binding the ^3S state of the deuteron but rather with those acting in the ^1S state of the n-p system, which, as we know, do not produce a bound state.

It is usual to introduce as a simplifying working hypothesis the assumption that nuclear forces are the same—for the same spin and angular momentum states—for n-p, p-p, and n-n. This assumption is usually expressed with the statement that *nuclear forces are charge independent*:

$$(\text{n-n}) = (\text{p-p}) = (\text{n-p}). \tag{2}$$

We shall see that charge independence is in agreement with all known facts of nuclear physics. It is found, for instance, that the S-wave nuclear scattering of n-n and n-p is the same in the singlet S state where the comparison is possible (3.4); that equivalent states of nuclei such as C^{14} ($Z = 6, N = 8$), N^{14} ($Z = 7, N = 7$, the interesting state in this case is an excited state), and O^{14} ($Z = 8, N = 6$) are equally bound (2.14a); that high-energy nucleon-nucleon scattering does not violate charge independence (3.55), etc.

In view of this experimental evidence, we can regard charge-independence as one of the basic properties of nuclear forces, and in what follows we shall develop a formalism appropriate to its mathematical formulation.

1.32 The Isospin Formalism

a. Introduction to Isospin. As a consequence of charge independence, it becomes fruitful to regard neutrons and protons as two almost degenerate states of the same particle, the nucleon. The obvious differences between neutron and proton seem to play a secondary role in determining nuclear binding, and the two nucleons can be considered members of an almost degenerate doublet corresponding to two values of some new internal variable.

The expression "doublet" reminds us of the one used for spin multiplicity, and in effect it is possible to construct an *isotopic spin* (*isospin*)[1] formalism, in every way similar to that of usual spin, which is of great help in the treatment of the multiplicities arising in nuclear physics because of the similar behavior of neutrons and protons.

We say that the nucleon $\mathcal{N}$ is a particle of isospin $\frac{1}{2}$, which can exist in two states, the proton p and the neutron n according to whether the isospin points "up" or "down."[2] The isospin is a vector in a three-dimensional space, called isospin space, which has no relation to physical space.

If we introduce a set of cartesian coordinates ξ, η, ζ in isospin space, the components of the isospin vector $\vec{T}$ are one half of the components of the vector operator $\vec{\tau}$:

$$\tau_\xi = \begin{pmatrix} 0 & 1 \\ 1 & 0 \end{pmatrix}, \quad \tau_\eta = \begin{pmatrix} 0 & -i \\ i & 0 \end{pmatrix}, \quad \tau_\zeta = \begin{pmatrix} 1 & 0 \\ 0 & -1 \end{pmatrix}, \tag{1}$$

which are formally identical to the Pauli matrices [1.14(7)]. As in usual spin, only one component, say τ_ζ; is measurable, and its eigenvalues are

$$\begin{aligned} \tau_\zeta &= +1 \quad \text{for proton,} \\ \tau_\zeta &= -1 \quad \text{for neutron,} \end{aligned} \tag{2}$$

corresponding to eigenvalues $\pm\frac{1}{2}$ for the ζ component of isospin.

All the formalism of physical spin (1.14b) can be used for isospin. For a proton

$$\psi = \begin{pmatrix} \psi_\mathrm{p} \\ 0 \end{pmatrix} = \mathrm{p} \tag{3}$$

and for a neutron

$$\psi = \begin{pmatrix} 0 \\ \psi_\mathrm{n} \end{pmatrix} = \mathrm{n}. \tag{4}$$

The symbols p and n replace the α and β of physical spin theory.

Formally, the nucleon state could be a mixture of neutron and proton, but physically *it is meaningless to add coherently the states* p *and* n of the same nucleon since the resulting state would not have a definite electric charge. Stated in other words, it is meaningless to add coherently proton and neutron states to form a particle polarized in the ξ or η direction of isospace.

[1] The name isospin cuts short the long-standing controversy in nomenclature between the partisans of "isotopic spin" and "isobaric spin."

[2] The convention that the proton has isospin "up" is usual in high-energy nuclear physics, whereas in the literature on low-energy physics it is often assumed that the isospin of the neutron is "up."

The operators

$$\Lambda_p = \tfrac{1}{2}(1 + \tau_\zeta), \quad \Lambda_n = \tfrac{1}{2}(1 - \tau_\zeta) \tag{5}$$

are projection operators for the neutron and the proton in complete analogy with 1.14(17).

Then the charge, mass, and magnetic moment operators of the nucleon are

$$q = \tfrac{1}{2}(1 + \tau_\zeta)\,|e|\,, \tag{6}$$

$$M = \tfrac{1}{2}(1 + \tau_\zeta)M_p + \tfrac{1}{2}(1 - \tau_\zeta)M_n, \tag{7}$$

$$\mu = \tfrac{1}{2}(1 + \tau_\zeta)\mu_p + \tfrac{1}{2}(1 - \tau_\zeta)\mu_n. \tag{8}$$

The components τ_ξ and τ_η, although not measurable, are essential to the formalism. It is often convenient to consider the components of $\vec{\tau}$ on the axes

$$\mp \frac{1}{\sqrt{2}}(\hat{\xi} \pm i\hat{\eta}) \qquad \text{and } \hat{\zeta},$$

and we can write, as in 1.14(19),

$$\tau^+ = \tfrac{1}{2}(\tau_\xi + i\tau_\eta) = -\frac{1}{\sqrt{2}}\tau_+ = \begin{pmatrix} 0 & 1 \\ 0 & 0 \end{pmatrix}, \tag{9}$$

$$\tau^- = \tfrac{1}{2}(\tau_\xi - i\tau_\eta) = \frac{1}{\sqrt{2}}\tau_- = \begin{pmatrix} 0 & 0 \\ 1 & 0 \end{pmatrix},$$

$$\tau_0 = \tau_\zeta = \begin{pmatrix} 1 & 0 \\ 0 & -1 \end{pmatrix}.$$

The operators τ^+ and τ^- transform a neutron into a proton and vice versa.

The wave functions ψ_p and ψ_n are, in turn, two-component Pauli functions, which describe the spin multiplicity. Relativistically, ψ_p and ψ_n are four-component Dirac spinors.

Keeping all these complications in mind, we will nevertheless often write, in short form ψ_p, $|p\rangle$, or p for $\begin{pmatrix} \psi_p \\ 0 \end{pmatrix}$, and similarly for the neutron, and

$$\psi_{p\uparrow},\ |p, +\tfrac{1}{2}\rangle, \text{ or } p_\uparrow \quad \text{for} \quad \begin{bmatrix} \begin{pmatrix} \psi \\ 0 \end{pmatrix} \\ \begin{pmatrix} 0 \\ 0 \end{pmatrix} \end{bmatrix},$$

etc.

It is also convenient to use the following graphical symbols:

proton with spin up,
proton with spin down,
neutron with spin up,
neutron with spin down.

b. Isospin of Many Nucleons. We shall assume that the isospin of a system of many particles can be obtained by means of the usual addition rules of angular momentum.

A single nucleon has isospin $\frac{1}{2}$ with ζ components $\pm\frac{1}{2}$. The total isospin operator of a system of A nucleons is

$$\vec{T} = \sum_{\alpha=1}^{A} \tfrac{1}{2}\vec{\tau}_\alpha. \tag{10}$$

The eigenvalues of T^2 are $T(T+1)$, where T can assume values between 0 and $A/2$. For each T there are $2T+1$ eigenvalues of T_ζ, which are integer or half-integer numbers with $-T \leq T_\zeta \leq T$.

Since $\tau_\zeta = \pm 1$ for proton and neutron, respectively, the eigenvalue of T_ζ is[1]

$$T_\zeta = \sum_{\alpha=1}^{A} \tfrac{1}{2}\tau_{\alpha\zeta} = \tfrac{1}{2}(Z - N); \tag{11}$$

from this it is immediately verified that (6) gives the correct nuclear charge:

$$\sum_{\alpha=1}^{A} q_\alpha = \sum_{\alpha=1}^{A} \tfrac{1}{2}(1 + \tau_{\alpha\zeta})|e| = \tfrac{1}{2}|A + 2T_\zeta|\,|e| = Z\,|e|.$$

The states of a system of A nucleons corresponding to the same value of T are said to form an isospin multiplet. There are $2T+1$ members of the multiplet, corresponding to different T_ζ and thus to different charge, the limits of Z being $A/2 \pm T$.

If there were no electromagnetic effects, all the members of the multiplet would have the same structure and the same binding energy.

c. Example for A = 2. Let us see how the law of addition for isotopic spin leads to a simple and meaningful classification of the states of two nucleons in the S state.

The states of two nucleons, 1 and 2, can be classified as isospin singlet and triplet according to whether $T = 0$ or 1. The singlet

$$\frac{1}{\sqrt{2}}\,[\psi_p(1)\,\psi_n(2) - \psi_n(1)\,\psi_p(2)] \tag{12}$$

[1] With our notation T_ζ is negative for complex nuclei that have $N > Z$. The sign would be positive if we had assigned $T_\zeta = +\frac{1}{2}$ to the neutron, as is sometimes done in the discussion of nuclear structure.

has necessarily $T_\zeta = 0$, thus $N = Z$. It represents some state of the neutron-proton system. The three components of the triplet for $T_\zeta = \pm 1$ and 0 are

$$\psi_p(1)\,\psi_p(2)$$

$$\frac{1}{\sqrt{2}}\,[\psi_p(1)\,\psi_n(2) + \psi_n(1)\,\psi_p(2)] \tag{13}$$

$$\psi_n(1)\,\psi_n(2)$$

and correspond, respectively, to two protons, to some state of neutron-proton, and to two neutrons.

The classification is meaningful for the following reason. A neutron and a proton in the S (or D) state can have either parallel or antiparallel physical spins (^3S or ^1S), whereas two protons and two neutrons are allowed to exist only with opposite spins (^1S). According to charge independence, the three ^1S states, pp, np, nn, behave in the same manner, and it is useful to group them together as the three isotriplet components (13). On the other hand, the physical spin triplet—whose ground state is the bound deuteron—is allowed only for different nucleons: in isospin notation it is singled out as the isosinglet state (12).

If we accept this classification of the $A = 2$ states, we note that all allowed $l = 0$ states are antisymmetrical in relation to the exchange of both $\boldsymbol{\sigma}$ and $\vec{\tau}$. This observation is a particular aspect of a general formulation of the exclusion principle for the nucleons presented in (d).

d. The Exclusion Principle for the Nucleons. The exclusion principle applies to identical particles of spin $\frac{1}{2}$. It can be stated as follows:

(14) *The wave function of N identical particles*

$$\psi(\mathbf{r}_1\boldsymbol{\sigma}_1, \cdots, \mathbf{r}_i\boldsymbol{\sigma}_i, \cdots, \mathbf{r}_j\boldsymbol{\sigma}_j, \cdots, \mathbf{r}_N\boldsymbol{\sigma}_N)$$

must be antisymmetrical in relation to the exchange of the space and spin coordinates $\mathbf{r}\boldsymbol{\sigma}$ *of any pair ij.*

The exclusion principle, as stated, applies to neutrons and to protons separately. It does not apply to nucleons because two nucleons in different charge states are obviously not identical.

But in the isotopic spin formalism *all* nucleons are considered identical, the difference between neutron and proton being only in the eigenvalues of the coordinate $\vec{\tau}$. The state of A nucleons is written as

$$\psi(\mathbf{r}_1\boldsymbol{\sigma}_1\vec{\tau}_1, \cdots, \mathbf{r}_i\boldsymbol{\sigma}_i\vec{\tau}_i, \cdots \mathbf{r}_j\boldsymbol{\sigma}_j\vec{\tau}_j, \cdots \mathbf{r}_A\boldsymbol{\sigma}_A\vec{\tau}_A). \tag{15}$$

We can now reformulate the exclusion principle:

(16) *The wave function of A nucleons must be antisymmetrical relative to the exchange of the space, spin, and isospin coordinates* $\mathbf{r}\boldsymbol{\sigma}\vec{\tau}$ *of any pair ij.*

Clearly, if the two nucleons are of the same kind, their wave function is symmetrical in $\vec{\tau}$ and the new formulation reduces to the old one. On the other hand, if the two nucleons are in a different charge state, their wave function can be either symmetrical or antisymmetrical in $\vec{\tau}$, and the new formulation allows all states in **r** and $\boldsymbol{\sigma}$.

Our classification of the states for $A = 2$ and $l = 0$ agrees with the new formulation of the exclusion principle. The bound state of the deuteron, an n-p system in an even angular momentum state and in an even physical spin state, must be an odd (singlet) isospin state.

e. Similarities and Differences between Spin and Isospin. In order to clarify the meaning of isotopic spin and its connection with the exclusion principle, let us consider two different approaches to atomic physics (neglecting, for simplicity, the physical spin of neutron and proton).

In our first approach we state that atoms are composed of four different elementary particles:

protons, p,
neutrons, n,
upelectrons, u,
downelectrons, d.

Just as protons and neutrons are easily recognizable by applying an electric field, so upelectrons and downelectrons are distinguishable in a magnetic field H. The following elementary particle reactions may occur:

$$\mathrm{n} \rightarrow \mathrm{p} + e + \bar{\nu} + 782\ \mathrm{keV}$$

$$\mathrm{u} \rightarrow \mathrm{d} + \hbar\omega, \quad \text{with } \hbar\omega = 2\mu_e H.$$

The four particles separately obey the exclusion principle, but protons do not exclude neutrons and upelectrons do not exclude downelectrons from the same orbital state.

Alternatively, we can say that atoms consist of only two different particles, namely

nucleons, $\mathcal{N}$
electrons, e,

but then we must reformulate the exclusion principle to take into account the different possible states of the nucleon and of the electron.

Some confusion may arise because the conventional presentation of atomic physics is an admixture of the two foregoing, in which upelectrons and downelectrons are considered as one particle, whereas protons and neutrons are regarded as distinct.

The similarity of the way in which spin and isospin enter into the formulation of the exclusion principle must not make us forget that they are two essentially different quantities and that the analogy does not extend to all their properties. The most conspicuous difference is the difference of mass of the two isospin states, which makes the neutron unstable even in the absence of external fields. It is also important to keep in mind that conservation of charge requires T_ζ to be a good quantum number, defining a privileged direction in isospace.

I.33 *The Charge-Independent Hamiltonian*

a. Conservation of Isotopic Spin. The assumption of charge independence asserts that the nuclear forces between two nucleons are independent of their charge states and thus of the values of τ_ζ. Since in our formalism the individual τ_ζ are not good quantum numbers, charge independence must be formulated in terms of the total isospin:

(1) *Fqr a given value of T the nuclear interaction is independent of T_ζ.*

This statement corresponds to complete degeneracy of the T-multiplets. These, however, are split because of electromagnetic effects by an amount that is small for light nuclei and that becomes more and more important for heavy nuclei (since, as we shall see, the nuclear binding increases linearly with A and the electrostatic repulsion energy increases with Z^2).

Another way of stating charge independence is the following:

(2) *The nuclear force Hamiltonian does not depend on the orientation of the total isospin vector $\vec{T}$,*

from which it follows that

(3) *isospin space is isotropic as far as nuclear interactions are concerned*[1].

Since isospin has all the properties of angular momentum, the isotropy of isospin space is equivalent to the

(4) *principle of conservation of isotopic spin $\vec{T}$.*

We are thus faced with a new conservation law that is only approximately valid, in the same manner that conservation of orbital angular momentum is only approximately valid in atomic physics because of spin-orbit coupling.

The component T_ζ is necessarily a constant of the motion due to conservation of charge; but we can also state that

(5) *if we neglect electromagnetic effects T^2 is a good quantum number.*

Let us comment briefly on the relation between charge independence and *charge symmetry*. We have seen in 1.31 that invariance under charge symmetry is a particular case of charge independence: it must therefore

[1] However, the electromagnetic interaction defines a privileged direction in isospace.

correspond to invariance under particular rotations in isospace. These rotations must transform all neutrons into all protons (and vice-versa) and thus change the sign of T_ζ: they must be identified with 180° rotations around an axis perpendicular to ζ. It is customary to represent the operation of charge symmetry with a rotation of 180° in the $\varphi = 0$ plane, that is, rotations around the second (η) isospin axis.

The application of the idea of isospin to nuclei with $A > 2$ is discussed in Chapter 2. In Chapters 7 and 8 we will find that isospin is useful in the theory of all strongly interacting particles.

b. The Charge-Independent Hamiltonian. In order to conform with isospin conservation, the Hamiltonian describing the interaction between two nucleons must be rotationally invariant in isospace. Thus it must contain scalar quantities formed with the isospins $\vec{\tau}_1$ and $\vec{\tau}_2$. Only two such linearly independent scalars exist: these can be chosen as 1 and $\vec{\tau}_1 \cdot \vec{\tau}_2$ or as

$$(6) \qquad 1 \quad \text{and} \quad \mathcal{T}_\tau = \tfrac{1}{2}(1 + \vec{\tau}_1 \cdot \vec{\tau}_2),$$

where $\mathcal{T}_\tau$ is the *isospin exchange operator* [compare with 1.14 (38)].

Thus, if we use 1.22 (12), the most general velocity independent interaction Hamiltonian between two nucleons can be written

$$(7) \quad [V_W(r) + V_\sigma(r)\mathcal{T}_\sigma + V_T(r)S_{12}] + \mathcal{T}_\tau[V_W'(r) + V_\sigma'(r)\mathcal{T}_\sigma + V_T'(r)S_{12}].$$

The central problem of nuclear physics is to establish whether (7) is correct—without addition of velocity-dependent forces or of terms violating charge independence—and to determine the functions of position appearing in it. Since no evidence to contradict charge independence has been found and velocity-dependent forces seem unimportant, at least for small velocities, the problem is reduced to the determination of the six $V(r)$.

This problem has been attacked with all the means at our disposal, but a final word still cannot be said.

Formula (7) has been compared with the properties of complex stable nuclei—not an easy job by far to carry out quantitatively because of the difficulties inherent in many body problems; scattering experiments at ever-increasing energies have been and are being performed in order to find the nuclear force interaction; new particles—mesons—have been invented to explain nuclear forces; the properties of the π mesons have been studied both theoretically and experimentally in the hope of throwing light on the fundamental problem of nuclear physics; other, unpredicted particles—the μ meson and the strange particles—were discovered in the process of these investigations, and we know that they must be related to the nuclear interactions.

As a result of all this labor, our knowledge has no doubt increased. But, after a succession of hopes and disappointments, the original goal has not yet been reached, and "strong interactions" are still not understood or only partly understood.

There has been, however, a step forward. If, twenty years ago, the purpose of nuclear physics was to describe nuclear forces by means of the six functions appearing in (7), today, owing to the progress in the field of elementary particles, we believe that it may be possible to arrive not only at a description but also at an understanding of nuclear forces in terms of the properties of mesons and hyperons.

c. Exchange Operators and Exchange Forces. We have already observed in 1.14 (38) that the operators $\mathcal{T}_\sigma$ and $\mathcal{T}_\tau$ effectively exchange the spin and the isospin of particles 1 and 2.

For two particles of equal mass relative to the common center of mass, $\psi(\mathbf{r}_1, \mathbf{r}_2) = \psi(\mathbf{r}_1, -\mathbf{r}_1)$; in this case the exchange operator $\mathcal{T}_r$ is equivalent to the orbital parity operator $P_r^{(0)}$ and its eigenvalues are $(-1)^l$, where l is the orbital angular momentum of the relative motion.

The meaning of the product $\mathcal{T}_\sigma\mathcal{T}_\tau$, which enters in the general Hamiltonian, can be easily understood if we remember that the exclusion principle demands

(8) $$\mathcal{T}_\tau\mathcal{T}_\sigma\mathcal{T}_r = -1,$$

where $\mathcal{T}_r$ is the *coordinate exchange* operator.

The exchange operators that can possibly enter in the interaction Hamiltonian between two nucleons are listed here with their eigenvalues.

The coordinate exchange operator or Majorana operator:

(9) $$\mathcal{T}_r, \text{ with eigenvalues } (-1)^l.$$

The spin exchange operator or Bartlett operator:

(10) $$\mathcal{T}_\sigma, \text{ with eigenvalues } (-1)^{S+1}.$$

The isospin exchange operator or Heisenberg operator:

(11) $$\mathcal{T}_\tau, \text{ with eigenvalues } (-1)^{T+1}.$$

Because of the exclusion principle (8), the quantum numbers l, S, T are restricted by the relation

(12) $$l + S + T \quad \text{must be odd.}$$

Let us note that states of different T do not mix because of charge independence and states of even l do not mix with states of odd l because of parity conservation. It follows that, for a pair of interacting nucleons, states of even S (triplets) do not mix with states of odd S (singlets). Thus in the two-body problem of nuclear physics

(13) $$S \text{ is a good quantum number.}$$

Historically, exchange operators were first considered by Heisenberg, who thought that nuclear forces were similar to the exchange forces in the hydrogen molecule. Because the atoms of the molecule exchange an electron, Heisenberg thought that the nucleons in the deuteron exchanged a charge (according to Yukawa, this would be associated with a meson), as described by the operator $\mathcal{T}_\tau$.

We have already discussed the presence of spin-dependent forces, requiring terms in $\mathcal{T}_\sigma$ in the Hamiltonian, and we shall see that other exchange forces are needed to account for the behavior of nuclear forces for different states of angular momentum.

References

Books

BW-52 J. M. Blatt and V. F. Weisskopf, *Theoretical Nuclear Physics*, Wiley, New York, 1952.

CS-57 E. U. Condon and G. H. Shortley, *The Theory of Atomic Spectra*, Cambridge University Press, 1957.

Ed-57 A. R. Edmonds, *Angular Momentum in Quantum Mechanics*, Princeton University Press, Princeton, N.J., 1957.

FR-59 U. Fano and G. Racah, *Irreducible Tensorial Sets*, Academic Press, New York, 1959.

Ra-53 N. F. Ramsey, *Nuclear Moments*, Wiley, New York, 1953.

Ra-56 N. F. Ramsey, *Molecular Beams*, Clarendon Press, Oxford, 1956.

Ro-57 M. E. Rose, *Elementary Theory of Angular Momentum*, Wiley, New York, 1957.

Sc-55 L. Schiff, *Quantum Mechanics*, McGraw-Hill, New York, 1955.

Wi-31 E. P. Wigner, *Gruppentheorie*, F. Vieweg and Sohn, Braunschweig, 1931.

Wi-59 E. P. Wigner, *Group Theory* (English translation), Academic Press, New York, 1959.

Articles

B-50 R. E. Bell and R. G. Elliot, *Phys. Rev.*, **79**, 282 (1950).

B-36 H. A. Bethe and R. F. Bacher, *Rev. Mod. Phys.*, **8**, 82 (1936).

C-57 M. H. Cohen and F. Reif, *Solid State Phys.*, **5**, 321 (1957).

E-41 L. Eisenbud and E. P. Wigner, *Proc. Nat. Acad. Sci., U.S.*, **27**, 281 (1941).

G-55 S. Gartenhaus, *Phys. Rev.*, **100**, 900 (1955).

J-54 Jaccarino, King, Satten, and Stroke, *Phys. Rev.*, **94**, 1798 (1954).

R-41 W. Rarita and J. Schwinger, *Phys. Rev.*, **59**, 436 (1941).

R-51 J. M. Robson, *Phys. Rev.*, **83**, 349 (1951).

R-55 J. M. Robson, *Phys. Rev.*, **100**, 933 (1955).

S-57 Smith, Purcell, and Ramsey, *Phys. Rev.*, **108**, 120 (1957).

TWO

Nuclear Models

2.1 Light Nuclei

2.11 *Nuclei with Three and Four Nucleons*

a. H^3 and He^3. We shall now try to understand, at least in a qualitative way, how the nucleon-nucleon forces described in Chapter 1 account for the properties of complex nuclei. We start our discussion with a description of light nuclei and, proceeding to larger and larger atomic numbers, we shall see how nuclear properties may be related to the fundamental interactions.

The character of this discussion is necessarily less precise than the treatment of Chapter 1; many of the ideas are at best semiquantitative and much of the presentation is purely descriptive.

Let us start with the nuclei containing three nucleons. For $A = 3$ the isospin can assume the values $\frac{3}{2}$ and $\frac{1}{2}$, giving rise to a quadruplet with $0 \leq Z \leq 3$ and a doublet with $1 \leq Z \leq 2$. The terms of the quadruplet would be the nuclei (nnn), (nnp), (npp), and (ppp), supposedly all equally bound and in the same space-spin state. It is well known that the tri-proton and the tri-neutron do not exist, and we conclude that all terms of the quadruplet are unbound. Thus H^3 and He^3, like n and p, belong to an isospin doublet. The data on these nuclei are reported in Table 1.

As for the deuteron, the values of spin and magnetic moments can be accounted for in the assumption of an almost pure S state. If all three nucleons are in the same state with zero orbital angular momentum (Fig. 2.11-1), the spin is necessarily $\frac{1}{2}$ because of the exclusion principle;

Table 2.11-1

	H^3	He^3
Atomic mass	3.01699	3.01697
Spin	$\frac{1}{2}$	$\frac{1}{2}$
Magnetic moment	2.9788	−2.1274
Binding energy B*	8.5 MeV	7.6 MeV
Binding energy per nucleon pair $B/3$	2.8	2.5
Decay mode	$H^3 \to He^3 + e + \bar{\nu}$	stable
Decay mean life	12.3 years	—
Decay energy (atomic mass difference)	18 keV	—

* The binding energy of an atom whose nucleus contains N neutrons and Z protons is determined from its mass by using the well-known relativistic relation between mass and energy:

$$B = [ZM_H + NM_n - M(Z, N)]c^2.$$

M_H is the mass of the hydrogen *atom* and $M(Z, N)$, the *atomic* mass of the isotope considered. The binding energy, thus defined, includes the binding energy of the atomic electrons.

the magnetic moments predicted for a pure S state are just μ_p and μ_n and differ by about 10% from the measured values.

Fig. 2.11-1. The state of the bound nuclei for $A = 3$.

The unbound members of the quadruplet would have an entirely different structure (see Fig. 2.11-2).

It is interesting to observe that the binding energy per pair of particles of these two nuclei is higher than the binding energy of the deuteron. This is because the range of nuclear forces is considerably smaller than the radius of the deuteron. If we add a third nucleon to the deuteron, we increase the number of particles from 2 to 3 and the number of interacting pairs from 1 to 3. Since there is more attraction per particle, the three nucleons are, on the average, closer to one another than the two nucleons in the deuteron. Thus they are more often within the attractive well, increasing the expectation value of the binding energy per pair.

b. Electrostatic Repulsion. The difference of mass between H^3 and He^3 can be expressed as follows.

(1) $[2M_n + M_H - (\text{nuclear binding energy of } H^3)]$
$- [M_n + 2M_H - (\text{nuclear binding energy of } He^3)$
$+ (\text{electrostatic energy between two protons})] = 18\text{ keV}.$

If nuclear forces are charge-symmetrical, the nuclear binding energies of H^3 and He^3 are identical and (1) reduces to

(2) $M_{\rm n} - M_{\rm H}$ + (electrostatic energy between two protons) = 18 keV,

from which we obtain

(3) electrostatic repulsion energy between two protons of He^3 = 764 keV.

Let us see if this can be simply explained. The energy of electrostatic repulsion between two protons 1 and 2, within a nucleus, can be computed in an elementary oversimplified way, assuming that the nucleus is a sphere

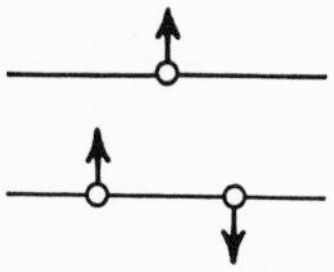

Fig. 2.11-2. The state of the trineutron.

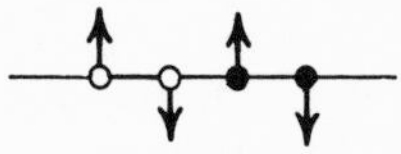

Fig. 2.11-3. State of He^4.

of radius R and that the probability of finding each proton is constant all over the nuclear volume. Then each proton produces a charge density $\rho = e/\frac{4}{3}\pi R^3$ and a potential $U(r) = 2\pi\rho[R^2 - (r^2/3)]$. The energy of the charge density of proton 1 in the potential due to proton 2 is

(4) $$E_{\rm coul} = \int U\rho\, d\mathbf{r} = 2\pi\rho^2 \int \left(R^2 - \frac{r^2}{3}\right) r^2\, dr\, d\Omega = \frac{32}{15}\pi^2\rho^2 R^5 = \frac{6}{5}\frac{e^2}{R}.$$

By equating (3) and (4) we find for the radius of He^3

(5) $$R = 2.3 \times 10^{-13}\ \text{cm}.$$

This value is quite reasonable and shows that the idea of charge symmetry leads to no contradiction, although we cannot expect that the results obtained from (4) will be accurate.

For comparison, we report that recent measurements (C-63) of the form factor of He^3 by high-energy electron scattering give a rms radius of $1.97 \pm 0.10 \cdot 10^{-13}$ cm for an assumed gaussian charge density distribution.

c. He^4. There is a single bound nucleus with $A = 4$. This is He^4, obviously an isospin singlet. Its spin is 0, as we can expect for four particles in an S state (Fig. 2.11-3).

The binding energy of He^4 is high: 28 MeV. The binding energy per pair, 28/6 MeV = 4.7 MeV, is the highest of all nuclei. Thus we expect the four nucleons of He^4 to be very close to one another and quite often within one another's potential well. This is confirmed by high-energy electron scattering experiments according to which He^4 is a gaussian distribution of charge with rms radius 1.61×10^{-13} cm (H-56).

2.12 Nuclei with Five Nucleons: Spin-Orbit Coupling and Saturation

a. A = 5. Scattering of Neutrons and Protons by He. Proceeding in order with our survey of nuclei, we find that *there is no stable*

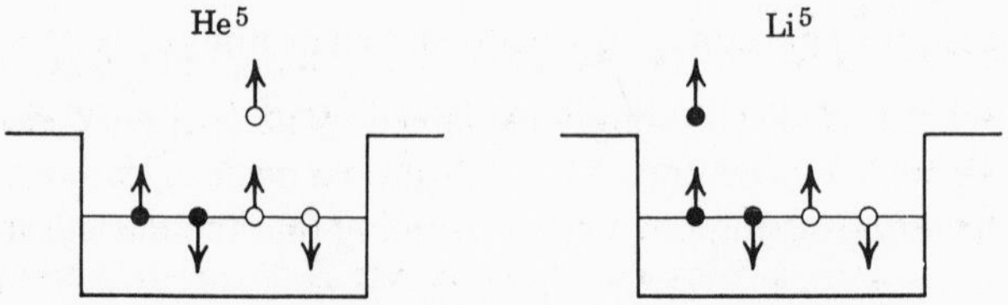

Fig. 2.12-1. Schematic representation of the state of five nucleons in He^5 and Li^5.

nucleus with $A = 5$. This is a rather unusual situation: in a nuclear chart ordered in A only the places $A = 5$ and $A = 8$ are empty. The binding energy per pair has been growing steadily up to He^4, and now we suddenly find no binding at all when we try to add another neutron or proton.

The reason is that the fifth particle cannot fit in the same state as the other four. The unbound He^5 and Li^5 can be intuitively represented by the diagram in Fig. 2.12-1.

Some information about the forces between the α particle and the extra nucleon can be obtained by studying the scattering of neutrons and protons in He.

Let us consider n-He scattering, which is easier to interpret because of

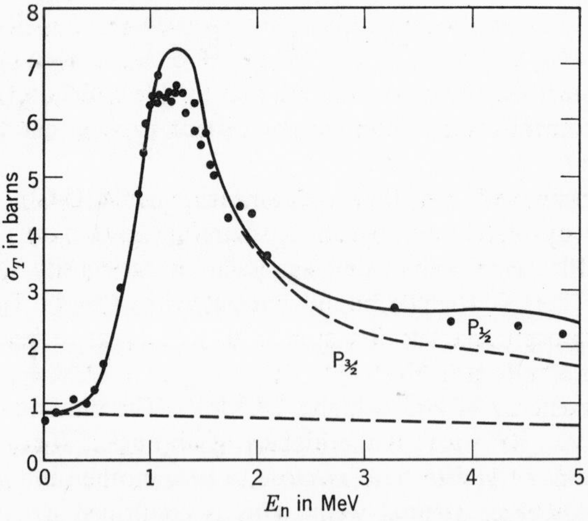

Fig. 2.12-2. Experimental points for total n-α cross section and decomposition from phase analysis. The dotted lines separate the contributions of the various partial cross sections [from R. K. Adair, *Phys. Rev.*, **86**, 160 (1952)].

the absence of coulomb (Rutherford) scattering. The total cross section shows a maximum at a center of mass energy of 0.95 MeV with a half-width of $\approx\frac{1}{2}$ MeV. A phase analysis (discussed in detail in 3.52) shows that this maximum is the result of an interaction of the neutron in a $P_{3/2}$ state. The contributions of the $P_{1/2}$ state and of the S state can also be resolved, as shown in Fig. 2.12-2.

The observed resonance can be interpreted as resulting from a virtual state of the He-n system, with a binding energy of ≈ -0.95 MeV and a mean life $\Delta t = \hbar/\Delta E \approx 10^{-21}$ sec. Though this mean life is short, it is considerably longer than the transit time of a neutron of $\approx$1 MeV (velocity $\approx 2 \times 10^9$ cm/sec) through the He nucleus ($\approx 2 \times 10^{-13}$ cm) and indicates the temporary formation of a state of He^5.

b. Spin-Orbit Coupling. From these considerations and from Fig. 2.12-2 we conclude that the lowest state of He^5 is an unbound $P_{3/2}$ state; the $P_{1/2}$ state is even more unbound, since it affects the scattering at still higher neutron energy. The different energy of the $P_{3/2}$ and $P_{1/2}$ states shows that nuclear forces have the property of *spin-orbit coupling*. The lowest term of the spin-orbit doublet is the one with the highest J, contrary to the situation prevailing in atomic physics. In nuclear physics we speak therefore of *inverted doublets*. The importance of spin-orbit coupling appears in the theory of nuclear shell structure.

The results obtained from the scattering of protons in He are similar to those just described for the neutrons. The only difference is caused by the electrostatic charge which makes the interpretation of the data more difficult and which raises the unbound levels of Li^5 (three proton pairs) above those of He^5 (one proton pair). It is interesting to observe that the difference in coulomb energy is now larger than the neutron-hydrogen mass difference, making the atom He^5, with the larger number of neutrons, the more stable of the doublet. The relative position of the levels is shown in Fig. 2.12-3.

c. Saturation and Exchange Character of Nuclear Forces. The tight binding of He^4 and the lack of binding of He^5 and Li^5 can be regarded as evidence in favor of exchange forces of the Majorana type 1.33 (9), attractive in the S state and repulsive in the P state. The existence of Majorana forces is also revealed in high-energy n-p scattering, and there is no doubt that this kind of force plays an important role in nuclear structure.

In the attempts to compute the interaction energy of complex nuclei we usually assume that the total interaction can be expressed as the sum of the interactions between any two nucleon pairs:

$$\mathcal{H} = \sum_{\text{all pairs}} \mathcal{H}_{ik}. \tag{1}$$

Since there are in all $\frac{1}{2}A(A-1)$ pairs, a normal square well potential

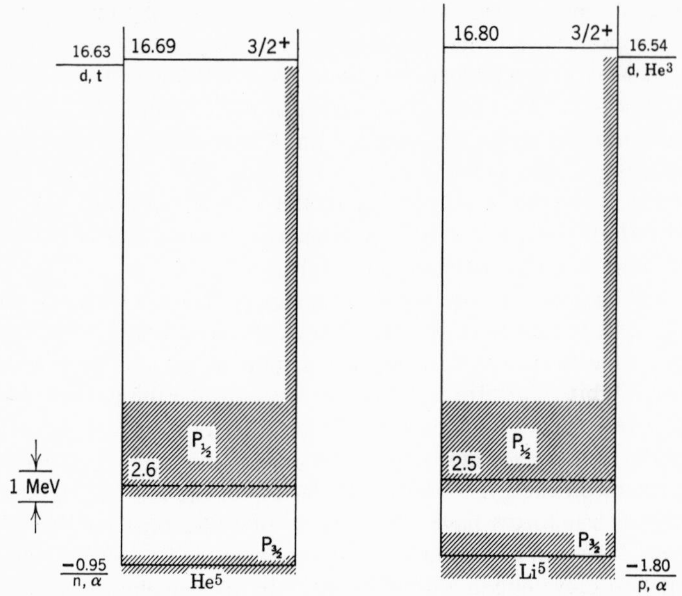

Fig. 2.12-3. The levels of He^5 and Li^5 showing the unstable inverted doublet in a scale of atomic masses (from *Am. Inst. Phys. Handbook*, McGraw-Hill, 1957, used by permission).

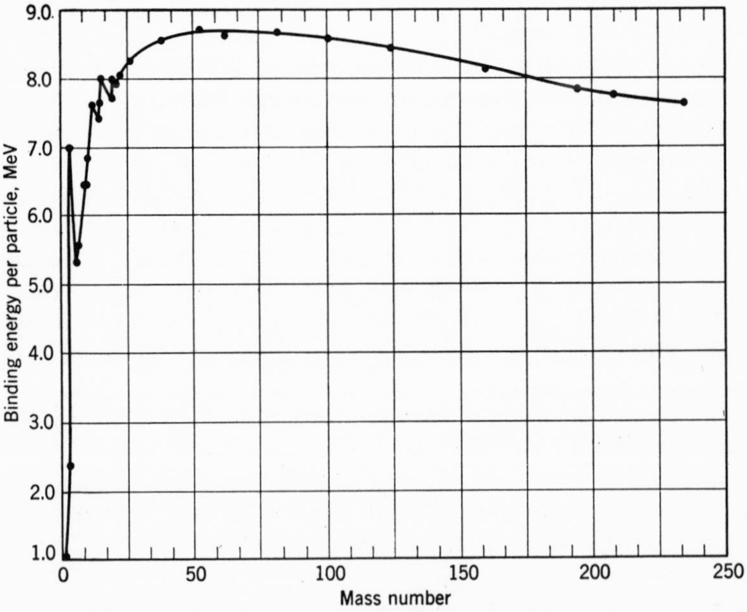

Fig. 2.12-4. Plot of binding energy per particle (reprinted with permission from D. Halliday, *Introductory Nuclear Physics*, Second Edition, Wiley, 1955, p. 261).

would give a binding energy increasing roughly as A^2. We have seen, in fact, that the binding energy varies even more rapidly than $\frac{1}{2}A(A - 1)$ for $A \leq 4$ because of the reduction of nuclear radius. If this trend continued, heavy nuclei would be very small and very strongly bound.

We find instead (Fig. 2.12-4) that the trend is suddenly interrupted at $A = 5$. For $A > 5$ the binding energy per particle B/A is about constant, although for light nuclei ($A < 16$) we observe some variations with the periodicity of 4. Also, for $A > 5$, nuclear radii increase as $A^{1/3}$, corresponding to a constant density of nuclear matter.

These features are attributed to the *saturation property of nuclear forces*, by which we mean that each nuclear particle can be strongly bound only to a limited number of others, a situation similar to the binding of atoms in condensed matter. In fact, condensed matter has constant density and a heat of evaporation (binding energy) proportional to weight.

Heisenberg was the first to suggest that nuclear forces could be exchange forces like those binding the hydrogen molecule. By analogy he suggested an exchange of charge [see 1.33 (11)]. The Heisenberg exchange operator $\mathfrak{I}_\tau$, however, produces attraction between nuclear pairs in different charge states and repulsion between like nucleons: the nuclear forces, attractive for the deuteron, could not produce the strong binding of H^3, He^3, and He^4.

Majorana exchange forces instead are attractive for all particles in the S state. This explains the rapid increase in binding up to He^4 and the saturation for four nucleons.

Under the assumption that the potential between pairs is given by square wells with normal and Majorana exchange forces,

$$\begin{aligned} V_{ij} &= V_W + V_M \mathfrak{I}_{r_{ij}} \qquad &(\text{for } r_{ij} < r_0), \\ &= 0 &(\text{for } r_{ij} > r_0), \end{aligned} \tag{2}$$

it can be proved (BW-52, Chapter III, p. 140) that saturation of nuclear forces occurs if

$$V_M > 4V_W. \tag{3}$$

A similar relation can be obtained if we include tensor forces and other kinds of exchange forces.

From some high-energy scattering experiments [3.53 (20)] we obtain instead

$$V_M \approx V_W. \tag{4}$$

Thus it seems that though exchange forces—and particularly Majorana forces—exist and are important, they cannot be the only reason for the observed saturation effects.

Obviously, the presence of a repulsive core in the nucleon-nucleon potential would help to explain the constant density of nuclei and the linear dependence of the binding energy on A. According to current ideas, such repulsive cores exist, as we have shown in Fig. 1.25-1. We can only conclude that—as in everything else in nuclear physics—the explanation of saturation is not a simple one and more than one feature of nuclear forces must be taken into account for a complete understanding of the facts.

2.13 Light Nuclei: Symmetry Effects

a. The Symmetry Effect. The bound nuclei for $1 \leq A \leq 16$ are shown in the Z-N plot of Fig. 2.13-1. From a first glance at the figure it is

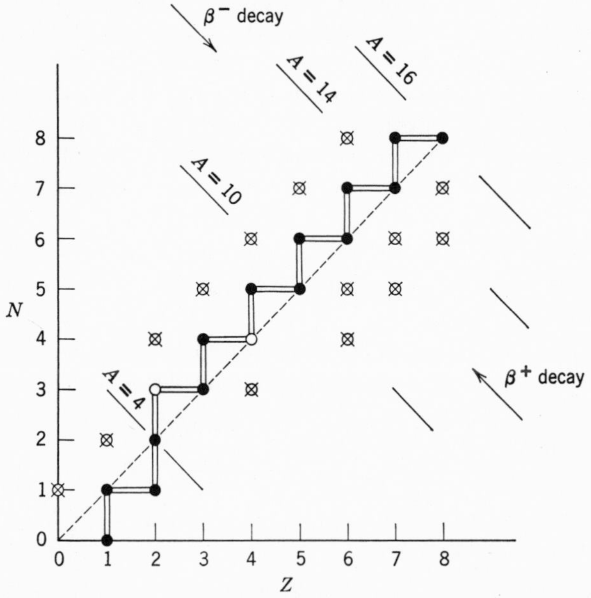

Fig. 2.13-1. The nuclei up to $A = 16$ in a Z-N plot: ● Stable nucleus; ⊠ β active nucleus; ○ most stable unbound nucleus for given A. A double line connects the most stable nuclei for each A.

apparent that the bound nuclei gather around the $N = Z$ line. This effect is called the "symmetry" effect. For each value of A the nuclei that are most bound have the smallest value of isotopic spin: $T = 0$ $(N = Z)$ for A even, and $T = \frac{1}{2}$ $(N = Z \pm 1)$ for A odd.

As a consequence of the exclusion principle, $\mathcal{T}_r\mathcal{T}_\sigma\mathcal{T}_\tau = -1$, the small isotopic spin (minimum symmetry in $\vec{\tau}$) corresponds to a maximum of symmetry in **r** and **σ**.

In order to discuss the symmetry properties of the nuclear states, we can make use of an "*independent particle model*" according to which each nucleon has its own state of motion (orbit), in some kind of total nuclear potential well, independently of the presence of the other nucleons.

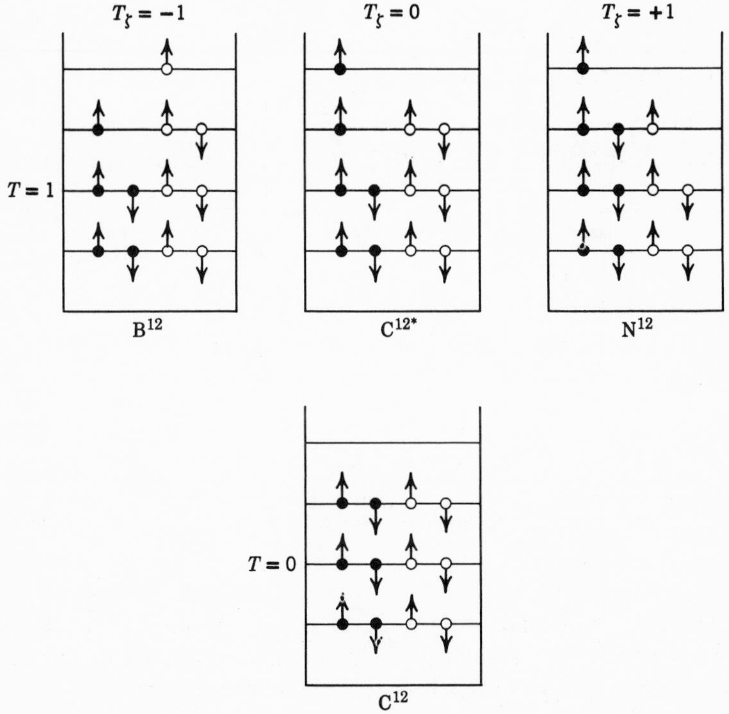

Fig. 2.13-2. Isospin singlet and triplet for $A = 12$ ($= 4 \times 3$), showing the greater space symmetry of the isosinglet.

It is convenient to represent independent-particle nuclear states with diagrams such as those in Figs. 2.13-2 and 2.13-3. Here the horizontal lines indicate given "spacial" states (given orbits) in order of increasing energy. Each such line can, at most, contain four nucleons in different spin and charge states. Nucleons along vertical lines are in the same spin-charge state. Thus the space wave function is necessarily symmetrical with respect to the exchange of two nucleons in the same horizontal line and antisymmetrical for nucleons in the same vertical line. Nucleon pairs whose members are neither in the same vertical nor horizontal line are with equal probability "spacially" even or odd.

From Fig. 2.13-2 and Fig. 2.13-3 it is clear that the state in which the nucleons are in the lowest possible energy level corresponds to a maximum of space symmetry as a consequence of the exclusion principle.

This principle, however, is not the only or the most important reason favoring space symmetry. Another is the short range of nuclear forces, which favors symmetrical pairs, since they are more often close to one another and therefore more often within one another's potential well.

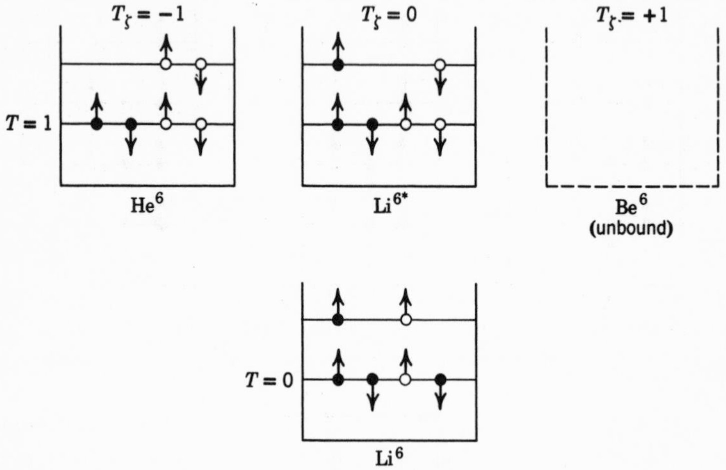

Fig. 2.13-3. Isospin singlet and triplet for $A = 6$ $(= 4 + 2)$, showing the greater spin symmetry of the isosinglet.

Probably the most important cause of space symmetry is the fact that the interaction Hamiltonian contains Majorana terms which are attractive for symmetrical pairs and repulsive for antisymmetric ones.

A detailed study of the symmetry properties of the nuclear wave function has been carried out by Wigner in his *supermultiplet* theory. This theory, which is not reported here, has proved successful in interpreting the binding energy of light nuclei.

b. Even-Odd Effects. A nucleus is called even-even, odd-odd, even-odd, according to whether N and Z are both even, both odd, or one even and one odd. Figure 2.13-2 shows how the space symmetry effect increases the stability of an even-even nucleus, such as C^{12}, in relation to its odd-odd neighbors B^{12} and N^{12}, which, with an excited state of C^{12}, form an isospin triplet with more isospin symmetry but less space symmetry than the ground state of C^{12}.

The effect of space symmetry is large, about 15 MeV (see Fig. 2.15-4), as indicated by the high energy of the radioactive decays of

B^{12} and N^{12}:

(1) $$B^{12} \rightarrow C^{12} + e^- + \bar{\nu} + 13.4 \text{ MeV},$$

(2) $$N^{12} \rightarrow C^{12} + e^+ + \nu + 16.7 \text{ MeV}.$$

Let us now consider in Fig. 2.13-3 the case of $A = 6$ ($A = 4n + 2$ is even but not a multiple of 4). Here the space symmetry is the same in the isospin singlet and triplet. It is the spin symmetry that is different: Li^6 has spin 1 and is a triplet; He^6 has spin 0 and is a singlet. The effect of spin symmetry is the same one that explains the stability of the deuteron and the instability of the di-neutron. Spin symmetry, however, is less important than space symmetry. In the case in question it contributes about 4 MeV (Fig. 2.15-1):

(3) $$He^6 \rightarrow Li^6 + e^- + \bar{\nu} + 3.55 \text{ MeV}.$$

For A odd the nuclei must be even-odd. The most space-spin symmetric state is an isospin doublet. The two members of the doublet, according to charge independence, should have the same structure, the same symmetry, and the same binding. They have been given the name "*mirror nuclei.*"

It is interesting to see how the symmetry effects produce a maximum of stability for $A = 4n$, N and Z even. These effects account for the periodicity of 4 in the B/A curve of Fig. 2.12-4 which has sometimes been interpreted in terms of an α particle structure.

For heavier nuclei the symmetry effects are mostly destroyed by the coulomb repulsion (2.14), but the even-odd effects remain. For $A > 14$ there are no odd-odd nuclei (the heaviest bound odd-odd nucleus is N^{14}); even-odd and odd-even nuclei are about equally bound, whereas all even-even nuclei have spin zero and are very stable. These effects are known as *pairing* and are discussed more fully in the remainder of this chapter.

2.14 Intermediate Nuclei: Electrostatic Effects

a. Coulomb Repulsion. We have seen that the symmetry effect is the result of charge symmetry of nuclear forces and the successful classification of states in isospin multiplets the result of charge independence.

Now we must consider the electromagnetic effects that oppose the tendency toward maximum symmetry since they destroy the equality of interaction between nucleon pairs. The electrostatic repulsion between the protons is the most obvious and most important of the electromagnetic effects.

Because electrostatic forces have long range and do not saturate, the electrostatic repulsion energy increases as the number of proton pairs $\frac{1}{2}Z(Z-1)$. It becomes more and more important—in relation to the binding energy due to nuclear forces proper—with increasing atomic number.

Let us attempt a semiquantitative computation of the electrostatic repulsion energy with the method used for $A = 3$. Applied to a nucleus containing Z protons, 2.11 (4) yields

$$E_{\text{coul}} = \frac{3}{5} Z(Z-1) \frac{e^2}{R_{\text{coul}}}, \tag{1}$$

where the coulomb radius R_{coul} is the radius of the nucleus considered as a sphere in which the protons are distributed with uniform probability. We can now write

$$R_{\text{coul}} = r_{0,\,\text{coul}} A^{1/3} \quad (r_{0,\,\text{coul}} \text{ constant}), \tag{2}$$

in order to express the constant density of nuclear matter (2.21), and obtain[1]

$$E_{\text{coul}}(Z, A) = \frac{3}{5} \frac{Z(Z-1)}{A^{1/3}} \frac{e^2}{r_{0,\,\text{coul}}}. \tag{3}$$

In order to study the validity of this expression, let us apply it to the "*mirror nuclei.*" These nuclei, as already mentioned, are the isospin doublets for A odd which are found symmetrically located about the $N = Z$ line. The first examples are n-p, H^3-He^3, He^5-Li^5, Li^7-Be^7, and the sequence continues with few interruptions up to $A = 39$. In the assumption of charge symmetry the difference in binding energy between the members of a mirror pair should be the result solely of electrostatic effects, and thus it is directly comparable with (3).

The heavier of the two members of the pair is radioactive and decays into the lighter. The maximum energy of β decay is a direct measure of the atomic-mass difference[2]. For $A = 1$ and $A = 3$ it is the proton-abundant nucleus that is stable, simply because the proton itself is lighter than the neutron. But already for $A = 5$ the electrostatic repulsion between protons is sufficient to overcome the inherent instability of the neutron, and it is the neutron-abundant nucleus that is stable.

[1] Observe that the coulomb energy (3) is the electrostatic energy of a sphere of charge Ze, minus Z times the electrostatic energy of a sphere of charge e. The subtraction is required to remove the effect of the repulsion of each proton on itself.

[2] It is easily seen that the following relations hold between the difference in *atomic* mass and the *kinetic* energies of the particles emitted in β decay,

$$\Delta M = E_{\text{max}}(e^-) \qquad \text{for } e^- + \bar{\nu} \text{ emission}$$
$$\Delta M = E_{\text{max}}(e^+) + 2mc^2 \qquad \text{for } e^+ + \nu \text{ emission}$$
$$\Delta M = E(\nu) \qquad \text{for } K \text{ capture.}$$

The difference in atomic mass between the proton-abundant and the neutron-abundant members of the pair is, from (3),

(4)

$$M(Z_2, A) - M(Z_1, A) = M\left(\frac{A+1}{2}, A\right) - M\left(\frac{A-1}{2}, A\right)$$

$$= M_p - M_n + E_{coul}\left(\frac{A+1}{2}, A\right) - E_{coul}\left(\frac{A-1}{2}, A\right)$$

$$= M_p - M_n + \frac{3}{5}\frac{A-1}{A^{1/3}}\frac{e^2}{r_{0,\,coul}}.$$

The agreement with experimental data is surprisingly good (Fig. 2.14-1) and confirms the assumption of charge symmetry. The numerical constant $r_{0,coul}$ is

(5) $$r_{0,coul} = 1.46 \times 10^{-13} \text{ cm}.$$

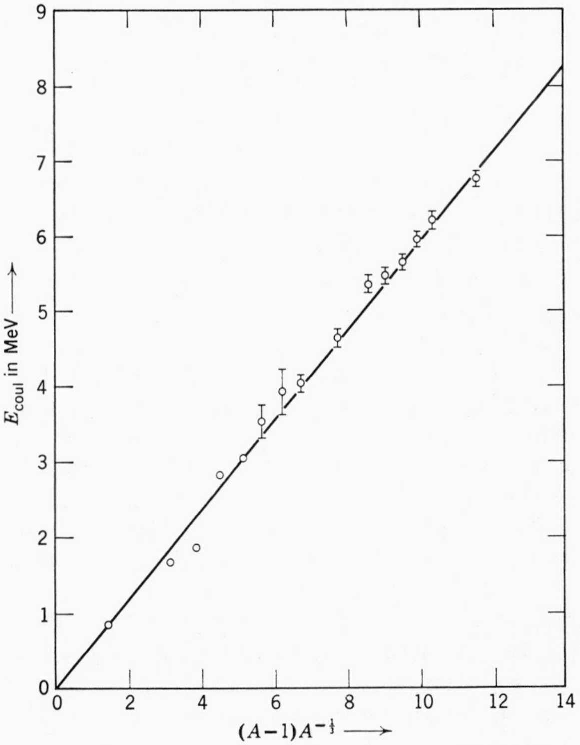

Fig. 2.14-1. Coulomb energy difference of mirror nuclei plotted versus $(A - 1)A^{-1/3}$ (reprinted with permission from J. M. Blatt and V. F. Weisskopf, *Theoretical Nuclear Physics*, Wiley, 1952, p. 228).

We can now apply (3) to the members of an isospin triplet in order to verify charge independence. The classical example is the triplet O^{14}, N^{14*}, C^{14}, for which the energy-level diagram is shown in Fig. 2.14-2.

If charge independence holds, the difference in mass between the three components of the isospin triplet should be due entirely to the difference

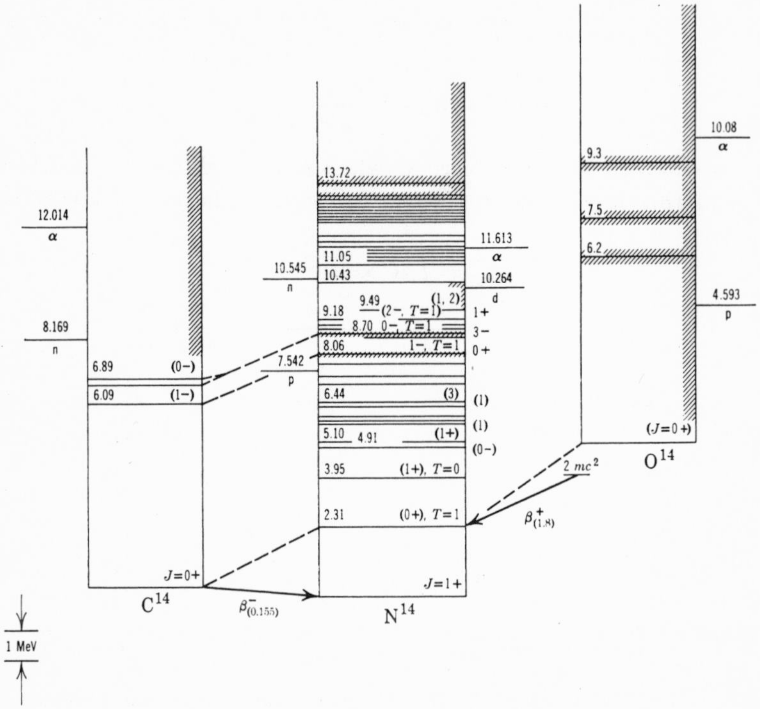

Fig. 2.14-2. The energy levels of C^{14}, N^{14}, O^{14}. Particularly important is the isotriplet C^{14}, N^{14*} (2.31 MeV) and O^{14} (from *Am. Inst. Phys. Handbook*, McGraw-Hill, 1957, p. 8–72; adapted to show atomic mass differences; used by permission).

in mass of the nucleons and to the electrostatic energy. It is found that in this case also the formula in (3) is in sufficiently good agreement with the data. This agreement applies also to other isospin triplets, and it is the first verification of charge independence encountered in this treatment.

b. Competition between Symmetry and Electrostatic Effects. For $A > 16$ the coulomb repulsion starts competing with the tendency toward symmetry and gradually overcomes it entirely. Fig. 2.14-3 shows how this happens in the usual N-Z plot.

First, for $A = 4n + 2$ the odd-odd nuclei with $N = Z = 2n + 1$ become unstable. N^{14} is the heaviest stable odd-odd nucleus. For

$A = 18$ the most stable nucleus is O^{18}, with $Z = 8$, $N = 10$, and not the symmetrical F^{18}, with $Z = 9$, $N = 9$.

For $A = 4n$ the even-even nuclei, for which the symmetry effect is stronger, remain on the $N = Z\,(= 2n)$ line up to $A = 40$, the last stable one being Ca^{40} ($Z = N = 20$).

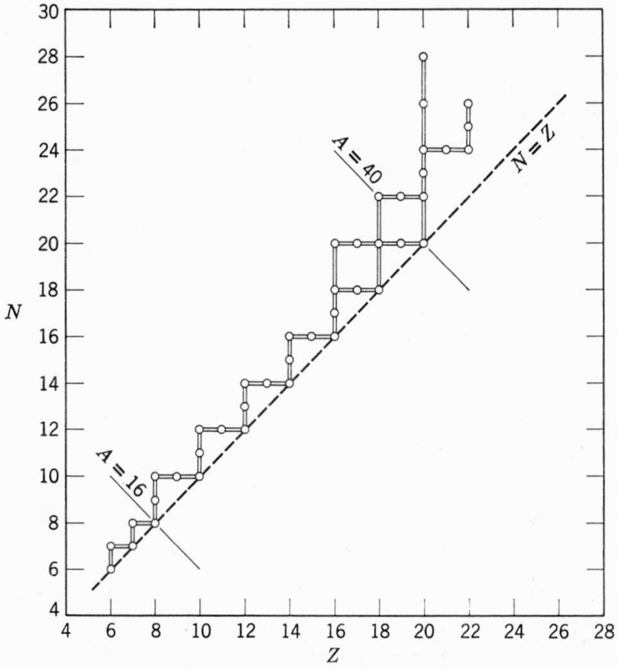

Fig. 2.14-3. Plot of stable nuclei in the region of intermediate mass numbers.

But for $A > 40$ all stable nuclei have $N > Z$; the symmetry is destroyed. The situation becomes more and more complicated and can be discussed only in terms of appropriate models in which the symmetry plays a secondary role.

2.15 *Energy Levels of Light Nuclei*

A large amount of information on the excited states of light nuclei has been accumulated through the analysis of scattering and of nuclear reactions. The principles on which the measurements are based are discussed in later chapters. Here we want to report only on some of the results.

The information is best presented in the form of level diagrams (AIP-57;

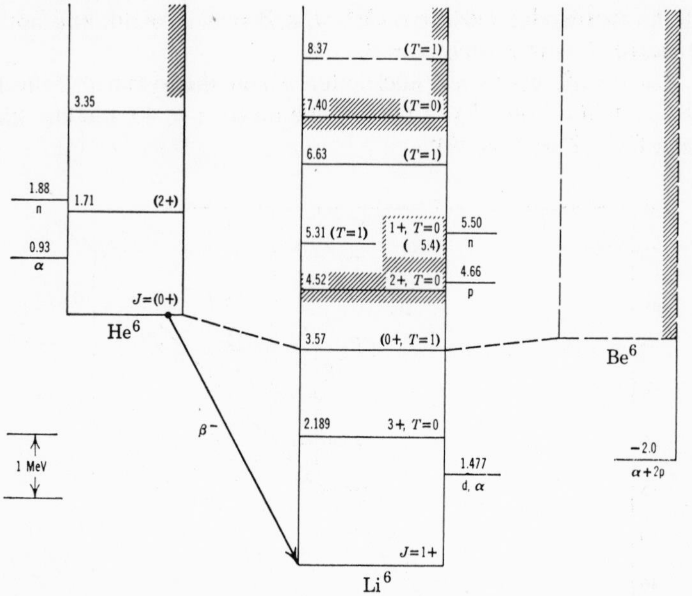

Fig. 2.15-1. Level schemes for $A = 6$ (from *Am. Inst. Phys. Handbook*, McGraw-Hill, 1957, p. 8–59; used by permission).

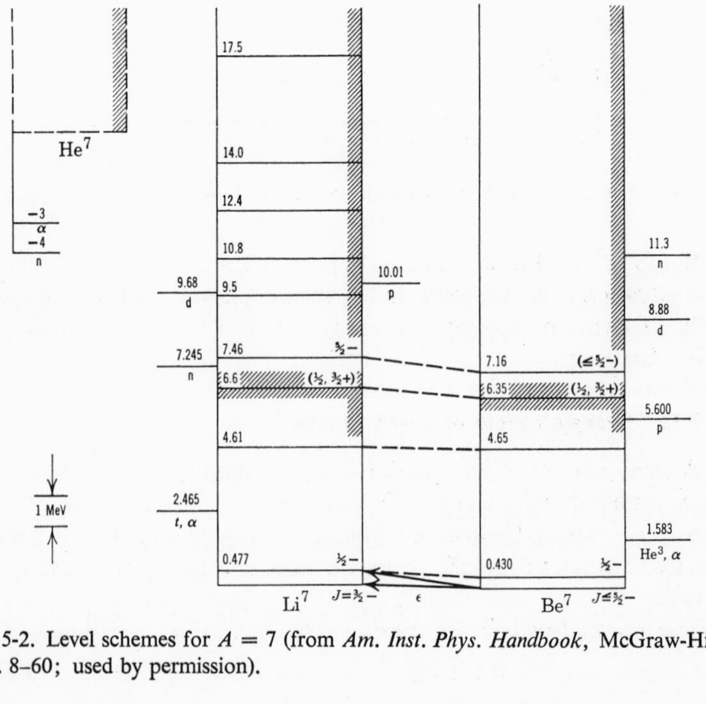

Fig. 2.15-2. Level schemes for $A = 7$ (from *Am. Inst. Phys. Handbook*, McGraw-Hill, 1957, p. 8–60; used by permission).

A-55) and often includes the spin, parity, and isospin quantum numbers as well as the energy and the width of the levels.

The diagram for $A = 5$ has been already reported in Fig. 2.12-3. For $A = 6$ (Fig. 2.15-1) there are two bound nuclei, He^6 and Li^6, but no bound excited states. (The diagram indicates that Li^6 disintegrates into d + α

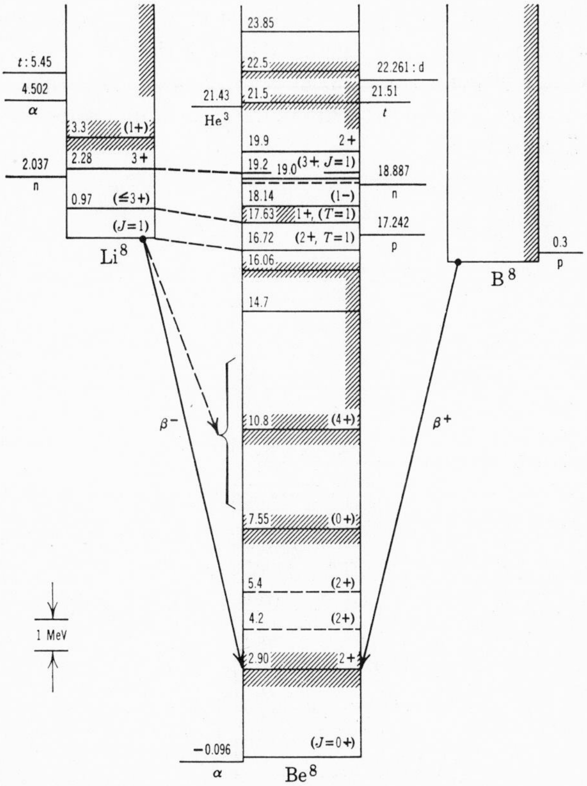

Fig. 2.15-3. Level schemes for $A = 8$ (from *Am. Inst. Phys. Handbook*, McGraw-Hill, 1957, p. 8–62; used by permission).

with the absorption of 1.477 MeV, an energy lower than that of the first excited state.) The magnetic moment of Li^6, 0.821, is close enough to $\mu_n + \mu_p$ to indicate a predominant ^3S state for this nucleus. The configuration, $p_{3/2}$, $p_{3/2}$, corresponds to one neutron and one proton in the lowest state of the inverted triplet.

The first two states of Li^6 have no equivalent in He^6 and are isospin singlets. However the third, at 3.57 MeV, has the same structure as He^6 and forms an isospin triplet, together with the unbound ground state of Be^6 ($Be^6 \rightarrow \alpha + 2p + 2$ MeV).

Let us now look at the isospin doublet Li^7 and Be^7 (Fig. 2.15-2). The magnetic moment of Li^7, 3.25, is most probably contributed by a proton in a $p_{3/2}$ state $(1 + 2.8 = 3.8)$, in agreement with the determination of spin and parity (Li^7 is $\frac{3}{2}-$; see 5.16c). Li^7 and Be^7 have a bound excited state, at 0.477 and 0.430 MeV, respectively. This state is a $p_{1/2}$ and, together with the $p_{3/2}$ ground state, furnishes another example of inverted doublet.

$A = 8$ (Fig. 2.15-3) is unique, since the ground state of the most stable nucleus, Be^8, is itself unstable against disintegration into two α particles. The lowest state of the isospin singlet is 16.72 MeV lower than the lowest state of the isospin triplet, which shows the great importance of symmetry for N and Z both even.

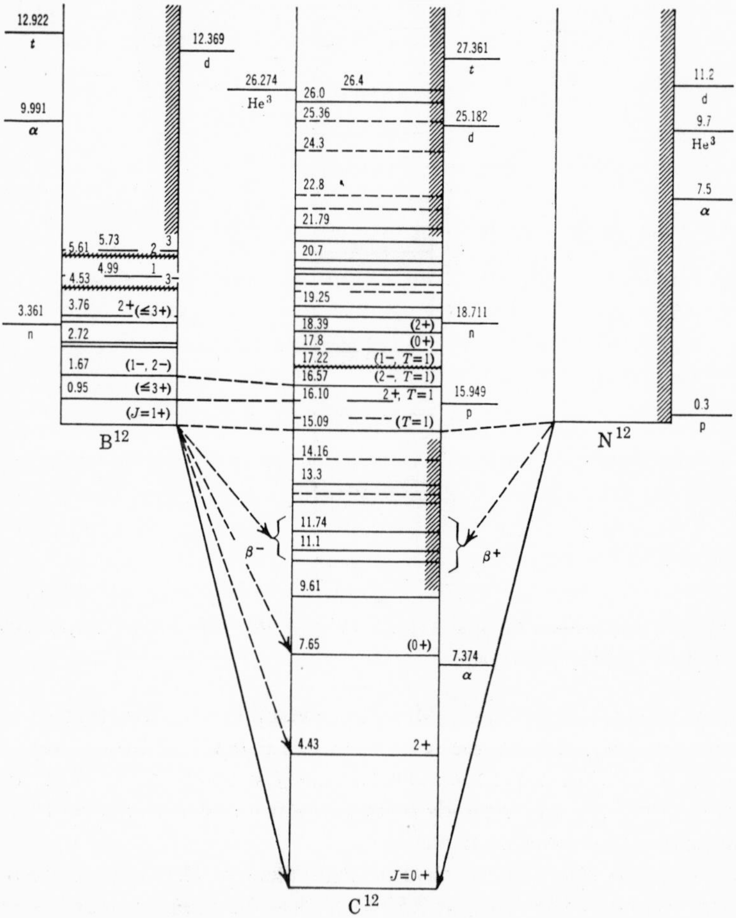

Fig. 2.15-4. Level schemes for $A = 12$ (from *Am. Inst. Phys. Handbook*, McGraw-Hill, 1957, p. 8–69; used by permission).

The diagram for $A = 12$ (Fig. 2.15-4) is similar, apart from the fact that C^{12} is stable. With increasing A, the density of excited states increases; it is also apparent that the energy levels are denser at high excitation energy.

As we shall see, the quantum numbers of the ground states and of some of the excited states can be interpreted by means of nuclear models. The energy of the levels is difficult to predict because of the complications of the many-body problem, but the width of the levels is often understood, at least qualitatively, in terms of selection rules and of potential barrier penetration.

If the position of each level remains unexplained, the general trends of the level density, particularly its increase with A and with excitation energy, finds a simple interpretation in terms of statistical considerations (2.24d).

2.2 Medium and Heavy Nuclei

2.21 The Density of Nuclear Matter

a. Nuclear Radii from the Coulomb Repulsion Energy. We have seen in 2.14 that the electrostatic energy of repulsion between the protons in mirror nuclei is consistent with an elementary treatment that allows the determination of a "coulomb" nuclear radius

$$R_{\text{coul}} = r_{0,\,\text{coul}} A^{1/3}, \quad r_{0,\,\text{coul}} = 1.46 \times 10^{-13} \text{ cm.}$$

The assumption of uniform charge distribution cannot be expected to be valid for light nuclei. It should be better applicable to heavy nuclei, since these can be considered, to a certain extent, to be composed of homogeneous nuclear matter.

But even for heavy nuclei we cannot expect that the radii obtained from 2.14(3) are correct. The electrostatic energy between a pair of protons, 1 and 2, in independent particle states $\psi_i(\mathbf{r})$ and $\psi_j(\mathbf{r})$ should be computed from the quantum mechanical equation

(1) $$(E_{\text{coul}})_{ij} = \left\langle \psi_{ij}(\mathbf{r}_1\mathbf{r}_2) \left| \frac{e^2}{r_{12}} \right| \psi_{ij}(\mathbf{r}_1\mathbf{r}_2) \right\rangle,$$

where $\psi_{ij}(\mathbf{r}_1\mathbf{r}_2)$ is the properly symmetrized or antisymmetrized wave function

(2) $$\psi_{ij} = \frac{1}{\sqrt{2}} [\psi_i(\mathbf{r}_1)\, \psi_j(\mathbf{r}_2) \pm \psi_i(\mathbf{r}_2)\, \psi_j(\mathbf{r}_1)].$$

The coulomb energy per pair contains exchange integrals and can be expressed in the form

$$(3) \qquad (E_{\text{coul}})_{ij} = \int |\psi_i(\mathbf{r}_1)|^2\, |\psi_j(\mathbf{r}_2)|^2 \frac{e^2}{r_{12}}\, d\mathbf{r}_1\, d\mathbf{r}_2 \pm \int \psi_i^*(\mathbf{r}_1)\, \psi_j^*(\mathbf{r}_2)\, \psi_i(\mathbf{r}_2)\, \psi_j(\mathbf{r}_1) \frac{e^2}{r_{12}}\, d\mathbf{r}_1\, d\mathbf{r}_2.$$

For $Z > 4$ there are more space-antisymmetric than space-symmetric proton pairs, as we can show with the method in 2.13. The first integral leads to an expression similar to 2.14(3), so that when the sum over all pairs is performed we have

$$(4) \qquad E_{\text{coul}} = \frac{3}{5} \frac{Z(Z-1)}{A^{1/3}} \frac{e^2}{r_0} - X,$$

where X is a positive quantity contributed by the exchange integrals (B-36; C-53; F-46) and r_0 is a new estimate of the nuclear radius constant, more accurate than the old $r_{0,\text{coul}}$. It follows from this and from 2.14(3) that

$$(5) \qquad r_0 < r_{0,\text{coul}}.$$

Because of our poor knowledge of nuclear wave functions it is not worthwhile to continue this discussion, and we must be satisfied with the conclusion that the analysis of the nuclear coulomb energy leads to a nuclear radius constant somewhat smaller than 1.46×10^{-13} cm[1].

b. Measurements of Nuclear Radii by Means of Strong Interacting Particles. Among the first estimates of nuclear sizes we must recall those obtained from the mean lives of α emitters and from the anomalous scattering of α particles.

More recent determinations were obtained from nuclear scattering of neutrons. In the simplifying assumptions that nuclear forces have negligible range, that the nuclear radius is much larger than the neutron's wavelength, and that the nucleus behaves as an opaque sphere, the neutron's total cross section is $2\pi R^2$ [see 3.51(3)]. Apart from possible complications arising from the finite range of nuclear forces, it is not easy to find an energy region in which the small wavelength and the opacity conditions are satisfied. Small neutron wavelengths require large energy, but nuclei are partly transparent for high-energy neutrons.

Numerous experiments of neutron scattering in the energy range of $\approx$10 MeV and above have been performed to study nuclear radii. The result of this kind of measurement leads to a nuclear radius constant $r_0 \simeq 1.5 \times 10^{-13}$ cm, in good agreement with the oversimplified interpretation of electrostatic repulsion effects. However, neutron scattering

[1] A recent analysis of mirror nuclei leads to $r_0 = (1.28 \pm 0.05) \times 10^{-13}$ cm (K-58).

experiments do not measure the nuclear radius proper—the radius at which the nuclear density vanishes—but rather the somewhat larger radius to which nuclear forces extend. Again, we expect the correct nuclear radius to be smaller than that obtained from these experiments.

c. Measurement of Nuclear Radii by Means of Electrons and Muons. Much more significant is the value of the nuclear radii obtained by exploring the distribution of nuclear electric charge. Since electrostatic forces are weak compared to nuclear forces, the density of protons—and thus the electric charge density—has very nearly the same distribution as the density of nuclear matter.

In order to find the "electrostatic" nuclear radius, we must experiment with charged particles that are not subject to nuclear forces. Such are electrons and muons[1].

Atomic electrons, however, travel in trajectories that are far removed from the nucleus: their wave functions overlap the nucleus only slightly, and the effects of nuclear size on atomic spectra are small. In order to study the shape of nuclei, we must make use of electrons of very small wavelength. With this in mind, the nuclear scattering of electrons up to energies of 900 MeV has been studied at Stanford University (H-56).

The results give an almost constant r_0 that confirms the constant density of nuclear matter. For heavy nuclei the Stanford group finds that $r_0 = 1.19 \times 10^{-13}$ cm, whereas for light nuclei the result is $r_0 = 1.3 \times 10^{-13}$ cm.

The experimental data make possible the determination of a second parameter to describe the charge distribution: this is a "skin depth" T (see Fig. 2.21-1 for definition) whose value is about 2.4×10^{-13} cm.

Experiments with muonic x rays were carried on first at Columbia University (F-53). Contrary to what happens with electrons, the muon atomic trajectory is close to the nucleus: in a heavy element, such as lead, the Bohr orbit would actually be inside the nucleus, where the muon will travel for some time before being captured as a result of weak interactions.

The values of r_0 obtained by Fitch and Rainwater are $10^{13} r_0 = 1.17$, 1.21, 1.22, 1.17 cm for $Z = 22$, 29, 51, and 82, respectively[2].

We shall therefore accept from experiment the nuclear radius constant

$$r_0 = 1.2 \times 10^{-13} \text{ cm}, \tag{6}$$

[1] We shall try to avoid the term μ meson, since we want to reserve the name "meson" for strong interacting particles with integral spin.

[2] More recent data have been obtained at the Carnegie Institute of Technology by Backenstoss and Sutton (B-58a).

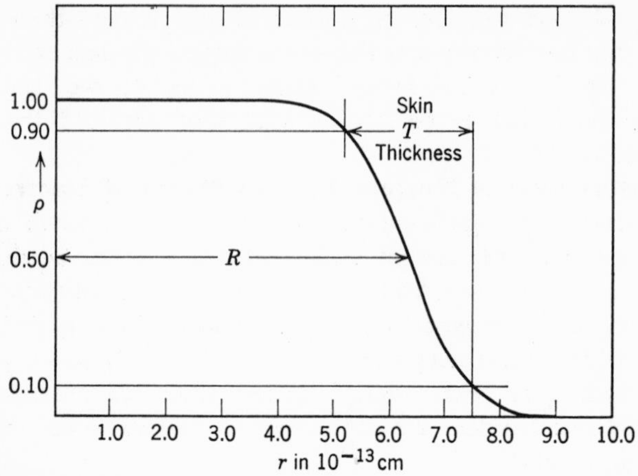

Fig. 2.21-1. Nuclear charge density distribution as a function of r; definition of the skin thickness T [from R. Hofstadter, *Rev. Mod. Phys.*, **28**, 220 (1956)].

from which it follows that the density of nuclear matter is

$$\begin{aligned} (\tfrac{4}{3}\pi r_0^3)^{-1} &= 1.3 \times 10^{38} \text{ nucleons/cm}^3, \\ &= 2.2 \times 10^{14} \text{ g/cm}^3, \\ &= 2.2 \times 10^{8} \text{ tons/cm}^3. \end{aligned} \tag{7}$$

2.22 *Independent Particle Discussion of Nuclear Magnetic Moments*

a. Even-Even Nuclei and Pairing Effects. In 1.16 we discussed the fundamental restrictions on the possible nonvanishing nuclear moments. Apart from these restrictions, we observe empirically that without exception *all even-even nuclei in the ground state have zero spin* and therefore no moment of any kind.

This observation can be related to the properties of the forces between nucleons (2.13b) and receives a simple explanation in the independent particle model, in which we assume that each particle has its own state of motion in an over-all nuclear potential well. In this model we must admit that each pair of equal nucleons has $J = 0$, a situation usually called *pairing*.

b. Even-Odd Nuclei. It then becomes natural to try to explain the spins and moments of even-odd nuclei in terms of the odd unpaired nucleons only.

In this assumption the orbital angular momentum of the unpaired particle can take only the values $l = J \pm \frac{1}{2}$, where J is the nuclear spin, and we can find the expectation value of the magnetic moment μ for each of the two possible values of l. The calculation is similar to that for the deuteron (1.24b), with

$$(1) \quad \begin{aligned} &g_l = 1,\ g_s = 2\mu_\text{p} \text{ if the odd particle is a proton,} \\ &g_l = 0,\ g_s = 2\mu_\text{n} \text{ if the odd particle is a neutron.} \end{aligned}$$

We proceed to compute

$$\begin{aligned} \mu &= \langle g_l L_z + g_s S_z \rangle_{JJ} \\ &= \left\langle g_l \frac{\mathbf{l} \cdot \mathbf{J}}{J^2} J_z + g_s \frac{\mathbf{s} \cdot \mathbf{J}}{J^2} J_z \right\rangle_{JJ} \\ &= \left\langle g_l \frac{l^2 + J^2 - s^2}{2J^2} J_z + g_s \frac{s^2 + J^2 - l^2}{2J^2} J_z \right\rangle_{JJ} \\ &= g_l \frac{l(l+1) + J)J+1) - s(s+1)}{2J(J+1)} J \\ &\quad + g_s \frac{s(s+1) + J(J+1) - l(l+1)}{2J(J+1)} J, \end{aligned}$$

with the result that

$$(2) \quad \begin{aligned} \mu &= J + 2.29 && \text{for odd } Z \quad l = J - \tfrac{1}{2}, \\ \mu &= \frac{J^2 - 1.29J}{J+1} && \text{for odd } Z \quad l = J + \tfrac{1}{2}, \\ \mu &= -1.91 && \text{for odd } N \quad l = J - \tfrac{1}{2}, \\ \mu &= \frac{1.91J}{J+1} && \text{for odd } N \quad l = J + \tfrac{1}{2}. \end{aligned}$$

These values are called the Schmidt limits for the nuclear magnetic moments.

In the strict single-particle model the nuclear magnetic moments should correspond to either one of the two limits, since states with $l = J \pm \frac{1}{2}$ do not mix. However, the experimental values (Figs. 2.22-1 and 2) are not always close to one of the limits; almost without exception they are found to fall between them.

The discrepancy is explained if we recall (1.21a, 1.24b) that the anomalous magnetic moments of the nucleons are produced by a "meson cloud" whose properties change when the nucleons are bound. According to this view, the gyromagnetic ratios of the proton and neutron in (1) must be replaced by

(3) $2 < g_s < 2\mu_\text{p}$ for the proton, $\quad 2\mu_\text{n} < g_s < 0$ for the neutron,

and we can easily understand why the experimental values do not agree with the limits (2).

It is important to note that in the single particle interpretation of the moments it is possible to assign the value of l (and thus the parity) of a nuclear state as the l of the Schmidt limit which is closer to the measured magnetic moment.

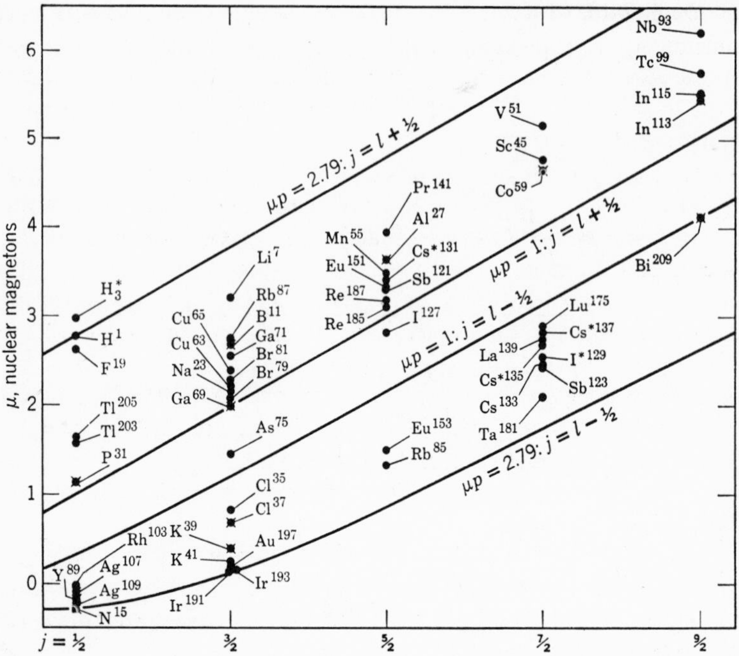

Fig. 2.22-1. Magnetic moments of nuclei with odd Z plotted against the spin (reprinted with permission from M. G. Mayer and J. H. Jensen, *Nuclear Shell Structure*, Wiley, 1955, p. 12).

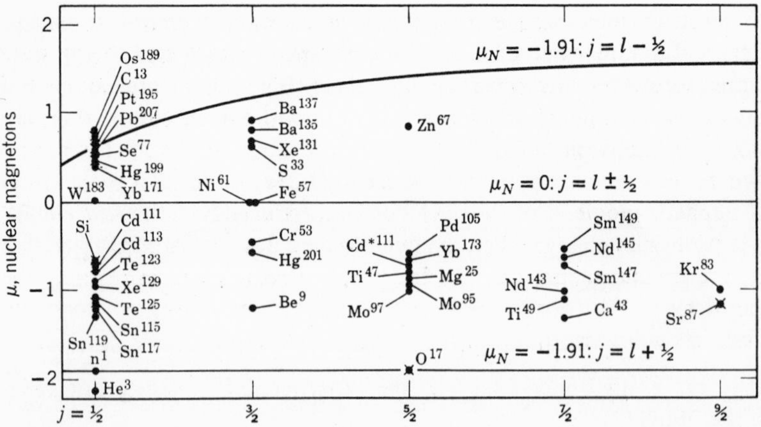

Fig. 2.22-2. Magnetic moments of nuclei with odd N plotted against the spin (reprinted with permission from M. G. Mayer and J. H. Jensen, *Nuclear Shell Structure*, Wiley, 1955, p. 13).

c. Odd-Odd Nuclei. The magnetic moment of odd-odd nuclei is contributed by the two odd particles. The deuteron and Li^6 have already been discussed. We must now consider the two stable nuclei B^{10} and N^{14} and the long-lived radioactive Na^{22}, for which the magnetic moment has been measured.

We suppose that the odd particles in all these nuclei are in the triplet state: then the gyromagnetic ratio corresponding to the total intrinsic spin $S = 1$ is $g = \mu_p + \mu_n = 0.88$ and that corresponding to the total orbital angular momentum is $\frac{1}{2}$. B^{10}, whose ground state has $J = 3$ and positive parity, could be a $^3D_3$, or $^3F_3$, or $^3G_3$. The first assignment leads to a theoretical magnetic moment of 1.88 in good agreement with the experimental value of 1.80.

Similarly, we find that the magnetic moment of N^{14} (1^+, $\mu = 0.40$) agrees better with $^3D_1$ than with $^3S_1$ or $^3P_1$. The case of Na^{22} (3^+, $\mu = 1.75$) is similar to B^{10} and also favors a $^3D_3$ state.

2.23 Is Nuclear Matter "Condensed" or "Gaseous"?

Nuclear matter has constant density and a binding energy proportional to its weight. These properties make it similar to *condensed matter*, such as matter in the familiar solid or liquid states.

On the other hand, there are other aspects of nuclear behavior—such as the magnetic moments—which are best explained in terms of an *independent particle model*. According to this model, the nucleons move freely—without affecting one another's motion—within the nuclear volume, a behavior that is characteristic of a perfect gas.

How can we reconcile these apparently contradictory views? A nucleus in its ground state is a system of Fermi particles in its lowest energy state and therefore at zero temperature. We may think that its behavior should be similar to that of any other system of fermions; for instance, a system of nitrogen atoms (G-58). The similarity between the nuclear forces and the forces between nitrogen atoms are, in effect, striking. Both forces have a repulsive core, a short-range attraction, and show saturation effects.

It is well known that when the temperature is lowered nitrogen liquefies and solidifies, losing all the independent particle properties proper to the gaseous state. Why does nuclear matter instead maintain some independent particle character?

In order to find the answer to this question, let us compare more closely the forces acting in the two cases, and we will find that there are some very significant differences.

The nuclear potential well is just deep enough to produce a bound state in the deuteron. If its depth were decreased by $\approx 10\%$, the deuteron would not be bound. The deuteron is, in effect, almost unbound, often being outside the attractive potential: it has no bound states for $l > 0$.

Instead the nitrogen molecule is, relatively speaking, much more bound: its S state is deep in the attractive well and many rotational states are bound. Of particular importance is the comparison of the depth of the well with the Fermi energy of the condensed state. For nuclear matter the well has a depth of ≈ 40 MeV, whereas the Fermi energy is ≈ 30 MeV (see 2.24a). In solid nitrogen the well is ≈ 10 eV deep, whereas the Fermi energy for an atomic spacing of $\approx 10^{-8}$ cm and a mass $14 \times 1.6 \times 10^{-24}$ g is only $\approx 10^{-2}$ eV.

As a result of the smallness of the interaction compared to statistical effects, the nucleons in a nucleus acquire a "rigidity" that allows their motion to proceed undisturbed by collisions with other nucleons: this is because nucleon 1, deeply embedded in a Fermi distribution, is not allowed to change its momentum when it collides with nucleon 2. The effective cross section becomes small and both nucleons behave as free.

We conclude that nuclear matter in the ground state behaves like a Fermi gas at the absolute zero. The high degeneracy is the result of high density, which in turn is related to the short range of the forces. Our intuitive understanding of normal matter cannot be expected to apply, and the high degeneracy eleminates the inconsistency between the independent particle motion and the condensed behavior. But, even if this were granted, it remains to be seen whether both these aspects are compatible with our knowledge of nuclear forces.

The relation between two-body forces and nuclear models has been investigated by Brueckner and collaborators in a long series of papers (B-54a; B-54b; B-55b; B-55c; E-55). These authors have arrived at the conclusion that forces consistent with meson theory and with the results of scattering experiments lead to "saturation" with the proper value of nuclear density and binding energy. Furthermore, they have obtained a transformation that approximately reduces the problem of many strong interacting particles to an alternative problem that can be studied with self-consistent field methods: the wave function of the reduced problem describes particles moving more or less freely in a collectively determined potential well.

Thus it appears that the models used in the description of nuclear states are not in contradiction with one another and with nuclear forces, and we shall proceed to their discussion.

2.24 The Fermi Gas Model

a. Symmetrical Nucleon Gas. In the "Fermi gas" model of the nucleus we assume that the nucleons are free to move in a volume $\Omega = \frac{4}{3}\pi r_0{}^3 A$. The attraction between the individual nucleon pairs is replaced by a common potential well of depth V_0, which holds the nucleons within the nuclear volume (Fig. 2.24-1). Let us neglect for the moment the electrostatic charge of the protons and suppose that our nucleus has $N = Z = A/2$.

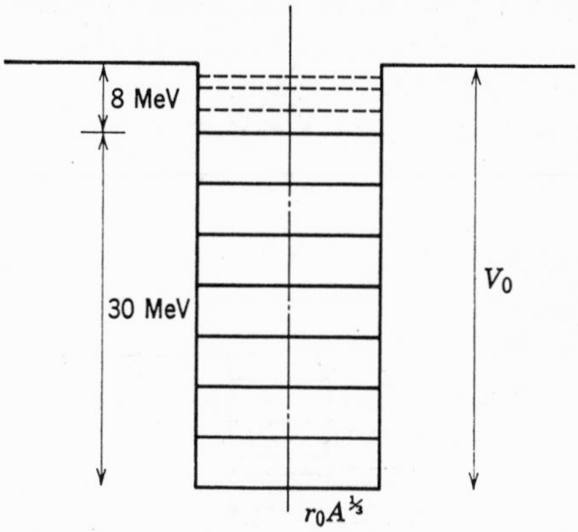

Fig. 2.24-1. The nuclear well with occupied single-particle states (solid line) and empty excited states (dotted lines).

According to the assumption of Fermi statistics, the number of neutron states per unit momentum interval is

(1) $$\frac{dN}{dp} = 2\frac{4\pi p^2\Omega}{(2\pi\hbar)^3} = \frac{\Omega p^2}{\pi^2\hbar^3},$$

and thus, at zero temperature, where only the lowest states are populated, our N neutrons occupy momentum states up to a maximum momentum $p_{\max}$ given by

(2) $$N = \int_0^{p_{\max}} \frac{dN}{dp}\, dp \doteq \frac{\Omega}{3\pi^2\hbar^3}\, p_{\max}^3.$$

It is well known that $p_{\max}$ and the corresponding kinetic energy $E_{\max} = p_{\max}^2/2M$ depend on the density

(3) $$p_{\max} = 3^{1/3}\pi^{2/3}\hbar\left(\frac{N}{\Omega}\right)^{1/3}$$

(4) $$E_{\max} = \frac{3^{2/3}\pi^{4/3}\hbar^2}{2M}\left(\frac{N}{\Omega}\right)^{2/3}.$$

From the known value of the density of nuclear matter we find

(5) $$k_{\max} = p_{\max}/\hbar = 1.2 \times 10^{13}\ \text{cm}^{-1},$$
$$E_{\max} = 30\ \text{MeV}.$$

Since it is known experimentally from photodisintegration experiments that the binding energy of the least bound neutron (ionization potential) of average heavy nuclei is ≈ 8 MeV, the potential V_0 is ≈ 38 MeV.

The total kinetic energy of the neutrons is

$$E_N = \int_0^{E\max} E \frac{dN}{dE}\, dE = \int_0^{E\max} E \frac{dN}{dp}\frac{dp}{dE}\, dE = C \frac{N^{5/3}}{A^{2/3}}, \tag{6}$$

where C is a positive constant.

For a symmetrical nucleon gas $N = Z = A/2$ the total kinetic energy is

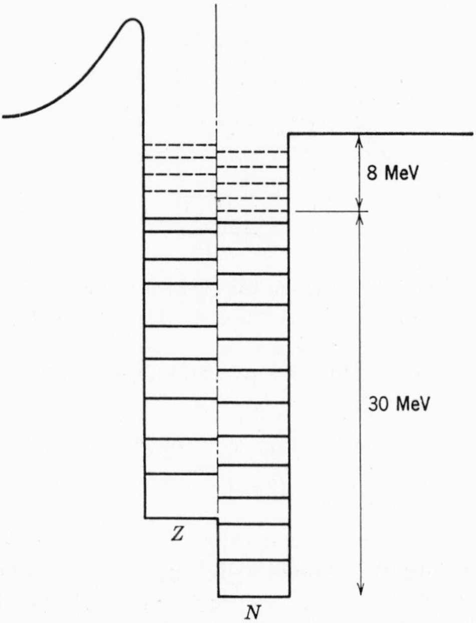

Fig. 2.24-2. The nuclear wells for neutrons and protons with single-particle states.

the sum of two equal terms ($E = E_N + E_Z = 2E_N$); the average kinetic energy is, for both neutrons and protons,

$$E_{\text{av}} = \tfrac{3}{5} 30 \text{ MeV} = 18 \text{ MeV}. \tag{7}$$

b. Nonsymmetrical Nucleon Gas. If we consider the electrostatic repulsion between the protons, the symmetry is destroyed. Our model must involve two separate gases, contained in two different wells and having different energy levels (Fig. 2.24-2).

The levels are occupied to the same height if the nucleus is β stable. Otherwise a sequence of β decays will occur until this situation is reached. For stable nuclei there will be an excess of neutrons because of the greater depth of the neutron well.

The kinetic energy of the zero-temperature neutron gas is now different from that of the proton gas. From (6) the total kinetic energy can be written

$$\frac{C}{A^{2/3}}(N^{5/3} + Z^{5/3}).$$

This value is larger than the energy computed for $N = Z$. Using the binomial expansion we determine that the difference, to the second order in $T_\zeta = \frac{1}{2}(Z - N)$ is

$$(8) \quad \frac{C}{A^{2/3}}\left[N^{5/3} + Z^{5/3} - 2\left(\frac{A}{2}\right)^{5/3}\right]$$

$$= \frac{C}{A^{2/3}}\left[\left(\frac{A}{2} - T_\zeta\right)^{5/3} + \left(\frac{A}{2} + T_\zeta\right)^{5/3} - 2\left(\frac{A}{2}\right)^{5/3}\right] \approx \text{constant}\ \frac{T_\zeta^2}{A}.$$

This is an expression of the symmetry energy due to the exclusion principle.

c. Experimental Studies of Internal Nuclear Motions. The momentum distribution of the particles within a nucleus has been investigated experimentally with the technique of "quasi-elastic" scattering of protons of 340 MeV (C-52; W-55). If a fast proton is scattered elastically by a nucleon at rest, the kinematical conditions define its energy for each angle of scattering. If it is scattered by a nucleon in motion, the energy distribution observed at each angle permits the determination of the momentum of the target nucleon.

When a 340-MeV proton collides with a nucleus, most of the collisions are inelastic: they give rise to nuclear reactions and frequently to stars. Some of the events, however, can be interpreted as elastic collisions with a single nucleon in motion within the nucleus; these are the "quasi-elastic events."

Quasi-elastic scattering studies on the deuteron reveal a momentum distribution in agreement with the Fourier transform of the Hulthen wave function [1.23(9)] for $\rho = R/7$. In Be and C the observed energy distribution can be fitted with a gaussian with $1/e$ value around 20 MeV.

Unfortunately, the data are not complete and the method cannot be applied to heavier elements; but the order of magnitude of the momentum distribution observed agrees with the present statistical considerations.

d. Excited States. Nuclei have many excited states. The low ones may be attributed to the excitation of a single particle, as in atomic physics, but highly excited nuclei are essentially different from excited atoms. In an atom the excitation energy is usually carried by one electron; in a nucleus it is often shared by many nucleons.

A nucleon in an excited state is no longer embedded in the Fermi gas. Its interactions with the remaining nucleons become more and more important with increasing excitation energy. For this reason highly excited states of nuclei are many-body states in which the energy is shared by many particles. An excited nucleus is more like a normal condensed material than a nucleus in the ground state.

For a nucleus composed of many particles the only practical way of describing nuclear excitation is in the statistical approach.

The excitation energy E^* raises the nuclear temperature to a value T, which depends on the particular model assumed to represent nuclear matter. For a Fermi gas of A particles the relation is a square dependence:

$$E^* = \frac{\pi^2}{4} A \frac{(kT)^2}{E_{\text{max}}} \approx \text{constant } AT^2. \tag{9}$$

An important application of the statistical approach is the estimate of the number of excited states. For this we first find the entropy S of the nucleus from the relation between E^* and T:

$$S = \int_0^T \frac{dE^*}{T} = \text{constant } \sqrt{AE^*}. \tag{10}$$

Then we interpret the entropy as the logarithm of the probability of realizing the excitation in a certain energy interval dE^* and thus as the logarithm of the number of states available in dE^*. We write

$$\frac{\text{density of states at temperature } T}{\text{density of states at temperature } 0} = \frac{w(T)}{w(0)} = e^{S/k}, \tag{11}$$

where k is Boltzmann's constant.

The result is that the density of states should depend on A and E^* according to the expression

$$w(T) \approx \exp(\text{constant } A^{1/2}E^{*1/2}). \tag{12}$$

Equation (12) is qualitatively verified in the sense that on the average heavy nuclei have denser excited states and that the level density increases with energy.

It is interesting to observe that for medium and heavy nuclei the statistical approach is applicable even to unbound states. The low unbound states have a long mean life and the corresponding levels are sharp (compound nucleus), since none of the particles has sufficient energy to escape unless all the energy is concentrated in it—statistically a rather improbable situation. The escape of a particle becomes similar to the slow evaporation of a molecule from a drop of liquid.

At high excitation energy the "drop" evaporates rapidly—it boils away—and we observe the production of characteristic "stars" in photographic emulsion.

We shall make use of these ideas in the discussion of nuclear reactions.

2.25 *The Semiempirical Mass Formula (Drop Model)*

a. The Mass Formula. We can make use of the ideas developed in the preceding sections in order to write a formula for the exact atomic masses. The formula (W-35) contains seven terms and four constants, α, β, γ, δ, which cannot be obtained from the theory and will be determined to fit the empirical data. The formula is

$$(1)\quad M = M_n N + M_H Z - \alpha A + \beta A^{2/3} + \gamma \frac{T_\zeta^2}{A} + \frac{3}{5}\frac{Z(Z-1)}{A^{1/3}}\frac{e^2}{r_{0,\,\mathrm{coul}}} + \delta(A, Z).$$

In this expression the terms $M_n N$ and $M_H Z$ are the *masses of the elementary particles* forming the atom. The numerical values of M_n and M_H can be found in 1.21a.

The term in α expresses the fact that because of *saturation* of nuclear forces the binding energy is proportional to A.

The term in β, proportional to the nuclear surface, is a correction attributed to the smaller binding of the particles near the surface of the nucleus. It is often called the surface energy, or *surface tension*, term.

The next term in γ has the form obtained in 2.24(8) and represents the *symmetry* effects that favor $N = Z$.

Next comes the *coulomb repulsion* already discussed in 2.21a. Numerically[1] for $r_{0,\mathrm{coul}} = 1.5 \times 10^{-13}$ cm,

$$(2)\quad \frac{3}{5}\frac{Z(Z-1)}{A^{1/3}}\frac{e^2}{r_{0,\mathrm{coul}}} = 0.000627\frac{Z(Z-1)}{A^{1/3}}\ \mathrm{MU} = 0.583\frac{Z(Z-1)}{A^{1/3}}\ \mathrm{MeV}.$$

Finally, the term δ describes the *effects of pairing*. A good fit to the data is obtained by taking δ as a function of A:

$$(3)\quad \begin{aligned} &\delta = -0.036A^{-3/4}\ \mathrm{MU} = -33A^{-3/4}\ \mathrm{MeV} \quad \text{for even-even nuclei,}\\ &\delta = 0 \quad \text{for even-odd nuclei,}\\ &\delta = +0.036A^{-3/4}\ \mathrm{MU} = +33A^{-3/4}\ \mathrm{MeV} \quad \text{for odd-odd nuclei.}\end{aligned}$$

[1] The numerical values for α, β, γ, and δ are taken from Fermi's lecture notes (Fe-50).

The symmetry term coefficient γ can be obtained by expressing (1) as a function of A and $T_\zeta = \frac{1}{2}(Z - N)$:

$$(1') \quad M = M_{\mathrm{n}}A - (M_{\mathrm{n}} - M_{\mathrm{H}})\left(\frac{A}{2} + T_\zeta\right) - \alpha A + \beta A^{2/3} + \gamma \frac{T_\zeta^{\,2}}{A} + 0.583 \text{ MeV} \frac{[(A/2) + T_\zeta]^2}{A^{1/3}} + \delta(A, T_\zeta)$$

(for simplicity $Z(Z - 1)$ has been replaced by Z^2 in the coulomb energy term) and writing that the most stable even-odd nucleus for a given A must have

$$(4) \quad \frac{\partial M(A, T_\zeta)}{\partial T_\zeta} = M_{\mathrm{H}} - M_{\mathrm{n}} + 2\gamma \frac{T_\zeta}{A} + 0.583 \text{ MeV} \times \frac{2}{A^{1/3}}\left(\frac{A}{2} + T_\zeta\right) = 0.$$

Comparison with the values of A and T_ζ for a known stable isotope gives us

$$(5) \quad \gamma = 0.083 \text{ MU} = 77 \text{ MeV}.$$

Equation (4) yields the most stable nucleus for each A. By calling Z_β the Z value of a β stable nucleus we have

$$(6) \quad Z_\beta = \frac{A}{1.98 + 0.015\, A^{2/3}}.$$

The curve (6) passes through the region of most stable nuclei for all values of A.

By substituting (6) in (1), we obtain the masses of stable nuclei $M_\beta(A)$, still expressed in terms of the unknown coefficients α and β. Comparison with the data yields

$$(7) \quad \begin{aligned} \alpha &= 0.015 \text{ MU} = 14 \text{ MeV} \\ \beta &= 0.014 \text{ MU} = 13 \text{ MeV}. \end{aligned}$$

With these numerical values (1) predicts atomic masses with an accuracy that in most cases is considerably better than 0.01 MU (one part in 10^{-4} for $A = 100$).

The Weizsäcker formula and Fermi treatment which we have reported have been considerably refined in the last decade. New terms have been added to the semiempirical mass formula which, in a recent paper (S-61)[1],

[1] The symmetry term in $|T_\zeta|$ was suggested by Wigner and the other modifications, by Brandt et al., and Salpeter and Mozer (see S-61 for references). The coulomb term corresponds to $r_0 = 1.07\ 10^{-13}$ cm, with trapezoidal charge distribution, and includes exchange effects.

is written as follows for odd A:

$$(8)\quad M = M_n N + M_H Z - \alpha A + \beta A^{2/3} + \left(\gamma - \frac{n}{A^{1/3}}\right)\left(\frac{T_\zeta^2 + 2\,|T_\zeta|}{A}\right) + 0.8076\,\frac{Z^2}{A^{1/3}}\left(1 - \frac{0.7636}{Z^{2/3}} - \frac{2.29}{A^{2/3}}\right).$$

The values of the coefficients, determined by least square fit performed with an electronic computer, are

$$\alpha = 16.11 \text{ MeV}$$
$$\beta = 20.21 \text{ MeV}$$
$$\gamma = 20.65 \text{ MeV}$$
$$n = 48.00 \text{ MeV}.$$

The differences between the measured masses and those computed from (8) correspond to a standard deviation of 2.61 MeV. The departures from the semiempirical formula, however, are not random. Definite systematic trends are observed (Fig. 2.25-1), and these are positive evidence of a shell structure.

b. Stability for Emission of Heavy Particles. The energy condition for spontaneous emission of a proton or a neutron by a nucleus is

$$(9a)\qquad M(N, Z) > M(N, Z-1) + M_H,$$

$$(9b)\qquad M(N, Z) > M(N-1, Z) + M_n,$$

or, approximately,

$$(10a)\qquad \frac{\partial M(N, Z)}{\partial Z} > M_H,$$

$$(10b)\qquad \frac{\partial M(N, Z)}{\partial N} > M_n.$$

These equations define regions in the ZN plane which are, respectively, in the neutron abundant and proton abundant side of the β stability line (Fig. 2.25-2). The neutron instability region is not far from this line, and neutron emission is actually observed in certain fission products.

However, the neutron and proton instability regions cross the β stable line only for very high values of A that are not observed for existing nuclei. This explains why there are no radioactive nuclei emitting protons or neutrons.

The condition for α emission is

$$(11)\qquad M(N, Z) > M(N-2, Z-2) + M(2, 2),$$

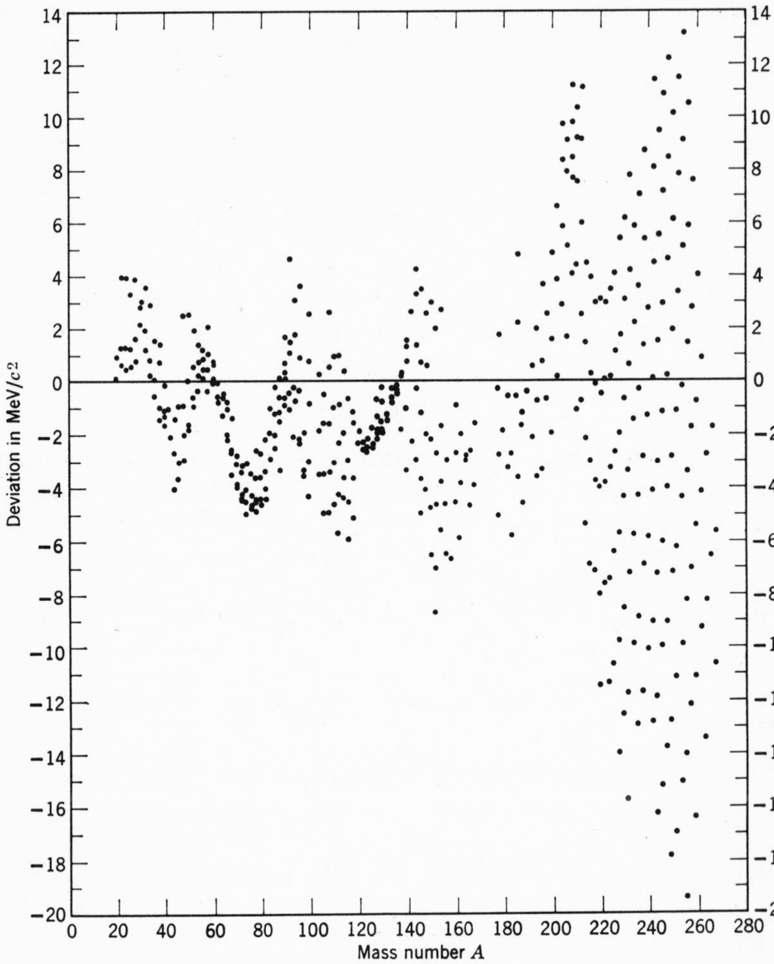

Fig. 2.25-1. Deviation of 488 atomic mass excesses for odd A from values calculated from formula (8) [from P. A. Seeger, *Nucl. Phys.*, **25**, 4 (1961)].

or

$$2\frac{\partial M}{\partial Z} + 2\frac{\partial M}{\partial N} > M(2, 2) = 2M_{\mathrm{H}} + 2M_{\mathrm{n}} - 28 \text{ MeV}. \tag{12}$$

Because of the binding energy of the α particle, (12) may be satisfied even when (10) is not. In fact, the region of α instability defined by (12) crosses the β stable line for $A \approx 150$.

From a table of nuclear data we find that the lightest α emitter is Sm^{152} and that the natural radioactive families start at $A \approx 210$. This is not unreasonable if we consider that, because of the small penetrability of the potential barrier, several MeV of excess energy are needed for the α particle to be emitted with a detectable half-life.

c. β-Stability of Isobars. The difference in mass between neighboring isobars determines the energy of β decay. From (1′) we see that the dominant term in T_ζ is the symmetry term in γT_ζ^2 and thus the curves $M(A, T_\zeta)$ for A constant are roughly parabolic.

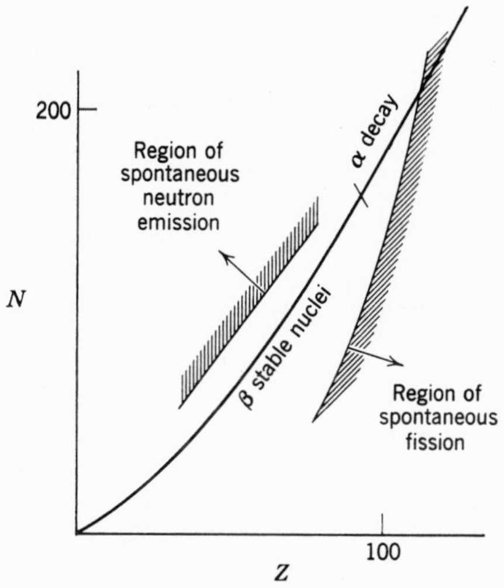

Fig. 2.25-2. Qualitative sketch showing some of the stability conditions which follow from the mass formula.

For A odd (even-odd nuclei, $\delta = 0$) there is only one such parabola (Fig. 2.25-3) and there is only one β stable nucleus, corresponding to the value of Z integer which gives the minimum M.

For A even (even-even or odd-odd nuclei) there are two parabolas displaced by 2δ (Fig. 2.25-4) and there may be several even-even β stable nuclei.

These remarks correspond to well-known empirical facts.

d. Excited States. The nuclear model usually associated with the semiempirical mass formula is a condensed matter model, since constant density, binding proportional to weight, and surface energy are properties of normal solids and liquids.

The excited states of the model correspond to vibrations. There are two kinds of vibrations to be considered: volume waves and surface waves or ripples.

Nuclear matter has constant density and is difficult to compress. Thus the volume waves have high frequency and high quantum energy. They can be disregarded for small excitation energies (~MeV).

The development of these ideas (B-37, p. 86) leads to the following relation between entropy and excitation energy:

$$S = \text{constant} A^{2/3} E^{*4/7}. \tag{13}$$

From this equation, as from 2.24(12), we predict an increase in the density of levels with A and E^*.

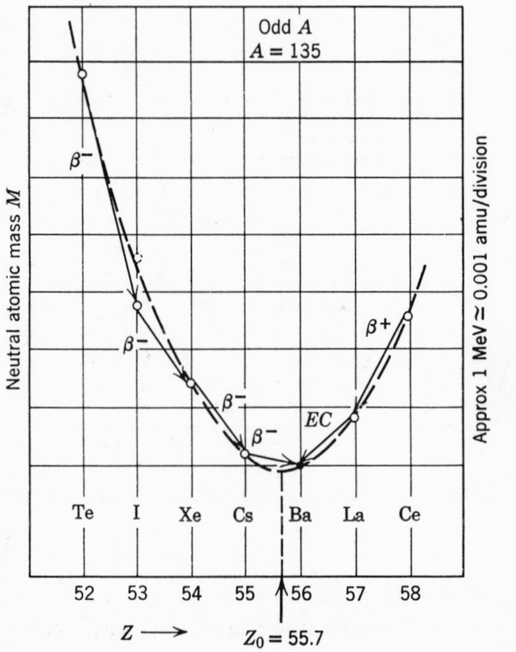

Fig. 2.25-3. Isobaric masses for $A = 135$ (odd). Note that the mass of I^{135} ($N = 82$) falls below the smooth curve (from R. D. Evans' *The Atomic Nucleus*, McGraw-Hill, 1955, used by permission).

Experimental evidence for nuclear vibrational excited states is presented in 2.27c.

e. Fission. An obvious consequence of the surface vibrations is fission. The fission of a mercury drop carrying a surface density of electricity has been discussed by Rayleigh, and the only difference in the nuclear case is that we must consider a volume distribution of charge. However, the phenomenon of fission was not theoretically predicted.

If a spherical nucleus undergoes a deformation at constant density, the surface term and the coulomb term of the mass formula are affected.

The surface energy increases and thus the surface forces oppose the deformation; the coulomb energy decreases and the electrostatic repulsion tends to make the deformation larger.

Let R be the radius of the undeformed nuclear sphere and let us describe the magnitude of the deformation by a parameter ε. The sphere is deformed into an ellipsoid of revolution whose semiaxes are $R(1 + \varepsilon)$ (along

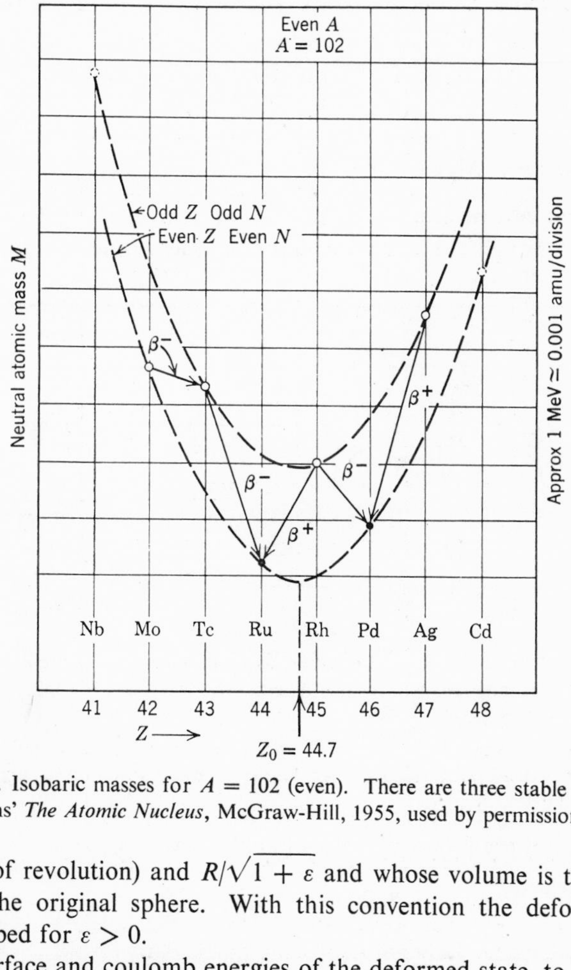

Fig. 2.25-4. Isobaric masses for $A = 102$ (even). There are three stable nuclei (from R. D. Evans' *The Atomic Nucleus*, McGraw-Hill, 1955, used by permission).

the axis of revolution) and $R/\sqrt{1 + \varepsilon}$ and whose volume is the same as that of the original sphere. With this convention the deformation is cigar-shaped for $\varepsilon > 0$.

The surface and coulomb energies of the deformed state, to the second power of ε, are, from (2) and (7),

$$\begin{aligned} &\text{surface energy} = 0.014A^{2/3}(1 + \tfrac{2}{5}\varepsilon^2 + \cdots)\ \text{MU}, \\ (14) \quad &\text{coulomb energy} = 0.000627\,\frac{Z^2}{A^{1/3}}(1 - \tfrac{1}{5}\varepsilon^2 + \cdots)\ \text{MU}. \end{aligned}$$

The nucleus is naturally unstable against fission if

$$0.000627\frac{1}{5}\frac{Z^2}{A^{1/3}} > 0.014\frac{2}{5}A^{2/3},$$

or

$$\frac{Z^2}{A} \geq 45, \tag{15}$$

which for β stable nuclei is satisfied for $Z \geq \approx 120$.

We stop this discussion at this point and refer to specialized books for further detail.

2.26 The Shell Model

a. Magic Numbers. A close look at a table of nuclear data will reveal that, though the main trends of nuclear properties are properly

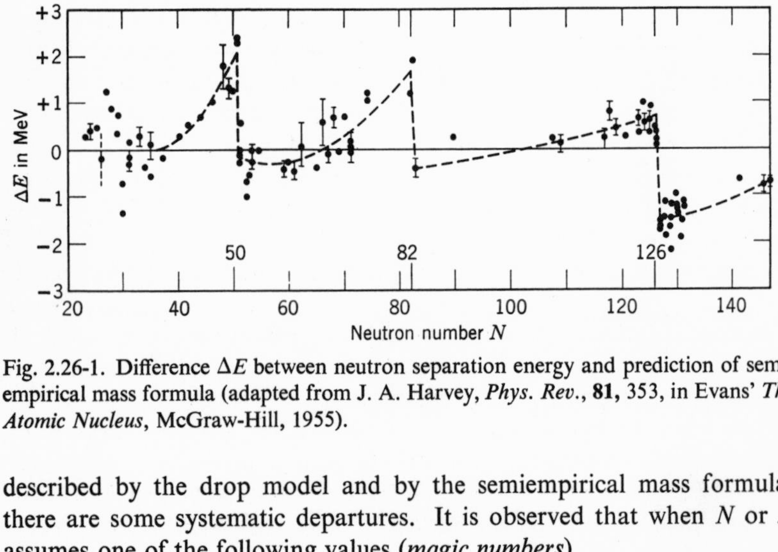

Fig. 2.26-1. Difference ΔE between neutron separation energy and prediction of semiempirical mass formula (adapted from J. A. Harvey, *Phys. Rev.*, **81**, 353, in Evans' *The Atomic Nucleus*, McGraw-Hill, 1955).

described by the drop model and by the semiempirical mass formula, there are some systematic departures. It is observed that when N or Z assumes one of the following values (*magic numbers*),

$$2, 8, 20, (28), 50, 82, 126, \tag{1}$$

the nuclei are particularly numerous and particularly stable. For instance, Ca($Z = 20$) has six and Sn($Z = 50$) has 10 stable isotopes; for $N = 20$ there are five stable nuclei, and for $N = 50$ their number is six, whereas the neighboring values of N and Z are less populated.

The unusually strong binding is revealed in plots of nuclear masses (Fig. 2.25-1) and of neutron separation energies—analogous to the atomic ionization potentials (Fig. 2.26-1). Also the energetics of β and α decay give evidence for magic numbers: for instance, the anomalously light I^{53} of Fig. 2.25-3 has $N = 82$.

b. Shells in a Square Well Potential. It is tempting to try to account for the stability of the magic-number nuclei in the same manner as we explain the chemical stability of the noble gases. In the atomic case we deal with electrons whose interactions with one another are in first approximation neglected compared to nuclear attraction. Such independent particle treatment of the electrons leads to the idea of complete shells corresponding to full energy levels and to spherically symmetric spinless atoms. When a shell is completed, or closed, we have a maximum of stability.

To transfer this idea to the nuclear case, we have to go back to the independent particle model. In the Fermi gas model (2.24) the shape of the well was left undefined, but now we shall attempt to classify the states according to the quantum numbers appropriate to the motion in a spherical well.

The order of levels in a spherical well of infinite depth is given by the order of the zeros in the Bessel functions. We indicate such levels in order of increasing energy in Fig. 2.26-2. Spectroscopic notation is used; $1s$ is the first level with $l = 0$, etc. (the number preceding the designation of angular momentum is one plus the number of radial nodes). The symbol for the level is followed by the number of equal particles it may contain $[2(2l + 1)]$ and by the predicted magic number $[\Sigma\, 2(2l + 1)]$. The vertical scale is an energy scale in units of $2\hbar^2/MR^2$.

Apart from the lowest magic numbers 2, 8, and 20, the agreement is poor. However, the square well which we have chosen is surely an oversimplification and we can vary it in order to fit the data; we are also allowed to invert the order of some levels, as inversions occur in atomic physics in the region of the rare earths.

We have the impression that we are facing a game of numbers that surely can be solved with a sufficient amount of ingenuity or trickery but whose solution is not very meaningful.

This impression, however, is false. There are many ways to check a proposed solution. For instance, any interpretation of the closed shells in terms of level ordering leads to a definite prediction for the spins and magnetic moments for the nuclei with N or Z equal magic number ± 1, according to the single particle theory in 2.22(2); many other less direct checks of internal consistency are also possible.

c. Shells in a Square Well with Spin-Orbit Coupling. The level system which is accepted at present involves the basic idea that each state of motion (apart from the S states) is split in two because of spin-orbit coupling[1]. The doublets are inverted, as we have seen for He^5 and

[1] This idea originated with M. G. Mayer and J. H. D. Jensen (MJ-55).

Li^5, meaning that the level with higher J is lower. Each split level now contains $2J + 1$ equal particles.

The scheme, and its connection with the level order in Fig. 2.26-2, is shown in Fig. 2.26-3.

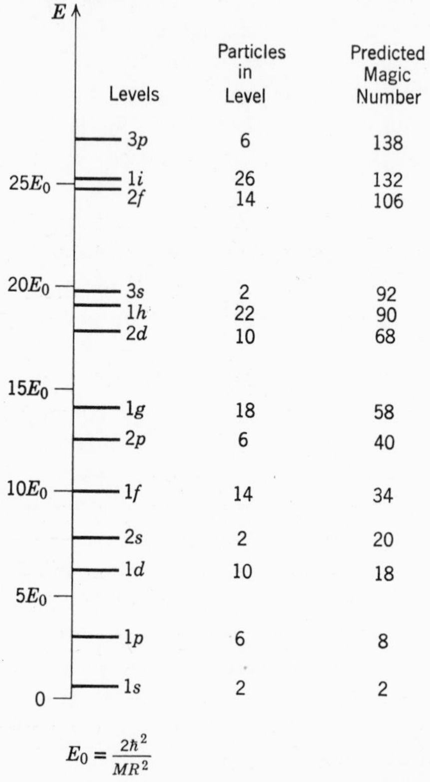

Fig. 2.26-2. Levels and magic numbers from infinitely deep square well of radius R (reprinted with permission from M. G. Mayer and J. H. Jenson, *Nuclear Shell Structure*, Wiley, 1955).

It would be too long to report here all of the arguments in favor of this scheme. We shall limit ourselves to a description of the nature of the evidence that enters into the discussion and to a few illustrative examples.

According to the scheme, all nuclei with 21 neutrons or protons should have spin $\frac{7}{2}$ and those with 19 neutrons or protons should have spin $\frac{3}{2}$. This is actually the case. The magnetic moments for N or $Z = 21$ should be those computed from 2.22(2) for a $f_{7/2}(l = 3, J = l + \frac{1}{2})$, and those for N or $Z = 19$ should agree with a $d_{3/2}$ state ($l = 2, J = l - \frac{1}{2}$). Here the agreement is not so good; but we know that magnetic moments are not easy to compute, and we can be satisfied with the fact that the observed moments are closer to the predicted Schmidt limit than to the other one. In $K^{41}(Z = 19)$ the moment is indeed very near to the limit predicted.

Concerning quadrupole moments, we expect those for Z equal to closed shell plus (or minus) one to be negative (or positive), and this is in agreement with the facts.

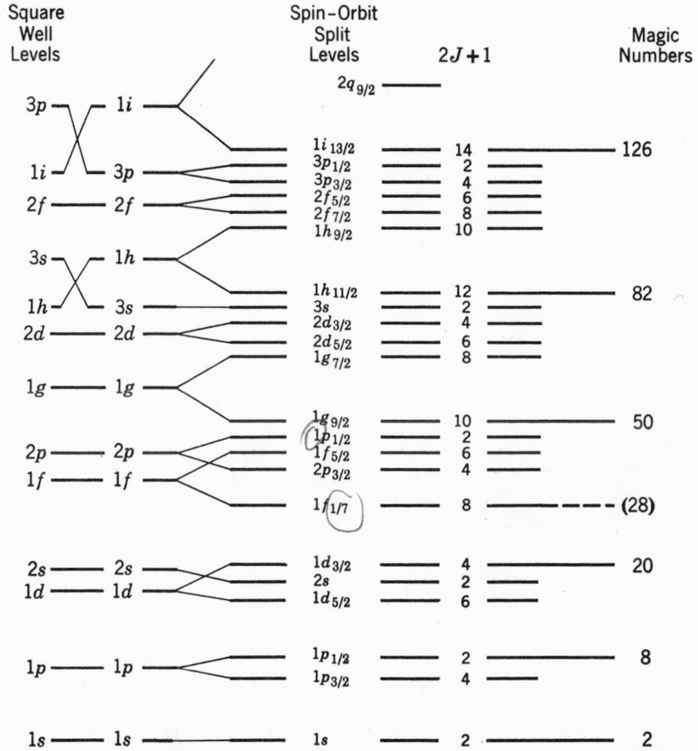

Fig. 2.26-3. The original level order of the shell model with spin-orbit coupling (some inversions are required according to recent work; see 2.28) (reprinted with permission from M. G. Mayer and J. H. Jenson, *Nuclear Shell Structure*, Wiley, 1955).

The predictions are sometimes made difficult by the fact that contiguous sublevels may have energies very close to one another. An interesting example is provided by the low levels of the even-odd isotopes of Te ($Z = 52$, $69 \leq N \leq 81$). The odd neutron may be in the $2d_{3/2}$, $3s$, or $1h_{11/2}$ state, which is observed either as ground or low excited state (Fig. 2.26-4). Because of the large angular momentum difference between the $h_{11/2}$ level and the others, γ transitions are highly forbidden (see 4.31), and this explains why we observe isomers for Te and neighboring nuclei.

The phenomenon of isomerism (long γ lives) is concentrated in *islands* whose locations correspond to the presence of neighboring levels of widely different J. In agreement with the level sequence of Fig. 2.26-3, isomeric islands are found for

$$38 \leq \text{odd } N \text{ or } Z \leq 50 \qquad (p_{1/2} \text{ and } g_{9/2} \text{ levels}),$$
$$64 \leq \text{odd } N \leq 82 \qquad (s_{1/2},\ d_{3/2}, \text{ and } h_{11/2} \text{ levels}), \tag{2}$$
$$100 \leq \text{odd } N \leq 126 \qquad (f_{5/2} \text{ and } i_{13/2} \text{ levels}).$$

d. Many-Particle Configurations. The shell model is most directly applicable to nuclei with a single particle or a single hole in the

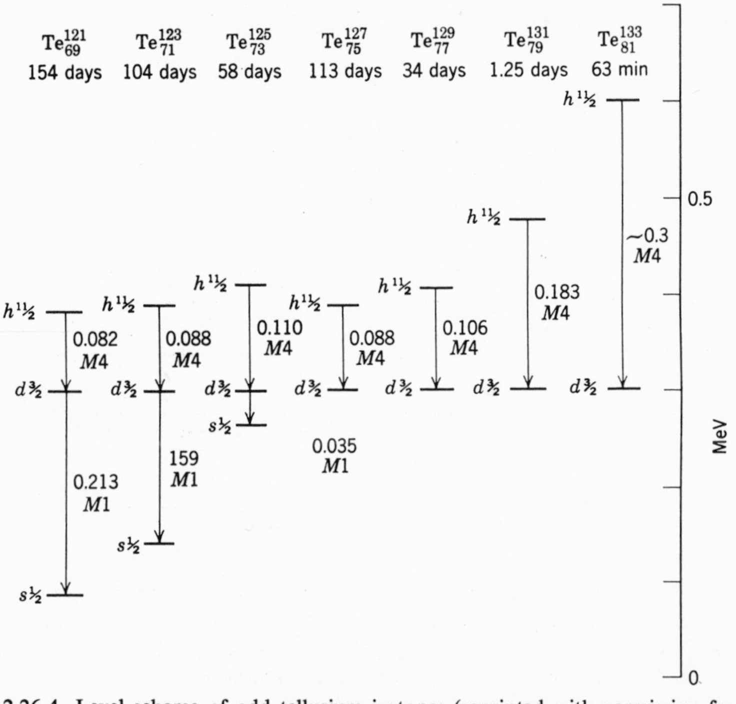

Fig. 2.26-4. Level scheme of odd tellurium isotopes (reprinted with permission from M. G. Mayer and J. H. Jensen, *Nuclear Shell Structure*, Wiley, 1955).

last shell; but we must consider more generally the effect of several particles (or holes) and study the configurations that may result.

Two unpaired particles in a j shell may give $2j + 1$ values of total angular momentum J, from 0 to $2j$. However, some of these values are excluded because of the restriction of Fermi statistics, which allows only antisymmetric states. By writing the two particle wave function with the help of Clebsch-Gordan coefficients, we see that only the states with J even have the required symmetry.

The situation is more complicated if more than two particles (or holes) are considered. We report (MJ-55) the possible values of total angular momentum in Table 2.26-1.

In the independent-particle model the different values of J are degenerate, and we cannot predict the spin of the ground state. It is known, however, that if the number of particles in the j shell is even the ground state has

Table 2.26-1

j	Number of Unpaired Particles (or Holes) in j Shell	Possible J Values
$\frac{1}{2}$	1	$\frac{1}{2}$
$\frac{3}{2}$	1	$\frac{3}{2}$
	2	0, 2
$\frac{5}{2}$	1	$\frac{5}{2}$
	2	0, 2, 4
	3	$\frac{3}{2}, \frac{5}{2}, \frac{9}{2}$

$J = 0$; if it is odd, we observe $J = j$ because of the pairing of the even particles.

We can prove that if the ground state has $J = j$ the single-particle calculation of the magnetic moments (2.22b) still gives the correct results; but other electromagnetic properties, such as quadrupole moments and transition probabilities, cannot be computed from the single-particle model (2.33).

These questions are more fully discussed in 2.3, where we develop theoretical techniques appropriate to the treatment of many-body problems.

2.27 *Collective Motions and the Unified Model of Bohr and Mottelson*

a. Description of the Model. Certain nuclear data can neither be explained with the independent particle model nor in terms of a spherical drop of condensed matter. They require the assumption of collective motions and of nonspherically symmetric deformations of the potential well in which the individual independent particles move.

Let us consider first the electric quadrupole moments. For odd Z these moments are of the sign predicted from the state of the odd proton, but their value is often much larger than that computed for the wave function of a single proton. For odd N the quadrupole moment may be different from zero; the sign agrees with that predicted in the assumption that the odd neutron is positively charged! Typical is the case of S^{33} ($N = 17, J = \frac{3}{2}$, one neutron in $d_{3/2}$ state) with $Q < 0$ and of S^{35} ($N = 19, J = \frac{3}{2}$, one neutron missing from the complete $d_{3/2}$ level) with $Q > 0$.

These observations can be explained, assuming a *deformation of the core.* In an early model (R-51) it was assumed that the deformation resulted from the attraction between the odd particle and the other nucleons. The amount of deformation was obtained with a perturbation calculation (H-52; H-53) and obviously depended on the strength of the attraction and the surface energy.

It is expected that the deformation will be small for nuclei close to magic numbers with high binding energy and thus large rigidity.

It has been found empirically that for most configurations the equilibrium deformation possesses axial symmetry and the nuclear potential well can be regarded as an ellipsoid of revolution. Excited states involve the consideration of oscillations of the nucleus as a whole around the equilibrium shape and rotations with preservation of shape and internal structure. Such oscillations and rotations are typically *collective motions.*

b. Collective Rotational States. For large deformations—as observed away from magic numbers—the rotational states are lower than the vibrational ones. We shall discuss rotations first.

In order to visualize the motion that results from the core rotation, we must imagine that the core affects any one single particle only because it produces the potential well in which the particle moves. According to this model, the rotations of the well around its own axes of symmetry have no effect on the nucleon's motion: no mass moves.

The moment of inertia is zero and the rotational states infinitely high [see (2)]. Rotations around an axis perpendicular to the symmetry axis instead carry along some nuclear matter. They may be responsible for motions similar to those illustrated in Fig. 2.27-1[1].

The total angular momentum of the nucleus is composed of two parts: a first part contributed by the rapid motion of the independent particles within the deformed well and a second due to the slower revolution of the well as a whole around nonsymmetry axes.

If the slowly rotating well has an axis of symmetry z, the projection of the total angular momentum of the individual particles on this axis is a good quantum number. Let us call this projection $\Omega = \sum_{\alpha} j_{\alpha z}$ (Fig. 2.27-2),

[1] See the article by A. Bohr and B. B. Mottelson in *β and γ Spectroscopy* (B-55a). This article contains references to the original work. For a more modern review see D. M. Brink (B-60b).

and let **R** be the angular momentum of the collective motion, which, as we have said, is perpendicular to the symmetry axis.

In order to obtain the total angular momentum of the nucleus J, we must add $\mathbf{\Omega}$ and $\mathbf{R}$ according to the coupling scheme of Fig. 2.27-2.

When the addition is performed according to the rules of quantum

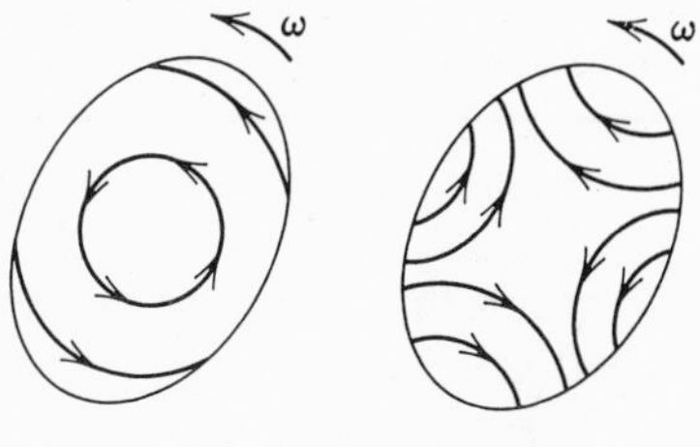

(a) (b)

Fig. 2.27-1. Distribution of internal velocities within a revolving non-spherical potential well. (*a*) Rigid rotation, (*b*) irrotational (**curl v** = 0) motion (from A. Bohr and B. R. Mottelson in *β and γ Spectroscopy*, North Holland, 1955, K. Siegbahn, editor).

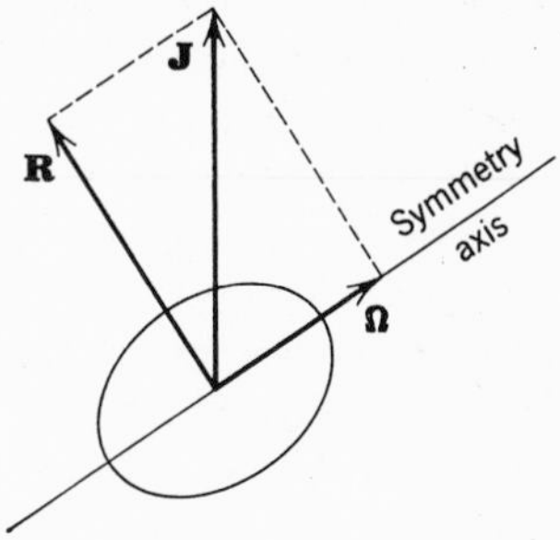

Fig. 2.27-2. Coupling scheme in the collective motion model (from A. Bohr and B. R. Mottelson, in *β and γ Spectroscopy*, North Holland, 1955, K. Siegbahn, editor).

mechanics, we find that J can assume values $\Omega, \Omega + 1, \cdots$, and that the rotational energy is given by

$$(1) \qquad E_{\text{rot}} = \frac{\hbar^2}{2\mathfrak{J}} [J(J + 1) + a(-1)^{J+\frac{1}{2}}(J + \tfrac{1}{2})\delta_{\Omega,\frac{1}{2}}],$$

where $\mathfrak{J}$ is the moment of inertia about $\mathbf{R}$, $\delta_{\Omega,\frac{1}{2}} = 1$ or 0 for $\Omega = \frac{1}{2}$ or $\Omega \neq \frac{1}{2}$,

$$a = \sum_j (-1)^{j-\frac{1}{2}}(j + \tfrac{1}{2})\,|C_j|^2,$$

and $|C_j|^2$ is the probability that the last odd particle has angular momentum j.

Let us apply these considerations to deformed even-even nuclei. In this case we know that $J = 0$ in the ground state[1] and we can also assume $\mathbf{R} = \mathbf{\Omega} = 0$. The excited states resulting from collective rotations without change of internal structure have $\Omega = 0$, $\mathbf{R} = \mathbf{J}$. Thus $\delta_{\Omega,\frac{1}{2}} = 0$ and the energy levels are given by the simple formula

$$(2) \qquad E^* = \frac{\hbar^2}{2\mathfrak{J}_{\text{eff}}} J(J + 1),$$

[1] Such ground states are spherically symmetrical because there is no preferential axis relative to which the deformed nucleus could be aligned.

where $\mathfrak{J}_{\text{eff}}$ is the moment of inertia for the axis of rotation, which is perpendicular to the symmetry axis. If we assume, in particular, that the system is symmetrical relative to inversion of the symmetry axis, as in an ellipsoid of revolution, only even values of J are allowed. The situation is the same as that of a homonuclear molecule whose nuclei satisfy Bose statistics.

There is unambiguous evidence that (2) properly describes the low excited states of many even-even nuclei away from magic numbers. It

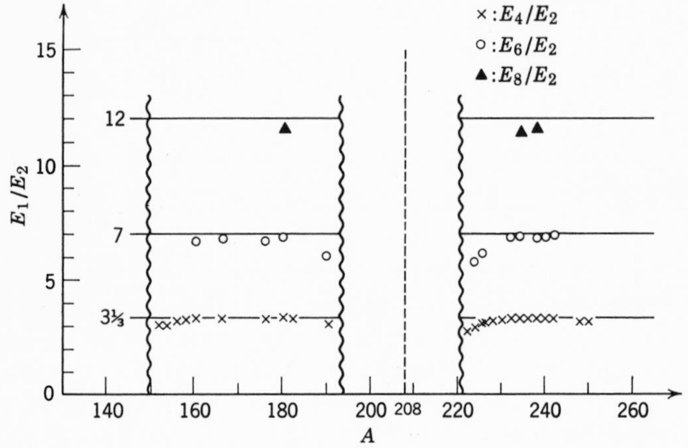

Fig. 2.27-3. Experimental ratios of excited-state energy of even-even nuclei compared with predictions of rotational model [from Alder et al., *Rev. Mod. Phys.*, **28,** 432 (1956)].

follows from (2) that the ratios of excitation energies of successive levels ($J = 2n$) to that of the first excited states ($J = 2$) should be

$$\frac{E_{2n}^*}{E_2^*} = \frac{2n(2n+1)}{2 \times 3} = \frac{n(2n+1)}{3}, \quad n = 2, 3, 4, \tag{3}$$

from which we obtain

$$\frac{E_4^*}{E_2^*} = 3\tfrac{1}{3}; \quad \frac{E_6^*}{E_2^*} = 7; \quad \frac{E_8^*}{E_2^*} = 12; \quad \text{etc.}$$

Such ratios are indeed often observed (Fig. 2.27-3) and sometimes with amazing accuracy (Fig. 2.27-4). Furthermore, the excitation energy E_1^* of the first rotational state of deformed nuclei shows a smooth variation with A (Fig. 2.27-5), whereas magic and near-magic nuclei, which are spherical, show no rotational spectrum.

From the data in Fig. 2.27-5 and with the help of (2) we can obtain the effective moments of inertia of the various nuclei. Since $E^* \simeq \mathfrak{J}_{\text{eff}}^{-1}$, the effective moment of inertia is small for magic nuclei, which are spherically symmetrical, and large for highly deformed nuclei, away from magic numbers. This is in agreement with the model described.

The values of the effective moments of inertia will help us to understand the kind of rotational motion that occurs. Let us call R the mean radius of the well and ΔR the difference between the major and minor semiaxis of the deformed well. Then, if we define a deformation parameter

$$(4) \qquad \beta = \frac{4}{3}\left(\frac{\pi}{5}\right)^{1/2}\frac{\Delta R}{R} = 1.06\,\frac{\Delta R}{R},$$

the *rigid* moment of inertia is

$$(5) \qquad \mathfrak{J}_{\mathrm{rig}} = \tfrac{2}{5}AMR^2(1 + 0.31\beta + \cdots).$$

The values of R are known from 2.21, and the values of β can be obtained from the observed γ transition probabilities, so that $\mathfrak{J}_{\mathrm{rig}}$ can be computed and compared with the $\mathfrak{J}_{\mathrm{eff}}$ obtained from the experiment. The comparison is shown in Fig. 2.27-6.

We see that for small β—almost spherically symmetrical nuclei—the empirical moment of inertia is indeed much smaller than the one computed for a rigid body. On the other hand, $\mathfrak{J}_{\mathrm{eff}}$ is larger than the moment of inertia for an irrotational motion such as that indicated in Fig. 2.27-1*b*.

For A odd the rotational bands are more complicated because of the contribution $\mathbf{\Omega}$ of the independent particles to the total angular momentum. In the ground state $J = \Omega$, and for the successive excited rotational states $J_1 = \Omega + 1$, $J_2 = \Omega + 2$, etc. An illustrative example of two sets of rotational states in the same nucleus is provided by W^{183} (Fig. 2.27-7).

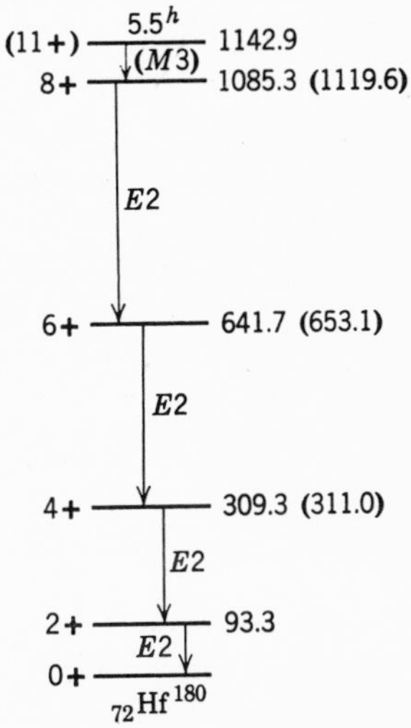

Fig. 2.27-4. The excited states of Hf^{180}. The excitation energy in keV is compared with the predictions of the rotational model (in parenthesis) (from A. Bohr and B. R. Mottelson, in *β and γ Spectroscopy*, North Holland, 1955, K. Siegbahn, editor).

c. Vibrations and Other Collective Motions. The nucleus as a whole can oscillate as well as rotate, and the resulting collective vibrations are equivalent to the surface waves of the old drop model. Dipole collective oscillations, which correspond to a displacement of the whole nucleus, cannot occur because of conservation of momentum, and the simplest oscillations have quadrupole character. The excitation energies of the vibrational levels are evenly spaced, as expected from the excitation of an integral number of "phonons."

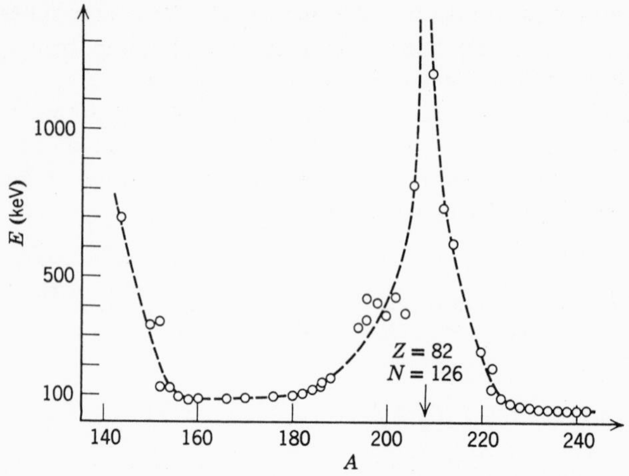

Fig. 2.27-5. Energy of first excited state of even-even nuclei with $A > 140$ (from A. Bohr and B. R. Mottelson, in *β and γ Spectroscopy*, North Holland, 1955, K. Siegbahn, editor).

Taking into account the rules of addition of angular momentum and the restrictions of Bose statistics for the phonons, we obtain the successive excited states due to perfectly harmonic quadrupole surface waves as shown in Table 2.27-1.

Table 2.27-1

Ground state	no phonon	excitation energy 0	angular momentum 0
First excited state	1 phonon	excitation energy $\hbar\omega$	angular momentum 2
Second excited state	2 phonons	excitation energy $2\hbar\omega$	angular momentum 0, 2, 4
Third excited state	3 phonons	excitation energy $3\hbar\omega$	angular momentum 0, 2, 3, 4, 6

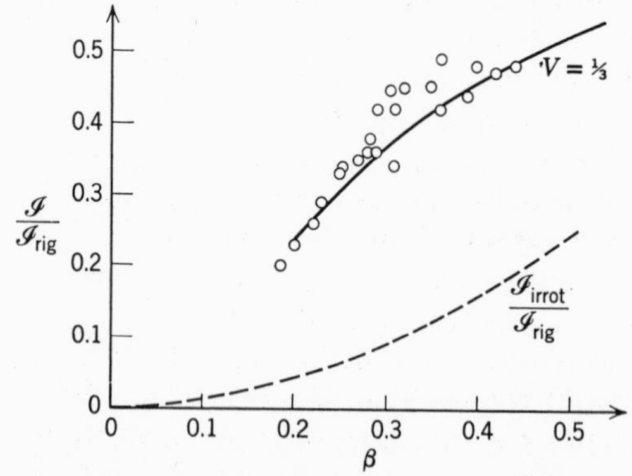

Fig. 2.27-6. Moments of inertia of nuclear motion compared with rigid moments of inertia [from Alder et al., *Rev. Mod. Phys.*, **28**, 529 (1956)].

If we remove the restriction that the oscillator be harmonic, we remove the degeneracy of the states of different angular momentum.

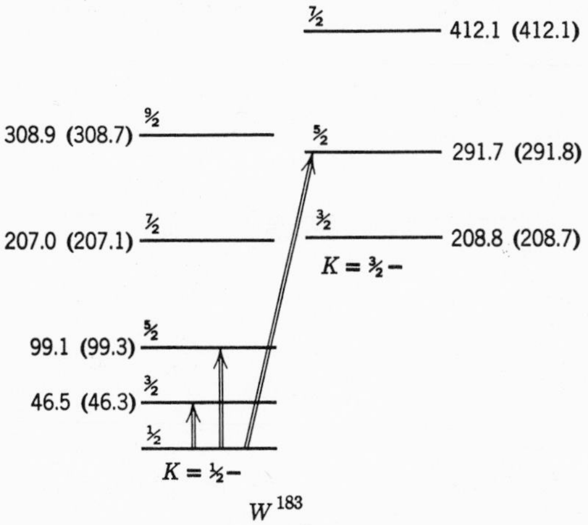

Fig. 2.27-7. Levels of the odd nucleus W^{183} showing two sets of rotational states. Experiment is compared with theory (in parenthesis) [from Alder et al., *Rev. Mod. Phys.*, **28**, 534 (1956)].

A typical example of a spectrum interpreted in terms of almost harmonic vibrations is provided by Pd^{108} (Fig. 2.27-8).

Before closing the subject of collective vibrations, we should mention the *giant dipole resonances* observed in the cross section for γ absorption and photo disintegration of all nuclei around 18 MeV; these resonances are attributed to the opposite vibrations of the proton and neutron fluids within the nucleus (See 4.43b).

Collective *octupole oscillations* are also observed. These appear as low-lying 3^- levels in nuclei such as Sr^{88} or Pb^{208} and, more prominently, as an enhancement of the inelastic proton scattering cross section in a large range of atomic numbers from 50 to 150, for excitation energies of about 2.5 MeV.

d. Shell Model in a Nonspherical Potential Well. The theory of the deformed shell model has been treated in some detail by Nilsson (N-55). Rather

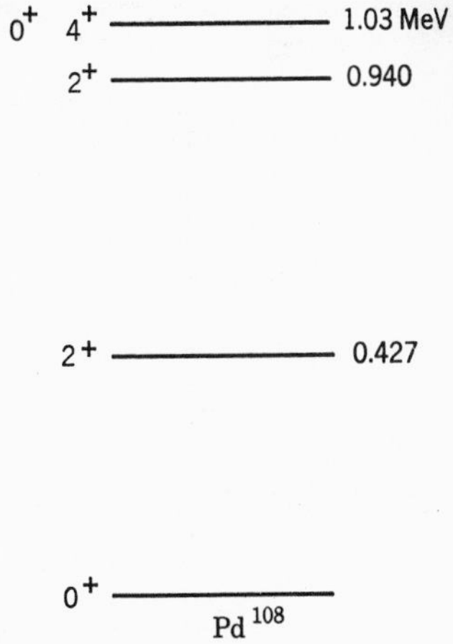

Fig. 2.27-8. The low excited states of Pd^{108}.

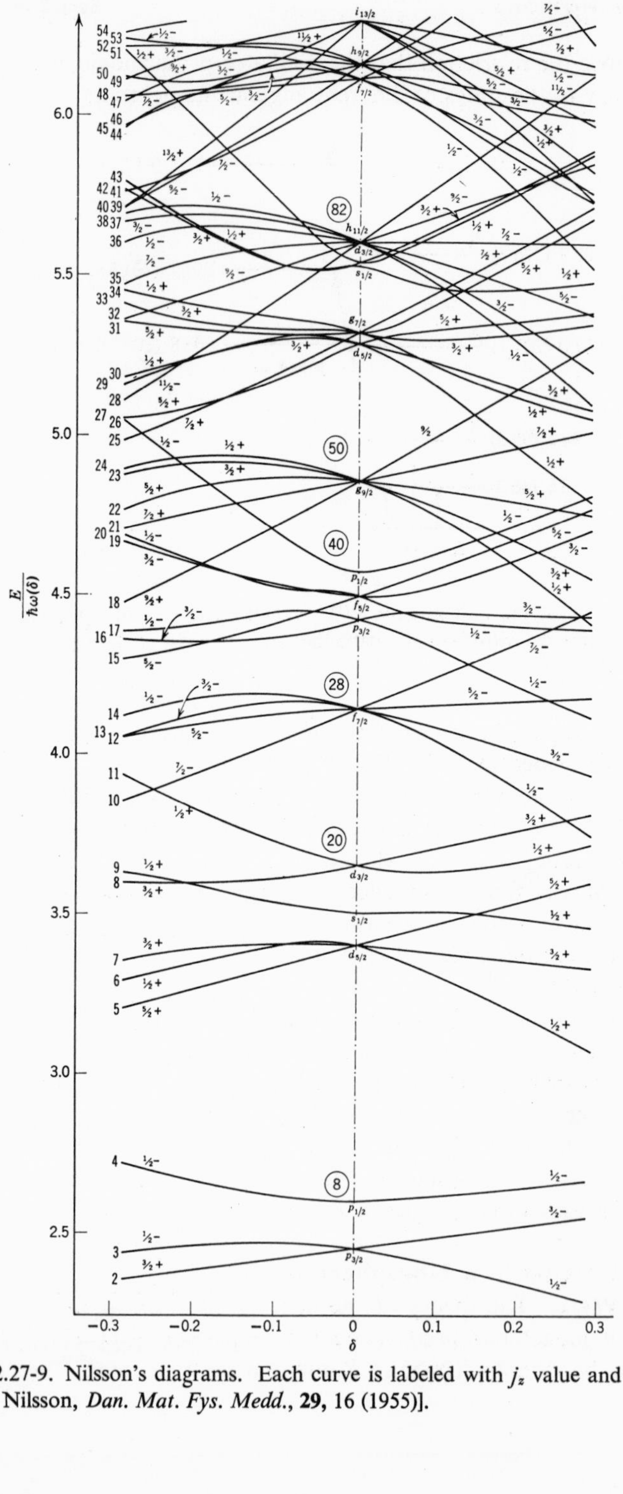

Fig. 2.27-9. Nilsson's diagrams. Each curve is labeled with j_z value and parity [from S. G. Nilsson, *Dan. Mat. Fys. Medd.*, **29**, 16 (1955)].

than discussing a distorted square well, this author introduces the following Hamiltonian for the single particles in a distorted oscillator potential

$$\mathcal{H} = \frac{p^2}{2M} + \frac{M}{2}(\omega_x^{\ 2}x^2 + \omega_y^{\ 2}y^2 + \omega_z^{\ 2}z^2) + C\mathbf{l}\cdot\mathbf{s} + Dl^2. \tag{6}$$

In this formula the first term is the kinetic energy, the second is the potential energy for a nonspherical oscillator, the third expresses spin-orbit coupling, and the last introduces a correction to the oscillator potential, depressing the high angular momentum states and leading to better agreement with the conventional order of the levels.

For cylindrical symmetry ($\omega_x = \omega_y$), j_z is a good quantum number for each particle, and so is $\Omega = \Sigma j_z$. However, the single particle values of l^2, l_z and s_z are no longer good quantum numbers because the forces are not central. The single particle levels, whose energy depended only on j^2 in the spherical well, are split in the deformed well into $\frac{1}{2}(2j + 1)$ twice-degenerate levels according to the value of $|j_z|$.

From the quantitative development of these ideas Nilsson has obtained some by now famous diagrams (Fig. 2.27-9) in which the single particle level energy is plotted as a function of a deformation parameter $\delta \simeq \Delta R/R$.

2.3 Many-Body Theory of Nuclear Models

2.31 The Shell Model with Interactions

a. Introduction to the Model. In the first two parts of this chapter we described a variety of nuclear models, each useful to explain some of the nuclear data, but we have made no serious attempt to formulate a more generally consistent theory of nuclear matter. We shall now present a formalism with which to compute the behavior of systems of many equal fermions under different assumptions on their interaction, and we shall see how this formalism, with an appropriate choice of interaction, might explain from a unique viewpoint the various and apparently contradictory properties of nuclei.

Since the exclusion principle plays a predominant role in our problem, we shall start (2.32) by introducing a technique with which to take into account the antisymmetrization of the states of many fermions without resorting to the cumbersome procedure of writing determinant wave functions.

Then we shall assume that single-particle states of the nucleons are obtained in first approximation from the simplest form of Mayer-Jensen shell model, with spherical nuclei and spin-orbit coupling, and finally we shall take into account some interaction between the particles moving in the shells.

This approach can be justified by saying that the main part of the forces between nucleon pairs "coalesce" to give an average spherical potential within which the nucleons move almost freely but that there remains some residual effect of the elementary interaction that must be separately considered.

This picture has some similarity with that used in the discussion of conduction electrons within a metal. The electrons are located in an average well whose depth is the Fermi energy plus the thermoionic work function. They also interact with one another. These interactions are very important near the absolute zero and are responsible for the phenomenon of superconductivity.

In fact, some of our theoretical techniques (2.35) are borrowed from the theory of superconductivity.

The treatment that follows is formal and quantitative and presents a logical framework for a general description of the properties of nuclear matter. In our discussion the residual forces are introduced in a modelistic manner, to account for observations on complex nuclei, rather than derived from our knowledge of the elementary interactions. Because of inadequate knowledge of the forces, the theory does not yet lead to precise agreement with experiment, and despite the more general and logically consistent structure it only explains trends and gives no more than a semiquantitative description of the facts.

It is, however, possible to give a theoretical justification of the shell model with interactions. One can show with a variational calculation (Hartree-Fock) that the Hamiltonian of interacting nucleons

$$\mathcal{H} = \sum_{\alpha} T_{\alpha} + \sum_{\alpha\beta} V_{\alpha\beta}$$

(T_{α} is the kinetic energy and $V_{\alpha\beta}$, the potential acting between the $\alpha\beta$ pair) is approximately equivalent to the sum of a Hamiltonian of independent particles moving in an average potential (shell model) and of residual terms. We do not intend to discuss here the more formal aspects of the theory, and we shall proceed with a more intuitive presentation.

b. Energy Gap and Pairing Forces. In Sections 2.13b, 2.22a, and 2.25a we have seen that nuclear forces cause the pairing of equal nucleons in states with $J = 0$, but the pairing effects were not included in our treatment of the shell model.

It is easily understood, therefore, that the shell model without pairing fails to account for certain features of nuclear spectra, to which it should be directly applicable.

Let us compare, for example, the spectra of Pb^{207} and Pb^{206} (Fig. 2.31-1).

The excited levels of Pb^{207} ($Z = 82$, magic; $N = 125$, magic minus one) result from lifting one neutron from an inner level into the "hole" in the 126-neutron shell and can be explained consistently with the shell model (though several inversions in the level order of Fig. 2.26-3 are needed: the inner levels of the 126 shell should be in the order $2f_{7/2}$, $1i_{13/2}$, $3p_{3/2}$, $2f_{5/2}$, $3p_{1/2}$ rather than $2f_{7/2}$, $2f_{5/2}$, $3p_{3/2}$, $3p_{1/2}$, $1i_{13/2}$). The excited states of Pb^{206} should agree with the same single-particle levels, considering two neutron holes instead of one: the first excited states of Pb^{206} should be as indicated in Fig. 2.31-1*b*. Experimentally, instead, we find the level scheme of

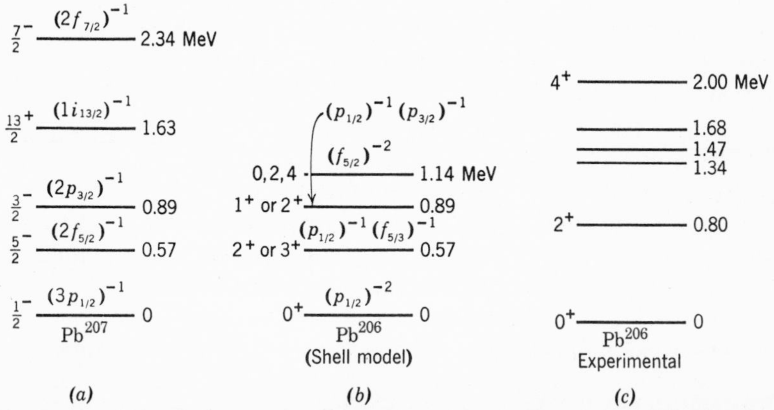

Fig. 2.31-1. (*a*) Level scheme of Pb^{207} interpreted according to the shell model; (*b*) the expected level scheme of Pb^{206}; (*c*) the observed level scheme of Pb^{206} showing the "energy gap."

Fig. 2.31-1*c*. The separation of the levels is larger than expected: we observe what has come to be called an "energy gap."

The existence of these gaps is easily explained by the pairing of nucleons; in the ground state of Pb^{206} all neutrons are paired, each pair having $J = 0$, whereas the pairing is broken when we build the excited states. The theory of superconductivity is similarly based on the pairing of conduction electrons and also involves an energy gap.

In our discussion of the shell model with interaction the pairing effects are taken into account by introducing *ad hoc* pairing forces (2.34 and 2.35) as a residual interaction.

c. Long-Range Forces and Collective Behavior. It is usually assumed that the pairing effects can be described with a δ-function interaction. But the collective behavior of nuclear matter can be explained only in terms of forces with a relatively long range.

Many such forces have been introduced in the discussion of the shell model with interaction.

It is first of all tempting to try to account for nuclear deformations by means of a suitably chosen distorting force superimposed on the spherical shell model (2.36d). It is known that the deformation of the deuteron is the result of tensor forces; but it is more convenient to introduce in our model of heavy nuclei a distorting force with simpler analytical properties whose strength can be chosen to account for nuclear quadrupole moments and moments of inertia for a large number of nuclei.

Several authors have discussed the properties of nuclear ground and excited nuclear states with a shell model to which is added an interaction that may typically have the form

$$V(r) = \frac{e^{-\mu r}}{r}(W + B\mathcal{T}_\sigma + H\mathcal{T}_\tau + M\mathcal{T}_\sigma\mathcal{T}_\tau),$$

where the $\mathcal{T}$'s are the exchange operators of 1.33c, μ is a range parameter, and W, B, H, M are other constants (for Wigner, Bartlett, Heisenberg, and Majorana forces) to be determined from a best fit to the data.

Without further discussion of these aspects of the theory, we develop in what follows the general formalism of the shell model with interaction and its application to the pairing forces.

2.32 *Many-Body States and Observables*

a. Antisymmetrized States of Many Fermions. The work that we propose to report in the remaining part of this chapter has been carried out mostly at the Institute of Theoretical Physics in Copenhagen by A. Bohr and B. Mottelson and by people of their school. Unfortunately, it is difficult to give references to the literature on this subject. Though many papers have been published on particular aspects of the theory, the general treatment can be found only on informally reproduced lecture notes, of which there exist several sets[1].

Proceeding according to the scheme of 3.31a, let us consider a system of equal fermions (Di-47, Section 65), in our case either protons or neutrons, to which certain states m (short for all quantum numbers n, l, j, s_z, j_z) are available. We shall suppose at the beginning that the fermions do not interact, as in the shell model of 2.26.

Each state m can be either unoccupied or occupied by one of the fermions. Since we have to do with two and only two possibilities, we

[1] B. R. Mottelson, Lectures at Les Houches (*The Many Body Problem*, C. DeWitt and P. Nozieres, editors, Wiley, New York, 1959); B. F. Bayman, Lectures at Princeton University (1960); R. A. Sorensen, Lectures in Buenos Aires (1961).

The present author is particularly indebted to M. Baranger and R. A. Sorensen for many illuminating conversations.

can make use of spin $\frac{1}{2}$ formalism and represent with $\begin{pmatrix}1\\0\end{pmatrix}_m$ the situation in which the state under consideration is unoccupied and with $\begin{pmatrix}0\\1\end{pmatrix}_m$ the same state occupied by one particle. Then the spin step-up and step-down operators become operators that annihilate and create particles in the state m. We write

(1)
$$\mathrm{a}_m = \begin{pmatrix}0 & 1\\0 & 0\end{pmatrix}_m \equiv \text{annihilation operator for the state } m$$
$$\mathrm{a}_m^{\dagger} = \begin{pmatrix}0 & 0\\1 & 0\end{pmatrix}_m \equiv \text{creation operator for state } m.$$

We can also introduce the symbol

(2) $$|0_m\rangle = \begin{pmatrix}1\\0\end{pmatrix}_m = \textit{vacuum} \text{ (or empty) } \textit{state}, \text{ with } \langle 0_m \mid 0_m\rangle = 1;$$

with this notation

(3) $$\mathrm{a}_m^{\dagger}\,|0_m\rangle = \begin{pmatrix}0\\1\end{pmatrix}_m = |m\rangle = \text{state with one particle in } m.$$

From the definition of step up and step down operators (1) we obtain

(4*a*) $$\mathrm{a}_m\mathrm{a}_m = \mathrm{a}_m^{\dagger}\mathrm{a}_m^{\dagger} = 0,$$
(4*b*) $$\mathrm{a}_m\mathrm{a}_m^{\dagger} + \mathrm{a}_m^{\dagger}\mathrm{a}_m = 1.$$

From (4*a*) it follows that $\mathrm{a}_m^{\dagger}\mathrm{a}_m^{\dagger}\,|0_m\rangle = 0$, in accordance with the exclusion principle. The operator

(5) $$N_m = \mathrm{a}_m^{\dagger}\mathrm{a}_m = \begin{pmatrix}0 & 0\\0 & 1\end{pmatrix}_m$$

has eigenvalues 0 and 1 for the empty and occupied states, respectively, and can be properly called the *number of particles operator* for the state m.

Let us now consider two particles in two levels m and n; if both levels are occupied, the state can be obtained by operating on the vacuum with the two creation operators $\mathrm{a}_m^{\dagger}$ and $\mathrm{a}_n^{\dagger}$:

(6) $$\mathrm{a}_n^{\dagger}\mathrm{a}_m^{\dagger}\,|0\rangle = |n, m\rangle,$$

where $|0\rangle$ now means that both states m and n are empty. In order to make sure that the state is properly antisymmetrized, we must assume that $\mathrm{a}_m^{\dagger}$

and $a_n^\dagger$ *anticommute*, so that

$$a_n^\dagger a_m^\dagger = \tfrac{1}{2}(a_n^\dagger a_m^\dagger - a_m^\dagger a_n^\dagger). \tag{7}$$

Thus the creation and annihilation operators for two states are conveniently assumed to have the following properties:

$$a_n a_m + a_m a_n = a_n^\dagger a_m^\dagger + a_m^\dagger a_n^\dagger = 0, \tag{8a}$$

$$a_m a_n^\dagger + a_n^\dagger a_m = \delta_{mn}, \tag{8b}$$

which reduce to (4) for $n = m$. These properties must be kept constantly in mind in all algebraic operations involving the creation and annihilation operators.

With the help of (8) it is easily seen that the state in (6) is conveniently normalized:

$$(9)\quad \langle 0|\, a_m a_n a_n^\dagger a_m^\dagger\, |0\rangle = -\langle 0|\, a_m a_n a_m^\dagger a_n^\dagger\, |0\rangle$$
$$= -\langle 0|\, a_m(\delta_{mn} - a_m^\dagger a_n) a_n^\dagger\, |0\rangle = -\delta_{mn} + 1 = \begin{cases} 0 \text{ for } n = m, \\ 1 \text{ for } n \neq m. \end{cases}$$

In general, the properly antisymmetrized and normalized state of N particles (determinant wave function) is simply

$$a_1^\dagger a_2^\dagger \cdots a_N^\dagger\, |0\rangle, \tag{10}$$

where $|0\rangle = \begin{pmatrix}1\\0\end{pmatrix}_1 \begin{pmatrix}1\\0\end{pmatrix}_2 \cdots \begin{pmatrix}1\\0\end{pmatrix}_N$; the total number of particles is given by the eigenvalues of the operator

$$N = \sum_m N_m = \sum_m a_m^\dagger a_m, \tag{11}$$

and the total number of holes by the eigenvalues of

$$\sum_m a_m a_m^\dagger = \sum_m (1 - a_m^\dagger a_m). \tag{12}$$

b. Many-Body Observables. In order to compute nuclear properties involving the contribution of several nucleons, we must learn to handle observables (operators) with the many-body technique.

Let us first consider an operator U that depends on the coordinate of one particle at a time. U could, for instance, be the energy in some external potential or the magnetic or quadrupole moment whose single-particle contributions can be separately computed and then added.

The matrix elements of U between single-particle states $|p\rangle = a_p^\dagger\, |0\rangle$ and $|k\rangle = a_k^\dagger\, |0\rangle$ can be written in two equivalent ways:

$$\langle p|\, U\, |k\rangle \quad \text{or} \quad \langle 0|\, a_p U a_k^\dagger\, |0\rangle; \tag{13}$$

since $a_m a_k^\dagger |0\rangle = \delta_{mk} |0\rangle$ and $\langle 0| a_p a_n^\dagger = \langle 0| \delta_{pn}$, the relation between U and U is

$$(14) \qquad \mathsf{U} = \sum_{m,n} \langle n| U |m\rangle a_n^\dagger a_m.$$

The second form of (13) has the advantage that it can be profitably generalized to many-particle states.

In fact, we shall now prove that the matrix elements of U between two-particle states $a_l^\dagger a_k^\dagger |0\rangle$ and $a_p^\dagger a_q^\dagger |0\rangle$:

$$(15) \qquad \langle 0| a_q a_p \left(\sum_{m,n} \langle n| U |m\rangle a_n^\dagger a_m \right) a_l^\dagger a_k^\dagger |0\rangle$$

are the properly summed matrix elements of U between the properly antisymmetrized two-particle states.

Let us first expand the matrix element without making use of creation and annihilation operators. If U operates only on one particle, say 1, its matrix elements for the states of two distinguishable particles are

$$\langle p(1), q(2)| U(1) |l(1), k(2)\rangle = \langle p| U(1) |l\rangle \delta_{qk}.$$

However, if the operator operates in the same manner on two distinguishable particles 1 and 2, $U(1)$ must be replaced by $U(1) + U(2)$ and the matrix element on a two-particle state becomes

$$\langle p(1), q(2)| U(1) + U(2) |l(1), k(2)\rangle$$
$$= \langle p(1)| U(1) |l(1)\rangle \delta_{qk} + \langle q(2)| U(2) |k(2)\rangle \delta_{pl}.$$

Finally, if the two particles are indistinguishable fermions, their state must be antisymmetrized, and the correct matrix element must be written

$$(16) \quad \tfrac{1}{2}\langle p(1)q(2) - p(2)q(1)| U(1) + U(2) |l(1)k(2) - l(2)k(1)\rangle$$
$$= \langle p| U |l\rangle \delta_{qk} + \langle q| U |k\rangle \delta_{pl} - \langle p| U |k\rangle \delta_{ql} - \langle q| U |l\rangle \delta_{pk}.$$

We shall now show that (15) is identical to (16). For this we can rewrite (15) in the form

$$\sum_{mn} \langle n| U |m\rangle \langle 0| a_q a_p a_n^\dagger a_m a_l^\dagger a_k^\dagger |0\rangle,$$

and observe that the sum has only four nonvanishing terms: for $m = k$ or l, and for $n = p$ or q. Thus (15) becomes

$$\langle p| U |l\rangle \langle 0| a_q a_p a_p^\dagger a_l a_l^\dagger a_k^\dagger |0\rangle + \langle p| U |k\rangle \langle 0| a_q a_p a_p^\dagger a_k a_l^\dagger a_k^\dagger |0\rangle$$
$$+ \langle q| U |l\rangle \langle 0| a_q a_p a_q^\dagger a_l a_l^\dagger a_k^\dagger |0\rangle + \langle q| U |k\rangle \langle 0| a_q a_p a_q^\dagger a_k a_l^\dagger a_k^\dagger |0\rangle.$$

But using (8) we can write

$$a_k a_l^\dagger a_k^\dagger |0\rangle = -(1 - \delta_{lk}) a_l^\dagger |0\rangle, \qquad a_l a_l^\dagger a_k^\dagger |0\rangle = (1 - \delta_{lk}) a_k^\dagger |0\rangle,$$
$$\langle 0| a_q a_p a_q^\dagger = -\langle 0| a_p (1 - \delta_{pq}), \qquad \langle 0| a_q a_p a_p^\dagger = \langle 0| a_q (1 - \delta_{pq}).$$

Thus (15) gives zero for $l = k$ or $p = q$, as required by the exclusion principle. For $l \neq k$, $p \neq q$ the δ-symbols vanish; if we make use of the resulting equalities and consider that $\mathsf{a}_p\mathsf{a}_k^\dagger\,|0\rangle = \delta_{pk}\,|0\rangle$, etc., (15) reduces to (16), as we wanted to prove.

The same formalism can be extended to states of more than two particles.

We must now consider operators that depend on the coordinates of two particles. A particularly interesting example is the potential energy of interaction between a pair of particles, which we need to describe the pairing forces. In this case, by following a procedure similar to that used for one-body operators, one can prove that the interesting matrix element between properly antisymmetrized many-particle states is the matrix element of

$$\sum_{nn'mm'} \langle nn'|\,U\,|mm'\rangle \mathsf{a}_n^\dagger \mathsf{a}_{n'}^\dagger \mathsf{a}_m \mathsf{a}_{m'} \tag{17}$$

between the many-particle states written in the form $\cdots \mathsf{a}_l^\dagger \mathsf{a}_k^\dagger\,|0\rangle$.

With the formalism just introduced, in which many-particle states are described by means of creation and annihilation operators and observables are represented by expressions such as (14) and (17), it is possible to solve many-body problems with relative ease. In all computations we must make constant use of the properties of the operators given in (8).

2.33 *Pairing Effects and the Calculation of Quadrupole Moments*

a. Introduction of Pairing Effects. We shall now discuss as an example the magnetic and quadrupole moments of nuclei, considering the possible contribution of many particles in an incomplete shell. A spherical shell model is assumed and no "collective" contribution to the moments are considered.

In accordance with the observation that $J = 0$ for even-even nuclei, we shall suppose that all even particles are paired in pairs with $J = 0$.

Thus an odd nucleus with n particles in an incomplete shell contains, in its ground state, one odd particle and $p = \frac{1}{2}(n - 1)$ pairs in the last shell. The nuclear spin is contributed exclusively by the odd particle, and the configuration is $(j^n)_j = (j^{2p+1})_j$. The value of p varies from 0 (one particle) to $j - \frac{1}{2}$ (one hole in the incomplete shell).

The magnetic moments are not affected by the presence of paired particles that do not alter the predictions of the single-particle model in 2.22. This is because the Landé factor for all equal nucleons in the j shell is the same, and nucleons paired with $J = 0$ cancel their contribution to the magnetic moment[1].

[1] See also footnote 2 on page 127.

The contribution of paired particles to the quadrupole moment, however, does not vanish and is computed in what follows. But before proceeding to the solution of this problem we must develop a formalism for the treatment of paired particles. The same formalism can be applied to the calculation of other interesting nuclear properties, such as the probability of emission of γ rays.

b. Paired Particles Operators and States. Let us consider the operators $a_m^\dagger$ and $a_{-m}^\dagger$ which create particles in states of opposite j_z:

(1) $$a_m^\dagger |0\rangle = |jm\rangle, \qquad a_{-m}^\dagger |0\rangle = |j\ -m\rangle.$$

Again, we use the condensed notation of the preceding section: the index $\pm m$ stands briefly for all the quantum numbers, $n, l, j, \pm j_z$.

We now want to introduce an operator $A^\dagger$ that creates two paired particles, with $J = 0$, in the shell j. The state $A^\dagger |0\rangle$ must be a spherically symmetrical linear combination of the states $a_m^\dagger a_{-m}^\dagger |0\rangle$. Apart from a constant of normalization, the coefficients must be the vector addition coefficients $C(jj0; m\ -m) = (-1)^{j-m}/(2j+1)^{1/2}$. We define the $J = 0$ pair creation operator as follows:

(2) $$A^\dagger = \sum_{m>0} (-1)^{j-m} a_m^\dagger a_{-m}^\dagger.$$

With this definition the state $A^\dagger |0\rangle$ is not normalized to unity. It follows from the orthonormal properties of the states $a_m^\dagger a_{-m}^\dagger |0\rangle$ [2.32(9)] that each of the $j + \frac{1}{2}$ terms[1] of the sum (2) contributes a unity to the square of $A^\dagger |0\rangle$; thus

(3) $$\begin{aligned}\langle 0| AA^\dagger |0\rangle &= \langle 0| \sum_{mn>0} (-1)^{2j-m-n} a_{-n} a_n a_m^\dagger a_{-m}^\dagger |0\rangle \\ &= \langle 0| \sum_{mn>0} (-1)^{2j-m-n} \delta_{mn} |0\rangle = \langle 0| \sum_{m>0} 1 |0\rangle = j + \tfrac{1}{2}.\end{aligned}$$

Paired particles satisfy Bose statistics, and more than one pair may exist in the same shell. In the sums describing each pair, however, the terms with the same quantum number for the single-particle creation operators are automatically suppressed because of the exclusion principle. For instance, a state of two pairs is

(4) $$\begin{aligned}A^\dagger A^\dagger |0\rangle = A^{\dagger 2} |0\rangle &= \sum_{m>0} a_m^\dagger a_{-m}^\dagger \sum_{n>0} a_n^\dagger a_{-n}^\dagger |0\rangle \\ &= \sum_{m>0} a_m^\dagger a_{-m}^\dagger \sum_{\substack{n>0 \\ n\neq m}} a_n^\dagger a_{-n}^\dagger |0\rangle.\end{aligned}$$

[1] The quantum numbers j and m are always half integers.

Thus the normalization of a two-pair state is

$$\langle 0|\, A^2A^{\dagger 2}\,|0\rangle = \langle 0|\sum_{p>0} a_{-p}a_p \sum_{\substack{q>0\\ q\neq p}} a_{-q}a_q \sum_{m>0} a_m{}^{\dagger}a_{-m}{}^{\dagger} \sum_{\substack{n>0\\ n\neq m}} a_n{}^{\dagger}a_{-n}{}^{\dagger}\,|0\rangle$$
$$= 2\langle 0|\sum_{m>0}\ \sum_{\substack{n>0\\ n\neq m}} 1\,|0\rangle = 2(j+\tfrac{1}{2})(j+\tfrac{1}{2}-1).$$

This procedure can be extended to many-pair states; we obtain for p pairs

(5)
$$\langle 0|\, A^pA^{\dagger p}\,|0\rangle = p!(j+\tfrac{1}{2})(j+\tfrac{1}{2}-1)\cdots(j+\tfrac{1}{2}-p+1) = \frac{p!\,(j+\frac{1}{2})!}{(j+\frac{1}{2}-p)!}.$$

Now let us consider states containing one pair plus one odd particle in the same shell. Such states can be written $A^{\dagger}a_m{}^{\dagger}\,|0\rangle$. Because of the exclusion principle the state m is suppressed in the paired particle sums:

$$A^{\dagger}a_m{}^{\dagger}\,|0\rangle = \sum_{n>0}(-1)^{j-n}a_n{}^{\dagger}a_{-n}{}^{\dagger}a_m{}^{\dagger}\,|0\rangle = \sum_{\substack{n>0\\ n\neq m}}(-1)^{j-n}a_n{}^{\dagger}a_{-n}{}^{\dagger}a_m{}^{\dagger}\,|0\rangle.$$

When we compute the square of this state we must consider that the sum now has only $j-\frac{1}{2}$ terms; we obtain

(6)
$$\langle 0|\, a_mAA^{\dagger}a_m{}^{\dagger}\,|0\rangle = j-\tfrac{1}{2}.$$

Similarly, we can compute the square of a state of one particle plus p pairs $(0 \le p \le j-\frac{1}{2})$:

(7)
$$\langle 0|\, a_mA^pA^{\dagger p}a_m{}^{\dagger}\,|0\rangle = \frac{p!\,(j-\frac{1}{2})!}{(j-\frac{1}{2}-p)!}.$$

The square of a state with two particles and p pairs is

(8)
$$\langle 0|\, a_ma_nA^pA^{\dagger p}a_n{}^{\dagger}a_m{}^{\dagger}\,|0\rangle = \begin{cases} 0 & \text{for } m=n,\\ \dfrac{p!\,(j-\frac{1}{2})!}{(j-\frac{1}{2}-p)!} & \text{for } m=-n,\\ \dfrac{p!\,(j-\frac{3}{2})!}{(j-\frac{3}{2}-p)!} & \text{for } m\neq \pm n,\end{cases}$$

and so on.

The commutators between these operators are useful also and can be computed easily. For instance,

(9)
$$[A^{\dagger}, A^{\dagger}] = [A, A] = [A^{\dagger}, a_m{}^{\dagger}] = [A, a_m] = 0,$$
$$[a_m, A^{\dagger}] = (-1)^{j-m}a_{-m}{}^{\dagger}; \qquad [a_m{}^{\dagger}, A] = -(-1)^{j-m}a_{-m}.$$

The computation of the commutator $[A, A^{\dagger}]$ which we shall need in our future work, is a little more complicated; we obtain the result[1]

$$[A, A^\dagger] = j + \tfrac{1}{2} - N, \tag{10}$$

where N is the number-of-particles operator.

c. Evaluation of the Quadrupole Moments. The quadrupole moment of a nuclear ground state with one odd particle and p pairs in an incomplete shell can be computed from 2.32(15). Considering that the states with paired particles are not normalized to unity, we must write

$$Q = \frac{\langle 0|\, a_j A^p \left(\sum_{m=-j}^{j} \langle m|\, Q\, |m\rangle a_m^\dagger a_m \right) A^{\dagger p} a_j^\dagger\, |0\rangle}{\langle 0|\, a_j A^p A^{\dagger p} a_j^\dagger\, |0\rangle}, \tag{11}$$

where the state $a_j^\dagger\, |0\rangle$ is the state with $m_j = j$.

By commuting the factors $a_m^\dagger a_m$ $(= 1 - a_m a_m^\dagger)$ we obtain

$$Q = \sum_{m=-j}^{j} \langle m|\, Q\, |m\rangle \left(1 - \frac{\langle 0|\, a_j a_m A^p A^{\dagger p} a_m^\dagger a_j^\dagger\, |0\rangle}{\langle 0|\, a_j A^p A^{\dagger p} a_j^\dagger\, |0\rangle}\right);$$

and, by making use of (7) and (8), this becomes

$$Q = \langle j|\, Q\, |j\rangle \times 1 + \langle -j|\, Q\, |-j\rangle \times 0 + \sum_{m \neq \pm j} \frac{p}{j - \frac{1}{2}} \langle m|\, Q\, |m\rangle.$$

Considering now that $\langle m|\, Q\, |m\rangle = \langle -m|\, Q\, |-m\rangle$ and that

$$\sum_{m=-j}^{j} \langle m|\, Q\, |m\rangle = 0,$$[2]

we obtain the result

$$Q = \left(1 - \frac{2p}{j - \frac{1}{2}}\right) \langle j|\, Q\, |j\rangle. \tag{12}$$

We conclude that the single-particle value is multiplied by $1 - 2p/(j - \frac{1}{2})$.

[1]
$$[A, A^\dagger] = \left[\sum_{m>0} (-1)^{j-m} a_{-m} a_m\, , \sum_{n>0} (-1)^{j-n} a_n^\dagger a_{-n}^\dagger \right].$$

But

$$[a_{-m} a_m\, , a_n^\dagger a_{-n}^\dagger] = 0 \quad \text{if} \quad n \neq m.$$

Thus

$$\begin{aligned} [A, A^\dagger] &= \sum_{m>0} [a_{-m} a_m\, , a_m^\dagger a_{-m}^\dagger] \\ &= \sum_{m>0} [a_{-m} a_m a_m^\dagger a_{-m}^\dagger - a_m^\dagger a_{-m}^\dagger a_{-m} a_m] \\ &= \sum_{m>0} [(1 - N_m)(1 - N_{-m}) - N_m N_{-m}] \\ &= \sum_{m>0} (1 - N_m - N_{-m}) = j + \tfrac{1}{2} - N. \end{aligned}$$

[2] Observe that for the magnetic moment $\langle m|\mu|m\rangle = -\langle -m\, |\mu|\, -m\rangle$. The sum $\sum_{m \neq j}$ vanishes and we obtain the single-particle value without any contribution from the pairs.

For one particle ($p = 0$) this factor is 1, and for one hole ($p = j - \frac{1}{2}$) it is -1. Between these two extremes the quadrupole moment varies linearly with the number of pairs.

2.34 *Pairing Interaction and Seniority within a Shell*

a. The Hamiltonian of the Shell Model with Pairing Forces. So far we have studied the effect of pairing only in connection with nuclear ground states, assuming that all even particles are paired. It would obviously be of some interest to study the excited states resulting from the breaking of these pairs and, if possible, to compute the corresponding energy of excitation. The number of unpaired particles in a certain state is called the *seniority* of the state.

In order to make quantitative predictions concerning excitation energy, it will be necessary to introduce a Hamiltonian. Let us first write the Hamiltonian of the independent particle shell model in the many-body formalism. Using the index j to specify the shell and m to indicate the z component of angular momentum[1] we obtain

$$\mathcal{H}_{\rm ip} = \sum_j \varepsilon_j \sum_m \mathsf{a}_{jm}{}^\dagger \mathsf{a}_{jm}, \tag{1}$$

where ε_j is the energy of the shell considered and $\Sigma\, \mathsf{a}_{jm}{}^\dagger \mathsf{a}_{jm}$ is the operator of the number of particles that it contains. This Hamiltonian is diagonal for states containing a definite number of particles in each shell; such states are eigenstates of (1).

Observe that (1) has the form of the operator in 2.32(14) and is appropriate to the method of computation developed in that section.

We must now add to the independent particle Hamiltonian (1) a term to express the pairing interaction for the particles belonging to the same shell. For this purpose we can write the total Hamiltonian as

$$\begin{aligned}\mathcal{H} = \mathcal{H}_{\rm ip} + \mathcal{H}_{\rm pf} &= \sum_j \varepsilon_j \sum_m \mathsf{a}_{jm}{}^\dagger \mathsf{a}_{jm} - G \sum_j \mathsf{A}_j{}^\dagger \mathsf{A}_j \\ &= \sum_j \varepsilon_j \sum_m \mathsf{a}_{jm}{}^\dagger \mathsf{a}_{jm} \\ &\quad - G \sum_j \sum_{mm'>0} (-1)^{j-m}(-1)^{j-m'} \mathsf{a}_{jm}{}^\dagger \mathsf{a}_{j-m}{}^\dagger \mathsf{a}_{j-m'} \mathsf{a}_{jm'},\end{aligned} \tag{2}$$

where G is a positive constant to be determined from the experiment. The added term is purely "modelistic" in the sense that it does not aim to describe correctly the nucleon-nucleon forces obtained from the scattering of elementary particles.

The pairing Hamiltonian has the proper form [2.32(17)] for an operator involving the coordinates of two particles. It is seen that unpaired particles are eigenstates of $\mathcal{H}_{\rm pf}$ corresponding to energy eigenvalue 0

[1] With a slight change in notation, the index j now stands for the quantum numbers n, l, and j and the index m refers to m_j.

and do not contribute to the pairing energy. The energy of paired particles is discussed in (b).

Observe that seniority commutes with the pairing Hamiltonian (2), but it is not a good quantum number if the forces between the particles in shell-model states have a more general character.

b. Calculation of Pairing Energy and Seniority. Let us consider a state of n particles and suppose that its pairing energy is E_n: we now show that the addition of a $J = 0$ pair to such a state increases the binding energy (decreases the pairing energy) by the amount $G(j + \frac{1}{2} - n)$. More formally stated, if

(3) $$\mathcal{H}_{\text{pf}}\mathsf{a}_1^\dagger \cdots \mathsf{a}_n^\dagger\,|0\rangle = E_n\,\mathsf{a}_1^\dagger \cdots \mathsf{a}_n^\dagger\,|0\rangle,$$

then

(4) $$\mathcal{H}_{\text{pf}}\mathsf{A}^\dagger\mathsf{a}_1^\dagger \cdots \mathsf{a}_n^\dagger\,|0\rangle = [E_n - G(j + \tfrac{1}{2} - n)]\mathsf{A}^\dagger\mathsf{a}_1^\dagger \cdots \mathsf{a}_n^\dagger\,|0\rangle.$$

For this proof let us first compute the commutator $[\mathcal{H}_{\text{pf}}, \mathsf{A}^\dagger]$. Making use of 2.33(10), we have

$$\begin{aligned}[\mathcal{H}_{\text{pf}}, \mathsf{A}^\dagger] = \mathcal{H}_{\text{pf}}\mathsf{A}^\dagger - \mathsf{A}^\dagger\mathcal{H}_{\text{pf}} &= -G[\mathsf{A}^\dagger\mathsf{A}\mathsf{A}^\dagger - \mathsf{A}^\dagger\mathsf{A}^\dagger\mathsf{A}]\\ &= -G\mathsf{A}^\dagger[\mathsf{A}, \mathsf{A}^\dagger] = -G\mathsf{A}^\dagger(j + \tfrac{1}{2} - N).\end{aligned}$$

From this we obtain immediately

$$\begin{aligned}\mathcal{H}_{\text{pf}}\mathsf{A}^\dagger\mathsf{a}_1^\dagger \cdots \mathsf{a}_n^\dagger\,|0\rangle &= \mathsf{A}^\dagger[\mathcal{H}_{\text{pf}} - G(j + \tfrac{1}{2} - N)]\mathsf{a}_1^\dagger \cdots \mathsf{a}_n^\dagger\,|0\rangle\\ &= \mathsf{A}^\dagger[E_n - G(j + \tfrac{1}{2} - n)]\mathsf{a}_1^\dagger \cdots \mathsf{a}_n^\dagger\,|0\rangle,\end{aligned}$$

which is equivalent to (4).

We are now in position to compute the pairing energy of a state of n particles in any given shell, assuming that s particles are unpaired and $n - s$ are paired. [n and s must be both even or both odd, since the number of pairs is $(n - s)/2$]. Such a state is said to have seniority s; ground states always have seniority zero for n even and 1 for n odd.

For the computation we consider that the s unpaired particles have pairing energy zero and that the addition of the first pair contributes $-G(j + \frac{1}{2} - s)$; the addition of the second pair, $-G[j + \frac{1}{2} - (s + 2)]$; and, finally, the addition of the last pair gives an energy $-G[j + \frac{1}{2} - (n - 2)]$. In total we obtain an easily summed arithmetic progression of $(n - s)/2$ terms:

(5)
$$\begin{aligned}E_{n,s} &= -G[(j + \tfrac{1}{2} - s) + (j + \tfrac{1}{2} - s - 2) + \cdots + (j + \tfrac{1}{2} - n + 2)]\\ &= -G\frac{n - s}{4}[(j + \tfrac{1}{2} - s) + (j + \tfrac{1}{2} - n + 2)]\\ &= -\frac{G}{4}[n(2j + 3 - n) - s(2j + 3 - s)].\end{aligned}$$

In order to account for gaps of the order of MeV (see Fig. 2.31-1), (5) requires $G \approx 1$ MeV if $s \approx j \approx 1$, and $G \approx 0.1$ MeV for $s = 2, j \approx \frac{5}{2}$.

2.35 *Nuclear Ground States with Pairing Interaction between Different Shells*

a. Introductory Discussion. We must now explore the consequences of a pairing interaction acting between particles of different shells. For clarity and simplicity we shall start considering only two shells, j_1 and j_2.

The Hamiltonian for the two shells can be written as a generalization of the Hamiltonian of the preceding section:

$$(1a)\quad \begin{aligned}\mathcal{H} = \mathcal{H}_{\text{ip}} + \mathcal{H}_{\text{pf}} &= \sum_{j=j_1,j_2} \varepsilon_j \sum_m \mathsf{a}_{jm}{}^\dagger \mathsf{a}_{jm} - G \sum_{j,j'=j_1,j_2} \mathsf{A}_{j'}^\dagger \mathsf{A}_j \\ &= \sum_{\substack{m \\ j=j_1,j_2}} \varepsilon_j \mathsf{a}_{jm}{}^\dagger \mathsf{a}_{jm} - G \sum_{\substack{mm'>0 \\ j,j'=j_1,j_2}} ff' \mathsf{a}_{j'm'}^\dagger \mathsf{a}_{j'-m'}^\dagger \mathsf{a}_{j-m} \mathsf{a}_{jm}.\end{aligned}$$

Consistently with our choice of phases, the factors f, f' are given by[1]

$$(1b)\qquad f = (-1)^{l+j-m}; \qquad f' = (-1)^{l'+j'-m'}.$$

[1] The new phase factor $(-1)^{l+l'}$ (which reduces to unity if the particle pairs belong to the same shell) is justified if we assume that the pairing forces have short range corresponding approximately to a δ-function potential. The rest of this footnote is meant to show that the matrix elements of a δ-function potential in fact contains a factor $(-1)^{l-l'}$; the argument presented is a simplified form of one found in Bayman's notes.

If $\psi_{lj}{}^{m_j}(\mathbf{r}\boldsymbol{\sigma}) = u_l(\mathbf{r})\mathcal{Y}^{m_j}_{l\frac{1}{2}j}(\theta\varphi\boldsymbol{\sigma})$ is the wave function of a particle in the lj shell, a $J = 0$ pair in this shell is

$$\Psi_{jl,J=0}(\mathbf{r}_1\boldsymbol{\sigma}_1\mathbf{r}_2\boldsymbol{\sigma}_2) = \frac{1}{\sqrt{2}}\frac{1}{\sqrt{2j+1}} \sum_{m_j>0} (-1)^{j-m_j} [\psi_{lj}{}^{m_j}(\mathbf{r}_1\boldsymbol{\sigma}_1)\psi_{lj}{}^{-m_j}(\mathbf{r}_2\boldsymbol{\sigma}_2) - \psi_{lj}^{-m_j}(\mathbf{r}_1\boldsymbol{\sigma}_1)\psi_{lj}{}^{m_j}(\mathbf{r}_2\boldsymbol{\sigma}_2)].$$

Let us suppose that the pair is lowered in energy because of a short-range attraction $\delta(\mathbf{r}_1 - \mathbf{r}_2)$ between the two paired particles. This attraction, considered as an operator, has diagonal matrix elements between pairs with the same jl and nondiagonal matrix elements between pairs in $jl, j'l'$. In general, the matrix elements are

$$\sum_{\text{spins}} \int \Psi^*_{jl,J=0}(\mathbf{r}_1\boldsymbol{\sigma}_1\mathbf{r}_2\boldsymbol{\sigma}_2)\, \delta(\mathbf{r}_1 - \mathbf{r}_2)\, \Psi_{j'l',J'=0}(\mathbf{r}_1\boldsymbol{\sigma}_1\mathbf{r}_2\boldsymbol{\sigma}_2)\, d^3\mathbf{r}_1\, d^3\mathbf{r}_2 = \int \sum_{\text{spins}} \Psi^*_{jl,J=0}(\mathbf{r}\boldsymbol{\sigma}_1\boldsymbol{\sigma}_2)\Psi_{j'l',J'=0}(\mathbf{r}\boldsymbol{\sigma}_1\boldsymbol{\sigma}_2)\, d^3\mathbf{r}.$$

Since the integrands are invariant under rotation, they may be computed along the z axis where

$$Y_l^{m_l}(\theta = 0) = \delta_{m_l 0}\sqrt{\frac{2l+1}{4\pi}}.$$

Thus the only values of m_j for which $\mathcal{Y}_l^{m_j}(\theta = 0, \boldsymbol{\sigma})$ is nonzero are $m_j = m_s = \pm\frac{1}{2}$. For these values we have

$$\mathcal{Y}_l^{\pm\frac{1}{2}}(\theta = 0, \boldsymbol{\sigma}) = C(l\tfrac{1}{2}j;\ 0 \pm\tfrac{1}{2})\sqrt{\frac{2l+1}{4\pi}}\, \zeta_{\frac{1}{2}}^{\pm\frac{1}{2}}.$$

Though (1) is formally similar to 2.34(2), its consequences are quite different, for the pairing Hamiltonian now contains terms with $j \neq j'$. For instance, the term

$$\sum_{mm'>0} ff' \mathrm{a}^{\dagger}_{j_1 m'} \mathrm{a}^{\dagger}_{j_1 -m'} \mathrm{a}_{j_2 -m} \mathrm{a}_{j_2 m}$$

destroys a pair in the j_2 shell and recreates it in the j_1 shell. Terms of this kind are a perturbing interaction which occurs between nucleons in different shells and mixes the shell states (*configuration mixing*): now, a

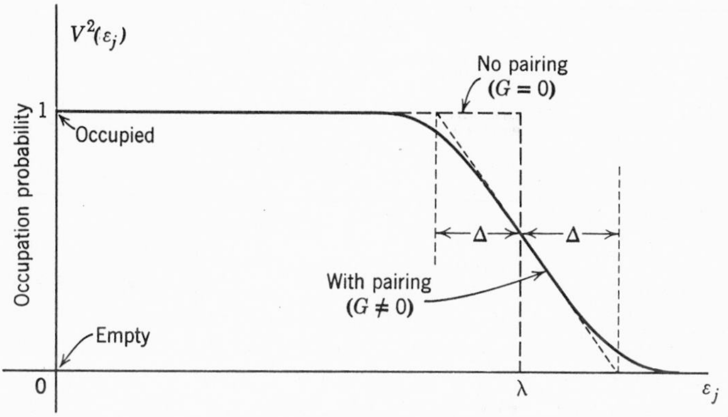

Fig. 2.35-1. Ground state occupation probability as a function of shell energy. Dashed line: no pairing interaction between shells. Full line: with pairing interaction between shells.

particle can be found in more than one shell, and the shells may be partly occupied.

A more quantitative discussion of these effects can be carried on by employing the theoretical methods developed by Bardeen and collaborators (B-57) for the theory of superconductivity. Before reporting on these rather involved calculations, it seems useful to describe intuitively the results that are obtained.

For this purpose let us consider a large number of shells—so large that their energy ε_j may be treated as a continuous variable—and plot the occupation probability as a continuous function of ε_j (Fig. 2.35-1). In

---

The $\sum_{m_j>0}$ in the definition of Ψ' has, for $\theta = 0$, a single term. The spin state in the antisymmetrized sum is a singlet, and we have, using a property of the vector addition coefficients [1.17(7)],

$$\Psi'_{jl,J=0}(r, \theta = 0, \sigma_1\sigma_2) = u_l^2 \zeta_0^{\,0}(-1)^{j-\frac{1}{2}} C(l\tfrac{1}{2}j;\ 0\tfrac{1}{2}) C(l\tfrac{1}{2}j;\ 0-\tfrac{1}{2})$$
$$= u_l^2 \zeta_0^{\,0}(-1)^{j-\frac{1}{2}}(-1)^{l+\frac{1}{2}-j}\,|C(l\tfrac{1}{2}j;\ \sigma\tfrac{1}{2})|^2 \simeq (-1)^l;$$

thus the matrix element contains a factor $(-1)^{l+l'}$.

the independent particle shell model (dashed curve) the levels are occupied up to a certain maximum energy λ which may be called the *chemical potential* and which is determined by the density of particles in accordance with the exclusion principle. For energies larger than λ the occupation probability suddenly drops to zero.

The intershell interaction produces configuration mixing with the result that the states near λ are only partly occupied. This is indicated by the full curve of Fig. 2.35-1, which shows that the Fermi surface loses its sharpness and is replaced by a transition region of depth 2Δ.

As a result of a variational calculation, it is possible to compute λ and Δ from the parameters of the shell theory and from the pairing interaction constant G. The value of Δ is proportional to G and naturally goes to zero in the independent particle model, with $G = 0$.

The curves of Fig. 2.35-1 refer to ground states of even nuclei which are states of maximum pair binding or of minimum seniority. For the excited states the occupation probability changes. In the independent particle model the excitation corresponds to the creation of particles in previously empty shells and of holes in previously full shells. When intershell interactions are considered, the excitations in the region of partial occupancy are less than whole particles and holes and are called *quasi-particles*. The concept of quasi-particle is more fully discussed in 2.36a, where an appropriate mathematical formalism is presented.

From the theory we can calculate that a quasi-particle in the j shell contributes an excitation energy

$$E_j = \sqrt{(\varepsilon_j - \lambda)^2 + \Delta^2}. \tag{2}$$

For shells away from the Fermi surface ($|\varepsilon_j - \lambda| \gg \Delta$) the excitation energy is $\varepsilon_j - \lambda$ and, apart from the additive constant λ, it is the same as that of the independent particle model. But the excitation energy can never be smaller than the gap Δ.

Even-even nuclei in their ground states have no quasi-particles: the ground state is the quasi-particle vacuum, and the excitations correspond to the formation of quasi-particle pairs. The creation of each quasi-particle requires a minimum energy Δ.

Even-odd nuclei have one quasi-particle (the unpaired particle) in the ground state, which can be excited to a higher energy without requiring any energy for its creation. Thus no gap is observed in the excitation spectrum.

The possible excitations are found to satisfy Fermi statistics. We can introduce quasi-particle creation and annihilation operators $\alpha_{jm}{}^\dagger$ and α_{jm}, which satisfy the same commutation rules as the $\mathrm{a}_{jm}{}^\dagger$ and a_{jm}. The

Hamiltonian then assumes the simple form

$$\mathcal{H} = E_0 + \sum_{jm} E_j \alpha_{jm}^{\dagger} \alpha_{jm}, \tag{3}$$

where E_0 is the ground-state energy.

This preliminary discussion is meant to introduce a few intuitive concepts to be kept in mind while following the more formal approach. The meaning of these concepts will become more precise as the theory is developed.

b. Bardeen's Trial Wave Function. We shall find approximate eigenstates of the Hamiltonian (1), generalized to include any number of levels, by following a method developed by Bardeen and collaborators in their theory of superconductivity. Since the states may be partly occupied, we designate with U_{jm} and $V_{jm}(m > 0)$, respectively, the probability amplitude for states j, $\pm m$ to be empty or full. We assume that U_{jm} and V_{jm} are real and satisfy the normalization condition

$$U_{jm}^2 + V_{jm}^2 = 1. \tag{4}$$

Following Bardeen, we consider a state of the form

$$\psi_B = \prod_{\substack{m>0 \\ j}} (U_{jm} + f V_{jm} \mathrm{a}_{jm}^{\dagger} \mathrm{a}_{j-m}^{\dagger}) \, |0\rangle \tag{5}$$

which we call the Bardeen trial state. As a consequence of (4), each of the factors in ψ_B, and thus ψ_B itself, is normalized to unity.

It is important to observe that ψ_B *does not correspond to a definite number of particles* (not only in any one shell, but in total). The average number of particles n, corresponding to ψ_B, is the expectation value of the number-of-particles operator in 2.32(11):

$$\begin{aligned} n &= \langle \psi_B | \, N \, | \psi_B \rangle \\ &= \langle 0 | \prod_{\substack{m'>0 \\ j'}} (U_{j'm'} + f' V_{j'm'} \mathrm{a}_{j'-m'} \mathrm{a}_{j'm'}) \left| \sum_{jm} \mathrm{a}_{jm}^{\dagger} \mathrm{a}_{jm} \right| \\ &\qquad \prod_{\substack{m''>0 \\ j''}} (U_{j''m''} + f'' V_{j''m''} \mathrm{a}_{j''m''}^{\dagger} \mathrm{a}_{j''-m''}^{\dagger}) \, |0\rangle. \end{aligned} \tag{6}$$

Considering that the factors in ψ_B are separately normalized to unity and that the term $\mathrm{a}_{jm}^{\dagger}\mathrm{a}_{jm}$ commutes with all the factors not involving j and m, we can write[1]

$$\begin{aligned} n = \sum_{jm} \Big\langle 0 \Big| \, U_{j|m|} + f V_{j|m|} \mathrm{a}_{j-|m|} \mathrm{a}_{j|m|} \left| \mathrm{a}_{jm}^{\dagger} \mathrm{a}_{jm} \right| \\ U_{j|m|} + f V_{j|m|} \mathrm{a}_{j|m|}^{\dagger} \mathrm{a}_{j-|m|}^{\dagger} \Big| 0 \Big\rangle = 2 \sum_{j,m>0} V_{jm}^2. \end{aligned} \tag{7}$$

[1] The sum in (7) contributes V_{jm}^2 for $m = \pm|m|$. Thus the factor 2 in the last expression.

The distribution of the number of particles around this average is a binomial distribution. For n large—and this applies better to superconductivity than to nuclear physics—the weight of states with a different number of particles is sharply peaked about the average number n. In this sense, ψ_B approximately corresponds to a fixed number of particles.

c. The Variational Calculation. Following Bardeen, we use ψ_B as a trial state of a variational calculation, to be developed as follows:

(i) Introduce an indeterminate Lagrange multiplier λ (*chemical potential*) as an added term to the shell energy, so that the Hamiltonian (1) becomes

$$(8) \qquad \mathcal{H}' = \sum_{mj} (\varepsilon_j - \lambda) a_{jm}^{\dagger} a_{jm} - G \sum_{jj',mm'>0} ff' a_{j'm'}^{\dagger} a_{j'-m'}^{\dagger} a_{j-m} a_{jm}.$$

(ii) Compute the expectation value of $\mathcal{H}'$ in the state ψ_B [1]

$$(9) \quad \langle \psi_B | \mathcal{H}' | \psi_B \rangle = 2 \sum_{j,m>0} (\varepsilon_j - \lambda) V_{jm}^2 - G \sum_{jj',mm'>0} U_{j'm'} V_{j'm'} U_{jm} V_{jm} - G \sum_{j,m>0} V_{jm}^4.$$

(iii) Introduce the *gap constant* Δ with the definition

$$(10) \qquad \Delta = G \sum_{j,m>0} U_{jm} V_{jm}$$

(it is proved in (15) that the Δ thus defined has the intuitive meaning shown in Fig. 2.35-1).

(iv) Determine the chemical potential λ and the gap constant Δ by means of two equations obtained by minimizing the energy (9) and by imposing the condition that the average number of particles of ψ_B be the total number of particle n:

$$(11) \qquad d \langle \psi_B | \mathcal{H}' | \psi_B \rangle = 0,$$

$$(12) \qquad \langle \psi_B | N | \psi_B \rangle = 2 \sum_{j,m>0} V_{jm}^2 = n.$$

Before proceeding to develop this outline, let us make a simplifying assumption: since the theory is inaccurate for states containing a small

[1] The first term in $\mathcal{H}'$ contains $\sum a_{jm}^{\dagger} a_{jm}$ and is computed as in (6). It contributes

$$2 \sum_{m>0} (\varepsilon_j - \lambda) V_{jm}^2.$$

The second term contains a double sum. For its computation we must consider both the jm and $j'm'$ factors of ψ_B: by omitting the subscripts j and the factors that give unity, we have

$$\sum_{mm'>0} \langle 0 | (U_m + f V_m a_{-m} a_m)(U_{m'} + f' V_{m'} a_{-m'} a_{m'}) \, | ff' a_{m'}^{\dagger} a_{-m'}^{\dagger} a_{-m} a_m) | \times (U_{m'} + f' V_{m'} a_{m'}^{\dagger} a_{-m'}^{\dagger})(U_m + f V_m a_m^{\dagger} a_{-m}^{\dagger}) \, |0\rangle.$$

There are two kinds of nonvanishing terms: those with eight a's which contribute $\sum_{mm'>0} U_m V_{m'} U_{m'} V_m$ and those with twelve a's which contribute $\sum_{m>0} V_m^4$.

number of particles, we shall suppose that $j + \frac{1}{2}$ and $j' + \frac{1}{2}$ are large. Then, for the most interesting cases, the last sum in (9) (which is over $j + \frac{1}{2}$ or $j' + \frac{1}{2}$ values of m) can be neglected compared with the double sum [which contains $(j + \frac{1}{2}) \times (j' + \frac{1}{2})$ terms in m and m'].

We can now expand the differential in (11), using (9) without the last sum and considering the V_{jm} as independent variables. By equating to zero the coefficients of each dV_{jm}, we obtain the following set of equations[1]

$$(13) \qquad 2(\varepsilon_j - \lambda)V_{jm}U_{jm} = \Delta(U_{jm}^2 - V_{jm}^2).$$

These and the normalization condition (4) can be solved to obtain U_{jm} and V_{jm} in terms of ε_j, λ, and Δ. We easily verify that the lowest energy solution of (13) is

$$(14) \quad U_{jm}^2 = \frac{1}{2}\left(1 + \frac{\varepsilon_j - \lambda}{E_j}\right), \quad V_{jm}^2 = \frac{1}{2}\left(1 - \frac{\varepsilon_j - \lambda}{E_j}\right), \quad V_{jm}U_{jm} = \frac{\Delta}{2E_j},$$

where E_j is as introduced in (2). The pair-occupation probability V_{jm}^2 of this solution is as indicated in the curve of Fig. 2.35-1. For $G = 0$ (no pairing), $\Delta = 0$ and $E_j = |\varepsilon_j - \lambda|$: V_{jm}^2 suddenly goes from 1 to 0 at $\varepsilon_j = \lambda$. For finite G, $\Delta \neq 0$ and the slope[2] of V_{jm}^2 at $\varepsilon_j = \lambda$ is

$$(15) \qquad \left[\frac{d(V_{jm}^2)}{d\varepsilon_j}\right]_{\varepsilon_j=\lambda} = \left(-\frac{V_{jm}}{E_j}\right)_{\varepsilon_j=\lambda} = -\frac{1}{2\Delta};$$

and thus Δ actually measures the thickness of the transition region.

[1] In the stated approximation (11) becomes

$$d\left[2\sum_{\substack{m>0\\ j}}(\varepsilon_j - \lambda)V_{jm}^2 - G\sum_{\substack{mm'>0\\ j,j'}} U_{j'm'}V_{j'm'}U_{jm}V_{jm}\right].$$

Differentiating the first term, we have $4\sum(\varepsilon_j - \lambda)V_{jm}\,dV_{jm}$. For the sum in the second term we have

$$\sum_{mm'>0} d(U_mV_mU_{m'}V_{m'})$$
$$= \sum_{mm'>0}\{U_{m'}V_{m'}(U_m\,dV_m + V_m\,dU_m) + U_mV_m(U_{m'}\,dV_{m'} + V_{m'}\,dU_{m'})\}$$
$$= 2\sum_{m'm>0} U_{m'}V_{m'}(U_m\,dV_m + V_m\,dU_m).$$

Considering now that because of (4) $dU_m = -V_m\,dV_m/U_m$ the last expression becomes

$$2\sum_{mm'>0} U_{m'}V_{m'}(U_m^2 - V_m^2)\,dV_m/U_m.$$

From this, and considering (10), we easily obtain (13).

[2] Again, ε_j is treated here as a continuous variable.

We observe finally that summing the last of (14) over jm and using (10) we obtain

(16) $$\frac{G}{2}\sum_{j,m>0}\frac{1}{E_j} = 1 \qquad \text{(gap equation)},$$

whereas (12) becomes

(17) $$\sum_{jm}\left(1 - \frac{\varepsilon_j - \lambda}{E_j}\right) = n \qquad \text{(number equation)}.$$

These two equations determine λ and Δ in terms of G.

We conclude that the ground state ψ_0 of the Hamiltonian (1) is given approximately (for large number of particles and large j) by the Bardeen trial state ψ_B, in which the quantities V_{jm} and U_{jm} satisfy (14) and λ and Δ satisfy (16) and (17).

2.36 Quasi-Particles and Excited States

a. The Quasi-Particle Formalism. Let us now see more precisely how the excitations of the shell model with pairing interactions can be described by means of quasi-particle creation and annihilation operators. With the help of these operators we can develop a formalism in which the ground state of the nucleus plays the role of quasi-particle vacuum, and the quasi-particles themselves behave like fermions, whose production, scattering, interactions, and annihilation can be studied with techniques borrowed from the theory of elementary particles.

Let us start introducing the *quasi-particle production and annihilation operators* (B-58b; B-58c; V-58) for a state jm:

(1) $$\begin{aligned}\alpha_{jm}{}^{\dagger} &= U_{jm}\mathrm{a}_{jm}{}^{\dagger} - fV_{jm}\mathrm{a}_{j-m},\\ \alpha_{jm} &= U_{jm}\mathrm{a}_{jm} - fV_{jm}\mathrm{a}_{j-m}^{\dagger};\end{aligned}$$

The corresponding operators for the state $j, -m$ are obtained by changing the sign of m and of $f[(-1)^{-m} = -(-1)^m$, since m is a half-integer]:

(2) $$\begin{aligned}\alpha_{j-m}^{\dagger} &= U_{jm}\mathrm{a}_{j-m}^{\dagger} + fV_{jm}\mathrm{a}_{jm}\\ \alpha_{j-m} &= U_{jm}\mathrm{a}_{j-m} + fV_{jm}\mathrm{a}_{j-m}^{\dagger}.\end{aligned}$$

In these definitions it is understood that the quantities $U_{j\pm m}$, $V_{j\pm m}$ correspond to the ground-state solution 2.35(14).

Let us also use the notation $|\text{“0”}\rangle$ for the ground state ψ_0, to make clear that it behaves like a vacuum for the quasi-particles. The correctness of this statement can readily be proved, since it is easily verified that[1]

(3) $$\alpha_{jm}\,|\text{“0”}\rangle = \alpha_{j-m}\,|\text{“0”}\rangle = 0.$$

[1] By applying α_{jm} to the (jm)th factor of $|\text{“0”}\rangle$, we have

$$\begin{aligned}\alpha_{jm}\,|\text{“}0_{jm}\text{”}\rangle &= (U_{jm}\mathrm{a}_{jm} - fV_{jm}\mathrm{a}_{j-m}^{\dagger})(U_{jm} + fV_{jm}\mathrm{a}_{jm}{}^{\dagger}\mathrm{a}_{j-m}^{\dagger})\,|0\rangle\\ &= (U_{jm}fV_{jm} - fV_{jm}U_{jm})\mathrm{a}_{j-m}^{\dagger}\,|0\rangle = 0.\end{aligned}$$

If we apply the quasi-particle creation operator to the vacuum $|\text{“}0\text{”}\rangle$, we obtain

$$\alpha_{jm}^{\dagger}\,|\text{“}0\text{”}\rangle = a_{jm}^{\dagger} \prod_{j'm' \neq jm} (U_{j'm'} + f'V_{j'm'}a_{j'm'}^{\dagger}a_{j'-m'}^{\dagger})\,|0\rangle, \tag{4}$$

as we can show by carrying out the computation in detail for the (jm)th factor of $|\text{“}0\text{”}\rangle$, which is the only one to be affected:

$$\begin{aligned}\alpha_{jm}^{\dagger}(U_{jm} + fV_{jm}a_{jm}^{\dagger}a_{j-m}^{\dagger})\,|0\rangle \\ &= (U_{jm}a_{jm}^{\dagger} - fV_{jm}a_{j-m})(U_{jm} + fV_{jm}a_{jm}^{\dagger}a_{j-m}^{\dagger})\,|0\rangle \\ &= (U_{jm}^{2} + f^{2}V_{jm}^{2})a_{jm}^{\dagger}\,|0\rangle = a_{jm}^{\dagger}\,|0\rangle.\end{aligned}$$

The meaning of these operators is now clear: *for energies well above the Fermi surface* ($U_{jm} = 1$, $V_{jm} = 0$) *the operator* $\alpha_{jm}^{\dagger}$ *creates a particle in the state jm; for energies well below the Fermi surface* ($U_{jm} = 0$, $V_{jm} = 1$), $\alpha_{jm}^{\dagger}$ *destroys the particle j, −m (leaving a hole that behaves like a particle in the state jm).*

In the intermediate region, around the Fermi surface, $\alpha_{jm}^{\dagger}$ *does a little of both creating and annihilating: it "fills in" completely the state jm and "empties out" entirely the state j, −m.*

It is easily verified that the *quasi-particle states are normalized to unity* in their own vacuum. By using (4) we obtain immediately

$$\langle\text{“}0\text{”}|\,\alpha_{jm}\alpha_{jm}^{\dagger}\,|\text{“}0\text{”}\rangle = \langle 0|\,a_{jm}a_{jm}^{\dagger}\,|0\rangle. \tag{5}$$

We must now prove a very important property of the quasi-particles: *The state* $\alpha_{jm}^{\dagger}\,|\text{“}0\text{”}\rangle$ *is an eigenstate of the Hamiltonian* 2.35(8) corresponding to excitation energy 2.35(2):

$$E^{*} = E_{j} = \sqrt{(\varepsilon_{j} - \lambda)^{2} + \Delta^{2}}. \tag{6}$$

For the proof we must consider that the excitation energy is the difference between the energy of the excited state and that of the ground state

$$E^{*} = \langle\text{“}0\text{”}|\,\alpha_{jm}\mathcal{H}'\alpha_{jm}^{\dagger}\,|\text{“}0\text{”}\rangle - \langle\text{“}0\text{”}|\,\mathcal{H}'\,|\text{“}0\text{”}\rangle.$$

The ground-state energy has already been computed in 2.35(9); for the excited state $\alpha_{jm}^{\dagger}\,|\text{“}0_{jm}\text{”}\rangle = (U_{jm})^{-1}a_{jm}^{\dagger}\,|0\rangle$ the jm term of the first sum in 2.35(8) gives $(\varepsilon_{j} - \lambda)$ instead of $2(\varepsilon_{j} - \lambda)V_{jm}^{2}$ and the j, m terms in the sums expressing the pairing interaction are suppressed[1]. If small terms

[1] In the sum $\sum_{m'm''>0} U_{m'}V_{m'}U_{m''}V_{m''}$ the terms with $m' = m$ and $m'' = m$ are suppressed. These give

$$\sum_{m''>0} U_{m}V_{m}U_{m''}V_{m''} + \sum_{m'=0} U_{m'}V_{m'}U_{m}V_{m} = 2U_{m}V_{m}\sum_{m'>0} U_{m'}V_{m'}.$$

are again neglected, the excitation energy is [use 2.35(10) and (14) for the transformations]

$$E^* = (1 - 2V_{jm}^2)(\varepsilon_j - \lambda) + 2GU_{jm}V_{jm} \sum_{j',m'>0} U_{j'm'}V_{j'm'}$$
$$= \frac{(\varepsilon_j - \lambda)^2}{E_j} + \frac{\Delta^2}{E_j} = \frac{E_j^2}{E_j} = E_j,$$

as we wanted to prove[1].

Also important is the fact that *the quasi-particles behave like fermions.* This follows from the commutation rules of the α's, which may be obtained by using the definitions (1) and (2), and which are found to be the same as those of the a's:

$$\alpha_m \alpha_{m'} + \alpha_{m'}\alpha_m = \alpha_m^\dagger \alpha_{m'}^\dagger + \alpha_{m'}^\dagger \alpha_m^\dagger = 0,$$
(7)
$$\alpha_m \alpha_{m'}^\dagger + \alpha_{m'}^\dagger \alpha_m = \delta_{mm'}.$$

b. Graphical Representation for Interacting Quasi-Particles. We have seen that the quasi-particles are—at least approximately—eigenstates of the Hamiltonian of the shell model with pairing forces and behave like free fermions. But, if other interactions are taken into account, the quasi-particles do not propagate freely. They may be scattered and created in particle-hole pairs, just like any other fermion.

These effects are treated by using techniques originally developed for the interactions of elementary particles, and which are discussed in Chapter 3 (scattering) and Chapter 6 (Feynman diagrams).

At this point we want only to describe a graphical method that is often used to represent interacting quasi-particles or just to talk about them. Though we can attach a quantitative meaning to this method, the reader who is not yet familiar with Feynman graphs cannot derive more than an intuitive understanding from the present description.

On a piece of white paper (the quasi-particle vacuum $|``0"\rangle$) we fix the upward direction as representing that of increasing time: the top of the sheet is the future and the bottom is the past. Then a quasi-particle state ($\alpha_{jm}^\dagger |``0"\rangle$ for $\varepsilon_j > \lambda$) is represented by a line (not necessarily straight) pointing up to indicate the continued and unchanged presence in time of

[1] We must show that the excitation energy (6) does not contradict the results of 2.34, where we computed the seniority excitation of s unpaired particles in the same shell.

For this we must remember that the value of E_j to be used in (6) must satisfy the gap equation 2.35(16). If a single shell is considered there is no sum over j in this equation, and the sum over m consists of $j + \frac{1}{2}$ equal terms. Thus we obtain $E_j = (G/2)(j + \frac{1}{2})$. On the other hand, the seniority excitation energy 2.34(5) reduces to $E_{ns} - E_{n0} = s(G/2)(j + \frac{1}{2})$, provided $j + \frac{1}{2} \gg 1$ and $j + \frac{1}{2} \gg s$. Thus the general theory with inter-shell interaction reduces to the more accurate single-shell computation if j is large [see comments after 2.35(12)] and if the seniority is not too high.

the quasi-particle (Fig. 2.36-1*a*). We shall see that it is convenient to represent an antiquasi-particle, or quasi-hole ($\alpha_{jm}{}^{\dagger}\,|``0"\rangle$ for $\varepsilon_j < \lambda$) by a line pointing down[1]. The elementary interaction between two quasi-particles is conventionally indicated by means of two crossing upward

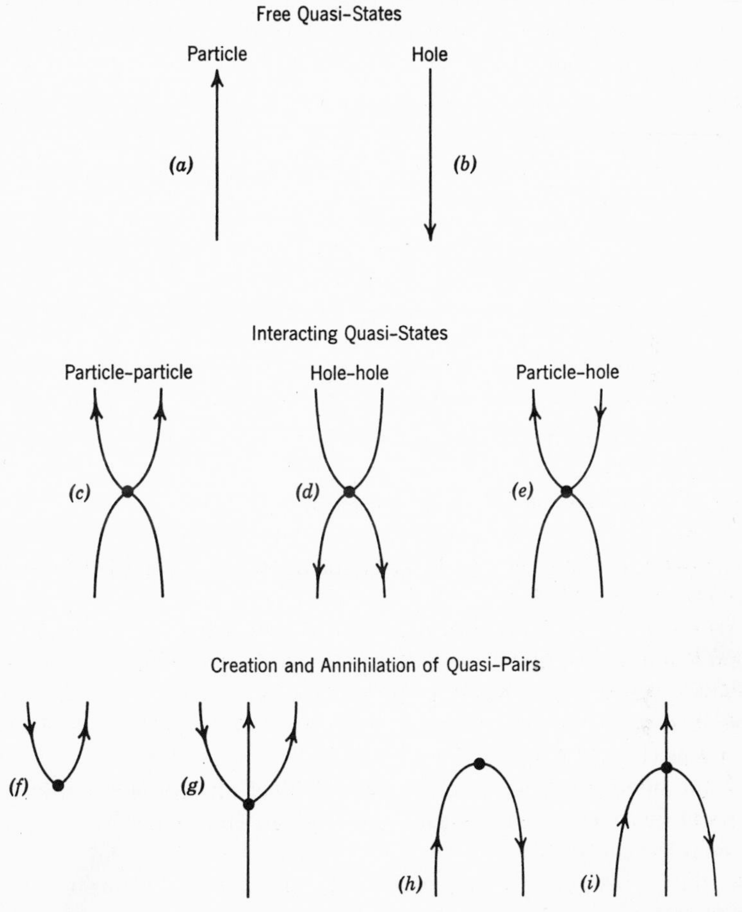

Fig. 2.36-1. Graphical representation of quasi-particles and of their interaction.

lines, and so on, as shown in Fig. 2.36-1*b*; the creation of quasi-particle pairs is the sudden appearance of an upward and downward line (Fig. 2.36-1*c*) and, similarly, the annihilation of a pair is the sudden disappearance of such lines.

[1] The distinction between quasi-particles and quasi-holes is somewhat artificial, but it is not essential to the method. Some authors omit the upward and downward arrows in the graphs.

Interactions with other forces (electromagnetic or elastic: photons or phonons) are indicated with wavy lines as shown in Fig. 2.36-2.

c. Nuclear Excited States. Let us first describe the excited states of nuclei neglecting quasi-particle interaction. As usual, it is useful to distinguish between even and odd nuclei. Odd nuclei have an unpaired particle (quasi-particle) in their ground states. Their lower excited states consist of the excited states of this quasi-particle; there are also higher excited states containing quasi-particles pairs in addition to the original quasi-particle.

The lowest excited states of an even nucleus, whose ground state is the quasi-particle vacuum, can be formed only by breaking a $J = 0$ pair, and

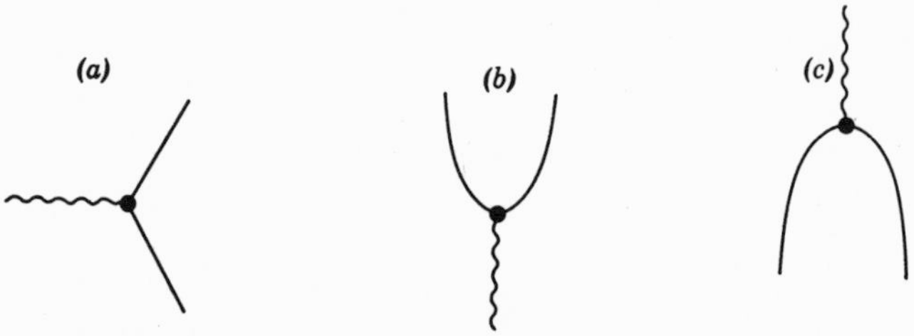

Fig. 2.36-2. Scattering (*a*), production (*b*), and annihilation (*c*) of quasi-particles due to interactions with perturbing quanta such as photons of phonons.

their spectrum shows a gap characteristic of the energy needed for quasi-particle pair production.

When interactions between quasi-particles are taken into account, the excited states assume a complicated structure. The nucleus becomes a complex system of interacting quasi-particles which can be intuitively described—and also quantitatively discussed—with the help of intricate diagrams (Fig. 2.36-3).

If the interactions are strong, the individual quasi-particles lose their importance and excited nuclear states may be best described as heated gaseous systems (2.24d).

If the forces acting between the quasi-particles have long range the scattering is no longer incoherent: one obtains coherent motions which may be identified as collective excitations. Thus the formalism of interacting quasi-particles accounts also for the existence of rotational and vibrational excited states.

d. The Distorting Interaction. The form of long-range residual interaction that has been most extensively and successfully studied is the so-called *distorting interaction* or P_2 *force* (B-59).

In order to introduce this interaction, let us consider two particles, i and j, whose position is defined by the vectors $\mathbf{r}_i$ and $\mathbf{r}_j$, measured from the center of the nucleus. An arbitrary scalar, spin-independent potential acting between the two particles can be expanded in Legendre polynomials $P_l(\cos\theta_{ij})$, where $\cos\theta_{ij} = (\mathbf{r}_i \cdot \mathbf{r}_j)/|\mathbf{r}_i|\,|\mathbf{r}_j|$.

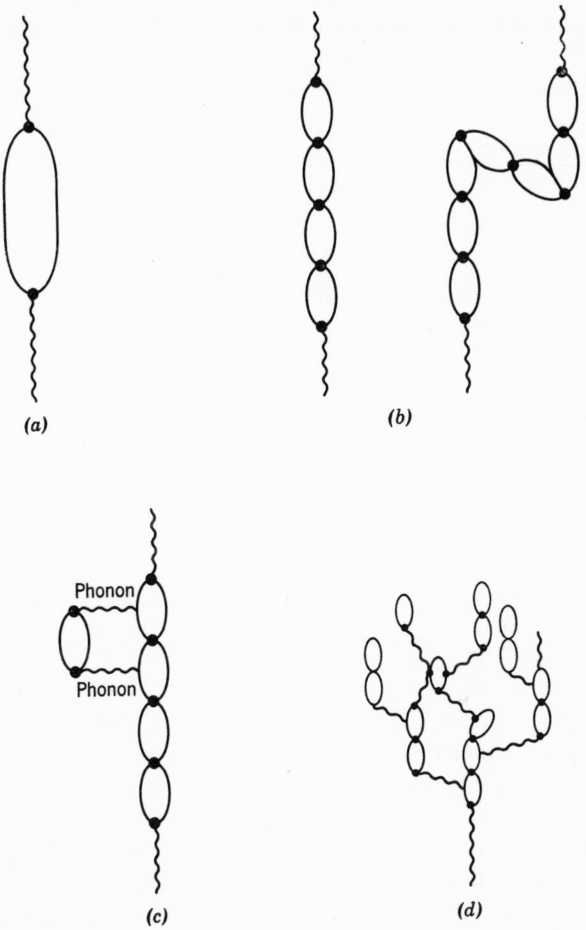

Fig. 2.36-3. Excitations of an even nucleus resulting from the absorption of a γ ray. In (*a*), (*b*) and (*c*) the γ ray is re-emitted: (*a*) pair of noninteracting quasi-particles; (*b*) pairs of quasi-particles interacting with each other; (*c*) pairs of quasi-particles interacting with each other and with other mechanisms of nuclear excitation; (*d*) pairs of strongly interacting quasi-particles leading to a complex compound nucleus.

The spherically symmetrical term in $l = 0$ can be neglected: its effect on the ground states is already included in the assumption of a spherical well, and its contributions to the excited states would be in the form of vibrations with volume change, which are not observed.

The $l = 1$ term must vanish because it would tend to move the center of mass of nuclear matter in relation to the center of the well.

Thus the $l = 2$ or P_2 term is the first of some importance: it can produce spheroidal deformations of the nucleus and may be considered responsible for nuclear quadrupole moments. Though it is known that the quadrupole moment of the deuteron is due to tensor forces, we obtain a simpler modelistic description of the deformations in heavy nuclei if we attribute them to a $P_2(\cos\theta_{ij})$ interaction.

Thus we suppose that between the two particles i and j there exists a force corresponding to a potential energy

$$-\chi\, F(\mathbf{r}_i, \mathbf{r}_j) P_2(\cos\theta_{ij}), \tag{8}$$

where χ is a constant and F is a function of $|\mathbf{r}_i - \mathbf{r}_j|$ which may be chosen to fit the experimental data.

The P_2 potential favors values of the angle θ_{ij} near 0 or π. Then, if F has a relatively long range, all particles tend to align to produce the desired quadrupole distortion of the nucleus as a whole.

Expressed in "many-body" notation, the Hamiltonian of a nuclear model including pairing and distorting residual interactions consists of three terms.

$$\begin{aligned}\mathcal{H} = \sum_{jm} \varepsilon_j \mathsf{a}_{jm}{}^{\dagger} \mathsf{a}_{jm} &- G \sum_{\substack{m,m'>0 \\ jj'}} ff' \mathsf{a}^{\dagger}_{j'm'} \mathsf{a}^{\dagger}_{j'-m'} \mathsf{a}_{j-m} \mathsf{a}_{jm} \\ &- \chi \sum_{\substack{j_1 j_2 j_1' j_2' \\ m_1 m_2 m_1' m_2'}} \langle j_1' m_1' j_2' m_2' \,|\, \mathsf{P}_2 \,|\, j_2 m_2 j_1 m_1 \rangle\, \mathsf{a}^{\dagger}_{j_1' m_1'} \mathsf{a}^{\dagger}_{j_2' m_2'} \mathsf{a}_{j_2 m_2} \mathsf{a}_{j_1 m_1}.\end{aligned} \tag{9}$$

where P_2 is the operator corresponding to the potential (8).

This model is capable of accounting for many nuclear collective properties, assuming that the quantities G and χ are slowly varying functions of the mass number (for instance $G \approx 0.12$ MeV has been used for $A \approx 200$, $G \approx 0.2$ MeV for $A \approx 100$). The theoretical results on ground-state deformation (B-61) and on moments of inertia (G-60) are in agreement with the experiment, and in some cases it is possible to obtain a fairly good description of low-energy excited states. The calculation of the excited states of nuclei in which either neutrons or protons are in a closed shell (K-60) has the simplifying feature of a spherical equilibrium shape and is particularly successful.

As already noted in c, the long-range forces also make the connection between the quasi-particles and the collective approach (B-59; B-60a), since they "scatter" the quasi-particles coherently and produce collective excitations. Thus the phonon and the quasi-particle aspect merge in the model corresponding to the Hamiltonian (9).

Complete wave functions of nuclear excited states, including quasi-particle and quadrupole phonons, may be computed (K-63). From these functions we obtain magnetic and quadrupole moments, electromagnetic transition probabilities, and other nuclear properties that can be compared with the experiment. Though much remains to be done both from the experimental and the theoretical viewpoint, the comparison between the model and the experiment so far seems satisfactory, and we can hope that further developments may bring a fuller understanding of the complex problem of nuclear states.

References

Books

AIP-57 *Am. Inst. Phys. Handbook*, McGraw-Hill, New York, 1957, Section 8e.
BW-52 J. M. Blatt and V. F. Weisskopf, *Theoretical Nuclear Physics*, Wiley, New York, 1952.
Di-47 P. A. M. Dirac, *Principles of Quantum Mechanics*, Clarendon Press, Oxford, 1947.
Fe-50 E. Fermi, *Nuclear Physics*, University of Chicago Press, 1950.
MJ-55 M. G. Mayer and J. H. D. Jensen, *Nuclear Shell Structure*, Wiley, New York, 1955.

Articles

A-55 F. Ajzenberg-Selove and T. Lauritsen, *Rev. Mod. Phys.*, **27,** 77 (1955).
B-36 H. Bethe and R. F. Becker, *Rev. Mod. Phys.*, **8,** 82, 162 (1936).
B-37 H. Bethe, *Rev. Mod. Phys.*, **9,** 69 (1937).
B-54a K. A. Brueckner, *Phys. Rev.*, **96,** 508 (1954).
B-54b Brueckner, Levinson, and Mahmoud, *Phys. Rev.*, **95,** 217 (1954).
B-55a A. Bohr and B. B. Mottelson, in *β and γ Spectroscopy* (edited by K. Siegbahn) North Holland, Amsterdam, 1955.
B-55b K. A. Brueckner, *Phys. Rev.*, **97,** 1353 (1955).
B-55c K. A. Brueckner and C. A. Levinson, *Phys. Rev.*, **97,** 1344 (1955).
B-57 Bardeen, Cooper, and Schrieffer, *Phys. Rev.*, **108,** 1175 (1957).
B-58a G. C. Backenstoss and R. B. Sutton (unpublished) (1958).
B-58b N. N. Bogolyubov, *J. Exptl. Theoret. Phys.*, **34,** 58 (1958).
B-58c N. N. Bogolyubov, *Nuovo Cimento* **7,** 794 (1958).
B-59 S. T. Balyaev, *Kgl. Danske Videnskab. Selskab, Mat. Fys. Medd.*, **31,** No. 11 (1959).
B-60a M. Baranger, *Phys. Rev.*, **120,** 957 (1960).
B-60b D. M. Brink, *Progr. Nucl. Phys.*, **8,** 97 (1960).
B-61 D. R. Bes and Z. Szymanski, *Nucl. Phys.*, **28,** 42 (1961).
C-52 Cladis, Hess, and Moyer, *Phys. Rev.*, **87,** 425 (1952).
C-53 L. N. Cooper and E. M. Henley, *Phys. Rev.*, **92,** 801 (1953).

C-63 Collard, Hofstadter, Johansson, Parks, Ryneveld, Walker, Yearian, Day, and Wagner, *Phys. Rev. Letters*, **11**, 132 (1963).
E-55 R. J. Eden and N. C. Francis, *Phys. Rev.*, **97**, 1366 (1955).
F-46 E. Feenberg and G. Goertzel, *Phys. Rev.*, **70**, 597 (1946).
F-53 V. L. Fitch and J. Rainwater, *Phys. Rev.*, **92**, 789 (1953).
G-58 Gomes, Walecka, and Weisskopf, *Ann. Phys., N.Y.*, **3**, 241 (1958).
G-60 J. J. Griffin and M. Rich, *Phys. Rev.*, **118**, 850 (1960).
H-52 Hardy, Silvey, and Townes, *Phys. Rev.*, **86**, 608 (1952).
H-53 Hardy, Silvey, Townes, Burke, Strandberg, Parker, and Cohen, *Phys. Rev.*, **92**, 1532 (1953).
H-56 R. Hofstadter, *Rev. Mod. Phys.*, **28**, 215 (1956).
K-58 O. Kofoed-Hansen, *Rev. Mod. Phys.*, **30**, 449 (1958).
K-60 L. S. Kisslinger and R. A. Sorensen, *Kgl. Danske Videnskab. Selskab, Mat. Fys. Medd.*, **32**, No. 9 (1960).
K-63 L. S. Kisslinger and R. A. Sorensen (in print), 1963.
N-55 S. G. Nilsson, *Kgl. Danske Videnskab. Selskab, Mat. Fys. Medd.*, **29**, No. 16 (1955).
R-51 J. Rainwater, *Phys. Rev.*, **79**, 432 (1951).
S-61 P. A. Seeger, *Nucl. Phys.*, **25**, 1 (1961).
V-58 J. G. Valatin, *Nuovo Cimento*, **7**, 843 (1958).
W-35 C. F. V. Weizsäcker, *Z. Physik*, **96**, 431 (1935).
W-55 J. M. Wilcox and B. J. Moyer, *Phys. Rev.*, **99**, 875 (1955).

THREE

Analysis of Scattering Experiments

3.1 The Scattering of *S*-Wave Neutrons

3.11 Experimental Measurements of Neutron Cross Sections for Energies under 10 MeV

The experimental techniques used to study the scattering of neutrons under 10 MeV have been developed to a considerable degree of perfection and the cross sections are known with remarkable accuracy. A full understanding of the experimental methods requires, in many cases, some of the knowledge of neutron behavior which is presented in the later pages of this Chapter. We shall, however, give a brief preliminary account of experimental matters to indicate how the data have been obtained.

If the wavelength of the neutrons is of the order of 10^{-12} cm or larger (energy smaller than $\approx$10 MeV), only the S wave overlaps appreciably with the nuclear potential and is scattered. The scattering is spherically symmetrical, and the only quantity to be measured is the total cross section. Rather intense neutron beams, produced by nuclear reactors and accelerators, are available for these measurements (Hu-53).

The spectrum of neutrons emerging from a reactor or from a moderated accelerator beam consists mostly of a Maxwell distribution peaked at the moderator's temperature, and of a high energy tail whose flux goes as $1/E$ [see 3.21(11)]. At room temperature the velocity of thermal ($E = kT = \frac{1}{40}$ eV) neutrons is 2.2×10^5 cm/sec and their wavelength is 1.8 Å, of the order of magnitude of interatomic spacing in solids.

Various filters can be used for the selection of particular bands of the spectrum. Crystalline substances are transparent only for "very cold" neutrons; cadmium absorbers affect only thermal and cold neutrons; indium has a sharp absorption peak at 1.5 eV; Li and B have an absorption cross section proportional to $1/\sqrt{E}$ and are transparent only to fast neutrons, and so on. A judicious and ingenious use of these filters allows us to separate "groups" of neutrons in various energy bands.

But much more useful are the techniques that employ monochromatic neutron beams.

We can select neutron energies in the same manner as we select energies of x rays—by Bragg scattering on crystals. The method is useful in the region of thermal neutrons and can be used up to energies $\approx 10^2$ to 10^3 eV, with decreasing resolution because of the decreased wavelength.

It is also possible to select the neutron velocities mechanically by means of a velocity selector consisting of a rotating cylinder with helical holes.

Instead of producing a monochromatic beam, we can measure electronically the neutron's velocity. For this purpose the source of neutrons is either pulsed—this is readily done for a cyclotron—or "chopped" by rotating an absorber with a hole in a reactor's beam. The detector, usually a counter containing boron and responding to the α particles from the reaction $n + B^{10} \rightarrow He^4 + Li^7$, is located at some distance away. By means of an electronic circuit we select the detector's pulses according to the neutron's time of flight.

All these methods fail for large velocities. Mechanical selectors have obvious limitations in speed; fast pulsing of an accelerator gives a fast pulse of high-energy neutrons, but a slower pulse of slow neutrons, since the time required for the slowing down is not negligible.

Different methods must be used at higher energies. Among these we should mention the production of monoenergetic neutrons from a thin target by a beam of charged particles accelerated in a well-stabilized Van de Graaff machine.

Polarized beams of slow neutrons can be obtained by filtering through magnetized iron (3.31) or by reflection by magnetic mirrors. For higher energies, in the MeV region, polarized neutrons are obtained by scattering in He or as a product of certain reactions.

The art of detecting neutrons is also highly developed. We have already mentioned the boron counters, which are useful mostly at low energy but can be used at higher energies when surrounded by a paraffin moderator. There are also various radioactive detectors or foils. Indium responds to thermal and epithermal neutrons and, when surrounded by cadmium, to epithermal neutrons only. Other foils become radioactive only when exposed to neutrons above a certain energy and are used as threshold detectors to measure the upper part of the spectrum from a source.

In this chapter we discuss almost exclusively the interaction of neutrons

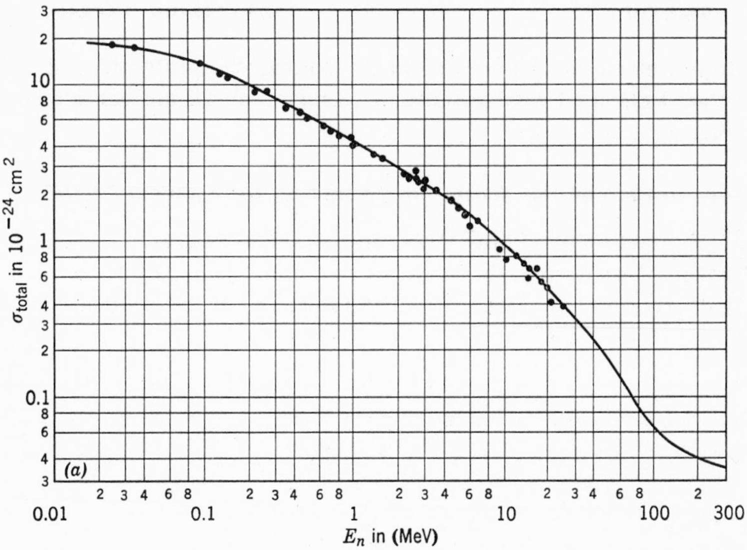

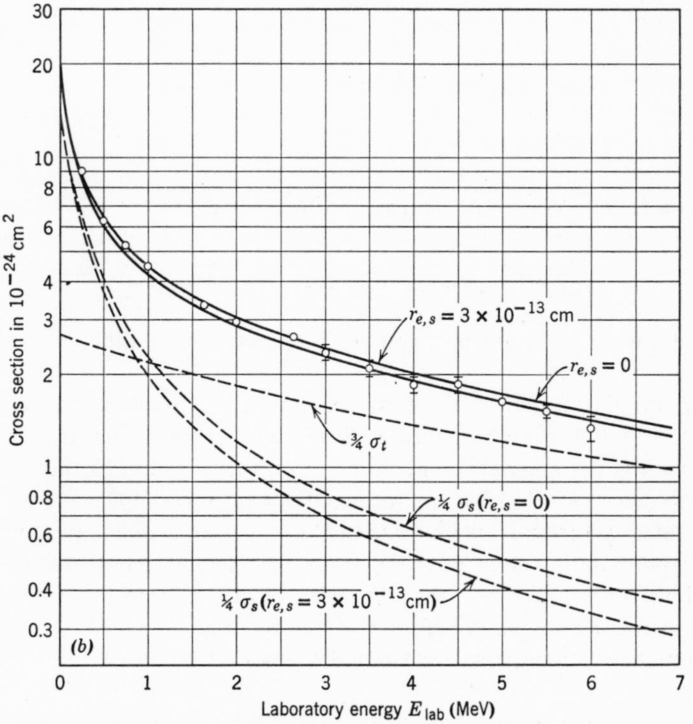

Fig. 3.11-1. (*a*) Experimental results on total n–p scattering cross section (N. F. Ramsey, *Experimental Nuclear Physics*, Wiley, 1960, E. Segré, editor). (*b*) Same data compared with theoretical curves to be explained in the course of this chapter (reprinted from J. M. Blatt and V. F. Weisskopf, *Theoretical Nuclear Physics*, Wiley, 1952).

with the elementary particles of stable matter: the proton (Fig. 3.11-1) and the electron. Cross sections for complex nuclei are considered in Chapter 5.

3.12 Review of the Scattering Formalism for Spinless Particles

a. Expansion of a Plane Wave in Spherical Waves. In a classical treatment of scattering, the particles in the incident parallel beam are divided according to their impact parameters; then the deflection is

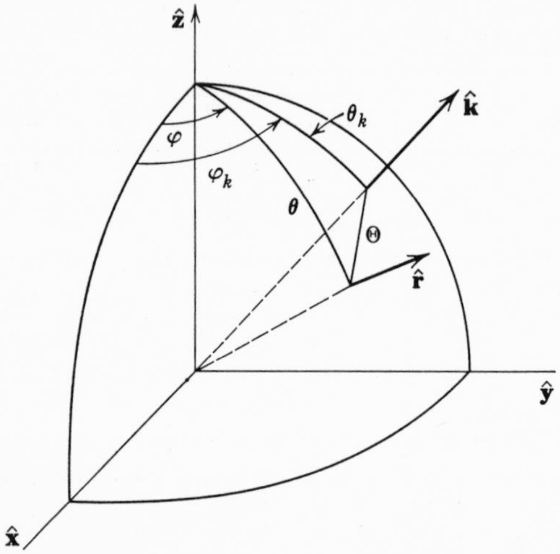

Fig. 3.12-1. Definition of the polar angles θ, φ and θ_k, φ_k.

studied for each parameter, and from the result the differential cross section is obtained.

In quantum mechanics we must decompose the incoming plane wave in a somewhat similar manner. The quantity replacing the impact parameter is the angular momentum, which is a constant of the motion, and the decomposition has the form of the expansion of a plane wave in eigenstates of orbital angular momentum, which are spherical waves. The expansion is surely possible, since the angular momentum eigenfunctions form a complete set. The way of determining the coefficients of the expansions is described in many classical books (MM-33; Sc-49). For a plane wave propagating along the z axis the result is[1]

(1)
$$e^{ikz} = \sum_{l=0}^{\infty} i^l \sqrt{4\pi(2l+1)}\, j_l(kr)\, Y_l^0(\theta)$$
$$\cong \sum_{l=0}^{\infty} i^l \sqrt{4\pi(2l+1)}\, \frac{\sin\left(kr - \frac{1}{2}l\pi\right)}{kr}\, Y_l^0(\theta)$$

In this formula k is the wave number; the coordinates xyz (or $r\theta\varphi$ with polar axis along z), which are used to describe plane and spherical waves, are measured from an arbitrary origin where we may eventually locate a scattering center; the functions $j_l(kr)$ and $Y_l^0(\theta)$ have been defined in 1.13d.

The expansion applies to a wave describing a particle without spin. There is no privileged direction, apart from the axis of propagation z, from which θ is measured. The $Y_l^0(\theta)$ do not depend on φ and cylindrical symmetry is assured.

If the plane wave propagates in an arbitrary direction, defined by the wave vector $\mathbf{k}$, its expansion in spherical waves contains the spherical functions of the angle Θ, between $\hat{\mathbf{k}}$ and the variable point defined by the unit vector $\hat{\mathbf{r}}$. But these can be expressed with the aid of the addition theorem 1.13(15) in terms of the spherical harmonics of the angles $\theta\varphi$ and $\theta_k\varphi_k$, defined in Fig. 3.12-1. We obtain in this manner

$$(2) \qquad e^{i\mathbf{k}\cdot\mathbf{r}} = 4\pi \sum_{l=0}^{\infty} \sum_{m=-l}^{l} i^l j_l(kr)[Y_l^m(\theta_k\varphi_k)]^* Y_l^m(\theta\varphi)$$

$$= 4\pi \sum_{l=0}^{\infty} i^l j_l(kr)[Y_l^0(\theta_k) Y_l^0(\theta) + \text{terms containing a factor } \cos m(\varphi - \varphi_k)].$$

b. The Scattering Formalism. We may suppose that the beam described by a plane wave eventually meets a scattering center fixed at the origin; or, if we want to describe the collision of an incident particle of mass m_1 with a target particle of mass m_2, we locate at the origin their center of mass. In this last case the k of formulas (1) and (2) is the wave number of the relative motion:

$$(3) \qquad k = \sqrt{\frac{2\mu E}{\hbar^2}} \quad \text{with} \quad \frac{1}{\mu} = \frac{1}{m_1} + \frac{1}{m_2} \quad \text{and} \quad E = \frac{m_2}{m_1 + m_2} E_L,$$

where E is the energy in the center of mass system and E_L, the kinetic energy of the incident particle in the laboratory, where the target is at rest.

We shall always assume that the interaction occurs through a potential that falls with distance rapidly enough to allow the usual mathematical treatment. This is always the case for short-range nuclear potentials.

We must look for solutions of the wave equation of the asymptotic form

$$(4) \qquad \psi \simeq e^{ikz} + f(\theta)\frac{e^{ikr}}{r},$$

since we must add to the incoming beam an outgoing spherical wave, describing the scattering. The complex function $f(\theta)$ is called the *scattering*

[1] Equalities $\simeq$ are valid asymptotically for large r. Formula 1.13(18) has been used for the asymptotic value of (1).

amplitude and has the dimensions of length[1]. It does not depend on φ because of the axial symmetry of the problem considered. The function $f(\theta)$ can also be expanded in Legendre polynomials or in Y_l^0:

$$f(\theta) = \sum_{l=0}^{\infty} (2l+1)a_l P_l(\cos\theta) = \sum_{l=0}^{\infty} \sqrt{4\pi(2l+1)}\, a_l\, Y_l^0(\theta). \tag{5}$$

Each coefficient a_l (also a length) that enters into this expansion is called the *scattering amplitude of the* lth *angular momentum wave.* We shall introduce as usual a set of real angles δ_l, such that

$$a_l = \frac{e^{2i\delta_l} - 1}{2ik} = \frac{e^{i\delta_l}}{k} \sin\delta_l = \frac{1}{k\cot\delta_l - ik} \tag{6}$$

These angles are called the *scattering phase shifts* of the respective waves. The reason for this name is that the lth term in the asymptotic expansion of (4) can be written, by making use of (1), (5), and (6),

$$\psi_l \cong \sqrt{4\pi(2l+1)}\frac{1}{kr}\left[i^l \sin(kr - \tfrac{1}{2}l\pi) + \frac{e^{2i\delta_l} - 1}{2i} e^{ikr}\right] Y_l^0(\theta) \tag{7a}$$

and this, with a little algebra, becomes

$$\psi_l \cong \frac{\sqrt{4\pi(2l+1)}}{kr}\, i^l e^{i\delta_l} \sin(kr - \tfrac{1}{2}l\pi + \delta_l)\, Y_l^0(\theta). \tag{7b}$$

Thus, apart from the complex phase factor $e^{i\delta_l}$, the lth term of (4) behaves asymptotically as the lth term of a free wave shifted by a phase angle δ_l.

If in particular δ_l is small or near π, $\cot\delta_l$ is large and the amplitude a_l becomes approximately real[2]

$$a_l \approx \frac{1}{k\cot\delta_l} = \begin{cases} \delta_l/k & \text{for } |\delta_l| \ll 1, \\ (\delta_l - \pi)/k & \text{for } |\delta_l - \pi| \ll 1. \end{cases} \tag{8}$$

The differential scattering cross section is given by

$$\sigma(\theta) = |f(\theta)|^2 \tag{9}$$

and the total cross section by

$$\sigma = \int |f(\theta)|^2\, d\Omega. \tag{10}$$

If, in this formula, we substitute (5) and (6), the mixed terms of the square

[1] More precisely, we should say that $f(\theta)$ is the amplitude of the scattered beam at unit distance from the origin.

[2] Observe, however, that the second-order term in the expansion of (6) is the imaginary quantity $i\delta_l^2/k$, as required by the optical theorem [3.19(8)].

vanish because of the orthogonality of the $Y_l^0(\theta)$ and we obtain

(11) $$\sigma = \sum_{l=0}^{\infty} 4\pi(2l+1)\,|a_l|^2 = \frac{4\pi}{k^2}\sum_{l=0}^{\infty}(2l+1)\sin^2\delta_l.$$

c. Energy Dependence of Phases for Short-Range Scattering Potential. In our discussion of the deuteron we concluded that the shorter the range of the forces r_0, the greater the potential well depth V_0 needed to produce a certain effect. As for the deuteron, we shall speak of short range whenever V_0 is much larger than all of the other energies involved in our problem, so that the energy variation of the wave functions for $r < r_0$ may be neglected.

Under the assumption of short range we can prove that the phase shifts δ_l of the lth angular momentum wave satisfy the relation

(12) $$k^{2l+1}\cot\delta_l = \text{constant} \quad \text{for } kr_0 \ll 1$$

and in particular

(13) $$\delta_l \approx k^{2l+1} \quad \text{for } kr_0 \ll 1,\ |\delta_l| \ll 1.$$

The proof follows.

From (7*b*) we see that the radial part of the l-wave solution $u_l(r) = r\psi_l$ of the Schrödinger equation corresponding to phase shifts δ_l varies asymptotically as

(14)
$$u_l(r) \simeq \sin(kr - \tfrac{1}{2}l\pi + \delta_l) = \sin(kr - \tfrac{1}{2}l\pi)\cos\delta_l + \cos(kr - \tfrac{1}{2}l\pi)\sin\delta_l.$$

Thus, if the scattering potential vanishes for $r > r_0$, we can write, for $r > r_0$,

(15) $$u_l(r > r_0) = kr[j_l(kr)\cos\delta_l + n_l(kr)\sin\delta_l].$$

If $r_0 \ll 1/k$, we can use the approximation valid near the origin [1.13(18)] in order to express the function (15) for values of r just larger than r_0:

(16) $$u_l(r = r_0 + \varepsilon) = \frac{(kr)^{l+1}}{(2l+1)!!}\cos\delta_l + \frac{(2l-1)!!}{(kr)^l}\sin\delta_l.$$

We can now compute the logarithmic derivative of u_l for $r = r_0$, which we call ρ_l/r_0:

(17) $$\rho_l = r_0\left(\frac{1}{u_l}\frac{du_l}{dr}\right)_{r=r_0} = \frac{\dfrac{l+1}{(2l+1)!!}(kr_0)^{l+1}\cos\delta_l - l\dfrac{(2l-1)!!}{(kr_0)^l}\sin\delta_l}{\dfrac{(kr_0)^{l+1}}{(2l+1)!!}\cos\delta_l + \dfrac{(2l-1)!!}{(kr_0)^l}\sin\delta_l},$$

from which we obtain

$$\tan \delta_l = \frac{(l+1) - \rho_l}{l + \rho_l} \frac{(kr_0)^{2l+1}}{(2l+1)!!\,(2l-1)!!}, \tag{18}$$

or

$$(kr_0)^{2l+1} \cot \delta_l = (2l+1)!!\,(2l-1)!! \frac{l + \rho_l}{l + 1 - \rho_l}. \tag{19}$$

The continuity of the logarithmic derivative requires that ρ_l be determined by the wave function for $r < r_0$. But we have assumed that the energy dependence of this wave function can be neglected: thus ρ_l can be considered constant and (12) is proved.

Note that the proof does not hold for $\rho_l \approx -l$ ($\theta_l \approx \pi/2$, resonance) nor for $\rho_l \approx l + 1$.

3.13 S-Wave Scattering for Spin 0 and for Spin $\frac{1}{2}$

a. S-Wave Scattering Amplitude and Scattering Length. The cross section for *S*-wave scattering for spinless particles is, from 3.12(11),

$$\sigma = 4\pi a_0{}^2 = \frac{4\pi}{k^2} \sin^2 \delta_0 = \frac{4\pi}{k^2 + k^2 \cot^2 \delta_0}. \tag{1}$$

We want to discuss now the approximations valid for small k, which are of special interest for slow neutrons.

Because of the short range of nuclear forces $k \cot \delta_0$ is approximately constant [3.12(12)]; thus for small k the amplitude a_0 is real [3.12(8)], and it is convenient to define a real constant, the *scattering length* a, from the relation

$$\mathrm{a} = \lim_{k \to 0} (-a_0) = \lim_{k \to 0} \frac{-1}{k \cot \delta_0}; \tag{2}$$

then, for sufficiently small k, (1) becomes

$$\sigma = \frac{4\pi}{k^2 + (1/\mathrm{a}^2)} \quad (k \text{ small}). \tag{3}$$

The scattering length has a simple geometrical meaning. Let us consider the $l = 0$ part of the asymptotic wave function $r\psi$, which varies with r as $\sin(kr + \delta_0)$, and extend it to small and negative values of r, introducing a function v (Fig. 3.13-1) defined everywhere by

$$v = \text{constant} \times \sin(kr + \delta_0). \tag{4}$$

If the range of the forces is short, the wave function $r\psi$ for $r < r_0$ depends only on the interaction potential; for $kr \ll 1$ the function v is the straight line

$$v = \text{constant} \times (kr \cos \delta_0 + \sin \delta_0)$$

and intercepts the r axis at

(5) $$r = -\frac{1}{k \cot \delta_0} = \mathrm{a}$$

(Fig. 3.13-1). Thus a is the position of the first zero of v for k small.

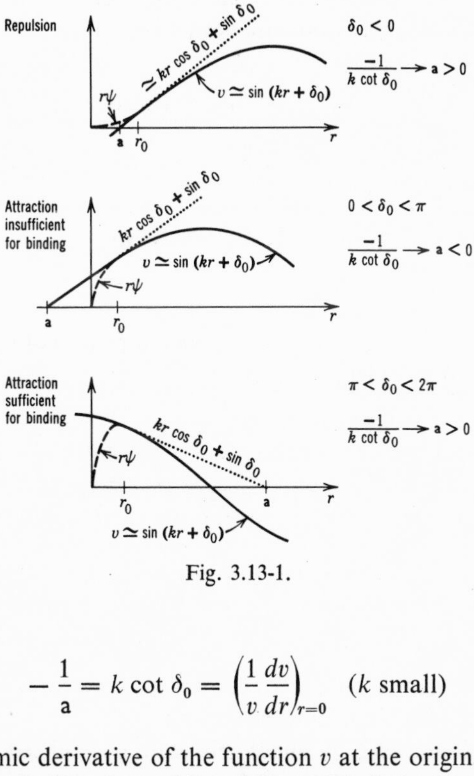

Fig. 3.13-1.

Moreover

(6) $$-\frac{1}{\mathrm{a}} = k \cot \delta_0 = \left(\frac{1}{v}\frac{dv}{dr}\right)_{r=0} \qquad (k \text{ small})$$

is the logarithmic derivative of the function v at the origin.

b. S-Wave Scattering of Particles with Spin $\frac{1}{2}$. If the colliding particles have spins s_1 and s_2, the incident scalar plane wave and the scattered scalar spherical wave in 3.12(4) are not a sufficient description of the scattering process: the spin states before and after scattering must be specified.

There are, in general, $(2s_1 + 1)(2s_2 + 1)$ such states. However, the spin states of the scattered beam are limited by conservation of angular momentum to those having the same eigenvalues of J and M_J (for S scattering $\mathbf{J} = \mathbf{s}_1 + \mathbf{s}_2$) as the incident state.

The simplest case is the scattering of a particle of spin $\frac{1}{2}$ by one of spin 0. Conservation of angular momentum requires that, for S scattering, the spin of the scattered particle remain unchanged. Thus the two terms of 3.12(4) are multiplied by the same spin function and nothing of interest happens.

Next, let us consider the case of two particles, 1 and 2, with spin $\frac{1}{2}$. There are now four independent spin states, and the scattering amplitude may depend on the state of the incident and scattered wave.

If we want to stress the total angular momentum, it will be appropriate to choose the set of states [compare with 1.14(35)]

$$\tag{7} \begin{aligned} \zeta_s &= \frac{1}{\sqrt{2}}(\alpha_1\beta_2 - \beta_1\alpha_2), \\ \zeta_t^+ &= \alpha_1\alpha_2, \\ \zeta_t^0 &= \frac{1}{\sqrt{2}}(\alpha_1\beta_2 + \beta_1\alpha_2), \\ \zeta_t^- &= \beta_1\beta_2, \end{aligned}$$

whereas, if we want to keep track of the spin direction of the two particles we can take the four independent states

$$\tag{8} \begin{aligned} \zeta^{++} &= \alpha_1\alpha_2 = \zeta_t^+, \\ \zeta^{+-} &= \alpha_1\beta_2 = \frac{1}{\sqrt{2}}(\zeta_t^0 + \zeta_s), \\ \zeta^{-+} &= \beta_1\alpha_2 = \frac{1}{\sqrt{2}}(\zeta_t^0 - \zeta_s), \\ \zeta^{--} &= \beta_1\beta_2 = \zeta_t^-. \end{aligned}$$

It is often convenient to take the direction of propagation of the incident wave as the axis of quantization of the spin.

If ζ_i is the initial and ζ_f the final spin state normalized to unity, the S part of the asymptotic solution of the wave equation can be written [from 3.12(1), (4), (5)]

$$\tag{9} \psi_0 \cong \zeta_i \frac{\sin kr}{kr} + \zeta_f a_{0,fi} \frac{e^{ikr}}{r}.$$

It is convenient to introduce an operator A_0, such that

$$\tag{10} A_0\zeta_i = a_{0,fi}\zeta_f,$$

and write

$$\psi_0 \cong \left(\frac{\sin kr}{kr} + A_0 \frac{e^{ikr}}{r}\right)\zeta_i. \tag{11}$$

The matrix elements of the operator A_0 are the amplitudes for scattering from initial spin state ζ_i to final spin state ζ_f:

$$a_{0,fi} = \langle f| \, A_0 \, |i\rangle. \tag{12}$$

Their squares are proportional to the cross sections for the corresponding spin transitions.

For two particles of spin ½ the S scattering amplitude is a 4 × 4 matrix which contains 16 elements. This matrix is considerably simplified if we apply conservation of angular momentum and parity. For this purpose it is convenient to refer the matrix A_0 to the states (7). In this representation the matrix is necessarily diagonal (since states of different J and M_J do not mix). It contains at most four elements: $a_{0,s}$, $a_{0,t}^{+}$, $a_{0,t}^{0}$, $a_{0,t}^{-}$. But the last three of these quantities must be equal to one another because the process of S scattering does not involve any privileged axis.

The S-scattering-amplitude matrix has only two independent elements $a_{0,s}$ and $a_{0,t}$. It is

$$\begin{array}{c|cccc} & \zeta_s & \zeta_t^- & \zeta_t^0 & \zeta_t^+ \\ \zeta_s & a_{0,s} & 0 & 0 & 0 \\ \zeta_t^- & 0 & a_{0,t} & 0 & 0 \\ \zeta_t^0 & 0 & 0 & a_{0,t} & 0 \\ \zeta_t^+ & 0 & 0 & 0 & a_{0,t} \end{array} \tag{13}$$

A practical way of writing (13) is by means of the triplet and singlet projection operators 1.14(37) whose eigenvalues are, respectively, 0 in the singlet, 1 in the triplet, and vice versa. Then the matrix (13) becomes

$$A_0 = \Lambda_s a_{0,s} + \Lambda_t a_{0,t}. \tag{14}$$

Referred to the states (8), the matrix A_0 is not diagonal. Its elements can easily be computed; for instance,

$$\begin{aligned} \langle \alpha_1\beta_2| \, A_0 \, |\alpha_1\beta_2\rangle &= \left\langle \frac{1}{\sqrt{2}}(\zeta_s + \zeta_t^0) \right| A_0 \left| \frac{1}{\sqrt{2}}(\zeta_s + \zeta_t^0) \right\rangle \\ &= \tfrac{1}{2}(a_{0,s} + a_{0,t}), \\ \langle \alpha_1\beta_2| \, A_0 \, |\beta_1\alpha_2\rangle &= \left\langle \frac{1}{\sqrt{2}}(\zeta_s + \zeta_t^0) \right| A_0 \left| \frac{1}{\sqrt{2}}(\zeta_t^0 - \zeta_s) \right\rangle \\ &= \tfrac{1}{2}(a_{0,t} - a_{0,s}). \end{aligned} \tag{15}$$

The complete matrix is

$$
(16)\qquad
\begin{array}{c|cccc}
 & \alpha_1\alpha_2 & \alpha_1\beta_2 & \beta_1\alpha_2 & \beta_1\beta_2 \\
\alpha_1\alpha_2 & a_{0,t} & 0 & 0 & 0 \\
\alpha_1\beta_2 & 0 & \frac{1}{2}(a_{0,t}+a_{0,s}) & \frac{1}{2}(a_{0,t}-a_{0,s}) & 0 \\
\beta_1\alpha_2 & 0 & \frac{1}{2}(a_{0,t}-a_{0,s}) & \frac{1}{2}(a_{0,t}+a_{0,s}) & 0 \\
\beta_1\beta_2 & 0 & 0 & 0 & a_{0,t}
\end{array}
$$

We note that the scattering includes the process of *spin flip* because of the nondiagonal elements of (16). These elements produce a scattered wave in a $\beta_1\alpha_2$ state from an incident spin state $\alpha_1\beta_2$, and vice versa, with an amplitude proportional to the difference $a_{0,t} - a_{0,s}$. Thus spin flip is a consequence of the spin dependence of the forces.

c. Scattering of Unpolarized Beams. The cross section for unpolarized spin $\frac{1}{2}$ particles is obtained by averaging (1) over the initial spin states[1]

$$(17)\qquad \sigma = 4\pi(\tfrac{3}{4}\,|a_{0,t}|^2 + \tfrac{1}{4}\,|a_{0,s}|^2)$$

since the triplet and singlet states do not mix.

By making use of (16), we can compute separately the cross sections for the various initial and final spin states of the two particles:

$$
(18)\qquad
\begin{aligned}
\sigma(\alpha_1\alpha_2 \to \alpha_1\alpha_2) &= \sigma(\beta_1\beta_2 \to \beta_1\beta_2) = 4\pi\,|a_{0,t}|^2 && \text{(no flip)},\\
\sigma(\alpha_1\beta_2 \to \alpha_1\beta_2) &= \sigma(\beta_1\alpha_2 \to \beta_1\alpha_2) = 4\pi\tfrac{1}{4}\,|a_{0,t} + a_{0,s}|^2 && \text{(no flip)},\\
\sigma(\alpha_1\beta_2 \to \beta_1\alpha_2) &= \sigma(\beta_1\alpha_2 \to \alpha_1\beta_2) = 4\pi\tfrac{1}{4}\,|a_{0,t} - a_{0,s}|^2 && \text{(flip)}.
\end{aligned}
$$

If beam and target are not polarized, the parts of the cross section corresponding to no flip and to flip are obtained by averaging over the initial states and summing over the pertinent final states:

$$(19)\qquad \sigma_{\text{no flip}} = 4\pi\tfrac{1}{2}[|a_{0,t}|^2 + \tfrac{1}{4}\,|a_{0,t} + a_{0,s}|^2]$$

and, similarly,

$$(20)\qquad \sigma_{\text{flip}} = 4\pi\tfrac{1}{2}\,\tfrac{1}{4}\,|a_{0,t} - a_{0,s}|^2.$$

3.14 *Zero-Range Discussion of n-p Scattering*

a. The Zero-Range Approximation at Zero Kinetic Energy. If the range of nuclear forces is small, the potential well is deep, and the neutron-proton wave function within the well varies only slightly with energy: it can be assumed to be the same for $E = -B = -2.22$ MeV and for $0 \le E \le \sim$MeV.

[1] Formula (17) holds if the scattering is incoherent: for instance, if the target atoms are randomly arranged. See 3.13a for discussion of coherence.

In this approximation the triplet scattering length a_t can be obtained assuming that the function $u = r\psi$, for $r \leq r_0 \ll R \ll 1/k$, is just the deuteron wave function. In the zero-range approximation the deuteron u function is $Ke^{-r/R}$ (K is a normalization constant), and thus the logarithmic derivative is

(1) $$\left(\frac{1}{u_D}\frac{du_D}{dr}\right) = -\frac{1}{R} \qquad \text{(for deuteron).}$$

By comparing this with 3.13(6) in order to match logarithmic derivatives

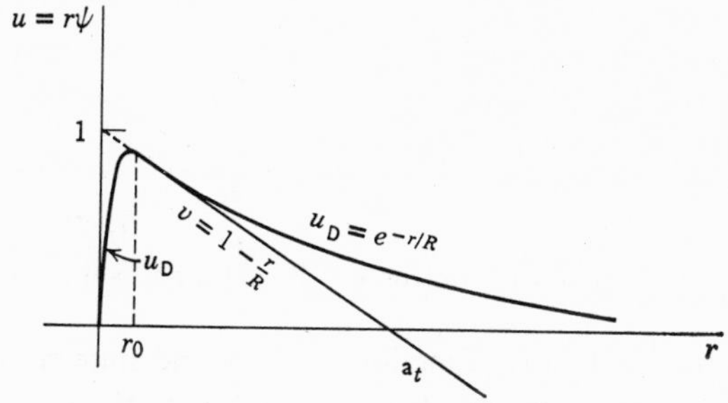

Fig. 3.14-1. For $r < r_0 \ll R$, $u = u_D$ (deuteron solution). For $r > r_0$ the zero energy scattering solution u, a sine wave of infinite wavelength, is extrapolated linearly. The normalization constant has been put equal to unity in this figure.

we can write

(2) $$a_t = R.$$

These considerations are illustrated in Fig. 3.14-1.

From this we expect, by introducing (2) in 3.13(3),

(3) $$\sigma_t = 4\pi R^2 = 2.33 \times 10^{-24}\ \text{cm}^2 \quad \text{for } k = 0.$$

This value must be compared with the experimental value of the scattering cross section for slow neutrons on free protons, which is $\approx 20 \times 10^{-24}$ cm^2.

The discrepancy must be attributed to a large contribution from the singlet state. For an unpolarized beam

(4) $$\sigma = \tfrac{3}{4}\sigma_t + \tfrac{1}{4}\sigma_s \approx 20 \times 10^{-24}\ \text{cm}^2$$

and thus

(5) $$\sigma_s = 4\pi a_s^2 \approx 73 \times 10^{-24}\ \text{cm}^2$$

and

(6) $$a_s \approx \pm 23 \times 10^{-13}\ \text{cm}.$$

We shall find a more accurate value of a_s with a more complete analysis, but (6) will be essentially confirmed.

In the same manner that a_t is related to the deuteron's internal wave function, so a_s is related to the internal wave function of the singlet state of the n-p system. The ambiguity of sign appearing in (6) (Fig. 3.14-2) means that the singlet state u function can have either positive or negative slope at the edge of the well. For $a_s > 0$ the slope would be negative, as for the triplet deuteron: a decreasing exponential could be smoothly

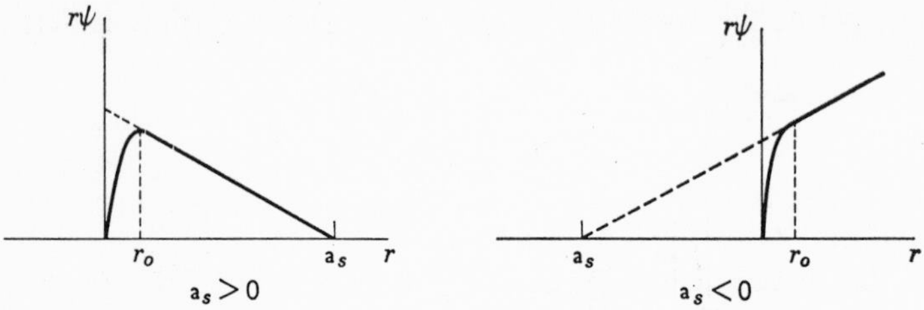

Fig. 3.14-2. The function $r\psi_s$ for $k = 0$, and for $a_s > 0$ and $a_s < 0$.

reattached to the inside wave function and a bound state could exist. For $a_s < 0$, instead, there is no possibility of binding in the singlet state.

The sign of a_s has been experimentally measured and has been found to be negative (see 3.16). The possibility of a bound state of the singlet deuteron is thus ruled out.

This elementary discussion contains all of the essential physical results from low energy n-p scattering.

b. The Zero-Range Approximation at Finite Energy. When the wavelength of the relative motion becomes comparable to the scattering lengths ($E \approx 10$ keV), the zero-energy approximation fails. If we maintain the assumption of zero range, however, the value of $k \cot \delta_0$ is energy-independent, and we can write for the triplet state

$$\sigma_t = \frac{4\pi}{k^2 + (1/R^2)} . \tag{7}$$

Similarly, we can define an appropriate scattering length for the singlet state

$$\lim_{k \to 0} (k \cot \delta_{0,s}) = -\frac{1}{a_s} , \tag{8}$$

and the total unpolarized cross section becomes

$$\sigma = \frac{3}{4} \frac{4\pi}{k^2 + (1/R^2)} + \frac{1}{4} \frac{4\pi}{k^2 + (1/a_s^2)} . \tag{9}$$

The energy dependence of the measured cross section is described fairly accurately by (9), and the value of $|a_s|$ can be determined to obtain a best fit. But the agreement between theory and experiment can be somewhat improved if we consider the finite range of nuclear forces.

3.15 *Shape-Independent Effective Range Theory*

a. Cross Section for a Square Well of Finite Width. The procedure in the preceding section can easily be extended to a square well of width r_0. The result (B-36) is, to the first order in r_0, for the triplet state

$$\sigma_t = \frac{4\pi}{[k^2 + (1/R^2)][1 - (r_0/R)]}.$$

But the square well is surely a naïve approximation, and we wonder whether we could do better: for some time it was hoped that the low-energy scattering experiments would provide information on the shape of the nuclear potential well.

It has become clear from further studies that the experimental data can be fitted with good accuracy with only two parameters for each spin state: a scattering length a, defined in 3.13(2), and an effective radius r_e, to be defined in what follows.

b. A Useful Identity of Shape-Independent Theory. The zero-range theory assumed that the wave function inside the well was independent of energy. We now consider that it may vary, but only slowly, with energy. We shall make no assumption on the well shape, apart from specifying that $V = 0$ for $r > r_0$: we shall try to describe the effect of the variation of the internal wave function with energy, without making use of a specific wave function at any energy (B-49).

In Fig. 3.15-1 we represent a typical u function, u_n, at energy E_n, wave number $k_n^2 = (M/\hbar^2)E_n$, and for an arbitrary spin state.[1]

For $r < r_0$, u_n is not specified because we do not know the details of the potential; for $r > r_0$, u_n = constant $\times$ $\sin(k_n r + \delta_n)$. We also define a function v_n such that

$$(1a) \qquad v_n = \frac{\sin(k_n r + \delta_n)}{\sin \delta_n} \quad \text{everywhere,}$$

which at the origin satisfies

$$(1b) \qquad \begin{aligned} v_n(0) &= 1 \\ v_n'(0) &= \left(\frac{dv_n}{dr}\right)_{r=0} = k_n \cot \delta_n. \end{aligned}$$

[1] The subscript 0 has been dropped from the phase-shift angle, since only S states are involved and there is no possible ambiguity. The subscript n refers to the energy.

and we fix the normalization of u_n so that $u_n = v_n$ for $r > r_0$:

$$u_n = u_n(r) \quad \text{(unspecified)} \quad \text{for } r < r_0,$$

(2)
$$u_n = \frac{\sin(k_n r + \delta_n)}{\sin \delta_n} \quad \text{for } r > r_0.$$

Let us now write the wave equation for two different energies, E_n and

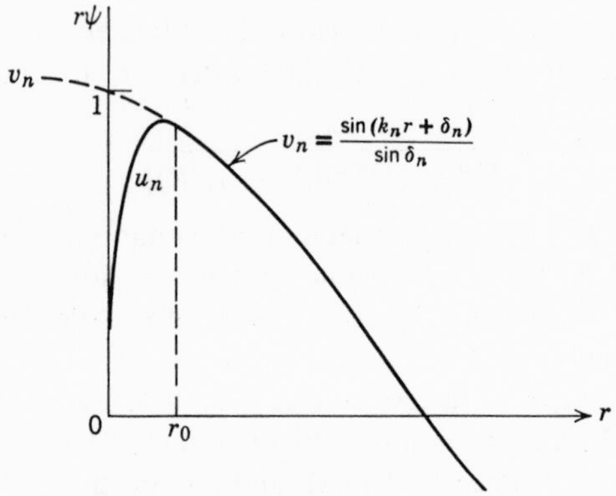

Fig. 3.15-1. Definition of the function u_n and v_n.

E_m, for the same (unspecified) potential $V(r)$:

(3a)
$$\frac{d^2u_n}{dr^2} - \frac{M}{\hbar^2} V(r)u_n = -k_n^2 u_n,$$

(3b)
$$\frac{d^2u_m}{dr^2} - \frac{M}{\hbar^2} V(r)u_m = -k_m^2 u_m.$$

Let us multiply (3a) by u_m, (3b) by u_n, and subtract to obtain

(4)
$$u_m \frac{d^2u_n}{dr^2} - u_n \frac{d^2u_m}{dr^2} = -(k_n^2 - k_m^2)u_n u_m,$$

which is equivalent to

(5)
$$\frac{d}{dr}(u_n u_m' - u_m u_n') = (k_n^2 - k_m^2)u_n u_m.$$

By using the same procedure for the functions v_n and v_m, which satisfy the wave equation with $V(r) = 0$, we can write

(6)
$$\frac{d}{dr}(v_n v_m' - v_m v_n') = (k_n^2 - k_m^2)v_n v_m.$$

Now subtract (6) from (5) and integrate over r from 0 to ∞, remembering that $u = v$ for $r \to \infty$:

$$(7) \qquad -(u_n u_m' - u_m u_n')_{r=0} + (v_n v_m' - v_m v_n')_{r=0} = (k_n^2 - k_m^2)\int_0^\infty (u_n u_m - v_n v_m)\, dr.$$

By using (1*b*) and remembering that $u(0) = 0$, we get

$$(8) \qquad k_n \cot \delta_n - k_m \cot \delta_m = (k_n^2 - k_m^2)\int_0^\infty (v_n v_m - u_n u_m)\, dr.$$

This equation is the identity that we wanted to prove. It is an exact equation, but it is expressed in a rather unconventional form, since $\int u_n u_m\, dr$, considered as a function of the momenta k_n and k_m, is zero for $n \neq m$ and has a discontinuity at $m = n$. However, the integral $\int v_n v_m\, dr$, which can be performed with the help of a convergence factor (A-58), also has a discontinuity at $m = n$. As a result of the cancellation of these discontinuities, the right-hand side of (8) is a well-behaved, slow-varying function of energy.

c. The Effective Range. We now replace the integral in (8) with the energy-independent positive quantity of the dimension of length

$$(9) \qquad \tfrac{1}{2} r_e = \int (v_0^2 - u_0^2)\, dr,$$

where r_e is called the *effective range* and v_0 and u_0 are the functions u and v for $E = 0$. This can be done without introducing large errors, since the integral in (8) is a slowly varying, continuous function of E_n and E_m. Indeed, the integrand in (9) vanishes for $r > r_0$, as does the integral in (8); for $r < r_0$ the variation of u with energy is slow because of the great depth of the well, whereas v, being necessarily unity at the origin, cannot vary rapidly near it.

With the definition of effective range (9), (8) becomes

$$(10) \qquad k_n \cot \delta_n - k_m \cot \delta_m = (k_n^2 - k_m^2)\tfrac{1}{2} r_e.$$

In particular, if we choose $E_m = 0$, we have $k_m = 0$, $k_m \cot \delta_m = v_m'(0) = -1/\mathrm{a}$, and we can write (leaving out the subscript n)

$$(11) \qquad k \cot \delta + \frac{1}{\mathrm{a}} = \frac{1}{2} r_e k^2.$$

If we choose instead, $E_m = -B < 0$, where B is the binding energy of some bound state, the corresponding k_m is $1/iR$, where R is the "radius" of the bound state and $k_m \cot \delta_m = -1/R$. Thus (8) becomes

$$(12) \qquad k \cot \delta + \frac{1}{R} = \left(k^2 + \frac{1}{R^2}\right)\frac{1}{2} r_e.$$

For $E_n = 0$, $E_m = -B$, (8) yields

$$-\frac{1}{\mathrm{a}} + \frac{1}{R} = \frac{r_e}{2R^2}. \tag{13}$$

Formulas (11) and (12) can be used in 3.13(1) in order to express the energy dependence of $k \cot \delta$ in terms of the effective range. Using (11) for the singlet and (12) for the triplet, the unpolarized n-p cross section becomes

$$\sigma = \frac{3}{4}\frac{4\pi}{k^2 + \{(1/R) - \frac{1}{2}r_{e,t}[k^2 + (1/R^2)]\}^2} + \frac{1}{4}\frac{4\pi}{k^2 + [(1/\mathrm{a}_s) - \frac{1}{2}r_{e,s}k^2]^2} \tag{14}$$

Equation (14) expresses the energy dependence of the cross section in terms of three parameters to be determined from comparison with the experiment. These are the singlet scattering length a_s and the singlet and triplet effective ranges $r_{e,s}$ and $r_{e,t}$.

Before analyzing the experimental data to obtain these parameters, we must describe the measurements of the coherent scattering length from which pertinent and more precise information is derived.

3.16 Coherent Scattering from Hydrogen Molecules and the Sign of a_s

a. Qualitative Discussion of Scattering from Ortho- and Parahydrogen. If two protons are at a distance smaller than the neutron's wavelength, they will scatter coherently: the scattered neutron waves interfere, and the relative phase can be measured. Thus the total scattering cross section of a hydrogen molecule for sufficiently cold neutrons depends on the relative sign of a_s and a_t, and its measurement allows us to find the sign of a_s.

The distance between the two protons of a hydrogen molecule is 0.74 Å. We suppose that the neutrons are of such low energy that their wavelength is much larger than this distance, and we neglect the thermal motion of the molecule, which is initially at rest. We consider only molecules in their lowest rotational states. In these conditions the parahydrogen molecules (antiparallel proton spins) have rotational quantum number $I = 0$; they can be regarded as rigid during the scattering, for the very slow neutrons have insufficient energy to excite vibrational or rotational states. Scattering with spin flip cannot occur because the transition of parahydrogen into orthohydrogen requires energy, since the lowest state of orthohydrogen has $I = 1$. Spin flips may occur in the scattering from orthohydrogen: the neutron may then be inelastically scattered with a gain in energy. We shall not compute this effect whose cross section is, of course, proportional to $(\mathrm{a}_t - \mathrm{a}_s)^2$.

b. Reduced Mass Correction in the Scattering from Bound Protons. The scattering cross section in the Born approximation is proportional to the square of the reduced mass μ of the incident and target particles.

This approximation was originally used by Fermi to compute the cross section of bound protons. Its validity is not obvious, since the nuclear potential well is very deep, but Bethe arrived at the conclusion that its

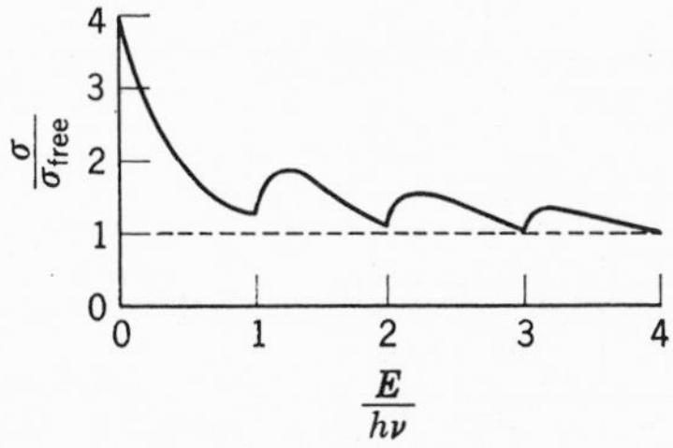

Fig. 3.16-1. Cross section for the scattering of neutrons by elastically bound protons; $h\nu = 0.4$ eV for the CH bond of paraffin (reprinted from H. A. Bethe and P. M. Morrison, *Elementary Nuclear Theory*, Wiley, 1956).

use is justified because the potential has a very short range and can be replaced by a much shallower long-range potential, which gives the same scattering length. We shall not enter into this discussion and we will be satisfied with the fact that the predictions of the Born approximation, as used by Fermi, agree with the experiment.

If the target proton is rigidly bound to a molecule of mass M_{mol}, we can write

$$(1)\qquad \frac{a_{\text{bound proton}}}{a_{\text{free proton}}} = \frac{\mu_{\text{bound}}}{\mu_{\text{free}}} = \frac{(1/M) + (1/M)}{(1/M) + (1/M_{\text{mol}})} = \frac{2}{1 + (M/M_{\text{mol}})}.$$

The ratio is 2 for $M_{\text{mol}} = \infty$ (protons in large molecules or in solids), $\frac{4}{3}$ for $M_{\text{mol}} = 2M$ (protons in H_2 molecules).

A proton can be considered rigidly bound when the energy of the neutron is not sufficient to produce transitions between the quantum states of the proton in the molecule or in the lattice, a condition that we supposed fulfilled. But, if the neutrons have energies comparable to those of the chemical bond, ≈ 1 eV, interesting solid-state and chemical effects can be observed in the energy dependence of the cross section (see Fig. 3.16-1).

c. The Cross Section for Ortho- and Parahydrogen. Using 3.13(14) and (1), the effective scattering amplitude for the two protons in a hydrogen molecule is, at small energy, a matrix

$$(2)\qquad A_{\text{mol}} = \tfrac{4}{3}(\Lambda_{s1}a_s + \Lambda_{t1}a_t + \Lambda_{s2}a_s + \Lambda_{t2}a_t),$$

where 1 and 2 refer to the two protons whose relative spin directions are still unspecified. By introducing 1.14(37), we have

$$(3) \qquad \begin{aligned} A_{\text{mol}} &= \tfrac{1}{3}[(1 - \boldsymbol{\sigma}_{\text{n}} \cdot \boldsymbol{\sigma}_1)\text{a}_s + (3 + \boldsymbol{\sigma}_{\text{n}} \cdot \boldsymbol{\sigma}_1)\text{a}_t \\ &\quad + (1 - \boldsymbol{\sigma}_{\text{n}} \cdot \boldsymbol{\sigma}_2)\text{a}_s + (3 + \boldsymbol{\sigma}_{\text{n}} \cdot \boldsymbol{\sigma}_2)\text{a}_t] \\ &= \tfrac{1}{3}[(2 - 2\boldsymbol{\sigma}_{\text{n}} \cdot \mathbf{S})\text{a}_s + (6 + 2\boldsymbol{\sigma}_{\text{n}} \cdot \mathbf{S})\text{a}_t] \\ &= \tfrac{2}{3}[(\text{a}_s + 3\text{a}_t) + (\text{a}_t - \text{a}_s)\boldsymbol{\sigma}_{\text{n}} \cdot \mathbf{S}], \end{aligned}$$

where $\boldsymbol{\sigma}_{\text{n}}/2$ is the spin of the neutron and $\mathbf{S} = \boldsymbol{\sigma}_1/2 + \boldsymbol{\sigma}_2/2$ is the total spin of the hydrogen molecule.

For parahydrogen, $S = 0$, we have immediately

$$(4) \qquad \sigma_{\text{para}} = 4\pi\langle A_{\text{mol}}^2\rangle = 4\pi\tfrac{16}{9}4(\tfrac{1}{4}\text{a}_s + \tfrac{3}{4}\text{a}_t)^2.$$

In this formula the factor $\frac{16}{9}$ results from the binding of the target protons, the factor 4 arises from the presence of two protons, and the factor in parentheses is the *coherent average of the scattering lengths* of the proton.

For orthohydrogen, $S = 1$, the collision may take place in states of total angular momentum $\frac{1}{2}$ and $\frac{3}{2}$, which occur with relative probabilities 2 and 4. Since the scattering from different molecules in a gas or liquid is incoherent, it is the cross section (and not the amplitude) that must be averaged over the two kinds of collisions. We easily obtain[1] $\boldsymbol{\sigma}_{\text{n}} \cdot \mathbf{S} = -2$ and $+1$ for $J = \frac{1}{2}$ and $\frac{3}{2}$, respectively; thus the average of $\boldsymbol{\sigma}_{\text{n}} \cdot \mathbf{S}$ is 0 and the average of $|\boldsymbol{\sigma}_{\text{n}} \cdot \mathbf{S}|^2$ is 2 for unpolarized beams.

Taking this into account, we have

$$(5) \qquad \sigma_{\text{ortho}} = 4\pi\langle A_{\text{mol}}^2\rangle = 4\pi\tfrac{4}{9}[(\text{a}_s + 3\text{a}_t)^2 + 2(\text{a}_t - \text{a}_s)^2].$$

Again note that equations (4) and (5) apply to elastic scattering and do not include the possibility of spin flip within the molecule (ortho $\rightleftharpoons$ para transitions).

d. Comparison with Experiment. After the pioneering work of Alvarez and Pitzer (A-40) and some early experiments by Sutton et al. (S-47), the most accurate measurements were performed by Squires and Stewart (S-55). In these experiments the scattering hydrogen was kept at 20°K, the boiling point of liquid hydrogen; the neutrons were produced by a cyclotron, slowed down in paraffin cooled by liquid oxygen, and selected for low velocities (λ up to $\approx$4 Å).

The most striking experimental result is that the cross section of parahydrogen is much smaller than that of free hydrogen. The value

$$\sigma_{\text{para}} \approx 4 \times 10^{-24}\ \text{cm}^2,$$

[1] $$\boldsymbol{\sigma} \cdot \mathbf{S} = 2\frac{\boldsymbol{\sigma}}{2} \cdot \mathbf{S} = -\mathbf{S}^2 - \left(\frac{\sigma}{2}\right)^2 + \left|\mathbf{S} + \frac{\boldsymbol{\sigma}}{2}\right|^2 = -2 - \tfrac{3}{4} + \tfrac{3}{4} = -2 \quad \text{for } J = \tfrac{1}{2},$$
$$= -2 - \tfrac{3}{4} + \tfrac{15}{4} = +1 \quad \text{for } J = \tfrac{3}{2}.$$

about five times smaller than σ_{free}, has been quoted from the measurements of Sutton et al. In order to explain this result, it is clear that the interference between singlet and triplet must be destructive and the signs of a_s and a_t must be opposite.

From the observed ortho-para result and from the best value of the free neutron cross section[1], Squires and Stewart obtain

$$a_t = (+5.37 \pm 0.04) \times 10^{-13}\,\text{cm}, \qquad (6)$$
$$a_s = (-23.73 \pm 0.07) \times 10^{-13}\,\text{cm}.$$

From the negative sign of a_s we conclude that the singlet state of the deuteron is unbound.

Comparing the value of a_t with the value of R by means of effective range theory [3.15(13)], we have

$$r_{e,t} = 1.65 \times 10^{-13}\,\text{cm}. \qquad (7)$$

For more accurate values see 3.19(13) to (17).

3.17 *S Scattering for Spins I and ½: the Spin of the Neutron*

a. *S* Scattering Matrix for Spins *I* and ½. We have assumed until now that the neutron has spin ½, but we have not yet given any experimental evidence for this assumption. We are now in a position to prove that the observed large ratio $\sigma_{\text{ortho}}/\sigma_{\text{para}}$ could not be explained if the spin of the neutron were larger than ½ (S-37).

For this purpose we must discuss the scattering of neutrons of arbitrary spin I on protons of spin ½.

We start by introducing a scattering length matrix that has $2(2I + 1)$ lines and columns. It is diagonal when referred to eigenstates of J^2 and M_J, where $\mathbf{J}$ is the sum of the spins of the two particles. All the elements for a given value of J are identical because of the absence of a privileged direction, and thus we have only two nonvanishing independent elements,

$$a_+ \quad \text{for } J = I + \tfrac{1}{2}, \qquad (1)$$
$$a_- \quad \text{for } J = I - \tfrac{1}{2}.$$

There will be $2(I + \frac{1}{2}) + 1 = 2I + 2$ states with scattering amplitude a_+ and $2(I - \frac{1}{2}) + 1 = 2I$ states with scattering amplitude a_-.

We can express the scattering matrix in terms of projection operators Λ_+ and Λ_-, for the $I + \frac{1}{2}$ and $I - \frac{1}{2}$ states. By analogy with 1.14(37) we look for these operators in the form $A + B\mathbf{I} \cdot \boldsymbol{\sigma}$, where A and B are

[1] $4\pi(\frac{3}{4}a_t^2 + \frac{1}{4}a_s^2) = (20.36 \pm 0.10) \times 10^{-24}\,\text{cm}^2$ (M-49).

constants. By computing first

$$\langle \mathbf{I}\cdot\boldsymbol{\sigma}\rangle_J = 2\left\langle \mathbf{I}\cdot\frac{\boldsymbol{\sigma}}{2}\right\rangle_J = J(J+1) - I(I+1) - \tfrac{3}{4} \tag{2}$$

$$= \begin{cases} I & \text{for } J = I + \tfrac{1}{2}, \\ -(I+1) & \text{for } J = I - \tfrac{1}{2}, \end{cases}$$

we obtain

$$\begin{aligned} \Lambda_+ &= \frac{1}{2I+1}[(I+1) + \boldsymbol{\sigma}\cdot\mathbf{I}], \\ \Lambda_- &= \frac{1}{2I+1}(I - \boldsymbol{\sigma}\cdot\mathbf{I}), \end{aligned} \tag{3}$$

and

$$A = \Lambda_+ \mathrm{a}_+ + \Lambda_- \mathrm{a}_-. \tag{4}$$

The unpolarized free particle n-p cross section is now

$$\sigma_{\text{free}} = \frac{I+1}{2I+1} 4\pi \mathrm{a}_+^{\,2} + \frac{I}{2I+1} 4\pi \mathrm{a}_-^{\,2}. \tag{5}$$

We know from experiment that $\sigma_{\text{free}} \approx 20 \times 10^{-24}\ \text{cm}^2$.

For $I = \frac{3}{2}$ the deuteron, whose spin is 1, would be in a $I - \frac{1}{2}$ state. Thus we can put $\mathrm{a}_- = R$ in (5) and solve for a_+. Numerically, we obtain

$$\mathrm{a}_- = 4.3 \times 10^{-13}\ \text{cm}, \qquad \mathrm{a}_+ = \pm 15.6 \times 10^{-13}\ \text{cm}. \tag{6}$$

b. Cross Sections of Neutrons of Arbitrary Spin in Ortho- and Parahydrogen. We are now in a position to proceed exactly as we did for neutron spin $\frac{1}{2}$. The effective scattering amplitude of two protons which scatter coherently in a molecule is

$$\begin{aligned} A_{\text{mol}} &= \tfrac{4}{3}(\Lambda_{+1}\mathrm{a}_+ + \Lambda_{-1}\mathrm{a}_- + \Lambda_{+2}\mathrm{a}_+ + \Lambda_{-2}\mathrm{a}_-) \\ &= \frac{4}{3}\frac{1}{2I+1}[2(I+1)\mathrm{a}_+ + 2I\mathrm{a}_- + (\boldsymbol{\sigma}_1+\boldsymbol{\sigma}_2)\cdot\mathbf{I}\mathrm{a}_+ - (\boldsymbol{\sigma}_1+\boldsymbol{\sigma}_2)\cdot\mathbf{I}\mathrm{a}_-] \\ &= \frac{4}{3}\frac{2}{2I+1}[(I+1)\mathrm{a}_+ + I\mathrm{a}_- + \mathbf{S}\cdot\mathbf{I}(\mathrm{a}_+ - \mathrm{a}_-)], \end{aligned} \tag{7}$$

where $\mathbf{S} = \frac{1}{2}(\boldsymbol{\sigma}_1 + \boldsymbol{\sigma}_2)$ is the spin of the molecule. When A_{mol} is squared to obtain the cross section, the term in $\mathbf{S}\cdot\mathbf{I}$ vanishes in the absence of polarization, and we have

$$\sigma = 4\pi\frac{16}{9}\frac{4}{(2I+1)^2}\{[(I+1)\mathrm{a}_+ + I\mathrm{a}_-]^2 + \langle(\mathbf{S}\cdot\mathbf{I})^2\rangle(\mathrm{a}_+ - \mathrm{a}_-)^2\}. \tag{8}$$

For parahydrogen ($S = 0$)

$$\langle(\mathbf{S}\cdot\mathbf{I})^2\rangle = 0 \qquad \text{(para)}. \tag{9}$$

For orthohydrogen ($S = 1$) the average is to be performed over the three orientations of $\mathbf{S}$ relative to $\mathbf{I}$. The three possible states of total angular momentum $I + 1$, I, and $I - 1$ have values of $\mathbf{S} \cdot \mathbf{I}$ equal to I, -1, and $-(I + 1)$, respectively, and occur with relative probabilities $2I + 3$, $2I + 1$, and $2I - 1$; thus we easily verify that $\langle \mathbf{S} \cdot \mathbf{I} \rangle = 0$, and we find

$$\langle (\mathbf{S} \cdot \mathbf{I})^2 \rangle = \tfrac{2}{3} I(I + 1) \qquad \text{(ortho)}. \tag{10}$$

In the assumption $I = \frac{3}{2}$ the theoretical ortho- and parahydrogen cross sections are obtained introducing (6) into (8). The result for parahydrogen is

$$\sigma_{\text{para}} = 116 \times 10^{-24}\ \text{cm}^2 \quad \text{for } \mathsf{a}_+ > 0,$$
$$\sigma_{\text{para}} = 60 \times 10^{-24}\ \text{cm}^2 \quad \text{for } \mathsf{a}_+ < 0.$$

The experimental value is more than an order of magnitude smaller than either of these, and we must conclude that the assignment of spin $\frac{3}{2}$ to the neutron is not tenable.

3.18 Coherent Scattering from Crystals

a. Coherent and Incoherent Scattering from Identical Centers. The same coherent scattering amplitude

$$\mathsf{a}_{\text{coh}} = \tfrac{1}{4}\mathsf{a}_s + \tfrac{3}{4}\mathsf{a}_t, \tag{1}$$

which enters in the cross section of parahydrogen [3.16(4)] can be measured more accurately from the coherent scattering of neutrons in crystals containing hydrogen. For this reason we shall pay some attention to the scattering of neutrons in crystals.

Let us first define what is meant by coherent scattering in the simple assumption of a crystal composed of atoms of only one species (no isotopic mixture) and with spin 0. We suppose also that the atoms are perfectly still and that the scattering nuclei are much smaller than the neutron's wavelength.

The asymptotic solution of the wave equation describing a parallel beam and an S wave scattered by a center at the origin is [from 3.12(4)] of the form

$$e^{ikz} - b\,\frac{\mathsf{a}}{r}\,e^{ikr}, \tag{2}$$

where $b = (A + 1)/A$ is the "binding factor" [3.16(1)] [1].

If there are N scattering centers ($N \gg 1$) at positions $\mathbf{r}_i (1 \leq i \leq N)$,

[1] In the present case $b = \mathsf{a}_{\text{bound}}/\mathsf{a}_{\text{free}} = \left(\frac{1}{M} + \frac{1}{M}\right) \Big/ \left(\frac{1}{MA} + \frac{1}{\infty}\right)$.

the total wave (neglecting multiple scattering) is

(3) $$e^{ikz} - \sum_{i=1}^{N} b \frac{\mathrm{a}}{d_i} e^{ik(z_i+d_i)},$$

where $d_i = |\mathbf{r} - \mathbf{r}_i|$ is the distance from the ith center to point $\mathbf{r}$ where the wave is observed (Fig. 3.18-1).

To find the intensity of the scattered wave at position r, we must square the summation appearing in (3). This gives rise to a double sum in i and j.

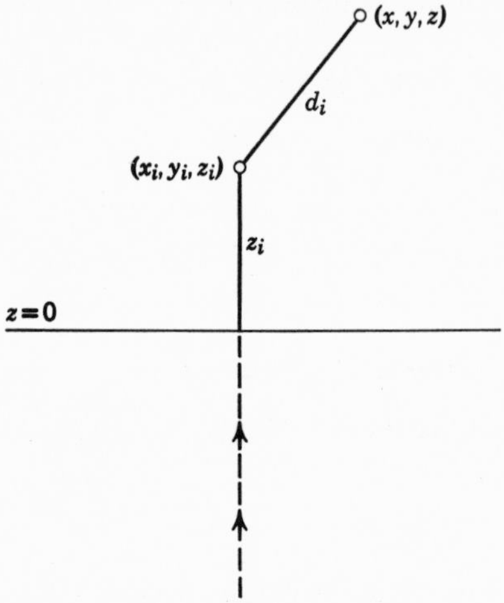

Fig. 3.18-1. Definitions of the quantities entering in (3).

It is convenient to discuss separately the terms with $i = j$ and those with $i \neq j$:

(4) $$|\psi_{sc}|^2 = b^2\mathrm{a}^2 \left| \sum_i \frac{\exp[ik(z_i + d_i)]}{d_i} \right|^2 = b^2\mathrm{a}^2 \sum_{ij} \frac{\exp[ik(z_i - z_j + d_i - d_j)]}{d_i\, d_j}$$

$$= b^2\mathrm{a}^2 \sum_i \frac{1}{d_i^2} + b^2\mathrm{a}^2 \sum_{i \neq j} \frac{\exp[ik(z_i - z_j + d_i - d_j)]}{d_i\, d_j}.$$

The first sum ($i = j$) is the *incoherent* scattering and the second ($i \neq j$), the *coherent* scattering intensity.

Incoherent scattering does not depend on direction. If the sample and the detector are small compared to their relative distance R, we can write $d_i \approx R$, and the incoherent intensity goes as

(5) $$|\psi_{\mathrm{inc}}|^2 \approx N b^2 \frac{\mathrm{a}^2}{R^2}.$$

Coherent scattering, instead, is strongly dependent on angle, and it is important only where $z_i - z_j + d_i - d_j = 2\pi n/k = n\lambda$ (n integer): thus in the forward direction ($n = 0$) and, if the centers are regularly spaced, at particular angles called the Bragg angles. In these directions the intensity goes as

$$|\psi_{\text{coh}}|^2 \approx N^2 b^2 \frac{\mathfrak{a}^2}{R^2}. \tag{6}$$

and is much larger than the incoherent intensity.

b. Coherent Scattering from Centers of Different Kinds. Let us suppose now that there are two different kinds of randomly distributed scattering centers, having scattering lengths $\mathfrak{a}_1$ and $\mathfrak{a}_2$. Let there be N_1 centers of the first kind and N_2 of the second, with relative concentration c_1 and c_2.

$$N_1 + N_2 = N, \qquad c_1 = \frac{N_1}{N}, \qquad c_2 = \frac{N_2}{N}. \tag{7}$$

The two kinds of centers may be two isotopes of the same element or—more important to us—may differ only in spin orientation.

In the new situation (4) must be replaced by

$$|\psi_{\text{sc}}|^2 = b^2 \left| \mathfrak{a}_1 \sum_{i=1}^{N_1} \frac{\exp[ik(z_i + d_i)]}{d_i} + \mathfrak{a}_2 \sum_{i=1}^{N_2} \frac{\exp[ik(z_i + d_i)]}{d_i} \right|^2 \tag{8}$$

and the coherent scattered intensity is[1] (in the proper directions):

$$|\psi_{\text{coh}}|^2 = b^2 \left| \mathfrak{a}_1 \frac{N_1}{R} + \mathfrak{a}_2 \frac{N_2}{R} \right|^2 = \frac{N^2}{R^2} b^2 (c_1\mathfrak{a}_1 + c_2\mathfrak{a}_2)^2. \tag{9}$$

It is the same as if the centers were all equal and had a common amplitude:

$$\mathfrak{a}_{\text{coh}} = c_1\mathfrak{a}_1 + c_2\mathfrak{a}_2. \tag{10}$$

If the centers differ only because of spin orientation, the two scattering lengths are $\mathfrak{a}_+$ and $\mathfrak{a}_-$, corresponding to $J = I + \frac{1}{2}$ and $J = I - \frac{1}{2}$; the concentrations expressing the chance of their occurrence are

$$c_+ = \frac{I + 1}{2I + 1}; \qquad c_- = \frac{I}{2I + 1}, \tag{11}$$

and thus

$$\mathfrak{a}_{\text{coh}} = \frac{I + 1}{2I + 1}\mathfrak{a}_+ + \frac{I}{2I + 1}\mathfrak{a}_-, \tag{12}$$

which, for $I = \frac{1}{2}$, reduces to (1).

[1] When the square of (8) is expanded, the squares of each of the sums contribute a coherent and an incoherent part, whereas the mixed terms between the two sums contribute only coherently. It is easily seen that the coherent terms can be grouped as in (9).

It is usual to define a cross section for coherent scattering:

$$\sigma_{\rm coh} = 4\pi b^2 a_{\rm coh}^2; \tag{13}$$

the coherent scattering intensity (9) is proportional to $\sigma_{\rm coh}$, but its dependence on the number of scattering centers is quadratic at the peak of the diffraction line. This is compensated by the fact that the lines become narrower when N increases.

c. Measurement of Coherent Scattering from Crystals Containing Hydrogen. The first experiment on coherent scattering of neutrons from hydrogen were performed (S-48; W-48) with a double crystal spectrometer. In this instrument the first crystal produces the monochromatic beam by Bragg reflection, and the second crystal is the substance under study.

The substance used was NaH. At the beginning of these experiments the crystal structure of NaH was not known because x ray diffraction cannot locate the position of the hydrogen atoms. Neutron diffraction established first that the structure of NaH was the same as that of NaCl. Then the coherent scattering cross section of hydrogen was measured, with the result[1] that

$$\sigma_{\rm coh} = 4\pi 4 a_{\rm coh}^2 = (2.0 \pm 0.3) \times 10^{-24}\ {\rm cm}^2. \tag{14}$$

This measurement, together with that of the free-proton cross section, led to

$$a_t = +5.22 \times 10^{-13}\ {\rm cm}, \tag{15}$$

$$a_s = -23.4 \times 10^{-13}\ {\rm cm},$$

and (from 3.15(13)) to

$$r_{e,t} = (1.6 \pm 0.2) \times 10^{-13}\ {\rm cm}. \tag{16}$$

3.19 *Index of Refraction of Neutron Waves*

a. The Optical Theorem. The optical theorem relates the index of refraction of a material with the scattering cross section of the individual atoms and nuclei of which it is composed.

Let us consider a plane wave e^{ikz} (Fig. 3.19-1) that traverses perpendicularly a thin slab of material of thickness t and index of refraction n. In traversing the slab the wave is shifted in phase, and it emerges as

$$\psi(z > t) = e^{i[k(z-t)+nkt]} \approx e^{ikz}[1 + ik(n-1)t]. \tag{1}$$

Let us now suppose that the material of the slab contains a density N of scattering centers, which scatter a *spherically symmetrical* wave with

[1] For hydrogen atoms bound to a solid lattice $b = 2$.

scattering length a. The wave at $z > t$ can then be expressed as[1]

(2) $$\psi(z > t) = e^{ikz} - \mathrm{a}Nt2\pi \int \rho\, d\rho\, \frac{e^{ikr}}{r}.$$

But $\rho\, d\rho = r\, dr$ and the integral can be performed easily with the help

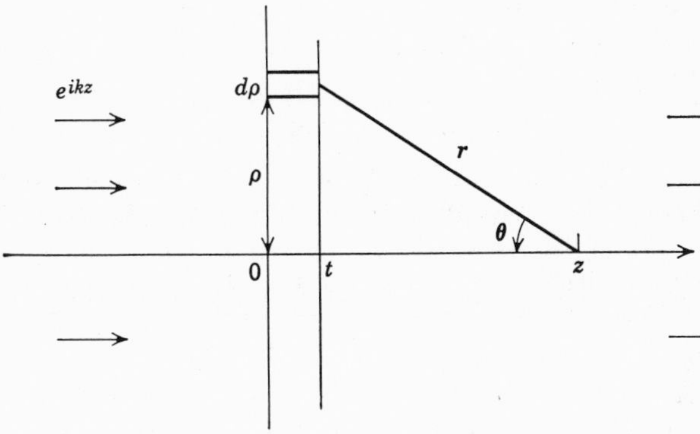

Fig. 3.19-1. Graphical definition of symbols used in the proof of the optical theorem.

of a convergence factor $\exp(-\omega r)$ $(\omega > 0)$.

(3) $$\int_z^\infty e^{ikr}\, dr = \lim_{\omega \to 0} \int_z^\infty e^{(ik-\omega)r}\, dr = -\frac{e^{ikz}}{ik},$$

so that

(4) $$\psi(z > t) = e^{ikz} + \mathrm{a}\frac{2\pi Nt}{ik} e^{ikz}.$$

By comparing (1) and (4) we obtain

(5) $$n - 1 = -\frac{2\pi N}{k^2}\mathrm{a}.$$

This equation can be extended to *nonspherically symmetrical* scattering, which corresponds to an amplitude $f(\theta)$. The derivation follows the same lines as the proof of (5). $f(\theta)$ is transformed into a function of r, $f(\theta) = f(\arcsin \rho/r) = \varphi(r)$, and the integral $\int \varphi(r)\, e^{ikr}\, dr$ is done by parts; one of the parts can be neglected under the assumption that $\varphi(r)$ does not vary appreciably over one wavelength and the result is

(6) $$n - 1 = \frac{2\pi N}{k^2} f(0),$$

where $f(0)$ is the forward scattering amplitude; this could have been

[1] The factor b is omitted in this derivation, and the scattering lengths must be considered as bound scattering lengths.

expected, considering that the index of refraction describes the propagation of the wave in the forward direction.

Formula (6) holds also if the index of refraction n contains an *imaginary part* that describes the attenuation of the beam. By separating the real and the imaginary part of (6) we can write

$$\text{Re}\,(n - 1) = \frac{2\pi N}{k^2}\,\text{Re}\,f(0),$$

(7)

$$\text{Im}\,n = \frac{2\pi N}{k^2}\,\text{Im}\,f(0).$$

The linear absorption coefficient corresponding to the imaginary part of n is obtained by squaring (1) and is $2k\,\text{Im}\,n$. The same absorption coefficient, computed from the particle viewpoint, is the inverse mean free path, $N\sigma_{\text{tot}}$. Thus it follows from the optical theorem that

(8) $$\sigma_{\text{tot}} = \frac{2k}{N}\,\text{Im}\,n = \frac{4\pi}{k}\,\text{Im}\,f(0).$$

Finally, we must observe that since the propagation of a wave in the forward direction is a coherent effect, $f(0)$ must be replaced by the corresponding *coherent amplitude* when more than one kind of scattering center is present: thus (6) becomes, in general,

(9*a*) $$n - 1 = \frac{2\pi N}{k^2} f_{\text{coh}}(0),$$

and for the scattering of slow neutrons

(9*b*) $$n - 1 = -\frac{2\pi N}{k^2}\,\mathfrak{a}_{\text{coh}}.$$

For $k\mathfrak{a}_{\text{coh}} \ll 1$ the imaginary part of the scattering amplitude is negligible [3.12(8)] and the index of refraction can be considered real.

b. Specular Reflection of Neutrons. Neutron indices of refraction are close to unity and difficult to measure. It has been found possible, however, to observe the reflection of neutrons from the interface of two materials and to measure the critical glancing angle for total reflection, θ_c. From these measurements we can obtain the coherent scattering amplitude:

$$\cos\theta_c = n = 1 - \frac{2\pi N}{k^2}\,\mathfrak{a}_{\text{coh}},$$

(10)

$$\theta_c \approx \frac{\sqrt{4\pi N \mathfrak{a}_{\text{coh}}}}{k}$$

The most accurate measurement of the coherent scattering length for neutrons in hydrogen has been obtained with this method by Hughes and collaborators (Hu-53), with the result

(11) $$b\mathrm{a}_{\mathrm{coh}} = 2\mathrm{a}_{\mathrm{coh}} = -(3.78 \pm 0.02) \times 10^{-13}\ \mathrm{cm}.$$

This value, together with the best determination of the free-proton scattering cross section, leads to an accurate value of a_s and a_t. From the value of a_t and the binding energy of the deuteron we obtain $r_{e,t}$, according to 3.15(13). The result is

(12) $$r_{e,t} = (1.7 \pm 0.03) \times 10^{-13}\ \mathrm{cm}.$$

The singlet effective range $r_{e,s}$ remains to be determined from the energy dependence of the free-proton scattering cross section [see 3.15(14), and Fig. 3.11-1].

Before closing the topic of low-energy n-p scattering, we report on the best values (HS-57) of the parameters entering into this process:

(13) $R = (4.3157 \pm 0.002) \times 10^{-13}$ cm, from $B = (2.226 \pm 0.002)$ MeV;

(14) $\mathrm{a}_t = (+5.415 \pm 0.012) \times 10^{-13}$ cm.

(15) $\mathrm{a}_s = (-23.806 \pm 0.028) \times 10^{-13}$ cm, from $\sigma_{\mathrm{free}} = (20.57 \pm 0.04) \times 10^{-24}\ \mathrm{cm}^2$, and from $2\mathrm{a}_{\mathrm{coh}} = (-3.78 \pm 0.02) \times 10^{-13}$ cm;

(16) $r_{e,t} = (1.704 \pm 0.028) \times 10^{-13}$ cm, from the values of R and a_t;

(17) $r_{e,s} = (2.49 \pm 0.24) \times 10^{-13}$ cm, from the energy dependence of n-p cross section (see Fig. 3.11-1*b*).

These numerical results contain all of the information that can be obtained on the neutron-proton force from low-energy scattering experiments.

3.2 Behavior of Neutrons in Matter

3.21 Slowing Down of Neutrons

a. Kinematics of S-Wave Collisions. The neutrons emitted in nuclear reactions have an energy of a few MeV. They are slowed down by successive S scatterings in matter until they reach thermal equilibrium with their surroundings. After this they diffuse like gaseous molecules until they are captured by nuclei.

The process of slowing down and thermal diffusion has been studied, mainly by Fermi, and it is of interest in any experiment involving neutrons. We discuss it following the lines of Fermi, but, to avoid complications, we neglect the possibility of capture during the slowing-down process.

Let M be the mass of the neutron, V_0 its speed in the laboratory system, MA the mass of the scattering nucleus, θ_L the scattering angle in the laboratory, and θ_0 the scattering angle in the center-of-mass system.

Then the speed of the center of mass, v_c, and the speed of the neutron in the center-of-mass system, v_0, are

(1)
$$v_c = \frac{V_0}{1 + A},$$
$$v_0 = V_0 - v_c = \frac{A}{1 + A} V_0.$$

From these, and from Fig. 3.21-1, we obtain the speed V_1 and the

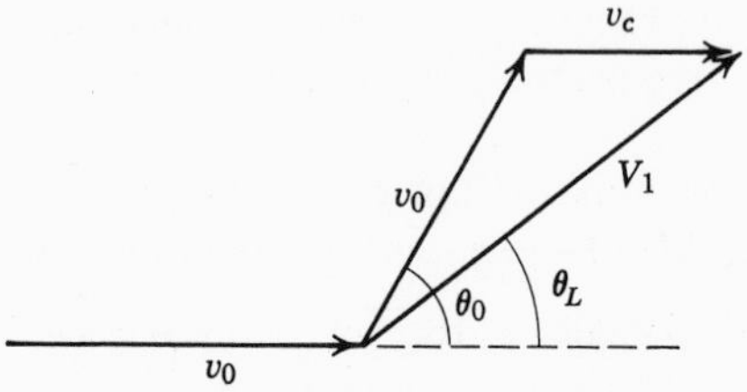

Fig. 3.21-1. Kinematics of neutron collision.

energy E_1 after collision as a function of the center-of-mass scattering angle:

(2)
$$V_1^2 = v_0^2 + v_c^2 + 2v_0v_c \cos \theta_0$$
$$= V_0^2\left[\left(\frac{A}{A + 1}\right)^2 + \left(\frac{1}{A + 1}\right)^2 + \frac{2A}{(A + 1)^2} \cos \theta_0\right],$$
$$E_1 = \frac{E_0}{(A + 1)^2}(1 + A^2 + 2A \cos \theta_0),$$

where $E_0 = \frac{1}{2}MV_0^2$ is the initial kinetic energy.

We can write

(3)
$$\frac{(A - 1)^2}{(A + 1)^2} E_0 \leq E_1 \leq E_0.$$

As a consequence of the S nature of the scattering, the number of scattering events per unit solid angle is constant in the center-of-mass system:

(4)
$$\frac{dN_1}{2\pi \sin \theta_0 \, d\theta_0} = \frac{1}{4\pi}.$$

It follows that the spectrum of the once-scattered neutrons is flat, as illustrated in Fig. 3.21-2:

(5)
$$\left|\frac{dN_1}{dE_1}\right| = \frac{dN_1}{d\theta_0}\left|\frac{d\theta_0}{dE_1}\right| = \frac{(A + 1)^2}{4A}\frac{1}{E_0}.$$

b. Rate of Energy Loss Due to Successive Collisions. In order to treat the effect of many collisions, Fermi introduced a method of averaging appropriate to a situation in which the average fractional energy loss per collision is always the same. He defined an *average*

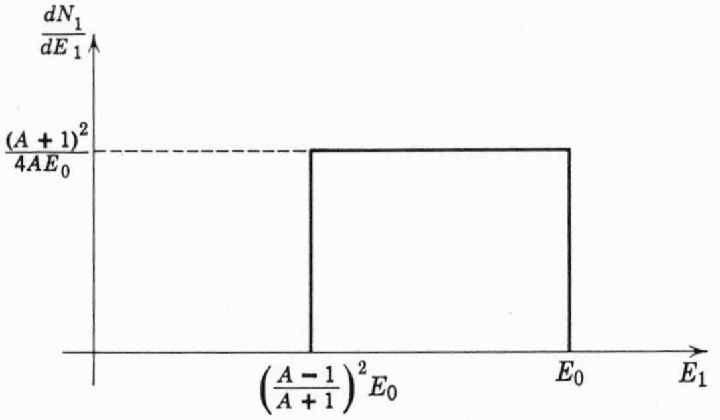

Fig. 3.21-2. The spectrum of once-scattered neutrons.

logarithmic energy loss,

(6)
$$\xi = \int \left(\log \frac{E_0}{E_1}\right) \left|\frac{dN_1}{dE_1}\right| dE_1 = \frac{(A+1)^2}{4AE_0} \int_{\left(\frac{A-1}{A+1}\right)^2 E_0}^{E_0} \log \frac{E_0}{E_1}\, dE_1$$
$$= 1 + \frac{(A-1)^2}{2A} \log \frac{A-1}{A+1},$$

which does not depend on E_0.

At each collision $\log E$ decreases, in average, by ξ. After ν collisions

(7)
$$\log E_\nu = \log E_0 - \xi\nu,$$

or

$$E_\nu = E_0 e^{-\xi\nu}.$$

By defining

(8)
$$\varepsilon = \log E,$$

we can think of the neutrons moving down the $\varepsilon = \log E$ axis; their average speed along this axis is

(9)
$$v_\varepsilon = \frac{d\varepsilon}{dt} = \frac{d \log E_\nu}{d\nu} \frac{d\nu}{dt} = -\xi \frac{V}{\lambda_s},$$

where λ_s is the scattering mean free path, and V/λ_s is the number of scattering collisions per unit time. We can also compute the speed along the E axis:

(10)
$$v_E = \frac{dE}{dt} = \frac{dE}{d \log E} \frac{d \log E}{dt} = -\frac{E\xi V}{\lambda_s}.$$

The spectrum of neutrons during the slowing-down process is obtained by considering that $N(E)v_E$ must not depend on energy *if there is no absorption*; thus the flux $N(E)V$ is inversely proportional to the energy

$$N(E)V \approx \frac{\text{constant}}{E}. \tag{11}$$

c. Diffusion in Space Accompanying the Loss of Energy. While the neutrons slow down they diffuse through the moderator. It is convenient to follow this process in the four-dimensional $xyz\,\varepsilon$ space. If n is the four-dimensional neutron density and $\mathbf{v}\,(v_x v_y v_z)$ is the velocity of the neutron fluid, distinct from the kinetic velocity of the individual neutrons V, the continuity equation (neglecting absorption) is

$$\frac{\partial n v_x}{\partial x} + \frac{\partial n v_y}{\partial y} + \frac{\partial n v_z}{\partial z} + \frac{\partial n v_\varepsilon}{\partial \varepsilon} = -\frac{dn}{dt}. \tag{12}$$

The diffusion in space can be treated according to the conventional diffusion equation,

$$n\mathbf{v} = -D\,\mathbf{grad}\,n, \tag{13}$$

and to kinetic theory, from which we know that the diffusion coefficient is

$$D = \frac{\lambda_t V}{3}, \tag{14}$$

where λ_t is the "transport mean free path," that is, the scattering mean free path corrected for the tendency of the neutrons to keep moving forward in the laboratory system

$$\lambda_t = \frac{\lambda_s}{1 - \langle\cos\theta_L\rangle} = \frac{\lambda_s}{1 - 2/(3A)}. \tag{15}$$

By introducing (13) and (14) in (12), we can write

$$-\text{div}\,\frac{\lambda_t V}{3}\,\mathbf{grad}\,n + \frac{\partial n v_\varepsilon}{\partial \varepsilon} = -\frac{dn}{dt}. \tag{16}$$

Considering that λ_t and V do not depend explicitly on position, this becomes

$$-\frac{\lambda_t}{3}\nabla^2(nV) + \frac{\partial n v_\varepsilon}{\partial \varepsilon} = -\frac{dn}{dt}. \tag{17}$$

d. Fermi's Age Equation. If we now define

$$q \equiv -n v_\varepsilon = \frac{\xi}{\lambda_s}\,nV \tag{18}$$

and

(19) $$\tau \equiv \int_{\varepsilon}^{\varepsilon_0} \frac{\lambda_s \lambda_t}{3\xi} \, d\varepsilon,$$

from which, if λ_s and λ_t do not depend on energy,

(20) $$\frac{d\tau}{d\varepsilon} = -\frac{\lambda_s \lambda_t}{3\xi},$$

Eq. (17) becomes, for a stationary state ($dn/dt = 0$),

(21) $$\nabla^2 q - \frac{\partial q}{\partial \tau} = 0.$$

Equation (21) is Fermi's celebrated age equation. In it q is the neutron current density along the ε axis, or the *slowing-down density*: it is the number of neutrons passing through the energy ε per unit volume and unit time. τ is the so-called *age*, which has the dimensions of a length squared and which is zero for "newborn" neutrons of initial energy E_0 and large for "old" neutrons of small energy.

Formally, (21) is exactly like the equation of heat diffusion (where q would be a quantity of heat and τ a time). Therefore its solutions are well studied.

For a point neutron source q is a gaussian function of r:

(22) $$q(r, \tau) = \frac{Q}{4\pi\tau^{3/2}} e^{-r^2/4\tau},$$

where Q is a constant related to source strength. The older the neutrons, the wider the gaussian. The average square distance traveled by neutrons of age τ is

(23) $$\langle R^2 \rangle = \frac{\int r^2 \exp(-r^2/4\tau) \, d\mathbf{r}}{\int \exp(-r^2/4\tau) \, d\mathbf{r}} = 6\tau.$$

It is actually possible to measure the slowing-down density by studying the radioactivity induced in "foils" which have a sharp resonance for the capture of neutrons of different energies.

3.22 Behavior of Thermal Neutrons

The slowing-down process terminates when the neutrons have reached thermal equilibrium with the surrounding medium. However, the diffusion process continues. In a good moderator such as C or D nearly all neutrons reach thermal energy. The function $q(\mathbf{r}, \tau_{\text{th}})$ obtained as the solution of 3.21(21) is the source of thermal neutrons per unit volume and unit time. The thermal neutrons survive until they are captured (they seldom live long enough to decay!): thus, if λ_a is the absorption mean free path, there is a sink of thermal neutrons $n_{th}V_{th}/\lambda_a$ per unit volume and per unit time.

In static conditions, $dn/dt = 0$, the continuity equation can be written

$$\text{div}\,(n_{th}\mathbf{v}_{th}) - q(\mathbf{r}, \tau_{th}) + \frac{n_{th}V_{th}}{\lambda_a} = 0. \tag{1}$$

By making use of the diffusion equation 3.21(13), with a thermal diffusion coefficient

$$D_{th} = \frac{\lambda_{th}V_{th}}{3} \tag{2}$$

and defining a *diffusion length* such that

$$L^2 = \frac{\lambda_t\lambda_a}{3}, \tag{3}$$

we have

$$\nabla^2 n_{th} + \frac{q(\mathbf{r}, \tau_{th})}{D} - \frac{n_{th}}{L^2} = 0. \tag{4}$$

Let us discuss as an example the application of (4) to one of the first measurements (A-36) of the capture cross section of neutrons by protons.

Let us slow down the neutrons from a source in a tank of paraffin or water, and let us work in a region in which the source of thermal neutrons $q(\mathbf{r}, \tau_{th})$ may be regarded as constant or, at least, does not vary in the z direction. In this region let us locate a plane absorber of thermal neutrons such as a sheet of Cd. If z is the distance from the sheet, (4) becomes

$$\frac{d^2n_{th}}{dz^2} + \frac{q}{D} - \frac{n_{th}}{L^2} = 0, \tag{5}$$

and its solution, appropriate to the situation described, is of the form

$$n \approx A + Be^{-z/L}. \tag{6}$$

We can now probe n by measuring the radioactivity induced by thermal neutrons in some appropriate small "foil" located at various z positions. From $n(z)$ we obtain L and λ_a [see (3)]. Thus the absorption cross section, mostly contributed by hydrogen, is determined. The result for absorption of thermal neutrons by protons is

$$\sigma_{abs} = 0.3 \times 10^{-24}\ \text{cm}^2. \tag{7}$$

The theory of capture of neutrons by protons is discussed in 4.2.

3.3 Interaction of Nucleons with Electrons

3.31 *Magnetic Interaction between Neutrons and Electrons*

a. Theory of Magnetic Scattering. An interaction between neutrons and electrons is expected as a consequence of the magnetic moment of the neutron. A neutron and an electron at rest should interact through a dipole-dipole potential of the type described in 1.22(9); and the magnetic moment of a neutron is also coupled to the magnetic field produced by the electron's current.

The scattering of neutrons from free electrons, however, is difficult to study experimentally, and the problem of interest is the scattering of neutrons from the electrons in magnetic materials. In nonmagnetic materials, of course, the electrons cancel one another's spin and angular momenta, and the net effect is zero.

We assume that the energy of interaction of a neutron in a magnetized material has the form

$$\mathcal{H}_m = -\frac{|e|\,\hbar}{2Mc}\,\boldsymbol{\mu}_n \cdot \mathbf{B}, \tag{1}$$

where $\boldsymbol{\mu}_n$ is the magnetic moment of the neutron in nuclear magnetons and $\mathbf{B}$ is the magnetic induction vector produced by the electron.

Other forms of interaction have been suggested (B-37); it has been shown (E-49) that these forms are equivalent to (1), apart from replacing $\mathbf{B}$ by $\mathbf{H} + 4\pi C\mathbf{m}$, where $\mathbf{m}$ is the magnetic moment density and C is an indeterminate constant whose value is between 0 and 1. It was finally proved experimentally (H-51a) that C is near to unity and that (1) is the correct formula.

We shall, however, rewrite (1) in a form that is more convenient for the calculation[1].

We consider the scattering of a neutron wave by an atom of magnetic moment $(|e|\hbar/2mc)\,\boldsymbol{\mu}_A$ distributed over the atomic volume according to a density $g(\mathbf{r}_A)$, with $\int g(\mathbf{r}_A)\,d\mathbf{r}_A = 1$. This distribution of magnetic moment corresponds to a distribution of current density

$$\frac{1}{c}\,\mathbf{j}(r_A) = \frac{|e|\,\hbar}{2mc}\,\mathbf{curl}\,[g(\mathbf{r}_A)\boldsymbol{\mu}_A], \tag{2}$$

which interacts with the vector potential produced by the magnetic moment

[1] The computation that follows is a simplified version of a paper by O. Halpern and M. H. Johnson (H-39). In the original paper the atom is treated relativistically and quantum mechanically, whereas here we use a classical description of a magnetic moment density.

of the neutron, whose coordinate is $\mathbf{r}_n$:

$$\mathbf{A}(r_A) = \frac{|e|\,\hbar}{2Mc}\,\boldsymbol{\mu}_n \times \nabla(|\mathbf{r}_n - \mathbf{r}_A|)^{-1}. \tag{3}$$

The energy density equivalent to (1) is minus the dot product of the vectors (2) and (3)[1] and the magnetic interaction Hamiltonian can be written

$$\mathcal{H}_m = -\frac{|e|\hbar}{2mc}\frac{|e|\hbar}{2Mc}\int \{\mathbf{curl}\,[g(\mathbf{r}_A)\boldsymbol{\mu}_A]\}\cdot\{\boldsymbol{\mu}_n \times \nabla(|\mathbf{r}_n - \mathbf{r}_A|)^{-1}\}\,d\mathbf{r}_A. \tag{4}$$

As a result of the interaction, the neutron is scattered. For slow neutrons the scattering amplitude of the whole atom is the sum of two terms:

$$f = -\mathfrak{a}_N + f_m. \tag{5}$$

The first term, $-\mathfrak{a}_N$, is constant with energy and angle and corresponds to nuclear scattering. The second term, f_m, describes the magnetic effects and depends on energy and angle, since the neutron wavelength is of the same order as the atomic size; f_m may depend on φ if the magnetization is perpendicular to the direction of propagation.

The magnetic scattering amplitude can be computed in the Born approximation. Introducing the momentum transfer $\hbar\mathbf{q} = \hbar\mathbf{k} - \hbar\mathbf{k}'$, where $\mathbf{k}'$ is the wave vector of the scattered wave, we have

$$\begin{aligned} f_m &= -\frac{M}{2\pi\hbar^2}\int e^{i\mathbf{q}\cdot\mathbf{r}_n}\,\mathcal{H}_m(r_n)\,d\mathbf{r}_n \\ &= \frac{1}{8\pi}\frac{e^2}{mc^2}\int e^{i\mathbf{q}\cdot\mathbf{r}_n}\{\mathbf{curl}\,[g(r_A)\boldsymbol{\mu}_A]\}\cdot\{\boldsymbol{\mu}_n \times \nabla(|\mathbf{r}_n - \mathbf{r}_A|)^{-1}\}\,d\mathbf{r}_A\,d\mathbf{r}_n. \end{aligned} \tag{6}$$

b. Computation of Magnetic Scattering Cross Section. If we write $\mathbf{r}_n - \mathbf{r}_A = \mathbf{r}$, the integral splits in two:

$$f_m = \frac{1}{8\pi}\frac{e^2}{mc^2}\left[\int e^{i\mathbf{q}\cdot\mathbf{r}_A}\,\mathbf{curl}\,[g(r_A)\boldsymbol{\mu}_A]\,d\mathbf{r}_A\right]\cdot\left[\int e^{i\mathbf{q}\cdot\mathbf{r}}\boldsymbol{\mu}_n \times \nabla\left(\frac{1}{r}\right)d\mathbf{r}\right]. \tag{7}$$

The first integral can be done writing $\mathbf{curl}\,[g(r_A)\,\boldsymbol{\mu}_A] = -\boldsymbol{\mu}_A \times \mathbf{grad}\,g(r_A)$, and then integrating by parts. The result is

$$iF\boldsymbol{\mu}_A \times \mathbf{q} \quad \text{with} \quad F = \int e^{i\mathbf{q}\cdot\mathbf{r}}g(r)\,d\mathbf{r}, \tag{8}$$

[1] By indicating with $\mathbf{m}$ the density of magnetization and using a well-known vector relation, we have

$$-\boldsymbol{\mu}\cdot\mathbf{B} \to -\int \mathbf{m}\cdot\mathbf{B}\,d\mathbf{r} = -\int \mathbf{m}\cdot\mathbf{curl}\,\mathbf{A}\,d\mathbf{r} = \int \mathrm{div}\,\mathbf{m}\times\mathbf{A}\,d\mathbf{r} - \int(\mathbf{curl}\,\mathbf{m})\cdot\mathbf{A}\,d\mathbf{r} = -\frac{1}{c}\int \mathbf{j}\cdot\mathbf{A}\,d\mathbf{r}.$$

where $F(q)$ is the "magnetic form factor," analogous to the atomic form factor, familiar from x ray scattering. The second integral is

$$(9) \qquad \boldsymbol{\mu}_n \times \int e^{i\mathbf{q}\cdot\mathbf{r}} \nabla\left(\frac{1}{r}\right) d\mathbf{r} = -\boldsymbol{\mu}_n \times \int e^{i\mathbf{q}\cdot\mathbf{r}} \frac{\mathbf{r}}{r^3} d\mathbf{r}.$$

If we take a system of coordinates with the z axis in the $\mathbf{q}$ direction, the x and y components of the integral vanish. By making use of the

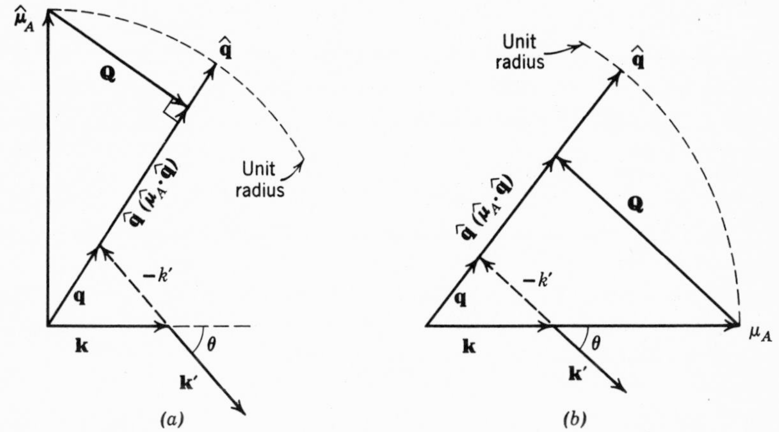

Fig. 3.31-1. Geometrical construction of the vector **Q** for scattering in the plane of magnetization; θ is the scattering angle, for μ_A transverse (*a*) and longitudinal (*b*).

integral 3.19(3) the expression in (9) becomes

$$(10) \qquad -\boldsymbol{\mu}_n \times \frac{\mathbf{q}}{|q|} \int e^{iqr\cos\theta} \frac{r\cos\theta}{r^3} r^2\, dr\, d\Omega = 4\pi\boldsymbol{\mu}_n \times \frac{\mathbf{q}}{|q|} \frac{1}{iq}.$$

Thus (7) can be written[1]

$$(11) \qquad f_m = \frac{1}{2}\frac{e^2}{mc^2} F\mu_A\mu_n(\hat{\boldsymbol{\mu}}_A \times \hat{\mathbf{q}}) \cdot (\hat{\boldsymbol{\mu}}_n \times \hat{\mathbf{q}}),$$

where $\hat{\boldsymbol{\mu}}_A$, $\hat{\boldsymbol{\mu}}_n$, $\hat{\mathbf{q}}$ are unit vectors in the direction of $\boldsymbol{\mu}_A$, $\boldsymbol{\mu}_n$, $\mathbf{q}$. We shall now make use of the vector identity:

$$(12) \qquad (\hat{\boldsymbol{\mu}}_A \times \hat{\mathbf{q}}) \cdot (\hat{\boldsymbol{\mu}}_n \times \hat{\mathbf{q}}) = -(\hat{\boldsymbol{\mu}}_A \cdot \hat{\mathbf{q}})(\hat{\boldsymbol{\mu}}_n \cdot \hat{\mathbf{q}}) + \hat{\boldsymbol{\mu}}_n \cdot \hat{\boldsymbol{\mu}}_A$$
$$= \hat{\boldsymbol{\mu}}_n \cdot [-\hat{\mathbf{q}}(\hat{\boldsymbol{\mu}}_A \cdot \hat{\mathbf{q}}) + \hat{\boldsymbol{\mu}}_A] = -\hat{\boldsymbol{\mu}}_n \cdot \mathbf{Q},$$

where **Q** is defined as

$$(13) \qquad \mathbf{Q} = (\hat{\boldsymbol{\mu}}_A \cdot \hat{\mathbf{q}})\hat{\mathbf{q}} - \hat{\boldsymbol{\mu}}_A.$$

When we consider that (see Fig. 3.31-1)

$$(14) \qquad |\mathbf{Q}| = \sin(\widehat{\mu_A, q}),$$

[1] In (11) and the following formulas μ_A and μ_n are positive numbers, and the unit vectors $\hat{\boldsymbol{\mu}}_A$ and $\hat{\boldsymbol{\mu}}_n$ are opposite to the spins of the atom and of the neutron.

(11) becomes

$$f_m = \pm \frac{1}{2} \frac{e^2}{mc^2} F\mu_A\mu_n \sin(\widehat{\mu_A, q}) \tag{15}$$

where the sign $\pm$ applies to neutrons with spin parallel or antiparallel to the direction of Q. The geometry is a little involved, but applications to particular cases can be made without great difficulty.

From (15) we obtain the differential atomic scattering cross section for neutrons polarized in the $\pm\mathbf{Q}$ direction:

$$\frac{d\sigma}{d\omega} = (a_N \pm |f_m|)^2. \tag{16}$$

If the neutrons are not polarized, we obtain by averaging over the two spin directions

$$\frac{d\sigma}{d\omega} = a_N^2 + f_m^2. \tag{17}$$

Finally, if the neutrons are not polarized and the iron is not magnetized, we must average f_m^2 over all directions of μ_A[1] and we get

$$\frac{d\sigma}{d\omega} = a_N^2 + \frac{2}{3}\left(\frac{1}{2}\frac{e^2}{mc^2} F\mu_A\mu_n\right)^2. \tag{18}$$

The forward scattering amplitude, from which we compute the index of refraction, is affected only by the longitudinal component of μ_A. This can be seen by averaging over φ the diagrams of Fig. 3.31-1 and considering that for almost forward scattering $\mathbf{q}$ is nearly transverse. The index of refraction for longitudinally polarized iron has two values, one for each of the two longitudinal polarizations:

$$n = 1 + \frac{2\pi N}{k^2}\left(-a_N \pm \frac{1}{2}\frac{e^2}{mc^2}\mu_A\mu_n\right). \tag{19}$$

In this equation F has been replaced by unity, since $\mathbf{q} = 0$ for forward scattering.

c. Experiments on Magnetic Scattering. We can deduce from (15) and (16) that the total scattering cross sections for neutrons traversing magnetized iron depends on the relative direction of μ_n and μ_A. It is thus possible to make neutron polarizers and analyzers by transmission in iron. This method has received many applications, in particular for the measurement of the neutron magnetic moment.

[1] The average must be performed by considering that nonmagnetized iron consists of randomly oriented magnetized domains. The result would be different for stainless steel or for a paramagnetic substance in which each atomic magnetic moment is averaged to zero.

By measuring the differential cross section for coherent scattering in polycrystalline iron (S-51b) it is possible to determine the form factor F (which depends on q and thus on angle). This magnetic form factor is of great interest in the solid-state theory of magnetic materials.

Another major contribution of the magnetic scattering of neutrons to our knowledge of solid state has been the discovery of antiferromagnetism and the studies that have followed (S-49; S-51a).

An interesting application of magnetic scattering is the reflection of neutrons from magnetic mirrors. As we saw in (19), a magnetic substance has two indices of refraction for neutrons: these indices can be written in the form (use $B_s \approx 4\pi\mathrm{m} = 4\pi N(e\hbar/2mc)\mu_A$; $k^2\hbar^2 = 2ME$)

$$n^2 \approx 1 - \frac{4\pi N}{k^2}\,\mathrm{a}_N \pm \frac{\mu_\mathrm{n} B_s}{E}, \tag{20}$$

where B_s is the saturation value of the magnetic induction and E is the neutron energy in the same units as $\mu_\mathrm{n} B_s$. Formula (20) holds whether the iron is magnetized or not in the macroscopic sense. The two indices of refraction correspond to two critical angles for glancing reflection; these angles have been measured and studied (H-51a). It is this kind of study that has made it possible to prove the correctness of the interaction (1).

Finally, we mention that it is possible to produce highly polarized ($100 \pm 5\%$) neutron beams by reflection from magnetized Co mirrors (H-49; H-51a). The nuclear scattering length of Co is such that $n - 1$ changes sign for the two spin states, and thus only one of the two neutron spins is totally reflected. Such beams have been used to study the β decay of polarized neutrons.

3.32 Other Interactions of Slow Neutrons and Electrons

a. Neutron-Electron Interactions. There are several reasons why the neutron should interact with electrons, apart from the magnetic interaction discussed in the preceding section.

There is first of all a relativistic effect that can be deduced from Dirac theory. It is well known that the relativistic theory of the electron predicts that the spin should be accompanied, even at rest, by a magnetic moment. We shall see in 6.15b that in a similar manner it follows from the Dirac equation that a neutral particle with a magnetic moment should interact, even at rest, with an electrostatic potential. The computed effect results in an attraction between neutron and electron. If we assume a square well of radius $e^2/mc^2 = 2.8 \times 10^{-13}$ cm, the theoretical depth is 3.9 keV.

Second, according to meson theories, the neutron has a certain probability of appearing as a proton surrounded by a negative meson cloud: there could be an additional electrostatic interaction because the neutron charge is not everywhere equal to zero.

Finally, some extremely weak (unobservable) electron-neutron forces should exist as a consequence of the β-decay interaction.

We shall now describe some of the information on nucleon-electron interaction, as obtained from low-energy neutron scattering.

b. Experimental Work. Several authors have attempted to detect experimentally a neutron-electron interaction distinct from the magnetic effect. For these experiments a nonmagnetic substance is used; the scattering due to the electrons is distinguished from the nuclear scattering either by its angular dependence or by the energy dependence of the form factor. Both methods are based on the fact that the "radius" of electronic orbits in an atom is not negligible compared to the neutron's wavelength.

Fermi and Marshall (F-49) looked for a departure from spherical symmetry in the scattering of neutrons from Xe. No angular dependence was observed. Assuming a well of radius $r_0 = e^2/mc^2$, its depth was computed to be -300 ± 5000 eV.

Using a similar, but somewhat refined, method, Hamermesh et al. (H-52a), obtained an attractive well of 5020 ($\pm 13\%$) eV in Kr and 2860 ($\pm 16\%$) in Xe. The average is 4100 ($\pm 10\%$) eV, very close to the relativistic effect computed from the anomalous magnetic moment.

A different technique was used by Havens, Rabi, and Rainwater (H-51b), who studied the cross section in Pb for thermal neutrons of different energy. A small effect was observed, corresponding to an attractive potential of around 2500 eV.

Hughes et al. (H-53) have used the method of glancing reflection from totally reflecting mirrors. The reflecting surface was the surface of separation between liquid oxygen and solid bismuth. In this case the critical angle θ_c [see 3.19(10)] is

$$\theta_c^2 = \frac{4\pi}{k^2}\{N_{\mathrm{O}}[\mathfrak{a}_{\mathrm{O}} - 8f_{el}(0)] - N_{\mathrm{Bi}}[\mathfrak{a}_{\mathrm{Bi}} - 83f_{el}(0)]\}. \tag{1}$$

Since the nucleon scattering powers of the two substances chosen were known and are very close ($N_{\mathrm{O}}\mathfrak{a}_{\mathrm{O}} \approx N_{\mathrm{Bi}}\mathfrak{a}_{\mathrm{Bi}}$), the effect of the electrons could be measured with some accuracy. The result obtained was 3860 $\pm$ 370 eV.

The latest determination was made at Columbia University (M-56); the energy dependence of the scattering was measured, with the result 4165 $\pm$ 265 eV.

These measurements are in agreement with the 3.9 keV predicted from the anomalous magnetic moment alone. No evidence of separation of charge over a finite volume is observed.

3.33 Scattering of High-Energy Electrons by Nucleons

a. Scattering of Electrons by Protons. The low-energy scattering of electrons by protons is essentially the result of electrostatic effects and follows the laws of Rutherford scattering. But, already at moderate energies, we must consider relativistic spin effects, together with those of the anomalous magnetic moment of the proton. The resulting scattering law can be computed by using Dirac theory, as discussed in Chapter 6.

Here, we are mainly concerned with the effects caused by the finite size of the nucleons (6.15c), which may give information on the electromagnetic structure of the proton. According to meson theory, the proton, as well as the neutron, should be surrounded by a meson "cloud" and consists of a distribution of charge of finite extent. Clearly, any information on this point is of great value to an understanding of the basic interactions between elementary particles.

Owing to the small "size" of the proton, electrons of small wavelength—thus of high energy—are required for the experimental investigation of these questions. Electron beams of increasing high energy have been made available at Stanford University by the construction and successive extensions of a linear accelerator; under the leadership of Hofstadter, these beams were used first for the determination of nuclear radii (2.21c), and—as soon as sufficient energy was available—for studies of the structure of the nucleons. Similar measurements have been carried on at Cornell University, using the beam of the 1.3 BeV electron synchrotron.

Already at 400 MeV (Fig. 3.33-1) the scattering cross section at large angle is noticeably different—smaller—than that expected for a point interaction. Since there is no reason to doubt, in the present state of our knowledge, that the electron is a point particle, the discrepancy is to be attributed to a finite size of the proton.

The electromagnetic interaction of the proton is described by its charge and by its anomalous magnetic moment[1], and we must consider as distinct the distribution of the charge and that of the anomalous moment. It is found, however, that (H-56) up to 400 MeV the experimental data can be explained by the assumption that the proton is an exponential distribution of charge and anomalous magnetic moment characterized by roughly equal radii:

$$r_c \approx r_\mu \approx 0.8 \times 10^{-13} \text{ cm.} \tag{1}$$

An alternative way of expressing the size of the proton is by giving the

[1] The nonanomalous, or Dirac, part of the magnetic moment is due to the charge itself and must not be regarded as an independent property.

form factors:

(2) F_{pe}, for the charge distribution,
$F_{p\mu}$, for the anomalous magnetic moment distribution.

The form factor associated with a distribution $g(r)$ has been defined in 3.31(8) as a function of the momentum transfer $\hbar q$. It is unity for a point charge and a decreasing function of q for a spread out charge distribution.

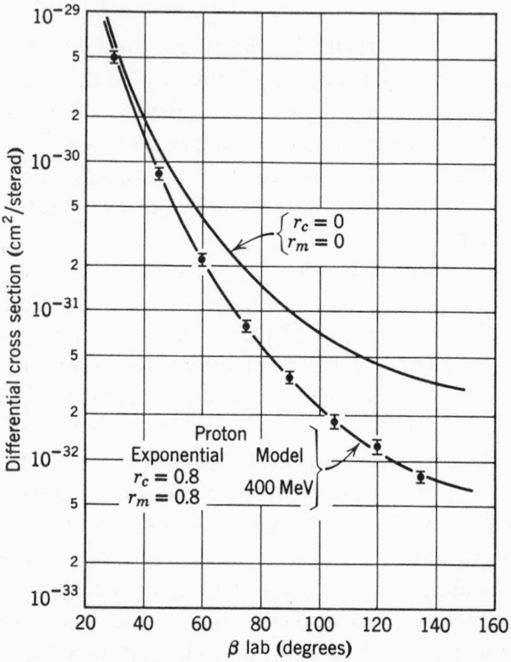

Fig. 3.33-1. Typical angular distribution for elastic scattering of 400-MeV electrons against protons. The solid lines are theoretical. The model providing the curve that agrees with experiment is an exponential with rms radii = 0.80×10^{-13} cm [(from R. Hofstadter, *Rev. Mod. Phys.*, **28**, 235 (1957)].

For the discussion of the scattering of high-energy electrons the definition of form factor 3.31(8) is not adequate and must be replaced with one that is relativistically invariant: for this purpose it is sufficient to replace the momentum transfer by a four-momentum transfer (of components $\hbar q_i = \hbar(k_i - k_i')$ and $(E' - E)/c$) and the vector **r** by the four-dimensional radius vector. In this manner the form factor describes a finite extension in time (retardation) as well as in space. However, for elastic scattering referred to the center-of-mass system the fourth component of the momentum transfer vanishes (since $E' = E$), and the form factors are functions of the magnitude of a space vector even in the relativistic case[1].

From the scattering at 900 MeV (Stanford; H-60b, H-61c, D-62) and at 1.3 beV (Cornell; L-61a) we find that for high four-momentum

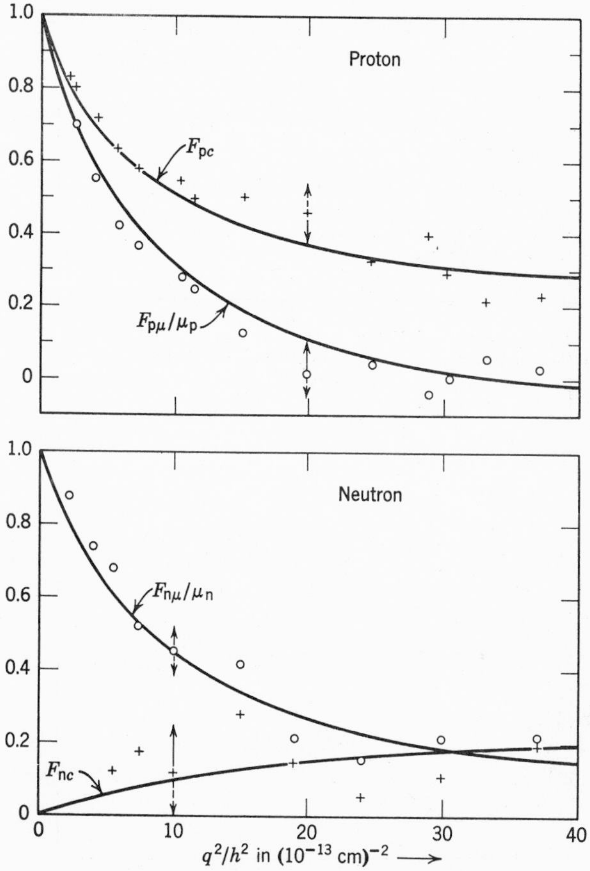

Fig. 3.33-2. Typical experimental results on the form factors of the nucleons. The solid curves are from equations (3) and (5) [from Littauer et al. (L-61a)].

transfers the charge and anomalous moment form factors differ from one another (Fig. 3.33-2) in the sense that corresponds to a wider distribution for the magnetic moment than for the charge. Apart from small discrepancies the results of the different groups are in agreement and the data can be roughly described by theoretical curves[2] (C-58, B-61, full

[1] See 6.15c and 6.24c for further discussion of these questions.
[2] See 7.38c for a more accurate theoretical formulation.

curves in Fig. 3.33-2), with numerical coefficients chosen to fit the experiment (L-61b). The equations of these curves are

$$(3)\qquad \begin{aligned} F_{\mathrm{p}c} &= 0.16 + \frac{0.29}{1 + q^2/4.4} + \frac{0.55}{1 + q^2/8.3}, \\ F_{\mathrm{p}\mu} &= -0.41 + \frac{0.09}{1 + q^2/4.4} + \frac{2.1}{1 + q^2/8.3}, \end{aligned}$$

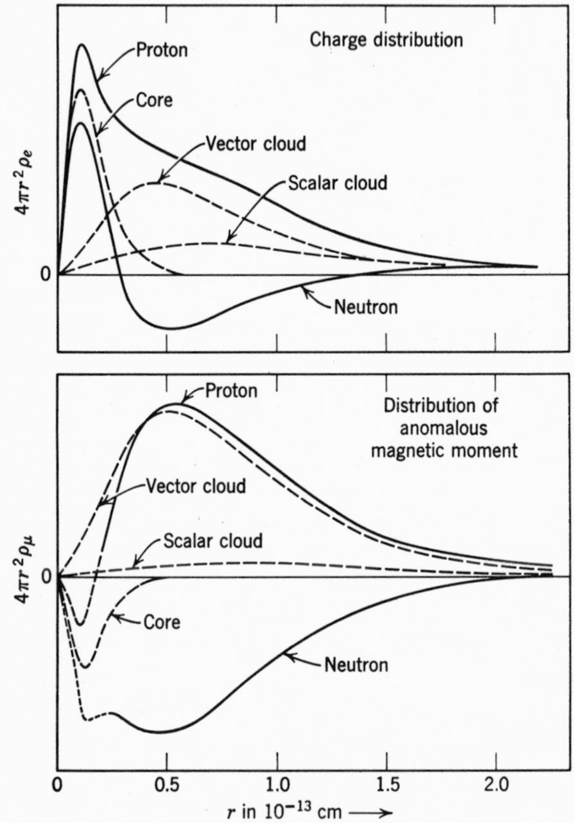

Fig. 3.33-3. The proton and neutron charge and anomolous moment density distributions given by the Fourier transforms of (3) and (5) [from Littauer et al. (L-61b)].

where q is expressed in 10^{13} cm^{-1}. The proton root-mean-square radii corresponding to these expressions are

$$(4)\qquad \begin{aligned} r_{\mathrm{p}c} &= 0.88 \times 10^{-13}\ \mathrm{cm}, \\ r_{\mathrm{p}\mu} &= 0.95 \times 10^{-13}\ \mathrm{cm}. \end{aligned}$$

b. Scattering of Electrons by Neutrons. Since neutron targets are not available, the information on the form factors of the neutron is obtained from the scattering of fast electrons by deuterons. Data up to 1.3 beV have been obtained (L-61a); since we have some knowledge of the deuteron wave function and of the form factor of the proton, it is possible to obtain the neutron form factor. The results are given in Fig. 3.33-2*b*, together with semitheoretical curves of equation:

$$F_{\mathrm{n}e} = 0.26 + \frac{0.29}{1 + q^2/4.4} - \frac{0.55}{1 + q^2/8.3},$$

(5)

$$F_{\mathrm{n}\mu} = 0.11 + \frac{0.09}{1 + q^2/4.4} - \frac{2.1}{1 + q^2/8.3}.$$

The root-mean-square radii corresponding to (5) are

$$r_{\mathrm{n}e} = 0.00 \times 10^{-13}\ \mathrm{cm},$$

(6)

$$r_{\mathrm{n}\mu} = 0.87 \times 10^{-13}\ \mathrm{cm}.$$

The root-mean-square radius of the neutron's charge distribution vanishes, and this is in agreement with the failure of the attempts to detect a distribution of charge by slow neutron scattering, as reported in 3.32.

The charge distributions obtained as the Fourier transforms of the form factors are reported in Fig. 3.33-3. The proton has a finite extent as if there were a finite probability of finding it decomposed into a neutron and a positive meson cloud. The structure of the neutron can be interpreted as due mostly to the decomposition into a positive proton surrounded by a negative meson cloud; but apparently we must also consider higher order effects that produce a positive charge density at larger distances.

Considering the difficulties of the experimental work and of the theoretical analysis, these conclusions must be considered as preliminary, for some of the details may change as a result of further investigation.

A more complete discussion of the form factors in terms of meson theories is presented in 7.38.

3.4 Low-Energy Scattering of Protons by Protons

3.41 S-Wave Nuclear Scattering of Protons by Protons

The scattering of protons by protons is as important as the scattering of neutrons by protons. Nevertheless, we shall dispose of it in a few sentences because, apart from the analytical complications introduced by the coulomb field, the treatment does not convey any new physical idea.

As we have already seen in the discussion of stable nuclei, the p-p force is composed of two parts: a long-range electrostatic repulsion and a short-range nuclear attractive potential of great depth.

As far as the S wave is concerned, the effect of the nuclear potential

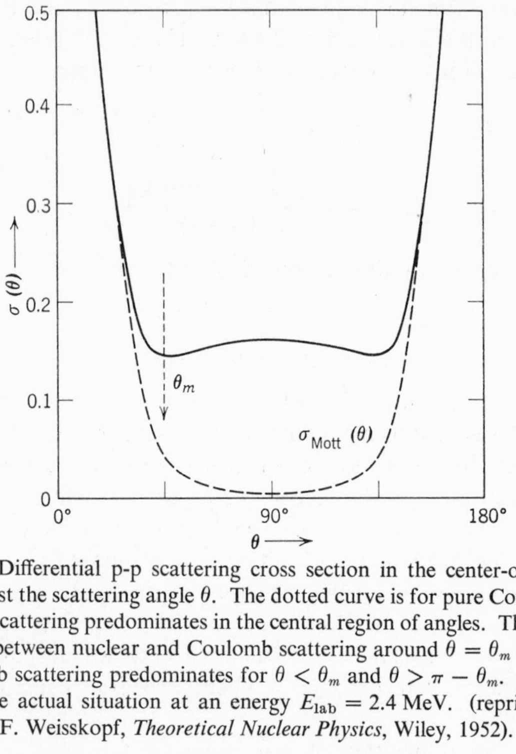

Fig. 3.41-1. Differential p-p scattering cross section in the center-of-gravity system, plotted against the scattering angle θ. The dotted curve is for pure Coulomb scattering. The nuclear scattering predominates in the central region of angles. There is destructive interference between nuclear and Coulomb scattering around $\theta = \theta_m$ and $\theta = \pi - \theta_m$. The Coulomb scattering predominates for $\theta < \theta_m$ and $\theta > \pi - \theta_m$. The figure corresponds to the actual situation at an energy $E_{\text{lab}} = 2.4$ MeV. (reprinted from J. M. Blatt and V. F. Weisskopf, *Theoretical Nuclear Physics*, Wiley, 1952).

can be described by two quantities having the dimensions of length:

a scattering length a_s

an effective radius $r_{e,s}$.

Because of the exclusion principle only the singlet state is allowed for $l = 0$.

The measurements of p-p scattering are simpler than those of n-p scattering. Because of their charge, protons can easily be accelerated and detected. The acceleration is usually achieved with a Van de Graaff machine and the detection by means of one of the standard counters for ionizing particles.

The coulomb repulsion masks the nuclear effect at low energy. Nuclear effects start appearing at $\approx$200 keV, and we can observe an interference between nuclear and coulomb scattering (Fig. 3.41-1).

In the center-of-mass system the cross section is symmetrical around 90° because of the indistinguishability of the two protons. At not too low energy ($\approx$MeV) the differential cross section is flat near 90°, where we observe almost exclusively the contribution of spherically symmetrical nuclear scattering, and increases rapidly in the forward and backward directions, due to coulomb (Rutherford, or if spin relativistic effects are included, Mott) scattering. In the intermediate region we observe a depression caused by the destructive interference of the two scattered waves.

The information obtained from these experiments allows the determination of a_s and of $r_{e,s}$, without any ambiguity in sign.

If we assume that the electrostatic interaction potential is everywhere e^2/r, the result from a shape-independent analysis is (HS-57)

$$(1) \qquad \begin{aligned} r_{e,s} &= 2.656 \pm 0.017 \times 10^{-13}\ \text{cm}, \\ a_s &= -7.694 \pm 0.012 \times 10^{-13}\ \text{cm}. \end{aligned}$$

These values are much more precise than the corresponding ones for the n-p system.

Although the values of $r_{e,s}$ for n-p and p-p may be the same, it is clear that the a_s are different. Does this contradict the assumption of charge independence?

In attempting to answer this question, let us observe first of all that though the value of a_s for p-p is about one third of that for n-p the corresponding difference in the nuclear potential depth is small: $a_s = -23 \times 10^{-13}$ cm corresponds to an energy of $\hbar^2/Ma_s^2 \approx 80$ keV for the "virtual" singlet state of the deuteron, and $a_s = -7.7 \times 10^{-13}$ cm to 0.7 MeV for the "virtual" singlet state of the diproton. The difference between these energies is indeed small compared to the depth of the nuclear well which is $\approx$50 MeV.

Furthermore, the values (1) have been obtained under the assumption that the electrostatic potential goes everywhere as $1/r$, or, in other words, that the protons possess a point electric charge. But we have seen in 3.33 that the proton's charge is distributed over a volume whose radius is of the order of 0.8×10^{-13} cm. Thus the shape-independent amplitude (1) includes not only the effect of nuclear forces but also the contribution of the departures of the electrostatic potential from the $1/r$ law.

An oversimplified square-well version of this argument is shown in Fig. 3.41-2. Since the finite size of the proton charge decreases the electrostatic repulsion, it affects the binding of the diproton. No final conclusion can be made without a detailed discussion of the electromagnetic effects.

A more quantitative comparison of p-p and n-p forces in the singlet S state is difficult. Even if the proton charge distribution were perfectly known, the shape-independent analysis of nuclear forces would not be adequate in the p-p case. This is easily seen, assuming that the nuclear forces have a repulsive core: in this case the effect of a given electrostatic potential would obviously depend on the radius of the core,

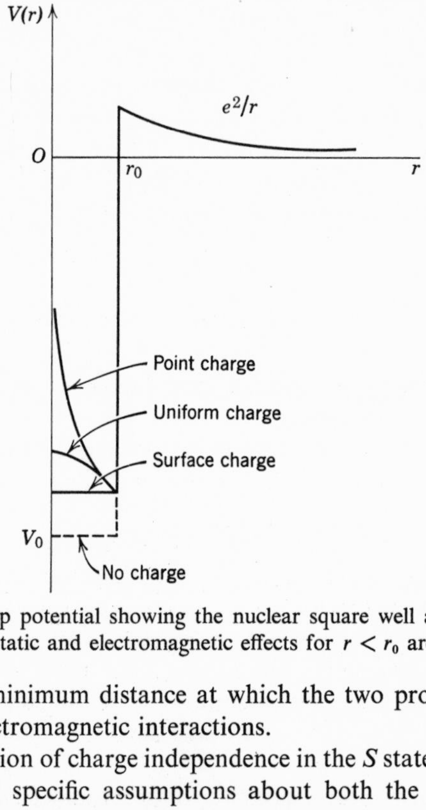

Fig. 3.41-2. The p-p potential showing the nuclear square well and the electrostatic effect. The electrostatic and electromagnetic effects for $r < r_0$ are not well known.

that is, on the minimum distance at which the two protons can explore their mutual electromagnetic interactions.

Thus the question of charge independence in the S state can be discussed only by making specific assumptions about both the electrostatic and nuclear potential, and our present knowledge is not sufficient for such a detailed analysis. To this we should add that the interaction between magnetic moments must also be taken into account in the discussion.

All considered, we can say first that the apparent disagreement between the values of a_s in (1) and in 3.19(15) corresponds to a very small percentage of difference in the depth of the nuclear well and second that, owing to the uncertainty in potential shapes, even this small difference may not be inconsistent with charge independence. In short, we can conclude that no violation of charge independence is observed in nucleon-nucleon scattering at low energy.

3.5 Scattering of High-Energy Nucleons

3.51 Partial Wave Analysis for Particles with Spin

a. Scattering of Spin-Zero Particles. The general formulation of the analysis in partial waves, needed for the more complete treatment of scattering of particles of spin zero, has been presented in 3.12, and we shall not enter here into the detailed application to scattering from different potentials, which is of limited interest in nuclear physics.

We observe only that each wave has its own scattering amplitude a_l and that there are no transitions between different partial waves because of conservation of orbital angular momentum. The scattering amplitude is a diagonal matrix when referred to states of different l:

$$\begin{matrix} a_0 & 0 & 0\cdots \\ 0 & a_1 & 0\cdots \\ 0 & 0 & a_2\cdots \\ \cdot & \cdot & \cdot \end{matrix} \tag{1}$$

As a simple example of scattering involving many angular momentum waves, we shall treat the scattering from a large impenetrable reflecting sphere of radius $R \gg 1/k$. Such a sphere can be represented by a potential

$$\begin{aligned} V(r) &= \infty \text{ for } r \leq R, \\ V(r) &= 0 \text{ for } r > R. \end{aligned} \tag{2}$$

All the spherical waves must be zero at $r = R$. This condition does not affect appreciably the incident waves with $l > kR$, which are nearly zero at $kr < l$, since the first point of inflection of the lth Bessel function is at $kr = [l(l+1)]^{1/2}$.

For $l < kR$, we require $\sin(kR - \frac{1}{2}l\pi + \delta_l) = 0$, or

$$\delta_l = n\pi + \tfrac{1}{2}l\pi - kR$$

(n integer). Thus, using 3.12(11),

$$\begin{aligned} \sigma &= \frac{4\pi}{k^2}\left[\sum_{l\text{ even}}^{kR}(2l+1)\sin^2 kR + \sum_{l\text{ odd}}^{kR}(2l+1)(1-\sin^2 kR)\right] \\ &= \frac{4\pi}{k^2}\left[\sum_{l\text{ odd}}^{kR}(2l+1) + \sin^2 kR\left(\sum_{l\text{ even}}^{kR}(2l+1) - \sum_{l\text{ odd}}^{kR}(2l+1)\right)\right]. \end{aligned}$$

For kR large the last two sums cancel. The first sum contains $kR/2$ terms, whose average value is $\approx kR$; thus

$$\sigma = \frac{4\pi}{k^2}\frac{kR}{2}kR = 2\pi R^2. \tag{3}$$

This well-known result is twice as large as the geometric cross section and includes the geometrical shadow and the diffraction scattering effects.

b. Scattering of Particles with Spin. When spins are present, the state of the incident beam must be written as the product of a plane wave and of a spin function ζ, which describes the spin state of the incident particle and of the target. Similarly, the scattered wave must contain information about the spins, expressed by a spin function ζ'.

We are led to consider solutions of the wave equation having the asymptotic form[1]

$$\psi \simeq \zeta e^{ikz} + \zeta'(\theta, \phi)\frac{e^{ikr}}{r}. \tag{4}$$

If the spin of the incident particle is s_1 and the spin of the target s_2, there are in all

$$g = (2s_1 + 1)(2s_2 + 1) \tag{5}$$

independent spin states.

Let us indicate with ζ_S an orthonormal set of such states and expand the states ζ and ζ' of (4) as a sum of ζ_S; then for each ζ_S the angular dependence of the incident and scattered waves can be expanded in spherical harmonics as usual. Thus the plane wave is decomposed in a sum over the indices l, S, and the scattered wave in a sum over the indices l', S'.

Orbital angular momentum and spin, however, are not good quantum numbers, and a partial wave corresponding to a certain l and S may give rise to a scattered wave with $l' \neq l$, $S' \neq S$. If we consider that the good quantum numbers are total angular momentum and parity, the amplitudes of the scattered waves form a matrix whose elements depend on many indices and may be written

$$a_{J,l'l,S'S}, \tag{6}$$

where $\mathbf{J} = \mathbf{l} + \mathbf{S} = \mathbf{l}' + \mathbf{S}'$, l' and S' take any value compatible with the conservation laws, and precisely

$$|l' - S'| \leq J \leq |l' + S'|; \qquad (-1)^l = (-1)^{l'}. \tag{7}$$

The amplitudes (6) are complex numbers with a meaning similar to that discussed for zero spin.

Each amplitude corresponds to a phase shift,

$$\delta_{J,l'l,S'S}, \tag{8}$$

[1] For more details see 3.59. The theoretically inclined reader may wish to start from the general treatment of 3.59 and then come back to Sections 3.51, 52, 53, and 54.

to which it is related by a formula similar to 3.12(6). If the scattering is elastic, the phase shifts for definite J and parity are real.

This formalism is clarified by the examples that follow.

c. Spin 0 and $\frac{1}{2}$. If the spins of the two particles are 0 and $\frac{1}{2}$, the eigenstates of J, divided according to parity, are

$$\text{(9)}\qquad \begin{array}{ll} \text{even states:} & S_{1/2}\quad D_{3/2}\quad D_{5/2}\cdots \\ \text{odd states:} & P_{1/2}\quad P_{3/2}\quad F_{5/2}\quad F_{7/2}\cdots \end{array}$$

If the scattering potential contains a spin-orbit coupling term, each one of the foregoing states has its own scattering amplitude. However, there are no possible transitions between any pair of states, since all such transitions would violate either the conservation of angular momentum or that of parity.

The matrix of the scattering amplitudes is again diagonal; its elements a_{lJ} are

(10)

	$S_{1/2}$	$P_{1/2}$	$P_{3/2}$	$D_{3/2}$	$D_{5/2}$
$S_{1/2}$	a_0	0	0	0	0
$P_{1/2}$	0	$a_{1,1/2}$	0	0	0
$P_{3/2}$	0	0	$a_{1,3/2}$	0	0
$D_{3/2}$	0	0	0	$a_{2,3/2}$	0
$D_{5/2}$	0	0	0	0	$a_{2,5/2}$

In order to give a quantitative meaning to the various a_{lJ}, let us consider an incident wave with the spin pointing along the direction of propagation. This wave, αe^{ikz}, can be expanded in eigenfunctions of J and l, making use of 3.12(1), 1.14(31), and Table 1.14-1:

$$\text{(11)}\quad \alpha e^{ikz} = \sum_{l=0}^{\infty} i^l\sqrt{4\pi(2l+1)}\, j_l(kr)\,\alpha Y_l^0(\theta)$$
$$= \sum_{l=0}^{\infty} i\sqrt{4\pi(2l+1)}\, j_l(kr)\left(-\sqrt{\frac{l}{2l+1}}\,\mathcal{Y}^{1/2}_{l-1/2} + \sqrt{\frac{l+1}{2l+1}}\,\mathcal{Y}^{1/2}_{l+1/2}\right).$$

We assign an amplitude $a_{l,l\pm 1/2}$ to each of the partial waves $\mathcal{Y}^{1/2}_{l\pm 1/2}$ in such a way that the total scattered amplitude $f(\theta)$ may be expressed similarly to 3.12(5):

(12)

$$f(\theta) = \sum_{l=0}^{\infty}\sqrt{4\pi(2l+1)}\left[-\sqrt{\frac{l}{2l+1}}\,a_{l,l-1/2}\mathcal{Y}^{1/2}_{l-1/2} + \sqrt{\frac{l+1}{2l+1}}\,a_{l,l+1/2}\mathcal{Y}^{1/2}_{l+1/2}\right].$$

We can now define a scattering phase $\delta_{l,l\pm 1/2}$ for each $a_{l,l\pm 1/2}$ by a relation similar to 3.12(6). The phases introduced keep the meaning of phase shifts of partial waves. We may use a *phase shift matrix* as well as an amplitude matrix.

The differential cross section is obtained by squaring (12): it results in a double sum containing interference terms between the different waves. Because of the orthonormality of the waves, the interference terms disappear in the total cross section:

$$\sigma_{\text{tot}} = \int |f(\theta)|^2 \, d\omega = 4\pi \sum_{l=0}^{\infty} [l a^2_{l,l-\frac{1}{2}} + (l+1) a^2_{l,l+\frac{1}{2}}] = \frac{2\pi}{k^2} \sum_{lJ} (2J+1) \sin^2 \delta_{lJ}. \tag{13}$$

A similar discussion can be made by starting with a wave βe^{ikz} with spin in the $-z$ direction. The total cross section does not contain α and β and is the same for both cases.

d. Spin ½ and ½: Nucleon-Nucleon Scattering. The states of two particles of spin ½ can be divided into singlet and triplets. When different orbital angular momenta are considered, the possible states are

$$\begin{aligned} &\text{even states: } {}^1S_0,\ {}^3S_1,\ {}^1D_2,\ {}^3D_1,\ {}^3D_2,\ {}^3D_3,\ {}^1G_4,\ {}^3G_3,\ {}^3G_4,\ {}^3G_5,\ \cdots, \\ &\text{odd states: } {}^1P_1,\ {}^3P_0,\ {}^3P_1,\ {}^3P_2,\ {}^1F_3,\ {}^3F_2,\ {}^3F_3,\ {}^3F_4,\ \cdots. \end{aligned} \tag{14}$$

Now the scattering may be accompanied by transitions between different lJ states, compatibly with the conservation of total angular momentum. The possible transitions are indicated by arrows in (14). Each state (14) corresponds to a diagonal element in the amplitude matrix and each arrow to a nondiagonal one[1].

If the two particles are nucleons, conservation of isospin (charge independence) requires that the states with $T = 0$ do not mix with those with $T = 1$. The states, and the transitions corresponding to independent amplitudes, can be ordered as follows:

$$\begin{aligned} &T = 0 \begin{cases} \text{even triplets: } \overset{\varepsilon_1}{{}^3S_1 \leftrightarrow {}^3D_1},\ {}^3D_2,\ \overset{\varepsilon_3}{{}^3D_3 \leftrightarrow {}^3G_3},\ {}^3G_4,\ {}^3G_5,\ \cdots, \\ \text{odd singlets: } {}^1P_1,\ {}^1F_3,\ {}^1H_4,\ \cdots, \end{cases} \\ &T = 1 \begin{cases} \text{even singlets: } {}^1S_0,\ {}^1D_2,\ {}^1G_4,\ \cdots, \\ \text{odd triplets: } {}^3P_0,\ {}^3P_1,\ \underset{\varepsilon_2}{{}^3P_2 \leftrightarrow {}^3F_2},\ {}^3F_3,\ \underset{\varepsilon_4}{{}^3F_4 \leftrightarrow {}^3H_4},\ {}^3H_5,\ {}^3H_6,\ \cdots. \end{cases} \end{aligned} \tag{15}$$

[1] The amplitude matrix can be diagonalized by taking linear combinations of the states corresponding to definite J and parity. The phase shifts corresponding to the diagonalized matrix are real.

The result of charge independence is to forbid triplet $\rightleftharpoons$ singlet transitions such as ${}^1D_2 \rightleftharpoons {}^3D_2$. This is in agreement with our remark in 1.33(13) that S is a good quantum number in the interaction between two nucleons.

All the amplitudes (15) may enter in n-p scattering, but in the case of p-p scattering only those for $T = 1$ must be considered.

e. Cross Sections, Polarization, and Spin-Flips. So far we have considered the amplitudes as depending on l and J; in this way the discussion is simplified by the direct application of the conservation principles.

However, in order to describe the angular distribution by means of a differential cross section, we must keep track of the separate orbital angular momentum functions $Y_l^m(\theta, \varphi)$; and, if we want to compute polarization and spin effects, we must refer to the separate functions of spins of the two particles $\zeta_{s_1}^{m_1}, \zeta_{s_2}^{m_2}$.

For this analysis each lJ state must be decomposed into the substates corresponding to definite values of the magnetic quantum numbers. The amplitude may be considered as a matrix in these substates; spin flips are possible and the matrix is not necessarily diagonal. We shall illustrate the situation with the example of the scattering of neutrons in He (3.52).

If beam and target are polarized, we are interested in the cross section, differential or total, of a given spin state ζ_i. However, if we do not select the polarization after scattering, we must sum the cross section[1] over all orthogonal final states ζ_f:

$$\sigma_\zeta = \sum_f \sigma_{\zeta_i \to \zeta_f}. \tag{16}$$

And, finally, if the initial beam and target are not polarized, we must average over the unobserved initial spins:

$$\sigma = \frac{1}{g} \sum_{i,f} \sigma_{\zeta_i \to \zeta_f}. \tag{17}$$

We have already made use of these ideas in the special case of scattering for $l = 0$.

3.52 *Scattering of Neutrons in He*

a. The Structure of the Amplitude Matrix. We have reported in 2.12 some of the conclusions that can be drawn from the scattering of neutrons in He, but we have not explained how such conclusions are derived from the experimental data.

We must consider for our discussion the experimental results on the n-He differential scattering cross section as a function of energy. Some

[1] The scattering is supposed to be incoherent.

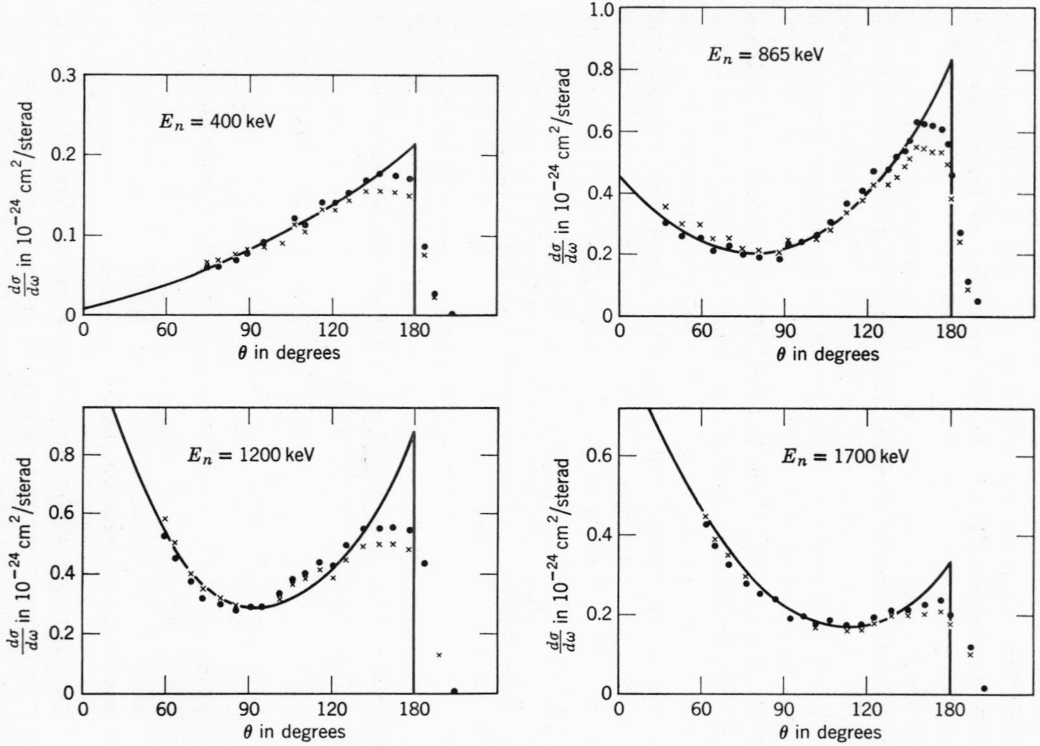

Fig. 3.52-1. The center-of-mass angular distribution for n-He scattering at various bombarding energies [from R. K. Adair, *Phys. Rev.*, **86,** 157, 158 (1952)].

of the data (A-52, S-53) are shown in Fig. 3.52-1, with continuous curves corresponding to the equation

$$\frac{d\sigma}{d\omega} = A(k) + B(k)\cos\theta + C(k)\cos^2\theta, \tag{1}$$

where the coefficients $A(k)$, $B(k)$, and $C(k)$ are chosen for a best fit with the experiment.

The purpose of the present analysis[1] is to determine the scattering amplitudes, as a function of energy, from the empirical coefficients $A(k)$, $B(k)$, and $C(k)$.

Since the data are adequately represented without the use of powers of $\cos\theta$ higher than the second, the scattering can be interpreted in terms of S and P waves only.

The partial wave-scattering amplitudes form a matrix, A, as shown in 3.51(10), with only three diagonal elements, which we call a_0, a_1, and a_3:

(2)

	$S_{1/2}$	$P_{1/2}$	$P_{3/2}$
$S_{1/2}$	a_0	0	0
$P_{1/2}$	0	a_1	0
$P_{3/2}$	0	0	a_3

In order to interpret the observed angular distributions, it is necessary to refer (2) to eigenstates of l and m_l, since each value of m_l has its characteristic angular dependence.

If we consider that the states $S_{1/2}$, $P_{1/2}$, and $P_{3/2}$ have multiplicity 2, 2, and 4, the scattering amplitude becomes an 8×8 matrix when referred to eigenstates of l, m_s, and m_l. It takes the following form:

(3)

scatt ↓ \ inc →	αY_0^0	βY_0^0	αY_1^{+1}	αY_1^0	αY_1^{-1}	βY_1^{+1}	βY_1^0	βY_1^{-1}
αY_0^0	a_0	0	0	0	0	0	0	0
βY_0^0	0	a_0	0	0	0	0	0	0
αY_1^{+1}	0	0	a_3	0	0	0	0	0
αY_1^0	0	0	0	$a_{\alpha\alpha}$	0	$x_{\alpha\beta}$	0	0
αY_1^{-1}	0	0	0	0	$x_{\alpha\alpha}$	0	$a_{\alpha\beta}$	0
βY_1^1	0	0	0	$a_{\beta\alpha}$	0	$x_{\beta\beta}$	0	0
βY_1^0	0	0	0	0	$x_{\beta\alpha}$	0	$a_{\beta\beta}$	0
βY_1^{-1}	0	0	0	0	0	0	0	a_3

[1] The present treatment applies in its entirety to the scattering of π mesons (spin 0) by nucleons (spin $\frac{1}{2}$), and it is for this reason that we carry on the analysis in considerable detail.

All of the diagonal elements may be different from zero; furthermore, there may be some nonvanishing nondiagonal elements corresponding to spin-flip transitions compatible with the conservation laws.

If we now choose the axis of quantization in the direction of the incoming beam, the incident wave must have $m_l = 0$ because of the axial symmetry of the problem. The initial states to be considered and the interesting matrix elements are those encircled in (3).

We can easily compute (with the help of Table 1.14-3)

$$\begin{aligned} a_{\alpha\alpha} = a_{\beta\beta} &= \langle \alpha Y_1{}^0 \,|A|\, \alpha Y_1{}^0 \rangle \\ &= \langle \sqrt{\tfrac{2}{3}}\mathcal{Y}^{1/2}_{3/2} - \sqrt{\tfrac{1}{3}}\mathcal{Y}^{1/2}_{1/2} \,|A|\, \sqrt{\tfrac{2}{3}}\mathcal{Y}^{1/2}_{3/2} - \sqrt{\tfrac{1}{3}}\mathcal{Y}^{1/2}_{1/2} \rangle \\ &= \tfrac{2}{3}a_3 + \tfrac{1}{3}a_1. \end{aligned} \tag{4}$$

$$\begin{aligned} a_{\beta\alpha} = a_{\alpha\beta} &= \langle \beta Y_1{}^1 \,|A|\, \alpha Y_1{}^0 \rangle \\ &= \langle \sqrt{\tfrac{1}{3}}\mathcal{Y}^{1/2}_{3/2} + \sqrt{\tfrac{2}{3}}\mathcal{Y}^{1/2}_{1/2} \,|A|\, \sqrt{\tfrac{2}{3}}\mathcal{Y}^{1/2}_{3/2} - \sqrt{\tfrac{1}{3}}\mathcal{Y}^{1/2}_{1/2} \rangle \\ &= \frac{\sqrt{2}}{3}\,a_3 - \frac{\sqrt{2}}{3}\,a_1. \end{aligned} \tag{5}$$

It is seen that spin flips ($a_{\beta\alpha} \neq 0$) are predicted only if there is spin-orbit coupling ($a_3 \neq a_1$).

b. Determination of the Scattering Phases from the Differential Cross Section. Let us assume that the incident beam is polarized along the direction of propagation, which has been chosen as the axis of quantization. Then the amplitude of the scattered wave can be obtained from 3.51(12):

$$f_\alpha = \sqrt{4\pi}\,a_0\mathcal{Y}^{1/2}_{0\,1/2\,1/2} + \sqrt{4\pi}\sqrt{3}\left(-\sqrt{\tfrac{1}{3}}\,a_1\mathcal{Y}^{1/2}_{1\,1/2\,1/2} + \sqrt{\tfrac{2}{3}}\,a_3\mathcal{Y}^{1/2}_{1\,1/2\,3/2}\right).$$

From this, using the law of addition of angular momentum,

$$\begin{aligned} \mathcal{Y}^{1/2}_{1\,1/2\,1/2} &= -\sqrt{\tfrac{1}{3}}Y_1{}^0\alpha + \sqrt{\tfrac{2}{3}}Y_1{}^1\beta, \\ \mathcal{Y}^{1/2}_{1\,1/2\,3/2} &= \sqrt{\tfrac{2}{3}}Y_1{}^0\alpha + \sqrt{\tfrac{1}{3}}Y_1{}^1\beta, \end{aligned}$$

we obtain

$$f_\alpha = \sqrt{4\pi}\,a_0Y_0{}^0\alpha + \sqrt{4\pi}\sqrt{3}\left[(\tfrac{1}{3}a_1 + \tfrac{2}{3}a_3)Y_1{}^0\alpha + \left(-\frac{\sqrt{2}}{3}\,a_1 + \frac{\sqrt{2}}{3}\,a_3\right)Y_1{}^1\beta\right].$$

This equation, in agreement with (4) and (5), shows that the partial wave $Y_1{}^0\alpha$ scatters with amplitude $a_{\alpha\alpha}$ and gives rise to a spin-flipped wave $Y_1{}^1\beta$ with amplitude $a_{\beta\alpha}$.

Finally, when the expressions for the spherical harmonics 1.13(11) are used, f_α assumes the form

$$f_\alpha = a_0\alpha + (2a_3 + a_1)\alpha\cos\theta + (a_1 - a_3)\beta\sin\theta e^{i\varphi}. \tag{6a}$$

If, instead, we had started from an initial state β, we would have obtained

$$f_\beta = a_0\beta + (2a_3 + a_1)\beta\cos\theta - (a_1 - a_3)\alpha\sin\theta e^{-i\varphi}. \tag{6b}$$

Let us now apply this formalism to the determination of the phase shifts from the measurements of cross section.

If the initial beam is not polarized, it can be considered as an incoherent mixture of α and β with equal probability. Since $|f_\alpha|^2 = |f_\beta|^2$, the angular distribution of the scattering is the same for initial polarization α, β, or for an unpolarized beam; namely

$$|f_\alpha|^2 = |f_\beta|^2 = |a_0 + (2a_3 + a_1)\cos\theta|^2 + |a_1 - a_3|^2(1 - \cos^2\theta). \tag{7}$$

This formula can be compared directly with (1), and we obtain the equations

$$\begin{aligned} A(k) &= |a_0|^2 + |a_1 - a_3|^2, \\ B(k) &= 2\,\mathrm{Re}\, a_0^*(2a_3 + a_1), \\ C(k) &= |2a_3 + a_1|^2 - |a_1 - a_3|^2. \end{aligned} \tag{8}$$

Each amplitude a_i can be expressed by a real phase δ_i, and (8) can be solved for δ_0, δ_1, and δ_3. The results are plotted in Fig. 3.52-2. It is clear that the first resonance occurs where $\delta_3 = 90°$ and that it is due to the $P_{3/2}$ state.

c. Polarization Effects. According to conservation of parity, the vector **k**, and thus the z direction, cannot define a privileged axis for spin orientation, but the pseudovector $\mathbf{k} \times \mathbf{k}'$ ($\mathbf{k}'$ is the wave vector of the scattered neutron), perpendicular to the scattering plane, can be coupled with the spin. Thus a beam of neutrons scattered by He can be polarized in the direction perpendicular to the plane of scattering.

The origin of this polarization can be understood with a simple classical argument. Let us consider a particle scattered by an attractive center and suppose that the scattering occurs only if the spin is parallel to the orbital angular momentum. This corresponds to an extreme case of spin-orbit coupling: $a_1 = 0$, $a_3 \neq 0$.

It is seen in Fig. 3.52-3 that in this assumption the particles deflected to the right are polarized with spin down and those deflected to the left are polarized with spin up.

Let us go back to the quantum mechanical treatment of n-He scattering[1] by supposing that the scattering occurs in the xz plane (Fig. 3.52-4).

[1] We follow a paper by Fermi (F-53a), in which this calculation is developed because of its interest in π-p scattering.

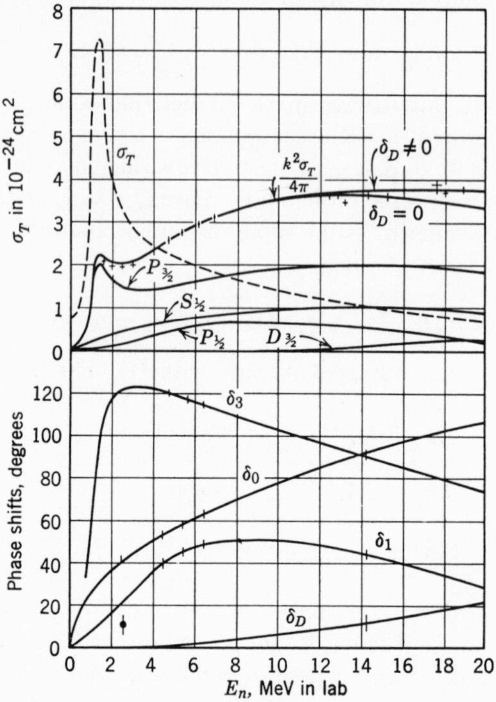

Fig. 3.52-2. Total cross section (upper part) and phase shifts (lower part) for n-α scattering up to 20 MeV. Experimental points, in the form $k^2\sigma_T/4\pi$, are compared with the cross sections of the partial waves, computed from the phase shifts of the lower figure [from J. D. Seagrave, *Phys. Rev.*, **92,** 1227 (1953)].

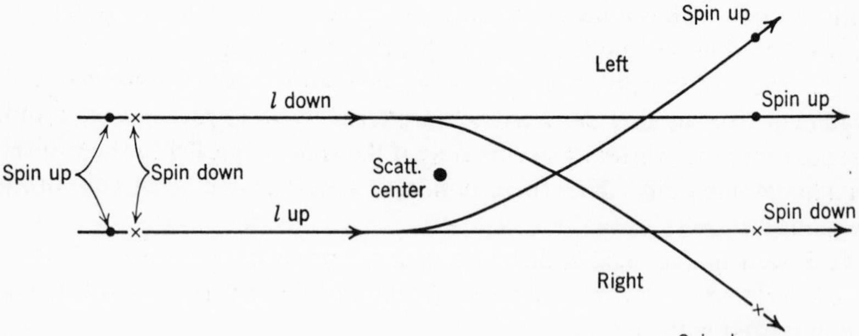

Fig. 3.52-3. Classical explanation of polarization effects in the case of extreme spin-orbit coupling. One assumes attraction for $P_{3/2}$ and no interaction for the other partial waves.

It is useful to introduce a matrix F whose elements, referred to the spin states α and β, are

$$
\begin{aligned}
F_{\alpha\alpha} &= F_{\beta\beta} = a_0 + (2a_3 + a_1)\cos\theta, \\
F_{\alpha\beta} &= -(a_1 - a_3)\sin\theta\, e^{-i\varphi}, \\
F_{\beta\alpha} &= (a_1 - a_3)\sin\theta\, e^{i\varphi}.
\end{aligned} \tag{9}
$$

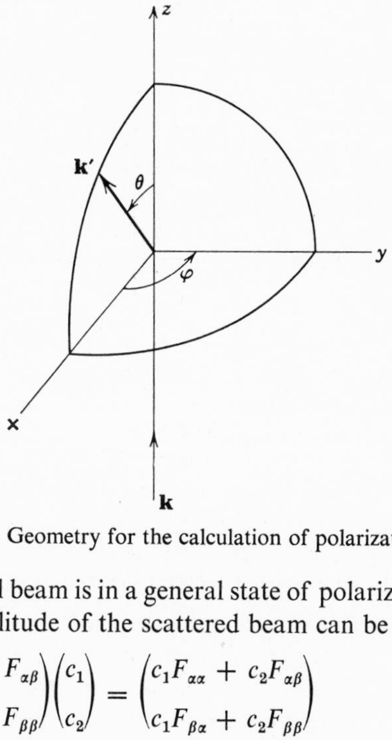

Fig. 3.52-4. Geometry for the calculation of polarization effects.

Then, if the initial beam is in a general state of polarization $\zeta_i = \begin{pmatrix} c_1 \\ c_2 \end{pmatrix} = c_1\alpha + c_2\beta$, the amplitude of the scattered beam can be written

$$
\begin{aligned}
F_{\zeta_i} &= \begin{pmatrix} F_{\alpha\alpha} & F_{\alpha\beta} \\ F_{\beta\alpha} & F_{\beta\beta} \end{pmatrix}\begin{pmatrix} c_1 \\ c_2 \end{pmatrix} = \begin{pmatrix} c_1F_{\alpha\alpha} + c_2F_{\alpha\beta} \\ c_1F_{\beta\alpha} + c_2F_{\beta\beta} \end{pmatrix} \\
&= (c_1F_{\alpha\alpha} + c_2F_{\alpha\beta})\alpha + (c_1F_{\beta\alpha} + c_2F_{\beta\beta})\beta = c_1f_\alpha + c_2f_\beta.
\end{aligned} \tag{10}
$$

The matrix F, like the matrix A, completely describes the scattering law for S and P waves. The elements of F depend on the direction of the scattering, since they refer to spin states, whereas the elements of A do not depend on the scattering angle which is contained in the eigenstates of orbital angular momentum.

The scattering amplitudes (9) for scattering to the left ($\varphi = 0$; $e^{\pm i\varphi} = 1$) are

$$
\begin{aligned}
(F_{\alpha\alpha})_{\text{left}} &= (F_{\beta\beta})_{\text{left}} = a_0 + (2a_3 + a_1)\cos\theta, \\
(F_{\alpha\beta})_{\text{left}} &= -(F_{\beta\alpha})_{\text{left}} = -(a_1 - a_3)\sin\theta,
\end{aligned} \tag{11}
$$

whereas, if the scattering is to the "right" ($\varphi = \pi$; $e^{\pm i\varphi} = -1$) the sign of $\sin\theta$ is inverted. Thus, if the incident beam is not polarized, the final wave contains the states α and β with equal probability to the left as well as to the right: as expected, there is no polarization in the direction of the incident beam.

Let us now study the probability of finding the neutron spin directed along the $\pm y$ direction. The spin eigenstates for the $\pm y$ direction ($\theta = \pi/2$, $\varphi = \pm\pi/2$) are [use 1.14(12) multiplied, for convenience, by a unitary phase factor exp $[\pm i(\pi/4)]$, which does not affect the calculation of the probabilities]:

$$(12) \quad \exp[\pm i(\pi/4)]\begin{pmatrix} \cos\frac{\pi}{4}\exp[\mp i(\pi/4)] \\ \sin\frac{\pi}{4}\exp[\pm i(\pi/4)] \end{pmatrix} = \frac{1}{\sqrt{2}}\begin{pmatrix} 1 \\ \pm i \end{pmatrix} = \frac{1}{\sqrt{2}}(\alpha \pm i\beta).$$

For initial state α the probability amplitude for scattered spin in the $\pm y$ direction is, for scattering to the left, the projection of the scattered wave on the states (12):

$$(13) \quad \frac{1}{\sqrt{2}}(\alpha \pm i\beta)^{\dagger}[(F_{\alpha\alpha})_{\text{left}}\,\alpha + (F_{\beta\alpha})_{\text{left}}\,\beta] = \frac{1}{\sqrt{2}}[(F_{\alpha\alpha})_{\text{left}} \mp i(F_{\beta\alpha})_{\text{left}}].$$

Apart from phase factors, this amplitude is the same for initial spin α or β. Thus the intensities for scattered spin in the $\pm y$ direction are obtained by squaring (13):

(14)

$$(I_{\pm y})_{\text{left}} = |(F_{\alpha\alpha})_{\text{left}} \mp i(F_{\beta\alpha})_{\text{left}}|^2 = |a_0 + (2a_3 + a_1)\cos\theta \mp i(a_1 - a_3)\sin\theta|^2$$

Since the amplitudes are complex, the intensities for $\pm y$ spin are different. Equation (14) refers to scattering to the left; for scattering to the right the two intensities are interchanged. As expected, there is no polarization for $\theta = 0$ nor for $a_1 = a_3$.

The *polarization* of the beam can be obtained from (14)

$$(15) \qquad P = \frac{I_+ - I_-}{I_+ + I_-} = \frac{2\,\text{Im}\,F_{\alpha\alpha}{}^*F_{\beta\alpha}}{|F_{\alpha\alpha}|^2 + |F_{\beta\beta}|^2}.$$

If the incident beam is polarized, say in the $+y$ direction, this polarization is maintained after the scattering, but the intensities on the right and left side may be different; we speak then of left-right *asymmetry*. Formally, if the initial state is $(1/\sqrt{2})(\alpha + i\beta)$, the scattered wave is

$$\frac{1}{\sqrt{2}}(F_{\alpha\alpha}\alpha + F_{\beta\alpha}\beta) + \frac{i}{\sqrt{2}}(F_{\alpha\beta}\alpha + F_{\beta\beta}\beta);$$

considering that $F_{\beta\alpha} = -F_{\alpha\beta} = \pm(a_1 - a_3)\sin\theta$ for left and right scattering, we can easily see that the left and right scattered intensity is given by an expression similar to (14):

$$I_{\substack{\text{left}\\\text{right}}} = |a_0 + (2a_3 + a_1)\cos\theta \mp i(a_1 - a_3)\sin\theta|^2, \tag{16}$$

and finally the asymmetry is given by the same expression as the polarization (15):

$$A = \frac{(I)_{\text{left}} - (I)_{\text{right}}}{(I)_{\text{left}} + (I)_{\text{right}}} = \frac{2\,\text{Im}\,F_{\alpha\alpha}{}^*F_{\beta\alpha}}{|F_{\alpha\alpha}|^2 + |F_{\beta\beta}|^2}. \tag{17}$$

d. Polarization Experiments. We have shown how it is possible to use right or left scattering of neutrons in He as a *polarizer* or *analyzer* of fast neutrons. It is also useful to employ, as in optics, a polarizer followed by an analyzer. This leads us to consider double scattering.

A double-scattering experiment reveals an asymmetry defined as

$$e = \frac{(LL) - (LR)}{(LL) + (LR)}, \tag{18}$$

where (LL) stands for the intensity of a beam scattered twice to the left, etc.

Let us assume that the beam scattered a first time to the left has a polarization P_1. Thus, apart from a constant,

$$I_+ = \frac{1 + P_1}{2}, \qquad I_- = \frac{1 - P_1}{2}. \tag{19}$$

In a second scattering the $\frac{1}{2}(1 + P_1)$ neutrons with spin up have a probability $\frac{1}{2}(1 + P_2)$ of being scattered again to the left and a probability $\frac{1}{2}(1 - P_2)$ of being scattered to the right (again apart from a common factor); the situation is reversed for the spin-down neutrons. Thus

$$\begin{aligned} (LL) &\simeq (1 + P_1)(1 + P_2) + (1 - P_1)(1 - P_2) = 2(1 + P_1P_2), \\ (LR) &\simeq (1 + P_1)(1 - P_2) + (1 - P_1)(1 + P_2) = 2(1 - P_1P_2), \end{aligned} \tag{20}$$

from which

$$e = \frac{1 + P_1P_2 - (1 - P_1P_2)}{1 + P_1P_2 + (1 - P_1P_2)} = P_1P_2. \tag{21}$$

If the conditions of the first and second scattering are the same (same angle and small energy difference), the polarization can be measured

$$P = \sqrt{e}. \tag{22}$$

Measurements of polarization are valuable in a phase analysis of the scattering. It sometimes happens that two sets of phases represent equally well the unpolarized cross sections and that the *ambiguity* may be resolved by means of polarization measurements.

This has happened both for n-He and for π-$\mathcal{N}$ scattering. The polarization experiments with n-He of Levintov et al. (L-57) have proved that the phases of Seagrave (Fig. 3.52-2) were correct, and that another set, due to Huber and Baldinger (H-52b) should be discarded.

3.53 High-Energy Scattering in the Born Approximation

a. Normal Potential. As the energy increases, more and more partial waves must be considered. The partial-wave analysis becomes very involved and is fit for electronic computation rather than for analytical discussion. However, it is possible to analyze some aspects of scattering experiments without decomposing the beams into partial angular momentum waves. In this section we discuss the characteristics of the scattering predicted by the Born approximation—which may be used at energies of the order of several hundred MeV—for some of the different types of nuclear forces described in 1.2 and 1.3.

Let us start with the case of "normal" or "Wigner" forces, corresponding to a potential $V(r)$ which depends on position only and does not involve spin or isospin operators. At sufficiently high energy the scattering amplitude can be written

$$(1) \qquad f(\theta) = -\frac{\mu}{2\pi\hbar^2}\int e^{-i\mathbf{k}'\cdot\mathbf{r}}V(r)e^{i\mathbf{k}\cdot\mathbf{r}}\,d\mathbf{r} = -\frac{\mu}{2\pi\hbar^2}\int e^{i\mathbf{q}\cdot\mathbf{r}}\,V(r)\,d\mathbf{r},$$

where $\mathbf{k}$ and $\mathbf{k}'$ are the initial and final wave vectors, μ is the reduced mass, and

$$(2) \qquad \mathbf{q} = \mathbf{k} - \mathbf{k}'; \qquad |q| = 2k \sin\frac{\theta}{2}.$$

If $V(r)$ is a square well of radius r_0 and depth V_0, the integral becomes

$$(3) \qquad \begin{aligned} -V_0\int e^{iqr\cos\theta}\,2\pi r^2\,dr d\cos\theta &= V_0\int \frac{1}{iqr}(e^{iqr} - e^{-iqr})2\pi r^2\,dr \\ &= \frac{4\pi V_0}{q}\int_0^{r_0}(\sin qr)r\,dr. \end{aligned}$$

The integral is small if $\sin qr$ has many oscillations between 0 and r_0. Thus only small values of q contribute, and the scattering is limited to a *forward* cone defined by

$$(4) \qquad qr_0 < 1, \qquad \sin\frac{\theta}{2} < \frac{1}{2kr_0}.$$

In a nucleon-nucleon collision with sufficiently high energy (several hundred MeV), $kr_0 \gg 1$, and the aperture of the cone is simply

$$\theta < \frac{1}{kr_0}. \tag{5}$$

b. Majorana Exchange Forces. Let us now consider the scattering of two nucleons, assuming that the potential is an exchange potential of the Majorana type containing the operator $\mathcal{P}_r$ (1.33). In this case the scattering amplitude in the Born approximation is

$$\begin{aligned} f(r) &= -\frac{\mu}{2\pi\hbar^2}\int e^{-i\mathbf{k}'\cdot\mathbf{r}}\, V(r)\, \mathcal{P}_r e^{i\mathbf{k}\cdot\mathbf{r}}\, d\mathbf{r} \\ &= -\frac{\mu}{2\pi\hbar^2}\int e^{-i\mathbf{k}'\cdot\mathbf{r}}\, V(r) e^{-i\mathbf{k}\cdot\mathbf{r}}\, d\mathbf{r} \\ &= -\frac{\mu}{2\pi\hbar^2}\int e^{-i\mathbf{Q}\cdot\mathbf{r}}\, V(r)\, d\mathbf{r}, \end{aligned} \tag{6}$$

where

$$\mathbf{Q} = \mathbf{k} + \mathbf{k}', \quad |Q| = 2k\cos\frac{\theta}{2}. \tag{7}$$

For a square well of radius r_0 the scattering is limited to the *backward* cone

$$Qr_0 < 1, \quad \cos\frac{\theta}{2} < \frac{1}{2kr_0}. \tag{8}$$

For $kr_0 \gg 1$ the aperture of the cone reduces to

$$\pi - \theta < \frac{1}{kr_0}. \tag{9}$$

c. Spin Orbit Coupling. We now discuss the scattering of a particle of spin $\frac{1}{2}$ by a nucleus in the assumption of spin-orbit coupling. Typical is the scattering of protons from carbon, which is often used to produce high-energy polarized proton beams[1].

Let us assume a potential

$$V(r) + \frac{1}{\hbar}W(r)\frac{\boldsymbol{\sigma}}{2}\cdot\mathbf{L}, \tag{10}$$

where $\mathbf{L}$ is the usual orbital angular momentum operator [1.13(2)], and define for convenience a function $Y(r)$ from

$$W(r) = -\left(\frac{\hbar}{\mu c}\right)^2 \frac{1}{r}\frac{dY}{dr}. \tag{11}$$

[1] The present section, and much of the rest of the discussion of polarization, follows the lines of L. Wolfenstein (W-56).

The factors are chosen in such a way that the functions V, W, and Y have the same dimensions.

The scattering amplitude is composed of two parts,

$$f = f_V + f_W; \tag{12}$$

f_V has been discussed in the Born approximation in (a) and (b), and

$$\begin{aligned} f_W &= \frac{-i}{4\pi\mu c^2}\int e^{-i\mathbf{k}'\cdot\mathbf{r}}\frac{1}{r}\frac{dY}{dr}\,\boldsymbol{\sigma}\cdot(\mathbf{r}\times\nabla\, e^{i\mathbf{k}\cdot\mathbf{r}})\,d\mathbf{r} \\ &= \frac{-1}{4\pi\mu c^2}\,\boldsymbol{\sigma}\times\mathbf{k}\cdot\int e^{i(\mathbf{k}-\mathbf{k}')\cdot\mathbf{r}}\frac{dY}{dr}\nabla r\,d\mathbf{r}. \end{aligned} \tag{13}$$

Integrating by parts we obtain

$$\begin{aligned} f_W &= \frac{-1}{4\pi\mu c^2}\,\boldsymbol{\sigma}\times\mathbf{k}\cdot\int e^{i(\mathbf{k}-\mathbf{k}')\cdot\mathbf{r}}\,\nabla Y\,d\mathbf{r} \\ &= \frac{i}{4\pi\mu c^2}\,\boldsymbol{\sigma}\times\mathbf{k}\cdot(\mathbf{k}-\mathbf{k}')\int Y e^{i\mathbf{q}\cdot\mathbf{r}}\,d\mathbf{r}. \end{aligned} \tag{14}$$

But, since $\boldsymbol{\sigma}\times\mathbf{k}\cdot\mathbf{k} = 0$,

$$f_W = \frac{-i}{4\pi\mu c^2}\,\boldsymbol{\sigma}\cdot\mathbf{k}\times\mathbf{k}'\int Y e^{i\mathbf{q}\cdot\mathbf{r}}\,d\mathbf{r}. \tag{15}$$

In the usual assumption that Y is real this amplitude is imaginary.

The angular dependence of f_W is determined by two factors: one is the integral which, as we have seen, has a maximum in the forward direction, and the other is the cross product $\mathbf{k}\times\mathbf{k}'$ whose magnitude is $k^2\sin\theta$ and has a maximum at 90°. The differential cross section corresponding to spin-orbit coupling should vary with angle less rapidly than that due to central forces.

Let us now discuss the polarization. We can observe that

$$f_W = \mp\frac{i}{4\pi\mu c^2}k^2\sin\theta\int Y e^{i\mathbf{q}\cdot\mathbf{r}}\,d\mathbf{r}, \tag{16}$$

where the sign $\mp$ has to be chosen according to whether the spin is parallel or antiparallel to the vector $\mathbf{k}\times\mathbf{k}'$.

It follows from (16) that no polarization is expected in the Born approximation if both $V(r)$ and $W(r)$ are real: in this case f_V is real and f_W is pure imaginary and the cross section is proportional to $|f_V|^2 + |f_W|^2$ for either sign in (16).

If $W(r)$ is taken as real, we expect polarization effects only if $V(r)$, and thus f_V, is complex. A complex potential, as well as a complex index of refraction, corresponds to absorption: since fast nucleons produce stars and other reactions in collisions with nuclei, the potentials are complex and polarization effects are expected in the Born approximation.

If, for example, we assume

$$(17)\qquad \begin{aligned} &V(r) = V_1 + iV_2; \qquad Y(r) = Y \quad \text{for } r < r_0, \\ &V(r) = Y(r) = 0 \qquad\qquad\qquad \text{for } r > r_0, \end{aligned}$$

in which V_1, V_2, and Y are real constants, the amplitude is, from (12), (1), (3), and (16),

$$(18)\qquad f = -\frac{2\mu}{\hbar^2 q}\left(V_1 + iV_2 \pm iY\frac{\hbar^2}{2\mu^2c^2}k^2\sin\theta\right)\int_0^{r_0}(\sin qr)\,r\,dr$$

and the differential scattering cross section is

$$(19)\qquad |f|^2 = \frac{4\mu^2}{\hbar^4 q^2}\left(V_1^2 + V_2^2 + Y^2\frac{\hbar^4}{4\mu^4c^4}k^4\sin^2\theta \pm V_2Y\frac{\hbar^2}{\mu^2c^2}k^2\sin\theta\right) \times \left[\int_0^{r_0}(\sin qr)r\,dr\right]^2.$$

d. Comparison with Experiment. The high energy ($\approx$ 500 MeV) scattering cross section of neutrons by protons (Fig. 3.57-2) shows two maxima, in the forward and backward directions. The cross section is almost symmetrical around 90°.

From (5) and (9) these maxima could be interpreted as the result of an equal amount of normal and Majorana-exchange forces. A force of this type

$$(20)\qquad \tfrac{1}{2}(1 + \mathfrak{I}_r)\,V(r)$$

is called a "Serber" force.[1]

The proton-proton cross section, instead, is almost spherically symmetrical at the same energy, and this fact can be interpreted as evidence in favor of spin-orbit or tensor forces.

From the practical point of view, we can use the exchange nature of the forces in order to produce beams of high-energy neutrons. The proton beam of a synchrocyclotron is made to strike an internal target from which a sizable percentage of the protons is scattered backward in the center-of-mass system, ejecting forward neutrons in the laboratory system. The process may be regarded equally well as a forward scattering of protons which have flipped their isotopic spin by exchanging their charge with a neutron of the target.

Polarization effects are also observed. If we introduce an internal carbon target into a synchrocyclotron and study the scattered beam that

[1] The "Serber" force is not in quantitative agreement with experiment. See 3.57 for a more up-to-date discussion of n-p scattering.

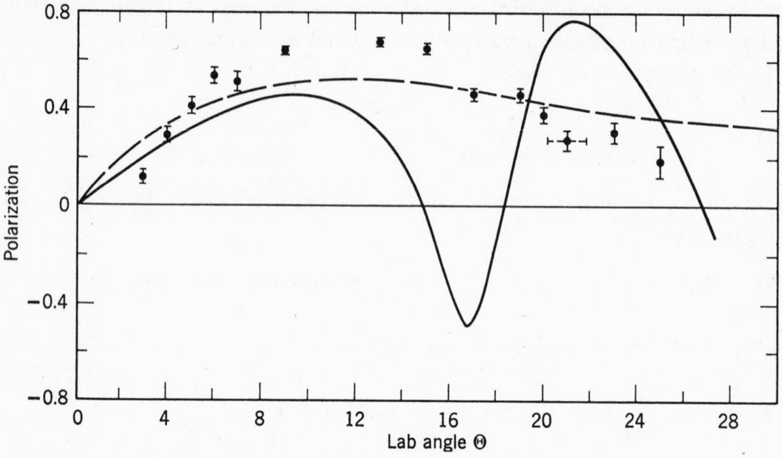

Fig. 3.53-1. Experimental data on polarization for 313-MeV protons scattered by carbon, compared with Born approximation calculations (dashed line) [from L. Wolfenstein, *Ann. Rev. Nucl. Sci.*, **6,** 55 (1956)].

emerges from the machine, we find that it is polarized. The polarization may be measured with a double-scattering experiment, and the results (Fig. 3.53-1) are in rough agreement with the prediction of the Born approximation.

In other cases (Fig. 3.53-2) the Born approximation is not adequate, and a better fit can be obtained with a more accurate treatment.

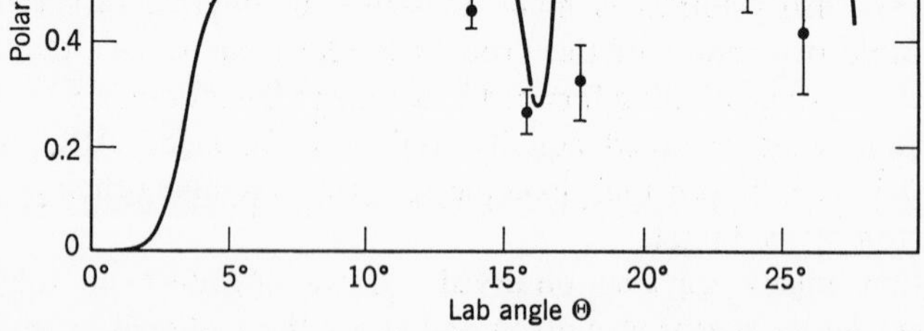

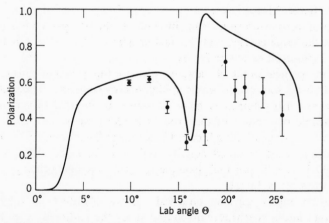

Fig. 3.53-2. Experimental data on polarization for 300-MeV protons scattered by aluminum and theoretical fit due to Sternheimer [from L. Wolfenstein, *Ann. Rev. Nucl. Sci.*, **6,** 56 (1956)].

The production of polarized beams of high-energy protons is of considerable interest in the study of nucleon-nucleon interactions.

3.54 *Polarization Measurements in the Scattering of Spin $\frac{1}{2}$ Particles*

a. Spin 0 and $\frac{1}{2}$. We shall now discuss some of the features in the scattering of spin $\frac{1}{2}$ particles without resorting to the expansion in a finite number of partial waves or to any other approximate method. We focus our attention on the behavior of the spin rather than on the angular distribution.

If the scattering process involves two particles of spin 0 and $\frac{1}{2}$, the complete asymptotic wave function which solves the Schrödinger equation with the scattering potential takes the form

$$\begin{pmatrix} a \\ b \end{pmatrix} e^{i\mathbf{k}\cdot\mathbf{r}} + \begin{pmatrix} u(\theta, \varphi) \\ v(\theta, \varphi) \end{pmatrix} \frac{e^{ikr}}{r}, \tag{1}$$

where a and b (normalized so that $|a|^2 + |b|^2 = 1$) are constants describing the spin of the incident wave, and u and v are complex functions of the scattering angles θ and φ. The spin function $\begin{pmatrix} u \\ v \end{pmatrix}$ is not normalized, and its square describes the intensity of the scattered beam.

In order to obtain the scattering amplitude for a beam in a general state of polarization $\begin{pmatrix} a \\ b \end{pmatrix} = a\alpha + b\beta$, it is sufficient to know the amplitudes for the states α and β; but, if we choose the axis of spin quantization along the direction of incidence, the amplitudes for these two states are related by invariance under reflection. Thus it is sufficient to determine experimentally the scattering amplitudes for only one initial state of polarization. For this purpose we need to perform three measurements at each angle, since we must find the functions $|u|$ and $|v|$ and their phase difference.

In order to determine what kind of measurements must be made, let us introduce

$$|f(\theta, \varphi)|^2 = |u(\theta, \varphi)|^2 + |v(\theta, \varphi)|^2 \tag{2}$$

and describe the direction of polarization of the scattered beam through the angles θ_s and φ_s (functions of θ, φ) expressing the direction of the spin:

$$\frac{1}{|f|} \begin{pmatrix} u(\theta, \varphi) \\ v(\theta, \varphi) \end{pmatrix} = \begin{pmatrix} \cos(\theta_s/2) \exp[-i(\varphi_s/2)] \\ \sin(\theta_s/2) \exp[i(\varphi_s/2)] \end{pmatrix}. \tag{3}$$

It is clear that a complete study of scattering, at each scattering angle θ, requires a measurement of the differential cross section

$$\frac{d\sigma}{d\omega} = |f|^2 = |u|^2 + |v|^2, \tag{4}$$

and a measurement of the angles θ_s and φ_s.

The angle θ_s can be determined from the polarization of the scattered beam measured from the normal to the plane of scattering

$$P = \frac{u^2 - v^2}{u^2 + v^2} = \frac{\cos^2(\theta_s/2) - \sin^2(\theta_s/2)}{\cos^2(\theta_s/2) + \sin^2(\theta_s/2)} = \cos\theta_s, \tag{5}$$

and can be obtained with a double-scattering experiment, as described in 3.52.

The determination of φ_s requires a measurement of triple scattering.

The problem of the scattering of two particles of spin 0 and $\frac{1}{2}$ can also be treated with the help of an *amplitude matrix* F. For the situation described in (1) the amplitude matrix is such that[1]

$$\begin{pmatrix} u(\theta, \varphi) \\ v(\theta, \varphi) \end{pmatrix} = F(\theta, \varphi)\begin{pmatrix} a \\ b \end{pmatrix}. \tag{6}$$

Since it is a 2×2 matrix, it can be expanded as a sum, with appropriate coefficients, of the unit matrix and of the three Pauli spin matrices. The coefficients are limited by the restriction that the scattering matrix must be a scalar, since it transforms a spin $\frac{1}{2}$ function into another function for the same spin. Thus the matrix $\boldsymbol{\sigma}$ must be dotted with a pseudovector, depending on the geometry of the scattering: since the only pseudovector is the normal to the scattering plane

$$\hat{\mathbf{n}} = \frac{\mathbf{k} \times \mathbf{k}'}{kk' \sin\theta},$$

we can write

$$F(\theta, \varphi) = g(\theta, \varphi) + h(\theta, \varphi)\boldsymbol{\sigma} \cdot \hat{\mathbf{n}}, \tag{7}$$

where g and h are complex functions of direction.

If the z axis is taken as usual in the direction of incidence and the plane of scattering is the xz plane

$$F(\theta, 0) = g(\theta, 0)1 + h(\theta, 0)\sigma_y = \begin{pmatrix} g & -ih \\ ih & g \end{pmatrix} \tag{8}$$

(in the application of this formula θ is positive to the left and negative to

[1] The amplitude matrix for the n-He problem has already been introduced in 3.52(9): however, the matrix elements were limited to S and P scattering, whereas (6) defines $F(\theta, \varphi)$ independently of the partial wave analysis.

the right); if the z axis is taken along $\hat{\mathbf{n}}$,

$$F = \begin{pmatrix} g + h & 0 \\ 0 & g - h \end{pmatrix}. \tag{9}$$

Again, we can see that the complete study of the scattering requires three experiments at each θ, since the absolute values of g and h and their phase difference have to be determined.

b. Spins ½ and ½. More interesting for the study of nuclear forces is the case of two particles of spin ½ in which the wave function of the scattering problem has the form

$$\begin{pmatrix} a \\ b \\ c \\ d \end{pmatrix} e^{i\mathbf{k}\cdot\mathbf{r}} + \begin{pmatrix} u(\theta, \varphi) \\ v(\theta, \varphi) \\ w(\theta, \varphi) \\ z(\theta, \varphi) \end{pmatrix} \frac{e^{ikr}}{r} \tag{10}$$

For each initial state a, b, c, d the complete description of the scattering is obtained when the four complex functions u, v, w, z are measured. This requires seven measurements at each angle, corresponding to the four magnitudes $|u|, |v|, |w|, |z|$ and to the three relative phases.

But we cannot expect that all initial states behave in the same manner: the triplets, for instance, may behave differently from the singlets. The seven measurements must be performed for different incident spin states, and the description of the law of scattering may be quite complicated. In what follows we show that it is complete when six complex functions (or 11 real ones) are determined.

We start, as before, by defining a scattering matrix $F(\theta, \varphi)$ such that

$$\begin{pmatrix} u \\ v \\ w \\ z \end{pmatrix} = F(\theta, \varphi) \begin{pmatrix} a \\ b \\ c \\ d \end{pmatrix}. \tag{11}$$

F is now a 4×4 matrix. Since it must be a scalar, its most general form (W-52) is a linear combination of the scalars obtained by dotting 16 spin tensors of the type in 1.22(13) with the momentum tensors:

(12)

1	(scalar)	$+$
$\mathbf{k}' - \mathbf{k} = \mathbf{K}$	(vector)	$+$
$\mathbf{k}' \times \mathbf{k} = \mathbf{n}$	(pseudovector)	$-$
$\mathbf{n} \times \mathbf{K} = \mathbf{P}$	(vector)	$-$
$K_iK_j,\ n_in_j,\ P_iP_j$	(symm. tensors)	$+$
$K_iP_j + K_jP_i$	(symm. tensor)	$-$

The sign (+ or −) stands for even or odd time-reversal behavior. (Under time reversal $\mathbf{k} \rightleftharpoons -\mathbf{k}'$; thus $\mathbf{k}' - \mathbf{k} = -\mathbf{k} + \mathbf{k}'$, even; $\mathbf{k}' \times \mathbf{k} = (-\mathbf{k}) \times (-\mathbf{k}') = -\mathbf{k}' \times \mathbf{k}$, odd; etc.)

We find that we can construct six linearly independent, scalar, time-reversible operators. Their most general linear combination, which is the most general form of F, is

$$F = A + B(\boldsymbol{\sigma}_1 \cdot \boldsymbol{\sigma}_2 + 1) + C(\boldsymbol{\sigma}_1 + \boldsymbol{\sigma}_2) \cdot \mathbf{n} + D(\boldsymbol{\sigma}_1 - \boldsymbol{\sigma}_2) \cdot \mathbf{n} + E(\boldsymbol{\sigma}_1 \cdot \mathbf{K})(\boldsymbol{\sigma}_2 \cdot \mathbf{K}) + G(\boldsymbol{\sigma}_1 \cdot \mathbf{P})(\boldsymbol{\sigma}_2 \cdot \mathbf{P}). \tag{13}$$

The quantities A, B, C, D, E, G are complex functions of scattering angles and energy. In order to find these six functions and their five phase differences, 11 different single and multiple scattering experiments are required.

The situation is somewhat simplified if we assume charge independence, in which case we must have $D = 0$, since $\boldsymbol{\sigma}_1 - \boldsymbol{\sigma}_2$ mixes singlets and triplets. Thus no more than five complex functions of the scattering angle (or nine real ones) may enter into the description of nucleon-nucleon elastic scattering for any given energy.

The nature of the measurements needed in order to reconstruct the nucleon-nucleon scattering matrix—a "complete set" of experiments—has been discussed in a recent paper (S-61). Apart from the measurements of cross section and polarization, a "complete set" must include experiments performed with polarized initial beams, and possibly polarized targets, in order to establish how the scattering affects the spin states. The relation between initial and final spins can be expressed by means of tensors, such as the polarization correlation tensor C_{ij}, the depolarization tensor D_{ij}, and the polarization transfer tensor K_{ij}, which are defined and used in the literature.

Unitarity restrictions (see 5.14d) further reduce the number of experiments required for a complete set.

3.55 *High Energy Scattering and Charge Independence*

a. Nucleon-Nucleon Scattering. It has been found by experiment that the values of the cross sections for n-p scattering are different from those of p-p scattering. This fact, however, does not necessarily violate the assumptions of charge independence, since the exclusion principle does not allow for p-p all of the states that are possible for n-p.

In this section, as a consequence of charge independence, we derive a simple inequality (7), which can easily be compared with the experimental results of high-energy scattering.

Before proceeding with the derivation, let us observe that neutron-proton scattering—which, as a matter of convenience, is studied with a neutron beam and a hydrogen target—can be investigated experimentally with either a neutron or a proton counter. In the first case we measure the scattered particle and in the second, the recoil. We can also say that the neutron counter measures the scattering with retention of charge (r), or with no isospin flip, at the angle at which it is located, whereas the proton counter yields information, at its own angle, on the scattering with charge exchange (x) or with isospin flip.

Since charge independence requires isospin conservation, we can treat the isospins of two nucleons in the same way as we have treated their physical spins for an S wave (F-53b) (orbital angular momentum has no analogy in isotopic spin space). The elements of the amplitude matrix[1] can be divided into isospin singlets and triplets $F_{fi,s}$ and $F_{fi,t}$; they can also be written as operators in isospin space, similar to 3.13(14):

$$F_{fi} = \Lambda_s F_{fi,s} + \Lambda_t F_{fi,t}, \tag{1}$$

where the projection operators Λ_s and Λ_t are formally the same as in 1.14(37), apart from the substitution of isospin for physical spin.

Since two protons are necessarily in isospin triplet, the p-p scattering amplitudes are

$$F_{fi,\text{pp}} = F_{fi,t}. \tag{2}$$

The p-n system can be decomposed in isospin singlet and triplet. We compute the scattering amplitudes, for charge retention and charge exchange in the same manner as the scattering with and without physical spin flip was computed in 3.13(16). Thus

$$F_{fi,r} = \tfrac{1}{2}(F_{fi,t} + F_{fi,s}) \tag{3}$$

$$F_{fi,x} = \tfrac{1}{2}(F_{fi,t} - F_{fi,s}). \tag{4}$$

The amplitudes (2), (3), and (4) form a triangle in the complex plane, as shown in Fig. 3.55-1, and the following inequality necessarily holds:

$$|F_{fi,\text{pp}}(\theta, \varphi)| \leq |F_{fi,r}(\theta, \varphi)| + |F_{fi,x}(\theta, \varphi)|. \tag{5}$$

But the amplitudes for charge retention and exchange are related by the fact that neutron and proton move in opposite directions in the

[1] The indices i and f stand for initial and final spin states, as explained in detail in 3.59.

center-of-mass system; thus in this system we can write

$$(6a) \qquad |F_{fi,\text{pp}}(\theta, \varphi)| \leq |F_{fi,r}(\theta, \varphi)| + |F_{fi,r}(\pi - \theta, \pi + \varphi)|,$$

and in particular at 90° (charge retention scattering is simply n-p scattering):

$$(6b) \qquad \left|F_{fi,\text{pp}}\left(\frac{\pi}{2}, 0\right)\right| \leq \left|F_{fi,\text{np}}\left(\frac{\pi}{2}, 0\right)\right| + \left|F_{fi,\text{np}}\left(\frac{\pi}{2}, \pi\right)\right|.$$

If the nucleons had no spin, the two terms at the right-hand side would be equal to each other (since no right-left asymmetry could occur) and by

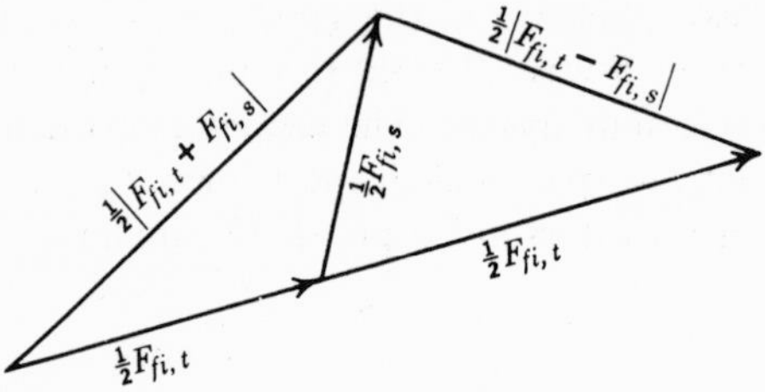

Fig. 3.55-1. Relation between the p-p scattering amplitude (F_t) and the n-p amplitude without and with charge exchange $\frac{1}{2}(F_t + F_s)$ and $\frac{1}{2}(F_t - F_s)$.

squaring (6*b*) we would obtain immediately

$$(7) \qquad \sigma_{\text{pp}}\left(\frac{\pi}{2}\right) \leq 4\sigma_{\text{np}}\left(\frac{\pi}{2}\right),$$

which is the inequality we wanted to prove.

In the actual case of spin ½ nucleons the same relation can be proved for the spin-averaged cross sections. For this purpose (6*b*) must be squared, summed over *f* and averaged over *i*; then, considering that the spin average must be the same at $\varphi = 0$ and $\varphi = \pi$, the right-hand side gives $\sigma_{\text{np}}(\pi/2, 0) + \sigma_{\text{np}}(\pi/2, \pi) = 2\sigma_{\text{np}}(\pi/2)$, plus double-product terms which are smaller than[1] $2[\sigma_{\text{np}}(\pi/2, 0)]^{1/2}[\sigma_{\text{np}}(\pi/2, \pi)]^{1/2} = 2\sigma_{\text{np}}(\pi/2)$, and (7) is proven.

The comparison of this inequality with experiment is discussed in 3.57.

b. Meson-Nucleon Scattering. Inequalities similar to (7) can be obtained (F-56; S-57a) as a consequence of charge independence for interacting particles of different isotopic spin. One of these inequalities, valid for isotopic spin 1 and ½ (pion-nucleon scattering) is

$$(8) \qquad 2\frac{d\sigma_0}{d\omega} \leq \left|\sqrt{\frac{d\sigma_-}{d\omega}} + \sqrt{\frac{d\sigma_+}{d\omega}}\right|^2,$$

[1] If a_i and b_i are nonnegative, $\sum a_i b_i \leq \sum a_i \sum b_i$.

where

σ_+ is the elastic scattering cross section of $\pi^+ + p$

$$(\pi^+ + p \rightarrow \pi^+ + p),$$

σ_- is the charge retention cross section of $\pi^- + p$

$$(\pi^- + p \rightarrow \pi^- + p),$$

σ_0 is the charge exchange cross section of $\pi^- + p$

$$(\pi^- + p \rightarrow \pi^0 + n).$$

The proof is left as a problem.

3.56 *Results of High-Energy Proton-Proton Scattering*

a. Description of the Experiments. The goal of any experimental investigation of scattering must be the complete determination of the scattering amplitude matrix. We have seen in 3.54 that in nucleon-nucleon scattering the conservation principles specify that nine experiments must be carried out at each angle and at each energy.

There may be, however, other restrictions that will allow us to obtain the desired information with a smaller number of experiments. We already know that for neutrons of sufficiently small energy only *S* scattering is allowed; the problem is reduced to the determination of two real scattering lengths, a_s and a_t. These are obtainable from three pieces of experimental information: total unpolarized cross section, coherent unpolarized cross section, and the existence of the deuteron (which fixes the sign of a_t).

More generally, owing to the short range of nuclear forces, it becomes possible to describe the scattering in terms of a relatively small number of phase shifts. Thus experiments at different angles are not entirely independent, and the knowledge of the angular distribution may make unnecessary the complete study of polarization at each angle, as we have seen for n-He scattering in 3.52. Furthermore, the number of independent experiments is restricted by the condition of unitarity of the scattering matrix (see 5.14d).

In practice, considering the unavailability of polarized targets, the experiments are limited to the determination of some of the following five parameters:

(i) Unpolarized cross section: $\sigma(\theta)$.
(ii) Polarization: $P(\theta)$.
(iii) Coplanar triple scattering measuring the depolarization produced by the second scatterer: $D(\theta)$.

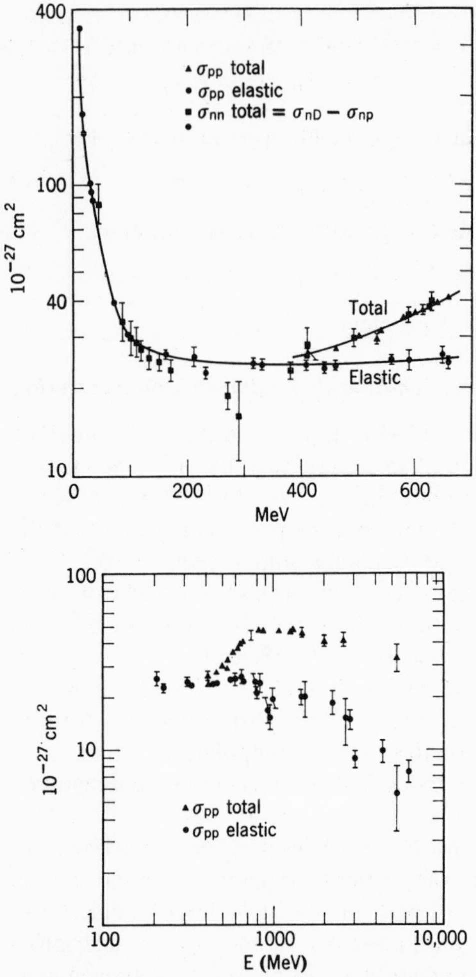

Fig. 3.56-1. Total and total-elastic p-p cross sections [from W. N. Hess, *Rev. Mod. Phys.*, **30**, 369, 370 (1958)].

(iv) Triple scattering with successive planes at right angles, measuring the rotation of the polarization in the second scatterer: $R(\theta)$.

(v) Polarization measurements with incident longitudinal polarization: $A(\theta)$. For this one performs a triple scattering experiment with a magnetic field before the second scatterer: the first scatterer polarizes transversely and the magnetic field rotates the spin to a direction parallel to the beam.

b. Experimental Data. The experimental data on nucleon-nucleon scattering at high energies have been collected in a review article which appeared in 1958 (H-58). Since that time, a few groups have concentrated in the accurate determination of the scattering amplitudes at particular energies. Worth mentioning is the work at 95 and 140 MeV at Harvard University (R. Wilson et al.), and that at 210 MeV at the University of Rochester (J. G. Tinlot et al.).

Some of the data for p-p scattering are reported in Figs. 3.56-1, 2, and 3.

One of the most striking features of the p-p scattering cross section is its constancy with angles up to high energies ($\approx$500 MeV, Fig. 3.56-2). From normal central forces we expect some P-wave contribution at $\approx$10 MeV, but the cross section at this energy is flat. We can explain the absence of P-wave scattering with exchange forces of the Serber type [3.53(20)], but according to these forces we should observe D-wave scattering at somewhat larger energy. The cross section instead remains nearly spherically symmetrical up to $\approx$500 MeV, despite the fact that it becomes larger than $4\pi\lambda\!\!\!^{-2}$, the maximum value for a pure S wave.

The observed behavior has been interpreted as evidence of considerable amounts of noncentral forces (spin-orbit or tensor) (C-50).

Above 500 MeV we observe an appreciable contribution of inelastic scattering, which is due to the production of π and K mesons. This effect results in an increase of the total cross section (Fig. 3.56-1); the elastic part of the cross section becomes peaked in the forward direction, as expected from diffraction by an opaque sphere.

c. Phase Shift Analysis. If the experimental information is sufficiently complete and accurate, it is possible to obtain numerical values for the scattering phases at any one energy. It is usual to consider a set of 14 phase shifts for $T = 1$, as described in 3.51(15).

The analysis, which assumes real phase shifts, is valid as long as the scattering is essentially elastic and thus up to about 400 MeV.

A computation, known under the initials SYM (S-57c), was performed in 1957, starting from the data at 310 MeV, an energy at which many experiments have been performed, including triple scattering. As a result, five sets of phases were obtained, each giving a satisfactory account of the measurements. Each of these solutions, labeled 1 to 5, appears in two slightly different forms, called "nuclear bar" and "BB,"[1] according to different methods of taking the coulomb interaction into account.

In order to reduce the ambiguities, a "modified" method of analysis was suggested (C-59). In the modified method we are guided by an approximate form of meson theory (OPEC, one-pion-exchange-contribution, or OPEP, one-pion-exchange-potential) in the selection of the best set of solutions.

[1] Blatt-Biedenharn.

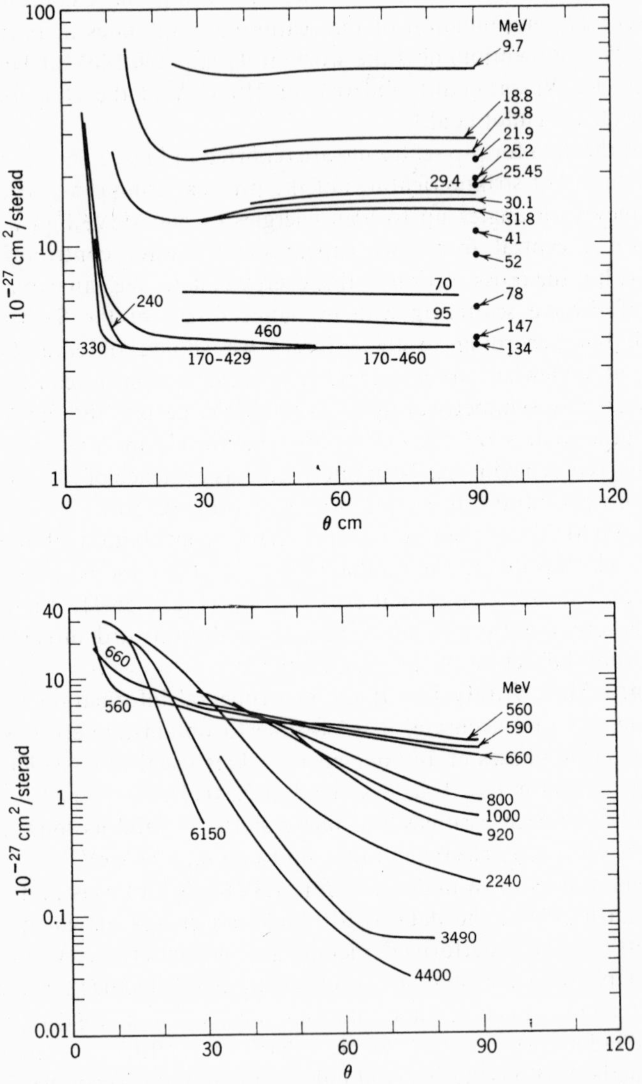

Fig. 3.56-2. Differential p-p cross section [from W. N. Hess, *Rev. Mod. Phys.*, **30,** 379 (1958)].

OPEP, which is assumed valid at large distances (for closer range many-pion-exchange-potential, MPEP, must be considered, since the range is inversely proportional to the exchanged mass), is used to compute the phases for high angular momenta.

By comparing OPEC with SYM it is found (M-59) that SYM 1 and SYM 2 are acceptable and that the three other SYM solutions must be discarded.

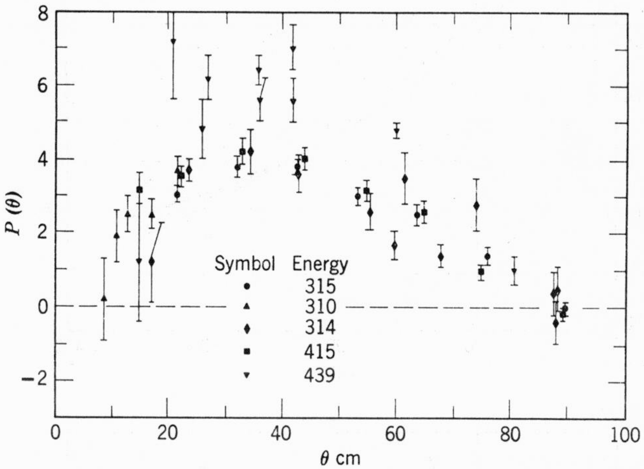

Fig. 3.56-3. Polarization in p-p scattering around 400 MeV [from W. N. Hess, *Rev. Mod. Phys.*, **30**, 396 (1958)].

Very similar solutions are found at 210 MeV. Finally, recent measurements of the parameter *A* at 210 MeV and large angles (E-60) make it probable that one of the two remaining solutions is spurious, and thus it is reasonable to assume (N-60) that SYM 1 is the only acceptable solution at 200–300 MeV.

At 145 MeV there are two sets of experiments that are not in agreement with each other, and it seems useless to consider a phase analysis.

Under reasonable assumptions we obtain a unique set of phases from the data at 95 MeV (M-61b; P-58; T-60). This set agrees with OPEP, and the "goodness of fit" has a sharp maximum (S-60b) for pion mass 125 MeV close to the true mass of 135 MeV.

Extensive computations for p-p phases from 9.7 to 345 MeV have been performed by Breit and collaborators (B-60b). These authors remark that the analysis of scattering data at one energy may yield many possible solutions but that there are theoretical guides for the classification of the energy dependence of the phases into reasonable and unreasonable categories. For instance, the *S* wave should dominate at low energy and

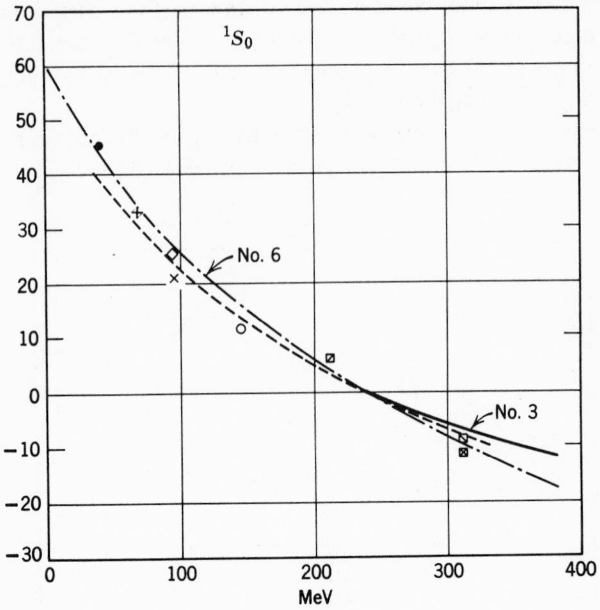

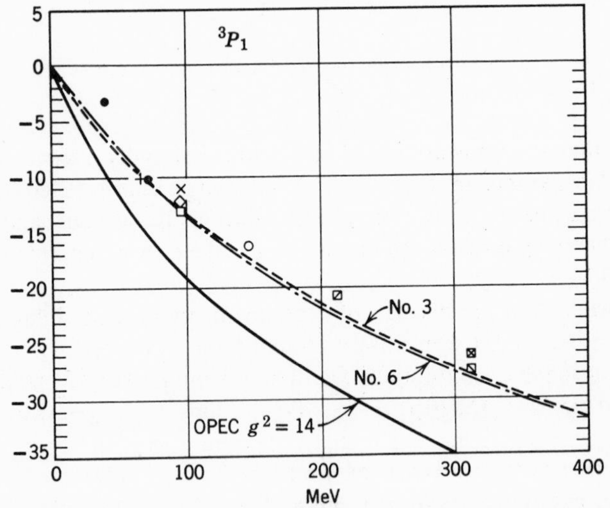

the other angular momentum waves should appear successively as the energy increases. Therefore, by studying the variation with energy of the different solutions, it is possible to discard some spurious sets. We can also note occasional errors in the experimental data when they result in unreasonable jumps in the energy dependence.

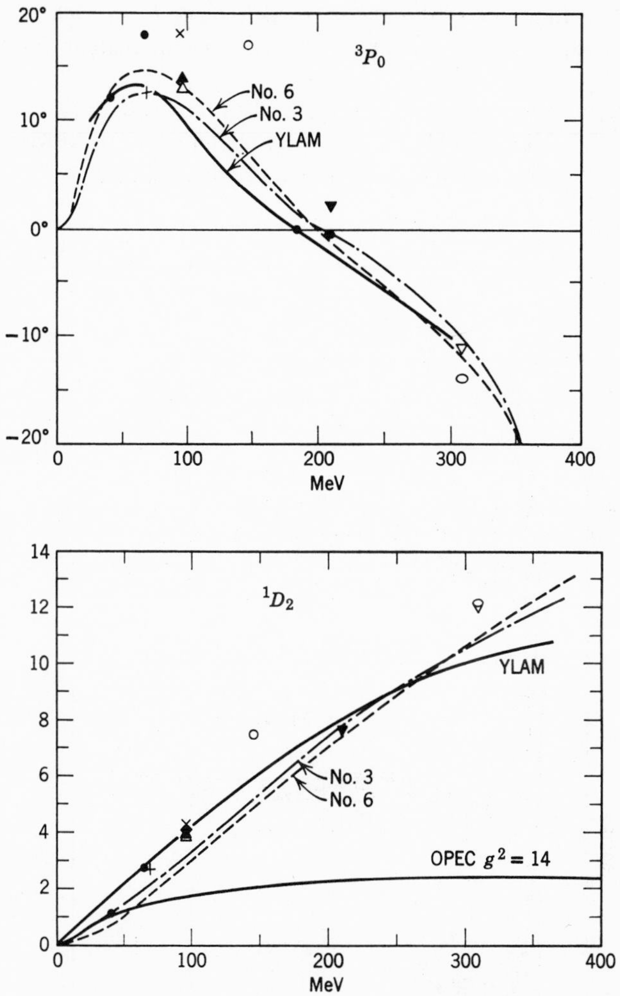

Fig. 3.56-4. Comparison of different sets of energy-dependent partial wave phase shifts in typical cases (from Stapp, Moravcsik, and Noyes, in *Proc. Int. Conf. High En. Physics*, Rochester, Interscience, New York, 1960).

Using these criteria and starting from preceding solutions for definite energy, families of energy-dependent phase shifts are found. These families behave similarly; the solution that gives the best fit to the data is referred to as YLAM (Fig. 3.56-4). Some examples of comparison with experiment are shown in Fig. 3.56-5.

The situation has been reviewed at the 1960 Rochester meeting, and several papers on this subject appear in the proceedings (B-60b; S-60c). Stapp, Moravcsik and Noyes present preliminary results of a phase analysis as a function of the energy, which starts from SYM 1, and in which they require, for continuity, that $k \cot \delta$ be an analytic function of energy.

The results are presented in the form of graphs (Fig. 3.56-4) and are compared with YLAM. The $^1S_0$ and $^3P_2$ are almost identical for the two computations. The F phases also show a rough similarity.

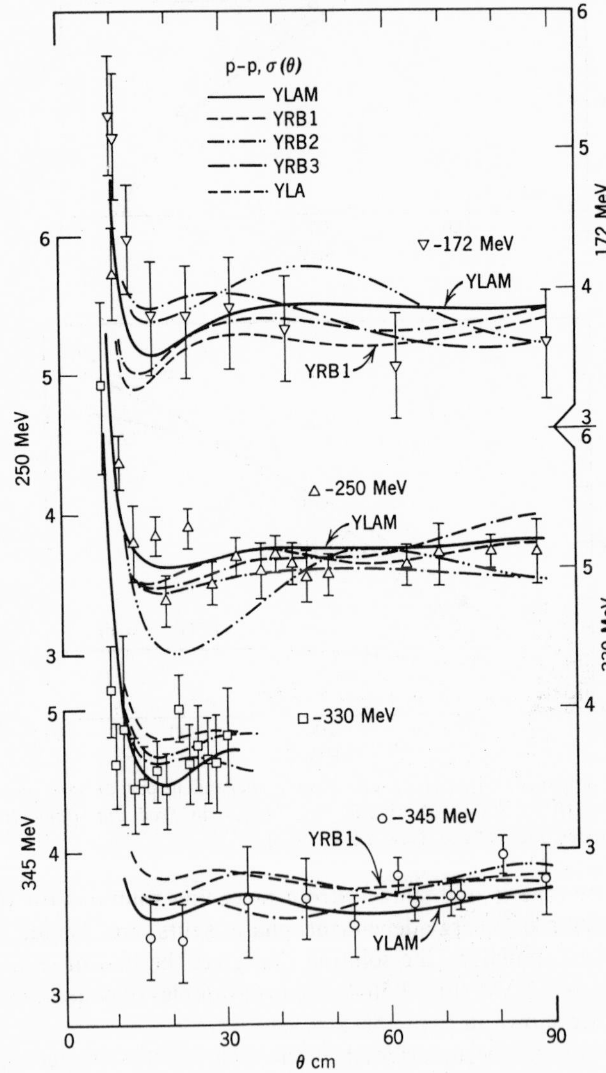

(*a*)

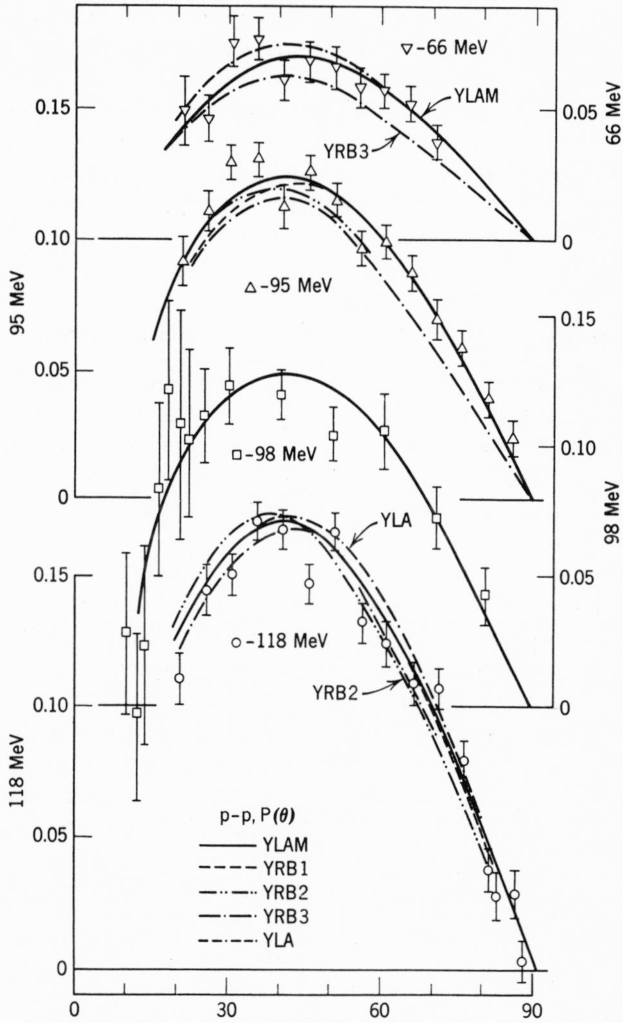

(b)

Fig. 3.56-5. (*a*) Comparison between experimental results on differential p-p cross sections, and computations from YLAM and other phase shifts. All cross sections are in 10^{-27} cm²/ster; (*b*) same comparison for polarization [from G. Breit et al., *Phys. Rev.*, **120,** 2240–2241 (1960)].

We can conclude that the attempts to analyze the p-p scattering data in terms of phase shifts have met some measure of success. The different groups engaged in this work are in almost quantitative agreement on a set of phase shifts which explains the data without ambiguity and which has a reasonable energy dependence.

Furthermore, the phase shifts for large orbital angular momentum agree with the prediction of meson theory in the one-meson exchange approximation. This agreement is significant because, at least at 95 MeV, it depends critically on the value of the mass of the meson and, in general, requires the same[1] meson-nucleon coupling constant that is obtained from meson-nucleon scattering experiments.

3.57 *Results on High-Energy Neutron-Proton Scattering*

a. Experimental Data. The total and differential cross sections of neutron-proton scattering shown in Figs. 3.57-1 and 2 are reported from Hess's paper. The same paper contains results of polarization experiments.

The differential cross section presents the forward-backward symmetry which we have already mentioned and which, historically, was attributed by Serber to an equal amount of normal and Majorana forces.

When the data on n-p are compared with those of p-p, we note some striking differences and are led to question whether these are compatible with charge independence. In this connection, Jastrow (J-51) was the first to remark that n-p and p-p scattering could be explained by a common interaction if the interaction contained a repulsive core.

More formally, charge independence can be tested by means of the considerations of 3.55a, which predict that the inequality $\sigma_{\mathrm{pp}}(\pi/2) \leq 4\sigma_{\mathrm{np}}(\pi/2)$ cannot be violated if charge independence holds. Fig. 3.57-3 shows the comparison of the pertinent experimental data, and from it we may conclude that there is no evidence against charge independence.

b. Phase Analysis of n-p Scattering. The phase analysis of n-p scattering is obviously more complicated than that of p-p scattering, since the n-p system can be found in both isospin triplet and singlet. According to charge independence, however, the $T = 1$ phases must be the same for p-p and n-p, and only the $T = 0$ phases of 3.51(15) remain to be determined from the analysis of n-p scattering.

An analysis at 95 MeV, at which energy the isospin triplet phases are uniquely determined, has been published (M-61a). Only one set of isospin singlet phases gives a good least-square fit to the experimental data.

[1] Actually the coupling constant required in p-p scattering is slightly larger than that of meson-nucleon scattering and the discrepancy is unexplained.

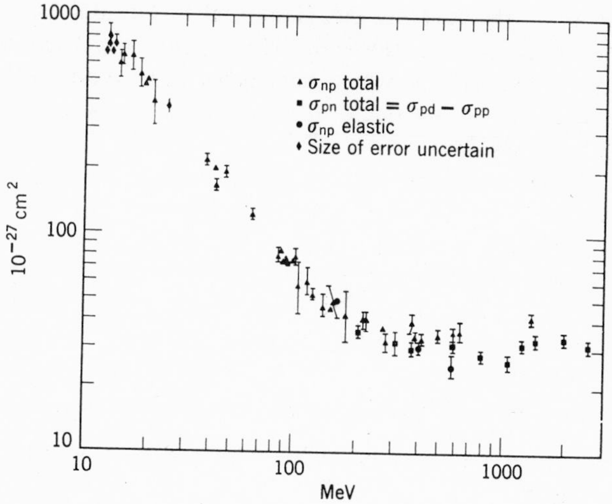

Fig. 3.57-1. Total n-p scattering cross section [from W. N. Hess, *Rev. Mod. Phys.*, **30,** 369 (1958)].

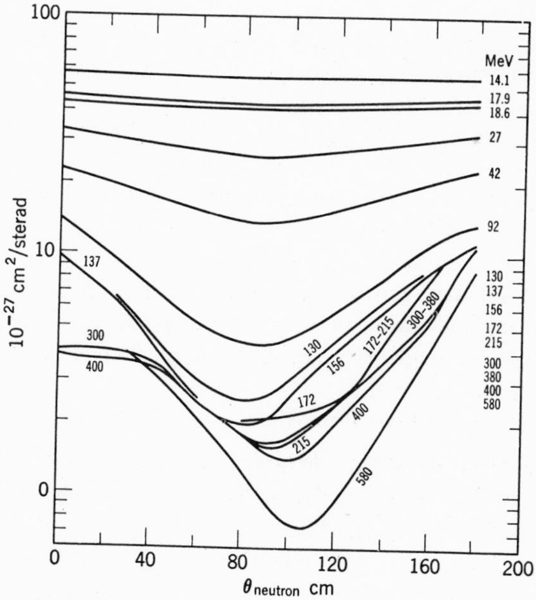

Fig. 3.57-2. Differential n-p scattering cross section [from W. N. Hess, *Rev. Mod. Phys.*, **30,** 379 (1958)].

More extensive work, covering energies from 13.7 to 350 MeV, was performed by the Yale group (H-61a). These authors reached several sets of phases, named YLAN, which are not essentially different from one another and all account satisfactorily for the data; the best agreement is obtained with YLAN3M.

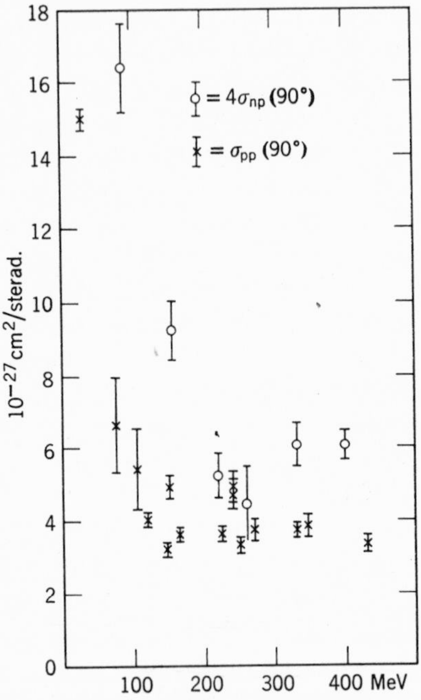

Fig. 3.57-3. Comparison of $4\sigma_{np}(\pi/2)$ and $\sigma_{pp}(\pi/2)$ (from L. Hulthen and M. Sugawara, *Handbook of Physics*, **39**, 126, Springer-Verlag, Berlin, 1957).

The fact that the data can be explained by using the isotriplet phases from p-p scattering and without mixing of $T = 0$ and $T = 1$ states again shows that there is no evidence against charge independence.

3.58 *Nuclear Interaction Potentials*

a. The Significance of Potentials. The search for a nuclear interaction potential has been for many years the basic problem of nuclear physics. In a sense, this problem has been solved because we have some "models" of potentials that account fairly well for the scattering data; but in another sense the solution of the problem still seems far away, since we have no hope of obtaining a unique, accurate form of the interaction in the near future. As a result, one has lost interest somewhat in fitting the data with potentials, and no paper of this kind was presented at the high energy conference of 1962.

If the forces are short-range the experiments cannot probe the potentials directly; they give information only on the asymptotic behavior of the wave functions. Since the theory should not introduce quantities incapable of being measured, it may be inappropriate to speak about potentials, and the treatment should be confined to asymptotic behavior, which are adequately represented by the phase shifts of the different J, ll', and ss' waves or by the amplitude matrix 3.54(11).

The problem of finding a form of potential that accounts for the scattering matrix becomes of secondary importance in the description of the data and in the prediction of the results of new experiments. Nevertheless, if a satisfactory analytical expression for a nuclear potential, valid at all energies, could be found—and this is not at all assured—we would have the feeling of having reached a more profound understanding of nuclear interactions. In this sense, a discussion on nuclear potentials is worth reporting.

b. Potentials from Meson Theories. We have already mentioned some of the ideas presented to explain high-energy scattering: these include exchange forces of the Serber type, repulsive cores, strong tensor forces, and spin-orbit coupling.

Parallel to these qualitative considerations much work has been devoted to the study of meson theories in the hope of obtaining from them the correct nucleon-nucleon interaction. After some encouraging beginnings, there was a period during which these efforts seemed vain because of the impossibility of finding an exact solution and because of the lack of a suitable method of approximation. The interest in meson potentials was revived in 1952 by Levy, who showed that the pseudoscalar meson theory may give nondivergent results for the two-nucleon system.

In 1954–1955 Chew and Low were able to account for low-energy meson-nucleon scattering by using a nonrelativistic, extended-source, static form of meson theory (see 7.25). This led Gartenhaus to use the same form of theory, including one- and two-meson exchanges, in the computation of the nucleon-nucleon interaction (G-55, see 7.18 and 7.26.)

The Gartenhaus potential, Fig. 3.58-1, accounts satisfactorily for the structure of the deuteron (see 1.25b), and it was natural to compare its predictions with the high-energy scattering data. The necessary computations were carried on by Gammel and Thaler, (G-56) but the results were most disappointing, chiefly for high-energy p-p scattering.

c. Phenomenological Potentials. After the failure of their attempt to explain the scattering with the Gartenhaus potential, Gammel

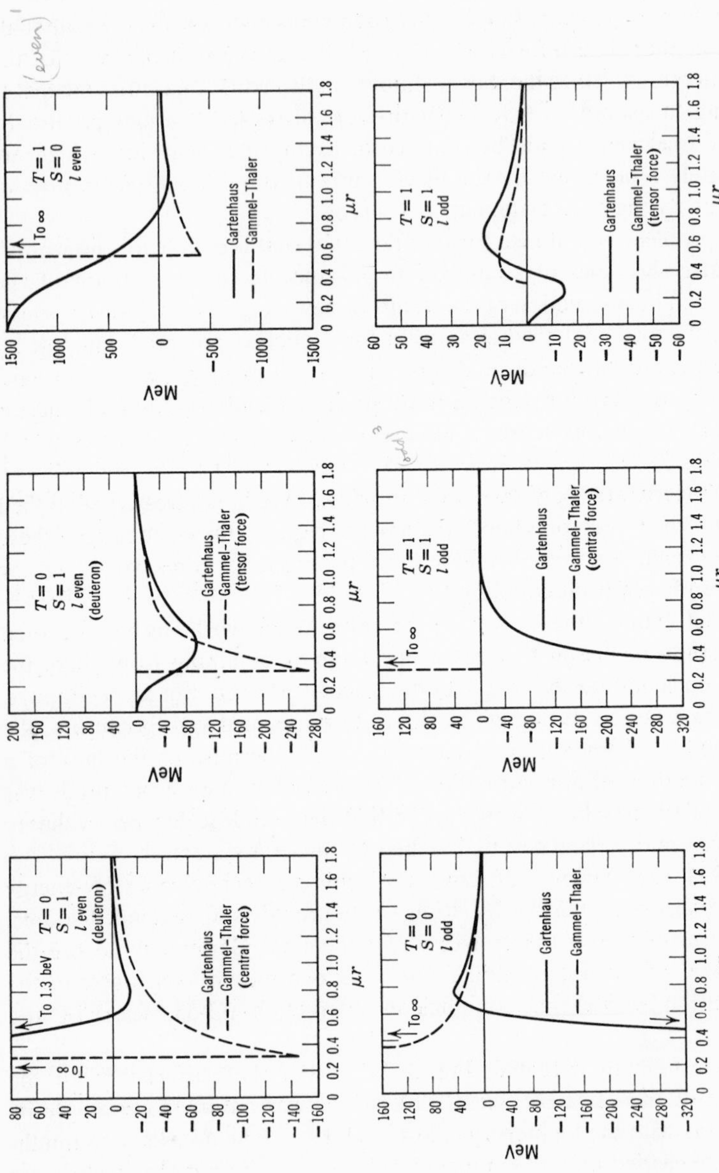

Fig. 3.58-1. The potentials of Gartenhaus and Gammel-Thaler. $\mu \approx 1.4 \times 10^{-13}$ cm [from P. S. Signell and R. E. Marshak, *Phys. Rev.*, **109**, 1229 (1958)].

and Thaler tried an entirely different approach. They looked for a phenomenological potential (G-57) which could account for the phases obtained by Stapp et al., and particularly for the solution SYM 1. Because of Majorana exchange, the potential had to be assumed to be different in even and odd orbital states, and, guided by the behavior of the SYM 1 phases, Gammel and Thaler chose the following form:

for singlet even states

$$(1a) \qquad {}^1V^+(r) = \begin{cases} +\infty & \text{for } r < {}^1r_0^+, \\ -{}^1V_C^+ \dfrac{\exp(-{}^1\mu_C r)}{{}^1\mu_C^+ r} & \text{for } r > r_0^+; \end{cases}$$

for triplet odd states

$$(1b) \qquad V(r) = \begin{cases} +\infty & \text{for } r < r_0, \\ -\left(S_{12} V_T \dfrac{\exp(-\mu_T r)}{\mu_T r} + \mathbf{L}\cdot\mathbf{S}\, V_{LS} \dfrac{\exp(-\mu_{LS} r)}{\mu_{LS} r}\right) & \text{for } r > r_0. \end{cases}$$

In other words, the singlet-even states have a repulsive core surrounded by an attractive Yukawa-like central potential, whereas the triplet-odd states have a repulsive core, no central attraction, a Yukawa-like tensor potential, and a spin orbit force.

Numerical computation was used to obtain the values of the constants in (1) for a best fit of the experimental data. The result is

$${}^1r_0^+ = 0.4 \times 10^{-13}\text{ cm}; \quad {}^1\mu_C^+ = 1.45 \times 10^{13}\text{ cm}^{-1}; \quad {}^1V_C^+ = 425.5\text{ MeV};$$
$$r_0 = 0.4125 \times 10^{-13}\text{ cm}; \quad \mu_T = 0.8 \times 10^{13}\text{ cm}^{-1}; \quad V_T = -22\text{ MeV};$$
$$\mu_{LS} = 3.7 \times 10^{13}\text{ cm}^{-1}; \quad V_{LS} = 7317.5\text{ MeV}.$$

The potentials obtained are shown in Fig. 3.58-1.

d. Semiphenomenological Potentials. In a series of papers, Signell and Marshak (S-57b; S-58a; S-58b; S-60a) discuss a form of interaction by means of which they obtain a good description of the experimental data. The interaction consists of the Gartenhaus potential to which a short range spin-orbit coupling force (Case and Pais) has been added.

The addition of spin-orbit coupling to the potential of Gartenhaus is not unnatural. The Gartenhaus computation was performed with a "static" meson theory in which the mass of the nucleon is supposed to be infinite: thus Gartenhaus' nucleons cannot move, and the lack of spin-orbit coupling is a necessary consequence of the approximation made. Adding the spin-orbit interaction may be considered as an attempt to compensate for a previous omission.

The papers of Signell and Marshak contain numerous figures which show the agreement of the scattering and polarization data with the predictions of an appropriately chosen $G + CP$[1] form of interaction (Fig. 3.58-2).

Further work on a static plus spin-orbit coupling potential has been reported by Bryan (B-60c) who has reached an improved agreement for p-p scattering in the 40 to 310 MeV energy range.

Other authors have tried to account for nuclear forces with potentials

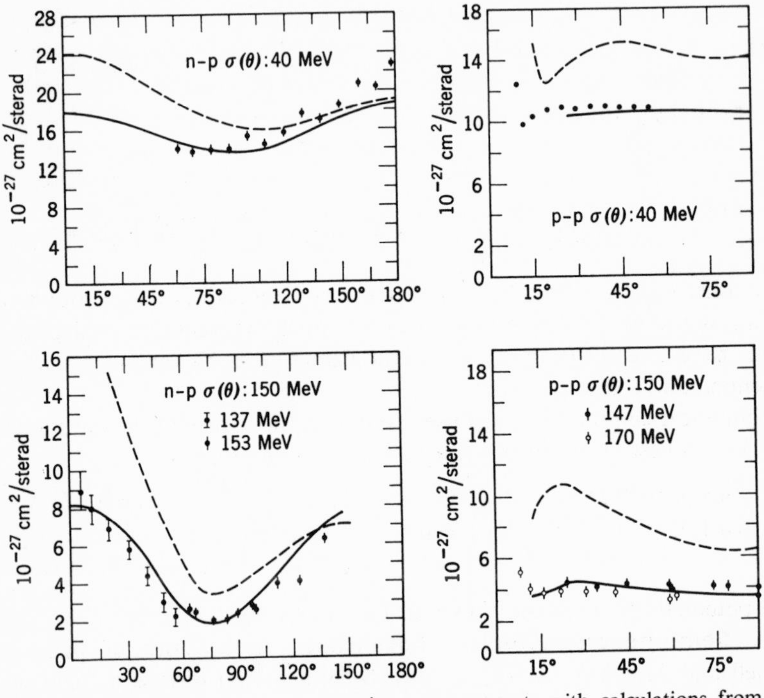

Fig. 3.58-2. Comparison of cross section measurements with calculations from the Gartenhaus (dashed line) and Signell-Marshak potentials (full line) [from P. S. Signell and R. E. Marshak, *Phys. Rev.*, **106**, 832, 833 (1958)].

that are partly derived from meson theory but contain adjustable parameters. Some of these attempts (F-61; H-59; H-60a) have met with considerable success in accounting for the data.

In conclusion it can be stated that it is presently possible to obtain potentials that account for the experimental data. Though the determination of the potential is not unique and we cannot say anything final about the choice of the parameters and about the detailed form of the interaction, certain features are definitely established. Among them we

[1] For Gartenhaus and Case-Pais.

can count the validity of the OPEP approximation at large distances ($r > \sim 1$ to 2 pion Compton wavelengths), the strong tensor forces, and the repulsive cores.

3.59 *The Amplitude Matrix and the Density Matrix for Arbitrary Spin and Polarization*

a. The Amplitude Matrix for Arbitrary Spins. In this section we intend to review the theory of scattering of particles with spins and to present it in a somewhat more general form than we have already used in this chapter. If our purpose had been to stress the theoretical aspects of scattering rather than the experimental information on nuclear interactions, this section could well have been written at the beginning of the chapter. In its present location it may be regarded as a theoretical appendix to our treatment of scattering.

Let us suppose in general that the incident particles have spin s_1 and the target particles spin s_2. Let us consider a complete set of orthonormal spin states of the incident and target particle system, ζ_s, with $0 \leq s \leq g$ [see 3.51(5)], and call ζ and $\zeta'(\theta, \varphi)$ the spin functions before and after scattering. The asymptotic form of the solution of the scattering problem is

(1*a*)
$$\psi \simeq \zeta e^{i\mathbf{k}\cdot\mathbf{r}} + \zeta'(\theta, \varphi)\frac{e^{ikr}}{r},$$

or

(1*b*)
$$\psi \simeq \begin{pmatrix} c_1 \\ c_2 \\ \cdot \\ \cdot \\ \cdot \\ c_g \end{pmatrix} e^{i\mathbf{k}\cdot\mathbf{r}} + \begin{pmatrix} c_1'(\theta, \varphi) \\ c_2'(\theta, \varphi) \\ \cdot \\ \cdot \\ \cdot \\ c_g'(\theta, \varphi) \end{pmatrix} \frac{e^{ikr}}{r}$$

where $c_s = \zeta_s^\dagger \zeta$, $c_s' = \zeta_s^\dagger \zeta'$.

As in the preceding sections, we shall assume that the initial spin state is normalized to unity,

(2)
$$\sum_s |c_s|^2 = 1,$$

whereas the final spin state is normalized so that $|c_s'(\theta, \varphi)|^2/r^2$ is the density of scattered particles of polarization s. Thus the coefficients c_s' are related to the differential scattering cross section:

(3)
$$\sigma(\theta, \varphi) = \sum_s |c_s'(\theta, \varphi)|^2.$$

Let us consider in particular the case in which the initial state is one of the basic spin states, say ζ_i, and expand the final state ζ' as a sum over the basic states. The corresponding asymptotic solution of the scattering problem can be written

$$\psi_i \cong \zeta_i e^{i\mathbf{k}\cdot\mathbf{r}} + \sum_f F_{fi}(\theta, \varphi)\zeta_f \frac{e^{ikr}}{r}. \tag{4}$$

The coefficients $F_{fi}(\theta, \varphi)$ of the expansion of the final state are the elements of the direction-dependent *scattering amplitude matrix* $F(\theta, \varphi)$.

The more general formulation (1) is obtained by summing the solutions ψ_i with amplitudes c_i:

$$\psi = \sum_i c_i \psi_i, \qquad c_s' = \sum_i c_i F_{si}(\theta, \varphi). \tag{5}$$

From this formalism we can obtain the partial cross section from a given incident polarized state of beam and target to a selected final state of polarization of the scattered and recoil particles. Obviously

$$\sigma_{if}(\theta, \varphi) = \sigma_{\zeta_i \to \zeta_f}(\theta, \varphi) = |F_{fi}(\theta, \varphi)|^2. \tag{6}$$

In order to obtain the unpolarized incoherent cross section, we must, as usual, sum over f and average over i:

$$\sigma = \frac{1}{g}\sum_{if} \sigma_{if} = \frac{1}{g}\sum_{if} |F_{fi}|^2 = \frac{1}{g}\sum_{if} F_{fi}^* F_{fi} = \frac{1}{g}\sum_{if} F_{if}^{\dagger} F_{fi} \tag{7}$$

But the sum extends to a complete set of states; thus we can write

$$\sigma(\theta, \varphi) = \frac{1}{g}\sum_i (F^{\dagger}F)_{ii} = \frac{1}{g} \text{ trace } F^{\dagger}F. \tag{8}$$

The spin sums and averages of the ortho-parahydrogen problem 3.16 and 3.17 could have been computed with the help of (8). Such computation is left as an exercise in the use of the method of traces.

b. Polarized, Unpolarized, and Partially Polarized Beams. A spin function $\begin{pmatrix} c_1 \\ c_2 \\ \cdot \\ \cdot \\ \cdot \\ c_g \end{pmatrix}$ completely defines the state of polarization of one or more particles; if all particles in a system have the same spin function, the polarization is 100%. If we add *coherently* different spin functions, we still obtain a 100% polarized system:

$$\begin{pmatrix} c_1 \\ c_2 \\ \cdot \\ \cdot \\ \cdot \\ c_g \end{pmatrix} + \begin{pmatrix} c_1' \\ c_2' \\ \cdot \\ \cdot \\ \cdot \\ c_g' \end{pmatrix} = \begin{pmatrix} c_1 + c_1' \\ c_2 + c_2' \\ \cdots\cdots \\ \\ c_g + c_g' \end{pmatrix} \tag{9}$$

The sum-state is a state of perfectly definite spins, just as are the states that have been added.

For instance, if we add *coherently* α and β, we obtain a new spin state

$$\frac{1}{\sqrt{2}}\begin{pmatrix}1\\0\end{pmatrix} + \frac{1}{\sqrt{2}}\begin{pmatrix}0\\1\end{pmatrix} = \frac{1}{\sqrt{2}}\begin{pmatrix}1\\1\end{pmatrix}, \tag{10}$$

whose spin points in the x direction. This is easily verified, since

$$\frac{1}{\sqrt{2}}\begin{pmatrix}1\\1\end{pmatrix} = \begin{pmatrix}\cos\left(\frac{1}{2}\frac{\pi}{2}\right)e^{0}\\ \sin\left(\frac{1}{2}\frac{\pi}{2}\right)e^{0}\end{pmatrix} \tag{11}$$

and

$$\sigma_x\begin{pmatrix}1\\1\end{pmatrix} = \begin{pmatrix}0 & 1\\1 & 0\end{pmatrix}\begin{pmatrix}1\\1\end{pmatrix} = \begin{pmatrix}1\\1\end{pmatrix}. \tag{12}$$

In order to obtain partially polarized or unpolarized systems, the spin states must be added *incoherently*. In an unpolarized beam there are no interference effects between the different spin states, which correspond to different, phase-unrelated particles, and the probabilities rather than the amplitudes are additive. This is the rule that we have followed in the calculation of unpolarized scattering cross sections.

For a partially polarized beam of N particles of spin $\frac{1}{2}$, the polarization along the z axis, according to 3.52(15), is the difference of the normalized probabilities of finding spin α and spin β. If the spin state is the superimposition of many spin states,

$$\zeta^{(n)} = \begin{pmatrix}a^{(n)}\\b^{(n)}\end{pmatrix},$$

each denoted by a superscript (n), coherently or incoherently added, the polarization along the z axis is

$$P_z = \frac{\sum_n [|a^{(n)}|^2 - |b^{(n)}|^2]}{\sum_n [|a^{(n)}|^2 + |b^{(n)}|^2]}. \tag{13a}$$

If we superimpose α and β with equal probability, either incoherently or coherently, we obtain $P_z = 0$. However, in the first case (50% of the states α and 50% β) the polarization is zero in all directions, whereas in the second (each state in $\alpha + \beta$ or $\alpha + i\beta$) there is polarization perpendicular to the z axis.

For each state (n) the relative probability amplitudes of finding the spin in the $\pm x$ or $\pm y$ direction are

$$\frac{1}{\sqrt{2}}(1 \pm 1)\begin{pmatrix} a^{(n)} \\ b^{(n)} \end{pmatrix} = \frac{1}{\sqrt{2}}[a^{(n)} \pm b^{(n)}],$$

$$\frac{1}{\sqrt{2}}(1 \mp i)\begin{pmatrix} a^{(n)} \\ b^{(n)} \end{pmatrix} = \frac{1}{\sqrt{2}}[a^{(n)} \mp ib^{(n)}].$$

From these we obtain the amount of polarization along the x and y axes for the same beam whose polarization along the z axis was given by (13a):

(13b)
$$P_x = \frac{\sum_n [\frac{1}{2}|a^{(n)} + b^{(n)}|^2 - \frac{1}{2}|a^{(n)} - b^{(n)}|^2]}{\sum_n [\frac{1}{2}|a^{(n)} + b^{(n)}|^2 + \frac{1}{2}|a^{(n)} - b^{(n)}|^2]}$$

$$= \frac{2\,\mathrm{Re}\sum_n a^{(n)*}b^{(n)}}{\sum_n [|a^{(n)}|^2 + |b^{(n)}|^2]}.$$

(13c)
$$P_y = \frac{2\,\mathrm{Im}\sum_n a^{(n)*}b^{(n)}}{\sum_n [|a^{(n)}|^2 + |b^{(n)}|^2]}.$$

In particular, each state (n) may be identified with the state of one particle.. Then it is appropriate to use the normalization $|a^{(n)}|^2 + |b^{(n)}|^2 = 1$, and it is easily seen that for N particles (13a, b, c) are equivalent to

(13d)
$$\mathbf{P} = \frac{1}{N}\sum_{n=1}^{N} \langle\zeta^{(n)}|\,\boldsymbol{\sigma}\,|\zeta^{(n)}\rangle.$$

We conclude, as expected, that if the beam is not totally polarized along the z axis (in which case either all $a^{(n)}$ or all $b^{(n)}$ would vanish) and if the phases are not completely random (in which case the $\sum_n$ at the numerators would vanish) the beam is necessarily polarized in the x or y direction.

P_x, P_y, and P_z can be considered as the components of a pseudovector, whose magnitude P, the amount of beam polarization independently of direction, is given by

(14)
$$P^2 = P_x^{\,2} + P_y^{\,2} + P_z^{\,2}.$$

c. The Density Matrix. A complete description of polarization in the case of arbitrary spin (W-56) must allow us to predict the result of any experiment involving spin. Let s_1 and s_2 be the spins of the incident and target particles. Then a spin state (n) is given by

(15) $$\zeta^{(n)} = \begin{pmatrix} c_1^{(n)} \\ c_2^{(n)} \\ \cdot \\ \cdot \\ \cdot \\ c_g^{(n)} \end{pmatrix}; \qquad g = (2s_1 + 1)(2s_2 + 1).$$

Any observation on the spin is a measurement of a spin-dependent dynamical variable, which corresponds to an operator $\mathcal{O}$ and is represented by a matrix of g lines and columns. In the state (n) the expectation value of $\mathcal{O}$, which gives the result of the observation, is

(16) $$\langle \mathcal{O} \rangle_n = \frac{\zeta^{(n)\dagger} \mathcal{O} \zeta^{(n)}}{\zeta^{(n)\dagger}\zeta^{(n)}} = \frac{\sum_k \sum_j c_k^{(n)*} c_j^{(n)} \mathcal{O}_{kj}}{\sum_j |c_j^{(n)}|^2}.$$

(The denominator is unity if $\zeta^{(n)}$ is normalized; we do not normalize $\zeta^{(n)}$ to unity because we want to allow different probabilities $\zeta^{(n)\dagger}\zeta^{(n)}$ for each n.)

If incident beam and target are a superimposition (coherent or incoherent) of spin states, the expectation value of $\mathcal{O}$ must be averaged over n:

(17) $$\overline{\langle \mathcal{O} \rangle_n} = \frac{\sum_n \zeta^{(n)\dagger}\zeta^{(n)} \langle \mathcal{O} \rangle_n}{\sum_n \zeta^{(n)\dagger}\zeta^{(n)}} = \frac{\sum_n \sum_k \sum_j c_j^{(n)} c_k^{(n)*} \mathcal{O}_{kj}}{\sum_n \sum_j |c_j^{(n)}|^2}.$$

Let us now introduce a *density matrix* (F-57):

(18) $$\rho_{jk} = \sum_n c_j^{(n)} c_k^{(n)*};$$

then

(19) $$\overline{\langle \mathcal{O} \rangle_n} = \frac{\sum_k \sum_j \rho_{jk} \mathcal{O}_{kj}}{\text{trace } \rho} = \frac{\sum_j (\rho\mathcal{O})_{jj}}{\text{trace } \rho} = \frac{\text{trace } \rho\mathcal{O}}{\text{trace } \rho}.$$

The last formula shows that if the *density matrix* ρ is known we can predict the result of any observation on the beam. Thus the density matrix describes completely the polarization of a beam.

For simplicity, let us fix our attention on only one kind of particle as, for instance, in the problem of scattering a beam of N particles per unit volume by a spinless or unpolarized target. It is convenient to fix the normalization such that $\zeta^{(n)\dagger}\zeta^{(n)} = \sum_j c_j^{(n)*}c_j^{(n)}$ is the probability density of finding a particle in the spin state (n), and the intensity of the beam is

$$N = \sum_{n,j} c_j^{(n)*}c_j^{(n)} = \text{trace } \rho. \tag{20}$$

As an example, let us compute the density matrices for a beam of N particles of spin $\frac{1}{2}$. From (18) these matrices are

	polarization in x direction	polarization in y direction	polarization in z direction	no polarization
(21)	$\frac{N}{2}\begin{pmatrix}1 & 1\\ 1 & 1\end{pmatrix}$	$\frac{N}{2}\begin{pmatrix}1 & -i\\ i & 1\end{pmatrix}$	$N\begin{pmatrix}1 & 0\\ 0 & 0\end{pmatrix}$	$\frac{N}{2}\begin{pmatrix}1 & 0\\ 0 & 1\end{pmatrix}.$

In general, we can verify that the density matrix for an unpolarized beam of N particles of spin s is

$$\frac{N}{2s+1}\,1, \tag{22}$$

where 1 is the unit matrix of $2s + 1$ lines and columns. The computation of density matrices for spins larger than $\frac{1}{2}$ is suggested as an exercise.

d. Use of the Density Matrix in Scattering Problems. The problem of the scattering of systems of arbitrary polarization can be stated as follows:

Given the density matrix ρ of the incident system and the amplitude matrix F, which defines the scattering law, find the density matrix ρ' of the scattered system at unit distance ($r = 1$).

The solution is as follows. At $r = 1$ the scattered and incident spin amplitudes for polarized beams are connected by the relation (4), and the density matrix after scattering is

$$\begin{aligned}\rho_{jk}' &= \sum_n \Big[\sum_l F_{jl}c_l^{(n)}\Big]\Big[\sum_m F_{km}c_m^{(n)}\Big]^* \\ &= \sum_{lm} F_{jl}\Big[\sum_n c_l^{(n)}c_m^{(n)*}\Big]F_{km}^* \\ &= \sum_{lm} F_{jl}\rho_{lm}F_{km}^* \\ &= \sum_{lm} F_{jl}\rho_{lm}F_{mk}^\dagger \\ &= (F\rho F^\dagger)_{jk}.\end{aligned} \tag{23}$$

The differential scattering cross section (see 20) is

$$\sigma = \frac{\text{trace } \rho'}{\text{trace } \rho} = \frac{\text{trace } F\rho F^\dagger}{\text{trace } \rho}, \tag{24}$$

which, for unpolarized beams (see 22), reduces to (8).

The computation of the polarization effects for the He-n scattering problem (3.52) can be performed with the technique of the scattering and density matrices and is left as a problem.

References

Books

Hu-53 D. J. Hughes, *Pile Neutron Research*, Addison-Wesley, Cambridge Mass., 1953, p. 309.

HS-57 L. Hulthen and M. Sugawara, *Handbook of Physics*, Vol. 39, Springer-Verlag, Berlin, 1957, p. 3, 51.

MM-33 N. F. Mott and H. S. W. Massey, *The Theory of Atomic Collisions*, Clarendon Press, Oxford, 1933.

Sc-49 L. I. Schiff, *Quantum Mechanics*, McGraw-Hill, New York, 1949.

Articles

A-36 E. Amaldi and E. Fermi, *Phys. Rev.*, **50,** 899 (1936).

A-40 L. A. Alvarez and K. S. Pitzer, *Phys. Rev.*, **58,** 1003 (1940).

A-52 R. K. Adair, *Phys. Rev.*, **86,** 155 (1952).

A-58 N. Austern, *Nucl. Phys.*, **7,** 195 (1958).

B-36 H. A. Bethe and R. F. Bacher, *Rev. Mod. Phys.*, **8,** 82 (1936).

B-37 F. Bloch, *Phys. Rev.*, **51,** 994 (1937).

B-49 H. A. Bethe, *Phys. Rev.*, **76,** 38 (1949).

B-60a Breit, Hull, Lassila, and Pyatt, *Phys. Rev.*, **120,** 2227 (1960).

B-60b G. Breit, *Proc. Int. Conf. High En. Phys.*, Rochester, Interscience, New York, 1960.

B-60c R. A. Bryan, *Nuovo Cimento*, **16,** 895 (1960).

B-61 Bergia, Stanghellini, Fubini, and Villi, *Phys. Rev. Letters*, **6,** 367 (1961).

C-50 K. M. Case and A. Pais, *Phys. Rev.*, **80,** 203 (1950).

C-58 E. Clementel and C. Villi, *Nuovo Cimento*, **4,** 1207 (1958).

C-59 Cziffra, MacGregor, Moravcsik, and Stapp, *Phys. Rev.*, **114,** 880 (1959).

D-62 de Vries, Hofstadter, and Herman, *Phys. Rev. Letters*, **8,** 381 (1962).

E-49 H. Ekstein, *Phys. Rev.*, **76,** 1328 (1949).

E-60 England, Gibson, Gotow, Heer, Tinlot, and Warner, *Proc. Int. Conf. High En. Phys.*, Rochester, Interscience, New York, 1960, p. 111.

F-49 E. Fermi and L. Marshall, *Phys. Rev.*, **72,** 1139 (1947).

F-53a E. Fermi, *Phys. Rev.*, **91,** 947 (1953).

F-53b D. Feldman, *Phys. Rev.*, **89,** 1159 (1953).

F-54 E. Fermi, *Nuovo Cimento*, **11,** 407 (1954).

F-56 D. Feldman, *Phys. Rev.*, **103,** 254 (1956).

F-57 U. Fano, *Rev. Mod. Phys.*, **29,** 74 (1957).

F-61 Feshbach, Lomon, and Tubis, *Phys. Rev. Letters*, **6,** 635 (1961).

G-55 S. Gartenhaus, *Phys. Rev.*, **100,** 900 (1955).

G-56 J. L. Gammel and R. M. Thaler, *Phys. Rev.*, **103,** 1874 (1956).
G-57 J. L. Gammel and R. M. Thaler, *Phys. Rev.*, **107**, 291 (1957).
H-39 O. Halpern and M. H. Johnson, *Phys. Rev.*, **55,** 898 (1939).
H-49 M. Hamermesh, *Phys. Rev.*, **75,** 1766 (1949).
H-51a D. J. Hughes and M. T. Burgy, *Phys. Rev.*, **81,** 498 (1951).
H-51b Havens, Rainwater, and Rabi, *Phys. Rev.*, **82,** 345 (1951).
H-52a Hamermesh, Ringo, and Wattenberg, *Phys. Rev.*, **85,** 483 (1952).
H-52b P. Huber and E. Baldinger, *Helv. Phys. Acta*, **25,** 435 (1952).
H-53 Hughes, Harvey, Goldberger, and Stafne, *Phys. Rev.*, **90,** 497 (1953).
H-56 R. Hofstadster, *Rev. Mod. Phys.*, **28,** 214 (1956).
H-58 W. N. Hess, *Rev. Mod. Phys.*, **30,** 368 (1958).
H-59 Hamada, Iwadare, Otsuki, Tamagaki, and Watari, *Progr. Theoret. Phys.*, **22,** 566 (1959).
H-60a T. Hamada, *Progr. Theoret. Phys.*, **24,** 1033 (1960).
H-60b Hofstadter, Bumiller, and Croissiaux, *Phys. Rev. Letters*, **5,** 263 (1960).
H-61a Hull, Lassila, Ruppel, McDonald, and Breit, *Phys. Rev.*, **122,** 1606 (1961).
H-61b Hofstadter, de Vries, and Herman, *Phys. Rev. Letters*, **6,** 290 (1961).
H-61c R. Hofstadter and R. Herman, *Phys. Rev. Letters*, **6,** 293 (1961).
J-51 R. Jastrow, *Phys. Rev.*, **81,** 165 (1951).
L-57 Levintov, Miller, and Shamshev, *Nucl. Phys.*, **3,** 221 (1957).
L-61a Littauer, Schopper, and Wilson, *Phys. Rev. Letters*, **7,** 141 (1961).
L-61b Littauer, Schopper, and Wilson, *Phys. Rev. Letters*, **7,** 144 (1961).
M-49 E. Melkonian, *Phys. Rev.*, **76,** 1744 (1949).
M-56 Melkonian, Rustad, and Havens, *Bull. Am. Phys. Soc.*, **1,** 62 (1956).
M-59 MacGregor, Moravcsik, and Stapp, *Phys. Rev.*, **116,** 1248 (1959).
M-61a M. MacGregor, *Phys. Rev.*, **123,** 2154 (1961).
M-61b MacGregor, Moravcsik, and Noyes, *Phys. Rev.*, **123,** 1835 (1961).
N-60 H. P. Noyes, *Proc. Int. Conf. High. En. Phys.*, Rochester, Interscience, New York, 1960, p. 117.
P-58 Palmieri, Cormack, Ramsey, and Wilson, *Ann. Phys.*, **5,** 299 (1958).
S-37 J. Schwinger, *Phys. Rev.*, **52,** 1250 (1937).
S-47 Sutton, Hall, Anderson, Bridge, DeWire, Lavatelli, Long, Snyder, and Williams, *Phys. Rev.*, **72,** 1147 (1947).
S-48 Shull, Wollan, Morton, and Davidson, *Phys. Rev.*, **73,** 842 (1948).
S-49 C. G. Shull and J. S. Smart, *Phys. Rev.*, **76,** 1256 (1949).
S-51a Shull, Strauser, and Wollan, *Phys. Rev.*, **83,** 333 (1951).
S-51b Shull, Wollan, and Koehler, *Phys. Rev.*, **84,** 912 (1951).
S-53 J. D. Seagrave, *Phys. Rev.*, **92,** 1222 (1953).
S-55 G. L. Squires and A. T. Stewart, *Proc. Roy. Soc.*, **A-230,** 19 (1955).
S-57a J. J. Sakurai, *Phys. Rev.*, **107,** 908 (1957).
S-57b P. S. Signell and R. E. Marshak, *Phys. Rev.*, **106,** 832 (1957).
S-57c Stapp, Ypsilantis, and Metropolis, *Phys. Rev.*, **105,** 302 (1957).
S-58a P. S. Signell and R. E. Marshak, *Phys. Rev.*, **109,** 1229 (1958).
S-58b P. S. Signell and R. E. Marshak, *Phys. Rev. Letters*, **1,** 416 (1958).
S-60a Saylor, Bryan, and Marshak, *Phys. Rev. Letters*, **5,** 266 (1960).

S-60b P. S. Signell, *Phys. Rev. Letters*, **5,** 474 (1960).
S-60c Stapp, Moravcsik, and Noyes, *Proc. Int. Conf. High En. Phys.*, Rochester, Interscience, New York, 1960.
S-61 C. R. Schumacher and H. A. Bethe, *Phys. Rev.*, **121,** 1534 (1961).
T-60 E. H. Thorndike and T. R. Ophel, *Phys. Rev.*, **119,** 362 (1960).
W-48 E. O. Wollan and C. G. Shull, *Phys. Rev.*, **73,** 830 (1948).
W-52 L. Wolfenstein and J. Ashkin, *Phys. Rev.*, **85,** 947 (1952).
W-56 L. Wolfenstein, *Ann. Rev. Nucl. Sci.*, **6,** 43 (1956).

FOUR

Interaction between Nucleons and Radiation

4.1 Theoretical Formulation

4.11 Semiclassical Treatment

a. Introduction. Up to this point we have discussed the strong forces acting between nucleons and responsible for binding nuclear matter. Our purpose was to relate the progress in the search for the law of strong interactions, and we were obliged to conclude that we are still far from a satisfactory formulation of nuclear forces.

The situation is completely different in the interaction of nucleons with radiation, which we propose to treat in this chapter. The electromagnetic interaction can be formulated with great accuracy, and in what follows we apply a well-established theory rather than look for new basic laws. The nucleons are treated nonrelativistically, since they move with small velocity in nuclear matter. They interact with the electromagnetic field through their charge and magnetic moment, whose value is taken from the experiment without any attempt at explanation. The finite size of the nucleons as well as other meson effects—such as "exchange currents"—are not taken into account in this part of our treatment.

Though the elementary interaction is well known in the stated approximation, its application to complex nuclei cannot be exact because of our poor knowledge of nuclear states. As we shall see, the main purpose of experimental and theoretical study of nuclear electromagnetic phenomena —γ emission, photodisintegration, etc.—is the search for new information on nuclear quantum numbers and nuclear wave functions.

b. The Hamiltonian. The absorption and the induced emission of light by atoms or nuclei can be treated semiclassically by means of perturbation theory. A nonquantized plane electromagnetic wave, propagating in the $+z$ direction, as described by the vector potential

(1) $$\mathbf{A} = 2\mathbf{A}_0 \cos(kz - \omega t) = \mathbf{A}_0 e^{i(kz-\omega t)} + \mathbf{A}_0 e^{-i(kz-\omega t)},$$

interacts with the charge and magnetic moments of the particles; this interaction is considered as a perturbation, which, according to time-dependent perturbation theory, induces transitions between the unperturbed energy levels of the system of particles.

The Hamiltonian of the particles in the presence of the potential vector (1) is

(2)
$$\mathcal{H} = V + \sum_\alpha \frac{1}{2M_\alpha}\left(\mathbf{p}_\alpha - \frac{e_\alpha}{c}\mathbf{A}\right)^2 - \sum_\alpha \frac{e\hbar}{2M_\alpha c}\boldsymbol{\mu}_\alpha \cdot \mathbf{curl}\,\mathbf{A}$$
$$= V + \sum_\alpha \left[\frac{p_\alpha{}^2}{2M_\alpha} - \frac{e_\alpha}{2M_\alpha c}(\mathbf{A}\cdot\mathbf{p}_\alpha + \mathbf{p}_\alpha\cdot\mathbf{A}) + \frac{e_\alpha{}^2}{2M_\alpha c^2}A^2 - \frac{e\hbar}{2M_\alpha c}\boldsymbol{\mu}_\alpha\cdot\mathbf{curl}\,\mathbf{A}\right].$$

where α is the order number of the particle and $\mathbf{A}$ is computed at position r_α. In this equation V is the unperturbed potential whose eigenstates are the levels of the atom or nucleus in the absence of radiation; M_α, e_α, μ_α are the mass, charge, and magnetic moment of the particles, and all the other symbols have their usual meaning. Together with the term in p^2, V forms the nonrelativistic unperturbed Hamiltonian:

(3) $$\mathcal{H}_0 = V + \sum_\alpha \frac{p_\alpha{}^2}{2M_\alpha}.$$

The next term (in $\mathbf{p}_\alpha$) of (2) has been written in a form valid if $\mathbf{A}$ is a general function of position which does not commute with $\mathbf{p}$: however, in what follows, we choose a gauge such that $\nabla \cdot \mathbf{A} = 0$ and write $2\mathbf{A}\cdot\mathbf{p}_\alpha$ instead of $\mathbf{A}\cdot\mathbf{p}_\alpha + \mathbf{p}_\alpha\cdot\mathbf{A}$.

Finally the term in A^2 is neglected, since A is supposed to produce a small perturbation.

With these assumptions, (2) becomes

(4) $$\mathcal{H} = \mathcal{H}_0 + \mathcal{H}'.$$

with

(5) $$\mathcal{H}' = -\sum_\alpha \left(\frac{e_\alpha}{M_\alpha c}\mathbf{A}\cdot\mathbf{p}_\alpha + \frac{e\hbar}{2M_\alpha c}\boldsymbol{\mu}_\alpha\cdot\mathbf{curl}\,\mathbf{A}\right).$$

The perturbation consists of two terms, which express the coupling of the field to the charges and to the magnetic moments of the particles.

c. Results of Perturbation Theory. When (1) is substituted into (4) we see that $\mathcal{H}'$ is composed of two parts: one with negative frequency [time dependence exp $(-i\omega t)$] and one with positive frequency. It can be proved that the negative frequency part of $\mathcal{H}'$ induces transitions from an initial state of energy E_i (time dependence exp $[-i(E_i/\hbar)t]$ to final states of energy $E_f = E_i + \hbar\omega$; such transitions are interpreted as absorption of light. Similarly the positive frequencies in $\mathcal{H}'$ result in transitions to states of lower energy and thus correspond to induced emission.

The transition rates can be computed by using time-dependent perturbation theory. The result is (Sc-49, Chapter VIII)

$$(6) \qquad w_{\substack{\text{absorption}\\ \text{induced emission}}} = \frac{2\pi}{\hbar}\,\rho_F(E)\left|\int \psi_f{}^*\mathcal{H}'(0)\,e^{\pm ikz}\psi_i\,d\mathbf{r}\right|^2$$

where $\rho_F(E)$ is the number of final states per unit energy interval (see 5.11), and $\mathcal{H}'(0)$ is the value of the perturbation (5) at $\mathbf{r} = t = 0$[1]:

$$(7) \qquad \mathcal{H}'(0) = \sum_\alpha \frac{1}{Mc}\left(-e_\alpha \mathbf{A}_0\cdot\mathbf{p}_\alpha \pm ie\frac{\hbar}{2}\mathbf{A}_0\times\mathbf{k}\cdot\boldsymbol{\mu}_\alpha\right).$$

The imaginary unit, expressing the shift in phase between electric and magnetic field, shows that there is no interference between the terms arising from the coupling to the charge and to the magnetic moment.

d. Introduction of Photons. In the treatment of (b) and (c) the electromagnetic wave can have any intensity, corresponding to arbitrary values of A_0. But we know that light is composed of photons, and we are interested in finding their effect.

For this we normalize the amplitude A_0 in such a way that the time-averaged energy density of the wave (1),

$$(8) \qquad \begin{aligned}\frac{1}{8\pi}(\langle\mathbf{E}^2\rangle + \langle\mathbf{H}^2\rangle) &= \frac{1}{8\pi c^2}\left\langle\left(\frac{\partial\mathbf{A}}{\partial t}\right)^2\right\rangle + \frac{1}{8\pi}\langle(\mathbf{curl\ A})^2\rangle\\ &= \frac{1}{4\pi c^2}\langle(2A_0\omega)^2\sin^2(kz-\omega t)\rangle = \frac{A_0{}^2\omega^2}{2\pi c^2},\end{aligned}$$

corresponds to n photons per unit volume:

$$(9) \qquad \frac{A_0{}^2\omega^2}{2\pi c^2} = n\hbar\omega.$$

We obtain

$$(10) \qquad \mathbf{A}_0 = \left(\frac{2\pi\hbar}{\omega}n\right)^{1/2} c\hat{\boldsymbol{\epsilon}}.$$

where $\hat{\boldsymbol{\epsilon}}$ is a unit vector which defines the polarization of the electromagnetic wave.

By substituting (10), with $n = 1$, into (6), we obtain the transition probability corresponding to one photon per unit volume or to a flux of c

[1] We write M instead of M_α since the nucleons have approximately equal mass.

photons per unit time. If we then divide by the flux c, we obtain the cross section for absorption or *induced* emission:

$$\sigma_{\substack{\text{absorption}\\ \text{induced emission}}} = \frac{1}{c}\, w_{\substack{\text{absorption}\\ \text{induced emission}}} \tag{11}$$

4.12 Quantization of the Radiation Field

a. The System of Particles and Radiation. The treatment of interactions between particles and radiation by means of perturbation theory, as presented in 4.11, is not completely satisfactory. First of all, it does not account—at least directly—for spontaneous emission; second, although it describes the transitions of the atom or nucleus, it does not tell—at least directly—what happens to the photon; and, finally, it is based on an asymmetry between "waves" and "particles," which is not in the spirit of quantum mechanics.

Instead of treating the particles as the "system" and the electromagnetic wave as the "perturbation," it is more satisfactory to treat photons and particles on the same basis.

For this let us consider a limited region of space, say a cubic box of unit side[1], which contains both massive particles and photons. The particles may be bound or unbound (free waves), but, because of the boundary conditions at the surface of the box, both bound and unbound states are quantized; so are the states of the photons.

The system consists now of both the particles and the photons contained in the box. Its state is specified by giving complete information on the content of the box. This information must include

(i) number of atoms and nuclei for each species, each internal state, and each state of motion and spin direction;
(ii) number of free particles for each wave number and spin direction;
(iii) number of photons for each wave number and polarization.

b. The States of the Free Radiation. Let us suppose that our box contains only radiation. The boundary conditions at the wall may correspond either to standing waves (reflecting walls, $\mathbf{A} = 0$ at the surface of the box) or traveling waves ($\mathbf{A}$ periodic at the surface). In what follows we confine our attention to standing waves, in which case the wave vectors of the photons are limited to those having components

$$k_x = \pi m_x, \qquad k_y = \pi m_y, \qquad k_z = \pi m_z, \tag{1}$$

[1] The normalization volume (volume of the box) does not appear in any of the formulas that can be compared with the experiment. For this reason it is convenient to speak of cubes of unit side and spheres of unit radius. The unit of length must be taken to be very large compared to all wavelengths of interest. A centimeter is adequate for γ rays. For radio waves we could take a light year or a parsec.

where m_x, m_y, and m_z are nonvanishing positive integers. For each possible wave vector there are two possible states of polarization.

Let us specify by λ a possible mode of vibration of the box: λ corresponds to a definite set of the numbers $m_x m_y m_z$ and to a definite polarization. Since photons satisfy Bose statistics, there may be an arbitrary number of photons for each λ: let n_λ be the number of photons in the state λ actually present in the box (*occupation number*). The set of numbers n_λ completely describes the state of the radiation in the box.

The angular frequency corresponding to a given λ is designated by

$$\omega_\lambda = ck_\lambda, \qquad k_\lambda = \pi(m_x^2 + m_y^2 + m_z^2)^{1/2}. \tag{2}$$

The energy levels of the mode λ are equally spaced; the spacing is $\hbar\omega_\lambda$ and corresponds to the addition of an extra photon to the mode.

We observe a striking similarity between the energy levels of each mode and those of an oscillator of the same frequency. The similarity between modes of vibrations and oscillators becomes even more apparent if we use the Hamiltonian formalism.

c. Hamiltonian of the Free Radiation. An arbitrary vector potential, which describes the state of radiation in the box classically can be decomposed as a sum of oscillatory components

$$\mathbf{A} = \sum_\lambda (q_\lambda \mathbf{A}_\lambda + q_\lambda^* \mathbf{A}_\lambda^*) \tag{3}$$

with

$$\mathbf{A}_\lambda = \hat{\boldsymbol{\epsilon}}_\lambda e^{i\mathbf{k}_\lambda \cdot \mathbf{r}}, \tag{4}$$

where $\hat{\boldsymbol{\epsilon}}_\lambda$ specifies the direction of polarization of the λ component ($\hat{\boldsymbol{\epsilon}}_\lambda$ may be complex if we use circular polarizations such as $\hat{\mathbf{x}} + i\hat{\mathbf{y}}$). Observe that $\mathbf{A}$, as written above, is real.

Classically, we could write $q_\lambda = q_{0\lambda} e^{-i\omega_\lambda t}$ with $q_{0\lambda}$ arbitrary constants. The state of radiation is decomposed, according to (3), into a set of polarized traveling plane waves similar to 4.11(1)

$$\mathbf{A}_\lambda = \hat{\boldsymbol{\epsilon}}_\lambda q_{0\lambda}\, 2\cos(\mathbf{k}_\lambda \cdot \mathbf{r} - \omega_\lambda t). \tag{5}$$

According to the ideas of quantum physics, the amplitudes q_λ must be quantized[1] in order to describe an integral number of photons. The q_λ must be considered as operators. From 4.11(10) we expect that, as the result of the quantization, the matrix elements for occupation number near n_λ are

$$\langle \approx n_\lambda |\, q_\lambda \,| \approx n_\lambda \rangle \approx c\left(\frac{2\pi\hbar n_\lambda}{\omega_\lambda}\right)^{1/2}, \qquad \text{for } n_\lambda \text{ large.} \tag{6}$$

Let us now proceed with the quantization of the field. It follows from the orthogonality of the A_λ that the Hamiltonian of the radiation field in

[1] A similar treatment is found in Fermi (Fe-51), Heitler (He-44).

the box of unit volume can be decomposed as a sum over the different modes:

(7) $$\mathcal{H} = \sum \mathcal{H}_\lambda,$$

with[1]

$$\mathcal{H}_\lambda = \frac{1}{8\pi} \int_{\substack{\text{unit}\\\text{cube}}} (\mathbf{E}_\lambda^2 + \mathbf{H}_\lambda^2)\, d\mathbf{r}$$

(8) $$= \frac{1}{8\pi} \int_{\substack{\text{unit}\\\text{cube}}} \left[\frac{1}{c^2} \left| \frac{\partial}{\partial t} (q_\lambda \mathbf{A}_\lambda + q_\lambda^\dagger \mathbf{A}_\lambda^*) \right|^2 + |\mathbf{curl}(q_\lambda \mathbf{A}_\lambda + q_\lambda^\dagger \mathbf{A}_\lambda^*)|^2 \right] d\mathbf{r}.$$

If we consider now that the q_λ must have frequency $\omega_\lambda = k_\lambda c$ so that[2]

(9) $$\dot{q}_\lambda = -i\omega_\lambda q_\lambda, \qquad \dot{q}_\lambda^\dagger = i\omega_\lambda q_\lambda^\dagger,$$

(8) can be put in the form

(10) $$\mathcal{H}_\lambda = \frac{k_\lambda^2}{8\pi} (|q_\lambda - q_\lambda^\dagger|^2 + |q_\lambda + q_\lambda^\dagger|^2).$$

Let us now introduce two hermitian operators

(11) $$Q_\lambda = q_\lambda + q_\lambda^\dagger, \qquad P_\lambda = \frac{-ik}{4\pi c}(q_\lambda - q_\lambda^\dagger) = \mathfrak{m}(\dot{q}_\lambda + \dot{q}_\lambda^\dagger)$$

with

(12) $$\mathfrak{m} \equiv \frac{1}{4\pi c^2}.$$

Then (10) becomes

(13) $$\mathcal{H}_\lambda = \frac{1}{2\mathfrak{m}} P_\lambda^2 + \tfrac{1}{2}\mathfrak{m}\omega_\lambda^2 Q_\lambda^2.$$

This is formally similar to the Hamiltonian of a linear oscillator of coordinate Q_λ, momentum P_λ, mass $\mathfrak{m}$, and angular frequency ω_λ.

d. Quantization of the Free Radiation Field. We can now quantize each mode of the radiation field in the same manner as we quantize a linear oscillator. The results are well known.

The energy eigenvalues are

(14) $$E_\lambda = (n_\lambda + \tfrac{1}{2})\hbar\omega_\lambda,$$

where the integers n_λ have the same meaning as the occupation numbers mentioned in (b). There is a zero point energy $\frac{1}{2}\hbar\omega_\lambda$ for each oscillator,

[1] We write $q\dagger$ in place of q^* because q is regarded as an operator.
[2] The equations in (9) are surely true if the q depends explicitly on time as $e^{\pm i\omega t}$ but are valid more generally [see (16) and (19)] as operator equations.

which contributes an infinite amount of zero point energy to the whole radiation field. We dispose of this infinite energy briefly by stating that we are interested only in energy differences and close our eyes to the difficulties arising from the infinite energy of the vacuum.

In the Heisenberg representation the operators q_λ vary with time as $\exp(\pm i\omega_\lambda t)$ and have a form that is close to that of a classical amplitude; but we choose the Schrödinger representation, in which operators do not depend on time. Then the matrix elements of Q_λ between two states of occupation numbers n_λ and n_λ' are $\langle n_\lambda'| Q_\lambda |n_\lambda\rangle$ and form the matrix

$$Q_\lambda = \left(\frac{2\pi\hbar}{\omega_\lambda}\right)^{1/2} c \begin{vmatrix} 0 & \sqrt{1} & 0 & 0 & \cdots \\ \sqrt{1} & 0 & \sqrt{2} & 0 & \cdots \\ 0 & \sqrt{2} & 0 & \sqrt{3} & \cdots \\ 0 & 0 & \sqrt{3} & 0 & \cdots \\ \cdots & \cdots & \cdots & \cdots & \cdots \end{vmatrix}, \tag{15}$$

where the n_λ and n_λ' vary from 0 (included) to infinity.

Thus (11) is satisfied by the operators

$$q_\lambda \rightarrow \left(\frac{2\pi\hbar}{\omega_\lambda}\right)^{1/2} c\mathrm{a}_\lambda, \qquad q_\lambda^\dagger \rightarrow \left(\frac{2\pi\hbar}{\omega_\lambda}\right)^{1/2} c\mathrm{a}_\lambda^\dagger, \tag{16}$$

where

$$\mathrm{a}_\lambda = \begin{vmatrix} 0 & \sqrt{1} & 0 & 0 & \cdots \\ 0 & 0 & \sqrt{2} & 0 & \cdots \\ 0 & 0 & 0 & \sqrt{3} & \cdots \\ 0 & 0 & 0 & 0 & \cdots \\ \cdots & \cdots & \cdots & \cdots & \cdots \end{vmatrix}, \qquad \mathrm{a}^\dagger = \begin{vmatrix} 0 & 0 & 0 & 0 & \cdots \\ \sqrt{1} & 0 & 0 & 0 & \cdots \\ 0 & \sqrt{2} & 0 & 0 & \cdots \\ 0 & 0 & \sqrt{3} & 0 & \cdots \\ \cdots & \cdots & \cdots & \cdots & \cdots \end{vmatrix}; \tag{17}$$

(16) and (17) must be compared with (6).

If we make use of (14), the time derivatives needed in (9) are

(18)

$$\frac{d}{dt}\langle n_\lambda'|\,\mathrm{a}_\lambda\,|n_\lambda\rangle = \left\langle n_\lambda' \left| \frac{1}{i\hbar}(\mathrm{a}_\lambda\mathcal{H} - \mathcal{H}\mathrm{a}_\lambda) \right| n_\lambda \right\rangle = \frac{(n_\lambda - n_\lambda')\omega_\lambda}{i}\langle n_\lambda'|\,\mathrm{a}_\lambda\,|n_\lambda\rangle,$$

$$\frac{d}{dt}\langle n_\lambda'|\,\mathrm{a}_\lambda^\dagger\,|n_\lambda\rangle = \left\langle n_\lambda' \left| \frac{1}{i\hbar}(\mathrm{a}_\lambda^\dagger\mathcal{H} - \mathcal{H}\mathrm{a}_\lambda^\dagger) \right| n_\lambda \right\rangle = \frac{(n_\lambda - n_\lambda')\omega_\lambda}{i}\langle n_\lambda'|\,\mathrm{a}_\lambda^\dagger\,|n_\lambda\rangle,$$

and correspond to the matrices

(19)
$$\dot{\mathbf{a}}_\lambda = \frac{\omega_\lambda}{i}\begin{vmatrix} 0 & \sqrt{1} & 0 & 0 & \cdots \\ 0 & 0 & \sqrt{2} & 0 & \cdots \\ 0 & 0 & 0 & \sqrt{3} & \cdots \\ 0 & 0 & 0 & 0 & \cdots \\ \cdots & \cdots & \cdots & \cdots & \cdots \end{vmatrix},$$
$$\dot{\mathbf{a}}_\lambda^\dagger = \frac{\omega_\lambda}{i}\begin{vmatrix} 0 & 0 & 0 & 0 & \cdots \\ -\sqrt{1} & 0 & 0 & 0 & \cdots \\ 0 & -\sqrt{2} & 0 & 0 & \cdots \\ 0 & 0 & -\sqrt{3} & 0 & \cdots \\ \cdots & \cdots & \cdots & \cdots & \cdots \end{vmatrix}.$$

By straightforward substitution one verifies that the energy (8) is a diagonal matrix, consistently with (14):

(14′)
$$\mathcal{H}_\lambda = \frac{1}{8\pi c^2}\frac{2\pi\hbar}{\omega_\lambda}c^2\omega_\lambda^{\,2}\begin{vmatrix} 1 & 0 & 0 & \cdots \\ 0 & 3 & 0 & \cdots \\ 0 & 0 & 5 & \cdots \\ \cdots & \cdots & \cdots & \cdots \end{vmatrix} + \frac{\omega_\lambda^{\,2}}{8\pi c^2}\frac{2\pi\hbar}{\omega_\lambda}c^2\begin{vmatrix} 1 & 0 & 0 & \cdots \\ 0 & 3 & 0 & \cdots \\ 0 & 0 & 5 & \cdots \\ \cdots & \cdots & \cdots & \cdots \end{vmatrix}$$

and that its eigenvalue in the state $|n_\lambda\rangle$ is $E_\lambda = (n_\lambda + \frac{1}{2})\hbar\omega_\lambda$.

The potential vector (3) and (4) is also a Hermitian operator, and its expansion in the different modes is

(20)
$$\mathbf{A} = \sqrt{2\pi\hbar}\, c \sum_\lambda \frac{1}{\sqrt{\omega_\lambda}}(\hat{\boldsymbol{\epsilon}}_\lambda \mathbf{a}_\lambda e^{i\mathbf{k}_\lambda\cdot\mathbf{r}} + \hat{\boldsymbol{\epsilon}}_\lambda^* \mathbf{a}_\lambda^\dagger e^{-i\mathbf{k}_\lambda\cdot\mathbf{r}}).$$

The operators $\mathbf{a}_\lambda$ and $\mathbf{a}_\lambda^\dagger$ are called the *annihilation and creation operators of the λ mode* because their matrix elements are different from 0 only for those states of the mode whose occupation numbers differ by ± 1.

Let us now refer the operators $\mathbf{a}_\lambda$ and $\mathbf{a}_\lambda^\dagger$ to the states of the electromagnetic field in our box. Each state is defined by a set of occupation numbers n_λ for each mode λ. Thus we have a double infinity of states, one for each of the possible occupation numbers (from 0 to ∞) of each possible mode:

$$\begin{aligned} \lambda = 1: &\quad n_\lambda = 0, 1, 2, 3, \cdots \\ \lambda = 2: &\quad n_\lambda = 0, 1, 2, 3, \cdots \\ \lambda = 3: &\quad n_\lambda = 0, 1, 2, 3, \cdots \\ &\cdots\cdots\cdots\cdots \end{aligned}$$

In this representation the operator a_λ, which leaves unchanged all modes but the λth, is

	λ	mode 1	mode 2	. . .	mode λ	. . .
λ'	n_λ \ n_λ'	0, 1, 2, . . .	0, 1, . . .		0, 1, . . .	
mode 1	0 1 2 . .	1 0 0 0 0 1 0 0 0 1 0	0	0	0	0
mode 2	0 1 . . .	0	1 0 0 0 1 . 0	0	0	0
. . .	0 1 . . .	0	0	1	0	0
mode λ	0 1 . . .	0	0	0	0 $\sqrt{1}$ 0 $\sqrt{2}$ 0	0
. . .		0	0	0	0	1

It is interesting to compare the photon (or boson) annihilation and creation operators (17) with the corresponding operators for nucleons (fermions) in 2.32(1). For fermions the matrices are 2×2, since there are only two possible states (full and empty) for each mode. Observe also that

$$a_\lambda^\dagger a_\lambda = \begin{vmatrix} 0 & 0 & 0 & \cdots \\ 0 & 1 & 0 & \cdots \\ 0 & 0 & 2 & \cdots \\ \cdots & \cdots & \cdots & \cdots \\ \cdots & \cdots & \cdots & \cdots \end{vmatrix}$$

is, like 2.32(5), a diagonal matrix whose elements are the number of particles in state, or mode, λ.

Although the fermion creation (or annihilation) operators for different modes must anticommute to obtain antisymmetric wave function, the corresponding boson operators *commute*.

e. Interaction between Particles and Radiation. Let us now suppose that our box contains both particles and radiation. In the absence of interaction between particles and radiation, its state can be designated by

(21) $$\Psi = |\psi_{\text{part}} n_1 n_2 \cdots n_\lambda \cdots\rangle$$

where ψ_{part} is the wave function of the particles and the numbers n_λ are the occupation numbers of the various modes of radiation.

The Hamiltonian is composed of three parts:

(22) $$\mathcal{H} = \mathcal{H}_{\text{part}} + \mathcal{H}_{\text{rad}} + \mathcal{H}'_{\text{int}},$$

where [as in 4.11(3)]

(23) $$\mathcal{H}_{\text{part}} = V + \sum_\alpha \frac{p_\alpha^{\,2}}{2M_\alpha}$$

and (see 7 and 8)

(24) $$\mathcal{H}_{\text{rad}} = \frac{1}{8\pi} \sum_\lambda \int (E_\lambda^{\,2} + H_\lambda^{\,2})\, d\mathbf{r}.$$

The sum

(25) $$\mathcal{H}_0 = \mathcal{H}_{\text{part}} + \mathcal{H}_{\text{rad}}$$

is the "unperturbed" Hamiltonian of which the states (21) are eigenstates.

The interaction Hamiltonian [see 4.11(5)] is

(26) $$\mathcal{H}' = -\sum_\alpha \frac{1}{Mc}\left(e_\alpha \mathbf{A} \cdot \mathbf{p}_\alpha + e\frac{\hbar}{2} \boldsymbol{\mu}_\alpha \cdot \mathbf{curl}\, \mathbf{A}\right)$$

with **A** expanded as in (20). In its quantized form the first term of (26) becomes

(27) $$\frac{e_\alpha}{Mc} \mathbf{A} \cdot \mathbf{p}_\alpha = \frac{e_\alpha}{Mc} \sqrt{2\pi\hbar}\, c \sum_\lambda \frac{1}{\sqrt{\omega_\lambda}} (\hat{\boldsymbol{\epsilon}}_\lambda \cdot \mathbf{p}_\alpha a_\lambda e^{i\mathbf{k}_\lambda \cdot \mathbf{r}_\alpha} + \hat{\boldsymbol{\epsilon}}_\lambda^* \cdot \mathbf{p}_\alpha a_\lambda^\dagger e^{-i\mathbf{k}_\lambda \cdot \mathbf{r}_\alpha})$$

and the second term is

$$(28) \quad \frac{e\hbar}{2Mc}\,\boldsymbol{\mu}_\alpha \cdot \text{curl}\,\mathbf{A}$$

$$= \frac{e\hbar}{2Mc}\sqrt{2\pi\hbar}\,c\sum_\lambda \frac{-i}{\sqrt{\omega_\lambda}}\,\boldsymbol{\mu}_\alpha \cdot (\hat{\boldsymbol{\epsilon}}_\lambda \times \mathbf{k}_\lambda \mathrm{a}_\lambda e^{i\mathbf{k}_\lambda\cdot\mathbf{r}_\alpha} - \hat{\boldsymbol{\epsilon}}_\lambda^* \times \mathbf{k}_\lambda \mathrm{a}_\lambda^\dagger e^{-i\mathbf{k}_\lambda\cdot\mathbf{r}_\alpha}.)$$

The interaction Hamiltonian is again considered as a perturbation that induces transitions between the stationary states (21) of $\mathcal{H}_0$ (25). The transition rates, in first order, are expressed by a formula similar to 4.11(6):

$$(29) \qquad w = \frac{2\pi}{\hbar}\,\rho_F(E)\,|\langle\Psi_f|\,\mathcal{H}'\,|\Psi_i\rangle|^2.$$

If we fix our attention on the absorption or the emission of a particular mode of radiation λ, the matrix element splits into two parts, which are the "particle" factor

$$(30) \quad \frac{-\hbar}{Mc}\left(\frac{2\pi\hbar}{\omega_\lambda}\right)^{1/2} c\sum_\alpha \int \psi_f^* e^{\pm i\mathbf{k}_\lambda\cdot\mathbf{r}_\alpha}\left[e_\alpha\hat{\boldsymbol{\epsilon}}_\lambda \cdot \frac{\mathbf{p}_\alpha}{\hbar} \pm \frac{e\mu_\alpha}{2i}(\hat{\boldsymbol{\epsilon}}_\lambda \times \mathbf{k}_\lambda)\right]\psi_i\,d\tau$$

(+ for absorption; − for emission; if $\hat{\boldsymbol{\epsilon}}$ is complex use $\hat{\boldsymbol{\epsilon}}^*$ for emission); and the radiation factor which is, for absorption:

$$(31a) \quad \langle n_1' \cdots n_\lambda' \cdots |\,\mathrm{a}_\lambda\,|n_1 \cdots n_\lambda \cdots\rangle = \delta_{n_1' n_1} \cdots \delta_{n_\lambda', n_\lambda - 1}\sqrt{n_\lambda} \cdots$$

and, for emission,

$$(31b) \quad \langle n_1' \cdots n_\lambda' \cdots |\,\mathrm{a}_\lambda^\dagger\,|n_1 \cdots n_\lambda \cdots\rangle = \delta_{n_1' n_1} \cdots \delta_{n_\lambda', n_\lambda + 1}\sqrt{n_\lambda + 1} \cdots$$

The theory describes both the change in state of the system of particles and the appearance or disappearance of a photon. It accounts for spontaneous emission, since (31*b*) is not zero even if there were no radiation in the initial state (all $n_\lambda = 0$).

4.13 *Introduction of the Multipole Fields*

a. Expansion of the Radiation Field in Spherical Waves. In 4.11 and 4.12 the electromagnetic field was expanded in a sum of proper modes in a cubic box. The modes chosen were plane waves, eigenfunctions of linear momentum $\hbar\mathbf{k}$; the expansion is justified because the plane waves form a complete set.

However, the expansion in plane waves is not always the most convenient. As we have seen for particles, the problem to be solved often presents spherical symmetry, and the treatment is simplified if we consider spherical waves. This is the case for a central potential, such as that responsible for the discontinuous, bound states of an atom or for the continuous states of the scattering problem.

Let us consider the transition between two atomic or nuclear states, accompanied by the emission of a quantum of radiation. The initial and final states of the system of particles are eigenstates of J, M_J, and P_r (parity), and the conservation principles require that the differences between the initial and final quantum numbers $J_i - J_f$, $M_i - M_f$, $\pi_i - \pi_f$ be found in the radiation field of the emitted wave.

Thus it may be useful to consider the waves emitted—or absorbed—by atoms and nuclei as eigenwaves of angular momentum and parity rather than as eigenwaves of linear momentum.

Such eigenwaves are called the *electric* or *magnetic multipole* fields. They form a complete set and can be used—in place of plane waves—as the modes into which an arbitrary field is expanded. In the quantization of the field each multipole wave corresponds to an oscillator whose nth level has energy $(n + \frac{1}{2})\hbar\omega$, corresponding to an integral number n of "spherical photons."

b. The Multipole Fields. The *multipole fields* are solutions of the wave equation in vacuum for given total angular momentum and parity. According to established conventions, the quantum numbers of the successive electric and magnetic multipoles are as follows:

(1$\mathcal{E}$) Electric 2^J pole: $\mathcal{E}J$; total angular momentum J; total parity $(-1)^J$;

(1$\mathcal{M}$) Magnetic 2^J pole: $\mathcal{M}J$; total angular momentum J; total parity $-(-1)^J$.

In more detail

(2)

Electric dipole	$\mathcal{E}1$:	$J = 1$	$\pi = -1$
Magnetic dipole	$\mathcal{M}1$:	1	+1
Electric quadrupole	$\mathcal{E}2$:	2	+1
Magnetic quadrupole	$\mathcal{M}2$:	2	−1
Electric octupole	$\mathcal{E}3$:	3	−1
etc.			

Each multipole field can be described either by giving the potential vector **A**, or one of the fields **E** and **H**. Since **A** and **E** are vectors—thus intrinsically odd—and **H** is a pseudovector—intrinsically even—the orbital parity of **A** and **E** is the opposite of that of **H** in each multipole (1.15d). In order to avoid confusion, the orbital parity of these vectors for different multipoles is indicated in Table 4.13-1.

Table 4.13-1

Multipole	Parity: Total	Parity: Orbital: E or A	Parity: Orbital: H
$\mathcal{E}J$	$(-1)^J$	$-(-1)^J$	$(-1)^J$
$\mathcal{M}J$	$-(-1)^J$	$(-1)^J$	$-(-1)^J$

c. Analytical Expression of the Multipole Fields. It is well known that the wave equation in vacuum

(3) $$(\nabla^2 + k^2)u = 0$$

admits scalar solutions that are eigenfunctions of angular momentum $L^2 \to l(l+1)\hbar$ and of its z component $(L_z \to m)$. These are

(4) $$u_l^m(kr) = j_l(kr)\, Y_l^m(\theta, \varphi),$$

where the functions j_l and Y_l^m have been introduced in 1.13d.

We shall now turn our attention to the vector solutions of the wave equation

(5) $$(\nabla^2 + k^2)\mathbf{A} = 0,$$

where the vector $\mathbf{A}$ represents the vector potential of an electromagnetic wave, and introduce the multipole fields $\mathbf{A}_\mu$ (F-60a)[1]:

(6$\mathcal{E}$) $$\mathbf{A}_{\mathcal{E}J}{}^M = \frac{\sqrt{2}}{\sqrt{J(J+1)}}\frac{1}{\hbar}\,\mathbf{curl}\,\mathbf{L}u_J{}^M(kr)$$

(6$\mathcal{M}$) $$\mathbf{A}_{\mathcal{M}J}{}^M = \frac{\sqrt{2}}{\sqrt{J(J+1)}}\frac{k}{\hbar}\,\mathbf{L}u_J{}^M(kr)$$

where $\mathbf{L}$ is the orbital angular momentum operator 1.13(2).

Observe that the expression $\mathbf{L}u_J{}^M$ can be expanded with the help of 1.13(25) and (27) and Table 1.14-4:

(7) $$\begin{aligned}\mathbf{L}u_J{}^M &= j_J(-L_-\hat{\mathbf{e}}_+ + L_0\hat{\mathbf{e}}_0 - L_+\hat{\mathbf{e}}_-)Y_J{}^M \\ &= \hbar j_J\{-[\tfrac{1}{2}(J+M)(J-M+1)]^{1/2}Y_J{}^{M-1}\hat{\mathbf{e}}_+ + MY_J{}^M\hat{\mathbf{e}}_0 \\ &\qquad + [\tfrac{1}{2}(J-M)(J+M+1)]^{1/2}Y_J^{M+1}\hat{\mathbf{e}}_-\} \\ &= \hbar j_J\sqrt{J(J+1)}[C(J1J;M-1,1)Y_J^{M-1}\hat{\mathbf{e}}_+ \\ &\qquad + C(J1J;M,0)Y_J{}^M\hat{\mathbf{e}}_0 + C(J1J;M+1,-1)Y_J^{M+1}\hat{\mathbf{e}}_-].\end{aligned}$$

[1] In our notation the index μ stands for parity ($\mathcal{M}$ or $\mathcal{E}$), J and M. We use the symbol $\mathbf{A}_{\pi J}{}^M$ to indicate a multiple of unspecified parity ($\mathcal{M}$ or $\mathcal{E}$) but of definite J and M.

The vector fields $\mathbf{A}_\mu$ describe spherical standing waves which have properties appropriate for electric ($\mathcal{E}$) and magnetic ($\mathcal{M}$) multipoles. These properties are described in detail in what follows:

(i) All fields $\mathbf{A}_\mu$ are divergenceless:

$$\text{div } \mathbf{A}_\mu = 0, \tag{8}$$

as it follows from the vector identities div **curl** = div **L** = 0.

(ii) The vector fields (6) are solutions of the wave equation (3) for wave number k. For magnetic multipoles this is easily seen from (7). For electric multipoles we first observe that because of (8) the wave equation can be written $(\mathbf{curl}\,\mathbf{curl} - k^2)\,\mathbf{A}_{\mathcal{E}J}{}^M = 0$; since **curl** obviously commutes with $(\mathbf{curl}\,\mathbf{curl} - k^2)$, we find that electric multipoles also satisfy the wave equation.

(iii) The vector fields (6) are eigenfields of J^2 and of J_z with eigenvalues $J(J+1)$ and M. For the magnetic multipoles this is seen by comparing (7) with the law of addition of angular momenta 1.14(30) and remembering that the unit vectors $\hat{\mathbf{e}}_+$, $\hat{\mathbf{e}}_0$, $\hat{\mathbf{e}}_-$ are the eigenvectors of spin 1 [1.14(25)]. For the electric multipoles the proof is immediate if we consider that J^2 and J_z commute with **curl** [1].

(iv) The orbital parity of $\mathbf{A}_{\mathcal{E}J}{}^M$ is $-(-1)^J$ and that of $\mathbf{A}_{\mathcal{M}J}{}^M$ is $(-1)^J$ in accord with the conventions (1) and (2). This can be shown by considering that each differential operator, or each factor r, changes the parity[2].

(v) The fields (6) are normalized to unity in a sphere of unit radius:

$$\int_0^1 r^2\,dr \int_{4\pi} |\mathbf{A}_\mu|^2\,d\Omega = 1. \tag{9}$$

In order to verify this relation for magnetic multipoles, we must compute expressions of the form

$$\frac{2}{J(J+1)}\,\frac{k^2}{\hbar^2} \int_0^1 |j_J(kr)|^2\,r^2\,dr \int |\mathbf{L}Y_J{}^M|^2\,d\Omega. \tag{10}$$

[1] To prove this point we write the operators in matrix form:

$$\mathbf{curl} = \begin{pmatrix} 0 & -\dfrac{\partial}{\partial z} & \dfrac{\partial}{\partial y} \\ \dfrac{\partial}{\partial z} & 0 & -\dfrac{\partial}{\partial x} \\ -\partial/\partial y & \partial/\partial x & 0 \end{pmatrix}, \qquad \frac{1}{k}J_z = \begin{pmatrix} L_z & -i & 0 \\ i & L_z & 0 \\ 0 & 0 & L_z \end{pmatrix}, \text{ etc.}$$

The commutation rules are found immediately by carrying out the matrix multiplications.

[2] The fields $\mathbf{A}_\mu$ represent vector potentials and are thus intrinsically odd. Thus equation (6$\mathcal{M}$) must be inverted in sign in left-handed coordinate systems.

The integration over the solid angle gives $J(J+1)\hbar^2$ as it can be proved by making use of (7). The radial integral can be computed easily if the unit radius contains many wavelengths ($k \gg 1$) and if the multipole is not too high ($J/k \ll 1$); in this case one is allowed to replace $j_J(kr)$ by $\{\sin[kr - l(\pi/2)]\}/kr$ and $|j_J(kr)|^2$ by its average $(2k^2r^2)^{-1}$.

Passing now to the integrals for the electric multipoles, we must remember that

$$|\mathbf{curl\ V}|^2 = (\mathbf{curl\ V}^*)\cdot(\mathbf{curl\ V}) = \text{div}\,[\mathbf{V} \times \mathbf{curl\ V}^*] + \mathbf{V}\ \mathbf{curl\ curl\ V}^*.$$

The divergence term vanishes upon integration; then by using the wave, equation, we obtain

$$\int |\mathbf{curl\ L}u_J{}^M|^2\, d\mathbf{r} = k^2 \int |\mathbf{L}u_J{}^M|^2\, d\mathbf{r}. \tag{11}$$

The normalization (9) is easily proved with the help of these relations.

4.14 The Multipole Fields Near the Origin

a. Approximations for $kr \ll 1$. The formulation of the multipole radiation given in the preceding section is exact. In order to carry out many computations of interest for the discussion of experimental results, it is convenient, however, to obtain simpler approximate expressions.

The approximations for $kr \ll 1$ are useful in the study of interaction with sources of small extent and thus, in most cases of interest, in the derivation of the transition probabilities for absorption and emission of radiation by atoms and nuclei.

The approximations for $kr \gg 1$ describe the behavior of the fields away from the source and can be applied to the computation of angular distributions and polarizations.

A first estimate of the vector potentials and of the magnetic fields near the origin ($kr \ll 1$) is obtained by using the approximations 1.13(18) in 4.13(6). Apart from factors of the order of unity, we can write near the origin[1]

$$\begin{aligned} |\mathbf{A}_{\mathcal{E}J}{}^M| &\cong k(kr)^{J-1}, \\ |\mathbf{H}_{\mathcal{E}J}{}^M| &\cong k^2(kr)^J, \end{aligned} \tag{1$\mathcal{E}$}$$

$$\begin{aligned} |\mathbf{A}_{\mathcal{M}J}{}^M| &\cong k(kr)^J, \\ |\mathbf{H}_{\mathcal{M}J}{}^M| &\cong k^2(kr)^{J-1}. \end{aligned} \tag{1$\mathcal{M}$}$$

[1] These estimates are obtained from 4.13(6) with $u_J \approx j_J \approx (kr)^J$, $L \approx 1$, **curl** $\approx 1/r$. The **curl curl** in $\mathbf{H}_{\varepsilon J}$ has been made equal to k^2 by the wave equation. The same estimates can be obtained from (6) and (8).

Observe that these formulas justify the classification of the multipoles into "electric" and "magnetic," since for $kr \ll 1$

$$|\mathbf{E}_{\mathcal{E}}| \cong k\,|\mathbf{A}_{\mathcal{E}}| \gg |\mathbf{H}_{\mathcal{E}}|$$

$$|\mathbf{E}_{\mathcal{M}}| \cong k\,|\mathbf{A}_{\mathcal{M}}| \ll |\mathbf{H}_{\mathcal{M}}|.$$

Though (1) is often sufficiently accurate for a rough estimate of the transition probabilities, we derive, for future reference, a more precise expression (S-52) by making use of the equality (which is not difficult to verify)

$$\text{(2)} \qquad \frac{1}{\hbar k}\,\mathbf{curl}\,\mathbf{L}u_J{}^M = \frac{i}{k}\left\{\nabla\left(1 + r\frac{\partial}{\partial r}\right) - \mathbf{r}\nabla^2\right\}u_J{}^M$$

and of the recurrence relation between the spherical Bessel functions[1]

$$\text{(3)} \qquad \left(1 + r\frac{d}{dr}\right)j_J(kr) = (J+1)j_J(kr) - (kr)j_{J+1}(kr).$$

We obtain exactly

$$\text{(4)} \quad \frac{1}{\hbar k}\,\mathbf{curl}\,\mathbf{L}u_J{}^M = \frac{i}{k}\,\mathbf{grad}\,[(J+1)u_J{}^M - kr\,j_{J+1}(kr)Y_J{}^M] + iku_J{}^M\,\mathbf{r}$$

In the approximation $kr \ll 1$ only the first term is important, and we can write

$$\text{(5)} \quad \frac{1}{\hbar k}\,\mathbf{curl}\,\mathbf{L}u_J{}^M \cong \frac{i}{k}(J+1)\,\mathbf{grad}\,u_J{}^M \cong \frac{i}{k}\frac{J+1}{(2J+1)!!}\,\mathbf{grad}\,[(kr)^J Y_J{}^M].$$

By introducing (5) into 4.13(6), we obtain, apart from phase factors, the following approximate expressions which are valid near the origin:

(6$\mathcal{E}$)

$$\mathbf{A}_{\mathcal{E}J}{}^M \cong \sqrt{\frac{2(J+1)}{J}}\,\frac{1}{(2J+1)!!}\,\mathbf{grad}\,[(kr)^J Y_J{}^M] \qquad (kr \ll 1),$$

(6$\mathcal{M}$)

$$\mathbf{A}_{\mathcal{M}J}{}^M \cong \sqrt{\frac{2}{J(J+1)}}\,\frac{k}{(2J+1)!!}\,\mathbf{r}\times\mathbf{grad}\,[(kr)^J Y_J{}^M] \qquad (kr \ll 1).$$

For the electric fields we can write, everywhere,

$$\text{(7)} \qquad \mathbf{E}_{\pi J}{}^M = -\frac{1}{c}\frac{\partial}{\partial t}\mathbf{A}_{\pi J}{}^M = \pm ik\mathbf{A}_{\pi J}{}^M.$$

[1] Equation (3) can be obtained for the usual form of the recurrence relation:

$$\frac{dj_J(kr)}{d(kr)} = \frac{J}{kr}j_J(kr) - j_{J+1}(kr)$$

multiplying by kr and adding j_J to both sides.

The magnetic fields can be computed as the **curl** of the vector potentials. Thus $\mathbf{H}_{\mathcal{M}J}{}^{M}$ has a form similar to that of $\mathbf{A}_{\mathcal{E}J}{}^{M}$, and $\mathbf{H}_{\mathcal{E}J}{}^{M}$ is obtained observing that **curl curl** $\mathbf{L}u_J{}^M = k^2 \mathbf{L}u_J{}^M$. The result is (neglecting phase factors)

(8ℰ)
$$\mathbf{H}_{\mathcal{E}J}{}^{M} \cong \sqrt{\frac{2}{J(J+1)}}\,\frac{k^2}{(2J+1)!!}\,\mathbf{r}\times \mathbf{grad}\,[(kr)^J Y_J{}^M] \qquad (kr \ll 1),$$

$$(8\mathcal{M})\quad \mathbf{H}_{\mathcal{M}J}{}^{M} \cong \sqrt{\frac{2(J+1)}{J}}\,\frac{k}{(2J+1)!!}\,\mathbf{grad}\,[(kr)^J Y_J{}^M] \qquad (kr \ll 1).$$

Let us apply these expressions to the dipole fields. By making use of 1.13(21) and (26), we see that

$$\mathbf{grad}\,(rY_1{}^0) = \sqrt{\frac{3}{4\pi}}\,\hat{\mathbf{z}} = \sqrt{\frac{3}{4\pi}}\,\hat{\mathbf{e}}_0.$$

$$\mathbf{grad}\,(rY_1{}^{\pm 1}) = \mp\sqrt{\frac{3}{8\pi}}\,(\hat{\mathbf{x}} \pm i\hat{\mathbf{y}}) = \sqrt{\frac{3}{4\pi}}\,\hat{\mathbf{e}}_{\pm},$$

from which we obtain for electric dipole

$$\mathbf{A}_{\mathcal{E}1}{}^{0} \cong \frac{1}{\sqrt{3\pi}}\,k\hat{\mathbf{e}}_0 \qquad \mathbf{A}_{\mathcal{E}1}{}^{\pm 1} \cong \frac{1}{\sqrt{3\pi}}\,k\hat{\mathbf{e}}_{\pm}$$

(9ℰ)

$$\mathbf{H}_{\mathcal{E}1}{}^{0} \cong \frac{k^3}{\sqrt{12\pi}}\,\mathbf{r}\times\hat{\mathbf{e}}_0 \qquad \mathbf{H}_{\mathcal{E}1}{}^{\pm 1} \cong \frac{k^3}{\sqrt{12\pi}}\,\mathbf{r}\times\hat{\mathbf{e}}_{\pm},$$

and for magnetic dipole

$$\mathbf{A}_{\mathcal{M}1}{}^{0} \cong \frac{k^2}{\sqrt{12\pi}}\,\mathbf{r}\times\hat{\mathbf{e}}_0 \qquad \mathbf{A}_{\mathcal{M}1}{}^{\pm 1} \cong \frac{k^2}{\sqrt{12\pi}}\,\mathbf{r}\times\hat{\mathbf{e}}_{\pm}$$

(9ℳ)

$$\mathbf{H}_{\mathcal{M}1}{}^{0} \cong \frac{k^2}{\sqrt{3\pi}}\,\hat{\mathbf{e}}_0 \qquad \mathbf{H}_{\mathcal{M}1}{}^{\pm 1} \cong \frac{k^2}{\sqrt{3\pi}}\,\hat{\mathbf{e}}_{\pm}.$$

b. The Intermediate Zone ($kr \approx 1$) and the Orbital Angular Momentum. The region $kr \approx 1$ is the most difficult to discuss quantitatively because no simple approximation can be made. In this region the fields are neither radial, as at the origin, nor tangential, as in the wave zone.

The Poynting vector $\mathbf{S} = (c/4\pi)\mathbf{E}\times\mathbf{H}$ is not radial in the intermediate zone, and in this region the fields carry a nonvanishing angular momentum density $\mathbf{r}\times\mathbf{S}$. The total angular momentum of the waves is obtained by integrating $\mathbf{r}\times\mathbf{S}$ all over space (F-50b; H-36), and the classical result agrees with what we would expect from the assumption of radiated photons: for each amount of radiated energy $\hbar\omega$, the angular momentum carried away by 2^J-pole radiation is $\sqrt{J(J+1)}\hbar$, with z component $M\hbar$.

4.15 *Angular Distribution and Polarization of the Multipole Fields in the Wave Zone*

a. Relation between Multipole Fields and Vector Spherical Harmonics. The angular distribution and polarization of the multipole fields in the wave zone are characteristic of vector spin-angle functions of definite total angular momentum and parity.

In order to discuss these properties, let us recall that a vector field has intrinsic angular momentum, or spin, $S = 1$ (1.14c). At each position in space a vector $\mathbf{V}(\mathbf{r})$ can be expressed as a sum of three components:

$$\mathbf{V}(\mathbf{r}) = -V_-(\mathbf{r})\hat{\mathbf{e}}_+ + V_0(\mathbf{r})\hat{\mathbf{e}}_0 - V_+(\mathbf{r})\hat{\mathbf{e}}_- \tag{1}$$

where the unit vectors $\hat{\mathbf{e}}_+$, $\hat{\mathbf{e}}_0$, and $\hat{\mathbf{e}}_-$ are eigenvectors of S^2 [for eigenvalues $S(S+1)\hbar^2 = 2\hbar^2$] and of S_z (for eigenvalues $+\hbar$, 0, and $-\hbar$).

The usual method of addition of angular momenta can be used to construct vector spin-angle functions of total angular momentum J and z-projection M, or *vector spherical harmonics*. Using 1.14(30) these functions can be written

$$\mathbf{Y}_{Jl1}^{M} = \sum_{m=-1}^{+1} C(l1J; M-m, m)\, Y_l^{M-m}(\theta\varphi)\hat{\mathbf{e}}_m. \tag{2}$$

The vector spherical harmonics (2) are normalized over the solid angle; they are a combination of the eigenstates of spin 1, $\hat{\mathbf{e}}_m$, with the eigenfunctions of orbital angular momentum l, $Y_l^{M-m}(\theta, \varphi)$.

For each value of J and M there are *three* vector spherical harmonics, for l equal to $J+1$, J, $J-1$. Each corresponds to the sum of three terms.

It is important to note that the orbital parity of $\mathbf{Y}_{J,J,1}^{M}$ is $(-1)^J$ and that of $\mathbf{Y}_{J,J\pm1,1}^{M}$ is $(-1)^{J+1}$.

The vector spherical harmonic $\mathbf{Y}_{J,J,1}^{M}$ is particularly useful and for brevity is called $\mathbf{X}_J^M$. It can be written more in detail by using Table 1.14-4:

$$\begin{aligned}\mathbf{X}_J^{M} = \mathbf{Y}_{J,J,1}^{M} &= -\left[\frac{(J+M)(J-M+1)}{2J(J+1)}\right]^{1/2} Y_J^{M-1}\hat{\mathbf{e}}_+ \\ &+ \frac{M}{\sqrt{J(J+1)}}\, Y_J^{M}\hat{\mathbf{e}}_0 \\ &+ \left[\frac{(J-M)(J+M+1)}{2J(J+1)}\right]^{1/2} Y_J^{M+1}\hat{\mathbf{e}}_-,\end{aligned} \tag{3}$$

Since the vector spherical harmonics form a complete set, an arbitrary vector field can be expanded as follows:

(4)
$$\mathbf{V}(\mathbf{r}) = \sum_{J=0}^{\infty} \sum_{M=-J}^{J} \frac{1}{r} [f_{JM}(r)\mathbf{Y}_{J,J,1}^{M} + g_{JM}(r)\mathbf{Y}_{J,J+1,1}^{M} + h_{JM}(r)\mathbf{Y}_{J,J-1,1}^{M}],$$

where $f_{JM}(r)$, $g_{JM}(r)$, $h_{JM}(r)$ are appropriate functions of r only.

The expansion of the multipole fields in vector spherical harmonics is particularly simple. Comparing with 4.13(7), we obtain immediately

$$\mathbf{L}Y_J{}^M = \hbar\sqrt{J(J+1)}\,\mathbf{X}_J{}^M, \tag{5}$$

and thus

$$\mathbf{A}_{\mathcal{E}J}{}^M = \sqrt{2}\,\mathbf{curl}\,[j_J(kr)\mathbf{X}_J{}^M], \tag{6$\mathcal{E}$}$$

$$\mathbf{A}_{\mathcal{M}J}{}^M = \sqrt{2}\,k\,j_J(kr)\mathbf{X}_J{}^M. \tag{6$\mathcal{M}$}$$

Using the wave equation ($\mathbf{curl\ curl\ A} - k^2\mathbf{A} = 0$), we can easily obtain the magnetic field of an electric multipole from the first of these equations; on the other hand, the electric field of a magnetic multipole can be computed as the time derivative of $\mathbf{A}_{\mathcal{M}J}{}^M$. Thus (apart from uninteresting phases)

$$\mathbf{H}_{\mathcal{E}J}{}^M = \mathbf{E}_{\mathcal{M}J}{}^M = \sqrt{2}\,k^2 j_J(kr)\mathbf{X}_J{}^M. \tag{7}$$

We know from electromagnetism that the fields (7) are tangential to the wavefront.

The remaining fields can be obtained in the wave zone by using the fact that $\mathbf{E}$ and $\mathbf{H}$ are perpendicular to $\mathbf{r}$ and to each other. Thus apart from phases

$$\mathbf{E}_{\mathcal{E}J}{}^M \cong \mathbf{H}_{\mathcal{M}J}{}^M \cong \sqrt{2}\,k^2 j_J(kr)\hat{\mathbf{r}} \times \mathbf{X}_J{}^M \qquad kr \gg 1; \tag{8}$$

(7) and (8), together with (3), completely specify the fields in the wave zone, where they can be experimentally investigated. It is seen that the magnetic multipoles are polarized at 90° from the electric ones.

Observe that (7) is valid also in the near zone, whereas (8) is not.

b. Dipole and Quadrupole Fields. For dipole radiation ($J = 1$) the electric field of the magnetic mode or the magnetic field of the electric mode, from (7) and (3), have the following spin-angle behavior:

$$\mathbf{E}_{\mathcal{M}1}{}^M \cong \mathbf{H}_{\mathcal{E}1}{}^M \cong \mathbf{X}_1{}^M$$
$$= -\left[\frac{(M+1)(2-M)}{4}\right]^{1/2} Y_1^{M-1}\hat{\mathbf{e}}_+ + \frac{M}{\sqrt{2}}\,Y_1{}^M\hat{\mathbf{e}}_0 \tag{9}$$
$$+ \left[\frac{(1-M)(2+M)}{4}\right]^{1/2} Y_1^{M+1}\hat{\mathbf{e}}_-.$$

Substitution of 1.13(11) and 1.13(21) yields

$$\mathbf{X}_1{}^0 = -\frac{1}{\sqrt{2}}\left(\sqrt{\frac{3}{8\pi}}\sin\theta e^{-i\varphi}\right)\left[-\frac{1}{\sqrt{2}}(\hat{\mathbf{x}}+i\hat{\mathbf{y}})\right]+0$$

$$(10)\qquad +\frac{1}{\sqrt{2}}\left(-\sqrt{\frac{3}{8\pi}}\sin\theta e^{i\varphi}\right)\left[\frac{1}{\sqrt{2}}(\hat{\mathbf{x}}-i\hat{\mathbf{y}})\right]$$

$$= \sqrt{\frac{3}{8\pi}}\, i\sin\theta(-\sin\varphi\,\hat{\mathbf{x}}+\cos\varphi\,\hat{\mathbf{y}})\Big],$$

$$(11)\qquad \mathbf{X}_1{}^{\pm1} = \sqrt{\frac{3}{8\pi}}\left(-\frac{\sin\theta}{\sqrt{2}}e^{\pm i\varphi}\hat{\mathbf{z}}+\cos\theta\frac{\hat{\mathbf{x}}\pm i\hat{\mathbf{y}}}{\sqrt{2}}\right).$$

The vector spherical harmonic $\mathbf{X}_1{}^0$ has the well-known dipole character. The intensity (Fig. 4.15-1*a*)

$$(12)\qquad |\mathbf{X}_1{}^0|^2 = \frac{3}{8\pi}\sin^2\theta$$

is zero along the polar axis; the vector $\mathbf{X}_1{}^0$ is always perpendicular to the z axis and to the radius vector.

The $\mathbf{X}_1{}^1$ and $\mathbf{X}_1{}^{-1}$ waves have an intensity (Fig. 4.15-1*b*)

$$(13)\quad |\mathbf{X}_1{}^1|^2 = |\mathbf{X}_1{}^{-1}|^2 = \frac{3}{8\pi}\left(\frac{1}{2}\sin^2\theta+\cos^2\theta\right) = \frac{3}{8\pi}\frac{1}{2}(1+\cos^2\theta);$$

for $\theta = 0$ they are circularly polarized along the z axis, as expected, since they carry one unit of angular momentum in this direction. The polarization is linear and parallel to the z axis for $\theta = \pi/2$; and, in intermediate directions, the radiation is elliptically polarized.

For quadrupole ($J = 2$) radiation we have

$$(14)\qquad \mathbf{E}_{\mathcal{M}2}{}^M = \mathbf{H}_{\mathcal{E}2}{}^M = \mathbf{X}_2{}^M$$

$$= -\left[\frac{(2+M)(3-M)}{12}\right]^{1/2} Y_2^{M-1}\hat{\mathbf{e}}_+ + \frac{M}{\sqrt{6}}Y_2{}^M\hat{\mathbf{e}}_0 + \left[\frac{(2-M)(3+M)}{12}\right]^{1/2} Y_2^{M+1}\hat{\mathbf{e}}_-.$$

Intensities and polarization can be computed, as we have shown for the dipole, by substituting the spherical harmonics. For instance we obtain, apart from constants, (Fig. 4.15-1*c*, *d*, *e*)

$$(15)\qquad \begin{aligned} |\mathbf{X}_2{}^0|^2 &\simeq \sin^2\theta\cos^2\theta, \\ |\mathbf{X}_2{}^1|^2 &\simeq 1 - 3\cos^2\theta + 4\cos^4\theta, \\ |\mathbf{X}_2{}^2|^2 &\simeq 1 - \cos^4\theta. \end{aligned}$$

Waves of higher polarity can be discussed in exactly the same manner.

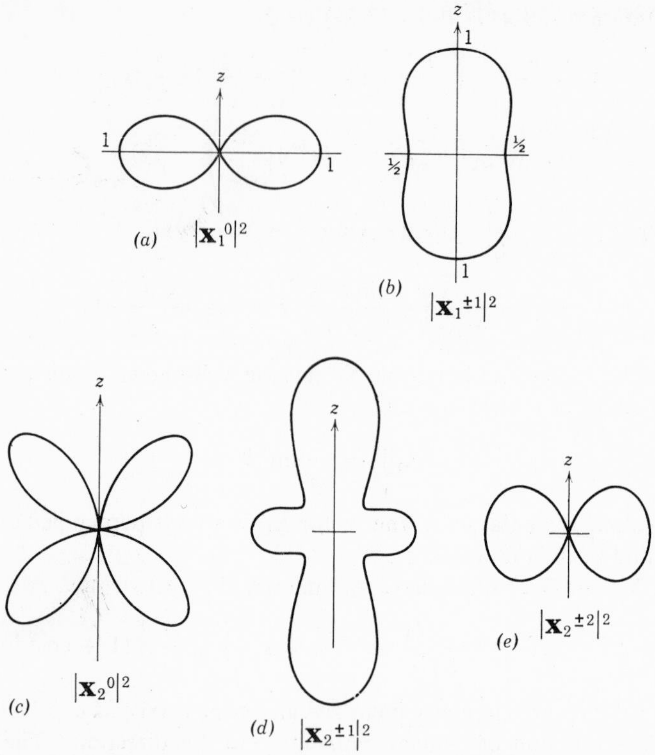

Fig. 4.15-1. Angular distributions of intensity of some simple multipole fields. (Reprinted with permission from J. D. Jackson, *Classical Electrodynamics*, Wiley, New York, 1962.)

4.16 Examples of Multipole Expansions

a. The Expansion of a Plane Wave. In order to clarify the connection between the analysis of the radiation field in plane waves and in multipoles, it is useful to expand a plane wave as a sum of multipoles.

Let us consider a plane wave of potential vector traveling along the z axis and polarized in the x direction:

$$\mathbf{A} = \hat{\mathbf{x}} e^{ikz}. \tag{1}$$

This wave can be decomposed into its circularly polarized components:

$$\mathbf{A} = \frac{-\mathbf{A}^+ + \mathbf{A}^-}{\sqrt{2}} = \frac{1}{\sqrt{2}}(-\hat{\mathbf{e}}_+ e^{ikz} + \hat{\mathbf{e}}_- e^{ikz}). \tag{2}$$

Then each circularly polarized component can be expanded in spherical waves according to 3.12(1):

$$\text{(3)} \qquad \mathbf{A}^{\pm} = \hat{\mathbf{e}}_{\pm} e^{ikz} = \sum_l i^l \sqrt{4\pi(2l+1)}\, j_l(kr)\, Y_l^0(\theta) \hat{\mathbf{e}}_{\pm}.$$

Finally, the products $Y_l^0(\theta)\hat{\mathbf{e}}_{\pm}$ can be expressed as a sum of vector spherical harmonics according to 1.14(31):

$$\text{(4)} \quad Y_l^0(\theta)\hat{\mathbf{e}}_{\pm} = \sum_{J=l-1}^{l+1} C(l1J; 0\ \pm 1)\mathbf{Y}_{Jl1}^{\pm 1}$$

$$= \left[\frac{l-1}{2(2l+1)}\right]^{1/2} \mathbf{Y}_{l-1,l,1}^{\pm 1} + \left[\frac{l+2}{2(2l+1)}\right]^{1/2} \mathbf{Y}_{l+1,l,1}^{\pm 1} \mp \frac{1}{\sqrt{2}} \mathbf{X}_l^{\pm 1}.$$

Substituting (4) into (3), we have

$$\text{(5)} \quad \mathbf{A}^{\pm} = \hat{\mathbf{e}}_{\pm} e^{ikz}$$

$$= \sum_l i^l \sqrt{4\pi}\, j_l(kr) \Bigg[\left(\frac{l+2}{2}\right)^{1/2} \mathbf{Y}_{l+1,l,1}^{\pm 1}$$

$$+ \left(\frac{l-1}{2}\right)^{1/2} \mathbf{Y}_{l-1,l,1}^{\pm 1} \mp \left(\frac{2l+1}{2}\right)^{1/2} \mathbf{X}_l^{\pm 1} \Bigg].$$

The sum (5) extends to $l = \infty$. The lowest values of l which contribute for $M = \pm 1$ are $l = 0$, $l = 2$, and $l = 1$ for the three terms in parentheses. We make the substitution $J = l + 1$ in the first term, $J = l - 1$ in the second, and $J = l$ in the third. Then all sums go from $J = 1$ to $J = \infty$, and we obtain

$$\text{(6)} \quad \mathbf{A}^{\pm} = \hat{\mathbf{e}}_{\pm} e^{ikz} = \sum_{J=1}^{\infty} i^J [2\pi(2J+1)]^{1/2}$$

$$\times \underbrace{\left[i^{-1} \left(\frac{J+1}{2J+1}\right)^{1/2} j_{J-1}(kr) \mathbf{Y}_{J,J-1,1}^{\pm 1} + i \left(\frac{J}{2J+1}\right)^{1/2} j_{J+1}(kr) \mathbf{Y}_{J,J+1,1}^{\pm 1}\right.}_{\mathcal{E}J}$$

$$\left. \mp \underbrace{j_J(kr) \mathbf{X}_J^{\pm 1}}_{\mathcal{M}J} \right]$$

In this expression the plane wave is resolved in a sum of terms of different J (total angular momentum); for each J the first two terms in the parentheses have orbital parity $-(-1)^J$ and are (see Table 4.13-1) the $\mathcal{E}J$ contribution; the last term, with orbital parity $(-1)^J$ is the $\mathcal{M}J$ part.

For small kr the electric dipole term in $j_0(kr)$ predominates. This is $\sqrt{2\pi 3}\,\sqrt{2/3}\,\mathbf{Y}_{1,0,1}^{\pm1} = \sqrt{4\pi}\,Y_0{}^0\hat{\mathbf{e}}_{\pm} = \hat{\mathbf{e}}_{\pm}$. Thus, near the origin, the electric dipole contribution can be obtained from the first term of the power-series expansion of the exponential: $e^{ikz} \approx 1$. As is well known, the second term of the series expansion ikz is a mixture of magnetic dipole and electric quadrupole, and so on.

b. The Radiation Field as a Sum of Quantized Multipoles. The electromagnetic field can be quantized as a sum of photons of definite multipolarity, following the procedure used in 4.12.

The cubic box of 4.12a is replaced by a spherical box of unit radius, whose proper modes are standing multipole waves with $k_\mu = m\pi$ (m integer). Each proper mode is characterized by a subscript μ, with which, in short, we represent all the quantum numbers k_μ, J, M, π. Thus the general field can be expanded exactly as in 4.12:

$$\mathbf{A} = \sum_\mu (q_\mu \mathbf{A}_\mu + q_\mu{}^\dagger \mathbf{A}_\mu{}^*), \tag{7}$$

where $\mathbf{A}_\mu$ are the multipole fields and q_μ their amplitudes to be quantized.

The quantized amplitudes are, as in 4.12(16),

$$q_\mu = \sqrt{\frac{2\pi\hbar}{\omega_\mu}}\, c\mathrm{a}_\mu, \tag{8}$$

where a_μ are annihilation operators [4.12(17)]. The interaction Hamiltonian can be expanded in production and annihilation operators as in 4.12(27) and (28). The term in $\mathbf{p}\cdot\mathbf{A}$ becomes

$$\frac{e_\alpha}{Mc}\mathbf{A}\cdot\mathbf{p}_\alpha = \frac{e_\alpha}{Mc}\sqrt{2\pi\hbar}\,c\sum_\mu \frac{1}{\sqrt{\omega_\mu}}[\mathbf{A}_\mu\cdot\mathbf{p}_\alpha\mathrm{a}_\mu + \mathbf{A}_\mu{}^*\cdot\mathbf{p}_\alpha\mathrm{a}_\mu{}^\dagger]; \tag{9}$$

and similarly the term in $\boldsymbol{\sigma}\cdot\mathbf{H}$ is

$$\frac{e\hbar}{2Mc}\mu_\alpha\boldsymbol{\sigma}\cdot\mathbf{H} = \frac{e}{2Mc}\mu_\alpha\sqrt{2\pi\hbar}\,c\boldsymbol{\sigma}\cdot\sum_\mu \frac{1}{\sqrt{\omega_\mu}}(\mathbf{curl}\,\mathbf{A}_\mu\mathrm{a}_\mu + \mathbf{curl}\,\mathbf{A}_\mu{}^*\mathrm{a}_\mu{}^\dagger). \tag{10}$$

4.17 Multipole Transition Rates

a. Matrix Elements. In order to compute the matrix elements of the transition probabilities for γ emission or absorption the quantized interaction Hamiltonians 4.16(8) and (9) must be integrated over the nuclear volume. If the nuclear radius R is much smaller than the wave number k_μ—as it occurs in most cases of interest—we can use the approximations for $kr \approx kR \ll 1$. Then, evaluating the momentum for each particle $\mathbf{p}_\alpha = -i\hbar\nabla_\alpha$ as $\approx\hbar/R$ and using 4.14(1), we obtain the following order of magnitude expressions, which indicate the relative importance of the matrix elements[1] in the single-particle model:

(1$\mathcal{E}$) $$\frac{e}{M}\sqrt{\frac{2\pi\hbar}{\omega}}\,\mathbf{A}_{\mathcal{E}J}{}^{M}\cdot\mathbf{p}\approx C\frac{\sqrt{k}}{R}(kR)^{J-1}$$ (electric multipole charge coupling)

(1$\mathcal{E}'$) $$\frac{e\hbar}{2M}\sqrt{\frac{2\pi\hbar}{\omega}}\,\mu\boldsymbol{\sigma}\cdot\mathbf{H}_{\mathcal{E}J}{}^{M}\approx C\frac{\sqrt{k}}{R}(kR)^{J+1}$$ (electric multipole magnetic moment coupling)

(1$\mathcal{M}$) $$\frac{e}{M}\sqrt{\frac{2\pi\hbar}{\omega}}\,\mathbf{A}_{\mathcal{M}J}{}^{M}\cdot\mathbf{p}\approx C\frac{\sqrt{k}}{R}(kR)^{J}$$ (magnetic multipole charge coupling)

(1$\mathcal{M}'$) $$\frac{e\hbar}{2M}\sqrt{\frac{2\pi\hbar}{\omega}}\,\mu\boldsymbol{\sigma}\cdot\mathbf{H}_{\mathcal{M}J}{}^{M}\approx C\frac{\sqrt{k}}{R}(kR)^{J}$$ (magnetic multipole magnetic moment coupling)

where

$$C=\frac{e}{M}\sqrt{\frac{2\pi\hbar^3}{c}}=\sqrt{2\pi}\,\frac{e}{\sqrt{\hbar c}}\,Mc^2\,\frac{\hbar^2}{M^2c^2}=\sqrt{\frac{2\pi}{137}}\,(Mc^2)\left(\frac{\hbar}{Mc}\right)^2.$$

A more accurate estimate of the nondiagonal matrix elements of the momentum can be obtained as follows:

(2) $$\langle f|\,p\,|i\rangle=M\frac{d}{dt}\langle f|\,r_\alpha\,|i\rangle=\frac{M}{i\hbar}\langle f|\,r_\alpha\mathcal{H}-\mathcal{H}r_\alpha\,|i\rangle$$
$$=\frac{M}{i\hbar}(E_i-E_f)\langle f|\,r_\alpha\,|i\rangle\approx\pm iM\omega R,$$

where, in the independent particle model, p_α is the momentum operator of a single particle and $\mathcal{H}$ the Hamiltonian which governs its motion. The estimate (2) is equivalent to the one used in (1) if $\hbar/R=M\omega R$ or if

$$\hbar\omega=\frac{\hbar^2}{MR^2}=2.2\text{ MeV}\left(\frac{R_{\text{deut}}}{R_{\text{nucl}}}\right)^2\approx\text{MeV}.$$

When (2) and 4.14(1) are used, the matrix element 4.16(9) becomes

(3$\mathcal{E}$) $$\frac{e}{M}\sqrt{\frac{2\pi\hbar}{\omega}}\,\mathbf{A}_{\mathcal{E}J}{}^{M}\cdot\mathbf{p}\approx C\frac{Mc}{\hbar}\sqrt{k}\,(kR)^{J};$$

(3$\mathcal{M}$) $$\frac{e}{M}\sqrt{\frac{2\pi\hbar}{\omega}}\,\mathbf{A}_{\mathcal{M}J}{}^{M}\cdot\mathbf{p}\approx C\frac{Mc}{\hbar}\sqrt{k}\,(kR)^{J+1},$$

where the constant is the same as in (1).

[1] The matrix elements have apparent dimensions (energy)(length)$^{1/2}$. This is because the radius of the normalization box has been taken as unity and does not appear in the formulas. If the normalization radius had been called L, there would have been an extra factor $L^{-1/2}$ and the matrix elements would have clearly the dimensions of an energy.

b. Transition Rates. The density of states for multipole waves in a unit sphere is[1]

$$\rho_F = 1/(\pi\hbar c) \tag{4}$$

and does not depend on energy. Thus the squares of (1) and (3) give the energy dependence of the transition probabilities. For example, we verify immediately from ($3\mathcal{E}$) that in accordance with elementary expectations[2] the electric dipole transition probability goes as R^2k^3.

By introducing the matrix elements (1) and the density of states (4) in 4.12(29), we obtain an estimate of the single particle transition probabilities. In order to avoid cumbersome constants, we shall use natural nuclear units:

$$\text{unit of length:}\quad \hbar/(Mc) = 0.21 \times 10^{-13}\ \text{cm}$$
$$\text{unit of time:}\quad \hbar/(Mc^2) = 0.7 \times 10^{-24}\ \text{sec}$$

and we obtain

$$w = \frac{4\pi}{137}\frac{k}{R^2}(kR)^{2J=2} \tag{5$\mathcal{E}$}$$

$$w = \frac{4\pi}{137}\frac{k}{R^2}(kR)^{2J+2} \tag{5$\mathcal{E}'$}$$

$$w = \frac{4\pi}{137}\frac{k}{R^2}(kR)^{2J} \tag{5$\mathcal{M}$}$$

$$w = \frac{4\pi}{137}\frac{k}{R^2}(kR)^{2J}. \tag{5$\mathcal{M}'$}$$

If we use the matrix elements ($3\mathcal{E}$) and ($3\mathcal{M}$) in place of ($1\mathcal{E}$) and ($1\mathcal{M}$), ($5\mathcal{E}$) and ($5\mathcal{M}$) are replaced by

$$w = \frac{4\pi}{137}k(kR)^{2J} \tag{6$\mathcal{E}$}$$

$$w = \frac{4\pi}{137}k(kR)^{2J+2} \tag{6$\mathcal{M}$}$$

More detailed estimates of radiative transition probabilities in nuclear physics are given in 4.34.

[1] From $k_\mu = m\pi$ (m integer) we have $dm = dk/\pi$; thus the number of states per unit energy is $dm/dE = (\pi\hbar c)^{-1}$.

[2] Classically the energy radiated per unit time dE/dt is proportional to the acceleration squared. For $x = R\sin\omega t$, $dE/dt \approx R^2\omega^4$. Thus the photon emission probability is $(\hbar\omega)^{-1}(dE/dt) \approx R^2\omega^3 \approx R^2k^3$.

4.2 Interaction of the Neutron-Proton System with Radiation

4.21 *Experimental Data and Qualitative Discussion on Deuteron Disintegration*

a. Experimental Introduction. The low-energy interaction of the neutron-proton system with radiation gives rise to the reactions

$$\mathrm{n} + \mathrm{p} \rightleftharpoons \mathrm{D} + \gamma. \tag{1}$$

Going from left to right, (1) describes the capture of neutrons by protons; in the opposite direction it corresponds to the photodisintegration of the deuteron.

These reactions are the only nuclear processes that can be computed with some accuracy from our knowledge of the interactions between the elementary particles. For this reason we treat them in some detail.

The photodisintegration of the deuteron is not easy to investigate experimentally. The determination of total cross section requires a quantitative measurement of γ-ray intensity, which is never so accurate as the measurement of a beam of charged particles. Nevertheless, data on the cross sections are available at several energies with an accuracy of $\approx 10\%$ (Figs. 4.21-1 and 4.21-2).

Several methods have been used for the observation of the reaction products. The most direct method of counting the photo-neutrons is not the most accurate; it is more convenient to count the photo-protons, in deuteron-impregnated photographic emulsions, or in deuteron-filled proportional counters and cloud chambers.

Besides measuring the total cross section, we can study the angular distribution of the disintegration products, which, as we shall see, is important to the determination of the angular momentum of the final state. The angular dependence is of the form

$$1 + A \sin^2 \theta, \tag{2}$$

where θ is the angle between the direction of the γ ray and that of the proton or neutron emitted. The coefficient A increases with energy.

The cross section of the inverse process, neutron capture by protons, is much smaller than the cross section for scattering of neutrons by protons. Thus the reaction is difficult to study and the value of the cross section is known accurately only for thermal neutrons:

$$\sigma = (0.329 \pm 0.004) \times 10^{-24}\ \mathrm{cm}^2. \tag{3}$$

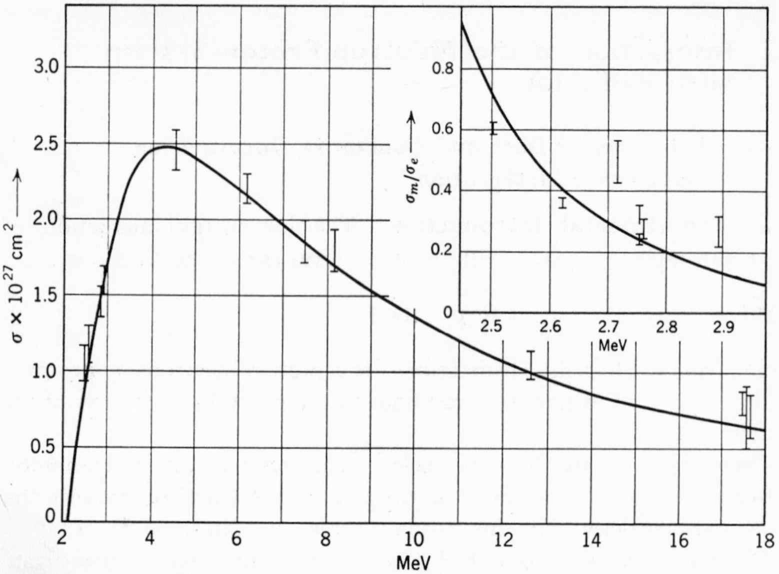

Fig. 4.21-1. Cross section of deuteron photodisintegration at low energy. [From L. Hulthen and M. Sugawara, *Handbook of Physics*, **39**, 112, Springer-Verlag, Berlin, (1957).]

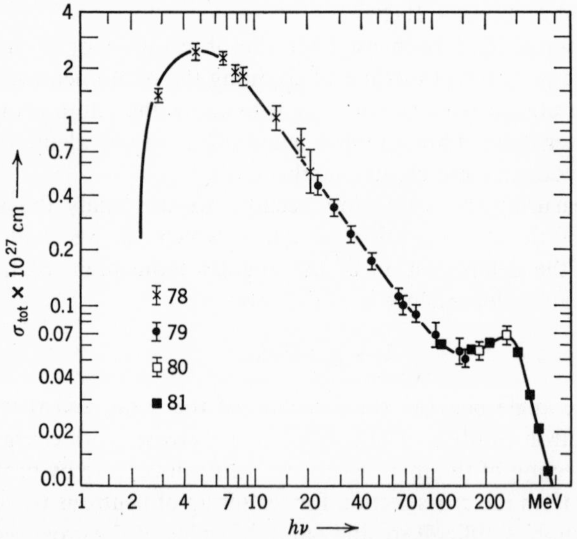

Fig. 4.21-2. Cross section of deuteron photodisintegration up to 400 MeV. [From L. Hulthen and M. Sugawara, *Handbook of Physics*, **39**, 14, Springer-Verlag, Berlin, (1957).]

An early measurement of this quantity was described in 3.22. The value (3) was obtained (H-53) by comparison with other well-known cross sections by studying the activation of iodine in a water solution of NaI irradiated with neutrons with and without the addition of boron salts.

b. Qualitative Discussion of the Process. We must discuss separately the photodisintegrations that produce spherically symmetrical protons from those producing protons with a $\sin^2 \theta$ angular distribution [see (2)].

In this last case the final state is a P state; the electromagnetic transition is an electric dipole transition—as are most atomic transitions—corresponding to the selection rule $\Delta l = \Delta J = 1$, $\Delta\pi \neq 0$. We may think that the electric vector of the incoming wave acts on the charge of the proton and ejects this particle in a direction that is preferentially perpendicular to that of the γ ray.

When the disintegration products are emitted with spherical symmetry, the final state must be an S state. Thus $\Delta l = 0$ [1]. We have to do with a transition from the bound ^3S to the unbound ^1S, caused by the coupling between the magnetic field of the wave and the magnetic moments of the nucleons. The quantum numbers of the particles change according to $\Delta J = 1$, $\Delta\pi = 0$, and the disintegration is due to the magnetic dipole part of the electromagnetic wave.

4.22 *Computation of the Photodisintegration Cross Section*

a. The Initial and Final States. The computation of the cross section of the photodisintegration of the deuteron is a direct application of the methods discussed in 4.1 concerning the interaction between particles and radiation. We discuss this problem in detail both because of its physical interest and as an illustration of the theory.

The cross section for the photoeffect is given by

$$\sigma = \frac{w}{c}, \tag{1}$$

where w is the transition probability of 4.12(29). The initial state appearing in this formula consists of the deuteron and of the incoming γ ray:

$$|\Psi_i\rangle = |\psi_i, 0, 0 \cdots 1_\lambda \cdots\rangle, \tag{2}$$

where ψ_i is the normalized deuteron wave function, and the occupation numbers of the radiation field are all zero, with the exception of the mode λ occupied by the incoming photon.

[1] We neglect the D state admixture in the deuteron.

If we suppose that the deuteron in the initial state moves with linear momentum $\hbar\mathbf{K}$, we can write

$$\psi_i = \exp(i\mathbf{K}\cdot\mathbf{R}_c)\psi_D(r), \tag{3}$$

where $\mathbf{R}_c$ is the coordinate of the deuteron's center of mass, and $\psi_D(r)$ is the internal deuteron wave function expressed in terms of the relative coordinate r (neutron-proton distance).

For the sake of simplicity we compute the cross section, assuming central forces in the zero-range approximation. In this case we obtain from 1.23(6), using appropriate normalization and including the spin part of the wave function,

$$\psi_D = \frac{1}{\sqrt{2\pi R}}\frac{e^{-r/R}}{r}\zeta_t. \tag{4}$$

We shall see that the zero-range approximation is fairly accurate. The case of finite range is more laborious and does not add a great deal to the understanding of the theory and the facts.

The final state contains no photons at all and can be described by

$$\langle\Psi_f| = \langle\psi_f, 0, 0\cdots|, \tag{5}$$

where ψ_f is the final state of the particles. The wave function ψ_f is a standing wave, normalized to unity over the volume in which the states of the free particles are quantized. The density of final states ρ_F must be calculated in this same volume.

The final state of the particles is an eigenstate of the unperturbed Hamiltonian, which includes the nuclear forces. We can use either spherical or "distorted" plane waves for the final state. If we choose spherical waves, they are conveniently normalized in a spherical box of unit radius; outside the range of nuclear forces (and everywhere in the zero-range approximation) we can write

$$\psi_f = e^{i\mathbf{K}'\cdot\mathbf{R}_c}\zeta_f\sqrt{2}k\,j_l(kr+\delta_l)\,Y_l^m(\theta,\varphi), \tag{6}$$

where $\hbar\mathbf{K}'$ is the final total momentum, $\hbar\mathbf{k}$ the momentum of the relative final motion[1], ζ_f is the final spin function, and the δ_l are the phase shifts due to the nuclear potential. The normalization is easily verified by using the asymptotic form of $j_l(kr)$, which is valid over most of the space for values of l that are not too large. Observe that, from conservation of energy,

$$\frac{\hbar^2k^2}{M} = \hbar\omega - B = \hbar\omega - \frac{\hbar^2}{MR^2}. \tag{7}$$

[1] See footnote, p. 46.

If (6) is used, the density of final states in the center of mass system computed in the same spherical box is[1]

(8) $$\rho_F = \frac{dn}{dE} = \frac{M}{2\pi}\frac{1}{\hbar^2 k}.$$

With (6) and (8), (1) gives the total cross section for transition to a final state of definite angular momentum. The angular distribution of the photo-protons is given by $|Y_l^m|^2$.

Alternatively, we can use for the final state a "distorted" (phase-shifted) plane wave traveling in the direction defined by the wave vector **k**. The distortion is necessary, since a free plane wave is not a solution of the unperturbed particle problem.

Outside the range of nuclear forces (and everywhere in the zero-range approximation) such a distorted plane wave is 3.12(1, 7b)

(9) $$\psi_f = e^{i\mathbf{K}'\cdot\mathbf{R}_c}\zeta_f \sum_l \sqrt{4\pi(2l+1)}\, i^l e^{i\delta_l} j_l(kr + \delta_l)\, Y_l^0(\cos \widehat{kr});$$

for $\delta_l = 0$ it reduces to a plane wave $e^{i\mathbf{k}\cdot\mathbf{r}}$, normalized in a cubic box of unit volume. For this same box the density of states in the solid angle $d\Omega$ around $\hat{\mathbf{k}}$ is (see 5.11)

(10) $$\rho_F = \frac{(\hbar k)^2\, d(\hbar k)\, d\Omega}{(2\pi\hbar)^3 \times 2\, d(\hbar^2 k^2/2M)} = \frac{d\Omega}{(2\pi\hbar)^3}\frac{M\hbar k}{2}.$$

If (9) and (10) are used in (1), we obtain the differential cross section for photo-protons emitted within $d\Omega$. The total cross section is then obtained by integration over the solid angle. The two methods are perfectly equivalent.

For the photodisintegration at low energy (smaller than $\approx$10 MeV) we can make the following approximations, which we know to be valid from scattering experiments:

(11) $$\begin{aligned} \delta_l &= 0 \quad \text{for} \quad l \neq 0, \\ \delta_0 &= \delta_t \quad \text{for} \quad \text{triplet } S, \\ \delta_0 &= \delta_s\,. \quad \text{for} \quad \text{singlet } S. \end{aligned}$$

b. The Interaction Hamiltonian. The matrix element is computed in the assumption

(12) $$k_\lambda R \ll 1,$$

where k_λ is the wave number of the γ ray and R is the radius of the deuteron. In the range of low-energy nuclear physics $1/k_\lambda$ is of the order of the electron's Compton wavelength, while R is of the order of the meson's Compton wavelength and (12) is sufficiently well satisfied.

[1] From $k = m\pi$ (m integer) and $E = \hbar^2 k^2/M$, we obtain $dm/dE = M\, dk/(2\pi\hbar^2 k\, dk)$.

The interaction Hamiltonian for an *incoming plane electromagnetic wave* is given by 4.12(26), (27), and (28), where for the states described above we can write $a_\lambda = 1$ and $a_\lambda^\dagger = 0$.

The momentum $\mathbf{p}_\alpha$ can be decomposed into the sum of the momentum due to the center-of-mass motion $\mathbf{P}_c$ and of the momentum of the proton relative to the center of mass, $\mathbf{p}_\mathrm{p} = M(\dot{\mathbf{r}}/2) = \mu\dot{\mathbf{r}} = \hbar\mathbf{k}$, where $\mathbf{r}$ is the relative coordinate (n-p distance) and μ, the reduced mass. Only the momentum $\mathbf{p}_\mathrm{p}$ needs to be included in the term $\mathbf{A}\cdot\mathbf{p}_\alpha$, since the operators $\mathbf{P}_c$ and $\mathbf{p}_\mathrm{n}$ have vanishing matrix elements in our problem (they do not disintegrate the deuteron).

The exponential $\exp(i\mathbf{k}_\lambda\cdot\mathbf{r}_\mathrm{p})$ can be decomposed into two factors $\exp(i\mathbf{k}_\lambda\cdot\mathbf{R}_c)\exp(i\mathbf{k}_\lambda\cdot\mathbf{r}/2)$, which must be integrated between the initial and final states in order to obtain the matrix element. Clearly, integration over the variable $\mathbf{R}_c$ ensures conservation of momentum, since the integral is nonzero only for $\mathbf{K}' = \mathbf{k}_\lambda + \mathbf{K}$: the particles recoil on absorption of the γ ray.

We are left with the integral over the relative coordinate $\mathbf{r}$. We shall consider only the first term in the expansion of the exponential and replace $\exp(i\mathbf{k}_\lambda\cdot\mathbf{r}/2)$ by unity. As explained at the end of 4.16a, this is equivalent to accepting only dipole contributions: electric for the term $\mathbf{A}\cdot\mathbf{p}$ and magnetic for $\boldsymbol{\mu}\cdot\mathbf{H}$.

We now compute the matrix elements of the particle perturbing Hamiltonian:

$$\mathcal{H}' = -\frac{e}{Mc}\sqrt{2\pi\hbar}\,c\,\frac{1}{\sqrt{\omega}}\,\hat{\boldsymbol{\epsilon}}_\lambda\cdot\mathbf{p}_\mathrm{p} + i\sqrt{2\pi\hbar}\,c\,\frac{1}{\sqrt{\omega}}\frac{e\hbar}{2Mc}(\mu_\mathrm{n}\boldsymbol{\sigma}_\mathrm{n} + \mu_\mathrm{p}\boldsymbol{\sigma}_\mathrm{p})\cdot\hat{\boldsymbol{\epsilon}}_\lambda\times\mathbf{k}_\lambda \tag{13}$$

between the initial and final states of the particles. In (13) the subscripts n and p refer to neutron and proton, and the magnetic moments are expressed in nuclear magnetons.

c. The Photoelectric Disintegration Cross Section. Since the two terms of (13) do not interfere, we compute separately the two disintegration cross sections: the corresponding processes are called, respectively, the *photoelectric* and the *photomagnetic* disintegration.

Let us choose final spherical waves and adopt the zero-range approximation. For the photoelectric cross section we must compute the matrix element of $\hat{\boldsymbol{\epsilon}}_\lambda\cdot\mathbf{p}_\mathrm{p}$ between the state of the deuteron (3) and the final state (6). If we assume that the γ ray is plane-polarized with the electric vector in the x direction, this matrix element is

$$\langle\psi_f|\hat{\mathbf{x}}\cdot\mathbf{p}_\mathrm{p}|\psi_i\rangle = \langle\psi_f|p_\mathrm{p}\cos\theta_x|\psi_i\rangle = \zeta_f^\dagger\zeta_t\sqrt{2}\,k\int j_1(kr)Y_1^0(\cos\theta_x)p_\mathrm{p}\cos\theta_x\frac{1}{\sqrt{2\pi R}}\frac{e^{-r/R}}{r}2\pi r^2\,dr\,d\cos\theta_x, \tag{14}$$

where, as required by conservation of angular momentum, we have chosen the final state with $l = 1$, $m_l = 0$; obviously we need $\zeta_f = \zeta_t$.

In (14) we can substitute the explicit form of j_1 and of Y_1^0 and write $i(M/2)\omega\mathbf{r}$ instead of $\mathbf{p}_{\mathrm{p}}$ [4.17(2)]. Then we have[1]

$$(15)\quad \langle \psi_f |\hat{\mathbf{x}} \cdot \mathbf{p}_{\mathrm{p}}| \psi_i \rangle$$

$$= i\sqrt{2}\sqrt{\frac{3}{4\pi}}\frac{M}{2}\omega\frac{2\pi}{\sqrt{2\pi R}}\int\frac{1}{r}\left(\frac{\sin kr}{kr} - \cos kr\right) r\cos^2\theta_x\frac{e^{-r/R}}{r}r^2\,dr\,d\cos\theta_x$$

$$= i\frac{2}{\sqrt{3}}\frac{M\omega}{\sqrt{R}}\frac{k^2}{(R^{-2}+k^2)^2}.$$

Collecting things together, from (1), (8), (13), and (15), we obtain

$$\sigma = \frac{w}{c} = \frac{2\pi}{\hbar c}\rho_F\,|\langle\Psi_f|\,\mathcal{H}'\,|\Psi_i\rangle|^2$$

$$(16)\qquad = \left(\frac{2\pi}{\hbar c}\right)\left(\frac{M}{2\pi}\frac{1}{\hbar^2 k}\right)\left(\frac{e^2}{M^2c^2}2\pi\hbar c^2\frac{1}{\omega}\right)\left[\frac{4}{3}\frac{M^2\omega^2}{R}\frac{k^4}{(R^{-2}+k^2)^4}\right]$$

$$= \frac{8\pi}{3}\frac{e^2}{\hbar^2 c}\frac{M}{R}\frac{\omega k^3}{(R^{-2}+k^2)^4}.$$

But ω can be eliminated by using (7) and (16) becomes

$$(17)\qquad \sigma = \frac{8\pi}{3}\frac{e^2}{\hbar c}\frac{1}{R}\frac{k^3}{(R^{-2}+k^2)^3}.$$

The angular distribution is given by the square of the final angular function $Y_1^0(\cos\theta_x)$; it is proportional to $\cos^2\theta_x$ around an axis in the direction of the polarization of the γ ray.

If the γ ray is not polarized, we must average over the two orthogonal polarizations. In this case the angular distribution must be axially symmetrical around the direction z of the incoming beam and it will be sufficient to determine it in the xz plane. By averaging over the x and y polarizations we obtain

$$(18)\qquad \langle\cos^2(\hat{\boldsymbol{\epsilon}}_\lambda, \mathbf{k})\rangle = \tfrac{1}{2}\cos^2\theta_x = \tfrac{1}{2}\sin^2\theta,$$

where θ is the angle between the direction of the incoming γ and that of the outgoing proton.

d. The Photomagnetic Disintegration Cross Section. We now turn our attention to the second term of the interaction Hamiltonian (13), which corresponds to the interaction between the magnetic field of the wave and the magnetic moments of the nucleons. In the deuteron the two magnetic moments, which have opposite sign, are antiparallel. The field tends to

[1] $\int_{-1}^{+1}\cos^2\theta_x\,d\cos\theta_x = \frac{2}{3}$; $\quad \int_0^\infty\left(\frac{\sin kr}{kr} - \cos kr\right)e^{-r/R}r\,dr = \frac{2k^2}{[R^{-2}+k^2]^2}.$

make them parallel and thus induces transitions from the triplet to the singlet state: the singlet is unbound and disintegration results.

This time we choose the polar axis $\hat{\mathbf{z}}$ in the direction of the magnetic field $\hat{\boldsymbol{\epsilon}}_\lambda \times \mathbf{k}_\lambda$; thus the particle perturbing Hamiltonian is simply

$$i\sqrt{2\pi\hbar}\, c \frac{k_\lambda}{\sqrt{\omega}} \frac{e\hbar}{2Mc} (\mu_n\sigma_{nz} + \mu_p\sigma_{pz}); \tag{19}$$

the perturbation acts on the spins but not on the orbital angular momentum. For this computation we must distinguish three initial states, according to the three orientations of the deuteron spin relative to the z axis, and the cross section must be averaged over them. The final state is the ${}^1S$ wave [see (6)]:

$$\frac{1}{\sqrt{2}}(\alpha_n\beta_p - \alpha_p\beta_n)\sqrt{2}k \frac{\sin(kr + \delta_s)}{kr} \frac{1}{\sqrt{4\pi}}. \tag{20}$$

Let us compute the matrix elements of the operator $(\mu_n\sigma_{nz} + \mu_p\sigma_{pz})$ between the three different initial states $\zeta_t^1 = \alpha_n\alpha_p$, $\zeta_t^0 = \sqrt{\tfrac{1}{2}}(\alpha_n\beta_p + \beta_n\alpha_p)$, $\zeta_t^{-1} = \beta_n\beta_p$, and the final state $\zeta_s = \sqrt{\tfrac{1}{2}}(\alpha_n\beta_p - \beta_n\alpha_p)$; we have

$$\begin{aligned}
\langle\zeta_s|\, \mu_n\sigma_{nz} + \mu_p\sigma_{pz}\, |\zeta_t^1\rangle &= \zeta_s^\dagger(\mu_n + \mu_p)\zeta_t^1 = 0,\\
\langle\zeta_s|\, \mu_n\sigma_{nz} + \mu_p\sigma_{pz}\, |\zeta_t^0\rangle &= \zeta_s^\dagger(\mu_n - \mu_p)\zeta_s^0 = \mu_n - \mu_p,\\
\langle\zeta_s|\, \mu_n\sigma_{nz} + \mu_p\sigma_{pz}\, |\zeta_t^{-1}\rangle &= \zeta_s^\dagger(-\mu_n - \mu_p)\zeta_t^{-1} = 0.
\end{aligned} \tag{21}$$

Thus the cross section, averaged over the three initial states, is[1]

$$\begin{aligned}
\sigma &= \frac{1}{3}\left(\frac{2\pi}{\hbar c}\right)\left(\frac{M}{2\pi}\frac{1}{\hbar^2 k}\right)(\mu_n - \mu_p)^2 \left| i\frac{\sqrt{2\pi\hbar}\, ck_\lambda}{\sqrt{\omega}} \frac{e\hbar}{2Mc}\right|^2\\
&\quad \times \left| \int \sqrt{2}\, k \frac{\sin(kr + \delta_s)}{kr} \frac{1}{\sqrt{4\pi}} \frac{1}{\sqrt{2\pi R}} \frac{e^{-r/R}}{r} 4\pi r^2\, dr\right|^2\\
&= \frac{2\pi}{3}\frac{e^2}{Mc^3}(\mu_n - \mu_p)^2 \frac{\omega}{kR}\left(\frac{(1/R)\sin\delta_s + k\cos\delta_s}{R^{-2} + k^2}\right)^2.
\end{aligned} \tag{22}$$

With the substitutions (7) and $k \cot \delta_s = -1/a_s$ [3.13(2)] we obtain, near threshold[2]

$$\sigma = \frac{2\pi}{3}\frac{e^2}{\hbar c}\left(\frac{\hbar}{Mc}\right)^2 (\mu_n - \mu_p)^2 \frac{k/R}{R^{-2} + k^2} \frac{[(a_s/R) - 1]^2}{1 + k^2 a_s^2}. \tag{23}$$

[1] Use

$$ck_\lambda = \omega; \qquad \int_0^\infty \sin(kr + \delta_s)\, e^{-r/R}\, dr = \frac{(1/R)\sin\delta_s + k\cos\delta_s}{R^{-2} + k^2};$$

the factor $\tfrac{1}{3}$ comes from averaging over the initial states.

[2] $$\left(\frac{1}{R}\sin\delta_s + k\cos\delta_s\right)^2 = \frac{1}{1 + \cot^2\delta_s}\left(\frac{1}{R} + k\cot\delta_s\right)^2 = \frac{k^2[(a_s/R) - 1]^2}{k^2 a_s^2 + 1}.$$

4.23 *Comparison of Theory and Experiment*

a. Photodisintegration. The disintegration cross sections computed in the preceding section [4.22(17) and (23)] are in satisfactory agreement with the experiment up to $\approx$10 MeV; the agreement is improved if finite range wave functions are used.

The photoelectric cross section is small at low energy:

(1) $$\sigma_{\text{photoel}} \approx \frac{8\pi}{3}\frac{1}{137} R^2(kR)^3, \qquad (kR \ll 1);$$

it increases with k^3 and has a maximum for $k = 1/R$.

The photomagnetic cross section is more important for k small:

(2) $$\sigma_{\text{photomag}} \approx \frac{2\pi}{3}\frac{1}{137}\left(\frac{\hbar}{Mc}\right)^2(\mu_{\text{n}} - \mu_{\text{p}})^2\left(\frac{a_s}{R} - 1\right)^2(kR), \qquad (kR \ll 1),$$

but increases less rapidly with k. For $kR \approx 1$ the photo effect predominates approximately in the ratio of R^2 (deuteron radius squared) to $(\hbar/Mc)^2$ (nucleon Compton wavelength squared).

The agreement between theory and experiment confirms our ideas about the deuteron and about low-energy n-p interactions but does not add to our knowledge of nuclear forces.

The problem of photodisintegration at high energy has been treated in many theoretical papers and has been the subject of considerable experimental investigation. The finite range of nuclear forces, the effect of radiation of higher multipolarity, and the contribution of π mesons must be considered, but we shall not enter in the discussion of these effects. For a review see HS-57.

b. Capture of Neutrons by Protons. Under time inversion the photodisintegration process becomes the capture of neutrons by protons. Because of time-inversion invariance, the transition probability *between any two states* of the n-p system must be the same in the two directions, and the capture cross section is related to the photodisintegration cross section:

(3) $$\frac{\sigma_{\text{capt}}}{\sigma_{\text{dis}}} = \frac{g_c}{g_d}\,\frac{\dfrac{1}{\text{neutron flux}}}{\dfrac{1}{\gamma\ \text{flux}}}\,\frac{\text{density of final } \gamma \text{ states}}{\text{density of final nucleon states}}.$$

In this expression the factors g come from the averaging over initial spin states and are

(4)
for electric radiation $g_c = \frac{3}{4}$,
for electric radiation $g_d = 1$,
for magnetic radiation $g_c = \frac{1}{4}$,
for magnetic radiation $g_d = \frac{1}{3}$.

For the computation of the fluxes and of the state densities it is convenient to use plane nucleon and γ waves normalized in a cube of unit volume. Thus [see 4.22(10) and 5.11(6)]

neutron flux	$\dfrac{\hbar k}{M}$,
density of final γ states	$\dfrac{d\Omega}{(2\pi\hbar)^3}\dfrac{\hbar^2\omega^2}{c^3}$,
γ flux	c,
density of final nucleon states	$\dfrac{d\Omega}{(2\pi\hbar)^3}\dfrac{1}{2}M\hbar k$,

and (3) yields, for magnetic transitions,

$$\frac{\sigma_{\text{capt}}}{\sigma_{\text{dis}}} = \frac{3}{2}\frac{\omega^2}{c^2k^2} \tag{5}$$

The theoretical capture cross section can be compared only with the experimental data for thermal neutrons. At this low energy the magnetic effect predominates and, from (2) and (5), we obtain

$$\sigma_{\text{capt thermal}} = \frac{\pi}{137}\left(\frac{\hbar}{Mc}\right)^2(\mu_{\text{n}} - \mu_{\text{p}})^2\left(\frac{\mathrm{a}_s}{R} - 1\right)^2\frac{R^2\omega^2}{c^2}\frac{1}{kR}. \tag{6}$$

The cross section goes as $1/k$; the factor $R^2\omega^2/c^2$ is

$$\frac{\hbar^2}{BM}\frac{B^2}{\hbar^2c^2} = \frac{B}{Mc^2} = \frac{2.2}{931}.$$

It is interesting to note that the cross section depends on the sign of a_s, thus on whether the singlet deuteron is bound or unbound. The almost perfect agreement of (6) with experiment confirms our conclusion that the singlet deuteron cannot be bound.

It is worth noticing, however, that even if the theory is improved with the inclusion of finite range effects there remains a difference of a few percent between theory and experiment. This difference can be attributed to the fact that meson exchange currents have been neglected in our discussion: unfortunately, our knowledge of nuclear interaction and of meson physics is too incomplete for a quantitatively reliable calculation of this effect.

4.3 Emission of Gamma Rays

4.31 *Spin and Parity Selection Rules for Multipole Radiation*

a. Importance of High Multipoles in Nuclear Physics. The emission of γ rays in transitions between nuclear states is essentially the same as the emission of light in atomic transitions. Although the wavelength $2\pi/k$ is considerably smaller in the nuclear problem so is the extension R of the radiating system, and the inequality $kR \ll 1$ holds in both cases. As a result, the lowest multipole transitions are faster than those corresponding to higher multipoles.

In atomic physics we usually consider only electric dipole transitions. Transitions for which the dipole selection rules are not satisfied are called "forbidden" and seldom discussed. An atomic excited state rarely decays with the improbable emission of high multipole radiation because, owing to collisions or other kinds of perturbations, the atomic states are seldom "pure." An atomic state which, if pure, would have a long mean life usually decays with the emission of an electric dipole wave. This is made possible by the admixture of a state with the appropriate quantum numbers.

The situation is different in nuclei because they are not so easily affected by external agents. A nuclear excited state for which all transitions involve large changes of angular momentum remains pure and eventually decays—possibly with a mean life measured in days or months—with the emission of radiation of high multipolarity (for an example, see Fig. 2.26-4.) This is the well-known phenomenon of *nuclear isomerism*.

The kind of radiation emitted can be studied experimentally with measurements of angular distribution and polarization (4.32, 4.33); internal conversion coefficients (4.35) also reveal the multipolarity of a transition; the mean life of the excited states also depends on multipolarity, though in a way which cannot be computed exactly because of our poor knowledge of nuclear wave functions (4.34 and 4.36).

Thus the study of high multipole radiation is of great importance in nuclear spectroscopy.

b. Angular Momentum and Parity Selection Rules. The selection rules for angular momentum and parity follow directly from the conservation principles.

Let us consider first (Fig. 4.31-1) the radiation emitted in the transition between a specified magnetic sublevel, M_i, of the initial state, and a final state of spin 0. The angular momentum and magnetic quantum number of the radiation are completely determined. Using quantum numbers as defined in the figure, we have the emission of

(1) $$2^{J_i}\text{-pole radiation,}$$

with angular distribution described, in the wave zone, by

(2) $$|\mathbf{X}_{J_i}{}^{M_i}|^2.$$

According to whether

(3) $$(-1)^{J_i} = \pm\pi_i\pi_f = \pm\pi,$$

the quantum emitted is

$$\text{(4)} \qquad \begin{array}{ll} \text{either} & \mathcal{E}J_i \\ \text{or} & \mathcal{M}J_i \end{array}$$

and its polarization is thus established.

Of greater practical importance is the case in which the magnetic sublevels are not specified (Fig. 4.31-2), but the spin and parities of initial

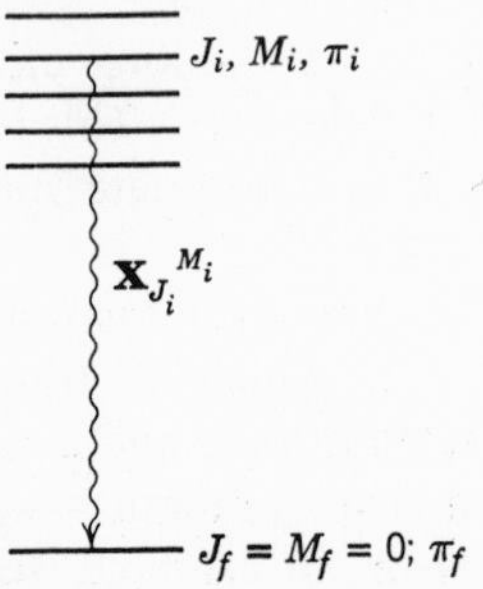

Fig. 4.31-1. The radiation field in the transition between a selected initial magnetic sublevel and a final state of 0 spin has definite values of $J = J_i$, $M = M_i$, and $\pi = \pi_i\pi_f$

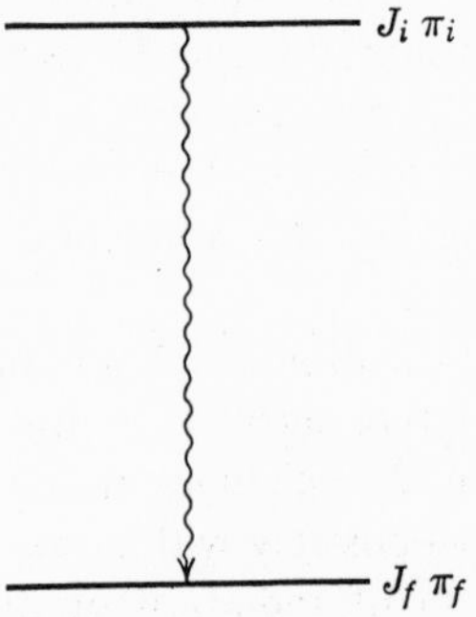

Fig. 4.31-2. In most experiments the magnetic sublevels of the initial and final state are not selected. The radiation is spherically symmetrical; its quantum numbers depend on J_i, π_i, J_f, and π_f but not on M_i and M_f.

and final states are known. The conservation of angular momentum (together with the law of vector addition of this quantity) requires that the multipoles 2^J emitted shall be limited to those for which

$$\text{(5)} \qquad |J_i - J_f| \leq J \leq J_i + J_f.$$

Let us introduce the notation

$$\text{(6)} \qquad J_0 = |J_i - J_f|$$

for the angular momentum of the lowest possible multipole and turn our attention to parity. For this purpose it is appropriate to discuss two separate cases.

Case 1, or parity favored case: the *lowest allowed* multipole is *electric*, a condition equivalent to

$$\text{(7a)} \qquad (-1)^{J_0} = \pi_i\pi_f = \pi.$$

Then all the allowed multipoles have parity (7*a*) and are

(8*a*) $$\mathcal{E}J_0,\ \mathcal{M}(J_0 + 1),\ \mathcal{E}(J_0 + 2), \cdots, \mathcal{E}(J_i + J_f).$$

Case 2, or parity unfavored case: the *lowest allowed* multipole is *magnetic*, equivalent to

(7*b*) $$-(-1)^{J_0} = \pi_i \pi_f = \pi.$$

Then the allowed multipoles are

(8*b*) $$\mathcal{M}J_0,\ \mathcal{E}(J_0 + 1), \cdots, \mathcal{M}(J_i + J_f).$$

More specifically, we can write the following table (zero poles do not exist for electromagnetic radiation!):

$J_0 = \lvert J_i - J_f\rvert$	$\pi_f\pi_0$	Allowed Multipoles
0 (no 0 → 0)	$-$	$\mathcal{E}1, \mathcal{M}2 \cdots$ up to $\mathcal{M}(J_1 + J_2)$
0 (no 0 → 0)	$+$	$\mathcal{M}1, \mathcal{E}2 \cdots$ up to $\mathcal{E}(J_1 + J_2)$
1	$-$	$\mathcal{E}1, \mathcal{M}2, \mathcal{E}3 \cdots$ up to $\mathcal{E}(J_1 + J_2)$
1	$+$	$\mathcal{M}1, \mathcal{E}2, \mathcal{M}3 \cdots$ up to $\mathcal{M}(J_1 + J_2)$
2	$-$	$\mathcal{M}2, \mathcal{E}3, \mathcal{M}4 \cdots$ up to $\mathcal{M}(J_1 + J_2)$
2	$+$	$\mathcal{E}2, \mathcal{M}3, \mathcal{E}4 \cdots$ up to $\mathcal{E}(J_1 + J_2)$
. . .	. . .	. . .

If $J_1 + J_2$ is large, there may be a mixture of many multipoles. We shall see, however, that in the approximation $kR \ll 1$ this mixture is limited in practice to only the first or the first two allowed multipoles.

c. "Purity" of the Multipoles. If we assume that the radiation is emitted in the transition of a single particle (independent particle model), the order of magnitude of the transition probability can be obtained from 4.17(5) and, apart from the common factor $4\pi/137$, is as follows:

Parity favored case:

$\mathcal{E}J_0$	charge coupling	$(k/R^2)(kR)^{2J_0-2} \times 1$
$\mathcal{E}J_0$	magnetic moment coupling	$(k/R^2)(kR)^{2J_0-2} \times (kR)^4$
$\mathcal{M}(J_0 + 1)$	charge coupling	$(k/R^2)(kR)^{2J_0-2} \times (kR)^4$
$\mathcal{M}(J_0 + 1)$	magnetic moment coupling	$(k/R^2)(kR)^{2J_0-2} \times (kR)^4$
$\mathcal{E}(J_0 + 2)$	charge coupling	$(k/R^2)(kR)^{2J_0-2} \times (kR)^4$
$\mathcal{E}(J_0 + 2)$	magnetic moment coupling	$(k/R^2)(kR)^{2J_0-2} \times (kR)^8$
. . .	. . .	. . .

Parity unfavored case:

$\mathcal{M}J_0$	charge coupling	$(k/R^2)(kR)^{2J_0-2} \times (kR)^2$
$\mathcal{M}J_0$	magnetic moment coupling	$(k/R^2)(kR)^{2J_0-2} \times (kR)^2$
$\mathcal{E}(J_0 + 1)$	charge coupling	$(k/R^2)(kR)^{2J_0-2} \times (kR)^2$
$\mathcal{E}(J_0 + 1)$	magnetic moment coupling	$(k/R^2)(kR)^{2J_0-2} \times (kR)^6$
$\mathcal{M}(J_0 + 2)$	charge coupling	$(k/R^2)(kR)^{2J_0-2} \times (kR)^6$
$\mathcal{M}(J_0 + 2)$	magnetic moment coupling	$(k/R^2)(kR)^{2J_0-2} \times (kR)^6$
....	....	....

It is clear that for $kR \ll 1$ only $\mathcal{E}J_0$ radiation is emitted with appreciable intensity in the parity favored transitions. In the parity unfavored case, instead, both $\mathcal{M}J_0$ and $\mathcal{E}(J_0 + 1)$ can be radiated with comparable intensities, and we can observe admixtures of these two multipoles.

For collective transitions the estimates are different, but also in this case the emission probability of the various "allowed" multipoles strongly restricts their mixing.

4.32 Direct Observation of Multipole Fields

a. Experimental Selection of Nuclear Transitions and Angular Distribution Measurements. In order to study experimentally the angular distribution $|\mathbf{X}_J{}^M|^2$, it is necessary to separate transitions corresponding to a given J and a given M. This is possible in principle and, in a few cases, also in practice (B-55; T-36). The case of Co^{60} is the classic example.

Let us consider a transition between a state with spin J_i and a state with $J_f = M_f = 0$. If we succeed in polarizing the initial spins along an arbitrary z axis, so that $M_i = J_i$, the J and M of the radiation are completely determined.

But the production of polarized nuclear sources is far from being easy. The magnetic energy $\mu H \approx (e\hbar/2Mc)H$ is $\approx 10^{-19}$ erg for a magnetic field of $\approx 2 \times 10^4$ gauss. Thus "brute force" polarization of nuclei, with conveniently available magnetic fields, requires a temperature of $\approx 10^{-3}$ °K.

In certain paramagnetic ions and in certain crystals, however, the magnetic field at the nucleus is $\approx 10^5$ to 10^6 gauss. Thus by taking advantage of the ionic or crystal fields we can prepare polarized samples of certain nuclei, such as the isotopes of Co and Mn (G-48b; R-49).

The decay scheme of Co^{60} is illustrated in Fig. 4.32-1. The radioactive nucleus has spin 5 and β decays with a half-life of 5.3 years to an excited state of Ni with spin 4. If Co^{60} is totally polarized, the polarization is maintained in the daughter state because of the selection rules for allowed β emission ($\Delta J = 0$ or 1, $\Delta M = 0$ or 1, $\Delta\pi = 0$). The two $\mathcal{E}2$ transitions that follow lead to the ground state of Ni^{60}. Both are expected to have an angular distribution $|\mathbf{X}_2{}^2|^2 \approx 1 - \cos^4 \theta$ [4.15(15)] and thus an anisotropy

(1)
$$\varepsilon = \frac{|\mathbf{X}(\pi/2)|^2 - |\mathbf{X}(0)|^2}{|\mathbf{X}(\pi/2)|^2}$$

equal to unity.

Ambler et al. (A-53) obtained the nuclear polarization by replacing

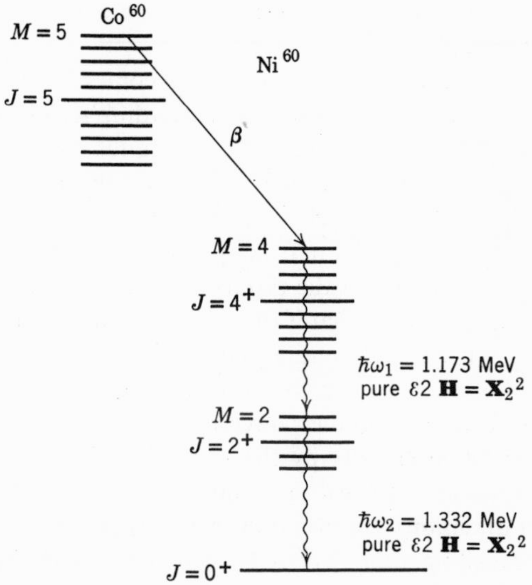

Fig. 4.32-1. The decay scheme of Co^{60} for polarized initial state.

with Co some of the Mg atoms in the mixed crystal $Ce_2(NO_3)_6 \cdot Mg_3(NO_3)_6 \cdot 24H_2O$ and cooling to 0.004 °K. The anisotropy was observed according to predictions.

Although experiments of this kind are difficult, they can in principle be used to determine the multipolarity of the radiation emitted and thus the angular momentum of nuclear excited states.

b. Measurements of Polarization. It is possible to build polarimeters to detect either plane or circular polarization of γ rays, taking advantage of some properties of the Compton effect.

The Compton scattering occurs preferentially in the plane of the magnetic vector of the incoming wave. This can be understood classically, considering that the wave induces oscillations of free electrons in a direction parallel to the electric vector and that the oscillating electrons radiate the scattered wave with a dipole distribution of intensity.

This effect can be used to build polarimeters for plane polarized radiation.

In order to measure circular polarization, one uses the fact that Compton scattering is "spin-dependent" in the sense that the cross section of a circularly polarized wave depends on whether the spin of the scattering electron is parallel or antiparallel to the angular momentum of the radiation. It follows, for instance, that the absorption in magnetized iron of right circularly polarized γ rays depends on whether the magnetization is parallel or antiparallel to the direction of propagation. The effect is small since only two of the 26 electrons of iron can be polarized, but it can easily be detected.

A complete understanding of these effects comes from the calculation of the Compton scattering cross section, according to Klein and Nishina. The outline of the calculation, which requires relativistic quantum electrodynamics, is discussed in 6.24 and the results are given in 6.24(2).

For the present we limit ourselves to reporting that circular polarization measurements on the radiation from polarized Co^{60} nuclei have been performed (see T-56) and that the results are in agreement with theory.

It is interesting to observe that if there is any radiation along the axis of nuclear polarization it must be entirely circularly polarized. This is because there is no orbital contribution to the magnetic quantum number if the direction of propagation is in the z direction. Thus the magnetic quantum number is contributed entirely by the spin of light, which assumes only the value ± 1. It also follows that states with $|M_i - M_f| \neq 1$ do not radiate in the z direction: for $\vartheta = 0$, $\mathbf{X}_J{}^M$ vanishes if $M \neq \pm 1$ (compare with 4,15(3), recalling that $Y_J{}^M(\vartheta = 0) = 0$ for $M \neq 0$, and see Fig. 4.15-1*a*, *c*, *e*).

4.33 Angular and Polarization Distributions and Correlations

a. Relative Transition Probabilities for Different Magnetic Substates. In order to discuss more general problems of angular distribution and polarization, we must consider the contribution of transitions with different M_i and M_f (Fig. 4.33-1). We can still regard J_i and J_f as fixed and treat only the emission of a pure multipole J. Multipole mixtures (as in the unfavored case in 4.31) are not considered.

In order to find the combined effects of the transitions for the different magnetic sublevels, we need to know the *relative* transition probabilities $w_{M_iM_f}$. These can be obtained simply and exactly by making use of the Wigner-Eckart theorem 1.14(34)[1]:

$$(1) \quad w_{M_fM_i} \simeq |C(J_iJJ_f;\, M_i,\, M_f - M_i)|^2 \simeq |C(J_fJJ_i;\, M_f,\, M_i - M_f)|^2.$$

This conclusion has been reached by making use of the conservation of angular momentum, and no approximations enter in the proof.

[1] Equalities $\simeq$ are exact apart from a constant which does not depend on M_i and M_f.

For those not familiar with the Wigner-Eckart theorem the same result can be obtained, less elegantly and less generally, by using the formalism of perturbation theory. We note that the transition probability is determined by a perturbing Hamiltonian obtained by dotting the multipole fields with the vector operators $\mathbf{p}$ and $\boldsymbol{\sigma}$. Thus the angular dependence of the Hamiltonian is that of the multipole fields, in which the eigenvectors of spin 1, $\hat{\mathbf{e}}_0$ and $\hat{\mathbf{e}}_\pm$ have been replaced by the scalar eigenfunctions of angular momentum 1, Y_1^0, and $Y_1^{\pm 1}$. We conclude that the Hamiltonian is a scalar function whose angular dependence is characteristic of the same angular momentum quantum numbers, J and M, which describe the emitted radiation: under rotations it must behave as the spherical harmonic Y_J^M for absorption and as $(Y_J^M)^*$ for emission.

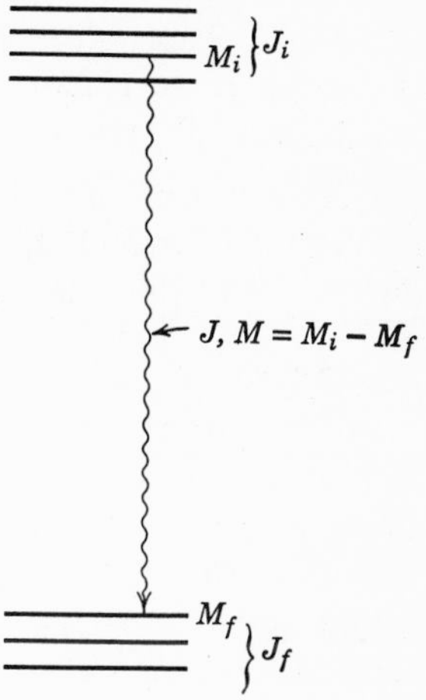

Fig. 4.33-1. Illustrating a 2^J-pole transition between given magnetic substates.

Then we may proceed to compute the matrix element for emission neglecting spin effects and assuming that the nuclear states are eigenstates of orbital angular momentum. We obtain expressions, apart from factors that do not depend on M_i and M_f (constants and radial integrals), which have the form

$$\int (Y_{J_f}{}^{M_f})^*(Y_J{}^M)^*(Y_{J_i}{}^{M_i})\, d\Omega. \tag{2}$$

But from 1.14(33) we immediately find that the dependence of these integrals on the magnetic quantum numbers is given by

$$C(J_iJJ_f;\ M_i - M), \tag{3}$$

and (1) is proven by squaring (3).

b. Angular and Polarization Distributions. Let us consider a partially polarized source of γ rays of spin J_i, with the different M_i states populated with a relative probability p_{M_i}. Let J_f be the spin of the final nucleus and M_f its magnetic quantum number, over which we have no control.

If the radiation emitted is a pure 2^J pole, the angular distribution of the intensity is given by

$$\mathfrak{J} = \sum_{M_i=-J_i}^{J_i} \sum_{M_f=-J_f}^{J_f} p_{M_i} w_{M_iM_f} |\mathbf{X}_J^{M_i-M_f}|^2. \tag{4}$$

The following examples of dipole transitions are left to the reader to compute[1] as a problem:

$$M_i = J_i \qquad J_f = J_i - 1 \qquad \mathfrak{J}(\theta) \simeq 1 + \cos^2\theta$$

$$M_i = J_i \qquad J_f = J_i \qquad \mathfrak{J}(\theta) \simeq 1 - \frac{2J_i - 1}{2J_i + 1}\cos^2\theta$$

$$M_i = J_i \qquad J_f = J_i + 1 \qquad \mathfrak{J}(\theta) \simeq 1 + \frac{J_i(2J_i - 1)}{2J_i^2 + 7J_i + 4}\cos^2\theta.$$

The treatment of polarization is more complicated because of the incoherent nature of the photons from different transitions. A general discussion requires the use of the density matrix (see D-55).

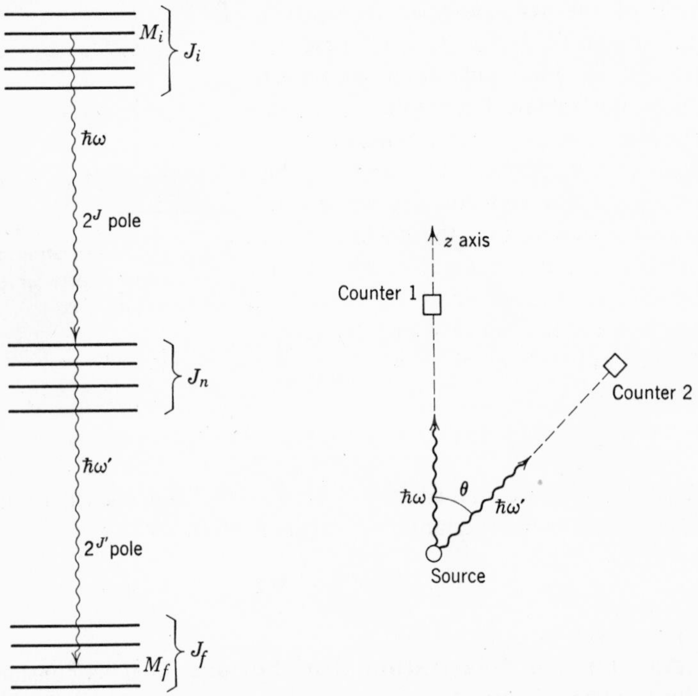

Fig. 4.33-2. Illustrating one of the cascade transitions giving rise to angular correlation effects.

c. Angular and Polarization Correlations (B-50; F-55, H-40; M-50). Of greater practical importance, because of the relative simplicity of the experimental techniques required, is the phenomenon of angular

[1] The computation is simplified if we consider that because of conservation of parity transitions with $\Delta M = 1$ and $\Delta M = -1$ have the same angular distribution.

correlation between two γ rays emitted in a cascade, as shown in Fig. 4.33-2. The experiments are easier because they do not require polarized nuclear sources.

The computation can be made in two steps. In the first we compute the populations of the sublevels M_n, assuming that the quantum $\hbar\omega$ has gone in the z direction, defined by the location of the first counter and used as axis of quantization. We obtain for an unpolarized source

$$p_{M_n} = \sum_{M_i} w_{M_i M_n} |\mathbf{X}_J^{M_i - M_n}(0)|^2, \tag{5}$$

where the $w_{M_i M_n}$ are given by (1) and $|\mathbf{X}_J^{M_i - M_n}(0)|^2$ is taken at $\theta = 0$.

Table 4.33-I

J_i	J	J_n	J'	J_f	$W(\theta)$
$\frac{1}{2}$	1	$\frac{1}{2}$	1	$\frac{1}{2}$	constant
$\frac{1}{2}$	1	$\frac{3}{2}$	1	$\frac{1}{2}$	$1 + \frac{3}{7}\cos^2\theta$
0	1	1	1	0	$1 + \cos^2\theta$
1	1	1	1	0	$1 - \frac{1}{3}\cos^2\theta$
2	1	1	1	0	$1 + \frac{1}{13}\cos^2\theta$
1	2	1	1	0	$1 - \frac{1}{3}\cos^2\theta$
2	2	1	1	0	$1 + \frac{3}{7}\cos^2\theta$
0	2	2	2	0	$1 - 3\cos^2\theta + 4\cos^4\theta$

But we have already observed (4.32b) that $\mathbf{X}_J{}^M(0)$ is nonzero only for $M = \pm 1$. Thus, for each M_n the sum has only two terms:

$$p_{M_n} = \sum_{\pm} w_{M_n \pm 1,\, M_n} |\mathbf{X}_J{}^{\pm 1}(0)|^2 \simeq \sum_{\pm} w_{M_n \pm 1,\, M_n}. \tag{6}$$

In the second step we compute the angular distribution of $\hbar\omega'$, by introducing (6) into (4)[1]. If θ defines the angle of the second counter, the angular distribution is (B-53a; F-50a; F-53; R-51a)

$$W(\theta) \simeq \sum_{M_n} \sum_{M_f} \sum_{\pm} w_{M_n \pm 1, M_n} w_{M_n M_f} |\mathbf{X}_{J'}^{M_n - M_f}(\theta)|^2. \tag{7}$$

Some simple results are given in Table 4.33-1 (B-50).

The phenomenon of angular correlation has been used extensively in order to determine the angular momentum of nuclear excited states. Angle-polarization correlation has also been studied experimentally (Fig. 4.33-3) and gives information on the parity of nuclear states.

d. Effect of Extranuclear Fields on Angular Correlation. If the nuclei of the source used in an angular correlation experiment are

[1] The contributions of the different intermediate states add incoherently because it is possible to observe whether the intermediate state was $M_i + 1$ or $M_i - 1$ by measuring the circular polarization of the first γ ray (L-51).

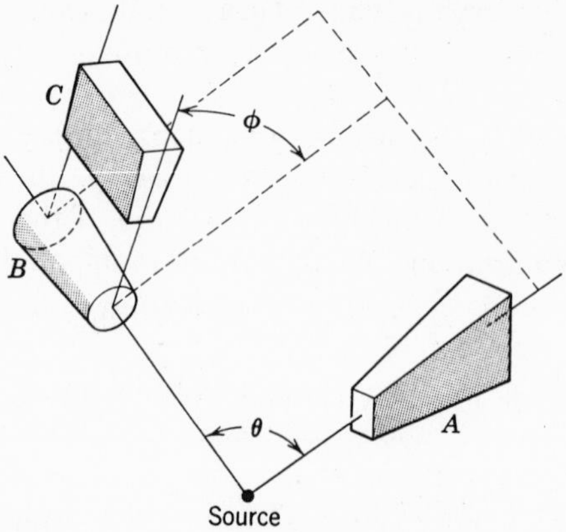

Fig. 4.33-3. Schematic diagram of γ-ray correlation polarimeter. Counter A detects the "first" γ; counter C detects the "second" γ after it has been Compton scattered by B. [From F. Metzger and M. Deutsch, *Phys. Rev.*, **78,** 551 (1950).]

located in a static field, they may experience a precession around the direction of the field. Of particular interest is the precession of the intermediate state n in the short time of its life: when this precession occurs around an axis perpendicular to the direction of the first γ ray (axis of quantization) with a period shorter than the mean life of the intermediate state, the levels M_n become mixed and the angular correlation is affected, as can be easily understood with a classical picture.

The field producing the precession may be a magnetic field H, in which

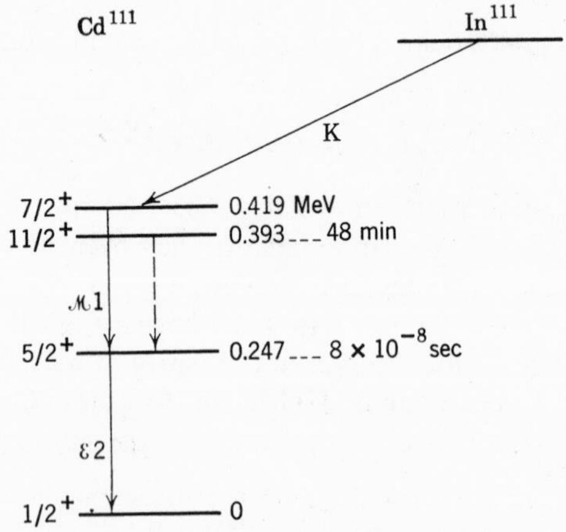

Fig. 4.33-4. The decay $In^{111} \rightarrow Cd^{111}$.

case the precession frequency is

$$\omega = \frac{1}{\hbar J_n} \boldsymbol{\mu}_n \cdot \mathbf{H}, \tag{8}$$

or an axially symmetrical electric field having a gradient $q = \partial E_z/\partial z$, in which case

$$\omega = \frac{3e(M_n^2 - M_n'^2)}{4\hbar J_n(2J_n - 1)} qQ_n, \tag{9}$$

where $\boldsymbol{\mu}_n$ and Q_n are the magnetic and quadrupole moments of the intermediate state.

In order to observe the effect—which consists in a reduction of the asymmetry—with available fields, the mean life of the intermediate state must not be too short: the classic example for these studies is the γ–γ cascade in the decay of In^{111} (Fig. 4.33-4), in which the intermediate state has a mean life of 8×10^{-8} sec. As a result of investigations of the effect of known extranuclear fields on angular correlation, we can measure the moments of the nuclear excited states μ_n and Q_n; if μ_n and Q_n are known, we can study the effective fields at the nucleus, a question of some interest in connection with the theory of solid state.

4.34 *Estimates of Radiative Transition Probabilities*

a. Estimates for Single Particle Transitions (G-55a; M-55; S-52). In order to compute the radiative transition probabilities between two nuclear states, it is necessary to know their wave functions. These being unknown, we can at best obtain some order of magnitude estimates. Even these estimates, however, are of interest, since the predictions from various multipoles differ by several orders of magnitude.

The transition probability in the absence of source polarization is obtained from 4.12(29). If we limit our attention to the emission of radiation of specified multipolarity μ [1]

$$w_\gamma = \frac{2\pi}{\hbar} \rho_F \frac{1}{2J_i + 1} \sum_{M_i} \sum_{M_f} |\langle \psi_f | \sum_\alpha \mathcal{H}'_{\mu,\alpha} | \psi_i \rangle|^2, \tag{1}$$

where $\sum_\alpha \mathcal{H}'_{\mu,\alpha}$ is the μ part of the Hamiltonian [4.16(9) and (10)] summed over all the particles in the nucleus ($1 \leq \alpha \leq A$); the density of final states ρ_F is given by 4.17(4).

In computing the matrix element, we make use of the single particle model, according to which only one nucleon is affected by the transition. This allows us to neglect the $\sum_\alpha$ and to regard ψ_i and ψ_f as one-particle wave functions.

[1] As in 4.13c, μ stands here for both J and parity.

It would seem at first sight that only proton transitions should be considered in the charge coupled term $e\mathbf{A}\cdot\mathbf{p}$. This, however, is not the case because of conservation of momentum: if a neutron undergoes a dipole transition, the rest of the nucleus recoils and radiation is produced. The recoil effect is taken into account by replacing the nucleon charge by an "effective charge" ϵ.

For a dipole transition the effective charge can be computed classically, considering that if a nucleon moves with velocity v, the net current ϵv is

$$\text{(2)}\qquad \begin{aligned} &\text{for a proton} && \epsilon v = ev - (Z-1)e\frac{v}{(A-1)} \approx \frac{e}{2}v, \\ &\text{for a neutron} && \epsilon v = -Ze\frac{v}{(A-1)} \approx -\frac{e}{2}v. \end{aligned}$$

Formulas for the effective charge to be used for multipole radiation of an arbitrary order can be found in the literature (G-55a), but, in view of uncertainties in the computation we shall simply take

$$\text{(3)}\qquad \begin{aligned} &\epsilon_J = \pm\tfrac{1}{2}e && \text{for } J = 1, \\ &\epsilon_J \approx \begin{cases} e \text{ for proton} \\ 0 \text{ for neutron} \end{cases} && \text{for } J \geq 2. \end{aligned}$$

Similarly, we can introduce an effective magnetic moment μ_J, which depends on the nature of the particle and the multipole order J.

By taking into account the effective charge and introducing in (1) the estimates (6$\mathcal{E}$), (5$\mathcal{E}'$), (6$\mathcal{M}$), and (5$\mathcal{M}'$) of 4.17, we obtain for single nucleon transitions of multipolarity J

$$\text{(4}\mathcal{E}\text{)}\qquad w_\gamma \approx \left(\frac{\epsilon_J}{e}\right)^2 \frac{4\pi}{137} k^{2J+1} R^{2J},$$

$$\text{(4}\mathcal{E}'\text{)}\qquad w_\gamma \approx \left(\frac{\mu_J}{\mu}\right)^2 \frac{4\pi}{137} k^{2J+3} R^{2J},$$

$$\text{(4}\mathcal{M}\text{)}\qquad w_\gamma \approx \left(\frac{\epsilon_J}{e}\right)^2 \frac{4\pi}{137} k^{2J+3} R^{2(J+1)},$$

$$\text{(4}\mathcal{M}'\text{)}\qquad w_\gamma \approx \left(\frac{\mu_J}{\mu}\right)^2 \frac{4\pi}{137} k^{2J+1} R^{2(J-1)}.$$

In these formulas all quantities are expressed in the nuclear units defined in 4.17. For numerical computation we may replace R by $r_0 \times A^{1/3} = 1.2 \times 10^{-13} A^{1/3}$ cm and introduce the γ energy $E_\gamma = \hbar kc$ in MeV; then

(4$\mathcal{E}$) becomes

(5$\mathcal{E}$) $$w_\gamma \simeq 1.3 \times 10^{23} \left(\frac{E_{\gamma\text{MeV}}}{930}\right)^{2J+1} (6A^{1/3})^{2J} \text{ sec}^{-1},$$

and the other expressions (4) can be similarly transformed.

b. More Accurate Evaluation of the Single-Particle Matrix Elements. For a more careful estimate, let us use the more accurate expressions 4.14(6) and (8) for the multipole fields near the origin [rather than 4.17(5) and (6), which were derived from 4.14(1)].

We shall discuss as an example the case of electric multipole charge coupling, in which the matrix element appearing in (1) is

(6) $$\sqrt{\frac{2\pi\hbar}{\omega}}\, c \frac{\epsilon_J}{Mc} \sqrt{\frac{2(J+1)}{J}} \frac{1}{(2J+1)!!} \int \psi_f{}^* \,\mathbf{grad}\, [(kr)^J Y_J{}^M]^* \cdot \mathbf{p}\psi_i \, d\mathbf{r}.$$

First we integrate by parts, using the relation

$$(\psi_f{}^*\mathbf{p}\psi_i) \cdot \mathbf{grad}\, [(kr)^J Y_J{}^M]^* = \text{div}\, [(kr)^J (Y_J{}^M)^* (\psi_f{}^*\mathbf{p}\psi_i)] - (kr)^J (Y_J{}^M)^* \,\text{div}\, (\psi_f{}^*\mathbf{p}\psi_i);$$

then, because of conservation of charge, we replace the factor div $(\psi_f{}^*\mathbf{p}\psi_i)$ in the nonvanishing integral by

$$-M \frac{\partial}{\partial t} (\psi_f{}^*\psi_i) = iM\omega\psi_f{}^*\psi_i.$$

Finally, the integral in (6) becomes (always apart from phase factors)

(7) $$M\omega \int \mathcal{R}_f{}^*(kr)^J \mathcal{R}_i r^2\, dr \int (\mathcal{Y}_{J_f}{}^{M_f})^* (Y_J{}^M)^* (\mathcal{Y}_{J_i}{}^{M_i})\, d\Omega,$$

where the wave functions have been decomposed into their spin angle ($\mathcal{Y}_J{}^M$) and radial ($\mathcal{R}$) parts.

The functions $\mathcal{R}$ are not known and, at best, can be estimated from nuclear models in some favorable case. In order to evaluate the order of magnitude of the radial integral, let us assume $\mathcal{R}$ = constant = $\sqrt{3/R^3}$ [so that $\int_0^R \mathcal{R}^2 r^2\, dr = \mathcal{R}^2(R^3/3) = 1$]. Then

(8) $$\int \mathcal{R}_f (kr)^J \mathcal{R}_i r^2\, dr = \frac{3}{R^3} k^J \frac{R^{J+3}}{J+3} = \frac{3}{J+3} (kR)^J;$$

this result must be considered as an upper limit, and the integral for the true radial functions could be 10 or 100 times smaller.

The integral over the solid angle expresses the conservation of angular momentum and involves the Clebsch-Gordan coefficients. The quantity

(9) $$S(J_i, J, J_f) = \frac{4\pi}{(2J_i+1)} \sum_{M_i} \sum_{M_f} \left| \int (\mathcal{Y}_f)^* Y^* \mathcal{Y}_i\, d\Omega \right|^2$$

is called the "statistical factor" and can be found tabulated (M-55). It is always of the order of unity.

By introducing the different estimates (2), (6), (7), (8), and (9) in (1), we obtain the following value for electric multipole transition probabilities, in the same notation as (4),

$$(10)\quad w_\gamma \approx \left(\frac{\epsilon_J}{e}\right)^2 \frac{S(J_i J J_f)}{137} \frac{2(J+1)}{J[(2J+1)!!]^2}\left(\frac{3}{J+3}\right)^2 k^{2J+1}R^{2J}$$

(electric multipole, charge coupling)

This formula agrees, apart from the factor $(\epsilon_J/e)^2 S$, with the estimate in Blatt and Weisskopf (BW-52, p. 627).

We shall not carry out the calculation for magnetic transitions in the same detail. We remark only that, according to 4.17(5), (6), the transition probabilities are decreased by a factor $(5\mathcal{M}')/(6\mathcal{E}) = (\hbar/McR)^2$ in relation to the electric ones. Considering, however, that the magnetic moments of the nucleons are larger than unity, Blatt and Weisskopf have increased the magnetic transition probabilities by a factor of 10 and write

$$(11)\quad w_\gamma \approx \frac{1}{137} \frac{20(J+1)}{J[(2J+1)!!]^2}\left(\frac{3}{J+3}\right)^2\left(\frac{\hbar}{McR}\right)^2 k^{2J+1}R^{2J}$$

(magnetic multipole, Blatt and Weisskopf)

These formulas have been widely used in the discussion of experimental results.

c. Transition Probabilities and Nuclear Models. If we specialize in a definite nuclear model, we can make precise computations of the transition probabilities (F-60); when the result is compared with the experiment, we obtain useful information on the reliability of the model.

The simplest model is to assume that the gamma rays are emitted in the transition of a given single particle between two states of a spherically symmetrical, independent particle shell model. The computation is exactly as outlined in (b); the only difference is that the radial functions are now spherical Bessel functions with a zero at the nuclear surface, and with a number of nodes appropriate to the shell being considered.

Still in the spherically symmetrical shell model we can introduce many-body effects with the formalism described in 2.3. If we consider only pairing within a shell, as in 2.33, the transition matrix element can be computed with the method used for the "many-body" quadrupole moment. One finds that the matrix element depends on the number of pairs p_i and p_f in the states involved. In states of seniority 0 and 1 the single-particle transition probability is multiplied by a factor

$$(12)\quad \begin{array}{ll} \dfrac{j_i+\frac{1}{2}-p_i}{j_i+\frac{1}{2}}\,\dfrac{j_f+\frac{1}{2}-p_f}{j_f+\frac{1}{2}} & \text{for odd particle transition} \\[2ex] \dfrac{p_i}{j_i+\frac{1}{2}}\,\dfrac{p_f}{j_f+\frac{1}{2}} & \text{for even particle transition} \end{array}$$

Thus the transition probability is decreased by the presence of paired particles (*suppression*).

If forces between different shells are considered, the transition may occur between quasi-particle states and the probability is smaller than that computed for states of full particles. It can be proved that the rates are multiplied by a factor

$$U_f U_i \pm V_f V_i, \tag{13}$$

where the + and − signs apply to magnetic and electric transitions, respectively. In a few cases, when comparison with experiment is possible, the agreement is satisfactory.

The effect of distortion and other long-range interactions between the particles of the shell model is to induce "collective" transitions which may be considerably faster than those expected from the single-particle model (*enhancement*) because of the coherent emission from many particles.

The rates may be computed from specific assumptions on nuclear shapes, moments of inertia, and other collective parameters. The theory of the shell model with interactions is often able to predict the parameters that lead to agreement with the experiment.

4.35 Internal Conversion

a. Description of the Process. The mean lives of the excited states of an isolated nucleus are the inverse of the radiative transition probabilities w_γ evaluated in 4.34. The excited states of the nucleus of a normal atom, however, have shorter mean lives because the presence of the atomic electrons provides an alternate way of decay to the ground state.

The process is similar to the Auger effect familiar in x rays and is called *internal conversion*. The nuclear transition occurs without the emission of radiation; the energy is found as kinetic energy of electrons, which are emitted with energy $\hbar\omega - E_I$, where E_I is the ionization potential of an atomic level. The process used to be treated as an internal photo effect, in which the nuclear γ ray was absorbed by the atomic electrons of the same atom; more correctly, it must be regarded as an added mode of decay which enhances the speed of the transition.

If w_e is the probability of electron emission, the mean life τ is given by

$$\frac{1}{\tau} = w_\gamma + w_e = w_\gamma + w_K + w_L + \cdots, \tag{1}$$

where K, L, etc., refer to the different atomic shells.

An interesting feature of the phenomenon is that the *internal conversion coefficients* for the various atomic shells

$$\alpha_K = \frac{w_K}{w_\gamma}, \qquad \alpha_L = \frac{w_L}{w_\gamma}, \cdots \tag{2}$$

can be computed without the knowledge of the nuclear wave functions[1] and thus, in principle at least, exactly. The $\alpha_K, \alpha_L, \cdots$ depend on the multipolarity of the transition, and an experimental measurement of conversion coefficients gives the same information as the study of the radiation field.

In practice, however, the computation of the coefficients of internal conversion is laborious. In order to obtain accurate results, we must use relativistic atomic wave functions and relativistic wave functions in the coulomb field of the atom for the final free electron.

b. Elementary Computation of Internal Conversion Coefficients for Electric Multipoles. Following the outline in Blatt and Weisskopf, we present a simplified discussion of the phenomenon of internal conversion. This discussion has to be considered semiquantitative; it does not aim to obtain accurate results but to clarify the nature of the effect and to indicate the procedure involved in a more exact computation.

We limit ourselves to pure electric multipole transitions (case 1 of 4.31b), to K shell electrons in a nonrelativistic approximation, and to transition energies well above the K edge. The region of validity of the result is for low Z and high, but nonrelativistic, energies.

The coefficients of internal conversion can be calculated from the formula

$$\alpha = \frac{w_e}{w_\gamma} = \frac{\rho_{F,e}}{\rho_{F,\gamma}} \frac{\sum\limits_{M_i}\sum\limits_{M_f} |\langle f_e|\,\mathcal{H}'\,|i\rangle|^2}{\sum\limits_{M_i}\sum\limits_{M_f} |\langle f_\gamma|\,\mathcal{H}'\,|i\rangle|^2}. \tag{3}$$

Since the denominator has already been computed in 4.34, using spherical outgoing electromagnetic waves, it is advantageous to use spherical waves for the emitted electrons appearing in the numerator. With 4.22(8) for $\rho_{F,e}$ (without the factor $\frac{1}{2}$ which was due to the reduced mass of the n-p system) and 4.17(4) for $\rho_{F,\gamma}$, we obtain

$$\frac{\rho_{F,e}}{\rho_{F,\gamma}} = \frac{m_e c}{\hbar k_e}. \tag{4}$$

The initial and final states must now include the description of the atomic electrons as well as that of the nucleus and of the radiation field. With self-explanatory notation:

$$\begin{aligned} |i\rangle &= |\psi_{iN}, \psi_{ie}, 0, 0, \cdots, 0\rangle, \\ \langle f_\gamma| &= \langle \psi_{fN}, \psi_{ie}, 0, 0, \cdots, 1, \cdots, 0|, \\ \langle f_e| &= \langle \psi_{fN}, \psi_{fe}, 0, 0, \cdots, 0|. \end{aligned} \tag{5}$$

[1] This is exactly true only if we neglect the radius of the nucleus compared to that of the electronic orbits.

If we consider only the electrons of the K shell, we can write nonrelativistically

$$\psi_{ie} = \left(\frac{Z^3}{\pi a^3}\right)^{1/2} \exp\left(-\frac{Zr_e}{a}\right), \tag{6}$$

where a is Bohr's radius ($a = 137\ \hbar/m_e c$). The undistorted, normalized final electron wave is [4.22(6)]

$$\psi_{fe} = \sqrt{2}k_e j_l(k_e r_e)\ Y_l^m(\theta_e, \varphi_e). \tag{7}$$

The nonrelativistic form (6) is valid for low Z ($Z \ll 137$, since the velocity in the K shell is $cZ/137$); (7) is valid for high transition energy, since we have neglected the coulomb distortion ($k_e \gg Z/a$).

The perturbing Hamiltonian is

$$\mathcal{H}' = \mathcal{H}_\gamma' + \mathcal{H}_e', \tag{8}$$

where $\mathcal{H}_\gamma'$ has already been discussed: it induces transitions between $|i\rangle$ and $\langle f_\gamma|$, with a matrix element estimated in 4.34.

In a complete theory the production of conversion electrons—which involves a change in both the nuclear and atomic states—must be treated as a second-order process (T-51). We must consider two intermediate states: $\psi_{fN}\psi_{ie}$ and $\psi_{iN}\psi_{fe}$, which are reached, without conservation of energy, with the emission of virtual photons. However, since it would be inaccurate to discuss nonrelativistically the exchange of photons coupled to the electron's current, we limit our attention to the electrostatic effects which are predominent at small velocities. These are adequately described by the interaction[1]

$$\begin{aligned}\mathcal{H}_e' &= \sum_\alpha \frac{e_\alpha e}{|\mathbf{r}_e - \mathbf{r}_\alpha|} \\ &= \sum_\alpha \sum_{J=0}^{\infty} \sum_{M=-J}^{+J} \frac{4\pi e_\alpha e}{2J+1} \frac{r_\alpha^J}{r_e^{J+1}} Y_J^M(\theta_e\varphi_e)[Y_J^M(\theta_\alpha\varphi_\alpha)]^*;\end{aligned} \tag{9}$$

in the second step we have used the expansion of $|\mathbf{r}_e - \mathbf{r}_\alpha|^{-1}$, valid for $r_e > r_\alpha$ [2].

It is immediately seen that for each nucleon (use the independent particle model, drop the subscript α, and use ϵ for the effective nucleon

[1] In the formalism of quantized field theory the coulomb interaction (9) is treated as an exchange of transverse virtual photons and actually corresponds to a second-order process.

[2] The contributions for $r_e < r_\alpha$ are discussed in (d).

charge)

$$\langle f|\,\mathcal{H}_e'\,|i\rangle = \langle \psi_{fN}\psi_{fe}|\,\mathcal{H}_e'\,|\psi_{iN}\psi_{ie}\rangle$$

(10) $$= \sum_{JM} e\epsilon \frac{4\pi}{2J+1}\left[\int \mathcal{R}_f^* r^J \mathcal{R}_i r^2\,dr \int (\mathcal{Y}_{J_f}{}^{M_f})^*[Y_J{}^M(\theta\varphi)]^*\mathcal{Y}_{J_i}{}^{M_i}\,d\Omega\right]$$

$$\times \left[\int \sqrt{2}\,k_e j_l(k_e r_e)\frac{1}{r_e^{J+1}}\sqrt{\frac{Z^3}{\pi a^3}}\exp\left(-\frac{Zr_e}{a}\right)r_e{}^2\,dr_e \int (Y_l{}^m)^* Y_J{}^M\,d\Omega_e\right].$$

If we limit our discussion to the case in which the lowest allowed multipole is electric, the nuclear integral contributes only for $J = |J_i - J_f|$, $M = M_i - M_f$, and the sum is reduced to a single term. Furthermore, the angular integral over the electron's coordinates vanishes unless $l = |J_i - J_f|$, $m = M_i - M_f$, and the electron is emitted with the angular momentum and the angular distribution appropriate to the nuclear transition considered.

It is important to observe that apart from a factor $k_\gamma{}^J$ the nuclear integrals are the same as those appearing in the denominator of (3). Thus they cancel in the computation of α, making the result *independent of the nuclear wave function*. This conclusion is quite general and does not depend on the nuclear model chosen.

The radial integral in the electron's coordinates can be written

(11) $$\sqrt{\frac{2Z^3}{\pi a^3}}\,k_e^{J-1}\int_0^\infty j_J(x)\exp\left(-\frac{Zx}{ka}\right)x^{-J+1}\,dx.$$

The integral appearing in (11) is a slow function of energy, and thus the dependence of the conversion electron coefficient on atomic number and energy is given primarily by

(12) $$\alpha \approx Z^3\frac{k_e^{2J-3}}{k_\gamma^{2J+1}}.$$

For large (but nonrelativistic) energy, $\hbar k_e{}^2/2mc = k_\gamma$ and

(13) $$\alpha \approx Z^3 k_\gamma{}^{-J-5/2}.$$

We conclude that conversion coefficients increase with Z^3 and decrease with k_γ. Internal conversion coefficients also increase with multipole order.

c. Determination of Multipolarity from Conversion Electron Measurements. Accurate calculation of *K*-shell conversion electron coefficients have been performed with electronic computers (R-51b) and are available in tabular form (R-55; Ro-58). As an example, a graphical presentation of the theoretical results for $Z = 40$ is given in Fig. 4.35-1.

For low-energy, high-multipolarity transitions the coefficients of internal conversion are considerably larger than unity, and internal conversion may increase the transition probability by several factors of 10.

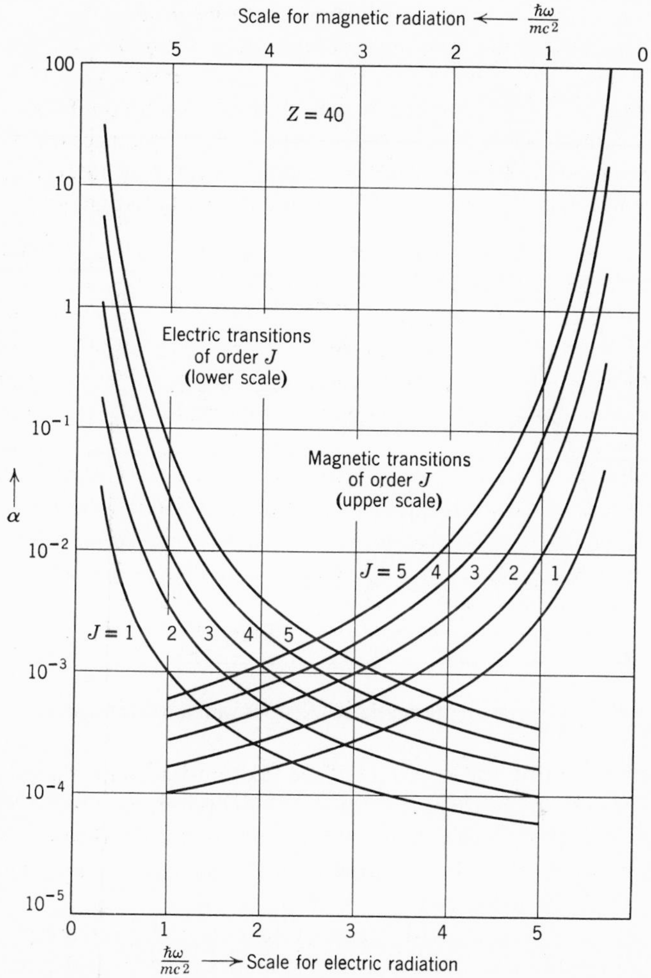

Fig. 4.35-1. Internal conversion coefficients for $Z = 40$. The lower scale applies to electric radiation, the upper one to magnetic radiation. The number J indicates the multipole order. The values are taken from the tables of Rose et al. (Reprinted with permission from J. M. Blatt and V. F. Weisskopf, *Nuclear Physics*, Wiley, New York, 1952, p. 619.)

A direct measurement of α_K requires a count of γ rays and of electrons. Since the absolute measurement of γ intensity is not always easy, one often resorts to less direct methods. If one studies with a β spectrograph a source of β rays followed by a γ transition in 100% of the cases, the coefficient of internal conversion can be obtained (Fig. 4.35-2) from the measurement of the area under the continuum ($w_\beta = w_\gamma + w_e$) and of the area under the conversion peaks (w_e).

In the more complicated decay schemes it is easier to measure the ratio α_K/α_L, α_K/α_M, etc., rather than the absolute values of α_K, α_L, α_M. These ratios are also dependent on the multipolarity of the transitions. Though the conversion coefficients for the L shell have not been computed with an accuracy comparable to that of the K shell, in many instances the ratios α_K/α_L, etc., are sufficiently well known from a theoretical interpolation of experimental data and may be used for multipolarity assignments.

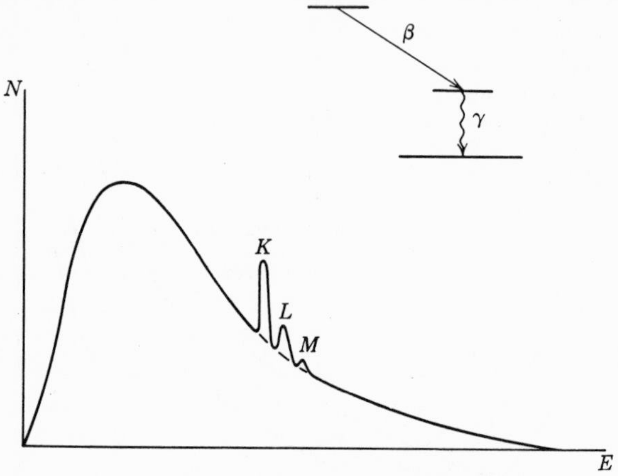

Fig. 4.35-2. Observation of conversion electrons with a β spectrograph.

d. Contributions for $r_e < r_\alpha$. If we take into account that nuclei have nonvanishing radii, there is a finite probability of finding the atomic electrons within the nuclear volume. This leads us to study the possibility $r_e < r_\alpha$ which was neglected in the expansion (9) and which is not included in the calculations of Rose et al.

For $r_e < r_\alpha$ the expansion of the Hamiltonian $\mathcal{H}_e'$ involves the powers r_e^J/r_α^{J+1}; the radial nuclear integrals in the matrix element (10) have the form $\int \mathcal{R}_f{}^* r_\alpha^{-(J+1)} \mathcal{R}_i r_\alpha{}^2\, dr_\alpha$ and—when introduced in (3)—do not cancel the integrals in the matrix elements for γ emission.

Thus the internal conversion coefficients depend—to a small extent in most cases—on the nuclear wave function and not only upon multipolarity. If the multipolarity is known, for instance, from angular correlation measurements, a determination of the conversion coefficient may furnish information on nuclear states.

It is interesting to observe that for $J = 0$ the radial integrals do not vanish, even if $J_i = J_f = 0$ (the corresponding integrals for the part $r_e > r_\alpha$ vanish because of the orthogonality of $\mathcal{R}_i$ and $\mathcal{R}_f$ for different energies). Thus, because of the $r_e < r_\alpha$ contribution, internal conversion provides a mechanism for the decay of excited states even when the only possible transition is $0 \rightarrow 0$ and γ emission is completely forbidden. In effect, we know of several $J = 0$ levels that decay exclusively by electron emission to a lower $J = 0$ state. Their mean life is in reasonable agreement with that computed from the process under study.

For excitation energies larger than $\approx$MeV, $0 \rightarrow 0$ transitions may take place with emission of positron-electron pairs. This process becomes more important than internal conversion at high energy and predominates in the decay of the first excited state of O^{16} (6.06 MeV). This mode of decay is discussed in 6.26c.

4.36 Mean Lives of Nuclear Excited States

We are now in position to discuss the experimental results on the mean lives of nuclear excited states.

The techniques used for the measurements vary with the order of magnitude of the times involved. Mean lives longer than seconds (*isomeric* states) can be timed with a stop watch; various mechanical methods may be used in the range between seconds and milliseconds; electronic delayed coincidence techniques are useful between $\approx 10^{-5}$ and $\approx 10^{-11}$ sec (*short-lived isomers*) (D-48); in some cases measurements of time of flight or line width have been used for shorter times. Measurements of coulomb-excitation cross sections (see 4.42) yield the matrix elements for absorption of radiation and are equivalent to a lifetime measurement.

The directly measured mean lives τ are the result of two different processes: emission of radiation and of internal conversion electrons, as indicated in 4.35(1). Thus it is necessary to know the electron decay probability, w_e, in order to obtain $\tau_\gamma = 1/w_\gamma$ to be compared with the estimates of 4.34. The internal conversion coefficient can either be measured directly or it can be computed from the theory with sufficient accuracy if the multipolarity is known.

A comparison between the values of τ_γ thus obtained from the experiment and the prediction of the theory is presented in graphical form in Figs. 4.36-1 and 2 (G-55a, b). In Fig. 4.36-1 the partial mean lives τ_γ from electric transitions are plotted versus neutron number after having been multiplied by an expression proportional to 4.34(4$\mathcal{E}$); in this manner we obtain "reduced" mean lives which, if the single-particle theory is applicable, should depend neither on energy nor on mass number but only on multipole order. For each J we expect a definite value which corresponds to the horizontal lines of Fig. 4.36-1.

Experimental points from single-particle transitions should be on or somewhat above the corresponding theoretical lines; points falling below these lines (*enhanced emission*) must be interpreted as evidence of coherent

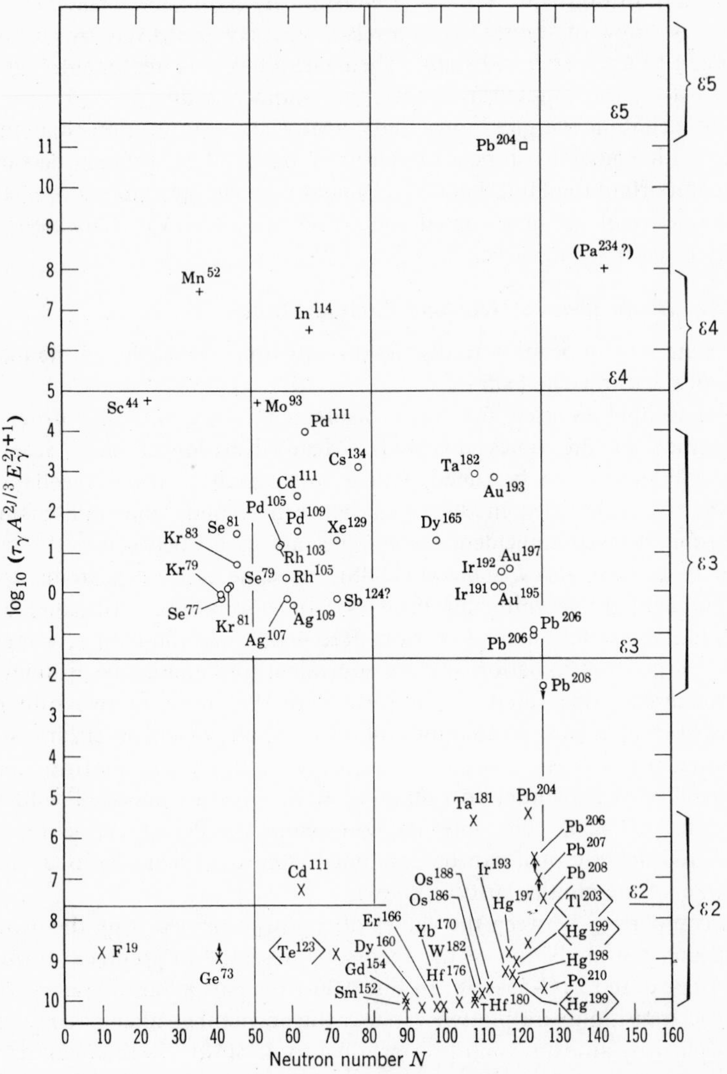

Fig. 4.36-1. Reduced lifetimes for ℰ2, ℰ3, ℰ4, and ℰ5 transitions plotted against the neutron number N. The lines correspond to the theoretical values for single proton transitions, with the statistical factor S taken equal to unity and the radius given by $R = 1.2 \times 10^{-13} A^{1/3}$ cm. [From M. Goldhaber and J. Wesener, *Ann. Rev. Nucl. Sci.*, **5**, 13 (1955).]

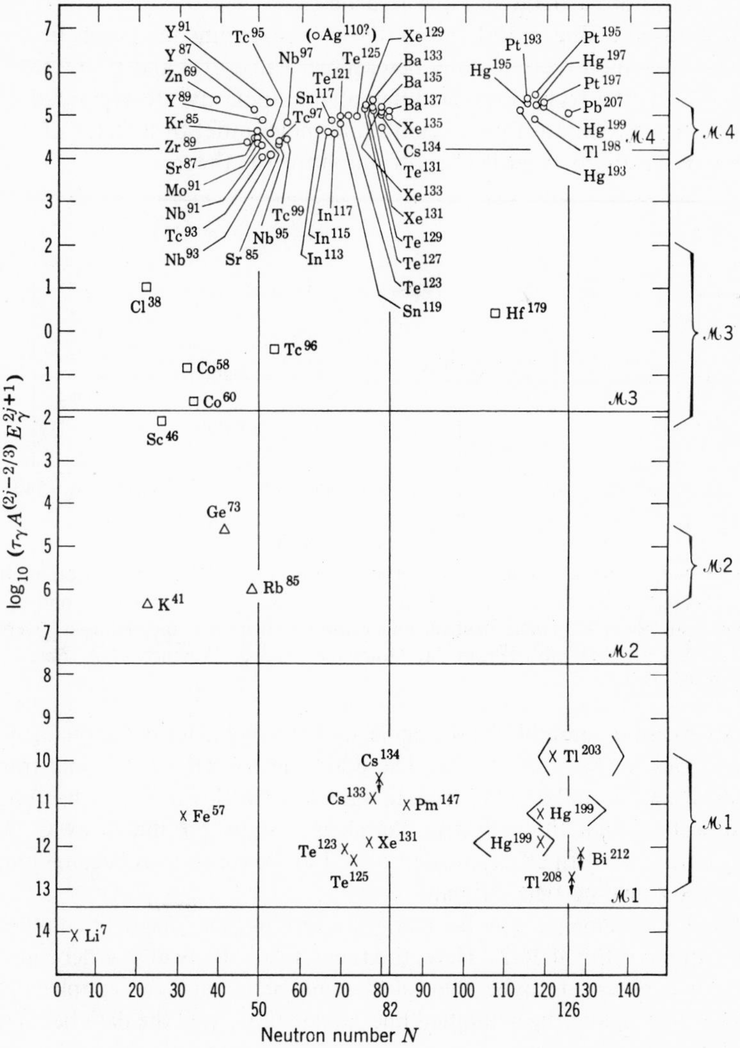

Fig. 4.36-2. Reduced lifetimes for $\mathcal{M}1$, $\mathcal{M}2$, $\mathcal{M}3$, and $\mathcal{M}4$ transitions plotted against the neutron number N. The lines correspond to the theoretical values for single proton transitions, with the statistical factor S taken equal to unity and the radius given by $R = 1.2 \times 10^{-13} A^{1/3}$ cm. [From M. Goldhaber and J. Wesener, *Ann. Rev. Nucl. Sci.*, **5**, 12 (1955).]

many particle transitions or "collective" emission; points well above the lines (*suppressed emission*) may be explained as transitions between many-body states of particles and quasi-particles.

Inspection of Fig. 4.36-1 shows that most experimental points lie above the line for the experimentally determined value of J and below the line for $J + 1$; the transitions of different multipolarity are separated, but, since the expectations for successive multipoles differ by a factor of $\approx 10^6$, this can hardly be regarded as a triumph for the theory.

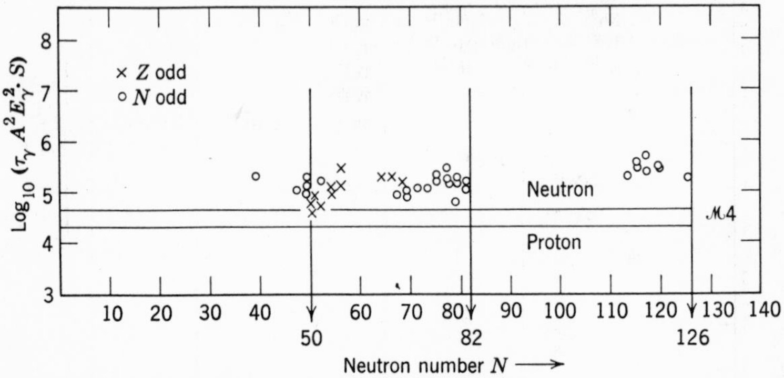

Fig. 4.36-3. Reduced lifetimes for $\mathcal{M}4$ transitions plotted against neutron number N. The relevant statistical factor S has been applied. The lines correspond to the theoretical values for single neutron and proton transitions; the radius is given by $R_0 = 1.2 \times 10^{-13} A^{1/3}$ cm. [From M. Goldhaber and J. Wesener, *Ann. Rev. Nucl. Sci.*, **5**, 16 (1955).]

An exception, notable for its regularity, is the behavior of the quadrupole transitions for $82 < N < 126$. These are the collective rotational transitions discussed in 2.27. We find, in agreement with what was observed in that section, that the collective character is more prominent away from magic numbers. In effect, around $N = 126$ the mean lives become longer than the single-particle estimates.

Similar comments can be made concerning the magnetic multipole transitions of Fig. 4.36-2. Here, the theoretical energy and A dependence has been assumed to be that of the magnetic moment coupled term 4.34(4.$\mathcal{M}'$); again, the computed lines divide fairly well the data belonging to different multipoles.

Of particular interest is the regularity observed for $\mathcal{M}4$ isomeric transitions, which becomes even more pronounced (Fig. 4.36-3) if we take into account that the theoretical prediction includes the "statistical factor" 4.34(9). These isomeric transitions belong to the "islands" mentioned in 2.26, which are well explained by the elementary shell model. It is understandable that the single-particle model should be applicable in this case.

Considerable progress has been made in explaining the position of some of the scattered points of Figs. 4.36-1 and 2 in terms of more refined nuclear models, as discussed in 4.34c.

In conclusion, the investigation of γ-transition matrix elements cannot be considered completed, and our understanding of the mean lives is still limited. However, the theory has been developed to the point of providing a semiquantitative interpretation of the data and of furnishing a powerful tool in the study of nuclear wave functions and models.

4.37 Isospin Selection Rules

a. Formulation of the Selection Rules. The Hamiltonian which describes the interaction of the nucleons with electromagnetic radiation involves the charges and magnetic moments of the nucleons. Thus it can be expressed with the help of the proton and neutron projection operators $\frac{1}{2}(1 \pm \tau_{\alpha\zeta})$ [see 1.32(6) and (8)]. If, for simplicity, we start with the nonquantized Hamiltonian, 4.11(5), we find that it can be decomposed into two parts:

(1) $$\mathcal{H}' = \mathcal{H}_S' + \mathcal{H}_V',$$

where the "isoscalar" term $\mathcal{H}_S'$ does not contain the isospin,

(2) $$\mathcal{H}_S' = -\sum_\alpha \frac{1}{2}\left[\frac{e}{Mc}\mathbf{A}\cdot\mathbf{p}_\alpha + \frac{e\hbar}{2Mc}(\boldsymbol{\mu}_\mathrm{p} + \boldsymbol{\mu}_\mathrm{n})\cdot \mathbf{curl}\,\mathbf{A}\right],$$

and the "isovector" term $\mathcal{H}_V'$ includes the terms with $\tau_{\alpha\zeta}$

(3) $$\mathcal{H}_V' = -\sum_\alpha \frac{1}{2}\tau_{\alpha\zeta}\left[\frac{e}{Mc}\mathbf{A}\cdot\mathbf{p}_\alpha + \frac{e\hbar}{2Mc}(\boldsymbol{\mu}_\mathrm{p} - \boldsymbol{\mu}_\mathrm{n})\cdot \mathbf{curl}\,\mathbf{A}\right].$$

In order to observe possible effects of isospin selection rules, we must, naturally, work with nuclei in definite isospin states, that is, with light nuclei for which coulomb repulsion effects are negligible.

But even in these cases we cannot speak of conservation of isotopic spin in the radiative process, since the electromagnetic interaction violates charge independence. This is clearly indicated by the fact that $\mathcal{H}'$ is the sum of two terms: the first, $\mathcal{H}_S'$, is a scalar in isospin space and corresponds to the emission of photons without change in isospin; the second, $\mathcal{H}_V'$, is the third component of an isospin vector and induces the emission of photons with change of one unit in the isospin of the source. If we wanted to assume conservation of isospin, we would be forced to say that the photon has isospin 0 and 1. Thus it is altogether meaningless to attribute a definite isospin quantum number to the photon, but we can say that a quantum of radiation cannot carry an isospin larger than 1.

Particularly interesting is the situation prevailing for electric dipole transitions (G-53) for which only photons of isospin 1 are allowed. This is because, the vector potential $\mathbf{A}(r_\alpha)$ entering in the interaction Hamiltonian can be replaced by a constant. Since $\Sigma\, \mathbf{p}_\alpha = 0$ in the center-of-mass system, the predominant term in (2) vanishes[1], and $\mathcal{H}_S{}'$ can be neglected altogether compared to $\mathcal{H}_V{}'\left(\sum_\alpha \tau_{\alpha\zeta}\mathbf{p}_\alpha\right.$ does not vanish!$\left.\right)$.

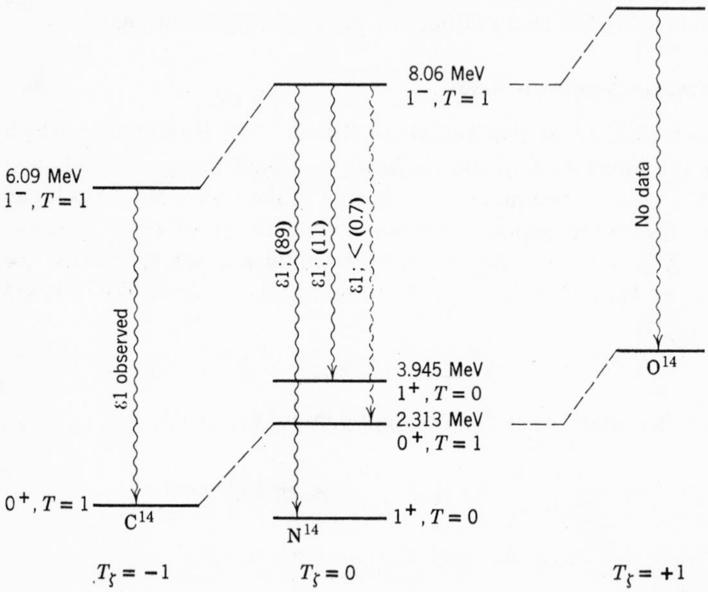

Fig. 4.37-1 (not to scale). Partial level diagram for $A = 14$, showing that the γ ray between the 8.06- and 2.313-MeV levels of N^{14} has not been observed (dotted wavy line, relative intensity < 0.7). Compare with Fig. 2.14-2.

Thus in a transition

$$\text{(4)} \qquad \Delta J:\ 1 \rightleftharpoons 0; \qquad \pi_i \pi_f = -1,$$

for which only $\mathcal{E}1$ radiation is allowed, an isospin selection rules determined by $\mathcal{H}_V$ only should be felt. Since the factor $\sum_\alpha \tau_{\alpha\zeta}\mathbf{p}_\alpha$ has the rotational behavior of $Y_1{}^0$ in isospin space, the isospin changes must be limited by the usual vector selection rule

$$\text{(5a)} \qquad \Delta T = \pm 1 \quad \text{or} \quad 0 \qquad (\text{no } 0 \to 0),$$

[1] The vanishing of electric dipole emission for the isoscalar part of the e.m. coupling can be understood intuitively, since for this part of the interaction both nucleons have charge $e/2$. Thus isoscalar dipole vibrations necessarily involve the motion of the center of mass of the nucleons.

with the added restriction

$$(5b) \qquad \Delta T = \pm 1 \text{ only, if } T_\zeta = 0,$$

which is a consequence of the fact that $C(j, 1, j; 0, 0) = 0$ (see Table 1.14-4)[1].

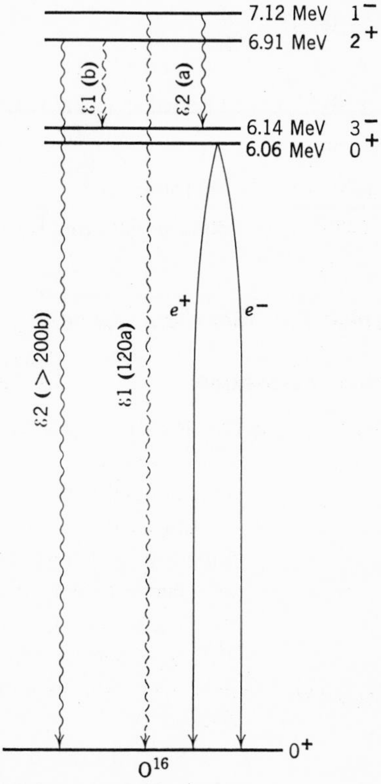

Fig. 4.37-2 (not to scale). Partial level diagram of O^{16}; all levels $T = 0$; isospin forbidden transitions indicated by dotted wavy lines.

b. Comparison with Experiment. Gell-Mann and Telegdi discuss two cases in which the isospin selection rules (5) should act. The first is the transition between two excited states of N^{14} ($T_\zeta = 0$) of energy 8.06 and 2.313 MeV, spin and parity 1^- and 0^+, and isospin 1 and 1 (Fig. 4.37-1). The γ ray should be forbidden because of (5*b*), whereas the corresponding γ rays of the two partners of the isospin triplet (C^{14} and O^{14}, $T_\zeta = \pm 1$; Fig. 2.14-2) should be allowed. This indeed seems to be borne out by the experimental results.

[1] For $\Delta T = 0$ the operator $\Sigma \tau_{\alpha\zeta}$ has eigenvalues $Z - N$ [see 1.32(11)] which vanish if $T_\zeta = 0$ ($N = Z$).

The low excited states of O^{16}, all $T = 0$, provide another interesting example. Here, all $\mathcal{E}1$ radiation should be forbidden as $0 \to 0$ isospin transition. The observed branching ratio of the 7.12- and 6.91-MeV levels are indeed affected by isospin selection rules, as shown in Fig. 4.37-2 and by the results reported below:

Decay of 7.12 MeV level:

$$\text{Ratio}\ \frac{\mathcal{E}1 \text{ to ground}}{\mathcal{E}2 \text{ to 6.14 MeV}} \begin{cases} = 120 \text{ (observed)} \\ 10^7 \text{ (expected ignoring isospin selection rule}^1\text{)} \end{cases}$$

Decay of 6.91 MeV level:

$$\text{Ratio}\ \frac{\mathcal{E}1 \text{ to 6.14 MeV}}{\mathcal{E}2 \text{ to ground}} \begin{cases} < 1/200 \text{ (observed)} \\ \approx 6 \text{ (expected ignoring isospin selection rule}^1\text{)} \end{cases}$$

4.4 Absorption of Gamma Rays

4.41 Resonance Absorption

a. Work Previous to the Mössbauer Effect. Nuclear absorption of γ rays is not easily observable because the electromagnetic radiation interacts with the atomic electrons whose absorption effects (photoelectric and Compton) hide the much smaller nuclear interactions. Nuclear absorption is observed with relative ease only if it results in a nuclear reaction—such as photodisintegration—whose products can be detected with appropriate counters.

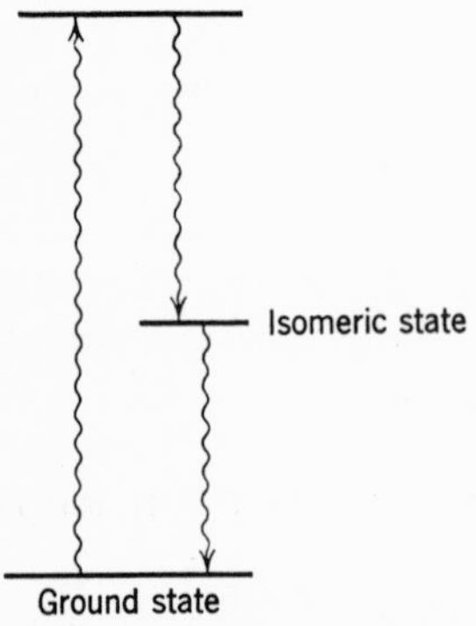

Fig. 4.41-1. Excitation of isomeric states by γ-ray absorption.

Absorption with transitions between bound states can be observed when it leads to an isomeric state. The experiment may be performed with an x-ray machine which produces a continuous spectrum of γ rays. The resonance radiation is absorbed (Fig. 4.41-1) leading to some excited state which, in turn, decays into an isomeric state whose radiation is conveniently studied after turning off the machine. Naturally, direct absorption to the isomeric state does not occur because the transition is highly forbidden.

Much more interesting are the attempts to observe nuclear resonance absorption—similar to the atomic absorption of sodium light by sodium

[1] Single particle estimate.

atoms—in which the γ rays emitted in the transition from an excited to a ground state would be absorbed in the opposite transition (Fig. 4.41-2).

This phenomenon is difficult to observe in nuclear physics because the frequencies ω_e and ω_a of the emitted and absorbed radiation are not exactly equal to the frequency $E/\hbar$ corresponding to the excitation energy. The difference E_r is the result of nuclear recoil and, as required by

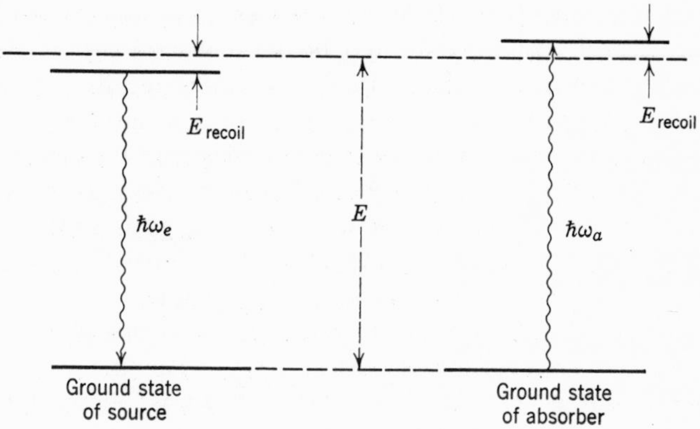

Fig. 4.41-2. Resonance absorption of γ rays.

conservation of momentum, amounts (for a free atom) to

(1) $$E_r = \frac{p^2}{2MA} = \frac{\hbar^2\omega^2}{2MAc^2} \approx \frac{(\hbar\omega)_{\text{Mev}}}{2A \times 930}\hbar\omega.$$

A numerical estimate for $A = 50$ shows that the recoil energy is ≈ 10 eV for $\hbar\omega \approx 1$ MeV. In the nuclear case E_r is much larger than the natural width of the line,

(2) $$\Gamma = \frac{\hbar}{\tau} \approx 10^{-2}\text{ eV}$$

(the numerical estimate is for $\tau \approx 10^{-13}$ sec) and often also appreciably larger than the Doppler width at room temperature:

(3) $$\Delta \approx \frac{2}{c}\sqrt{\frac{kT}{MA}}\,\hbar\omega \approx 10^{-5}\,\hbar\omega.$$

Thus there is no overlapping between the emitted frequency and the frequency needed for absorption, and resonance does not occur.

Only in exceptionally fast transitions (electric dipole) is the natural line width large enough for the observation of resonant absorption; the amount of absorption increases with temperature, since the Doppler effect further broadens the line.

By observations of resonant absorption—or resonant scattering—it has been possible to measure the mean life of some fast decaying nuclear excited states. Of particular interest is the 0.961 MeV, $1^- \rightarrow 0^+$ $\mathcal{E}1$ transition of Sm^{152}; the measured mean life is $(3 \pm 1) \times 10^{-14}$ sec (G-58). As we shall see, this determination is important in connection with the measurement of the helicity of neutrinos (8.21d).

b. The Mössbauer Effect. In 1958 Mössbauer (M-58a, b; M-59) showed that it is possible to obtain recoilless emission and absorption of γ rays when certain nuclei are strongly bound to a solid lattice. As long as the binding can be considered rigid, the lattice recoils as a whole, absorbing a negligible amount of energy because of its large mass.

The phenomenon can be understood considering that the vibrations of the lattice are quantized and that the recoil from the γ ray can excite only an integral number of phonons. When the γ energy is small and the binding of the lattice strong, the probability of γ emission or absorption without change in the number of phonons is significant.

Thus in an appreciable number of cases it has been possible to observe recoilless resonance absorption of nuclear γ rays. The first case, studied by Mössbauer, was a 129 keV γ line of Ir^{191}. This was followed by many other examples, and probably the transition that has been most extensively investigated is a 14 keV transition in Fe^{57}.

An interesting feature of nuclear resonance absorption is the extreme sharpness of the lines. For Fe^{57} the mean life of the excited state is $\approx 10^{-7}$ sec and thus

$$\frac{\Gamma}{E} \approx \frac{10^{-27}}{10^{-7}} \frac{1}{1.4 \times 10^4 \times 10^{-12}} \approx 10^{-12}.$$

Mössbauer proved that it is possible to destroy the resonance by introducing a Doppler shift. With appropriate mechanical equipment generating velocities of a few millimeters per second it is possible to shift the energy of the emitted γ rays by small known amounts and to explore the behavior of the absorption around the main resonance. In this manner the shape, structure, and position of the resonance line can be investigated, and these studies have led to the discovery of a number of effects of great interest in various fields of physics.

4.42 *Coulomb Excitation*

When stable nuclei are exposed to proton and α-particle beams from electrostatic generators, at *energy insufficient for the penetration* of the electrostatic potential barrier, we often observe the emission of characteristic nuclear γ lines, as if the nucleus had been excited by the passing ion. Coulomb excitation of collective rotational or vibrational states, which occurs with rather large cross sections, can be understood classically, but excitation to all kinds of states is possible, at least in principle.

The theoretical treatment of the effect is similar to that of internal conversion. In internal conversion a charged particle (electron) absorbs the nuclear excitation energy, whereas in coulomb excitation it is the nucleus that absorbs energy from a charged ion. The initial and final states of the "particles" are different, but the interaction Hamiltonian is the same for the two processes. The states of the ion in coulomb excitation are distorted plane waves corresponding to Rutherford scattering trajectories, and they can be discussed nonrelativistically in good approximation.

As in internal conversion, the transition matrix elements are composed of two factors: the "particle" factor, which can be computed, and the nuclear factor, which is the same as that of γ emission or absorption.

Thus a measurement of coulomb excitation cross section is equivalent to a measurement of γ mean life and gives the same kind of information on nuclear wave functions.

For an excellent theoretical and experimental review article the reader is referred to a paper by Alder et al. (A-56).

4.43 Photodisintegration of Complex Nuclei

a. Experimental Information. Photodisintegration experiments are usually carried out with bremsstrahlung radiation from a betatron. The emitted γ-rays have a continuous spectrum with a distribution of intensity proportional to $d\omega/\omega$, up to the energy of the electron beam. The results of measurements of neutron yield or of induced radioactivity are proportional to an integral of the photo cross section, and the cross section as a function of energy is obtained by taking the difference of data obtained at different energies. Typical results are shown in Fig. 4.43-1.

The curves can be divided into two parts. Near threshold ($\sim$10 MeV) the cross section is small, of the order of 10^{-27} cm^2, and does not vary rapidly with energy. In this region the photodisintegration can be explained with the absorption of $\mathcal{E}2$ γ rays. Around 20 to 25 MeV there is a peak, often called a *giant resonance* (see L-54, S-53, W-59).

In the photodisintegration at low energy one of the nucleons is directly ejected by the γ ray. The giant resonances, instead, are the result of a two-step process in which all the nucleons participate: the γ ray is first absorbed, leading to a "high temperature" nuclear state (compound nucleus), with excitation energy statistically distributed among the nucleons, until a neutron—or possibly a proton—is "evaporated."

b. Elementary Interpretation of the Giant Resonance. In order to explain the resonance, we shall describe an elementary model suggested by Goldhaber and Teller (G-48a) according to which the γ ray acts on all the nucleons producing oscillations of all protons relative to all neutrons.

Let R be the nuclear radius, ρ the density of protons (equal to the density of neutrons), and ξ the distance of separation of the neutron and proton

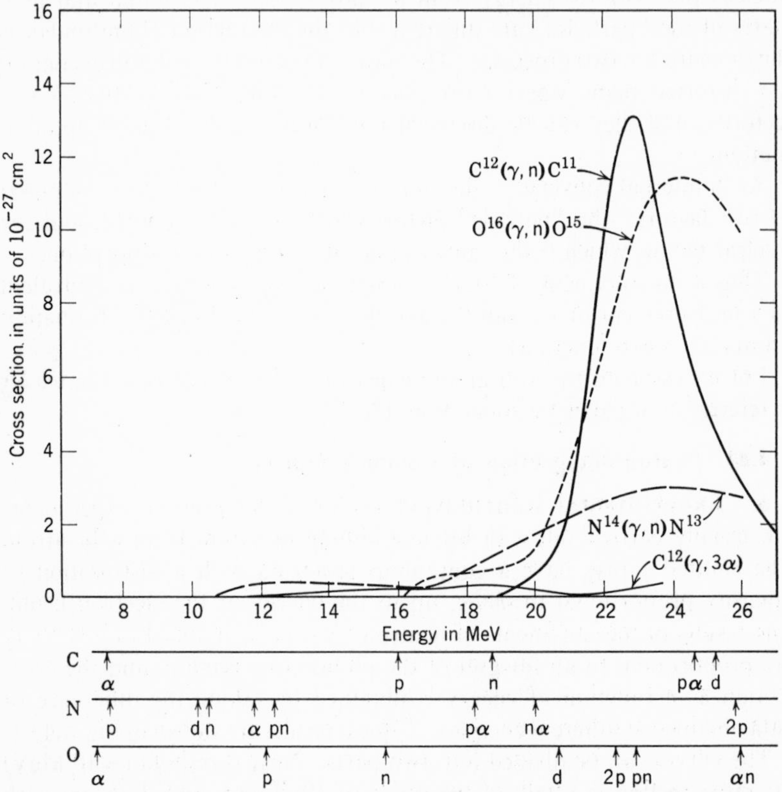

Fig. 4.43-1. Cross section curves for several photoreactions in C, N, and O. Thresholds for various x-ray and induced reactions are also indicated. [From K. Strauch, *Ann. Rev. Nucl. Sci.*, **2**, p. 111 (1953).]

"fluids" (Fig. 4.43-2). If ξ is smaller than the range of nuclear forces r_0, each proton is submitted to a restoring force, proportional to ξ. The energy required for the separation is $\frac{1}{2}K\xi^2$, where K is some constant.

But for $\xi \gg r_0$ there will be $2\pi R^2\rho\xi$ nucleon pairs which are completely separated. If V_0 is the depth of the attractive nuclear well, the energy required for separation is $2\pi R^2\rho\xi V_0$. If these two expressions of the separation energy are required to join smoothly at $\xi = r_0$, we must write $K = 4\pi R^2\rho V_0/r_0$.

Such a force constant acting on a mass $(4\pi/3)R^3\rho M$ produces a resonant frequency for small oscillations

$$\omega = \sqrt{\frac{K}{m}} = \sqrt{\frac{3V_0}{r_0RM}} \tag{1}$$

and thus a resonant energy $\hbar\omega$. Setting $r_0 = 2 \times 10^{-13}$ cm, $V_0 = 40$ MeV, we get

$$\hbar\omega = 16 \text{ MeV} \quad \text{for U,}$$
$$20 \text{ MeV} \quad \text{for Cu,}$$
$$26.5 \text{ MeV} \quad \text{for C.}$$

The agreement is as good as we can expect from these considerations.

Also the value of the cross section that can be computed turns out to be reasonable. It seems, therefore, that the idea of the participation of all nucleons in dipole oscillations must be taken seriously. This idea is developed quantum-mechanically in the next section.

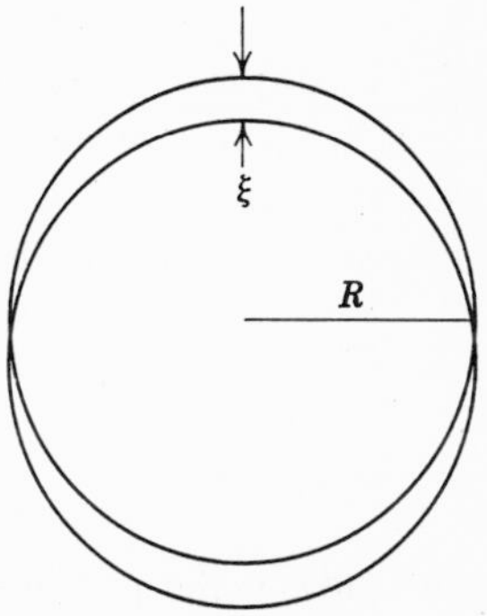

Fig. 4.43-2. Illustrating the model of Goldhaber and Teller.

c. Quantum-Mechanical Treatment. Use of the Sum Rules. We follow here, with some simplifications, the main lines of a paper by Levinger and Bethe (L-50) in which the photodisintegration cross section is calculated with the technique of the sum rules. Although this method is described in some books (BS-57), we will derive the necessary formulas.

First of all we must introduce some modifications to the cross section formula, since the first step of the absorption process leads to discontinuous final nuclear states ψ_f, to which the statistical computation of final state density is not applicable. We start with the expression

$$\sigma = \frac{2\pi}{\hbar c}\frac{1}{dE}\sum_f |\langle f|\, \mathcal{H}' \,|i\rangle|^2, \tag{2}$$

where the sum extends to all final states in the energy range dE. Since the experimental measurements are made with continuous spectra, it is appropriate to compute an integrated cross section:

$$\int_0^\infty \sigma\, dE = \frac{2\pi}{\hbar c}\sum_f |\langle f|\, \mathcal{H}' \,|i\rangle|^2, \tag{3}$$

where the sum extends to all final states. In order to compute the matrix element, we assume that all the Z protons and the N neutrons contribute to the dipole absorption with effective charge ε_α [4.34(2) and (3)], where

$$\varepsilon_\alpha = \frac{N}{A} e \quad \text{for } 1 \leq \alpha \leq Z \qquad \text{(protons)}$$

(4)

$$\varepsilon_\alpha = \frac{Z}{A} e \quad \text{for } Z + 1 \leq \alpha \leq A \qquad \text{(neutrons)}$$

Then, assuming polarization with the electric vector in the z direction, using 4.17(2), and disregarding phase factors, we have

$$\langle f| \mathcal{H}' |i\rangle = \langle f| \sum_\alpha \frac{\varepsilon_\alpha}{Mc} \mathbf{A} \cdot \mathbf{p}_\alpha |i\rangle = \sqrt{2\pi(E_f - E_i)} \sum_\alpha \varepsilon_\alpha \langle f| z_\alpha |i\rangle. \tag{5}$$

This expression must be squared and summed over all final states by taking advantage of the *sum rule*. This leads to a finite result without the need to specify the states involved.

We start expanding the square as a double sum over the nucleons:

$$\frac{1}{2\pi} \sum_f \left| \langle f| \mathcal{H}' |i\rangle \right|^2 = \sum_f (E_f - E_i) \sum_{\alpha,\beta=1}^{A} \varepsilon_\alpha \varepsilon_\beta \langle i| z_\alpha |f\rangle \langle f| z_\beta |i\rangle = \sum_f \sum_{\alpha\beta} \varepsilon_\alpha \varepsilon_\beta \langle i| z_\alpha |f\rangle (E_f - E_i) \langle f| z_\beta |i\rangle. \tag{6a}$$

We now make use of the nuclear Hamiltonian $\mathcal{H}$ in the assumption that it contains *no exchange operators*. Then we can write

$$z_\alpha \mathcal{H} |f\rangle = z_\alpha |f\rangle E_f \quad \text{and} \quad \langle i| \mathcal{H} z_\alpha = E_i \langle i| z_\alpha$$

and transform (6*a*) into

$$\frac{1}{2} \sum_f \sum_{\alpha\beta} \varepsilon_\alpha \varepsilon_\beta \{ \langle i \,|\, z_\alpha \mathcal{H} - \mathcal{H} z_\alpha \,|\, f\rangle \langle f \,|\, z_\beta \,|\, i\rangle + \langle i \,|\, z_\alpha \,|\, f\rangle \langle f \,|\, \mathcal{H} z_\beta - z_\beta \mathcal{H} \,|\, i\rangle \}, \tag{6b}$$

which, by use of $z_\alpha \mathcal{H} - \mathcal{H} z_\alpha = (i\hbar/M) p_{\alpha z}$ and of the matrix multiplication rule, becomes

$$\frac{i\hbar}{2M} \sum_{\alpha\beta} \varepsilon_\alpha \varepsilon_\beta \langle i| \, p_{\alpha z} z_\beta - z_\alpha p_{\beta z} \, |i\rangle. \tag{6c}$$

Thus the sum over f has been performed without computing the individual terms.

Finally, we can use the commutation relation between z_α and $p_{\alpha z}$. The terms with $\alpha = \beta$ yield

$$\frac{i\hbar}{2M} \sum_\alpha \varepsilon_\alpha^2 (-i\hbar) = \frac{\hbar^2 e^2}{2M} \left[Z \frac{N^2}{A^2} + N \frac{Z^2}{A^2} \right] = \frac{\hbar^2 e^2}{2M} \frac{ZN}{A}. \tag{7}$$

The terms with $\alpha \neq \beta$ vanish. However, if $\mathcal{H}$ contained exchange operators $\mathcal{T}_{\alpha\beta}$, we would have contributions from other terms to increase the theoretical cross section.

In conclusion we obtain (without exchange forces)

$$\int \sigma \, dE = 2\pi^2 \frac{e^2\hbar}{Mc} \frac{ZN}{A} \approx \frac{\pi^2}{137} \left(\frac{\hbar}{Mc}\right)^2 Mc^2 \frac{A}{2} \tag{8}$$
$$\approx 0.015A \; 10^{-24} \text{ cm}^2 \times \text{MeV}.$$

This result can be compared with the experimentally measured energy of the giant resonance and with the bremsstrahlung integrated cross section:

$$\int \sigma \, dE \approx E_{\text{res}} \int \sigma \frac{dE}{E} = 0.02A \; 10^{-24} \text{ cm}^2 \times \text{MeV}. \tag{9}$$

We obtain satisfactory agreement also by considering that exchange forces may increase the theoretical cross section (8).

The resonance energy can also be computed theoretically as the average value of the absorbed quantum energy:

$$E_{\text{res}} = \frac{\int (E_f - E_i)\sigma \, dE_f}{\int \sigma \, dE}. \tag{10}$$

The numerator of (10) can be transformed as follows:

$$\begin{aligned} \int (E_f - E_i)\sigma \, dE_f &= \frac{4\pi^2}{\hbar c} \sum_f (E_f - E_i)^2 \sum_{\alpha\beta} \varepsilon_\alpha \varepsilon_\beta \langle i | z_\alpha | f \rangle \langle f | z_\beta | i \rangle \\ &= \frac{4\pi^2}{\hbar c} \sum_f \sum_{\alpha\beta} \varepsilon_\alpha \varepsilon_\beta \langle i | z_\alpha \mathcal{H} - \mathcal{H} z_\alpha | f \rangle \langle f | \mathcal{H} z_\beta - z_\beta \mathcal{H} | i \rangle \\ &= \frac{4\pi^2}{\hbar c} \frac{\hbar^2}{M^2} \sum_{\alpha\beta} \varepsilon_\alpha \varepsilon_\beta \langle i | p_{\alpha z} p_{\beta z} | i \rangle. \end{aligned} \tag{11}$$

Here, too, the sum over f has been performed by use of the matrix multiplication rule.

We may drop the mixed terms in this last sum if we assume that there is no correlation between the motion of the different nucleons. In (11) we introduce $\varepsilon_\alpha \approx \varepsilon_\beta \approx e/2$ and compute $\langle p_{\alpha z}{}^2 \rangle \approx \langle p_{\beta z}{}^2 \rangle$ from the Fermi gas model of the nucleus (2.24), according to which the average value of the kinetic energy of a nucleon is 18 MeV and thus $\langle p_z{}^2 \rangle = 2M\frac{18}{3}$ MeV. Finally, using also (10) and (8), we obtain

$$E_{\text{res}} = \tfrac{4}{3} 18 \text{ MeV} = 24 \text{ MeV} \tag{12}$$

in sufficiently good agreement with experiment.

It is also possible to treat the absorption according to the independent particle model (with correlations) and to understand how the single-particle transitions contribute to the sum we have performed.

References

Books

BS-57 H. A. Bethe and E. E. Salpeter, *Quantum Mechanics of One and Two Electron Atoms*, Academic Press, New York, 1957.

BW-52 J. M. Blatt and V. F. Weisskopf, *Theoretical Nuclear Physics*, Wiley, New York, 1952.

Fe-51 E. Fermi, *Elementary Particles*, Yale University Press, 1951.

He-44 W. Heitler, *Quantum Theory of Radiation*, Oxford University Press, 1954.

HS-57 L. Hulthen and M. Sagawara, *Handbook of Physics*, Vol. **39**, Springer-Verlag, Berlin, 1957.

Ro-58 M. E. Rose "*Internal Conversion Coefficients*," North Holland Publishing Company (1958).

Sc-49 L. I. Schiff, *Quantum Mechanics*, McGraw-Hill, New York, 1949.

Articles

A-53 Ambler, Grace, Halban, Kurti, Durand, Johnson, and Lemmer, *Phil. Mag.*, **44**, Ser. 7, 216 (1953).

A-56 Alder, Bohr, Huus, Mottelson, and Winther, *Rev. Mod. Phys.*, **28**, 432 (1956).

B-50 E. L. Brady and M. Deutsch, *Phys. Rev.*, **78**, 558 (1950).

B-53a L. C. Biedenharn and M. E. Rose, *Rev. Mod. Phys.*, **25**, 729 (1953).

B-53b A. Bohr and B. R. Mottelson, *Kgl. Danske Videnskab. Selskab, Mat. Fys. Medd.*, **27**, No. 16 (1953).

B-55 Blin-Stoyle, Grace, and Halban, in *β and γ Spectroscopy* (edited by K. Siegbahn), North Holland, Amsterdam, 1955.

D-48 S. DeBenedetti and F. McGowan, *Phys. Rev.*, **74**, 128 (1948).

D-55 S. R. DeGroot and H. A. Tolhoek, in *β and γ Spectroscopy* (edited by K. Siegbahn), North Holland, Amsterdam, 1955, p. 613.

F-50a D. L. Falkoff and G. E. Uhlenbeck, *Phys. Rev.*, **79**, 323 (1950).

F-50b W. Franz, *A. Physik*, **127**, 363 (1950).

F-53 U. Fano, *Phys. Rev.*, **90**, 577 (1953).

F-55 H. Frauenfelder, in *β and γ Spectroscopy* (edited by K. Siegbahn), North Holland, Amsterdam, 1955, p. 531.

F-60 J. B. French, in *Nuclear Spectroscopy* (edited by V. Ajzenberg-Selove), Academic Press, New York, 1960.

G-48a M. Goldhaber and E. Teller, *Phys. Rev.*, **74**, 1046 (1948).

G-48b C. G. Gorter, *Physica*, **14**, 504 (1948).

G-53 M. Gell-Mann and V. Telegdi, *Phys. Rev.*, **91,** 169 (1953).
G-55a M. Goldhaber and J. Weneser, *Ann. Rev. Nucl. Sci.*, **5,** 1 (1955).
G-55b M. Goldhaber and A. W. Sunyar, in *β and γ Spectroscopy* (edited by K. Siegbahn), North Holland, Amsterdam, 1955, p. 453.
G-58 L. Grodzins, *Phys. Rev.*, **109,** 1014 (1958).
H-36 W. Heitler, *Proc. Cambridge Phil. Soc.*, **32,** 673 (1936).
H-40 D. R. Hamilton, *Phys. Rev.*, **58,** 122 (1940).
H-53 Hamermesh, Ringo, and Wexler, *Phys. Rev.*, **90,** 603 (1953).
L-50 J. S. Levinger and H. A. Bethe, *Phys. Rev.*, **78,** 115 (1950).
L-51 B. A. Lippmann, *Phys. Rev.*, **81,** 162 (1951).
L-54 J. S. Levinger, *Ann. Rev. Nucl. Sci.*, **4,** 13 (1954).
M-50 F. Metzger and M. Deutsch, *Phys. Rev.*, **78,** 551 (1950).
M-55 S. A. Mozkowski in *β and γ Spectroscopy* (edited by K. Siegbahn), North Holland, Amsterdam, 1955.
M-58a R. Mössbauer, *Z. Physik*, **151,** 124 (1958).
M-58b R. Mössbauer, *Naturiwiss.* **45,** 538 (1958).
M-59 R. Mössbauer, *Z. Naturforsch*, **14a,** 211 (1959).
R-49 M. E. Rose, *Phys. Rev.*, **75,** 213 (1949).
R-51a G. Racah, *Phys. Rev.*, **84,** 910 (1951).
R-51b Rose, Goertzel, Spinrad, Harr, and Strong, *Phys. Rev.*, **83,** 79 (1951).
R-55 M. E. Rose, Appendix IV in *β and γ Spectroscopy* (edited by K. Siegbahn), North Holland, Amsterdam, 1955, p. 905.
S-52 B. Stech, *Z. Naturforsch.*, **7a,** 401 (1952).
S-53 K. Strauch, *Ann. Rev. Nucl. Sci.*, **2,** 105 (1953).
T-51 N. Tralli and G. Goertzel, *Phys. Rev.*, **83,** 399 (1951).
T-56 H. A. Tolhoek, *Rev. Mod. Phys.*, **28,** 277 (1956).
W-59 D. H. Wilkinson, *Ann. Rev. Nucl. Sci.*, **9,** 1 (1959).

FIVE

Nuclear Reactions

5.1 Asymptotic Description of Nuclear Reactions

5.11 The Statistical Factors

a. The Available Phase Space. In the treatment of reactions between nuclei or between elementary particles, we are often faced with phenomena for which the law of interaction is unknown. It therefore often becomes useful to assume that the transition probability is simply proportional to the number of final quantum states available for the process under consideration. In the language of time-dependent perturbation theory this point of view is equivalent to the assumption that the square of the matrix element is constant, that is, it does not depend on the coordinates and momenta involved[1].

The computation of statistical factors provides us at least with a first guide in our attempts to interpret a new phenomenon: if the observed trends deviate from the statistical prediction, we obtain significant information on the unknown interaction, and, in particular, in perturbation theory, on the behavior of the matrix elements.

In our discussion we assume that the final products of a reaction contain some free particles. Unless otherwise specified, we shall assume that all particles have spin 0, in which case there is one final state in each phase space volume $(2\pi\hbar)^3$ for each particle; if the spin s is different from zero, the number of states is multiplied by $2s + 1$.

[1] We are obviously referring to matrix elements for plane final waves which do not contain energy-dependent normalization factors.

The general formulas are easily written. Let us consider the disintegration of a system, whose center of mass is at rest, into N particles whose momenta $\mathbf{p}_\alpha$ are in the range from $\mathbf{p}_\alpha$ to $\mathbf{p}_\alpha + d\mathbf{p}_\alpha$. Since

$$(1) \qquad \sum_{\alpha=1}^{N} \mathbf{p}_\alpha = 0,$$

because of conservation of momentum, only $N - 1$ momenta are independent; when the first $N - 1$ momenta are assigned, there is only one momentum state for the Nth particle, and thus the number of states per unit energy interval (in a box of unit geometrical volume) is

$$(2) \qquad \rho_F = \frac{1}{dE_0} \frac{d^3p_1}{(2\pi\hbar)^3} \frac{d^3p_2}{(2\pi\hbar)^3} \cdots \frac{d^3p_{N-1}}{(2\pi\hbar)^3},$$

where $E_0 = \sum_{\alpha=1}^{N} E_i$ is the total energy available for the process. It is often convenient to use polar coordinates in momentum space and to write $p_\alpha{}^2\, dp_\alpha\, d\Omega_\alpha$ in place of d^3p_α.

If one of the masses, say the Nth, is much larger than the others, the corresponding recoil energy is negligible and $dE_0 = \sum_{\alpha=1}^{N-1} dE_\alpha$. Thus the heavy particle does not enter at all into (2), and the density of states is the same as for $N - 1$ particles without the restriction of conservation of momentum.

In the general case the momentum spectrum of any one particle, say the first, can be obtained by integrating over all the other momenta[1]

$$(3) \qquad \rho_F(p_1)\, dp_1 = \frac{4\pi p_1{}^2\, dp_1}{(2\pi\hbar)^3} \frac{d}{dE_0} \prod_{\alpha=2}^{N-1} \int \frac{d^3p_\alpha}{(2\pi\hbar)^3}.$$

Finally, if different initial energies are possible, the expected energy dependence of the transition probability is obtained by integrating over all momenta:

$$(4) \qquad \rho_F(E) = \frac{d}{dE_0} \prod_{\alpha=1}^{N-1} \int \frac{d^3p_\alpha}{(2\pi\hbar)^3}.$$

These formulas are relativistically correct if the relativistic relation between energy and momenta is used. The relativistic computation of the statistical factors for several final particles may become rather involved, but explicit relativistic formulas for $N = 3, 4, 5$ can be found in the literature (B-56).

We will be satisfied here with the discussion of a few illustrative examples.

[1] The integral in (3) represents the number of states up to energy E_0 for fixed p_1. By taking the derivative we obtain the number of states per unit energy.

b. Nonrelativistic Examples from Nuclear Reactions. The case of nonrelativistic disintegration into two particles has already been treated in connection with the photodisintegration of the deuteron. In general, if the *disintegration* products have masses M_1 and M_2, we have from (2)

$$\rho_F = \frac{p_1^2\,dp_1\,d\Omega_1}{(2\pi\hbar)^3(dE_1 + dE_2)} = \frac{p_1^2\,dp_1\,d\Omega_1}{(2\pi\hbar)^3(1/M_1 + 1/M_2)p_1\,dp_1} = \frac{\mu p_1\,d\Omega_1}{(2\pi\hbar)^3}, \tag{5}$$

where μ is the reduced mass. This formula can be applied to the "*evaporation*" of a neutron from a heavy nucleus, in which case μ is—almost exactly—the mass of the neutron.

We have also computed the statistical factor for γ *emission*. For this we can use (2) with extreme relativistic ($M = 0$) kinematics for the photon:

$$\rho_F = \frac{1}{(2\pi\hbar)^3}\frac{p^2\,dp\,d\Omega}{c\,dp} = \frac{1}{(2\pi\hbar)^3}\frac{p^2}{c}\,d\Omega. \tag{6}$$

This same factor applies to the process of *K-electron capture*, where a massless neutrino is emitted.

We now turn our attention to the energy dependence of a few cross sections, using the formula

$$\sigma \simeq \frac{1}{v_i}\,\rho_F = \frac{\mu_i}{p_i}\,\rho_F, \tag{7}$$

where μ_i is the reduced mass and p_i the center-of-mass momentum of the incident particles.

For *elastic scattering* $p_i = p_f$, $\mu_i = \mu_f$, and we obtain

$$\sigma \simeq \mu_i^2\frac{p_f}{p_i}\,d\Omega = \text{constant}. \tag{8}$$

We have actually seen [3.12(11) and (12)] that the S-wave elastic-scattering cross section is constant for low energy and short-range forces. For higher values of l the cross section, instead, increases with energy approximately as $|\delta_l/k|^2 \simeq k^{4l} \simeq E^{2l}$ [see 3.12(11), (13)]. The energy dependence can be attributed to the penetrability of the "centrifugal potential barrier."

For an *exothermic reaction*—such as *neutron capture* followed by γ emission or by disintegration with emission of charged particles—we can neglect, for small incident energy, the energy dependence of ρ_F and write

$$\sigma \simeq \frac{1}{v_i}. \tag{9}$$

We have found that the energy dependence of the cross section of capture of neutrons by protons [4.23(6)] agrees with (9) at low energy. All neutron capture cross sections behave in this manner, and so do the cross sections for the neutron-induced exothermic particle disintegration of B and Li.

For *endothermic reactions*, characterized by a threshold energy E_0, the incident velocity near threshold is almost constant, whereas the available phase space increases as the momentum p_f of the emitted particles. Thus

$$\sigma \simeq p_f \simeq \sqrt{E - E_0}. \tag{10}$$

This is effectively the behavior near threshold for the photomagnetic disintegration of the deuteron [4.23(2)]. The photoelectric disintegration, instead, goes as $(p_f)^3$ because of the energy dependence of the electric dipole matrix element.

As an example of a disintegration into three bodies we shall study the statistical behavior of the *endothermic reaction* $(\gamma, 2n)$ *or* $(n, 2n)$. Two of the final particles have neutron mass M, and the third can be assumed to be infinitely heavy. If E_0 is the energy available for the disintegration (equal to the energy above the threshold of the reaction), the spectrum of one of the emitted neutrons is

$$\begin{aligned} \rho_F(p_1)\, dp_1 &= \frac{4\pi p_1^{\,2}\, dp_1}{(2\pi\hbar)^6} \frac{d}{dE_0} \int_0^{[2M(E_0-E_1)]^{1/2}} 4\pi p_2^{\,2}\, dp_2 \\ &\simeq \sqrt{E_1(E_0 - E_1)}\, dE_1. \end{aligned} \tag{11}$$

Near threshold ($v_i \approx$ threshold velocity) the cross section goes as

$$\sigma(E) \simeq \frac{1}{v_i} \int_0^{E_0} \rho_F(E_1)\, dE_1 \simeq \int_0^{E_0} \sqrt{E_1(E_0 - E_1)}\, dE_1 \sim E_0^{\,2}. \tag{12}$$

All the examples chosen are reactions that do not involve charged particles. Protons and α particles must penetrate the coulomb potential barrier in order to participate in a nuclear reaction, and this introduces a penetrability factor that varies strongly with energy and masks the statistical factors. The charged-particle disintegrations of Li and B are an exception because of the low value of Z and of the relatively large available energy.

c. Relativistic Examples from β Decay. (i) We start with the example of a phenomenon that cannot be explained by statistical factors alone: the two-body *decay of the* π *meson* which follows one of the two modes

$$\pi \to \mu + \nu, \tag{13μ}$$

$$\pi \to e + \nu. \tag{13e}$$

Here the total available energy is $m_\pi c^2$ and the momenta of the emitted particles are completely determined by the conservation of momentum and energy. We have for (13μ), assuming zero mass for the neutrino,

$$p_\mu c = p_\nu c = E_\nu = \frac{m_\pi^{\,2} - m_\mu^{\,2}}{2m_\pi} c^2, \tag{14a}$$

$$E_\mu = m_\pi c^2 - E_\nu = \frac{m_\pi^{\,2} + m_\mu^{\,2}}{2m_\pi} c^2. \tag{14b}$$

The statistical factor can be computed from (2); using the relations $E_\mu\, dE_\mu = c^2 p_\mu\, dp_\mu$ and $E_\nu\, dE_\nu = c^2 p_\nu\, dp_\nu = c^2 p_\mu\, dp_\mu$, we have

$$\rho_F = \frac{d\Omega_\mu}{(2\pi\hbar)^3} \frac{p_\mu^{\,2}\, dp_\mu}{dE_\mu + dE_\nu} = \frac{d\Omega_\mu}{(2\pi\hbar)^3} \frac{p_\mu}{c^2} \frac{E_\mu E_\nu}{E_\mu + E_\nu}, \tag{15}$$

which, by introducing (14) and integrating over the solid angle, becomes

$$\rho_F = \frac{4\pi c}{(2\pi\hbar)^3} \left(\frac{m_\pi^{\,2} - m_\mu^{\,2}}{2m_\pi}\right)^2 \frac{m_\pi^{\,2} + m_\mu^{\,2}}{2m_\pi^{\,2}}. \tag{16}$$

According to (16), we can predict the branching ratio of the reactions (13μ) and (13e), with the result

$$\frac{\pi \to e + \nu}{\pi \to \mu + \nu} = \frac{(m_\pi^{\,2} - m_e^{\,2})^2 (m_\pi^{\,2} + m_e^{\,2})}{(m_\pi^{\,2} - m_\mu)^2 (m_\pi^{\,2} + m_\mu^{\,2})} = 3.3. \tag{17}$$

Experimentally, the ratio (17) is $\approx 10^{-3}$. Obviously a more complete theory is needed in order to account for the facts. This is discussed in a later section (8.36b).

(ii) Let us now consider the *β decay of the neutron and of nuclei*, which is in fairly good agreement with statistical predictions. The β decay of the neutron

$$\mathrm{n} \to \mathrm{p} + e + \nu \tag{18}$$

or of a heavy nucleus is a disintegration into three particles, of which two, electron and neutrino, are to be treated relativistically, and the third, the residual nucleon or nucleus, can be considered as infinitely heavy. Let us assume this time that the neutrino has a finite mass and let us use (3) to find the spectrum of the electron:

$$\rho_F(p_e)\, dp_e = \frac{4\pi p_e^{\,2}\, dp_e}{(2\pi\hbar)^6} \frac{d}{dE_0} \int_0^{(1/c)[(E_0 - E_e)^2 - m_\nu^{\,2} c^4]^{1/2}} 4\pi p_\nu^{\,2}\, dp_\nu$$
$$= \frac{16\pi^2}{(2\pi\hbar)^6} \frac{1}{c^3} (E_0 - E_e) \sqrt{(E_0 - E_e)^2 - m_\nu^{\,2} c^4}\; p_e^{\,2}\, dp_e. \tag{19}$$

Experimental results are in agreement with this formula, provided we put $m_\nu = 0$. Thus (19) becomes

$$\rho_F(p_e)\,dp_e = \frac{16\pi^2}{(2\pi\hbar)^6}\frac{1}{c^3}\,p_e^2(E_0 - E_e)^2\,dp_e. \tag{20}$$

The inverse β mean lives should be proportional to the integral of (20), which, expressing the energies in units of mc^2, is

$$\frac{1}{\tau_\beta} \sim \int \rho_F(p_e)\,dp_e = \frac{16\pi^2}{(2\pi\hbar)^6}\frac{1}{c^6}\left[\frac{1}{60}\sqrt{E_0^2 - 1}\,(2E_0^4 - 9E_0^2 - 8) + \tfrac{1}{4}E_0 \log\left(E_0 + \sqrt{E_0^2 - 1}\right)\right]. \tag{21}$$

At high energy ($E_0 \gg mc^2$) the integral goes as E^5.

The predictions (20) and (21) are well verified for allowed β transitions (although a coulomb correction must be included) and, in particular, for the decay of mirror nuclei. For comparison with experiment see 8.11 and 8.12.

(iii) The computation of the statistical factors for the *decay of the muon* is a little more complicated, since none of the three particles resulting from the disintegration

$$\mu \rightarrow e + \nu_1 + \nu_2 \tag{22}$$

can be considered heavy. We carry out the computation because the result is of great significance. The statistical spectrum of the μ decay electrons from (3) is

$$\rho_F(p_e)\,dp_e = \frac{4\pi}{(2\pi\hbar)^6}\,p_e^2\,dp_e\,\frac{d}{dE_0}\int d^3p_{\nu_1}, \tag{23}$$

where the integral is the volume of phase space available to one of the neutrinos for fixed p_e and for $E \leqslant E_0$. For its evaluation we take $m_\nu = m_e = 0$ (this is justified, since $m_e \ll m_\mu$) and use the geometrical construction (Fe-51) of Fig. 5.11-1. Because of conservation of energy, the perimeter of the triangle ABC, of sides p_e, $p_{\nu 1}$, $p_{\nu 2}$, is $E_0/c\ (= m_\mu c)$; thus, if p_e and E_0 are held fixed, point C is bound to move on the surface of an ellipsoid of revolution whose volume is the integral required. The semiaxes a and b of the ellipsoid are readily computed and so is its volume:

$$\int d^3p_{\nu 1} = \tfrac{4}{3}\pi ab^2 = \tfrac{1}{6}\pi\left(\frac{E_0^3}{c^3} - 3\frac{E_0^2}{c^2}p_e + 2\frac{E_0}{c}p_e^2\right). \tag{24}$$

The statistical spectral shape is obtained by introducing (24) into (23):

$$\rho_F(p_e)\,dp_e = \frac{1}{96\pi^4\hbar^6 c}\,p_e^2(2p_e^2 - 6m_\mu c p_e + 3m_\mu^2 c^2)\,dp_e. \tag{25}$$

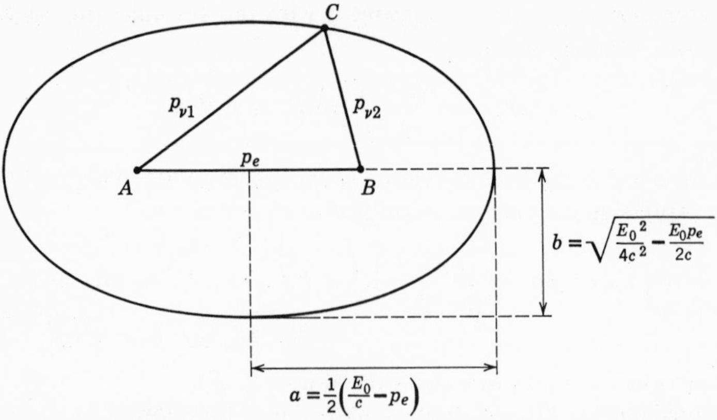

Fig. 5.11-1. Geometrical construction for the computation of the μ decay statistical factor.

The spectral shape is shown in Fig. 5.11-2 and is roughly in agreement with experimental results. Detailed comparison with the experiment is discussed later (8.31d, Fig. 8.36-2).

The integrated available phase space is

$$\int_0^{\frac{1}{2}m_\mu c} \rho_F(p_e)\, dp_e = \frac{7}{96 \times 160} \frac{c^4}{\pi^4 \hbar^6} m_\mu^5. \tag{26}$$

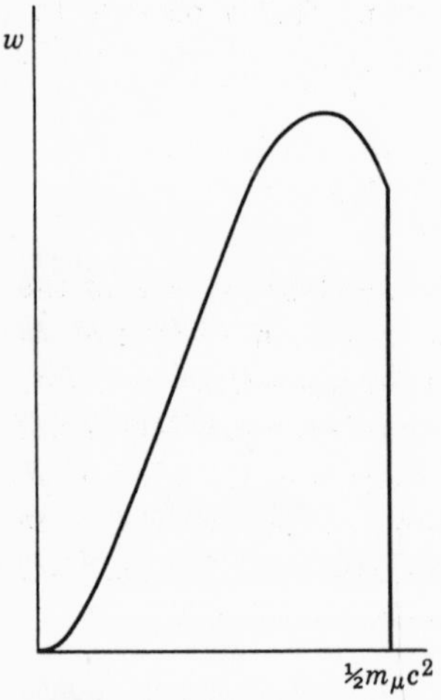

Fig. 5.11-2. Statistical spectrum of the electrons from muon decay. (From E. Fermi, *Elementary Particles*, Yale University Press, New Haven, Conn., 1951, p. 46.)

Most remarkable is the fact that the ratio of the measured neutron and muon decay rates is—within a factor ≈ 1—the same as the ratio of the integrated statistical factors (21) and (26):

$$\left(\frac{\tau_N}{\tau_\mu}\right)_{\text{exp}} \approx \frac{\int \rho_F(p_e)\, dp_e \quad \text{from (26)}}{\int \rho_F(p_e)\, dp_e \quad \text{from (21)}}. \tag{27}$$

Thus from statistical considerations alone we may conclude that the decay of the neutron and muon involves the same kind of interaction.

5.12 Partial Wave Analysis of Scattering with Absorption

a. Introduction of Complex Phase Shifts. In Chapter 4 we studied examples of nuclear reactions caused by electromagnetic interactions such as photodisintegration, capture, and coulomb excitation. By the use of the electromagnetic interaction Hamiltonian in first- or second-order perturbation it was possible to obtain a description of these reactions.

Most of the other nuclear reactions are the result of strong nuclear forces for which the Hamiltonian is not known and to which perturbation theory is probably not applicable. The close range (small r) mechanism of such reactions cannot be adequately treated, and we are limited to a more general asymptotic discussion (large r). In the rest of 5.1 we shall develop this asymptotic treatment and derive from it some conclusions that are more detailed than those obtained from the simple statistical approach; the second part of the chapter (5.2) is devoted to modelistic attempts at a short-range description of reactions involving complex nuclei.

The general theory of nuclear reactions is similar to the theory of scattering, since reactions can be regarded asymptotically as a form of scattering in which the particles change nature and in which kinetic energy is not conserved. However, for close distance between the colliding particles the two phenomena are—at least intuitively—essentially different; the interaction producing elastic scattering can (at least in principle) be represented by a real potential, whereas reactions are much more difficult to describe.

We start by showing how the partial wave analysis of scattering can be extended to include the possibility of absorption. For simplicity, we shall neglect the spins of all particles involved, as well as the possible electrostatic effects.

We have discussed in 3.12 the asymptotic form of the solution of the wave equation for the scattering problem. By using 3.12(7*b*) and expressing the sine function in terms of exponentials, this solution can be written[1]:

$$(1) \qquad \psi \cong \frac{\sqrt{\pi}}{k} \sum_l \sqrt{2l+1}\, i^{l+1} \frac{1}{r} [e^{-i(kr-\pi l/2)} - e^{2i\delta_l} e^{+i(kr-\pi l/2)}] Y_l^0 .$$

This equation shows that the outgoing partial spherical waves are shifted in phase in relation to the incoming waves. In the scattering problem the phases δ_l are real; the factors $e^{2i\delta_l}$ have modulus 1, and the intensities of the outgoing waves are equal to those of the incoming waves. This is clear if there is no absorption.

In order to obtain a wave that describes absorption as well as scattering, we must assume that the complex factors multiplying the outgoing wave may have modulus smaller than 1: stated in different, but perfectly

[1] As in 3.12 $\cong$ equalities hold asymptotically.

equivalent, words, this means that the phase shifts may be complex:

(2) $$e^{2i\delta_l} = e^{2i(\alpha_l+i\beta_l)} = e^{-2\beta_l}e^{2i\alpha_l}$$

where α_l and β_l are real and β_l must be positive.

The introduction of complex phase shifts describes the absorption as a dissipative process; the absorbed particle and its kinetic energy disappear. This view obviously violates conservation of energy, and it is not a complete picture of a nuclear reaction. The wave (1) with complex δ_l is not a solution of the wave equation for any Hamiltonian that satisfies the conservation principles.

A more adequate discussion of nuclear reactions is presented in 5.13; for the time being, we are satisfied to consider some of the consequences that follow from the partial description of the absorption process according to the assumption of complex wave shifts.

b. The Collision Amplitudes. The amplitude $e^{2i\delta_l}$ is called the *collision amplitude* of the lth angular momentum wave and is designated by the symbol S_l:

(3) $$S_l \equiv e^{2i\delta_l}, \qquad (|S_l|^2 \leq 1).$$

Observe that the scattering amplitudes a_l [3.12(6)] are the amplitudes of the scattered lth wave for a unit density incoming plane wave; the collision amplitudes S_l are the amplitudes (inverted in sign) of the outgoing lth spherical wave corresponding to an incoming lth spherical wave whose flux is equal to the velocity v of the bombarding particles[1]. It is convenient to normalize the spherical waves to unit flux: with this normalization we can write

(4) $$\psi_l \cong \frac{e^{-i(kr-\pi l/2)}}{r\sqrt{v}} Y_l^0 - S_l \frac{e^{i(kr-\pi l/2)}}{r\sqrt{v}} Y_l^0,$$

or, more simply,

(5) $$\psi_l \cong \mathfrak{I}_l - S_l \mathfrak{O}_l,$$

where $\mathfrak{I}_l$ and $\mathfrak{O}_l$ relate to incoming and outgoing lth spherical waves normalized to unit flux.

The collision amplitudes are simply related to the cross sections. The scattering cross section is immediately obtained by introducing (3) into 3.12(6) and (11):

(6) $$\sigma_{sc} = \sum_l \sigma_{sc,l} = \frac{\pi}{k^2} \sum_l (2l+1)\,|1 - S_l|^2;$$

[1] From the expression of flux over a sphere of arbitrary radius R,

$$\frac{\hbar}{2iM} \int \left(\frac{\partial \psi}{\partial r} \psi^* - \frac{\partial \psi^*}{\partial r} \psi \right)_{r=R} R^2 \, d\Omega,$$

it is easily seen that $(e^{\pm ikr}/r)Y_l^0$ corresponds to flux $\hbar k/M = v$.

the absorption cross section is

$$\sigma_a = \sum_l \sigma_{a,l} = \frac{\pi}{k^2} \sum_l (2l + 1)(1 - |S_l|^2), \tag{7}$$

since $1 - |S_l|^2$ is the difference between incoming and outgoing flux for the lth spherical wave.

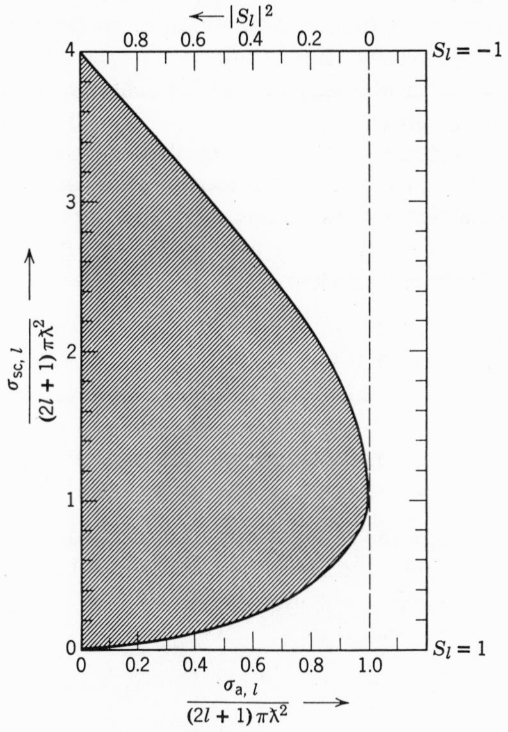

Fig. 5.12-1. For a given $\sigma_{a,l}$ the values of $\sigma_{sc,l}$ are limited to the shaded area. (Reprinted with permission from J. M. Blatt and V. F. Weisskopf, *Nuclear Physics*, Wiley, New York, 1952, p. 322.)

We can verify that the absorption cross section goes to zero if $|S_l| = 1$ and thus that scattering without absorption is possible. On the other hand, because of diffraction effects, it is not possible to have absorption ($|S_l| \neq 1$) without scattering.

The relation between scattering and absorption is illustrated in Fig. 5.12-1.

For a completely absorbing sphere of radius $R \gg 1/k$, $S_l = 0$ for $l < kR$ and $S_l = 1$ for $l > kR$; thus

$$\sigma_{sc} = \sigma_a = \frac{\pi}{k^2} \sum_{l=0}^{kR} (2l + 1) \approx \pi R^2. \tag{8}$$

Thus σ_{sc} and σ_a are each one half the scattering cross section for a perfectly reflecting sphere of the same radius 3.51(3). On the other hand, the total cross section

$$\sigma_t = \sigma_{sc} + \sigma_a = 2\pi R^2 \tag{9}$$

is the same as that of a perfectly reflecting sphere.

The expression in (9) receives an application in the determination of nuclear radii from measurements of total neutron cross sections.

c. Absorption and Scattering for Assigned Logarithmic Derivative on a Spherical Surface. For our study of nuclear reactions we find it useful to derive formulas that connect the cross sections (6) and (7) with the properties of the wave function at the surface of the nucleus[1]. For the derivation we assume that the target nucleus is a sphere of radius R, and we introduce the symbol ρ_l/R for the lth wave logarithmic derivative on the nuclear surface:

$$\rho_l = \text{Re}\ \rho_l + i\ \text{Im}\ \rho_l = \left(\frac{du_l/dr}{u_l/r}\right)_{r=R}, \tag{10}$$

where $u_l = r\psi_l$ and ψ_l is the lth angular momentum wave of the bombarding particle.

In order to describe both scattering and absorption, ρ_l is assumed to be a complex quantity whose value is a function of the bombarding energy.

(i) Let us start with the simplest case of neutral particles in an S state (*slow neutrons*). In this case the asymptotic form (4) is valid everywhere outside the nucleus and can be used directly in (10). We obtain

$$\rho_0 = -ikR\,\frac{e^{-2ikR} + S_0}{e^{-2ikR} - S_0} \tag{11}$$

from which

$$S_0 = \frac{\rho_0 + ikR}{\rho_0 - ikR}\,e^{-2ikR} = \left(1 + \frac{2ikR}{\rho_0 - ikR}\right)e^{-2ikR}. \tag{12}$$

The S wave scattering cross section from (6) and (12) is

$$\sigma_{sc,0} = \frac{\pi}{k^2}\left|e^{2ikR} - 1 - \frac{2ikR}{\rho_0 - ikR}\right|^2 \tag{13}$$

and the S wave absorption cross section from (7) and (12) is

$$\sigma_{a,0} = \frac{\pi}{k^2}\,\frac{-4kR\ \text{Im}\ \rho_0}{(\text{Re}\ \rho_0)^2 + (\text{Im}\ \rho_0 - kR)^2}. \tag{14}$$

(ii) For *fast neutrons* we must also consider the waves with $l \neq 0$. For $l \neq 0$ the asymptotic expressions $\exp\,[\pm i(kr - \pi l/2)]$ appearing in (4) are

[1] Or, more generally, at a spherical surface surrounding the nucleus.

not valid on the nuclear surface and must be replaced by the functions $krj_l^{\pm}(kr)$, where the $j_l^{\pm}(kr)$ are defined in 1.13(19).

The procedure is essentially the same as in (i) and the results of the computation can be found in Blatt and Weisskopf.

(iii) Further analytical complications arise in the case of *charged particles*, where the waves are distorted by the coulomb field of the nucleus. We shall not discuss this case because it adds nothing to our understanding of fundamental interactions. The interested reader is again referred to Blatt and Weisskopf.

5.13 Reaction Channels: The Collision (or Scattering) Matrix

a. Spin and Orbital Angular Momentum Channels. Let us consider the problem of elastic scattering including the effects of spin. For simplicity, the electrostatic effects (Rutherford scattering) are again disregarded.

By imagining that we have at our disposal adequate polarizers of the initial beam and target, as well as analyzers for the scattered beams and recoil particles, we shall be able to measure separately the features of the scattering for given initial and final spin states. The quantities that describe the scattering—cross sections, amplitudes, phase shifts, etc.—will, as we well know, depend on two indices that characterize the setting of the polarizer (or the initial spin state) and the analyzer (or the final spin state).

We now introduce a new term by saying that each polarizer and each analyzer setting defines a *spin channel*. The terms *spin channel* and *spin state* may be used interchangeably. The setting of the polarizer selects the initial spin or the *entrance spin channel*, whereas the setting of the analyzer selects the final spin or the *exit spin channel*.

The quantities, $S_l = e^{2i\delta_l}$, in 5.12 become matrices whose elements are labeled with channel indices and which operate on the spin states. The wave, which, in analogy with 5.12(4), describes entrance and exit channel, can be written

(1)

$$\zeta_\sigma \frac{\exp[-i(kr - \pi l/2)]}{r\sqrt{v}} Y_l^0 - \sum_{l'm'} (S_{l',l}^{m'0})_{\sigma'\sigma}\zeta_{\sigma'} \frac{\exp[+i(kr - \pi l/2)]}{r\sqrt{v}} Y_{l'}^{m'},$$

where ζ_σ and $\zeta_{\sigma'}$ define the entrance and exit spin channels. The sum over l' and m' is required in order to include flips in orbital angular momentum, which are allowed within the chosen channels. Observe that the analyzing polarimeters absorb some of the scattered particles and that $|S_{\sigma'\sigma}|^2$ may be smaller than unity.

b. Reaction Channels. We now wish to describe not only the elastic scattering but all of the possible reactions originated in the collision of two particles A_1 and A_2:

$$(2) \qquad A_1 + A_2 \rightarrow \begin{array}{l} A_1 + A_2 \quad \text{(elastic scattering)}^1 \\ B_1 + B_2 \\ C_1 + C_2 \\ \text{etc.} \end{array}$$

The distinction between the different particles can be made by appropriate instrumentation, such as mass spectrometers, range-ionization detectors, girls scanning photographic emulsions, etc., in the same manner in which the different spin states can be selected by analyzers and polarizers. We therefore use the term *channel* to designate the "kind" of reaction as well as the spin state.

In (2) $A_1 + A_2$ is the *entrance reaction channel*, and $A_1 + A_2$, $B_1 + B_2$, $C_1 + C_2$, etc., are different *exit reaction channels*.

Particles in different states of internal excitation are considered different, so that elastic and inelastic scattering are two distinct exit channels.

For compactness of notation we choose an index ρ to specify the channel and write (2) as

$$(3) \qquad N_{1\rho} + N_{2\rho} \rightarrow N_{1\rho'} + N_{2\rho'}$$

or still more briefly

$$(4) \qquad \rho \rightarrow \rho'.$$

In this notation elastic scattering corresponds to $\rho' = \rho$.

For $\rho' \neq \rho$ the velocities of the particles change during the reaction; we indicate with v_ρ the velocity for channel ρ and with $v_{\rho'}$ the velocity for channel ρ'.

The wave which, in analogy with 5.12(4), describes asymptotically the reaction (4) for orbital angular momentum l, is under the assumption of spin zero for all particles involved

$$(5) \qquad \left\{\psi_\rho \frac{\exp\left[-i(k_\rho r_\rho - \pi l/2)\right]}{r_\rho \sqrt{v_\rho}} - (S_l)_{\rho'\rho}\psi_{\rho'} \frac{\exp\left[i(k_{\rho'} r_{\rho'} - \pi l/2)\right]}{r_{\rho'}\sqrt{v_{\rho'}}}\right\} Y_l^0$$

where ψ_ρ and $\psi_{\rho'}$ are the internal wave functions of the particles in the entrance and exit channels and r_ρ, $r_{\rho'}$, their distances from the origin.

c. The Collision (or Scattering) Matrix. Let us remark that expressions such as (1) and (5) suffer the same limitations as the treatment of scattering with absorption in 5.12: only one final channel is included

[1] This includes the case $\delta_l = 0$ in which the incident beam proceeds without interaction.

in these expressions, which are neither a complete description of the collision nor a solution of an energy-conserving Schrödinger equation.

For a complete asymptotic description of the collision initiated by a given particle and spin channel $\sigma\rho$ we must *sum the outgoing waves for all possible exit channels* $\sigma'\rho'$. Our sums involve many indices, and a more compact notation becomes desirable. We write briefly

$$\begin{aligned} &\alpha \text{ for } \sigma, \rho; \qquad a \text{ for } \sigma, \rho, l, m = 0, \\ &\beta \text{ for } \sigma', \rho'; \qquad b \text{ for } \sigma', \rho', l', m'. \end{aligned} \tag{6}$$

The asymptotic expression for the wave describing a collision initiated in channel a becomes

$$\Psi_a \mathfrak{I}_a - \sum_b S_{ba} \Psi_b \mathfrak{O}_b; \tag{7}$$

$\mathfrak{I}_a$ and $\mathfrak{O}_b$ represent incoming and outgoing waves normalized to unit flux, which describe the initial and final state of motion:

$$\begin{aligned} \mathfrak{I}_a &= \frac{\exp\left[-i(k_\rho r_\rho - \pi l/2)\right]}{r_\rho \sqrt{v_\rho}} Y_l^0(\theta_\rho\, \varphi_\rho), \\ \mathfrak{O}_b &= \frac{\exp\left[i(k_{\rho'} r_{\rho'} - \pi l'/2)\right]}{r_{\rho'} \sqrt{v_{\rho'}}} Y_{l'}^{m'}(\theta_{\rho'}\, \varphi_{\rho'}), \end{aligned} \tag{8}$$

and Ψ_a and Ψ_b include the spin and internal wave function of the particles, normalized to unity:

$$\Psi_a = \psi_\rho \zeta_\sigma; \qquad \Psi_b = \psi_{\rho'} \zeta_{\sigma'}. \tag{9}$$

The coefficients S_{ba} are the elements of the *collision* (*or scattering*) *matrix*[1] S (B-52b; L-58; Sa-53; T-52).

A graphical clarification of the discussion is given in Fig. 5.13-1. The shaded area represents the region in which the collision takes place (small r). We make no attempt to describe what happens in this region, in which the nuclear forces act. The lines emerging from the shaded area are the different spin-particle channels, for which we write asymptotic waves: (a) is the elastic scattering with no spin [5.12(4)]; (b) corresponds to an exit channel which is different from the entrance channel, according to formulas (1) and (5); (c) is a complete description of the collision initiated by channel α, as given by (7).

d. Cross Sections. In order to compute cross sections, (7) must first be modified so that the incoming spherical waves are the same as for a plane wave of unit flux. This is easily done by multiplying by appropriate

[1] The name scattering matrix has been uniformly used in recent literature and will be adopted from now on.

factors[1] and summing over l:

$$(10)\qquad \frac{\sqrt{\pi}}{k_\rho}\sum_{l,m}\sqrt{2l+1}\; i^{l+1}\left(\delta_{m,0}\Psi_a\mathfrak{J}_a - \sum_b S_{ba}\Psi_b\mathfrak{O}_b\right).$$

The $a \to b$ cross section is the outgoing flux in the b channel, after subtracting the outgoing part of the plane wave. This subtraction is needed only in the elastic channel.

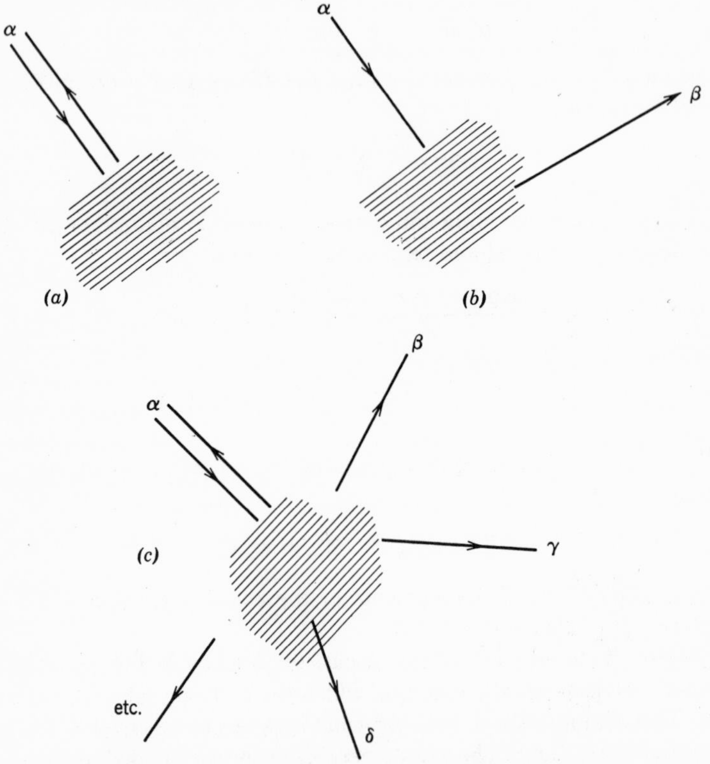

Fig. 5.13-1. An illustration of the discussion of nuclear reactions.

With this in mind, it becomes easy to express all kinds of partial and total cross sections in terms of the collision matrix. For instance, the cross section for the reaction $\alpha \to \beta$ ($\alpha \neq \beta$), with specification of the final orbital angular momentum state l', m', is

$$(11)\qquad \sigma_{\alpha\to\beta l'm'} = \frac{\pi}{k_\rho^{\,2}}\left|\sum_l i^l\sqrt{2l+1}\,S_{ba}\right|^2.$$

[1] See 5.12(1). The factor $\delta_{m,0}$ is appropriate for an incident wave propagating along the z axis.

Clearly, the angular distribution associated with this partial cross section is $|Y_{l'}^{m'}|^2$, whereas the angular distribution for the reaction $\alpha \to \beta$ is[1]

(12) $$d\sigma_{\alpha\to\beta}(\theta_{\rho'}, \varphi_{\rho'}) = \frac{\pi}{k_\rho^2} \left| \sum_{l'm'} \sum_{l} i^{l-l'} \sqrt{2l+1} S_{ba} Y_{l'}^{m'}(\theta_{\rho'}, \varphi_{\rho'}) \right|^2 d\Omega_{\rho'};$$

the total cross section, obtained by integrating over $d\Omega_{\rho'}$, is

(13) $$\sigma_{\alpha\to\beta} = \frac{\pi}{k_\rho^2} \sum_{l'm'} \left| \sum_{l} i^{l} \sqrt{2l+1} S_{ba} \right|^2 .$$

For elastic scattering we must subtract the outgoing part of the plane wave and (11) may be replaced by the more general formula:

(14) $$\sigma_{\alpha\to\beta l'm'} = \frac{\pi}{k_\rho^2} \left| \sum_{l} i^{l} \sqrt{2l+1} (S_{ba} - \delta_{\alpha\beta}) \right|^2 .$$

Similarly, (12) and (13) apply also to elastic scattering if we subtract $\delta_{\alpha\beta}$ from S_{ba}.

If we are interested in unpolarized cross sections, we must sum and average, as usual, over the spin channel indices.

5.14 *Properties of the Scattering Matrix*

a. Reciprocity. It follows from time-reversal invariance that the scattering matrix must be *symmetrical relative to the exchange of reaction channels*; it is not symmetric, however, in the exchange of spin channels, since the spin direction is inverted under time reversal.

This property of almost-symmetry is called *reciprocity*. We express it as

(1) $$S_{b(m'),a(m)} = S_{a(-m),b(-m')}$$

to indicate that in the inversion of the channels a and b all magnetic quantum numbers must be changed in sign.

b. The Principle of Detailed Balance. The principle of time-reversal invariance and the reciprocity properties of the scattering matrix can be used to relate the cross sections of inverse reactions.

A formula for the comparison of the cross section of photodisintegration of the deuteron with that of n-p capture has already been obtained in 4.23 by making use of first-order perturbation theory and of the hermitian properties of the electromagnetic interaction Hamiltonian. We are now in position to derive this and similar formulas from the general principle of time reversibility without making use of perturbation theory.

The spin-averaged cross section can be obtained from 5.13(13) by averaging over initial spins and summing over final spins. If all magnetic

[1] The phase $i^{-l'}$ comes from the factor $e^{-i\pi l'/2}$ in the outgoing wave [see (8)].

quantum numbers are equivalent, we can use the reciprocity property of the scattering matrix to obtain

$$\text{(2)} \qquad \frac{\langle d\sigma_{\rho\to\rho'}\rangle}{\langle d\sigma_{\rho'\to\rho}\rangle} = \frac{(2s_{\rho',1}+1)(2s_{\rho',2}+1)}{(2s_{\rho,1}+1)(2s_{\rho,2}+1)}\frac{k_{\rho'}^{2}}{k_{\rho}^{2}},$$

where the brackets indicate spin averaging and the $s_{\rho,1}$, etc., are the spins of the particles involved.

The relation between inverse reactions (2) is known as the *principle of detailed balance.*

This principle is applicable to most cases of interest, but it does not hold in general for separate spin states.

c. Unitarity. We have already observed that the fluxes of $\Psi_a \mathfrak{J}_a$ and of $\Psi_b \mathfrak{O}_b$ over any sphere surrounding the origin (center of mass) are unity. But the total flux of all the outgoing waves in 5.13(7) must also be unity if the particles of the entrance channel are not allowed to stick in the origin indefinitely without re-emitting the energy of the inelastic collision in some form. Thus we must have

$$\text{(3)} \qquad \sum_b |S_{ba}|^2 = \sum_b S_{ba}{}^*S_{ba} = 1.$$

Another relation between the elements of the collision matrix can be found from the orthogonality properties of the states. We have already made use of the fact that the waves Ψ_a and Ψ_b are orthogonal; but since the scalar product of two solutions of the same wave equation for the same energy does not depend on time[1], it follows that the waves which describe the collision initiated by subchannel a are also orthogonal to the waves describing the collision initiated by subchannel b. From this we obtain

$$\text{(4)} \qquad \sum_c S_{ca}{}^*S_{cb} = 0, \qquad (a \neq b).$$

When (1) and (2) are written together as

$$\text{(5)} \qquad \sum_c S_{ca}{}^*S_{cb} = \delta_{ab},$$

we recognize that the collision matrix must be unitary:

$$\text{(6)} \qquad S^\dagger S = 1.$$

For the elastic scattering of spinless particles the condition of unitarity in the collision matrix reduces to $|\eta_l|^2 = 1$ and requires that the phase shifts be real [see 5.12(3)].

d. Unitarity Restrictions for Elastic Scattering. The unitarity of the collision matrix can be expressed in form of relations between the

[1] For this we make use, somewhat intuitively, of the fact that the incoming and outgoing wave can be considered as forming a wave packet.

scattering amplitudes. In order to show the nature of these relations, let us consider the case of spinless elastic scattering, where the reality of the phase shifts δ_l is equivalent to the condition of unitarity.

If δ_l is real, we easily obtain from 3.12(6) the following equality for the partial wave-scattering amplitudes:

$$|a_l|^2 = a_l a_l^* = \frac{1}{2ik}(a_l - a_l^*) = \frac{1}{k}\operatorname{Im} a_l. \tag{7}$$

By using the expansion 3.12(5) and the addition theorem 1.13(15), (7) is transformed in a relation between θ-dependent amplitudes:

$$\int f(\theta_{kk''}) f^*(\theta_{k'k''})\, d\Omega'' = \frac{4\pi}{k}\operatorname{Im} f(\theta_{kk'}). \tag{8}$$

For $\mathbf{k} = \mathbf{k}'$ (8) reduces to the optical theorem 3.19(8); in general, it can be regarded as an extension of the optical theorem.

Similar, but more complicated, relations can be derived for the elastic scattering of particles with spin. These are particularly important in the discussion of nucleon-nucleon scattering because they introduce restrictions to the matrix of the scattering amplitudes beyond those imposed by the conservation principles already considered in the derivation of 3.54(13).

This question has been discussed by Puzilov et al. (P-57) who arrived at the result that the number of experiments required for the determination of the nucleon-nucleon scattering matrix is only five (rather than nine as concluded in 3.54 from the conservation of angular momentum, parity, time reversal, and iso-spin). This complete set of five experiments, however, must be performed as a function of angle, although a complete set at any one angle still consists of nine measurements.

5.15 Resonances

a. Resonances and Intermediate States. If we plot the cross section of certain nuclear reactions as a function of energy, we observe the presence of sharp maxima. The behavior of the cross section in the vicinity of a maximum is accurately accounted for by the formula

$$\sigma \simeq \frac{1}{(E - E_r)^2 + \Gamma^2/4}, \tag{1}$$

where E is the energy, E_r is the resonance energy, and Γ is the "full-width" at half-maximum.

Formulas similar to (1) are obtained for a variety of resonance phenomena. For instance, they express the amplitude of the forced vibrations of a damped oscillator (in which case E is a frequency and Γ is a damping coefficient) or the current in a resonating ac circuit. In optics a formula such as (1) describes the dispersion of light for frequencies close to the characteristic atomic frequencies, a problem that may be treated classically as a forced vibration or quantum mechanically by means of the second-order perturbation theory.

The interpretation of nuclear resonance is similar to that of optical dispersion; in both cases we assume that the reaction occurs in two steps:

$$A_1 + A_2 \rightarrow C \rightarrow B_1 + B_2, \tag{2}$$

where C represents a *compound state* (Bohr 1936) of energy E_r and a mean life of $\hbar/\Gamma$.

The dispersion formula was introduced in nuclear physics by Breit and Wigner (B-36); a satisfactory general proof, independent of particular models, was given by Wigner and Eisenbud (L-58, T-50, T-52, W-47, W-48), who used the formalism of the collision matrix. In what follows we sacrifice generality and rigor for the sake of brevity in the presentation of the essential physical facts.

b. Resonances as Zeros of the Logarithmic Derivative at the Nuclear Surface. If we accept the view that in the vicinity of a resonance a nuclear reaction is a two-step process (2) in which only one intermediate state enters, the cross section for selected channels can be written as a product of two factors: the cross section for the formation of the compound state from the input channel, and the relative probability of its decay into the exit channel.

Neglecting spins, we can write

$$\sigma_{\beta\alpha} = \sigma_{c\alpha}\frac{\Gamma_\beta}{\Gamma}, \tag{3}$$

where Γ_β is the partial width for exit channel β, and

$$\Gamma = \sum_\beta \Gamma_\beta \tag{4}$$

is the total width; σ_{ca} has the meaning of cross section for the formation of the compound state.

We now assume that the nucleus is a sphere of radius R and that the solution of the internal compound nucleus problem determines the logarithmic derivative of the wave function at the nuclear surface. Finally, for simplicity, we restrict our discussion to S waves ($kR \ll 1$) and no electrostatic effects (slow neutrons).

We are then allowed to use the formulas of 5.12c and, in particular, 5.12(13) and (14). It is reasonable to assume that resonances occur where the real part of ρ_0 vanishes. Not only does Re $\rho_0 = 0$ give a maximum in the cross section, but it also corresponds to a maximum of probability of penetration of the incoming particle into the nucleus, as shown intuitively in Fig. 5.15-1.

If we expand ρ_0 around the resonance energy

(5) $$\rho_0 = a(E - E_r) - ib$$

(a and b real constants) and substitute in 5.12(14), we obtain

(6) $$\sigma_{a,0} = \frac{\pi}{k^2} \frac{(2kR/a)(2b/a)}{(E - E_r)^2 + \frac{1}{4}(2b/a + 2kR/a)^2}.$$

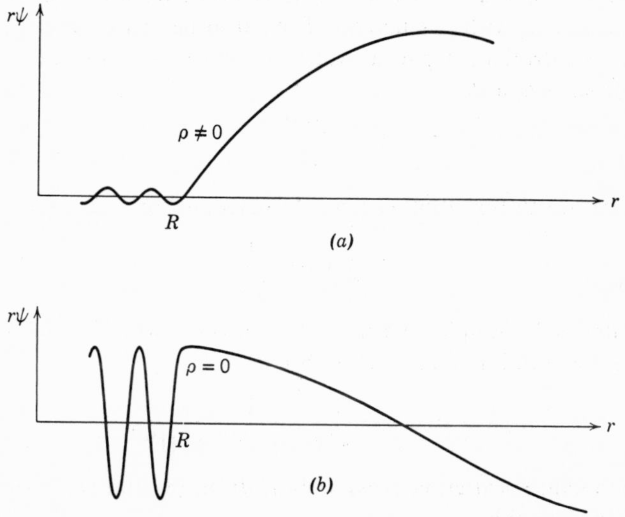

Fig. 5.15-1. The inside wave function has a small wavelength and thus a small amplitude compared to the outside wave function (a), unless the derivative at the surface vanishes (b), in which case the inside amplitude equals that outside.

The energy dependence of the cross section is in agreement with the dispersion formula. We recognize that the total width Γ is given by

(7) $$\Gamma = \frac{2b}{a} + \frac{2kR}{a}.$$

In order to understand the meaning of the two terms of (7), let us compute the scattering cross section near resonance by introducing (5) in 5.12(13):

(8) $$\sigma_{sc,0} = \frac{\pi}{k^2} \left| e^{2ikR} - 1 - \frac{2i(kR/a)}{(E - E_r) - i(b/a + kR/a)} \right|^2.$$

We see that the scattering amplitude is composed of two parts: a non-resonant part, which we call the potential scattering amplitude,

(9) $$A_{pot} = \frac{1}{k}(e^{2ikR} - 1) \qquad [\cong 2iR \quad \text{for} \quad kR \ll 1]$$

and a resonant part, which depends on the compound state parameters a and b,

$$A_{\text{res}} = -\frac{1}{k}\frac{2ikR/a}{(E - E_r) - i(b/a + kR/a)} \tag{10}$$

$$= -\frac{i}{k}\frac{2kR/a}{(E - E_r) - i\Gamma/2},$$

and which corresponds to the scattering resulting from the decay of the compound nucleus with re-emission of the absorbed particle.

If we now introduce a partial width for re-emission of the absorbed particle, or *particle width*,

$$\Gamma_\alpha = \frac{2kR}{a}, \tag{11}$$

and a partial width for all other kinds of reactions, or *reaction width*,

$$\Gamma_r = \sum_{\alpha \neq \beta} \Gamma_\beta = \frac{2b}{a}, \tag{12}$$

our formulas find a simple interpretation consistent with (3) and (4). The absorption, or reaction, cross section becomes

$$\sigma_{\text{a},0} = \sigma_{\alpha\to r,0} = \frac{\pi}{k^2}\frac{\Gamma_r\Gamma_\alpha}{(E - E_r)^2 + \frac{1}{4}\Gamma^2}, \tag{13}$$

and the resonance scattering cross section [from (8) and (11), neglecting potential scattering] is

$$\sigma_{\text{res sc},0} = \frac{\pi}{k^2}\frac{\Gamma_\alpha^{\ 2}}{(E - E_r)^2 + \frac{1}{4}\Gamma^2}; \tag{14}$$

hence for the total cross section for compound formation we obtain

$$\sigma_{\alpha\to c,0} = \sigma_{\text{a},0} + \sigma_{\text{res sc},0} = \frac{\pi}{k^2}\frac{\Gamma\Gamma_\alpha}{(E - E_r)^2 + \frac{1}{4}\Gamma^2}. \tag{15}$$

At resonance the cross section for compound formation is $(4\pi/k^2)(\Gamma_\alpha/\Gamma)$ and reduces to $4\pi/k^2$ if only elastic scattering is allowed, in agreement with the results in 3.12(11) for $\theta_0 = \pi/2$.

Near resonance the elastic scattering may show interference between the "potential" and "resonance" parts. Away from resonance the reaction cross section goes to zero, and the elastic scattering tends to a finite value

$$\sigma_{\text{sc},0} \approx 4\pi R^2, \qquad (kR \ll 1;\ E - E_r \gg \Gamma). \tag{16}$$

From this, as well as from (14) and (11), one sees that the scattering cross section is a constant at low energy, as expected from the statistical factors. From (13), (11), and (12) it appears instead that the reaction cross section goes as $1/k$ at low energy, which is also in agreement with statistical considerations.

These expressions are the one-level, spinless S-wave, Breit-Wigner formulas which are useful in the interpretation of neutron scattering data.

With some modifications they can be extended to higher angular momentum waves and to nuclei with spins. For angular momentum J an angular momentum factor $2J + 1$ appears; if the target nucleus has spin I and the compound state spin J, a statistical factor

$$\frac{2J + 1}{2(2I + 1)} \tag{17}$$

must be introduced in the spin-averaged neutron cross section.

The meaning of the widths remains the same for higher angular momentum and even for charged particles. The widths are, however, affected by factors expressing the penetrability of angular momentum and coulomb barriers.

5.16 *Angular Distribution of Reaction Products*

a. General Considerations. The laws of conservation of parity and angular momentum govern the angular distribution of nuclear reactions, as we have already seen in particular cases. A detailed calculation of angular distributions could be carried out in a manner similar to the treatment of γ-γ correlation, after constructing spin-angle-functions appropriate to the spins of each particle involved. The theory is rather complex and the reader is referred to specialized papers for its details (B-53).

In this section we intend to group together some general considerations and to illustrate their application with examples. For clarity, we shall consider two cases separately: in the first the reaction occurs in two steps, and it is studied near a resonance so that *only one* intermediate state is important; in the second case there is no resonance, or, even if a peak is observed, there are contributions of *more than one* intermediate state.

The study of the first case is important because the angular distribution reveals the unknown quantum numbers of the intermediate state if the other quantum numbers are known.

Since nuclear states can be classified as even and odd, it follows from conservation of parity that

(1) if the reaction occurs through a single intermediate state, the exit channel amplitude contains either only even or only odd powers of $\cos\theta$; thus the *differential cross-section must contain only even powers of* $\cos\theta$; the angular distribution must be *symmetrical around* 90° in the center of mass system.

Furthermore, it can be proved in general, from conservation of angular momentum that

(2) if the reaction occurs through an intermediate state of angular momentum J *the differential cross section cannot contain powers of* $\cos\theta$ *higher than* $(\cos\theta)^{2J}$.

And, finally, we must consider the restrictions for $kR \ll 1$ which limit the orbital angular momentum waves contributing to the reaction. It can be stated that:

(3) if the only orbital angular momentum waves contributing to the reactions are for $l \leq L$, *the differential cross section cannot include powers of* $\cos\theta$ *higher than* $(\cos\theta)^{2L}$.

The foregoing statements are almost trivial in the absence of spins and have been proved for the unpolarized average of arbitrary spins.

Let us now say a few words about the second case, in which the observations are not carried out at resonance or in which more than one intermediate state must be considered. Because of the interference of the contributions from intermediate states of different parity odd powers of $\cos\theta$ may appear in the angular distribution, as we have seen in the scattering of neutrons by He. A detailed phase-shift analysis is required in order to find the effects of all possible values of J and parity.

b. Consequences of Isospin Conservation. In connection with the application of the conservation principles to nuclear reactions it seems appropriate at this point to mention the consequences of isospin conservation.

Isospin conservation is important in reactions between elementary particles, and several examples are discussed in connection with pion physics (7.14d, 7.22, 7.34, etc.). In nuclear physics we expect the isospin conservation to be important in the reactions of light nuclei: in this case the resonances that are caused by an intermediate state of isospin different from that of the incoming particles should not be observed or, at least, should be strongly suppressed.

For instance, the first three excited states of Li^6 are as follows:

$$J = 3^+, \quad T = 0, \quad 2.19\ \text{MeV},$$
$$J = 0^+, \quad T = 1, \quad 3.57\ \text{MeV},$$
$$J = 2^+, \quad T = 0, \quad 4.52\ \text{MeV}.$$

In the scattering of deuteron by α particles ($T = 0$) we observe resonances corresponding to the first and third of these states, but the second state, with $T = 1$, is not formed as a compound nucleus.

c. Example: the Parity of Li^7. The reaction

$$Li^7 + p \rightarrow Be^{8*} \rightarrow He^4 + He^4 \tag{4}$$

has a resonance[1] corresponding to an excited state of Be^8. The spins of the initial and final particles in (4) are, in the order written $\frac{3}{2}$, $\frac{1}{2}$, 0, 0, and the angular distribution of the reaction products goes as $1 + A \cos^2 \theta$. From these data it is possible to deduce the parity of Li^7.

Since the two He^4 satisfy Bose statistics, they can exist only in even parity and even angular momentum states ($0^+, 2^+, 4^+, \cdots$). Only one of these states contributes to the reaction near the resonance. Consistently with conservation of angular momentum the initial state of $Li^7 + p$ could be ${}^5S_2$, ${}^3P_2$, ${}^5P_2$, ${}^3D_2$, ${}^5D_2$, ${}^5D_4$, ${}^3F_4$, etc.; but ${}^5S_2$ would give spherical symmetry of the reaction products, whereas D_2, F_4, etc., would give angular distributions including terms in $\cos^4 \theta$ that are not observed. Furthermore F states would not contribute significantly at the energy of the resonance and can be disregarded.

We conclude that the initial state must be P_2 and the resonant state of Be^8, 2^+. Conservation of parity requires that Li^7 be "intrinsically odd."

The odd parity of Li^7 is "intrinsic" only as long as we regard this nucleus as a particle without internal structure. We know, however, that the odd parity of Li^7 is the result of "internal" orbital parity.

d. Example: Quantum Numbers of the First Excited State of the Proton. In order to show how angular distributions may be used to find intrinsic properties of elementary particles, we now discuss the photoproduction of neutral pions (7.31 and 7.32):

$$\gamma + p \rightarrow \pi^0 + p. \tag{5}$$

The pion has spin zero and the final state has an angular distribution $1 + \frac{3}{2} \sin^2 \theta$. The cross section has a maximum at about 330 MeV, which indicates the existence of an intermediate state that must be considered as an excited state of the proton.

It is easily shown that the observed angular distribution agrees with absorption of dipole γ rays and spin $\frac{3}{2}$ for the intermediate state. For the proof we may use the method developed for γ-γ correlation. In Fig. 5.16-1 the lower state doublet represents the nucleon in its ground state and the higher state quadruplet, the nucleon in its excited state. The wavy lines represent the absorbed photons, and the numbers near them the relative transition probabilities between different magnetic substates (Clebsch-Gordan coefficients squared). The dashed lines stand for the emitted mesons; their relative transition probabilities and P wave angular distribution functions are written alongside. D waves, which would be

[1] This resonance was thought to be at or about 440 keV (A-55; C-41; Sa-53, p. 319).

allowed by conservation of angular momentum, would lead to disagreement with the experiment, showing that the parity of the $\frac{3}{2}$ state must be opposite to that of the pion.

The angular distribution computed from the Fig. 5.16-1 is

$$|Y_1^{-1}|^2 + \tfrac{1}{3}(\tfrac{1}{3}|Y_1^{+1}|^2 + \tfrac{2}{3}|Y_1^0|^2) = \frac{1}{6\pi}(1 + \tfrac{3}{2}\sin^2\theta) \tag{6}$$

in agreement with the observations.

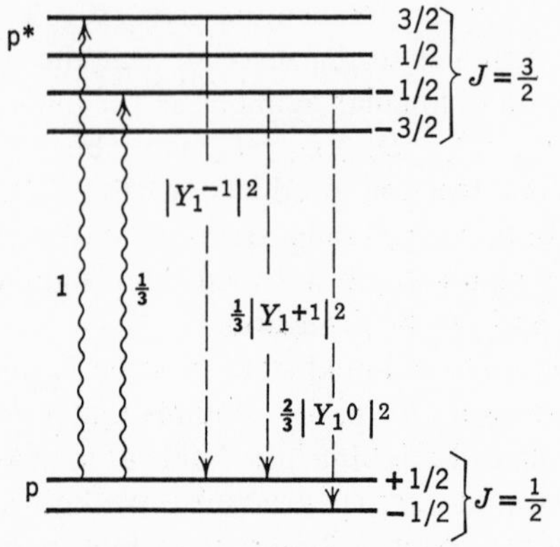

Fig. 5.16-1. The reaction of π^0-meson photoproduction through an intermediate excited state of the protons. Only the transitions for initial protons with spin up (relative to the direction of γ incidence) are indicated.

Other possible assignments of the spin of the excited state would not agree with the data.

5.2 Nuclear Reactions and Nuclear Models

5.21 *The Compound Nucleus*

a. Width of Slow Neutron Resonances. Reactions involving heavy nuclei are a complicated phenomenon on which a vast amount of empirical information has been accumulated: large books that contain nothing but experimental results on neutron cross sections are available (HS-58). A first look at the data reveals such complexity that any detailed theoretical explanation seems hopeless. Though it is indeed impossible to account for the many detailed aspects of each reaction, there are many trends that can be understood, as we shall try to make clear in what follows.

The simplest nuclear reactions are those produced by slow neutrons: that is, by neutrons interacting only in an S wave and having insufficient energy to excite the lowest excited state of the target nucleus: in practice this means neutrons of energy $E < \approx 100$ keV. Under these conditions inelastic scattering cannot occur, and, in most cases, only two reaction channels are open (Fig. 5.21-1)

(1) $\mathrm{n} + N \rightarrow \mathrm{n} + N$ (elastic scattering),

(2) $\mathrm{n} + N \rightarrow M + \gamma$ (radiative capture).

The exceptions are the slow neutron reactions in the light elements Li and B, which result in particle disintegration, and the absorption of

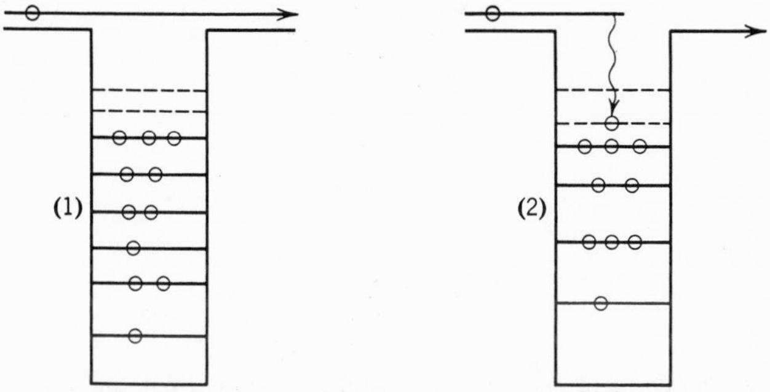

Fig. 5.21-1. Schematic description of elastic scattering (1) and capture (2) of slow neutrons by complex nuclei.

neutrons in certain heavy nuclei, which may be followed by fission. The exothermic disintegration of Li and B is fast and at low energy $\Gamma \gg |E - E_r|$; thus the energy dependence is $\approx 1/v$ [see 5.11(9) and 5.15(13); also Fig. 5.22-1]. In B the deviations from $1/v$ dependence (Fig. 5.21-2) indicate $E_r = 100$ keV, $\Gamma = 250$ keV. Induced fission, instead, is a slow process which does not change the general behavior of the cross section, as predicted from (1) and (2).

In all other cases, only (1) and (2) are energetically allowed, and the total cross section has *numerous and sharp resonances*, which indicate the formation of relatively *long-lived intermediate compound states.* For slow neutron resonances in the 0–100 keV region in medium-heavy nuclei the width is $\approx 10^{-1}$ eV. A typical spacing may be ≈ 10 eV (Fig. 5.21-3).

b. Condensed Matter Model of the Compound Nucleus. A width of ≈ 0.1 eV corresponds to a mean life of $\approx 10^{-14}$ sec, which is of the order of the time required for emission of $\mathcal{E}2$ γ rays to one of the low nuclear states in a single-particle transition. It is much longer, however, than the time that the neutron would spend to traverse the nucleus, which, for a velocity $\approx 10^9$ cm/sec (inside the nucleus the neutron acquires kinetic

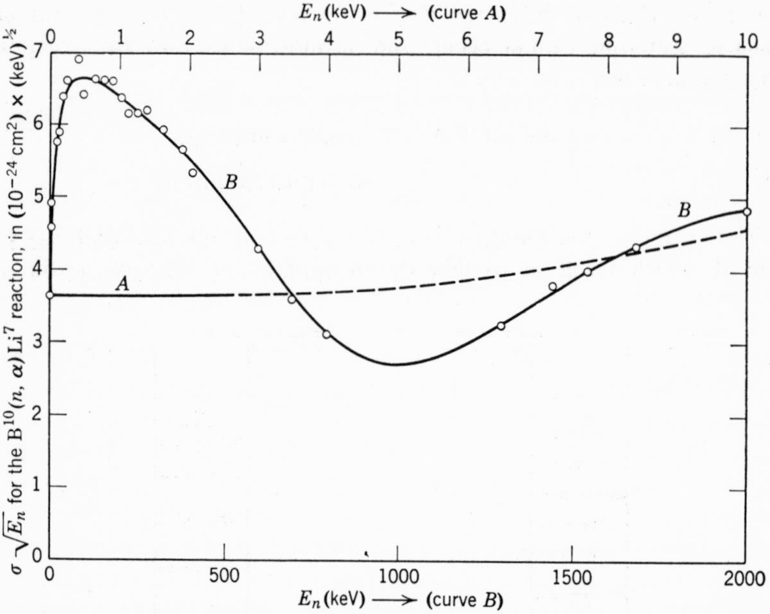

Fig. 5.21-2. Deviation of the B^{10} neutron cross section from the $1/v$ dependence. (Reprinted with permission from J. M. Blatt and V. F. Weisskopf, *Nuclear Physics*, Wiley, New York, 1952, p. 498.)

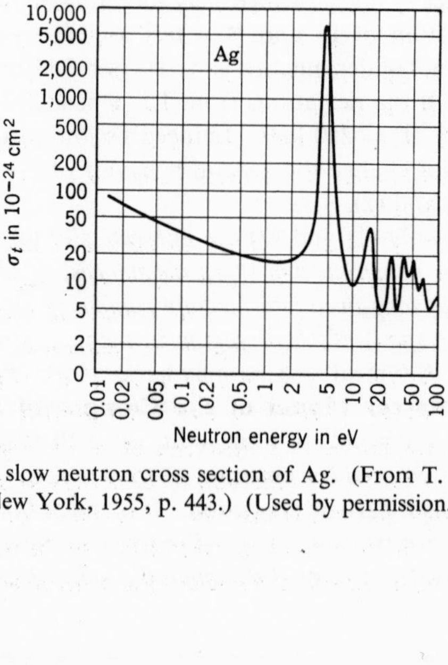

Fig. 5.21-3. The slow neutron cross section of Ag. (From T. Evans, *Nuclear Physics*, McGraw-Hill, New York, 1955, p. 443.) (Used by permission.)

energy because of the attractive potential) is $\approx 10^{-21}$ sec. In the single-particle model it is therefore impossible to explain why the neutron should stay in the nucleus long enough to account for the sharpness of the resonances and for the observed radiative capture.

If we compare the spectra of the nuclear excited states with those of an atom, we observe a striking difference: an atom has a continuum spectrum for excitations larger than the ionization potential while in a nucleus the line spectrum extends above the energy of dissociation. The continuity of the ionized atomic states corresponds to the fact than an electron with energy above the ionization potential is free to leave the atomic system; the sharpness of the neutron states above dissociation energy indicates that a neutron may linger in a nucleus for a much longer time than that required for its free escape. The reason for this different behavior is that an atom can be treated in good approximation as a system of independent particles, but a nucleus cannot.

A condensed-matter nuclear model is essential to interpret the sharpness of the unbound intermediate states formed in nuclear reactions (compound nuclei).

According to the model of the compound nucleus, the incoming neutron collides with a condensed many-particle system at 0°K, which can be pictured as a frozen drop. The energy of the neutron is shared among the many particles and raises the temperature of the drop. As a result, no neutron within the drop has, on the average, enough energy to escape. A quasi-stable system with sharp quantum levels is formed. Eventually this system will release the absorbed energy by radiation to a lower state [radiative capture (2)] or by evaporation of a neutron [resonance scattering (1)]. As in the conventional thermodynamical theory, evaporation occurs only when one of the particles gathers sufficient energy to escape as a result of a relatively improbable fluctuation.

Note that a classical "drop" model is better applicable to the compound nucleus—which has a finite temperature—than to a nuclear ground state which is at the absolute zero.

5.22 *Interpretation of Slow Neutron Cross Sections*

a. The Data. Some typical neutron cross section versus energy curves have been reproduced in Fig. 5.22-1 from the lowest measured energy to the first observed resonance. It can be seen that this resonance dominates the behavior of the cross section in the region considered, though the effect of other resonances not shown in the figure may be important for a quantitative interpretation. If E_r, Γ_n, and Γ_γ (or E_r, a and b) are taken from the experiment, 5.15(6) and (8) account quantitatively for the cross-sectional curves near resonance.

Let us have a closer look at the individual cases. The cross section of boron, and its almost exact $1/v$ dependence, was discussed in the preceding section. The isotopes Cd^{113} and Xe^{135} have a resonance in the 0.1 eV region with $\Gamma \approx E_r$; the resonance peak extends almost to zero energy,

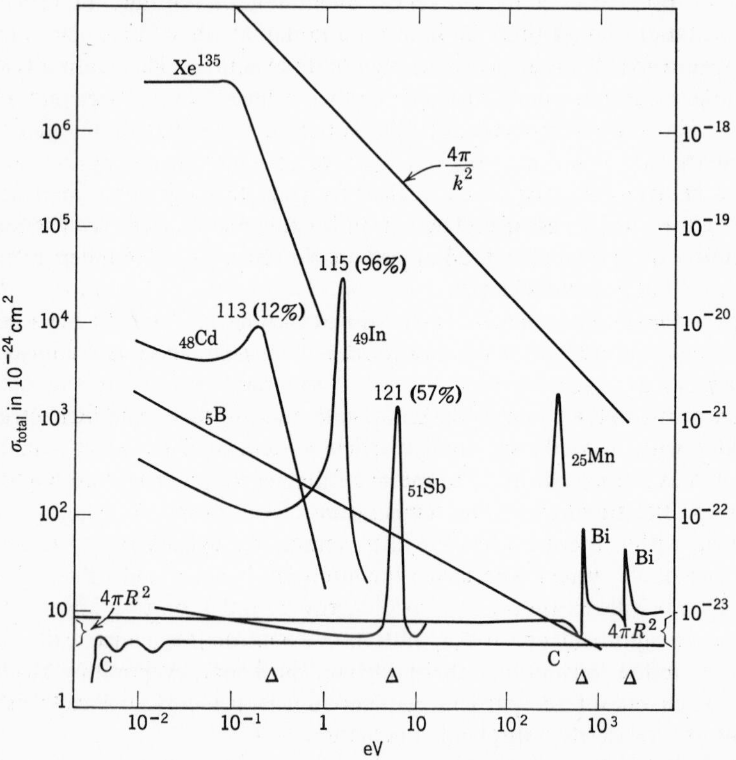

Fig. 5.22-1. Semiquantitative plot of the cross sections of different elements for low-energy neutrons in the region of the first resonance. Peaks are labeled with the mass number of the isotope responsible for the resonance and, in parentheses, with its percentage abundance. The triangles give an idea of instrumental resolution.

so that these nuclei are good absorbers of thermal neutrons and relatively transparent to neutrons of slightly higher energy.

In^{115} and Sb^{121} are shown as typical examples of isotopes whose first resonance is in the 1–10 eV region. These resonances are usually absorption resonances. If E_r is low and Γ_r sufficiently large, they contribute to the absorption in the thermal region, where the capture cross section goes as $1/v$.

If the first resonance is at relatively large energy (Bi) or if there are no resonances at all in the energy range considered (C), the low-energy cross section is mostly the result of potential scattering; it does not depend on energy and is of the order of $4\pi R^2$.

In the language of reactor engineering Xe^{135} is a "poison," a fission product that absorbs useful neutrons. Cd is used for control rods in thermal reactors. In and Sb are undesirable elements because of their large resonant capture. Bi has the properties of a good reactor "structural material" and may be used as a "coolant" because of its low melting point. C is a useful "moderator" because of its light weight and low absorption.

b. Relative Importance of Scattering and Radiative Capture. The capture width can be discussed, at least in principle, with the methods obtained in Chapter 4 for the probability of γ emission. It is not expected to vary with energy within the width of a level ($\sim$0.1 eV) because of the large energy available ($\sim$10 MeV). There may be differences from one level to another, but these differences are not very great because "allowed" transitions are always possible to one of the many final states available. Thus, at least as an order of magnitude, the capture, or γ, width can be considered as constant for slow neutrons.

The width for neutron re-emission, instead, is expected to vary linearly with k, according to 5.15(11). Thus we predict

(1) $$\frac{\sigma_{\mathrm{sc}}}{\sigma_{\mathrm{a}}} = \frac{\Gamma_\alpha}{\Gamma_r} \simeq k.$$

This relation is fairly well verified by the experimental results of Fig. 5.22-2. An extrapolation of these results (involving the assumption that all levels behave about in the same manner) leads to the conclusion that

(2) $$\sigma_{\mathrm{sc}} \approx \sigma_{\mathrm{a}} \quad \text{at } E \approx 10 \text{ eV}.$$

Thus thermal resonances are mostly absorption resonances, whereas resonances for $E > \sim 10$ eV are mostly scattering resonances.

In agreement with this view, the resonances of Bi ($E_r \approx 10^3$ eV; see Fig. 5.22-1) show the effects of interference between potential and resonant scattering amplitudes.

The total cross section for compound formation at resonance is

(3) $$\sigma_{\mathrm{compound}} = \frac{2J+1}{2(2I+1)} \frac{4\pi}{k^2} \frac{\Gamma_\alpha}{\Gamma}, \qquad (E = E_r)$$

[see 5.15(15) and (17)]. Thus the scattering absorption ratio can be obtained from the ratio of the peak cross section to $4\pi/k^2$. This is easily computed from Fig. 5.22-1 for each isotope after the data have been corrected for instrumental resolution.

c. Level Density. From the preceding discussion it appears that slow and thermal neutron cross sections could be understood if we could predict the exact location and width of the resonance levels from some kind of nuclear theory. We are obviously far from having such a theory, considering also that the energy of the levels must be known with an accuracy of ≈ 1 eV over ≈ 10 MeV.

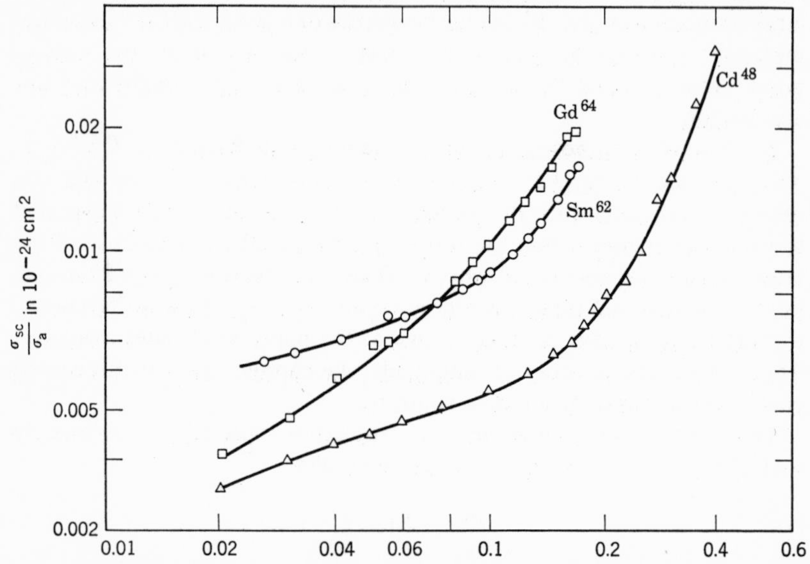

Fig. 5.22-2. Experimental ratios between scattering and absorption cross sections for slow neutron. (From D. J. Hughes, *Neutron Cross Sections*, Brookhaven National Laboratory, 1958, pp. 217, 252, 257.)

We can, however, obtain an estimate of the density of levels from the statistical considerations of 2.24, and in this manner we are able to interpret at least the general features of the cross-section curves. According to 2.24(12), the density of states for a Fermi gas model increases rapidly with the mass number and the excitation energy. This trend is semiquantitatively verified; the distance between levels is, on the average, smaller for heavy nuclei, and the density of unbound levels is much higher than that of the low excited states. Deviation from the independent particle model is expected, particularly for magic nuclei, which indeed have a smaller density of levels.

If the constants appearing in 2.24(12) are adjusted for a best fit to the experimental data, we reach a semiempirical description of the observed trends.

5.23 Neutron Cross Sections in the Nonelastic Region

a. Experimental Results. When the energy of the free neutron is sufficient to excite the target nucleus, inelastic scattering (Fig. 5.23-1*a*) becomes possible. With increasing energy, more and more states may be excited, and the number of "open" reaction channels increases. At $\sim$1 MeV (see Fig. 5.23-2) the nonelastic cross section increases rapidly with energy and soon becomes of the order of one half the total cross section,

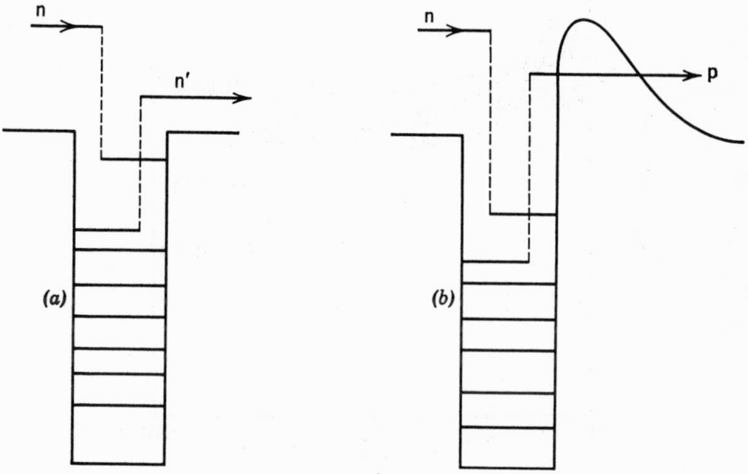

Fig. 5.23-1. (*a*) Inelastic scattering (n, n′) and (*b*) (n, p) reactions.

indicating that the only remaining elastic scattering is that resulting from diffraction.

At 10 MeV many partial angular momentum waves participate in the collision, and the total cross section becomes $\approx 2\pi R^2$ [5.12(9)].

The nonelastic break up of the intermediate nuclear state may occur in many different ways. Inelastic neutron scattering, however, predominates at not too high energies because charged particle emission is hindered by the coulomb potential barrier, particularly in heavy nuclei (Fig. 5.23-1*b*).

In general, there will be *competition* between the various final channels. The trend of the partial widths can usually be interpreted satisfactorily by considering statistical factors, density of states, and penetrability of barriers.

Experimentally, no sharp resonance is observed in the region in which nonelastic modes predominate. Though the flatness of the cross-section curves could be attributed to poor instrumental resolution, there are reasons to believe that resonances are actually absent in this energy range.

b. Continuum Theory of Nuclear Reactions. When nonelastic events predominate, the neutron wave function outside the nucleus still has an outgoing part corresponding to unscattered and diffraction-scattered neutrons. The internal wave function of the incoming neutron, however, consists only of ingoing waves whose intensity decreases going from the surface to the center of the nucleus. If K is the internal wave

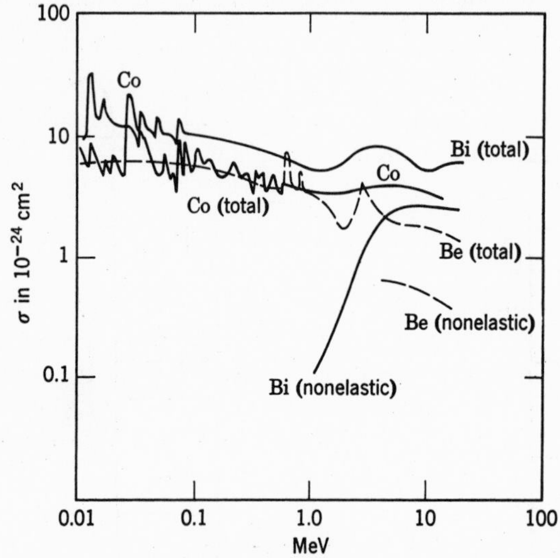

Fig. 5.23-2. Some cross sections in the nonelastic region.

number ($K \gg k$) and if we neglect the attenuation over a distance $1/K$, the internal wave function near the nuclear surface goes as

(1) $$r\psi = \text{constant } e^{-iKr}$$

and thus the S-wave logarithmic derivative at the nuclear surface becomes imaginary:

(2) $$\rho_0 = -iKR.$$

From this, and from 5.12(14), we obtain

(3) $$\sigma_{a,0} = \frac{\pi}{k^2} \frac{4kK}{(k+K)^2},$$

which shows no resonances. For pure S waves and no spins the cross section for a particular reaction channel $\alpha \to \beta$ becomes

(4) $$\sigma_0(\alpha \to \beta) = \frac{\pi}{k^2} \frac{4kK}{(k+K)^2} \frac{\Gamma_\beta}{\Gamma}.$$

At sufficiently high energy it will be necessary to include higher angular momentum waves, but this would not change the general conclusions nor the physical picture.

The formula (4) can also be derived as an average over many overlapping levels. If we call D the spacing of the levels, which, for simplicity, we shall assume constant, the cross section integrated over all S-wave resonances is in average

$$\sigma_0(\alpha \rightarrow \beta) = \frac{\pi}{k^2}\frac{\Gamma_\alpha\Gamma_\beta}{D}\int_0^\infty \frac{dE_r}{(E - E_r)^2 + \Gamma^2/4} = \frac{\pi^2}{k^2}\frac{\Gamma_\alpha\Gamma_\beta}{D\Gamma}. \tag{5}$$

A relation between D and Γ_n can be found. We note first that if the nuclear wave function is a combination of a number of states ϕ_n of energy $E_n = E_0 + nD$,

$$\psi = \sum_{n=1}^{N} a_n\phi_n e^{-i(E_nt/\hbar)} = e^{-i(E_0t/\hbar)}\sum_{n=1}^{N} a_n\phi_n e^{-i(nDt/\hbar)}, \tag{6}$$

its square has periodicity $2\pi\hbar/D$. The time $2\pi\hbar/D$ can be interpreted as the period of a wave packet within the nucleus. Thus, having entered the nucleus, a neutron hits the nuclear surface $D/\pi\hbar$ times per second. Each time its probability of escape is given by $4kK(k + K)^{-2}$, which, as can be easily verified, is the transparency of a potential step over which the wave number changes from k to K; then we can write

$$\Gamma_\alpha = \frac{D}{\pi}\frac{4kK}{(k + K)^2} \tag{7}$$

and the equivalence between (4) and (5) is proved.

c. The Spectrum of Inelastic Neutrons. The spectrum of the inelastic neutrons emitted in the reaction can be computed statistically with an accuracy depending on the usual limitations of the statistical model and its applicability.

Let us call E the energy of the incoming neutron and E^* the excitation energy of the residual nucleus. Then

$$E' = E - E^* \tag{8}$$

is the energy of the inelastically scattered neutron. The width for the emission of a neutron of energy E' varies as $\sqrt{E'}$ because of the number of states available to the free neutron. On the other hand, the number of states available to the final nucleus for E' in an interval dE' is $\rho(E - E')\,dE'$, where $\rho = 1/D$ is the density of final nuclear states. But $\rho(E^*)$ can be expressed by means of 2.24(12), and we obtain a spectral distribution

$$I(E')\,dE' \approx \sqrt{E'}\exp\left(\text{constant } A^{1/2}\sqrt{E - E'}\right) dE'. \tag{9}$$

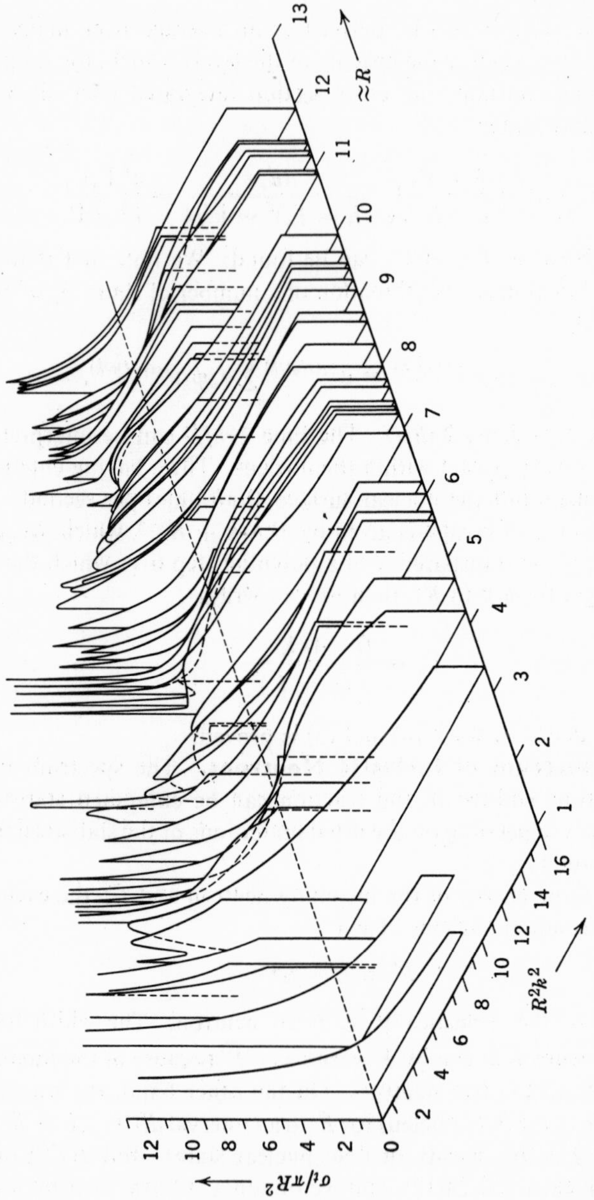

Fig. 5.24-1. Observed neutron total cross sections ($\sigma_t/\pi R^2$) as a function of energy (R^2k^2) and mass number ($\approx R \simeq A^{1/3}$). (From D. J. Hughes, *Neutron Cross Sections*, Pergamon, New York, 1957.)

This formula [particularly for $E' \ll E$, where $(E - E')^{1/2} \approx E^{1/2}(1 - \frac{1}{2}E'/E)$] has some similarity to a Maxwell distribution. Thus the model of "evaporation from a drop" is in a certain sense corroborated.

5.24 *The Optical Model of Neutron Cross Sections*

a. Intermediate Energy. Extensive data on neutron cross sections in the MeV energy range have been obtained by Barschall (B-52a). No sharp peaks were found in this region, and the individual curves exhibit no remarkable features. But by comparing the cross section of different elements, we observe regular trends as a function of atomic number which become particularly clear when we express the energy with the dimensionless parameter $(kR)^2$ and the cross sections with the dimensionless quantities $\sigma/\pi R^2$ (Fig. 5.24-1).

We have the impression that the cross sections do not depend on the internal nuclear structure, and we are led to interpret their features in terms of diffraction and absorption from a semitransparent homogeneous sphere.

This idea has been carried out in detail (F-54) and has proved quite successful. The corresponding model of nuclear reactions is called the *optical model* or, more informally, the *cloudy crystal-ball model.*

As in the independent-particle model, the nucleus is represented as a potential well, but an imaginary part is added to the potential in order to include the possibility of absorption. Phase shifts can be computed exactly from this complex potential, and the scattering and absorption of neutron waves are obtained in perfect analogy with the optical problem of the scattering and absorption of light from a semitransparent sphere.

The results are in remarkable agreement with the experiment, as shown by the curves of Fig. 5.24-2, which were computed by using the potential

$$V = V_0(1 + i\xi)\frac{1}{2}\left(1 - \tanh\frac{r - R}{d}\right) \tag{1}$$

with

$$R = 1.35 \times 10^{-13} A^{1/3} \text{ cm},$$
$$V_0 = -42 \text{ MeV},$$
$$\xi = 0.08,$$
$$d = 1.16 \times 10^{-13} \text{ cm}.$$

The radial dependence of this potential is plotted in Fig. 5.24-3 (compare with Fig. 2.21-1).

Measurements of angular distribution of scattered neutrons (Fig. 5.24-4) show diffraction effects in striking agreement with the optical model.

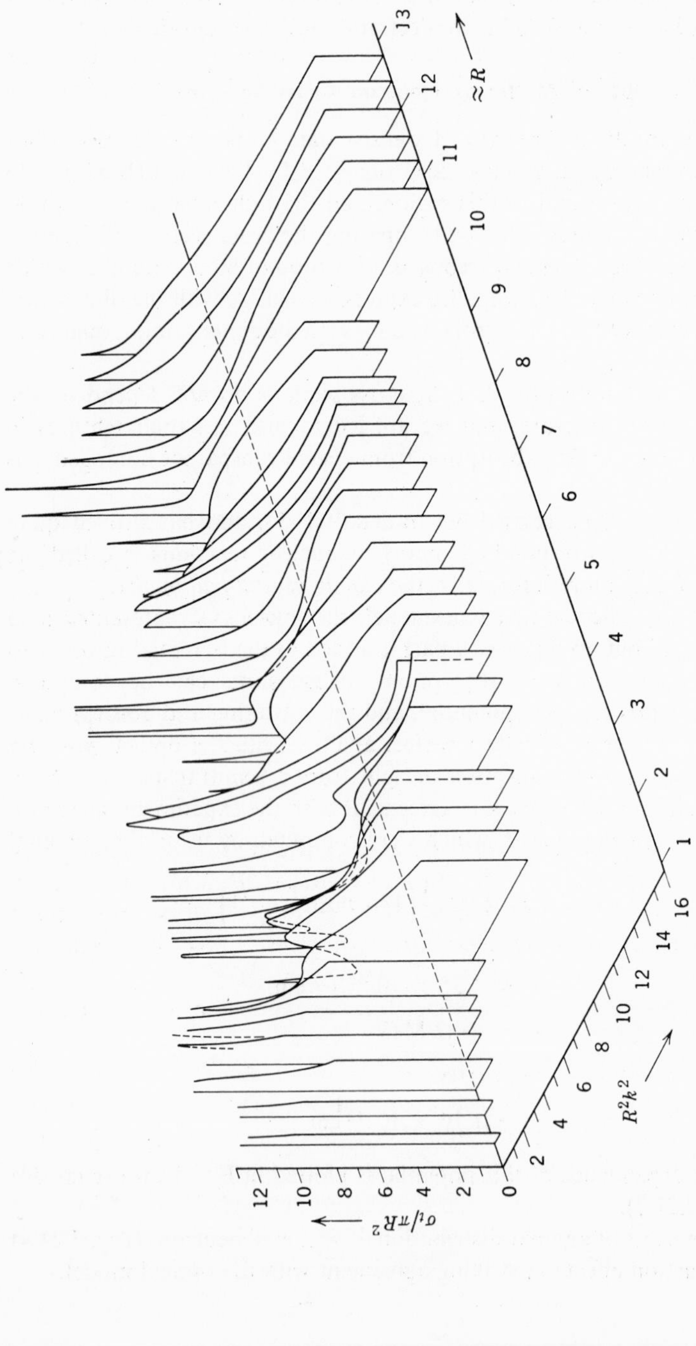

Fig. 5.24-2. Theoretical neutron total cross sections computed from the optical model potential of Fig. 5.24-3, with the parameters given in the text. (From D. J. Hughes, *Neutron Cross Sections*, Pergamon, New York, 1957.)

In conclusion we must recognize that the "compound-nucleus" and the "crystal-ball" models, though apparently mutually exclusive, have a certain range of validity. We are faced with the same situation we encountered in our discussion of static nuclear models in which both the "condensed" and "free particle" approaches had to be considered.

b. High-Energy Cross Sections and Star Production. The

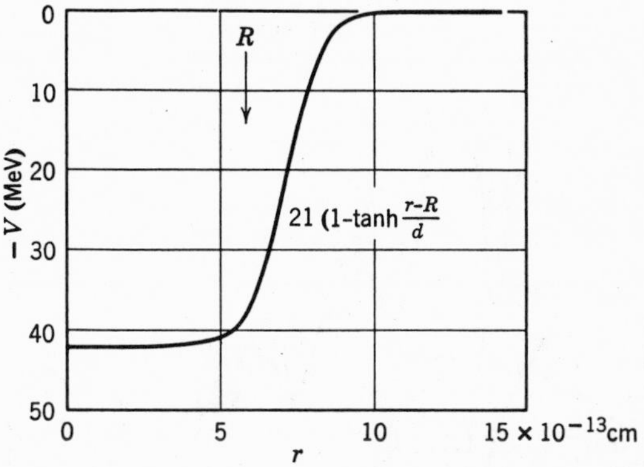

Fig. 5.24-3. The form of the potential well used in computations for the cloudy crystal-ball model; the real component of the well is shown, and in addition there is an 8% imaginary component of the same shape. (From D. J. Hughes, *Neutron Cross Sections*, Pergamon, New York, 1957, p. 71.)

cross sections in the high-energy region (50–500 MeV) can also be computed from a cloudy crystal-ball model (F-58). An effective nuclear radius

$$R = (1.25 \pm 0.05)A^{1/3} \times 10^{-13} \text{ cm}$$

is consistent with the results in this energy range. The real and imaginary part of the potential, however, must be varied as a function of energy in order to fit the experimental data. Some schemes to obtain the optical model potentials from the nucleon-nucleon phase shifts have been proposed.

High-energy nuclear reactions result in the emission of many particles, both neutral and charged, which give rise to characteristic "stars" in photographic emulsion.

The angular and energy distribution of star tracks show a few fast (gray) tracks in the forward direction and several slow (black) tracks isotropically distributed. Fast tracks are the direct result of nucleon-nucleon collision (single-particle interaction), and slow tracks are evaporated by the overheated nucleus (condensed compound-nucleus model).

At energies $\approx$ 0.5 beV meson production becomes important.

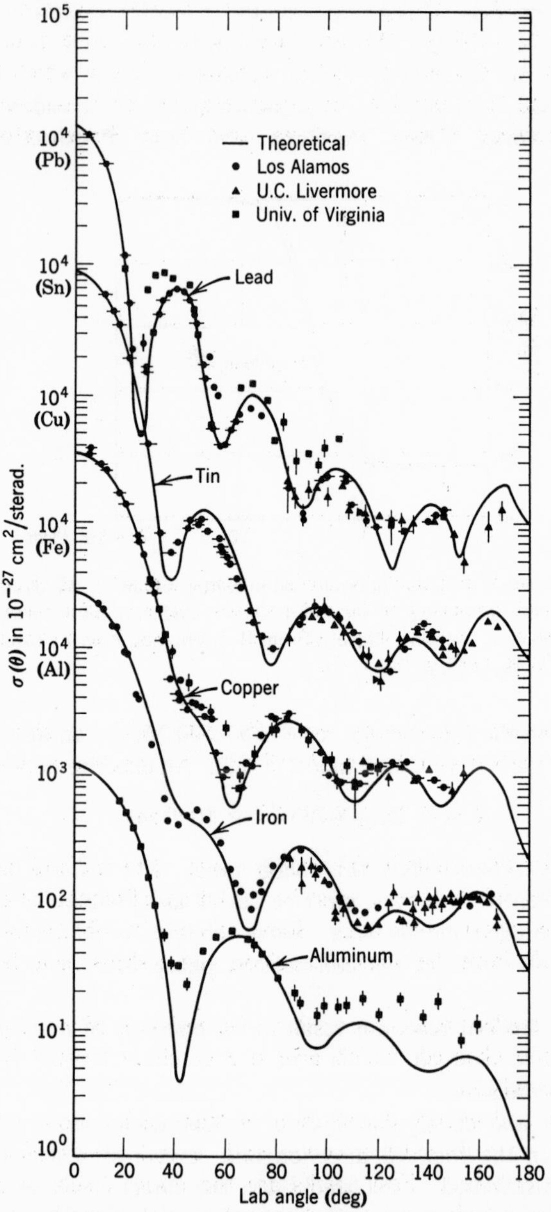

Fig. 5.24-4. Differential scattering cross sections for 14-MeV neutrons. Curves are theoretical, points experimental. [From S. Fernbach, *Rev. Mod. Phys.*, **30**, 415 (1958).]

5.25 *Stripping and Pickup*

a. Elementary Description of the Processes. As typical examples of a "direct" reaction for which it is possible to construct a fairly simple and satisfactory model, we shall discuss briefly the stripping process and its inverse, the pick-up reaction.

The simplest case of stripping is that of the deuteron, which corresponds to the reactions

$$\begin{aligned} &D + N \rightarrow N' + p \\ &D + N \rightarrow N'' + n, \end{aligned} \tag{1}$$

and from which the final proton or neutron emerges in the forward

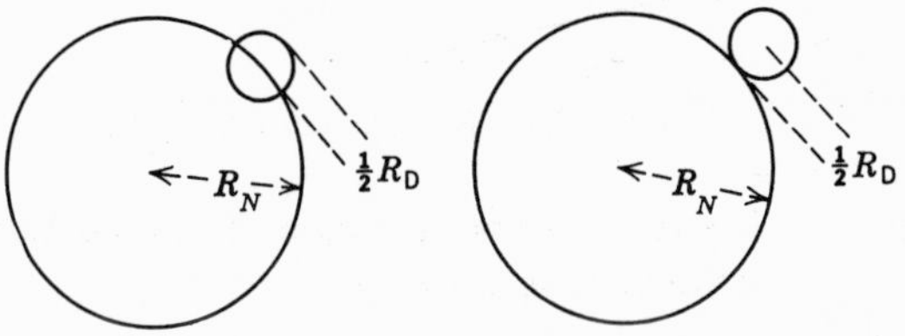

Fig. 5.25-1. Elementary model of stripping.

direction with nearly the same momentum as it possessed in the incoming deuteron. An elementary model of the process is obtained by assuming that "half" of the deuteron hits the nucleus near its edge; following the collision, the deuteron dissociates, one of the nucleons is absorbed, and the other proceeds almost undisturbed.

The inverse of this process is the pick-up of nucleons by protons or neutrons to form deuterons.

If the bombarding energy in a stripping experiment is small, the electrostatic field of the target nucleus polarizes the deuteron as a result of the repulsion exerted on the proton. An electric disintegration of the deuteron may result without actual "contact" with the nuclear surface, and the free neutron that is produced may be captured by the target nucleus.

When stripping is aided by electrostatic effects, we speak of the Oppenheimer-Phillips process.

If we neglect electrostatic effects, the stripping cross section can be estimated as follows. If R_N is the radius of the nucleus and $\frac{1}{2}R_D$ that of the deuteron[1], the useful impact parameter for "half-way hitting" is between R_N and $R_N + \frac{1}{2}R_D$ and the cross section is roughly (Fig. 5.25-1) $\pi(R_N + \frac{1}{2}R_D)^2 - \pi R_N^2 \approx \pi R_N R_D$. This is the correct order of magnitude for high-energy ($\approx$ 100 MeV) stripping.

[1] The factor $\frac{1}{2}$ is used so that $R_D = 4.3 \times 10^{-13}$ cm is, as usual, the n-p distance.

In this model the angular aperture of the forward particles is given by the ratio between the internal deuteron momentum and the momentum corresponding to the velocity of the bombarding beam. At 200 MeV bombarding energy the expected aperture is $\approx (2.2\text{ MeV}/200\text{ MeV})^{1/2} = 0.1\text{ rad} = 6°$, in agreement with observation. Under the same conditions the energy in the forward direction should be within the limits $[\frac{1}{2}(200 \pm 20]$ MeV and this also is borne out by the measurements (H-47; S-47).

A more careful estimate of the distribution of the internal momentum of the deuteron is obtained by computing the Fourier transform of its

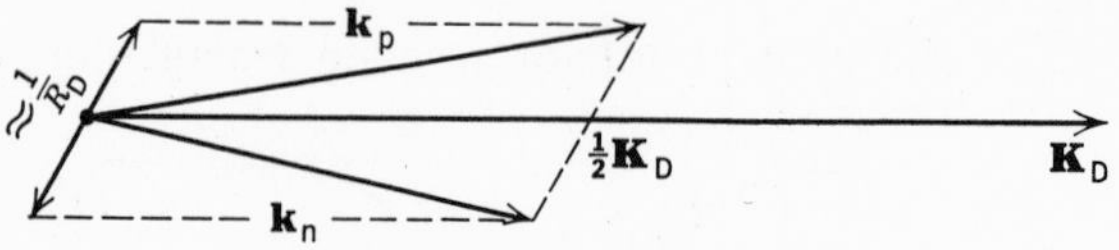

Fig. 5.25-2. Kinematics of stripping.

wave function. We can assume, for ease of computation, a zero-range wave function for the moving deuteron

$$\psi_D \simeq \left[\exp\left(i\mathbf{K}_D \cdot \frac{\mathbf{r}_n + \mathbf{r}_p}{2}\right)\right]\left[\frac{1}{r}\exp\left(-\frac{r}{R_D}\right)\right] \tag{2}$$

where $\hbar\mathbf{K}_D$ is the momentum of the incoming deuteron and $r = |\mathbf{r}_p - \mathbf{r}_n|$ (Fig. 5.25-2).

Then the probability amplitude for one of the nucleons, say the proton, to be found within a momentum interval $d\mathbf{k}_p$ is[1]

$$a(\mathbf{k}_p - \tfrac{1}{2}\mathbf{K}_D) \simeq \int \exp(-i\mathbf{k}_p \cdot \mathbf{r}_p)\psi_D(\mathbf{r}_n, \mathbf{r}_p)\, d\mathbf{r}_p = \frac{4\pi \exp(i\mathbf{k}_n \cdot \mathbf{r}_n)}{R_D^{-2} + |\mathbf{k}_p - \frac{1}{2}\mathbf{K}_D|^2}. \tag{3}$$

with $\mathbf{k}_n = \mathbf{K}_D - \mathbf{k}_p$.

The square of this expression would give the momentum spectrum and the angular distribution of the emerging protons if the stripping occurred with equal probability for all values of $\mathbf{k}_p$. In practice, it describes the rough features of the spectrum, but the understanding of its details requires a discussion of the capture probability.

b. Stripping and the Independent Particle Nuclear Model. The reactions of stripping and pickup have been extensively applied to

[1] It is convenient to perform the integration over the variable $\mathbf{r} = \mathbf{r}_p - \mathbf{r}_n$, since $d\mathbf{r} = d\mathbf{r}_p$ for $\mathbf{r}_n$ = constant. The finite range of nuclear forces can be taken into account by using the Hulthen form of the deuteron wave function, in which case (3) would contain two terms of the same form.

the investigation of bound nuclear states. In stripping the captured nucleon (say the neutron) occupies one of the available quantum states in the target nucleus, and the other (say the proton) carries some information concerning this state. Conversely, in pickup, the picked-up nucleon is removed from an occupied quantum state and the emerging deuteron conveys some information about this level.

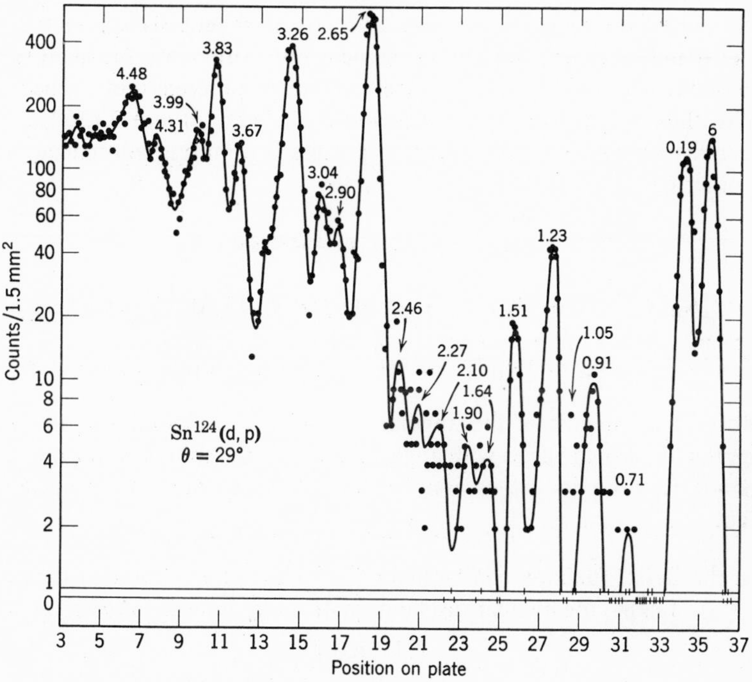

Fig. 5.25-3. Proton spectra from the reaction Sn^{124}(d, p). Each peak corresponds to a neutron capturing level of the target nucleus. [From B. L. Cohen and R. E. Price, *Phys. Rev.*, **121,** 1442 (1961).]

Thus stripping can be used to study unoccupied single-particle nuclear states and pickup to investigate occupied states.

Experimentally, we can measure the angular and energy distribution of the particle proceeding in the forward direction. In the case of stripping, for instance, an accurate measurement of the energy of the emerging proton (Fig. 5.25-3) determines the energy of the level in which the neutron has been captured, and the angular distribution determines the angular momentum of the state into which the capture has occurred.

A simplified discussion of the process, including the description of the capture, can be obtained in the Born approximation, disregarding spins and coulomb effects and assuming an infinitely heavy, spherically symmetrical nucleus. The transition amplitude is then the matrix element between the initial state of the deuteron (2) and a final state in which the neutron is in a single-particle nuclear state $u_l(r_n)\,Y_l^m(\theta_n\varphi_n)$, and the proton proceeds as a plane wave of momentum $\hbar\mathbf{k}_p$. The absolute value of $\mathbf{k}_p$ is fixed by conservation of energy, and the angular distribution of the protons is given by the square of the amplitude as computed below.

The perturbing potential $V(r_n)$ is taken to be spherically symmetrical and is assumed to depend only on the neutron coordinate: this is in the spirit of our model, according to which "the proton proceeds undisturbed."

With these assumptions, and with the use of (2), (3) and 3.12(1), the probability amplitude of the stripping process is (omitting normalization and other constants)

$$(4)\quad \int e^{-i\mathbf{k}_p\cdot\mathbf{r}_p}\,u_l(r_n)[Y_l^m(k_n)]^*\,V(r_n)\,\psi_D(\mathbf{r}_n,\mathbf{r}_p)\,d\mathbf{r}_n\,d\mathbf{r}_p$$

$$\simeq [R_D^{-2}+|\mathbf{k}_p-\tfrac{1}{2}\mathbf{K}_D|^2]^{-1}\int u_l(r_n)[Y_l^m(k_n)]^*\,V(r_n)e^{i\mathbf{k}_n\cdot\mathbf{r}_n}\,d\mathbf{r}_n$$

$$\simeq [R_D^{-2}+|\mathbf{k}_p-\tfrac{1}{2}\mathbf{K}_D|^2]^{-1}[Y_l^m(k_n)]^*\int_0^{R_N} u_l(r_n)\,V(r_n)\,j_l(k_n r_n)r_n^2\,dr_n.$$

Most of the details of the angular dependence are contained in the integral in dr_n which varies with angle faster than the spherical harmonic. To study its behavior let us assume that $V(r_n)$ acts only at the nuclear surface:

$$V(r_n) = V_0\,\delta(r_n - R_N).$$

Then the Bessel function can be taken out of the integral and written as $j_l(k_n R_N)$; finally, the angular distribution of the protons is found to go as

$$(5)\qquad I(\theta) \simeq \frac{[j_l(k_n R_N)]^2}{[R_D^{-2}+|\mathbf{k}_p-\tfrac{1}{2}\mathbf{K}_D|^2]^2}\,.$$

In this expression the denominator has a minimum for $\mathbf{k}_p = \tfrac{1}{2}\mathbf{K}_D$, which corresponds to the forward peak already discussed in (a). The Bessel function in the numerator modulates this peak in a manner that depends on the orbital angular momentum l of the neutron in its final state.

In order to understand even qualitatively the features of the modulation, k_n must be expressed as a function of the proton angle θ by means of the equations of conservation of momentum and of energy:

$$k_n^2 = k_p^2 + K_D^2 - 2k_pK_D\cos\theta$$

$$\frac{k_p^2}{2M} = \frac{K_D^2}{4M} + Q,$$

where Q is the energy liberated in the reaction, or the difference between the binding energy of the neutron in the deuteron and in the capturing nucleus.

Without developing the algebra any further, we refer to Fig. 5.25-4, in which the results of the theoretical analysis are compared with experimental data in a particular case. We see from this figure how it is possible to obtain the angular momentum of the capturing state from the measurement of the angular distribution of the stripped protons.

For a more complete account of theoretical work, the reader is referred to Butler (Bu-57).

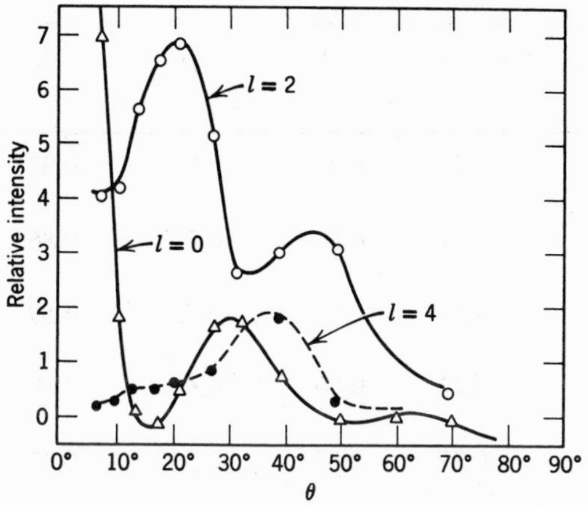

Fig. 5.25-4. Angular distribution of protons from $Sn^{116}(d, p)\ Sn^{117}$ revealing orbital angular momentum of capturing level. [From B. L. Cohen and R. E. Price, *Phys. Rev.*, **21**, 1441 (1961).]

c. Effect of Intershell Interactions. Besides giving information on the energy and orbital angular momentum of the capturing state, the experimental data can be analyzed in order to find the number of particles already existing in this state. Obviously the capture cannot occur in states l, j, which are completely full, and the cross section is expected to increase with the number of available holes.

According to the elementary shell model, the number of available states is an integer, but if forces acting between different shells are considered, as in 2.35, the states are only partly occupied and the number of available states is not necessarily integral.

We can therefore understand that (in the notation of 2.35) the stripping cross section with capture in a state j of the target nucleus is proportional to U_j^2, and the pickup cross section from the same state, to V_j^2.

These ideas have been used (C-61) in the interpretation of the results obtained on deuteron stripping (D, p) and pickup (D, t) reactions at 15 MeV, using tin targets of mass numbers 116, 118, 120, 122, 124 ($Z = 50$; $N = 66, 68, 70, 72, 74$). According to the elementary shell model of these nuclei (Fig. 2.26-3), the neutrons should fill successively the levels between the magic numbers 50 and 82: $1g_{7/2}$, $2d_{5/2}$, $3d_{3/2}$, $3s$, $1h_{11/2}$, each level being occupied by an integral number of neutrons between 0 and $2j + 1$. Since V_j^2 has the meaning of the occupation amplitude for each magnetic sublevel, the quantities $\sum_j (2j + 1)V_j^2$ should be integers.

From the experiment we obtain the values of V_j^2 reported in the following table:

	A = 116	118	120	122	124
	N = 66	68	70	72	74
	$N - 50$ = 16	18	20	22	24
$Z = 50$					
$1f_{7/2}$	0.78	0.86	0.89	(0.92)	(0.95)
$2d_{5/2}$	0.79	0.80	0.87	0.86	0.93
$2d_{3/2}$	0.25	0.33	0.55	0.59	0.68
$2s$	0.42	0.50	0.61	0.69	0.74
$1h_{11/2}$	0.27	0.33	0.35	0.47	0.55

It is easily verified that $\Sigma (2j + 1)V_j^2 = N - 50$ and that the population of all the j states increases with the number of neutrons, the lowest Mayer-Jensen levels being the first to fill up.

But, if we take the experimental V_j^2 at face value, the number of particles in each state is not an integer, in agreement with the assumption of residual interactions between particles in different levels. The fill-up order and the values of V_j are in reasonable agreement with calculations from pairing theory (K-60).

Though the interpretation of the experiment described may be opened to some doubt, the agreement with pairing theory is encouraging; and, more generally, it is interesting to see how the details of nuclear structure may be probed through the study of nuclear reactions.

References

Books

Bu-57 S. S. T. Butler, *Nuclear Stripping Reactions*, Wiley, New York, 1957.

BW-52 J. M. Blatt and V. F. Weisskopf, *Theoretical Nuclear Physics*, Wiley, New York, 1952.

Fe-51 E. Fermi, *Elementary Particles*, Yale University Press, 1951.
HS-58 D. J. Hughes and R. B. Schwartz, *Neutron Cross Sections*, BNL-325 U.S. Government Printing Office, 1958.
Sa-53 R. G. Sachs, *Nuclear Theory*, Addison-Wesley, Cambridge, Mass., 1953.

Articles

A-55 F. Ajzenberg and T. Lauritsen, *Rev. Mod. Phys.*, **27,** 77 (1955).
B-36 G. Breit and E. P. Wigner, *Phys. Rev.*, **49,** 519 (1936).
B-52a H. H. Barschall, *Phys. Rev.*, **86,** 431 (1952).
B-52b J. M. Blatt and L. C. Biedenharn, *Rev. Mod. Phys.*, **24,** 258 (1952).
B-53 L. C. Biedenharn and M. E. Rose, *Rev. Mod. Phys.*, **25,** 729 (1953).
B-56 M. M. Block, *Phys. Rev.*, **101,** 796 (1956).
C-41 C. L. Critchfield and E. Teller, *Phys. Rev.*, **60,** 10 (1941).
C-61 B. L. Cohen and R. E. Price, *Phys. Rev.*, **121,** 1441 (1961).
F-54 Feshbach, Porter, and Weisskopf, *Phys. Rev.*, **96,** 448 (1954).
F-58 S. Fernbach, *Rev. Mod. Phys.*, **30,** 414 (1958).
H-47 Helmholz, McMillan, and Sewell, *Phys. Rev.*, **72,** 1003 (1947).
K-60 L. S. Kisslinger and R. A. Sorensen, *Kgl. Danske Videnskab. Selskab, Mat. Fys. Medd.*, **32,** No. 9 (1960).
L-58 A. M. Lane and R. G. Thomas, *Rev. Mod. Phys.*, **30,** 257 (1958).
P-57 L. Puzilov, R. Ryndin, and Ya. Smorodinsky, *J. Exptl. Theor. Phys. (USSR)* **32,** 592 (1957); Translation: *Soviet Phys. JEPT*, **5,** 489 (1957).
S-47 R. Serber, *Phys. Rev.*, **72,** 1008 (1947).
T-50 T. Teichmann, *Phys. Rev.*, **77,** 506 (1950).
T-52 T. Teichmann and E. P. Wigner, *Phys. Rev.*, **87,** 123 (1952).
W-47 E. P. Wigner and L. Eisenbud, *Phys. Rev.*, **72,** 29 (1947).
W-48 E. P. Wigner, *Phys. Rev.*, **73,** 1002 (1948).

SIX

Relativistic Interaction between Fermions and Radiation

6.1 Formulation of Dirac Theory

6.11 Notation

a. Introduction. The present chapter is intended as a review of the Dirac wave equation, which is essential for the continuation of our treatment. We also outline briefly some results of relativistic perturbation theory, as applied to the interaction with electromagnetic radiation, since they are important in the discussion of weak interactions.

We have collected the formulas needed for future reference, without the intention of presenting comprehensive discussion of relativistic electron theory, which is properly treated in other courses and discussed in several books (Fe-61; Pa-33; Ro-61; SB-55). The formulas, however, are presented with a minimum of explanation and illustrated by examples of interest in nuclear physics and nuclear interactions.

b. Units. In what follows we have chosen our units so that

$$\hbar = c = 1. \tag{1}$$

Thus our formulas contain pure numbers such as

$$\pi = 3.1416 \cdots$$
$$e = 2.718 \cdots$$
$$\cdots,$$

and dimensionless coupling constants such as

$$e^2\left(=\frac{e^2}{\hbar c}\right)=\frac{1}{137} \qquad \text{(electromagnetic coupling)}$$

$$f^2 \approx 0.08 \qquad \text{(pion-nucleon coupling)}$$

$$\cdots .$$

Apart from these dimensionless quantities, the masses of particles will appear. According to the situation, always made clear by the [LMT] dimensions of any expression, a mass m may stand for

a mass [M],	m,
an inverse length [L^{-1}],	$\dfrac{mc}{\hbar}$,
an inverse time [T^{-1}],	$\dfrac{mc^2}{\hbar}$,
a momentum [MLT^{-1}],	mc,
an energy [ML^2T^{-2}],	mc^2,
etc.	

For instance, the mass of the electron may have the following numerical meanings:

(2)

$$\begin{aligned}
&[M], && m_e = 9.1\times 10^{-28}\ \text{g},\\
&[L^{-1}], && m_e = \frac{1}{3.86\times 10^{-11}}\ \text{cm}^{-1},\\
&[T^{-1}], && m_e = \frac{1}{1.288\times 10^{-21}}\ \text{sec}^{-1},\\
&[ML^2T^{-2}], && m_e = 0.511\ \text{MeV},\\
&\text{etc.}
\end{aligned}$$

Multiples and submultiples of physical interest are obtained by using the coupling constants as factors:

$$\begin{aligned}
&[L] && \frac{e^2}{m_e} \equiv \text{classical electron radius},\\
&[L] && \frac{1}{m_e} \equiv \text{Compton wavelength},\\
&[L] && \frac{1}{m_e e^2} \equiv \text{Bohr radius},\\
&[L] && \frac{1}{m_e e^4} \equiv \frac{1}{2}\times \text{wavelength of last hydrogen line},\\
& && \text{etc.}
\end{aligned}$$

A further simplification in the formulas can be introduced by taking as unit of mass the mass of a particular particle; we take advantage of this possibility in our discussion of pion physics. When this is done, only dimensionless physical quantities (mass ratios and coupling constants) remain: though present theory is not in position to attempt a derivation of these numbers, they might ultimately find a purely mathematical explanation.

However, if we select a system of units arbitrarily, one "universal constant" for each dimension will always come from the experiment. These empirical constants can be made to disappear with an appropriate choice of units, and, in the most ambitious theoretical dream, it may be possible to describe the universe with equations that do not contain experimental data at all!

c. Relativistic Notation. We refer the four-dimensional space time of special relativity to the four *real* orthogonal axes:

$$x_\mu \quad \text{or} \quad x_i, x_4, \qquad (\mu = 1, 2, 3, 4; \quad i = 1, 2, 3) \tag{3}$$

with

$$x_1 = x, \qquad x_2 = y, \qquad x_3 = z, \qquad x_4 = t.$$

A four-vector

$$\mathsf{v} \quad \text{or} \quad \mathbf{v}, v_4 \tag{4}$$

has components

$$v_1 = v_x, \qquad v_2 = v_y, \qquad v_3 = v_z, \qquad v_4 = v_t.$$

As in elementary physics, we assume that all vector (and tensor) components transform like coordinates (contravariantly).

The dot product of two four-vectors v and u is defined as

$$\mathsf{v} \cdot \mathsf{u} \equiv v_4 u_4 - \mathbf{v} \cdot \mathbf{u} \equiv \sum^{---+} v_\mu u_\mu \equiv v_\mu u_\mu. \tag{5}$$

We use different characters for the magnitudes of three- and four-vectors[1]:

$$\begin{aligned} v^2 &= \mathbf{v} \cdot \mathbf{v} = v_1{}^2 + v_2{}^2 + v_3{}^2 \\ \mathsf{v}^2 &= \mathsf{v} \cdot \mathsf{v} = -v_1{}^2 - v_2{}^2 - v_3{}^2 + v_4{}^2. \end{aligned} \tag{6}$$

Unless otherwise specified, *in this and in the following chapters the sums over space-time tensor indices must be understood to be always* $- - - +$.

[1] To avoid a misunderstanding of our use of type, the characters employed are shown below:

k, p, q, v, x, A, B, etc., are four-vectors
k, p, q, v, x, A, B, etc., are three-vectors
k, p, q, v, x, A, B, etc., are the magnitudes of four-vectors
k, p, q, v, x, A, B, etc., are the magnitudes of three-vectors

The definitions in (5) could be derived from the usual definition of scalar product by introducing covariant and contravariant components and assuming a metric:

(7) $$\delta_{\mu\nu}' = \begin{vmatrix} -1 & 0 & 0 & 0 \\ 0 & -1 & 0 & 0 \\ 0 & 0 & -1 & 0 \\ 0 & 0 & 0 & 1 \end{vmatrix}.$$

Since, however, we always use cartesian orthogonal axes[1], the distinction between covariant and contravariant components is unnecessary and is not made.

The symbol $\delta_{\mu\nu}'$ can be used to relate our $- - - +$ sums to the conventional ones. For instance,

(8) $$\begin{aligned} a_{\mu\nu}b_{\nu\lambda} &\equiv -a_{\mu1}b_{1\lambda} - a_{\mu2}b_{2\lambda} - a_{\mu3}b_{3\lambda} + a_{\mu4}b_{4\lambda} \\ &\equiv \overset{---+}{\sum_{\nu}} a_{\mu\nu}b_{\nu\lambda} = \overset{++++}{\sum_{\sigma\rho}} \delta_{\sigma\rho}' a_{\mu\sigma} b_{\rho\lambda}. \end{aligned}$$

Observe also that $\delta_{\mu\nu}'$ replaces the identity matrix in our summation convention:

(9) $$\delta_{\mu\nu}' x_\nu \equiv \overset{---+}{\sum_{\nu}} \delta_{\mu\nu}' x_\nu = \overset{++++}{\sum_{\nu}} \delta_{\mu\nu} x_\nu = x_\mu.$$

Some care must be used in connection with the four-gradient operator $\Box$, since its components are usually given in the covariant form $\partial/\partial x_\mu$. We introduce the contravariant components ∂_μ of the gradient as follows[2]:

(10) $$\Box_\mu = \partial_\mu = (\delta_{\mu\mu}')\frac{\partial}{\partial x_\mu} \qquad \left(\partial_i = -\frac{\partial}{\partial x_i} = -\nabla_i,\ \partial_t = \frac{\partial}{\partial t}\right).$$

Observe that, consistently with (5), we must write

(11) $$\partial_\mu v_\mu = \nabla \cdot \mathbf{v} + \frac{\partial v_4}{\partial t}; \qquad \Box^2 = \partial_\mu \partial_\mu = \frac{\partial^2}{\partial t^2} - \nabla^2.$$

The energy momentum four-vector $\mathbf{p}$ has components p_μ (or p_i, E). From (5) it is found that its square $E^2 - p^2$ is the square of the rest mass. The quantum mechanical transformations 1.12(3), (7) assume the form

(12) $$p_\mu \rightarrow i\partial_\mu \qquad \left(p_i = -i\frac{\partial}{\partial x_i},\quad p_t = E = i\frac{\partial}{\partial t}\right);$$

[1] Obviously this restriction does not exclude the possibility of using other systems of coordinates in three-dimensional space, as is usual in nonrelativistic theory.

[2] Observe that the covariant and contravariant components of the metric tensor (7) are identical. The parentheses in (10) and (13) are written to indicate that there are no sums over μ or ν.

one of the conveniences of a consistent contravariant notation is the elimination of the difference in sign between the space and the time components in these transformations.

If A_μ (or A_i, Φ where **A** is the vector and Φ the electrostatic potential) are the components of the electromagnetic four-vector potential, the doubly contravariant components of the field tensors are

$$F_{\mu\nu} = \partial_\mu A_\nu - \partial_\nu A_\mu = (\delta_{\mu\mu}')\frac{\partial}{\partial x_\mu} A_\nu - (\delta_{\nu\nu}')\frac{\partial}{\partial x_\nu} A_\mu; \tag{13}$$

these are related to the usual electric and magnetic fields as follows:

$$\begin{aligned} E_i &= F_{i4} = -\frac{\partial \Phi}{\partial x_i} - \frac{\partial A_i}{\partial t}, \\ H_i &= -F_{jk} = \frac{\partial A_k}{\partial x_j} - \frac{\partial A_j}{\partial x_k} \qquad (ijk \text{ cyclic}). \end{aligned} \tag{14}$$

6.12 Relativistic Wave Equations for Free Particles

a. Klein-Gordon Equation. From the relativistic mass-energy relation, which, in the notation of 6.11, is written

$$\mathsf{p}^2 - m^2 = 0 \tag{1}$$

and the quantum mechanical substitutions 6.11(12), we obtain the relativistic wave equation (Klein and Gordon)

$$(\Box^2 + m^2)\psi = 0 \qquad \left[\frac{\partial^2 \psi}{\partial t^2} = (\nabla^2 - m^2)\psi\right], \tag{2}$$

which must be satisfied by the wave function of all free particles. For $m = 0$, (2) becomes the law of propagation of each component of the electromagnetic field.

However (2) does not describe the relations between the different components of a many-component field, and thus it does not account completely for the propagation of fields corresponding to particles with spin. We know that the electromagnetic field satisfies the more restrictive Maxwell's equations. In a similar manner, particles of spin $\frac{1}{2}$ are properly described by the Dirac equation.

b. The γ Matrices. Dirac searched for a set of linear differential equations for the components of a complex, many-component wave function. In order to obtain these equations without changing the fundamental quantum mechanical operators for E and p [6.11(12)], we must obviously start from a linear mass-energy relation.

It is not possible to linearize (1) by using the laws of commutative algebra. At most, it can be linearized in one of the variables, say the energy, by writing

$$E = \pm\sqrt{p^2 + m^2}, \tag{1'}$$

with the very significant result that an ambiguity appears in the sign.

But (1) can be linearized in E and p_i if we use noncommutative coefficients. We must look for an expression of the form

$$\gamma_\mu p_\mu = -\boldsymbol{\gamma}\cdot\mathbf{p} + \gamma_4 p_4 = m, \tag{3}$$

which, however, must not contradict (1). By multiplying (3) by itself, we obtain

$$(\gamma_\mu p_\mu)(\gamma_\nu p_\nu) = m^2, \tag{4}$$

which reduces to (1), provided that the four γ_μ anticommute:

$$\gamma_\mu\gamma_\nu = -\gamma_\nu\gamma_\mu \qquad (\mu \neq \nu) \tag{5}$$

and

$$\gamma_i^2 = (\gamma_i)(\gamma_i) = -1, \quad \gamma_4^2 = (\gamma_4)(\gamma_4) = 1; \tag{6}$$

in short;

$$\tfrac{1}{2}(\gamma_\mu\gamma_\nu + \gamma_\nu\gamma_\mu) = \delta_{\mu\nu}'. \tag{7}$$

We shall see that $\boldsymbol{\gamma}, \gamma_4$ is a four-vector only in the sense that the expectation values of the operators $\gamma_4\gamma_\mu$ transform like the components of a four-vector (6.14).

The sign of m in (3) can be chosen arbitrarily. We assign the + sign to "particles," and we shall see that with this convention the − sign corresponds to "antiparticles"; $m = 0$ will be treated separately (8.23a).

It is customary to define also[1]

$$\gamma_5 = \gamma_1\gamma_2\gamma_3\gamma_4. \tag{8}$$

Observe that

$$\gamma_5\gamma_5 = -1, \qquad \gamma_5\gamma_\mu = -\gamma_\mu\gamma_5.$$

If we write

$$i\gamma_i\gamma_j = \sigma_k \qquad (ijk \text{ cyclic}), \tag{9}$$

we recognize that the σ_k have all the properties of the Pauli spin matrices. For instance,

$$\sigma_1\sigma_2 = ii(\gamma_2\gamma_3\gamma_3\gamma_1) = \gamma_2\gamma_1 = -\gamma_1\gamma_2 = i\sigma_3 \tag{10}$$

[compare with 1.14(8)].

[1] Other definitions of γ_5 differ by factors of i from the one given here. Schweber, Bethe, and DeHoffmann use $\gamma_5 = \gamma_4\gamma_1\gamma_2\gamma_3$, which differs in sign from our definition. Other authors use $\gamma_5 = \begin{pmatrix} 0 & 1 \\ 1 & 0 \end{pmatrix}$, which differs by a factor i [see (13d)].

Thus we obtain a relativistic generalization of the spin (a four-dimensional antisymmetrical tensor of zero trace; see 6.14):

(11) $$\sigma_{\mu\nu} = \frac{i}{2}(\gamma_\mu\gamma_\nu - \gamma_\nu\gamma_\mu) \qquad \sigma_{ij} = \sigma_k \quad \text{for } ijk \text{ cyclic.}$$

For future reference, it is also useful to observe that

$$i\gamma_4\gamma_5\gamma_1 = i\gamma_4\gamma_1\gamma_2\gamma_3\gamma_4\gamma_1 = i\gamma_2\gamma_3 = \sigma_1,$$
$$i\gamma_4\gamma_5\gamma_2 = \sigma_2, \qquad i\gamma_4\gamma_5\gamma_3 = \sigma_3,$$

and that we can write another relativistic generalization of the spin (a four-dimensional pseudovector, see 6.14):

(12) $$\sigma_\mu = i\gamma_4\gamma_5\gamma_\mu.$$

It is found that the relations (7) can be satisfied if the γ are 4×4 matrices. Then the four γ_μ, the six independent $\gamma_\mu\gamma_\nu$, the four independent $\gamma_\mu\gamma_\nu\gamma_\lambda$, together with γ_5 and the unit matrix, form a complete set of 16 independent 4×4 matrices.

A useful, but not unique, representation of the γ matrices can be obtained in terms of Pauli's 2×2 spin matrices 1.14(7). If we write

(13*a*) $$\gamma_i = \begin{pmatrix} 0 & \sigma_i \\ -\sigma_i & 0 \end{pmatrix}, \qquad \gamma_4 = \begin{pmatrix} 1 & 0 \\ 0 & -1 \end{pmatrix},$$

we can easily verify that the relations (5) to (10) are satisfied. In this representation the other independent 4×4 matrices are (with i, j, k cyclic)

(13*b*) $$\gamma_i\gamma_j = -i\begin{pmatrix} \sigma_k & 0 \\ 0 & \sigma_k \end{pmatrix}, \qquad \gamma_4\gamma_i = \begin{pmatrix} 0 & \sigma_i \\ \sigma_i & 0 \end{pmatrix}$$

(the matrices $\gamma_4\gamma_i$ are sometimes called the α_i matrices),

(13*c*) $$\gamma_i\gamma_j\gamma_k = i\begin{pmatrix} 0 & -1 \\ 1 & 0 \end{pmatrix}, \quad \gamma_i\gamma_j\gamma_4 = i\begin{pmatrix} -\sigma_k & 0 \\ 0 & \sigma_k \end{pmatrix},$$

(13*d*) $$\gamma_5 = \gamma_1\gamma_2\gamma_3\gamma_4 = i\begin{pmatrix} 0 & 1 \\ 1 & 0 \end{pmatrix},$$

and, naturally, the unit matrix, which is

$$1 = \begin{pmatrix} 1 & 0 \\ 0 & 1 \end{pmatrix}.$$

In the representation (13) the three matrices γ_i are antihermitian; moreover, all four γ_μ are unitary:

(14*a*) $$\gamma_i^\dagger = \gamma_i^{-1} = -\gamma_i; \qquad \gamma_4^\dagger = \gamma_4^{-1} = \gamma_4;$$

in short,

(14*b*) $$\gamma_\mu^{\dagger} = \gamma_\mu^{-1} = \gamma_4\gamma_\mu\gamma_4.$$

c. Slashed Vectors. Expressions of the type $\gamma_\mu A_\mu$ occur frequently in the development of the theory. It is convenient to use, with Feynman, the abbreviation

(15) $$\gamma_\mu A_\mu = \gamma_4 A_4 - \boldsymbol{\gamma}\cdot\mathbf{A} \equiv \not{A};$$

it is useful to note that from (14*b*) we have

(15′) $$\not{A}^{\dagger} = \gamma_4\not{A}\gamma_4.$$

A slashed vector is a scalar. For the commutation rules of slashed vectors with the γ matrices and with other slashed vectors we obtain

(16*a*) $$\gamma_\mu\not{A} = -\not{A}\gamma_\mu + 2A_\mu;$$

(16*b*) $$\not{A}\not{B} = -\not{B}\not{A} + 2\mathsf{A}\cdot\mathsf{B};\ (\not{A}\not{B} = -\not{B}\not{A} \text{ if } \mathsf{A}\cdot\mathsf{B} = 0);$$

(16*c*) $$\not{A}\not{A} = \mathsf{A}^2;$$

(16*d*) $$\not{A}\not{B} = \mathsf{A}\cdot\mathsf{B} - \frac{i}{2}\sigma_{\mu\nu}(A_\mu B_\nu - A_\nu B_\mu);$$

$$(\not{A}\not{B} = \not{B}\not{A} = \mathsf{A}\cdot\mathsf{B} \text{ if } \mathbf{A}\times\mathbf{B} = 0).$$

d. The Dirac Equation. The Dirac equation is obtained by substituting the familiar quantum mechanical energy and momentum operators in (3). Thus it can be written

(17*a*) $$(i\not{\partial} - m)\psi = 0,$$

or, more explicitly[1],

(17*b*) $$\left(i\gamma_4\frac{\partial}{\partial t} + i\boldsymbol{\gamma}\cdot\boldsymbol{\nabla} - m\right)\psi = 0.$$

Since the γ_μ are 4×4 matrices operating on the wave function ψ, this must have four components. It can be considered as a one-column matrix:

(18) $$\psi = \begin{pmatrix} \psi_{\mathrm{I}} \\ \psi_{\mathrm{II}} \\ \psi_{\mathrm{III}} \\ \psi_{\mathrm{IV}} \end{pmatrix}.$$

Roman subscripts are used to point out that there is no connection with the coordinate axes: the wave function is not a four-vector! For Roman

[1] Note that

$$\not{\partial} = \gamma_4\partial_4 - \gamma_1\partial_1 - \gamma_2\partial_2 - \gamma_3\partial_3 = \gamma_4\frac{\partial}{\partial x_4} + \gamma_1\frac{\partial}{\partial x_1} + \gamma_2\frac{\partial}{\partial x_2} + \gamma_3\frac{\partial}{\partial x_3}.$$

subscripts the conventional summation rule holds and the identity matrix is δ_{RS}.

Naturally, the elements of the operators acting on ψ (and in particular the γ matrices) are also labeled by roman subscripts; to the effect of multiplication the Dirac wave function itself can be considered as a 4×4 matrix whose only nonvanishing elements are those in the first column:

$$\psi = \begin{pmatrix} \psi_{\mathrm{I}} & 0 & 0 & 0 \\ \psi_{\mathrm{II}} & 0 & 0 & 0 \\ \psi_{\mathrm{III}} & 0 & 0 & 0 \\ \psi_{\mathrm{IV}} & 0 & 0 & 0 \end{pmatrix}.$$

The hermitian adjoint wave function is

(19) $$\psi^\dagger = \widetilde{\psi_{\mathrm{I}}^* \quad \psi_{\mathrm{II}}^* \quad \psi_{\mathrm{III}}^* \quad \psi_{\mathrm{IV}}^*}.$$

Observe that the product of two Dirac states ψ and ϕ can be written either as $\psi^\dagger\phi$ or as $\psi\phi^\dagger$. In the first case we obtain a matrix whose only nonvanishing element is in the upper left corner. Thus $\psi^\dagger\phi$ is a number:

(20) $$\psi^\dagger\phi = \psi_{\mathrm{I}}^*\phi_{\mathrm{I}} + \psi_{\mathrm{II}}^*\phi_{\mathrm{II}} + \psi_{\mathrm{III}}^*\phi_{\mathrm{III}} + \psi_{\mathrm{IV}}^*\phi_{\mathrm{IV}}$$

The product $\psi\phi^\dagger$, instead, is a complete matrix which, in the general case, has no vanishing elements. We can write

(21) $$(\psi\phi^\dagger)_{RS} = \psi_R\phi_S^*,$$

where capital indices such as S, P, Q, R [1] stand for Roman numerals.

Clearly (17) admits plane-wave solutions of the form

(22) $$\psi = ue^{-ip\cdot x} = ue^{i(\mathbf{p}\cdot\mathbf{x}-Et)}$$

if the four-component quantity u (Dirac spinor) satisfies

(23) $$(\not{p} - m)u = 0;$$

this equation does not contain differential operators, and u is independent of x and t.

The adjoint Dirac function (19) satisfies the adjoint equation

(24) $$\psi^\dagger(-i\gamma_\mu{}^\dagger\partial_\mu - m) = 0,$$

where the derivatives ∂_μ operate to the left.

Introducing

(25) $$\bar{\psi} = \psi^\dagger\gamma_4,$$

[1] The student is expected to know the classical meaning of these letters.

(24) can be written[1]

$$\bar{\psi}(-i\overleftarrow{\partial\!\!\!/} - m) = 0, \tag{26}$$

again with the understanding that the derivatives in the slashed vector $\overleftarrow{\partial\!\!\!/}$ operate to the left.

In the representation (13)

$$\bar{\psi} = \widetilde{\psi_{\rm I}^* \quad \psi_{\rm II}^* \quad -\psi_{\rm III}^* \quad -\psi_{\rm IV}^*}. \tag{27}$$

6.13 *Interpretation of the Solutions of the Dirac Equation*

a. Nonrelativistic Approximation. If we multiply to the left by γ_4 the Dirac equation 6.12(17*b*), we obtain

$$\left(i\frac{\partial}{\partial t} + i\gamma_4\boldsymbol{\gamma}\cdot\boldsymbol{\nabla} - m\gamma_4\right)\psi = 0. \tag{1}$$

We see that the operator

$$\mathcal{H} = -i\gamma_4\boldsymbol{\gamma}\cdot\boldsymbol{\nabla} + m\gamma_4 \tag{2}$$

has the meaning of the Hamiltonian of a free Dirac particle.

But, from 6.12(13),

$$\gamma_4\gamma_i = \begin{pmatrix} 0 & 1 \\ 1 & 0 \end{pmatrix}\sigma_i,$$

and thus the Dirac equation for energy E can be written

$$\left[\begin{pmatrix} 1 & 0 \\ 0 & 1 \end{pmatrix}E + i\begin{pmatrix} 0 & 1 \\ 1 & 0 \end{pmatrix}\boldsymbol{\sigma}\cdot\boldsymbol{\nabla} - \begin{pmatrix} 1 & 0 \\ 0 & -1 \end{pmatrix}m\right]\psi = 0. \tag{3}$$

Let us now consider separately the *upper* and *lower* components of ψ:

$$\psi = \psi_U + \psi_L, \quad \text{with} \quad \psi_U = \begin{pmatrix} \psi_{\rm I} \\ \psi_{\rm II} \\ 0 \\ 0 \end{pmatrix}, \quad \psi_L = \begin{pmatrix} 0 \\ 0 \\ \psi_{\rm III} \\ \psi_{\rm IV} \end{pmatrix}. \tag{4}$$

Then (3) splits into two parts:

$$\begin{cases} E\psi_U + i\boldsymbol{\sigma}\cdot\boldsymbol{\nabla}\psi_L - m\psi_U = 0 \\ E\psi_L + i\boldsymbol{\sigma}\cdot\boldsymbol{\nabla}\psi_U + m\psi_L = 0 \end{cases} \tag{5}$$

[1] Using (14*b*), we have

$$\psi^\dagger(-i\gamma_\mu{}^\dagger\overleftarrow{\partial}_\mu - m) = \psi^\dagger(-i\gamma_4\gamma_\mu\gamma_4\overleftarrow{\partial}_\mu - \gamma_4 m\gamma_4) = \bar{\psi}(-i\gamma_\mu\overleftarrow{\partial}_\mu - m)\gamma_4 = 0.$$

From these we have

$$\psi_U = -i\,\frac{\boldsymbol{\sigma}\cdot\boldsymbol{\nabla}\,\psi_L}{E-m}$$

(6)

$$\psi_L = -i\,\frac{\boldsymbol{\sigma}\cdot\boldsymbol{\nabla}\,\psi_U}{E+m}\;;$$

in the nonrelativistic approximation $E \approx m$ and

(7) $$\psi_U \gg \psi_L.$$

For $E \approx m$ the upper components are *large* and the lower components are *small*; the situation is reversed in negative energy states, $E \approx -m$.

For positive energy and $p \ll m$, we can write $E + m \approx 2m$. Thus the equation for the large components becomes [substituting the second of (6) into the first and considering the anticommutation relation of the σ_i]

(8) $$(E-m)\psi_U = -\frac{(\boldsymbol{\sigma}\cdot\boldsymbol{\nabla})(\boldsymbol{\sigma}\cdot\boldsymbol{\nabla})}{2m}\,\psi_U = -\frac{1}{2m}\,\nabla^2\psi_U.$$

This is the Schrödinger equation for a free particle of mass m and kinetic energy $E - m$.

The two-component wave functions ψ_U can be identified with a non-relativistic Pauli spinor.

b. The Four Solutions for Given Momentum. For assigned momentum **p** there are four independent solutions of the Dirac equation, $\psi_{(1)}, \psi_{(2)}, \psi_{(3)}$, and $\psi_{(4)}$. These are of the form

(9) $$\psi_{(s)} = u_{(s)}e^{-i(Et-\mathbf{p}\cdot\mathbf{x})} \qquad (s = 1, 2, 3, 4),$$

where $E = \pm\sqrt{p^2 + m^2}$ and the $u_{(s)}$ must satisfy the equation

(10) $$(\not{p} - m)u_{(s)} = 0.$$

Then, if ζ is an arbitrary Pauli spinor, we learn from (6) that the $u_{(s)}$ have the form

for $E > 0$ for $E < 0$

(11) $$\begin{pmatrix} \zeta \\ \dfrac{\boldsymbol{\sigma}\cdot\mathbf{p}}{|E|+m}\,\zeta \end{pmatrix} \qquad \begin{pmatrix} -\dfrac{\boldsymbol{\sigma}\cdot\mathbf{p}}{|E|+m}\,\zeta \\ \zeta \end{pmatrix}.$$

By choosing $\zeta = \begin{pmatrix}1\\0\end{pmatrix}$ and $\begin{pmatrix}0\\1\end{pmatrix}$ we can write four independent u's for assigned **p**:

$$
\begin{array}{cccc}
u_{(1)} & u_{(2)} & u_{(3)} & u_{(4)} \\
E > 0 & E > 0 & E < 0 & E < 0 \\
\text{spin up}^1 & \text{spin down} & \text{spin up} & \text{spin down}
\end{array}
$$

$$
(12)\qquad
\begin{pmatrix} 1 \\ 0 \\ \dfrac{p_z}{E+m} \\ \dfrac{p_x + ip_y}{E+m} \end{pmatrix}
\quad
\begin{pmatrix} 0 \\ 1 \\ \dfrac{p_x - ip_y}{E+m} \\ \dfrac{-p_z}{E+m} \end{pmatrix}
\quad
\begin{pmatrix} \dfrac{-p_z}{|E|+m} \\ \dfrac{-p_x - ip_y}{|E|+m} \\ 1 \\ 0 \end{pmatrix}
\quad
\begin{pmatrix} \dfrac{-p_x + ip_y}{|E|+m} \\ \dfrac{p_z}{|E|+m} \\ 0 \\ 1 \end{pmatrix}
$$

It is easily verified that for $\mathbf{p} = 0$ the eigenvalues of the Hamiltonian (2) are $+m$ for $u_{(1)}$ and $u_{(2)}$ and $-m$ for $u_{(3)}$ and $u_{(4)}$.

The spinors (11) and (12) are not normalized to unity, but they can be multiplied by a normalization factor

$$
(13)\qquad \left[1 + \frac{p^2}{(|E| + m)^2}\right]^{-\frac{1}{2}} = \left[\frac{|E| + m}{2\,|E|}\right]^{\frac{1}{2}},
$$

in order to obtain the usual normalization in a unit three-volume, $u^\dagger u = 1$. This normalization, however, is not relativistically invariant.

c. Expectation Values of the Dirac Matrices. Velocity and Current. With reference to the representation 6.12(13), it is seen that the expectation value of the Dirac matrices is large (≈ 1) in the nonrelativistic approximation if the upper left 2×2 submatrix is nonzero.

Thus among the 16 matrices in 6.12(13) 1, γ_4, $\gamma_i\gamma_j$, and $\gamma_i\gamma_j\gamma_4$ are the only ones to have a large nonrelativistic limit which is, respectively, 1, 1, $-i\sigma_k$, and $-i\sigma_k$.

The expectation value of $\gamma_4\gamma_i$ has the meaning of the ith velocity component (in units of c); this can be proved by making use of the Hamiltonian (2):

$$
(14)\qquad \frac{dx_i}{dt} = \frac{1}{i}(x_i\mathcal{H} - \mathcal{H}x_i) = -\gamma_4\gamma_i\left(x_i\frac{\partial}{\partial x_i} - \frac{\partial}{\partial x_i}x_i\right) = \gamma_4\gamma_i.
$$

In accord with this meaning the expectation values of $e\gamma_4\gamma_i$ are the components of the electric current; but these include not only the part

[1] The $u_{(s)}$ are not eigenvalues of $\sigma_z = \begin{pmatrix} \sigma_z & 0 \\ 0 & \sigma_z \end{pmatrix}$, and the classification according to spin up or down is appropriate only in the nonrelativistic limit.

due to the motion of the charge of the electron e but also the **curl** of the density of its magnetic moment, $e/2m$.

To prove this important statement, we use 6.12(26) and 6.12(17) and write the first component in the form

$$e\psi^\dagger\gamma_4\gamma_1\psi = \frac{e}{2m}[(\bar{\psi}m)\gamma_1\psi + \bar{\psi}\gamma_1(m\psi)]$$

$$= \frac{e}{2mi}[(\bar{\psi}\overleftarrow{\partial\!\!\!/})\gamma_1\psi - \bar{\psi}\gamma_1(\partial\!\!\!/\psi)]$$

$$= \frac{e}{2mi}[(\partial_4\bar{\psi}\gamma_4 - \partial_i\bar{\psi}\gamma_i)\gamma_1\psi - \bar{\psi}\gamma_1(\gamma_4\partial_4\psi - \gamma_i\partial_i\psi)].$$

Then it is seen that (for solutions of definite energy) the terms in ∂_4 cancel and those in ∂_1 are (nonrelativistically, for $\bar{\psi} \approx \psi^\dagger$) the current of a spinless particle

(15) $$\frac{e}{2mi}\left(-\frac{\partial\bar{\psi}}{\partial x_1}\psi + \bar{\psi}\frac{\partial\psi}{\partial x_1}\right);$$

finally, the terms in ∂_2 and ∂_3 give

(16) $$\frac{e}{2mi}\left(\frac{\partial\bar{\psi}}{\partial x_2}\gamma_2\gamma_1\psi + \frac{\partial\bar{\psi}}{\partial x_3}\gamma_3\gamma_1 - \bar{\psi}\gamma_1\gamma_2\frac{\partial\psi}{\partial x_2} - \bar{\psi}\gamma_1\gamma_3\frac{\partial\psi}{\partial x_3}\right)$$

$$= \frac{e}{2m}\left[\frac{\partial}{\partial x_2}(\bar{\psi}\sigma_3\psi) - \frac{\partial}{\partial x_3}(\bar{\psi}\sigma_2\psi)\right] = \frac{e}{2m}[\mathbf{curl}\,(\bar{\psi}\boldsymbol{\sigma}\psi)]_1,$$

which is the electric current produced by a density of magnetic moment $\approx(e/2m)\psi^\dagger\psi$ in the direction of the spin.

It is interesting to observe that although $\gamma_4\gamma_i = dx_i/dt$ has small expectation values, $(dx_i/dt)^2 = (\gamma_4\gamma_i)^2 = 1$ is large. This nonintuitive conclusion can be made plausible by using the uncertainty principle; it is said to correspond to a "zitterbewegung."

6.14 Invariance under Rotations, Inversion, and Lorentz Transformations

a. The General Lorentz Transformation. Since Lorentz's transformations are particular rotations in space time, we may treat them together with all other possible rotations and inversion of axes. Consider the general transformation

(1) $$x_\mu' = a_{\mu\nu}x_\nu$$

[sums over equal indices are understood and have the meaning defined by 6.11(5), so that the identity transformation is $a_{\mu\nu} = \delta_{\mu\nu}'$] with the orthogonality restriction

(2) $$a_{\mu\nu}a_{\mu\lambda} = \delta_{\nu\lambda}',$$

which is required to ensure the invariance of the dot product[1].

By the use of ++++ sums (1) can be written

(1′) $$x_\mu' = \sum_{\lambda\nu}^{++++} \delta_{\mu\nu}' a_{\lambda\nu} x_\nu,$$

which in the usual notation of covariant and contravariant components takes the form

(1″) $$x'^\mu = \sum_{\nu}^{++++} a_\nu{}^\mu x^\nu \quad \text{with} \quad a_\nu{}^\mu = \sum_{\lambda}^{++++} \delta_{\mu\lambda}' a_{\lambda\nu}.$$

If (2)[2] is satisfied, the determinant of the $\alpha_\nu{}^\mu$ can assume two values,

(3) $$\det a_\mu{}^\nu = \pm 1,$$

according to whether the four-volume[3] remains unchanged or changes sign under the transformation in (1).

If (3) is satisfied with the + sign, the transformation is called *proper*: it does not include reflections of an odd number of axes. In the opposite case the transformation is *improper* and includes parity and time-inversion transformations.

b. Transformation of ψ. The postulates of relativity and conservation of parity require that the form and the numerical coefficients of the Dirac equation remain unchanged in the transformation $x_\mu \to x_\mu'$. However, the four-vector $i\partial_\mu$ transforms like the coordinates, and the state ψ may also change into a different state ψ'. Let us define an operator S such that[4]

(4) $$\psi' = S\psi.$$

Then the Dirac equation

(5) $$(\gamma_\mu i\partial_\mu - m)\psi = 0$$

must become

(6*a*) $$(\gamma_\mu i\partial_\mu' - m)\psi' = (\gamma_\mu a_{\mu\nu} i\partial_\nu - m)S\psi = 0,$$

[1] $u_\mu' v_\mu' = a_{\mu\nu}u_\nu a_{\mu\lambda}v_\lambda = a_{\mu\nu}a_{\mu\lambda}u_\nu v_\lambda$.

[2] In covariant notation (2) becomes $\sum_{\mu}^{++++} a_\mu{}^\nu a_\lambda{}^\mu = \sum_{\mu}^{++++} a^{\mu\nu} a_{\lambda\mu} = \delta_\lambda{}^\nu$.

[3] $dx_1'\, dx_2'\, dx_3'\, dx_4' = (\det a_\mu{}^\nu)\, dx_1\, dx_2\, dx_3\, dx_4$.

[4] More precisely, $\psi_R'(\mathbf{x}') = \sum_S S_{RS}\, \psi_S(\mathbf{x})$, where x_μ' and x_ν are related by (1); R and S stand for Roman indices, introduced in 6.12d.

with γ_μ and m unchanged. If we multiply to the left by S^{-1}, we obtain

(6b) $$(S^{-1}\gamma_\mu S a_{\mu\nu} i\partial_\nu - m)\psi = 0.$$

But (5), (6a), and (6b) must have the same form, for which we need

$$S^{-1}\gamma_\mu S a_{\mu\nu} = \gamma_\nu.$$

By multiplying both sides by $a_{\lambda\nu}$ and using (2) we conclude that the transformation matrix S must satisfy the equation

(7) $$S^{-1}\gamma_\lambda S = a_{\lambda\nu}\gamma_\nu.$$

In words, S must be such that $S^{-1}\gamma_\mu S$ transforms like the coordinate x_μ.

c. The Transformation Matrices S. We can now verify that in our representation 6.12(13) the transformation matrices S can be written for all cases of interest:

Rotation of angle θ around space axis i [1]:

(8) $$S_{R,i} = \exp\left(-\tfrac{1}{2}\theta\gamma_j\gamma_k\right), \qquad (i, j, k \text{ cyclic}).$$

Lorentz transformation with speed v along axis i [2]:

(9) $$S_{L,i} = \exp\left(-\tfrac{1}{2}\theta\gamma_4\gamma_i\right), \qquad (v = \tanh\theta),$$

Inversion of space axis i:

(10) $$S_{P,i} = \pm\gamma_j\gamma_k\gamma_4, \qquad (i, j, k \text{ cyclic}).$$

[1] For instance, for space rotation around the axis 3

$$S_{R,3} = \exp\left(-\tfrac{1}{2}\theta\gamma_1\gamma_2\right); \qquad (S_{R,3})^{-1} = \exp\left(\tfrac{1}{2}\theta\gamma_1\gamma_2\right) = (S_{R,3})^\dagger.$$

We see that $S_{R,3}^{-1}\gamma_3 S_{R,3}$ remains invariant and that the other $S_{R,3}^{-1}\gamma_i S_{R,3}$ transforms like the coordinates:

$$(S_{R,3})^{-1}\gamma_1(S_{R,3}) = \exp\left(\tfrac{1}{2}\theta\gamma_1\gamma_2\right)\gamma_1\exp\left(-\tfrac{1}{2}\theta\gamma_1\gamma_2\right) = e^{\theta\gamma_1\gamma_2}\gamma_1$$

$$= \left(1 + \theta\gamma_1\gamma_2 - \frac{1}{2}\theta^2 - \frac{1}{3!}\theta^3\gamma_1\gamma_2 + \frac{1}{4!}\theta^4 + \cdots\right)\gamma_1 = \gamma_1\cos\theta + \gamma_2\sin\theta.$$

[2] For instance, for motion along the axis 1

$$S_{L,1} = \exp\left(-\tfrac{1}{2}\theta\gamma_4\gamma_1\right) = (S_{L,1})^\dagger; \qquad (S_{L,1})^{-1} = \exp\left(\tfrac{1}{2}\theta\gamma_4\gamma_1\right).$$

It is easily verified that $S_{L,1}^{-1}\gamma_1 S_{L,1}$ transforms like x_1 under the Lorentz transformation:

$$(S_{L,1})^{-1}\gamma_1(S_{L,1}) = \exp\left(\tfrac{1}{2}\theta\gamma_4\gamma_1\right)\gamma_1\exp\left(-\tfrac{1}{2}\theta\gamma_4\gamma_1\right) = \gamma_1 e^{-\theta\gamma_4\gamma_1}$$

$$= \gamma_1\left(1 - \theta\gamma_4\gamma_1 + \frac{\theta^2}{2} - \frac{\theta^3}{3!}\gamma_4\gamma_1 + \frac{1}{4!}\theta^4 + \cdots\right) = \gamma_1\cosh\theta - \gamma_4\sinh\theta$$

$$= (\gamma_1 - v\gamma_4)\cosh\theta = \frac{\gamma_1 - v\gamma_4}{\sqrt{1 - v^2}}.$$

Inversion of three-space axes (*parity operation*)[1]:

(11) $$S_{P,r} = \pm\gamma_4.$$

Inversion of time axis:

(12) $$S_{P,4} = \pm\gamma_1\gamma_2\gamma_3.$$

We introduce at this point the transformation matrices for *time reversal* S_T and *charge conjugation* S_C, using the definitions valid in the representation in 6.12(13):

(13) $$S_T = \pm\sigma_2 K = \pm i\gamma_3\gamma_1 K$$

and

(14) $$S_C = \pm\gamma_2 K,$$

where K is the operator of complex conjugation discussed in 1.17.

The study of these operators and the discussion of their physical meaning is postponed until 6.21, following the formulation of the electromagnetic interaction of Dirac particles presented in 6.15.

d. Transformation of $\bar{\psi}$. The transformation of $\bar{\psi}$ is obtained from its definition:

(15) $$(\bar{\psi})' = (\psi')^\dagger\gamma_4 = (S\psi)^\dagger\gamma_4 = \psi^\dagger S^\dagger\gamma_4.$$

It is easily verified that for (8), (9), (11), and (14)

$$S^\dagger\gamma_4 = \gamma_4 S^{-1}$$

and thus in these cases

(16) $$(\bar{\psi})' = \psi^\dagger\gamma_4 S^{-1} = \bar{\psi}S^{-1}.$$

The operation of time axis inversion (12) and that of time reversal (13) behave differently:

$$S_T{}^\dagger\gamma_4 = -\gamma_4 S_T{}^{-1};$$

Thus for (12) and (13)

(17) $$(\bar{\psi})' = -\bar{\psi}S^{-1}.$$

e. The Five Tensors of Dirac Theory. We are now in position to discuss the tensor properties of the expectation values of the 16 Dirac matrices.

[1] From $S_P = (S_P)^{-1} = (S_P)^\dagger = \pm\gamma_4$ we obtain $(S_P)^{-1}\gamma_i S_P = \gamma_4\gamma_i\gamma_4 = -\gamma_i$, which shows that the γ_i's invert their signs. More generally, we could have written $S_P = \pm\gamma_4$ or $\pm i\gamma_4$ (Y-50a), but the choice $S_P = \pm i\gamma_4$ has no physical meaning (W-52a).

By using (4), (7), and (16) it is easily found that (for transformations noninverting time)

(18) $\bar{\psi}\psi$ is a scalar,

(19) $\bar{\psi}\gamma_\mu\psi$ is a four-vector,

and

(20) $i\bar{\psi}\gamma_\mu\gamma_\nu\psi$ is a tensor.

The proof is immediate

$$\bar{\psi}'\psi' = (\bar{\psi}S^{-1})(S\psi) = \bar{\psi}\psi,$$
$$\bar{\psi}'\gamma_\mu\psi' = (\bar{\psi}S^{-1})\,\gamma_\mu(S\psi) = a_{\mu\nu}\bar{\psi}\gamma_\nu\psi.$$

We now prove that

(21) $\bar{\psi}\gamma_5\psi$ is a pseudoscalar.

For this we observe that γ_5 can be written in 4! different ways by permuting the γ_μ's and compensating for the change in sign with the symbol $\varepsilon_{\mu\nu\lambda\kappa}$:

$$\gamma_5 = (\varepsilon_{\mu\nu\lambda\kappa}\gamma_\mu\gamma_\nu\gamma_\lambda\gamma_\kappa)_{\text{no sum}}.$$

If we sum these 4! equal expressions, we obtain

$$4!\,\gamma_5 = \sum_{\mu\nu\lambda\kappa}^{++++} \varepsilon_{\mu\nu\lambda\kappa}\gamma_\mu\gamma_\nu\gamma_\lambda\gamma_\kappa$$

Then (21) can be proved by making use, exceptionally, of covariant-contravariant notation and of all $++++$ sums:

$$\begin{aligned} 4!\,\bar{\psi}'\gamma_5\psi' &= \sum_{\mu\nu\lambda\kappa} \varepsilon_{\mu\nu\lambda\kappa}\bar{\psi}'\gamma^\mu\gamma^\nu\gamma^\lambda\gamma^\kappa\psi' \\ &= \sum_{\mu\nu\lambda\kappa} \varepsilon_{\mu\nu\lambda\kappa}\bar{\psi}S^{-1}\gamma^\mu SS^{-1}\gamma^\nu SS^{-1}\gamma^\lambda SS^{-1}\gamma^\kappa S\psi \\ &= \sum_{\mu\nu\lambda\kappa}\sum_{\alpha\beta\gamma\delta} \varepsilon_{\mu\nu\lambda\kappa}a_\alpha{}^\mu a_\beta{}^\nu a_\gamma{}^\lambda a_\delta{}^\kappa\bar{\psi}\gamma^\alpha\gamma^\beta\gamma^\gamma\gamma^\delta\psi \\ &= \sum_{\alpha\beta\gamma\delta} (\det a_\mu{}^\nu)\varepsilon_{\alpha\beta\gamma\delta}\bar{\psi}\gamma^\alpha\gamma^\beta\gamma^\gamma\gamma^\delta\psi = 4!\,(\det a_\mu{}^\nu)\bar{\psi}\gamma_5\psi. \end{aligned}$$

Finally, from (19) and (21), it follows that for all different $\mu\nu\lambda\kappa$

(22) $i\bar{\psi}\gamma_\mu\gamma_\nu\gamma_\lambda\psi = \pm i\bar{\psi}\gamma_5\gamma_\kappa\psi$ is a four-pseudovector.

In order to study the behavior of the tensor components under time reversal or inversion, we must consider (17); but we shall not discuss this question any further.

f. Nonrelativistic Approximation of Dirac Tensors. The tensors (18), (19), (20), (21), and (22) are all hermitian with the factors i as written. Some insight on the physical meaning of these tensors is obtained from the nonrelativistic approximation of their expectation values:

$$\text{(18')} \qquad \bar{\psi}\psi = \psi^\dagger\gamma_4\psi \approx \psi^\dagger\psi \approx 1$$

$$\text{(19')} \qquad \bar{\psi}\gamma_\mu\psi = \psi^\dagger\gamma_4\gamma_\mu\psi = \begin{cases} \mu = 4: & \psi^\dagger\psi \approx 1 \\ \mu \neq 4: & \psi^\dagger\gamma_4\gamma_i\psi \approx v_i \ll \sim 1. \end{cases}$$

Thus the scalar (18) reduces to the density, and the vector (19) is the density-velocity four-vector, which multiplied by the electric charge becomes the four-current (compare with 6.13c). For small velocities, $v \ll 1$, the space components of this vector are much smaller than the time components.

The diagonal elements of $\gamma_\mu\gamma_\nu$ are ± 1 and their expectation values are the same as those for (18). They can be eliminated from the tensor (20), which then becomes [see 6.12(11)]

$$\text{(20')} \qquad \frac{i}{2}\,\bar{\psi}(\gamma_\mu\gamma_\nu - \gamma_\nu\gamma_\mu)\psi = \frac{i}{2}\,\psi^\dagger\gamma_4(\gamma_\mu\gamma_\nu - \gamma_\nu\gamma_\mu)\psi$$

$$= \begin{cases} \mu, \nu \neq 4: & \dfrac{i}{2}\,\psi^\dagger\gamma_4(\gamma_i\gamma_j - \gamma_j\gamma_i)\psi = \psi^\dagger\gamma_4\sigma_k\psi \approx \psi^\dagger\sigma_k\psi \sim 1, \\ \mu \text{ or } \nu = 4: & \dfrac{i}{2}\,\psi^\dagger\gamma_4(\gamma_4\gamma_i - \gamma_i\gamma_4)\psi = i\psi^\dagger\gamma_i\psi \approx v_i \ll \sim 1. \end{cases}$$

For small velocities the components for μ or $\nu = 4$ are negligible compared to those for $\mu, \nu \neq 4$, which are the components of the spin. Relativistically, the small components of the tensor (20) differ by a factor γ_4 from the small components of the vector (19).

The pseudoscalar (21) is of the order of v and is small if $v \ll 1$; this can be seen by writing

$$\text{(21')} \qquad \begin{aligned} \bar{\psi}\gamma_5\psi &= \psi^\dagger\gamma_4\gamma_1\gamma_2\gamma_3\gamma_4\psi = -\psi^\dagger\gamma_1\gamma_2\gamma_3\psi \\ &= i\psi^\dagger\gamma_1\sigma_1\psi = i\psi^\dagger\gamma_2\sigma_2\psi = i\psi^\dagger\gamma_3\sigma_3\psi \\ &\approx i\psi^\dagger\boldsymbol{\gamma}\cdot\boldsymbol{\sigma}\psi \approx \mathbf{v}\cdot\boldsymbol{\sigma} \ll \sim 1. \end{aligned}$$

Nonrelativistically, the pseudovector (22) reduces to the spin, and in this sense its components are the same as those of the space part of the tensor (20′). However, relativistically, there is a difference of a factor γ_4:

$$\text{(22')} \qquad i\bar{\psi}\gamma_5\gamma_\kappa\psi = i\psi^\dagger\gamma_4\gamma_1\gamma_2\gamma_3\gamma_4\gamma_\kappa\psi = -i\psi^\dagger\gamma_1\gamma_2\gamma_3\gamma_\kappa\psi$$

$$= \begin{cases} \kappa \neq 4: & \psi^\dagger\sigma_k\psi \sim 1, \\ \kappa = 4: & -i\psi^\dagger\gamma_5\psi \ll \sim 1. \end{cases}$$

The tensor (20) and the pseudovector (22) are two different four-dimensional generalizations of the Pauli spin operators.

6.15 Electromagnetic Interaction

a. Point Charge: Electrons and Muons. The electromagnetic interaction of a Dirac particle of point charge e is obtained by adding to the components of the four-momentum the usual gage invariant terms

$$\mathbf{p} \rightarrow \mathbf{p} - e\mathbf{A}, \tag{1}$$

where **A** is the four-potential of components

$$A_x, \quad A_y, \quad A_z, \quad A_4 = \Phi. \tag{2}$$

Thus the Dirac equation becomes

$$(i\not{\partial} - e\not{A} - m)\psi = 0, \tag{3}$$

with $e = -1/\sqrt{137}$ for a negative electron.

It is of interest to determine the effect of the electromagnetic field in the nonrelativistic approximation. Proceeding as in 6.13a, we find in place of 6.13(8)[1]

$$\begin{aligned}(E - e\Phi - m)\psi_U &= \frac{1}{2m}[\boldsymbol{\sigma}\cdot(-i\nabla - e\mathbf{A})][\boldsymbol{\sigma}\cdot(-i\nabla - e\mathbf{A})]\psi_U \\ &= \frac{1}{2m}[(\boldsymbol{\sigma}\cdot i\nabla)(\boldsymbol{\sigma}\cdot i\nabla) + e(\boldsymbol{\sigma}\cdot i\nabla)(\boldsymbol{\sigma}\cdot\mathbf{A}) + e(\boldsymbol{\sigma}\cdot\mathbf{A})(\boldsymbol{\sigma}\cdot i\nabla)]\psi_U \\ &= \left[\frac{-\nabla^2}{2m} + \frac{e}{2m}(i\nabla\cdot\mathbf{A} + \mathbf{A}\cdot i\nabla) - \frac{e}{2m}\boldsymbol{\sigma}\cdot\operatorname{curl}\mathbf{A}\right]\psi_U,\end{aligned} \tag{4}$$

which is a Schrödinger equation with kinetic energy $p^2/2m$ and interaction terms

$$e\Phi - \frac{e}{2m}(\mathbf{p}\cdot\mathbf{A} + \mathbf{A}\cdot\mathbf{p}) - \frac{e}{2m}\boldsymbol{\sigma}\cdot\operatorname{curl}\mathbf{A}. \tag{5}$$

The first two terms of the interaction are the same as those for the nonrelativistic charge coupling, of Chapter 4. The last term shows that the relativistic theory predicts that a point charge should interact, *even at rest*, with a magnetic field as if it possessed a magnetic moment $e/2m$ (Dirac moment). This prediction is in accord with the form of the current 6.13c and is well verified for electrons and muons.

If we take into account higher order corrections, the theoretically predicted magnetic moment of the electron is (S-57; S-58)

$$\mu_e = \frac{e}{2m}\left(1 + \frac{e^2}{2\pi} - 0.328\frac{e^4}{\pi^2} + \cdots\right) = \frac{e}{2m} \times 1.0011596,$$

[1] Terms in A^2 have been neglected in the second line of (4). The same approximation was used in Chapter 4.

and the experimental values from two independent measurements (G-51; F-56; K-52) are

$$\mu_e = \begin{cases} \dfrac{e}{2m}(1.001146 \pm 0.000012), \\ \\ \dfrac{e}{2m}(1.001165 \pm 0.000011). \end{cases}$$

b. Point Magnetic Moment: the Neutron. If a particle has a magnetic moment different from that predicted as a result of its charge, we speak of an anomalous contribution. Nonrelativistically, the interaction of the anomalous magnetic moment was represented by a term $-\mu_a \boldsymbol{\sigma} \cdot \mathbf{H}$. Relativistically, we must add the following term to the energy[1]:

$$\text{(6)} \qquad \mu_a \sigma_{\mu\nu}\, \partial_\mu A_\nu = \tfrac{1}{2}\mu_a \sigma_{\mu\nu} F_{\mu\nu} = \mu_a(-\boldsymbol{\sigma}\cdot\mathbf{H} + i\gamma_4 \boldsymbol{\gamma}\cdot\mathbf{E}).$$

where $\sigma_{\mu\nu}$ is given by 6.12(11) and $F_{\mu\nu}$ is the electromagnetic field tensor 6.11(13), (14).

The corresponding addition to the Dirac Hamiltonian is

$$\text{(7)} \qquad \mathcal{H}' = \mu_a(-\gamma_4 \boldsymbol{\sigma}\cdot\mathbf{H} + i\boldsymbol{\gamma}\cdot\mathbf{E}).$$

The term in $\boldsymbol{\sigma}\cdot\mathbf{H}$ does not require explanation, but the relativistic term in $\boldsymbol{\gamma}\cdot\mathbf{E}$ deserves some attention.

First of all we note that this term is *small* in the nonrelativistic approximation because the matrix $\boldsymbol{\gamma}$ has zeros in the upper left corner. Making a distinction between upper and lower components and using the representation 6.12(13), we find that its expectation value is

$$\text{(8a)} \quad \mathcal{H}'_{(\boldsymbol{\gamma}\cdot\mathbf{E})} = i\mu_a\langle\psi|\, \boldsymbol{\gamma}\cdot\mathbf{E}\, |\psi\rangle = i\mu_a\langle\psi_U|\, \boldsymbol{\sigma}\cdot\mathbf{E}\, |\psi_L\rangle - i\mu_a\langle\psi_L|\, \boldsymbol{\sigma}\cdot\mathbf{E}\, |\psi_U\rangle.$$

We now express the lower components in terms of the upper ones by means of 6.13(6),[2] using the approximation $E = m$ which is valid at low velocities. In this manner (8*a*) becomes

$$\text{(8b)} \quad \frac{\mu_a}{2m}\langle\psi_U|\, (\boldsymbol{\sigma}\cdot\mathbf{E})(\boldsymbol{\sigma}\cdot\boldsymbol{\nabla}) - (\boldsymbol{\sigma}\cdot\boldsymbol{\nabla})(\boldsymbol{\sigma}\cdot\mathbf{E})\, |\psi_U\rangle$$
$$= \frac{\mu_a}{2m}\langle\psi_U|\, \mathbf{E}\cdot\boldsymbol{\nabla} - \boldsymbol{\nabla}\cdot\mathbf{E} + i\boldsymbol{\sigma}\cdot(\mathbf{E}\times\boldsymbol{\nabla}) - i\boldsymbol{\sigma}\cdot(\boldsymbol{\nabla}\times\mathbf{E})\, |\psi_U\rangle.$$

[1] $\sigma_{12}\, \partial_1 A_2 + \sigma_{21}\, \partial_2 A_1 = \sigma_{12}(\partial_1 A_2 - \partial_2 A_1) = \sigma_{12}F_{12} = -\sigma_3 H_3$; $\sigma_{14}\, \partial_1 A_4 + \sigma_{41}\, \partial_4 A_1 = \sigma_{14}(\partial_1 A_4 - \partial_4 A_1) = \sigma_{14}F_{14} = \sigma_{14}E_1 = \frac{1}{2}i(\gamma_1\gamma_4 - \gamma_4\gamma_1)E_1 = i\gamma_1\gamma_4 E_1 = -i\gamma_4\gamma_1 E_1$. But the sign of the 1, 4 term must be inverted because of the $- - - +$ sum rule.

[2] In the case of electromagnetic interaction 6.13(6) should be modified, but the corrections contain higher powers of e and can be neglected.

But

$$-\nabla \cdot \mathbf{E}\psi_U = -\mathbf{E} \cdot \nabla\psi_U - (\nabla \cdot \mathbf{E})\psi_U,$$

and, since **curl E** $= 0$,

$$-\nabla \times \mathbf{E}\psi_U = \mathbf{E} \times \nabla\psi_U.$$

Finally, the interaction energy contributed by the $\boldsymbol{\gamma} \cdot \mathbf{E}$ term can be written

$$\frac{\mu_a}{2m} \langle\psi_U| -(\text{div } \mathbf{E}) + 2i\boldsymbol{\sigma} \cdot \mathbf{E} \times \nabla |\psi_U\rangle \tag{8c}$$

with the divergence operator *not operating* on ψ_U.

We conclude that *even at rest* ($\nabla\psi_U = 0$), there is an interaction between a neutral particle with an anomalous magnetic moment and an electrostatic field.

This conclusion can be applied to obtain the electrostatic neutron-electron interaction. The electric field produced by an electron (charge $-|e|$) satisfies the equation

$$\text{div } \mathbf{E} = -4\pi\,|e|\,|\psi_e|^2 \tag{9}$$

and thus the neutron-electron interaction energy at rest is

$$\mathcal{H}'_{(\boldsymbol{\gamma} \cdot \mathbf{E})} = \frac{\mu_{\text{n}}}{2M_{\text{n}}} 4\pi\,|e|\,|\psi_e|^2, \tag{10}$$

with $\mu_{\text{n}} = -1.91$. It is usual to express this interaction in terms of a potential well extending over a sphere of radius e^2/m. The depth of this potential is then

$$V_{(\boldsymbol{\gamma} \cdot \mathbf{E})} = \frac{\mu_{\text{n}}}{2M_{\text{n}}} \frac{4\pi\,|e|}{\frac{4}{3}\pi(e^2/m)^3} = -4080 \text{ eV}. \tag{11}$$

The potential is attractive and in almost perfect agreement with the experiments reported in 3.32.

The good agreement shows that there is no contribution from the finite size of the neutron.

c. Particles of Finite Size: Form Factors of the Nucleons. The electromagnetic interaction of a point charge and a point magnetic moment is not the most general interaction that may be used in the Dirac equation. Taking into account the fact that the operator $\Box^2$ is a scalar, we may write (F-52a, b)

$$\left[i\partial\!\!\!/ - m - \sum_{n=0}^{\infty} (e_n\Box^{2n}A\!\!\!/ + \mu_n\sigma_{\mu\nu}\Box^{2n}F_{\mu\nu})\right]\psi = 0. \tag{12}$$

The constants e_n and μ_n have the dimensions of ex^{2n} and μx^{2n}. In particular $e_0 = e$, $\mu_0 = \mu_a$.

The terms for $n \neq 0$ describe the interaction for a particle of finite size, and the coefficients e_n assume the meaning of even moments of the charge.

In order to show the relation between the coefficients e_n, the moments of the charge, and the form factors, let us rewrite in more detail the terms in $\gamma_4\Phi$ of (12):

$$-\sum_n e_n \Box^{2n}\gamma_4\Phi = -\gamma_4 \sum_n e_n \left(\frac{\partial^2}{\partial t^2} - \nabla^2\right)^n \Phi. \tag{13}$$

If the potential is static $[(\partial^2/\partial t^2)\Phi = 0]$, this expression can be compared with the electrostatic energy of a spherically symmetrical charge distribution $\rho(r)$ in the potential Φ:

$$\int \rho(r)\,\Phi(r)\,d^3\mathbf{r}$$

$$= \sum_{ijn} \frac{1}{i!\,j!\,(n-i-j)!}\left(\frac{\partial^n\Phi}{\partial x^i\,\partial y^j\,\partial z^{n-i-j}}\right)_{r=0} \int \rho(r) x^i y^j z^{n-i-j}\,d^3\mathbf{r}$$

$$= \Phi \int \rho(r)\,d^3\mathbf{r} + \frac{1}{2!}\nabla^2\Phi \int \rho(r) r^2\,d^3\mathbf{r} + \cdots.$$

As a result of the comparison, we obtain for the nonrelativistic static spherically symmetrical case

$$e_2 = \frac{1}{2!}\int \rho(r) r^2\,d^3\mathbf{r}, \tag{14}$$

and similar expressions can be derived for $n > 2$.

The successive moments are, in turn, related to the charge form factors, since

$$F_c(q) = \frac{1}{e}\int \rho(r) e^{i\mathbf{q}\cdot\mathbf{r}}\,d^3\mathbf{r} = \frac{1}{e}\int \rho(r)(1 - \tfrac{1}{6}q^2r^2 + \cdots)\,d^3\mathbf{r}.$$

By following essentially the same procedure, we can show that the coefficients μ_n are related to the moments and to the form factors for the density of anomalous magnetic moment.

The form of the Dirac equation (12) is needed to calculate the electromagnetic interaction of the nucleons, which, as we have already remarked on several occasions, are particles of finite size. The most interesting application is to the scattering of electrons by nucleons (3.33). Since the scattering is elastic, the energy transfer q_4 is zero in the center-of-mass system, and in this system the form factors depend only on q^2.

A more precise relativistic definition of the form factors and a discussion of the interaction of finite size nucleons with the quantized electromagnetic field can be found in 6.24c.

6.2 Electrons, Positrons, and Photons

6.21 *Free-Electron and Positron Spinors*

a. Normalization of Free-Electron Spinors. Before presenting the treatment of the interaction of electrons (or other charged spinors) with the electromagnetic field, we must describe the free states of the electron and of the positron in a way that we shall find useful in the development of the theory. The theory we are presenting has been known for several years and is mostly due to Dirac. However, the techniques of computation are due to Feynman, who introduced great simplifications and was also able to remove some of the remaining difficulties.

A free particle has a constant momentum **p**; in particular, a free fermion satisfies Dirac's equation and may exist—for assigned **p**—in four different states, each represented by a four-component spinor, as explained in 6.13b. The meaning of the four spinors $u_{(s)}$ in 6.13(12) is

$$\begin{array}{lllll} u_{(1)} & E > 0 & \text{spin up} & \text{or} & +\uparrow \text{ electron,} \\ u_{(2)} & E > 0 & \text{spin down} & \text{or} & +\downarrow \text{ electron,} \\ u_{(3)} & E < 0 & \text{spin up} & \text{or} & -\uparrow \text{ electron,} \\ u_{(4)} & E < 0 & \text{spin down} & \text{or} & -\downarrow \text{ electron,} \end{array} \tag{1}$$

and the Dirac equation for the $u_{(s)}$ can be written

$$(\not p - m)u_{(s)} = 0. \tag{2}$$

In the rest system ($\mathbf{p} = 0$) these spinors are orthogonal and normalized as usual: $u^{\dagger}_{(s)}u_{(s)} = 1$; nonrelativistically, the waves 6.13(12) can be normalized to unity in a unit volume by using the factor in 6.13(13).

If we want to consider rapidly moving particles, it will be convenient to normalize the wave functions in a volume that depends on velocity consistently with the Lorentz contraction: the normalization to unity is made over a volume $(1 - v^2)^{1/2} = m/|E|$, and this requires

$$u^{\dagger}_{(s)}u_{(s)} = \frac{|E|}{m}. \tag{3}$$

For this normalization the spinors in 6.13(12) must be multiplied by

$$\left(\frac{|E|}{m}\right)^{1/2}\left(\frac{|E| + m}{2\,|E|}\right)^{1/2} = \left(\frac{|E| + m}{2m}\right)^{1/2}. \tag{4}$$

But it is easily found[1] that $\bar{u}_{(s)}u_{(s)} = u^\dagger_{(s)}\gamma_4 u_{(s)} = (m/E)u^\dagger_{(s)}u_{(s)}$; and thus (3) can be expressed as

$$\bar{u}_{(s)}u_{(s)} = \frac{E}{|E|} = \begin{cases} +1 \text{ for positive energy states,} \\ -1 \text{ for negative energy states.} \end{cases} \tag{5}$$

b. Free Positron Spinors. Let us now study the charge conjugate solutions of the Dirac equation which correspond to the wave functions of positive electrons, or *positrons*. These are obtained by the application of the operator S_C given in 6.14(14). It is easily verified that the square of S_C is unity

$$S_C S_C = \gamma_2 K \gamma_2 K = -\gamma_2\gamma_2 = 1, \tag{6a}$$

and that[2]

$$S_C(i\partial\!\!\!/ - eA\!\!\!/ - m)S_C^{-1} = i\partial\!\!\!/ + eA\!\!\!/ - m. \tag{6b}$$

As appropriate to the operator of charge conjugation, S_C changes the charge, *and only the charge*, in the Dirac equation.

But the charge does not appear explicitly in the free-particle solutions of the equation and it is not immediately evident whether or how these transform under charge conjugation. In order to find the result of the transformation, let us formally apply the operator S_C to the free-electron state $\psi_{(1)}(\mathbf{p})$. Using from now on the + sign in 6.14(14) we obtain

$$S_C\psi_{(1)}(\mathbf{p}) = \begin{pmatrix} 0 & 0 & 0 & -i \\ 0 & 0 & i & 0 \\ 0 & i & 0 & 0 \\ -i & 0 & 0 & 0 \end{pmatrix} K \begin{pmatrix} 1 \\ 0 \\ p_z/(m+|E|) \\ (p_x + ip_y)/(m+|E|) \end{pmatrix} e^{-i\mathbf{p}\cdot\mathbf{x}}$$

$$= -i \begin{pmatrix} (p_x - ip_y)/(m+|E|) \\ -p_z/(m+|E|) \\ 0 \\ 1 \end{pmatrix} e^{i\mathbf{p}\cdot\mathbf{r}} = -i\psi_{(4)}(-\mathbf{p}).$$

[1] Multiply $(p\!\!\!/ - m)u_{(s)} = 0$ by $\bar{u}_{(s)}\gamma_4$ to the left; multiply $\bar{u}_{(s)}(p\!\!\!/ - m) = 0$ by $\gamma_4 u_{(s)}$ to the right; add to obtain $\bar{u}_{(s)}\gamma_4(p\!\!\!/ - m)u_{(s)} + \bar{u}_{(s)}(p\!\!\!/ - m)\gamma_4 u_{(s)} = 0$, or $2E\bar{u}_{(s)}u_{(s)} - 2mu^\dagger_{(s)}u_{(s)} = 0$.

[2] It would be useful for the student to verify (6*b*) term by term.

We can prove similarly that

$$
\begin{aligned}
S_C\psi_{(1)}(\mathbf{p}) &= -i\psi_{(4)}(-\mathbf{p}) \\
S_C\psi_{(2)}(\mathbf{p}) &= i\psi_{(3)}(-\mathbf{p}) \\
S_C\psi_{(3)}(\mathbf{p}) &= i\psi_{(2)}(-\mathbf{p}) \\
S_C\psi_{(4)}(\mathbf{p}) &= -i\psi_{(1)}(-\mathbf{p}).
\end{aligned}
\tag{7}
$$

We conclude that in the absence of external fields the solutions of the charge conjugate equation are the same as the solutions of the original equation, but the eigenvalue $\mathbf{p}$ of the momentum operator has changed sign; moreover, the order of the solutions has been rearranged to invert also the sign of the energy and the direction of the spin.

In short, even in the limit $A_\mu = 0$, charge conjugation inverts momentum, energy, and spin: the state $S_C\psi_{(1)}(\mathbf{p})$, which *is* that of a positron with momentum $\mathbf{p}$, positive energy, and spin up, *is formally equivalent* to the state of an electron with momentum $-\mathbf{p}$, negative energy, and spin down.

It is well known that the positron states can be intuitively understood in terms of the *theory of holes*, according to which a positron is a missing electron of opposite momentum, energy, and spin in a "sea" of negative energy electrons. But in what follows we intend to present a different interpretation which eliminates the negative energies and does not require the artifice of unobservable "seas."

For this purpose it is interesting to consider separately the effect of the operator S_C on the space-time independent part of the spinor $u_{(s)}$ and on the exponential $e^{-i\mathbf{p}\cdot\mathbf{x}}$ which describes the propagation of the free-electron wave. We have seen that, apart from phase factors, $u_{(1)}(\mathbf{p})$ is transformed into $u_{(4)}(-\mathbf{p})$, etc., and that the propagation of the charge conjugate wave corresponds to an inversion of both momentum and energy. As a result, the sign of the frequency has been inverted, though the direction of propagation has remained the same. This state of affairs can be interpreted in two different ways: we can say either that the charge conjugate state has opposite energy or that it *propagates backward in time* with unchanged energy.

In the remaining part of this section we shall take the second point of view; for this purpose the four spinors $u_{(s)}$, which belong to both signs of the energy, will be replaced with four spinors $w_{(s)}$ [see (12)] which belong to the two signs of the charge. The formal relation between the operators of charge conjugation and time reversal is discussed in subsection (e). In section 6.22 we use the idea of a positron as an *electron propagating backward in time* for the practical computation of matrix elements.

Let us first introduce four spinors $v_{(s)}$ appropriate to a *positron of momentum* **p**, making a table similar to (1):

$$v_{(1)}(\mathbf{p}) = S_C u_{(1)}(\mathbf{p}) = -iu_{(4)}(-\mathbf{p})$$
$$E > 0 \quad \text{spin up} \quad \text{or} \quad +\uparrow \text{ positron},$$
$$v_{(2)}(\mathbf{p}) = S_C u_{(2)}(\mathbf{p}) = iu_{(3)}(-\mathbf{p})$$
$$E > 0 \quad \text{spin down} \quad \text{or} \quad +\downarrow \text{ positron},$$
(8) $$v_{(3)}(\mathbf{p}) = S_C u_{(3)}(\mathbf{p}) = iu_{(2)}(-\mathbf{p})$$
$$E < 0 \quad \text{spin up} \quad \text{or} \quad -\uparrow \text{ positron},$$
$$v_{(4)}(\mathbf{p}) = S_C u_{(4)}(\mathbf{p}) = -iu_{(1)}(-\mathbf{p})$$
$$E < 0 \quad \text{spin down} \quad \text{or} \quad -\downarrow \text{ positron}.$$

Since, as we have already remarked, these charge conjugate spinors satisfy the original differential Dirac equation for four momentum eigenvalues $-\mathbf{p}$, we can write

(9) $$(\not{p} + m)v_{(s)} = 0;$$

this is the same as (2), apart from the inversion of the sign of the mass.

The relativistically invariant normalization of the $v_{(s)}$ must naturally be chosen so that

(10) $$v^{\dagger}_{(s)} v_{(s)} = \frac{|E|}{m}.$$

Proceeding as in the footnote on p. 383 but using (9) instead of (2), (10) is found to be equivalent to

(11) $$\bar{v}_{(s)} v_{(s)} = -\frac{|E|}{E} = \begin{cases} -1 \text{ for positive energy states,} \\ +1 \text{ for negative energy states.} \end{cases}$$

c. Free Spinors of Positive Energy. We have seen how we can give a complete set of spinors for momentum **p** in two different ways: either by specifying the electron spinors $u_{(s)}$ or the positron spinors $v_{(s)}$.

We now introduce a third way of listing the four solutions of the Dirac equation, which will enable us to get away from the fiction of negative energy states and holes in unobservable seas. We choose four independent spinors $w_{(s)}$, all corresponding to momentum **p** and positive energy:

(12) $$\begin{aligned} w_{(1)}(\mathbf{p}) &= u_{(1)}(\mathbf{p}) && \text{electron} \uparrow \quad E > 0, \\ w_{(2)}(\mathbf{p}) &= u_{(2)}(\mathbf{p}) && \text{electron} \downarrow \quad E > 0, \\ w_{(3)}(\mathbf{p}) = v_{(1)}(\mathbf{p}) &= -iu_{(4)}(-\mathbf{p}) && \text{positron} \uparrow \quad E > 0, \\ w_{(4)}(\mathbf{p}) = v_{(2)}(\mathbf{p}) &= iu_{(3)}(-\mathbf{p}) && \text{positron} \downarrow \quad E > 0. \end{aligned}$$

The explicit expression of these spinors can be obtained from 6.13(12) and from (7), (8) of this section. By including the normalization factor (4) we can write:

(13a)

$$w_{(1)} = \sqrt{\frac{E+m}{2m}} \begin{pmatrix} 1 \\ 0 \\ \dfrac{p_z}{E+m} \\ \dfrac{p_x+ip_y}{E+m} \end{pmatrix}, \qquad w_{(2)} = \sqrt{\frac{E+m}{2m}} \begin{pmatrix} 0 \\ 1 \\ \dfrac{p_x-ip_y}{E+m} \\ \dfrac{-p_z}{E+m} \end{pmatrix}$$

$$w_{(3)} = -i\sqrt{\frac{E+m}{2m}} \begin{pmatrix} \dfrac{p_x-ip_y}{E+m} \\ \dfrac{-p_z}{E+m} \\ 0 \\ 1 \end{pmatrix}, \qquad w_{(4)} = i\sqrt{\frac{E+m}{2m}} \begin{pmatrix} \dfrac{p_z}{E+m} \\ \dfrac{p_x+ip_y}{E+m} \\ 1 \\ 0 \end{pmatrix},$$

(13b)

$$\bar{w}_{(1)} = \sqrt{\frac{E+m}{2m}} \times \begin{pmatrix} 1 & 0 & \dfrac{-p_z}{E+m} & -\dfrac{p_x-ip_y}{E+m} \end{pmatrix},$$

$$\bar{w}_{(2)} = \sqrt{\frac{E+m}{2m}} \times \begin{pmatrix} 0 & 1 & -\dfrac{p_x+ip_y}{E+m} & -\dfrac{-p_z}{E+m} \end{pmatrix},$$

$$\bar{w}_{(3)} = i\sqrt{\frac{E+m}{2m}} \times \begin{pmatrix} \dfrac{p_x+ip_y}{E+m} & \dfrac{-p_z}{E+m} & 0 & -1 \end{pmatrix},$$

$$\bar{w}_{(4)} = -i\sqrt{\frac{E+m}{2m}} \times \begin{pmatrix} \dfrac{p_z}{E+m} & \dfrac{p_x-ip_y}{E+m} & -1 & 0 \end{pmatrix}.$$

In these formulas E is always positive.

The w are normalized in the following manner

(14) $\bar{w}_{(s)}w_{(s')} = \varepsilon_{(s)(s')}$ where $\varepsilon_{(s)(s')} = 0$ for $s \neq s'$
$= +1$ for $s = s' = 1, 2$
$= -1$ for $s = s' = 3, 4$

They also satisfy the relations:

(15)

$$\sum_{(s)} \bar{w}_{(s)}w_{(s)}\varepsilon_{(s)(s)} = 4,$$

$$\left(\sum_{(s)} w_{(s)}\bar{w}_{(s)}\varepsilon_{(s)(s)}\right)_{RS} = \delta_{RS}.$$

These expressions follow from the way the w's have been introduced, and their validity can be verified directly from the explicit form (13).

d. Projection Operators. We find it useful to introduce projection operators for free states of different charges. The electron and positron projection operators are

$$\Lambda_e = \frac{\not{p} + m}{2m}, \qquad \Lambda_p = \frac{\not{p} - m}{2m}, \tag{16}$$

since it is easily found from (2) and (9) that

$$\begin{aligned} &\Lambda_e w_{(1),(2)} = \Lambda_e u_{(1),(2)} = u_{(1),(2)}, \qquad \Lambda_e w_{(3),(4)} = \Lambda_e v_{(1),(2)} = 0, \\ &\Lambda_p w_{(1),(2)} = \Lambda_p u_{(1),(2)} = 0, \qquad \Lambda_p w_{(3),(4)} = \Lambda_p v_{(1),(2)} = -v_{(1),(2)}. \end{aligned} \tag{17}$$

Observe the minus sign in the last of (17): it is chosen in such a way that, considering the normalization of the positron wave function (11) and (12), the expectation value of Λ_p in positron states is positive: $\bar{v}_1\Lambda_p v_1 = \bar{v}_2\Lambda_p v_2 = +1$.

e. Relation between Time Inversion, Time Reversal, and Charge Conjugation. It is easily seen that when the operator of time-axis inversion $S_{P,4} = \gamma_1\gamma_2\gamma_3$ [6.14(12)], is applied to the wave equation the time part of all slashed vectors changes sign:

$$\begin{aligned} S_{P,4}(i\gamma_4\partial_4 + i\boldsymbol{\gamma}\cdot\boldsymbol{\nabla} - e\gamma_4 A_4 + e\boldsymbol{\gamma}\cdot\mathbf{A} - m)S_{P,4}^{-1} \\ = -i\gamma_4\partial_4 + i\boldsymbol{\gamma}\cdot\boldsymbol{\nabla} + e\gamma_4 A_4 + e\boldsymbol{\gamma}\cdot\mathbf{A} - m. \end{aligned}$$

Thus the operator $S_{P,4}$, besides inverting the sign of time, has also inverted the electric field and left invariant the magnetic field. Since time reversal must invert time and magnetic fields and leave electric fields unchanged (1.17b), clearly $S_{P,4}$ must be considered as the product of time reversal and charge conjugation. Introducing for convenience a phase factor i, we can write

$$S_{P,4} = \gamma_1\gamma_2\gamma_3 = iS_T S_C. \tag{18}$$

By multiplying by $S_C = \gamma_2 K$ to the right, we obtain

$$S_T = \frac{1}{i}\,\gamma_1\gamma_2\gamma_3\gamma_2 K = i\gamma_3\gamma_1 K, \tag{19}$$

and this justifies the definition 6.14(13) of the time-reversal operator.

Observe that S_T, as obtained in (19), commutes with S_C and that there is no ambiguity in the ordering of the product $S_C S_T$ in (18).

In the nonrelativistic limit the time-reversal operator reduces to $\sigma_2 K$, which is the operator introduced in 1.17.

6.22 *Propagation of Free Electrons and Positrons*[1]

a. The Wave Function as a Four-Flux. The behavior of the wave function of a fermion is governed by the Dirac equation, which is a first-order differential equation in the time variable. Thus, if a wave function is known all over space at time $t = 0$, it is possible to find its value, all over space, at any time $t > 0$. The wave equation can be solved step by step by adding together the changes occurring in infinitesimal time intervals, dt, or a formalism can be developed to pass directly over finite time intervals.

Following Feynman (F-49) we take this second approach, which is particularly useful in collision theory when we want to compute the state after the collision (final) from the state before the collision (initial) without being concerned with what has happened in between.

Since the time does not play any special role in a relativistic theory, we take a more general approach: let us indicate with $\psi(\mathbf{1})$, $\psi(\mathbf{2})$, etc., . . . the value of the wave function of a Dirac particle at space-time point $\mathbf{1}$ $(x_1y_1z_1t_1)$, $\mathbf{2}$ $(x_2y_2z_2t_2)$, etc., ... We want to find a method to compute $\psi(\mathbf{2})$ at any point $\mathbf{2}$ from the knowledge of ψ in a sufficiently large space-time region.

For this purpose let us remember that in the absence of fields, ψ satisfies the Dirac equation[2]

$$(i\partial\!\!\!/_1 - m)\,\psi(\mathbf{1}) = 0, \tag{1}$$

and let us introduce a Green's function (or better, a Green's matrix) $K^0(\mathbf{2}, \mathbf{1})$ as the solution of the equation[3]

$$(i\partial\!\!\!/_2 - m)\,K^0(\mathbf{2}, \mathbf{1}) = i\delta^4(\mathbf{2}, \mathbf{1}). \tag{2a}$$

[1] Sections 6.22 and 6.23 present a justification of the "rules" of quantum electrodynamics given in 6.24. Since these rules are finally justified by their success in predicting experimental results, some reader may prefer to skip these two sections and pass directly to 6.24.

[2] In (1) $\partial\!\!\!/_1$ stands for $\gamma_t(\partial/\partial t_1) + \gamma_x(\partial/\partial x_1) + \gamma_y(\partial/\partial y_1) + \gamma_z(\partial/\partial z_1)$ and, similarly, for $\partial\!\!\!/_2$ in (2).

[3] $\delta^4(\mathbf{2}, \mathbf{1})$ is the four-dimensional δ function

$$\delta^4(\mathbf{2}, \mathbf{1}) = \delta(x_2 - x_1)\,\delta(y_2 - y_1)\,\delta(z_2 - z_1)\,\delta(t_2 - t_1).$$

We shall find it convenient to use the following representation:

$$\delta(x_2 - x_1) = \lim_{A\to\infty} \frac{\sin A(x_2 - x_1)}{\pi(x_2 - x_1)} = \frac{1}{2\pi}\int_{-\infty}^{+\infty} e^{-ip_x(x_2 - x_1)}\,dp_x,$$

and thus we can write

$$\delta^4(\mathbf{2}, \mathbf{1}) = \delta^4(\mathbf{x}_2 - \mathbf{x}_1) = \frac{1}{(2\pi)^4}\int_{-\infty}^{+\infty} e^{-i\mathbf{p}\cdot(\mathbf{x}_2 - \mathbf{x}_1)}\,d^4\mathbf{p}.$$

By multiplying this equation on the right by $(-i\overleftarrow{\not\partial}_1 - m)$ and noting that $\partial_1\delta^4(\mathbf{2}, \mathbf{1}) = -\partial_2\delta^4(\mathbf{2}, \mathbf{1})$, we find

$$K^0(\mathbf{2}, \mathbf{1})(-i\overleftarrow{\not\partial}_1 - m) = i\delta^4(\mathbf{2}, \mathbf{1}). \tag{2b}$$

Let us now multiply (2b) to the right by $\psi(\mathbf{1})$ and (1) to the left by $K^0(\mathbf{2}, \mathbf{1})$, subtract and integrate over $d^4\mathbf{x}_1$; we obtain

$$\psi(\mathbf{2}) = -\int K^0(\mathbf{2}, \mathbf{1})(\overleftarrow{\not\partial}_1 + \overrightarrow{\not\partial}_1)\, \psi(\mathbf{1})\, d^4\mathbf{x}_1.$$

But the integrand $(\partial_\mu K^0)\gamma_\mu\psi + K^0\gamma_\mu(\partial_\mu\psi) = \partial_\mu(K^0\gamma_\mu\psi)$ is the four-divergence of $K^0(\mathbf{2}, \mathbf{1})\gamma_\mu\psi(\mathbf{1})$; thus the four-volume integral can be transformed

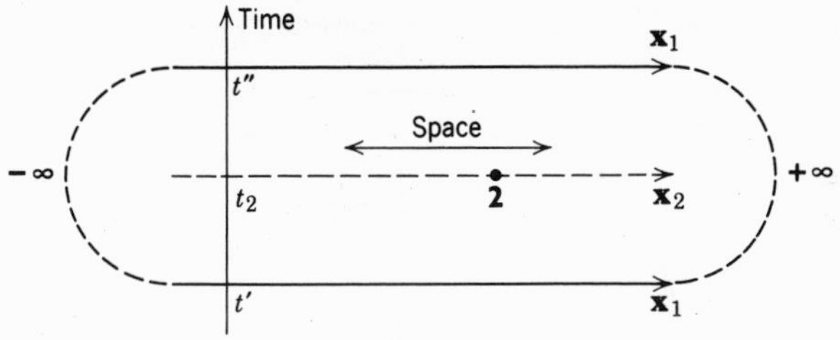

Fig. 6.22-1. Horizontal lines represent space for different times (vertical axis). The point 2 is surrounded by a 3-surface formed by all space at a past time t' and at a future time t''.

into a flux over a closed three-surface surrounding the point **2**:

$$\psi(\mathbf{2}) = \oint K^0(\mathbf{2}, \mathbf{1})\not{n}\psi(\mathbf{1})\, d^3\mathbf{x}_1, \tag{3}$$

where $\mathbf{n}$ is the inward unit normal to the surface itself.

In practice, (3) is used choosing a three-surface which simplifies the calculations but destroys the beautiful four-dimensional symmetry: the three-surface surrounding point **2** is taken to be all space at a past and at a future time (Fig. 6.22-1). Then (3) becomes

$$\psi(\mathbf{2}) = \int_{t'<t_2} K^0(\mathbf{2}, \mathbf{1})\gamma_4\psi(\mathbf{1})\, d^3\mathbf{x}_1 - \int_{t''>t_2} K^0(\mathbf{2}, \mathbf{1})\gamma_4\psi(\mathbf{1})\, d^3\mathbf{x}_1. \tag{4}$$

Though the derivation of these formulas is straightforward, their interpretation is far from obvious. In particular, the meaning of the contributions from the future must be clarified.

b. The Vacuum Kernel K^0 and its Poles. In order to find the kernel of the integral in (3), we must solve (2). It is easily verified by direct substitution that the solution of (2) is

$$K^0(\mathbf{2}, \mathbf{1}) = \frac{i}{(2\pi)^4}\int \frac{e^{-i\mathbf{p}\cdot(\mathbf{x}_2 - \mathbf{x}_1)}}{\not{p} - m}\, d^4\mathbf{p}. \tag{5a}$$

The factor $i(\not{p} - m)^{-1}$ is called the *propagator* of a fermion of mass m and momentum $\mathbf{p}$.

It will be useful to rewrite (5*a*) in other equivalent forms:

$$\text{(5b)} \qquad K^0(2, 1) = \frac{i}{(2\pi)^4} \int \frac{\not{p} + m}{\mathbf{p}^2 - m^2} e^{-i\mathbf{p}\cdot(\mathbf{x}_2 - \mathbf{x}_1)} \, d^4\mathbf{p}$$

$$\text{(5c)} \qquad = \frac{i}{(2\pi)^4} (i\not{\partial}_2 + m) \int \frac{e^{-i\mathbf{p}\cdot(\mathbf{x}_2 - \mathbf{x}_1)}}{\mathbf{p}^2 - m^2} \, d^4\mathbf{p}$$

$$\text{(5d)} \qquad = \frac{i}{(2\pi)^4} (i\not{\partial}_2 + m) \int e^{i\mathbf{p}\cdot(\mathbf{x}_2 - \mathbf{x}_1)} \, d^3\mathbf{p} \int \frac{e^{-ip_4(t_2 - t_1)}}{\mathbf{p}^2 - m^2} \, dp_4.$$

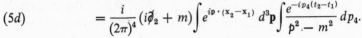

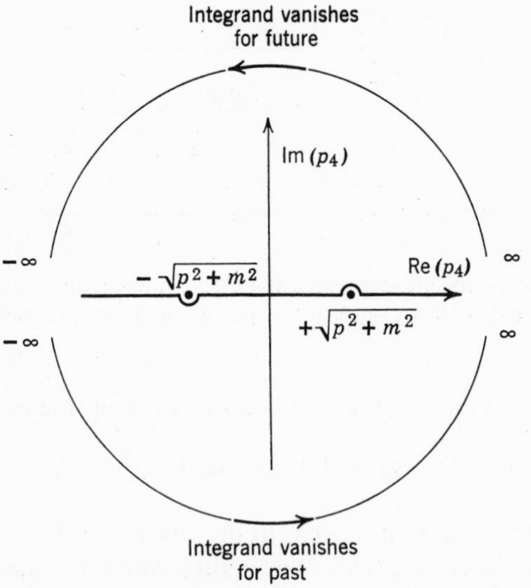

Fig. 6.22-2. Showing the Feynman paths of integration along the real p_4 axis and the closing infinite semicircles which give vanishing contributions from the past and from the future.

It is seen that the integrand has poles for

$$\text{(6)} \qquad \mathbf{p}^2 = m^2 \quad \text{or} \quad p_4 = \pm\sqrt{p^2 + m^2} \equiv \pm|E(p)|\,,$$

and thus the vacuum kernel is not definite until we specify how to handle the poles. Following Feynman, we set down the following rule:

(7)
accept contributions to the pole at $p_4 = +\sqrt{p^2 + m^2}$ (*electron pole*) *only from the past* (integral evaluated at $t_1 = t' < t_2$);
accept contributions to the pole at $p_4 = -\sqrt{p^2 + m^2}$ (*positron pole*) *only from the future* (integral evaluated at $t_1 = t'' > t_2$).

If the integral in dp_4 is performed in the complex plane, the choice (7) corresponds to the path of Fig. 6.22-2.[1] In fact, if we close the path of integration with an infinite noncontributing semicircle, we are obliged to choose the upper semicircle for the contribution from the future ($e^{-ip_4(t_2-t_1)} \rightarrow 0$ if $p_4 \rightarrow i\infty$ and $t_1 > t_2$), and the lower semicircle for the contribution from the past ($e^{-ip_4(t_2-t_1)} \rightarrow 0$ if $p_4 \rightarrow -i\infty$ and $t_1 < t_2$). Thus the path from the future encloses the positron pole, and the path from the past, the electron pole.

When the integration is performed over the paths indicated, by using Cauchy's theorem[2] we obtain for all times t_1

$$(8)\qquad \int_{-\infty}^{+\infty} \frac{e^{-ip_4(t_2-t_1)}}{p^2 - m^2}\, dp_4 = \int \frac{e^{-ip_4(t_2-t_1)}}{{p_4}^2 - E^2(p)}\, dp_4 = -\frac{\pi i}{|E(p)|}\, e^{-i|E(p)|\,|t_2-t_1|}.$$

c. Physical Interpretation. Let us explain once again the reason for accepting contributions from the future.

We could easily have chosen the path of integration to obtain contributions only from the past for both poles of $K^\circ(\mathbf{2}, \mathbf{1})$; but, in Feynman's words, the formulas arising from this choice would apply to Dirac's one-electron theory rather than to the theory of the positron. According to the one-electron theory, the amplitude proceeds toward increasing positive times with both positive and negative energy, that is, with both positive and negative rates of change of phase, corresponding to the four electron solutions $u_{(1)}$, $u_{(2)}$, $u_{(3)}$, and $u_{(4)}$.

The positron theory of 6.21c states instead that the negative energy states ($u_{(3)}$, $u_{(4)}$) are not available to the electron but that there are additional positive energy states ($v_{(1)}$, $v_{(2)}$) corresponding to positrons and propagating with negative rate of change of phase; since the phase contains the product of energy and propagation time and we chose an interpretation

[1] Instead of using a devious path around the poles, we could displace the negative energy pole slightly upward, the positive energy pole slightly downward, and integrate straight along the real axis. The required displacement of the poles is obtained by adding a small negative imaginary part, $-i\varepsilon$, to the mass of the particle: with this artifice the poles are located, as required, at

$$p_4 = \pm\sqrt{p^2 + |m - i\varepsilon|^2} \approx \pm\sqrt{p^2 + m^2 - 2im\varepsilon}.$$

[2] The residue of $\dfrac{e^{-ip_4(t_2-t_1)}}{(p_4 - |E|)(p_4 + |E|)}$ at $p_4 = \pm|E|$ is $\dfrac{e^{\mp i|E|(t_2-t_1)}}{\pm 2|E|}$. But the pole at $+|E|$ (from the past) is circled clockwise, whereas the pole at $-|E|$ (from the future) is circled anticlockwise.

that has only positive energy, we must invert the direction of propagation in time of the positrons.

This situation is illustrated in Fig. 6.22-3; it will become more meaningful after consideration of the effect of the electromagnetic field which is discussed in the next section.

It is possible to verify directly that (4) with the kernel (5d), (8), actually describes the propagation of free electron and positron waves. For the proof, which is left to the reader, the electron wave must be written

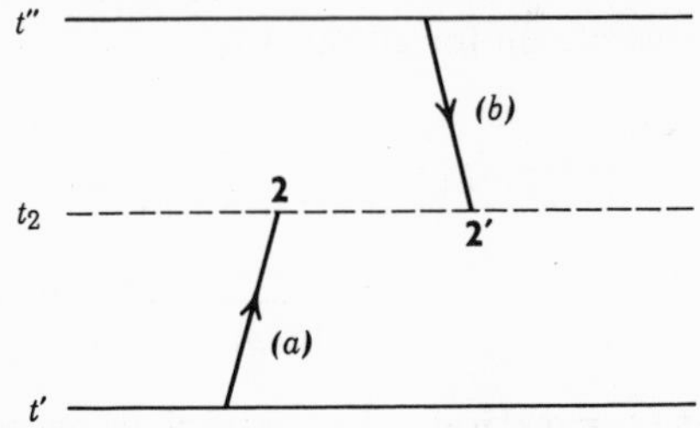

Fig. 6.22-3. Contributions to the state ψ (2), corresponding to the integral (4): (*a*) electrons coming from the past; (*b*) electrons coming from the future (positrons).

$u_{(1),(2)} \exp(-i\mathbf{p}\cdot\mathbf{x}_1)$, with $u_{(1),(2)}$ satisfying 6.21(2), and the positron wave must be written $u_{(3),(4)} \exp(i\mathbf{p}\cdot\mathbf{x}_1)$, with $u_{(3),(4)}$ satisfying 6.21(9).

6.23 Perturbation Theory[1]

a. The Interaction Kernel. In the presence of the electromagnetic field the electron satisfies the equation

$$(i\partial\!\!\!/_1 - eA\!\!\!/(\mathbf{1}) - m)\,\psi(\mathbf{1}) = 0 \tag{1}$$

and no longer propagates as described by the integral equation 6.22(3), in which K^0 satisfies 6.22(2).

Let us now introduce an interaction kernel $K(\mathbf{2}, \mathbf{1})$ as the solution of the equation

$$(i\partial\!\!\!/_2 - eA\!\!\!/(\mathbf{2}) - m)\,K(\mathbf{2}, \mathbf{1}) = i\delta^4(\mathbf{2}, \mathbf{1}). \tag{2}$$

We shall prove that the amplitude $\psi(\mathbf{2})$ is determined by an integral similar to 6.22(3), in which the vacuum kernel $K^0(\mathbf{2}, \mathbf{1})$ is replaced by the interaction kernel $K(\mathbf{2}, \mathbf{1})$.

But first let us study the solution of (2) and show how it can be written

[1] See footnote 1 on p. 388.

as a series (whose convergence we shall not investigate). Let us define

$$K^1(\mathbf{2}, \mathbf{1}) = -ie\int K^0(\mathbf{2}, \mathbf{3})\, \not{A}(\mathbf{3})\, K^0(\mathbf{3}, \mathbf{1})\, d^4\mathbf{x}_3,$$

$$K^2(\mathbf{2}, \mathbf{1}) = -ie\int K^0(\mathbf{2}, \mathbf{3})\, \not{A}(\mathbf{3})\, K^1(\mathbf{3}, \mathbf{1})\, d^4\mathbf{x}_3$$

(3) $$= -e^2\int K^0(\mathbf{2}, \mathbf{3})\, \not{A}(\mathbf{3})\, K^0(\mathbf{3}, \mathbf{4})\, \not{A}(\mathbf{4})\, K^0(\mathbf{4}, \mathbf{1})\, d^4\mathbf{x}_3\, d^4\mathbf{x}_4,$$

. . . . . .

. . . . . .

$$K^n(\mathbf{2}, \mathbf{1}) = -ie\int K^0(\mathbf{2}, \mathbf{3})\, \not{A}(\mathbf{3})\, K^{n-1}(\mathbf{3}, \mathbf{1})\, d^4\mathbf{x}_3,$$

. . . . . .

The K^n thus defined satisfy the equations[1]

(4)
$$(i\not{\partial}_2 - e\not{A}(\mathbf{2}) - m)\, K^0(\mathbf{2}, \mathbf{1}) = i\delta^4(\mathbf{2}, \mathbf{1}) - e\not{A}(\mathbf{2})\, K^0(\mathbf{2}, \mathbf{1}),$$
$$(i\not{\partial}_2 - e\not{A}(\mathbf{2}) - m)\, K^1(\mathbf{2}, \mathbf{1}) = e\not{A}(\mathbf{2})\, K^0(\mathbf{2}, \mathbf{1}) - e\not{A}(\mathbf{2})\, K^1(\mathbf{2}, \mathbf{1}).$$

. . . . . .

Now, by adding $n + 1$ such equations we obtain

(5) $$(i\not{\partial}_2 - e\not{A}(\mathbf{2}) - m)[K^0(\mathbf{2}, \mathbf{1}) + K^1(\mathbf{2}, \mathbf{1}) + \cdots + K^n(\mathbf{2}, \mathbf{1})] = i\delta^4(\mathbf{2}, \mathbf{1}) + R^{(n)},$$

where $R^{(n)}$ is a residue of order $(eA)^n$, which is presumably negligible in the usual sense of perturbation theory. Thus

(6) $$K(\mathbf{2}, \mathbf{1}) = K^0(\mathbf{2}, \mathbf{1}) + K^1(\mathbf{2}, \mathbf{1}) + \cdots$$

is the solution of (2).

We can now prove that $K(\mathbf{2}, \mathbf{1})$ is the appropriate kernel in the presence of electromagnetic field.

For this purpose let us note that the hermitian conjugate of (2) can be written

$$\bar{K}(\mathbf{1}, \mathbf{2})[-i\overleftarrow{\not{\partial}}_1 - e\not{A}(\mathbf{1}) - m] = -i\gamma_4\, \delta^4(\mathbf{2}, \mathbf{1}).$$

Let us multiply this equation by $\psi(\mathbf{1})$ to the right and (1) by $\bar{K}(\mathbf{1}, \mathbf{2})$ to the left. If we subtract the two expressions obtained and integrate over all space $\mathbf{x}_1$, we get

$$\psi(\mathbf{2}) = \int \gamma_4 \bar{K}(\mathbf{1}, \mathbf{2})(\overleftarrow{\not{\partial}} + \overrightarrow{\not{\partial}})\, \psi(\mathbf{1})\, d^4\mathbf{x}_1.$$

[1] The first of (4) is obtained by adding $-e\not{A}(\mathbf{2})\, K^0(\mathbf{2}, \mathbf{1})$ to both sides of 6.22(2); the second by changing 1 into 3 in 6.22(2), multiplying by $\not{A}(\mathbf{3})\, K^0(\mathbf{3}, \mathbf{1})$ to the right. integrating over $d^4\mathbf{x}_3$, and finally adding $-e\not{A}(\mathbf{2})\, K^1(\mathbf{2}, \mathbf{1})$ to both sides; and so on . . . ,

We can verify [using 6.22(5*b*), 6.12(15′) and (3)] that for each term of the expansion (5) we have $\gamma_4\bar{K}^n(\mathbf{1},\mathbf{2}) = -K^n(\mathbf{2},\mathbf{1})$; thus the foregoing expression for $\psi(\mathbf{2})$ will have the same form as the equation preceding 6.22(3). With this remark the proof is completed.

b. First-Order Transition Amplitude. The zeroth-order propagation of the electron is described by the vacuum kernel $K^0(\mathbf{2},\mathbf{1})$:

$$\psi^0(\mathbf{2}) = \oint K^0(\mathbf{2},\mathbf{1})\not{n}\,\psi(\mathbf{1})\,d^3\mathbf{x}_1, \tag{7}$$

with the integration extended to the flux coming from all space, both past and future.

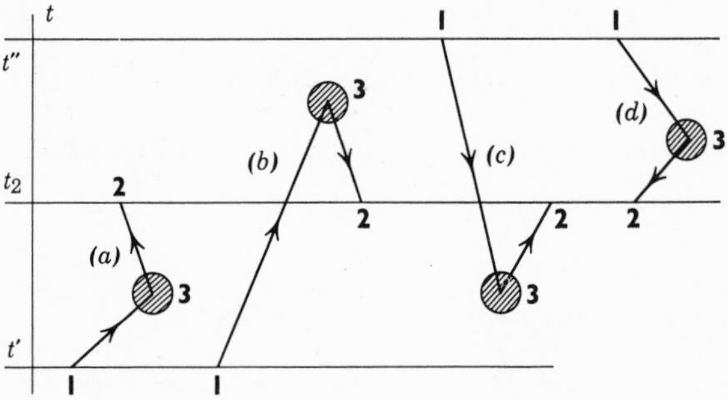

Fig. 6.23-1. Different contributions to the first order amplitude $\psi^1(\mathbf{2})$, included in the integral (8): (*a*) forward scattering at **3** of an electron coming from the past (normal electron scattering at **3**); (*b*) backward scattering of an electron coming from the past (annihilation of an electron with a positron at **3**); (*c*) forward scattering at **3** of an electron coming from the future (pair production at **3**); (*d*) backward scattering of an electron coming from the future (positron scattering at **3**).

The electromagnetic field contributes a new term to the amplitude $\psi(\mathbf{2})$. The first-order contribution is obtained from the vacuum kernel $K^1(\mathbf{2},\mathbf{1})$:

$$\begin{aligned}\psi^1(\mathbf{2}) &= \oint K^1(\mathbf{2},\mathbf{1})\not{n}\,\psi(\mathbf{1})\,d^3\mathbf{x}_1 \\ &= -ie\oint d^3\mathbf{x}_1\int K^0(\mathbf{2},\mathbf{3})\,\not{A}(\mathbf{3})\,K^0(\mathbf{3},\mathbf{1})\not{n}\,\psi(\mathbf{1})\,d^4\mathbf{x}_3.\end{aligned} \tag{8}$$

As (7) expresses "direct" propagation from **1** and **2**, so (8) can be interpreted as describing direct propagation from **1** to **3**, interaction at **3**, and direct propagation from **3** to **2**. Since K^0 propagates forward and backward in time we have contributions to the integral for all values of t_3 (before and after t_2) at which the interaction may take place. The different processes corresponding to first-order contribution (only one interaction) are explained with the illustration of Fig. 6.23-1.

Let us consider now the transition amplitude (matrix element) in a process induced in first order by the electromagnetic interaction. For this we specify two orthogonal "unperturbed" states, initial and final,

(9)
$$\psi_{\mathrm{I}}(\mathbf{1}) = w_{\mathrm{I}}(\mathbf{p}_{\mathrm{I}})e^{\mp i\mathbf{p}_{\mathrm{I}}\cdot\mathbf{x}_1}$$
$$\psi_{\mathrm{F}}(\mathbf{1}) = w_{\mathrm{F}}(\mathbf{p}_{\mathrm{F}})e^{\mp i\mathbf{p}_{\mathrm{F}}\cdot\mathbf{x}_1},$$

where the spinors w_{I} and w_{F} specify spin and charge (electron or positron) state. If, for instance, we are interested in the processes originated by an electron, the initial state propagates forward in time from (**1**) to (**2**) and becomes

(10)
$$\psi_{\mathrm{I}}(\mathbf{2}) = \psi_{\mathrm{I}}^{0}(\mathbf{2}) + \psi_{\mathrm{I}}^{1}(\mathbf{2}) + \cdots$$
$$= \int K^0(\mathbf{2},\mathbf{1})\gamma_4\psi_{\mathrm{I}}(\mathbf{1})\,d^3\mathbf{x}_1 + \int K^1(\mathbf{2},\mathbf{1})\gamma_4\psi_{\mathrm{I}}(\mathbf{1})\,d^3\mathbf{x}_1 + \cdots.$$

Since $\psi_{\mathrm{I}}^{0}(\mathbf{2})$ is orthogonal to $\psi_{\mathrm{F}}^{0}(\mathbf{2})$, the amplitude of final state contained in the expression (10) is[1]

(11)
$$\langle\psi_{\mathrm{F}}^{0}(t_2)\mid\psi_{\mathrm{I}}^{1}(t_2)\rangle$$
$$= \int \bar\psi_{\mathrm{F}}^{0}(\mathbf{2})\gamma_4\,\psi_{\mathrm{I}}^{1}(\mathbf{2})\,d^3\mathbf{x}_2$$
$$= \int \bar\psi_{\mathrm{F}}^{0}(\mathbf{2})\gamma_4\,K^1(\mathbf{2},\mathbf{1})\gamma_4\,\psi_{\mathrm{I}}(\mathbf{1})\,d^3\mathbf{x}_2\,d^3\mathbf{x}_1$$
$$= -ie\int \bar\psi_{\mathrm{F}}^{0}(\mathbf{2})\gamma_4\,K^0(\mathbf{2},\mathbf{3})\,A\!\!\!/(\mathbf{3})\,K^0(\mathbf{3},\mathbf{1})\gamma_4\,\psi_{\mathrm{I}}(\mathbf{1})\,d^3\mathbf{x}_2\,d^4\mathbf{x}_3\,d^3\mathbf{x}_1$$
$$= -ie\int \bar\psi_{\mathrm{F}}^{0}(\mathbf{3})\,A\!\!\!/(\mathbf{3})\,\psi_{\mathrm{I}}^{0}(\mathbf{3})\,d^4\mathbf{x}_3$$
$$= -ie\int (\bar w_{\mathrm{F}}\,A\!\!\!/(\mathbf{3})w_{\mathrm{I}})e^{i(\mathbf{p}_{\mathrm{F}}-\mathbf{p}_{\mathrm{I}})\cdot\mathbf{x}_3}\,d^4\mathbf{x}_3$$

c. First-Order Transition Probability: Interaction with Virtual Photons. The probability of transition between the (unperturbed) states ψ_{I} and ψ_{F} is given by the square of (11). If many final states are considered, the transition probability must be summed over all of them. If we assume that there are $\rho(E_{\mathrm{F}})$ equivalent states per unit final energy E_{F}, the integrated transition probability is

(12)
$$w_f = \int \rho(E_{\mathrm{F}})\,|\langle\psi_{\mathrm{F}}^{0}|\,\psi_{\mathrm{I}}^{1}\rangle|^2\,dE_{\mathrm{F}}$$
$$= \int \rho(E_{\mathrm{F}})\,dE_{\mathrm{F}}\left|-ie\int(\bar w_{\mathrm{F}}A\!\!\!/(\mathbf{x})w_{\mathrm{I}})e^{i(\mathbf{p}_{\mathrm{F}}-\mathbf{p}_{\mathrm{I}})\cdot\mathbf{x}}\,d^4\mathbf{x}\right|^2$$

[1] For the transformations of (11) we use successively (10), (3), 6.22(3), and (9).

Let us assume that $\mathbf{A}$ varies with time with frequency ω,

$$\mathbf{A}(\mathbf{x}) = \mathbf{A}_0(\mathbf{x})e^{\mp i\omega t}, \tag{13}$$

and observe that the square of the integral in dt can be written

$$\left| \int e^{i(E_F - E_I \mp \omega)t}\, dt \right|^2 = 2\pi\delta(E_F - E_I \mp \omega)\int e^{i(E_F - E_I \mp \omega)t}\, dt; \tag{14}$$

the δ function ensures conservation of energy, if the upper (lower) sign corresponds to absorption (emission). The integral in dt is now at the first power. Then (12) becomes

$$w_f = \left| -ie\int (\bar{w}_F \not{A}_0(\mathbf{x}) w_I) e^{-i(\mathbf{p}_F - \mathbf{p}_I)\cdot\mathbf{x}}\, d^3\mathbf{x} \right|^2 \times 2\pi \int \rho(E_F) e^{i(E_F - E_I \mp \omega)t}\, \delta(E_F - E_I \mp \omega)\, dE_F\, dt. \tag{15}$$

The integral in dE_F is immediately performed because of the δ function, and the last integral is

$$\rho(E_I \pm \omega)\int dt.$$

The transition probability is proportional to the time of integration, which can be considered as the time during which the perturbation acts. Thus we have found a formula for the transition probability per unit time:

$$w = 2\pi\rho(E_F)\,|M^{(1)}|^2, \tag{16}$$

where $E_F = E_I \pm \omega$, and the "*first-order matrix element*" is[1]

$$M^{(1)} = -ie\int (\bar{w}_F \not{A}_0(\mathbf{x}) w_I) e^{-i(\mathbf{p}_F - \mathbf{p}_I)\cdot\mathbf{x}}\, d^3\mathbf{x}. \tag{17}$$

We have reached a formulation of the theory similar to that used in Chapter 4. Though the matrix elements have a different form, they are three-dimensional integrals, and their relation to the transition probability is the same as in the nonrelativistic case.

The integral in $d^3\mathbf{x}$ vanishes unless the electromagnetic field $\mathbf{A}_0(\mathbf{x})$ has components that vary with position as $e^{i(\mathbf{p}_F - \mathbf{p}_I)\cdot\mathbf{x}}$; in other words, (17) automatically selects the Fourier components of $\mathbf{A}_0(\mathbf{x})$, which are appropriate for the conservation of momentum between the electron and the electromagnetic field.

Formula 17 is simplified if we use a special symbol for such components:

$$\not{a}(\mathbf{q}) = \int \not{A}_0(\mathbf{x}) e^{-i\mathbf{q}\cdot\mathbf{x}}\, d^3\mathbf{x}, \tag{18}$$

[1] There is a phase difference $-i$ relative to the matrix elements of the perturbing Hamiltonian.

in which case we may write

(19) $$M^{(1)} = -ie(\bar{w}_F \not{a}(\mathbf{p}_F - \mathbf{p}_I) w_I).$$

The interacting particle receives from the field an amount of energy and momentum "as if" it had absorbed a quantum of energy $\omega_F - \omega_I$ and momentum $\mathbf{p}_F - \mathbf{p}_I$. Though this quantum is an oscillatory component of an electromagnetic field, it cannot properly be called a photon, since its rest mass, $|\omega_F - \omega_1|^2 - |\mathbf{p}_F - \mathbf{p}_I|^2$, is different from zero. But it has become quite usual to describe the interaction with the field as the interaction with a "*virtual*" *photon* or with a photon that is "*not on the mass shell.*"

It is important to remember that the absorption or emission of a "*real*" photon ($k^2 = 0$) by a free particle of nonvanishing mass violates the laws of conservation of energy and momentum.

d. Interaction with Point Particles. Of particular interest in nuclear physics is the case in which the field $\mathbf{A}_0(\mathbf{x})$ acting on the electron is produced by a point particle.

For a spinless point particle of mass M, charge Ze, and momentum $\mathbf{P}$ we may write[1]

(20*a*) $$A_{0\mu} = \frac{j_\mu}{r} \quad \text{with} \quad j_\mu = ZeP_\mu/M,$$

from which[2]

(20*b*) $$\not{a}(q) = \frac{Ze}{M}\frac{4\pi}{q^2}\not{P}.$$

Thus (19) becomes

(21) $$M^{(1)} = -i\frac{Ze^2}{M}(\bar{w}_F \not{P} w_I)\frac{4\pi}{|\mathbf{p}_F - \mathbf{p}_I|^2}.$$

This formula is applicable to the coulomb scattering of electrons. The computations is developed in 6.26a.

If, instead, the field $\mathbf{A}_0(\mathbf{x})$ acting on the electron (a) is produced by another particle (b) of charge Ze and spin $\frac{1}{2}$,

(22) $$A_{0\mu} = \frac{j_\mu}{r} \quad \text{with} \quad j_\mu = Ze(\bar{w}_F^{(b)} \gamma_\mu^{(b)} w_I^{(b)}),$$

[1] In the gage where div $\mathbf{A} = 0$.

[2] $$\int \frac{e^{-i\mathbf{q}\cdot\mathbf{x}}}{r}\,d\mathbf{x} = -2\pi \int e^{-iqr\cos\theta}\, r\,dr\,d\cos\theta = 4\pi \int \frac{e^{iqr} - e^{-iqr}}{2iq}\,dr$$
$$= \frac{4\pi}{q}\int \sin(qr)\,dr = \frac{4\pi}{q^2}\lim_{a^2\to 0}\int e^{-a^2x}\sin x\,dx = \frac{4\pi}{q^2}.$$

In (20*b*) and (21) P_μ stands for the matrix element of P_μ between the initial and final state of the particle of mass M, which produces the field.

and (19) becomes

(23) $$M^{(1)} = -4\pi i Z e^2 \frac{(\bar{w}_F^{(a)} \gamma_\mu^{(a)} w_I^{(a)})(\bar{w}_F^{(b)} \gamma_\mu^{(b)} w_I^{(b)})}{|\mathbf{p}_F^{(a)} - \mathbf{p}_I^{(a)}|^2}.$$

In this form the first-order matrix element can be used for electron-electron scattering [6.24(5)].

e. Higher Order Processes. The transition amplitude for order n is obtained as in (11) by writing $\psi_I{}^n$ and $K^n(2, 1)$ in place of $\psi_I{}^1$ and $K^1(2, 1)$.

For instance, we obtain in second order for an initial electron

(24) $$\langle \psi_F{}^0(t_2) \mid \psi_I{}^2(t_2) \rangle$$
$$= \int \bar{\psi}_F{}^0(2)\gamma_4\, K^2(2, 1)\gamma_4\, \psi_I(1)\, d^3\mathbf{x}_2\, d^3\mathbf{x}_1$$
$$= (-ie)^2 \int \bar{\psi}_F{}^0(2)\gamma_4\, K^0(2, 3)\, A\!\!\!/(3)\, K^0(3, 4)$$
$$\times\, A\!\!\!/(4)\, K^0(4, 1)\gamma_4\, \psi_I(1)\, d^3\mathbf{x}_2\, d^4\mathbf{x}_3\, d^4\mathbf{x}_4\, d^3\mathbf{x}_1$$
$$= (-ie)^2 \int [\bar{w}_F\, A\!\!\!/(3)\, K^0(3, 4)\, A\!\!\!/(4) w_I] e^{i(\mathbf{p}_F \cdot \mathbf{x}_3 - \mathbf{p}_I \cdot \mathbf{x}_4)}\, d^4\mathbf{x}_3\, d^4\mathbf{x}_4.$$

The integrated transition probability is, as in (12),

(25) $$w_f = \int \rho(E_F)\, |\langle \psi_F{}^0 \mid \psi_I{}^2 \rangle|^2\, dE_F.$$

Let us assume, as in (13),

(26) $$\mathbf{A}(\mathbf{x}_3) = \mathbf{A}_0(\mathbf{x}_3) e^{\mp i\omega_3 t_3}; \qquad \mathbf{A}(\mathbf{x}_4) = \mathbf{A}_0(\mathbf{x}_4) e^{\mp i\omega_4 t_4}$$

(again the upper sign corresponds to absorption and the lower to emission) and let us introduce in (25) the expression of $K^0(3, 4)$ from 6.22(5*a*). Then we can treat the square of the integral in dt_3 and the integral in dE_F as was done in (c). Observing that the integral in dt_4 is $2\pi\delta(E - E_I \mp \omega_4)$, the integral in dE (fourth component of p) is performed by replacing E with $E_I \pm \omega_4$. We find that the transition probability per unit time is given by an expression like (16), with $M^{(1)}$ replaced by the *second-order matrix element*

(27) $$M^{(2)} = \frac{(-ie)^2}{(2\pi)^3} \int \left(\bar{w}_F\, A\!\!\!/_0(\mathbf{x}_3) \frac{i}{p\!\!\!/ - m} A\!\!\!/_0(\mathbf{x}_4) w_I \right)$$
$$\times\, e^{i(\mathbf{p} - \mathbf{p}_F) \cdot \mathbf{x}_3} e^{i(\mathbf{p}_I - \mathbf{p}) \cdot \mathbf{x}_4}\, d^3\mathbf{x}_3\, d^3\mathbf{x}_4\, d^3\mathbf{p},$$

with the time component of $p\!\!\!/$ equal to $\gamma_4(E_I \pm \omega_4)$.

In the notation introduced in (18), (27) becomes

(28) $$M^{(2)} = (-ie)^2 \int \left(\bar{w}_F a\!\!\!/(\mathbf{p}_F - \mathbf{p}) \frac{i}{p\!\!\!/ - m} a\!\!\!/(\mathbf{p} - \mathbf{p}_I) w_I \right) \frac{d^3\mathbf{p}}{(2\pi^3)};$$

the integration extends to all intermediate momentum states, whose number, in conformity with 5.11(2), is $\int (2\pi)^{-3} d^3\mathbf{p}$ for a unit normalization volume.

Formula 28 describes the interaction with two virtual photons corresponding to the factors $\not{a}(\mathbf{p} - \mathbf{p}_I)$ and $\not{a}(\mathbf{p}_F - \mathbf{p})$, whereas the factor $i(\not{p} - m)^{-1}$ represents the free propagation of the electron in the intermediate state between the points of interaction $\mathbf{x}_3$ and $\mathbf{x}_4$.

The matrix elements of still higher order can be obtained as an obvious extension of the analytical procedure. More directly, they can be written by extending intuitively the result of the computation (28) to include more interactions and more free propagations: for this purpose the use of diagrams, described in 6.24, is helpful.

f. Interaction with Real Photons. The most interesting application of second- and higher order perturbation theory is to the absorption and emission of real photons, which is forbidden in first order because of conservation of energy and momentum.

The different second-order processes initiated by an electron (arrow pointing upward in initial state) are illustrated in Fig. 6.23-2. In these processes the electron passes through an intermediate state which propagates forward or backward and can be interpreted as an intermediate electron or positron.

Diagrams (*a*) and (*b*) correspond to Compton scattering if the interactions at **3** and **4** are with real photons, of which one is absorbed and the other emitted. The same diagrams represent second-order scattering in an external field if the two photons are virtual. If one of the photons is virtual and the other is real, they describe the scattering in an external field accompanied by the emission of a quantum (x-ray emission, bremsstrahlung[1]).

Similarly (*c*) and (*d*) represent two-quantum annihilation, and (*e*) and (*f*) two-quantum pair production.

Finally if the sense of the arrows is inverted the diagrams of Fig. 6.23-2 describe the same processes initiated by a positron.

Since the time integrals have already been performed and the time dependance has been eliminated from the states and fields appearing in the matrix elements (27) and (28), the integrals are three-dimensional as are those in Chapter 4, and we can use the techniques developed there.

Let us develop a little further the interaction of an electron with two real photons such as in the Compton effect. Let us call $\mathbf{k}_3 = (k_3, \omega_3)$ and $\mathbf{k}_4 = (k_4, \omega_4)$ the four-momenta of the photons interacting at points **3** and **4**; let us also suppose, for simplicity, that absorption processes occur from single-photon states ($\mathsf{a} = 1$) and emission processes from no-photon

[1] In 6.24 this process is called third order, counting also the interaction of the electromagnetic field with the heavy charge which produces the field.

states ($a^\dagger = 1$). In order to compute the matrix element the fields $\mathbf{A}_0(\mathbf{x}_3)$ or $\mathbf{A}_0(\mathbf{x}_4)$ are expanded in creation and annihilation operators according to 4.12(20) and the appropriate terms are used in (27):

$$A\!\!\!/_0(3) \to \sqrt{\frac{2\pi}{\omega_3}}\, \not{\epsilon}_3 e^{\pm i\mathbf{k}_3\cdot\mathbf{x}_3}$$

(29)

$$A\!\!\!/_0(4) \to \sqrt{\frac{2\pi}{\omega_4}}\, \not{\epsilon}_4 e^{\pm i\mathbf{k}_4\cdot\mathbf{x}_4},$$

$\hat{\boldsymbol{\epsilon}}_3$ and $\hat{\boldsymbol{\epsilon}}_4$ are the unit vectors (assumed real) defining the polarization of the two quanta.

The specification of the momenta of the interacting photons fixes the Fourier component of the field and determines the momentum of the

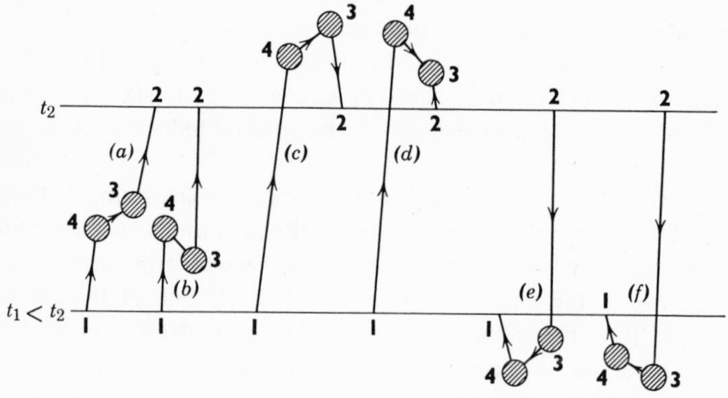

Fig. 6.23-2. Second order processes initiated by an electron.

intermediate state[1]. Thus there is no need to sum over intermediate momentum states as in (28), and we obtain a matrix element

$$M^{(2)} = (-ie)^2\left(\bar{w}_F \sqrt{\frac{2\pi}{\omega_3}}\, \not{\epsilon}_3 \frac{i}{\not{p} - m} \sqrt{\frac{2\pi}{\omega_4}}\, \not{\epsilon}_4 w_I\right), \tag{30}$$

with $\mathbf{p} = \mathbf{p}_I \pm \mathbf{k}_4 = \mathbf{p}_F \mp \mathbf{k}_3$, where the upper sign refers to absorption and the lower sign, to emission.

This formula has an almost graphical meaning. We see that the initial electron (factor w_I) interacts with the absorption or emission of the

[1] If we introduce (29) into (27), the integral in $d^3\mathbf{x}_4$ is

$$\int e^{i(\mathbf{p}_I - \mathbf{p} \pm \mathbf{k}_4)\cdot\mathbf{x}_4}\, d^3\mathbf{x}_4 = (2\pi)^3\, \delta(\mathbf{p}_I \pm \mathbf{k}_4 - \mathbf{p}).$$

Thus the value of $\mathbf{p}$ is fixed and the other integrals are immediately performed. We obtain (30) if $\mathbf{p}_F - \mathbf{p}_I = \pm\, \mathbf{k}_3 \pm \mathbf{k}_4$; otherwise the result is zero.

photon $\mathbf{k}_4$ (factor $-ie\sqrt{2\pi/\omega_4}\,\not{e}_4$), propagates freely with four-momentum $\mathbf{p}_\mathrm{I} \pm \mathbf{k}_4$ [factor $i(\not{p} - m)^{-1}$] until it interacts with the photon $\mathbf{k}_3$ (factor $-ie\sqrt{2\pi/\omega_3}\,\not{e}_3$), and finally reaches the final state ($\bar{w}_\mathrm{F}$). factor).

The four-momentum of the intermediate electron is such that $p^2 = (\mathbf{p}_\mathrm{I} \pm \mathbf{k}_4)^2 = p_\mathrm{I}{}^2 + k_4{}^2 \pm 2\mathbf{p}_\mathrm{I} \cdot \mathbf{k}_4 = m^2 + 0 \pm 2\mathbf{p}_\mathrm{I} \cdot \mathbf{k}_4 \neq m^2$. Thus the intermediate electron does not satisfy the kinematics of a particle of mass m; this situation is described by saying that *the intermediate electron is "virtual," or is not on the "mass shell,"* or (as in the older literature) that momentum, but not energy, is conserved in transitions to intermediate states.

Higher order matrix elements can be computed with the procedure developed here; but since the intuitive meaning of the formulas is now clear, they can also be written directly. For this purpose it is useful to make use of graphs, as we shall see in Section 6.24.

An example of computation of a second-order process is given in 6.27.

6.24 *Feynman Diagrams and Matrix Elements*

a. Processes Involving Electrons and Photons. The matrix element for electromagnetic processes—not involving bound states—is most easily written with the help of the famous Feynman diagrams, which are an intuitive graphical method of describing both the physical process and the perturbation calculation.

In drawing the diagrams, each electron is represented by a continuous line with arrows indicating its direction of propagation. In our convention the arrows point up (toward the future) for negative electrons and down (towards the past) for positrons.

Each photon, real or virtual, is represented by a wavy line.

The process is broken down in a succession of *elementary interactions*; in each interaction there is the *absorption* or the *emission of a single photon* (electron-photon vertex). Since each absorption or emission involves a factor $\approx 1/\sqrt{137}$ in the amplitude, the diagrams with the *minimum number of photons* are the most important. Only these are considered in the present discussion[1].

However, *all different diagrams* involving the minimum number of photons must be drawn. Two diagrams are different if they differ in the order of the absorptions and emissions, since the corresponding amplitudes do not commute.

Fig. 6.24-1 shows the two diagrams of Compton scattering constructed according to these rules.

[1] Higher order diagrams give divergent contributions to the matrix element if we do not use appropriate renormalization procedures.

In order to define the notation, it is useful to write next to the lines of the incident and emerging particles the symbols used for their momenta. Intermediate momenta are then computed whenever possible assuming conservation at each vertex, and written next to the appropriate lines.

We can now indicate in the diagram the factors entering the matrix element (circled symbols in Fig. 6.24-1). These factors are obtained from

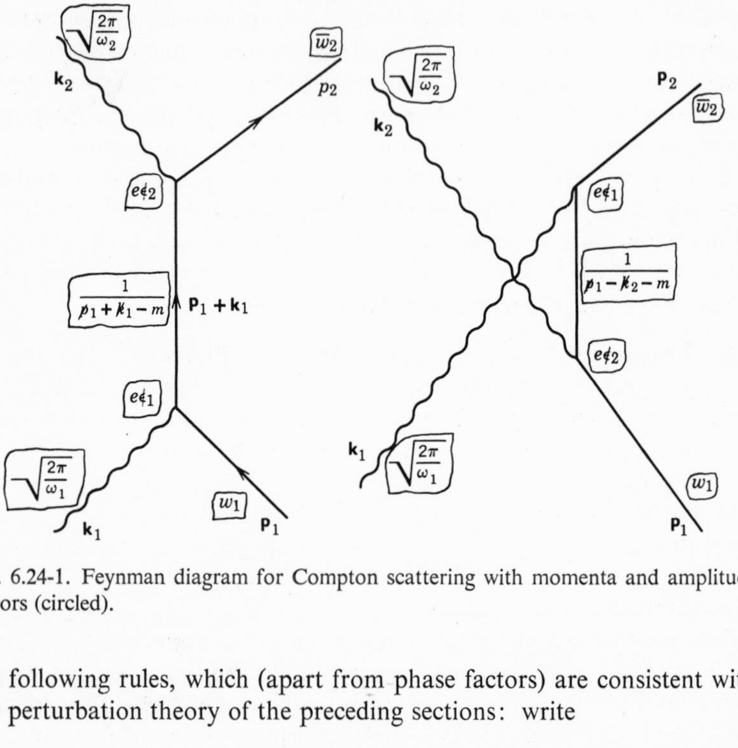

Fig. 6.24-1. Feynman diagram for Compton scattering with momenta and amplitude factors (circled).

the following rules, which (apart from phase factors) are consistent with the perturbation theory of the preceding sections: write

- a factor $w(\mathbf{p})$ next to each entering electron line (initial spinor normalized so that $w^\dagger w = E/m$);
- a factor $\bar{w}(\mathbf{p})$ next to each outgoing electron line (final spinor normalized so that $w^\dagger w = E/m$);
- a factor $\sqrt{2\pi/\omega}$ next to each entering or outgoing photon line (normalization of each photon);
- a factor $e\not{\epsilon}$ next to each real photon vertex (e is the charge of the particle, and $\hat{\boldsymbol{\epsilon}}$, a unit vector in the direction of polarization of the photon);
- a factor $e\not{a}$ next to each virtual photon vertex representing the interaction of the electron with an external field; in the interaction between point particles the factor at the virtual fermion-photon vertex may be written

$e\gamma_\mu$, provided we introduce a virtual photon propagator[1] $-4\pi/k^2$ (6.23d);

a factor $(\not{p} - m)^{-1}$ next to each virtual electron line propagating between two vertices (electron propagator in momentum representation).

Finally we collect the factors in a formula (following the diagrams in the direction of the arrows and writing from right to left) and integrate ($\int (2\pi)^{-3}\, d^3\mathbf{p}$) over the intermediate momenta which remain indeterminate. The contributions of the different diagrams are added together, symmetrizing over undistinguishable photons, and antisymmetrizing over undistinguishable electrons.

It is not difficult to verify that the squares of the matrix elements obtained from this procedure are the same as those predicted by the perturbation theory of 6.23. The phase factors of our rules have been chosen to agree, in the nonrelativistic limit, with those of the matrix elements of the perturbing Hamiltonian.

We now present examples of the application of the rules to writing matrix elements for some fundamental processes. In 6.26 and 6.27 we develop a few examples of detailed computation of cross sections and transition probabilities.

b. Examples

(i) *Compton Effect.* The diagrams in Fig. 6.24-1 describe the absorption of a photon of momentum $\mathbf{k}_1$ and the emission of a photon of momentum $\mathbf{k}_2$ by an electron.

[1] The free photon propagation kernel $K_\gamma(\mathbf{2}, \mathbf{1})$ can be introduced similarly to the electron kernel [see 6.22(2)] from the equation $\Box^2 K_\gamma(\mathbf{2}, \mathbf{1}) = 4\pi\delta(\mathbf{2}, \mathbf{1})$. The factor 4π multiplying the δ function is needed to conform with our choice of electromagnetic units: it is convenient if we want to use $K_\gamma(\mathbf{2}, \mathbf{1})$ as a Green's function to solve the inhomogeneous equation $\Box^2 A_\mu = 4\pi j_\mu$.

By solving the equation for $K_\gamma(\mathbf{2}, \mathbf{1})$ we obtain

$$K_\gamma(\mathbf{2}, \mathbf{1}) = -\frac{4\pi}{(2\pi)^4} \int \frac{e^{-i\mathbf{k}\cdot(\mathbf{x}_2 - \mathbf{x}_1)}}{k^2}\, d^4\mathbf{k}.$$

The ambiguity in the integration around the pole at $k^2 = 0$ is removed if we specify that the photon propagates only forward in time. Thus the path of integration must be closed following the lower infinite semicircle, and we must pass above the pole at $k_4 = k$; or alternatively, the pole could be lowered by assigning a small negative imaginary mass to the photon.

The Fourier component of $K_\gamma(\mathbf{2}, \mathbf{1})$, to be used in the matrix element, is $-4\pi/k^2$. This is in agreement with the result of perturbation theory (6.23d).

Stated in simple words, the $1/k^2$ form of the photon propagator corresponds to the $1/r$ dependence of electromagnetic potential (see footnote on page 397).

Following the rules, we obtain the matrix element

$$(1)\quad e^2\frac{2\pi}{\sqrt{\omega_1\omega_2}}\left[\left(\bar{w}_2\not{e}_2\frac{1}{\not{p}_1+\not{k}_1-m}\not{e}_1w_1\right)+\left(\bar{w}_2\not{e}_1\frac{1}{\not{p}_1-\not{k}_2-m}\not{e}_2w_1\right)\right].$$

The cross section obtained from this diagram was first computed by Klein and Nishina: they obtained, for plane polarized photons[1]

$$(2a)\qquad \sigma=\frac{e^4}{4m^2}\frac{\omega_2^{\,2}}{\omega_1^{\,2}}\,d\Omega_2\left[\frac{\omega_2}{\omega_1}+\frac{\omega_1}{\omega_2}-2+4(\hat{\epsilon}_1\cdot\hat{\epsilon}_2)^2\right],$$

and, averaging over polarizations

$$(2b)\qquad \sigma=\frac{e^4}{2m^2}\frac{\omega_2^{\,2}}{\omega_1^{\,2}}\,d\Omega_2\left(\frac{\omega_2}{\omega_1}+\frac{\omega_1}{\omega_2}-\sin^2\theta\right),$$

where θ is the Compton scattering angle.

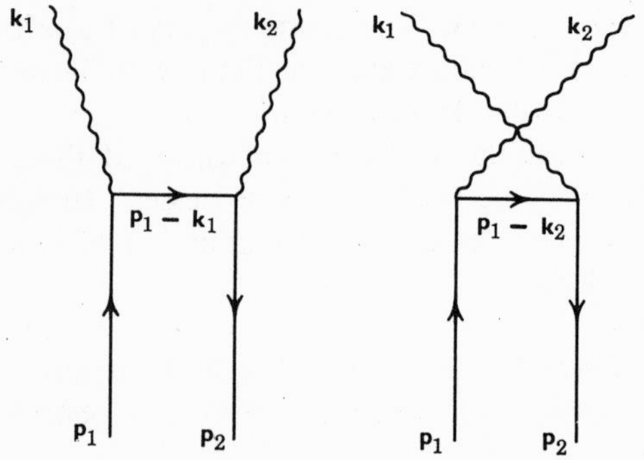

Fig. 6.24-2. Feynman diagrams for two quantum annihilation.

For circularly polarized photons on polarized electrons we find

$$(2c)\qquad \frac{d\sigma}{d\omega}=\frac{e^4}{2m^2}\frac{\omega_2^{\,2}}{\omega_1^{\,2}}\left[\left(\frac{\omega_1}{\omega_2}+\frac{\omega_2}{\omega_1}-\sin^2\theta\right)\pm\left(\frac{\omega_1}{\omega_2}-\frac{\omega_2}{\omega_1}\right)\cos\theta\right]$$

with the + sign valid if the electron's spin is parallel to the angular momentum of the γ ray.

(ii) *Pair Annihilation.* The annihilation of a pair of electrons and positrons must be at least a second-order process for conservation of energy and momentum. The diagrams in Fig. 6.24-2 correspond to the two-step scattering of an electron from forward to backward propagation in time.

From the diagrams we easily obtain the amplitude

$$(3)\quad -e^2\frac{2\pi}{\sqrt{\omega_1\omega_2}}\left[\left(\bar{w}_1\not{e}_2\frac{1}{\not{p}_1-\not{k}_1-m}\not{e}_1w_1\right)+\left(\bar{w}_2\not{e}_1\frac{1}{\not{p}_1-\not{k}_2-m}\not{e}_2w_1\right)\right].$$

[1] For the details of the computation in modern notation see (Fe-61).

The annihilation cross section for positrons of energy E colliding with electrons at rest is

$$(4)\quad \sigma = \frac{\pi e^4}{m^2}\frac{1}{E+m}\left[\frac{E^2+4mE+m^2}{E^2-m^2}\times\log\left(\frac{E}{m}+\sqrt{\frac{E^2-m^2}{m^2}}\right)-\frac{E+3m}{\sqrt{E^2-m^2}}\right].$$

In 6.27 we compute this cross section in the limit $E\to m$.

(iii) *Electron-electron Scattering.* The process in Fig. 6.24-3 is described as the exchange of a virtual photon between two electrons. Since the

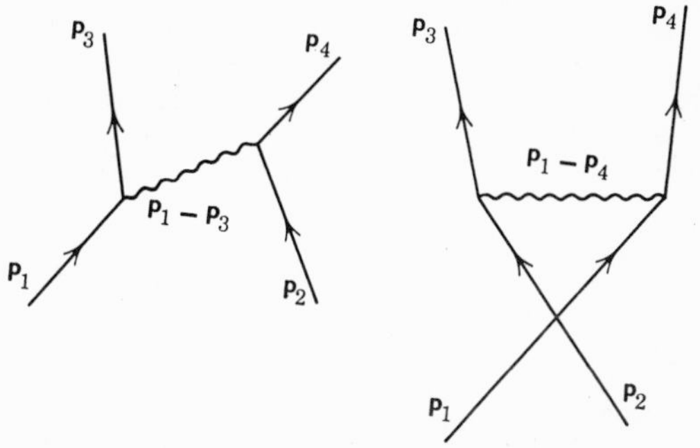

Fig. 6.24-3. Diagrams for electron-electron (Møller) scattering.

amplitude must now be antisymmetrized between the electrons, we obtain the matrix element:

$$(5)\qquad -4\pi e^2\left[\frac{(\bar{w}_4\gamma_\mu w_2)(\bar{w}_3\gamma_\mu w_1)}{|\mathbf{p}_1-\mathbf{p}_3|^2}-\frac{(\bar{w}_4\gamma_\mu w_1)(\bar{w}_3\gamma_\mu w_2)}{|\mathbf{p}_4-\mathbf{p}_1|^2}\right]$$

Observe that (5) is consistent with 6.23(23)[1].

The cross section obtained from (5) is the Moeller scattering cross section:

$$(6)\quad d\sigma = \frac{2e^4p\,d\Omega}{E^3}\left[\frac{4x+8x\cos\theta-2\sin^2\theta+4\cos\theta}{1-\cos\theta}+\frac{4x^2-8x\cos\theta+2\sin^2\theta-4\cos\theta}{(1+\cos\theta)^2}+\frac{4(1+x)(x-3)}{(1-\cos\theta)(1+\cos\theta)}\right]$$

where $x = E^2/p^2$.

(iv) *Higher Order Processes.* As examples of third-order process (three acts of emission and absorption), we reproduce in Fig. 6.24-4 and 5 one of

[1] For comparison with 6.23(23) note that in the center-of-mass system $p_{1t}-p_{3t} = p_{1t}-p_{4t} = 0$. Note also that the electrostatic part of the direct (not exchange) matrix element is positive ($\gamma_4\gamma_4 = 1$, $|\mathbf{p}_1-\mathbf{p}_3|^2 = -|\mathbf{p}_1-\mathbf{p}_3|^2$) as it should be for a repulsive force.

the diagrams for double Compton scattering and for three-quantum annihilation.

Other processes of the same order include the radiative correction to coulomb scattering (emission of bremsstrahlung, Fig. 6.24-6) and pair production in the field of a nucleus (Fig. 6.24-7).

c. Processes Involving Nucleons. (i) *Low Energy Approximations.* Nucleons are fermions and their interaction with the electromagnetic field is similar to that of electrons. In low-energy nuclear physics, however,

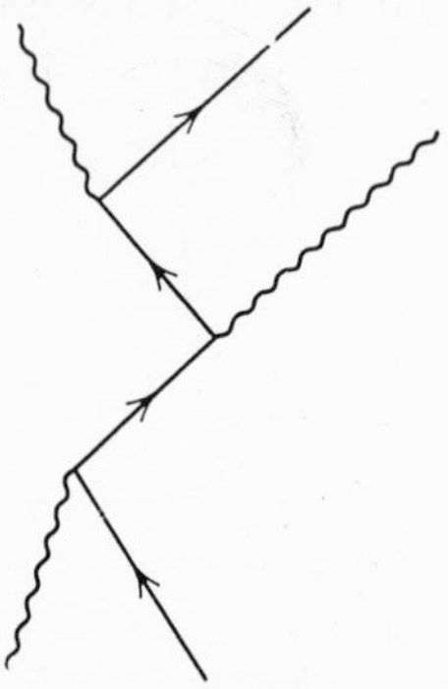

Fig. 6.24-4. One of the diagrams for double Compton scattering.

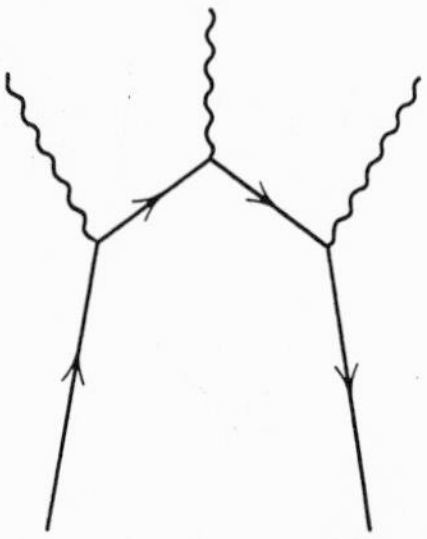

Fig. 6.24-5. One of the diagrams for three-quantum annihilation.

the approximations for $v \ll 1$ are often valid (Chapter 4), and we can make the following simplifications:

The factors w are replaced by Pauli spinors (and the space part of the wave function is a solution of Schrödinger equation);

The nucleon-photon vertex $e\not{\epsilon} = e(-\boldsymbol{\gamma} \cdot \hat{\boldsymbol{\epsilon}})$ becomes[1] $\approx -(e_\alpha/M)\hat{\boldsymbol{\epsilon}} \cdot \mathbf{p}$ with $e_\alpha = \frac{1}{2}(1 + \tau_\zeta)e$; but to this factor we must add the zero-velocity relativistic effects such as the interaction of the Dirac magnetic moment and the electrostatic neutron interaction (6.15b), and the coupling of the anomalous part of the moment. In conclusion we revert to the coupling of Chapter 4, corresponding to a vertex factor $-[(e_\alpha/M)\hat{\boldsymbol{\epsilon}} \cdot \mathbf{p}_\alpha + \mu_\alpha \boldsymbol{\sigma}_\alpha \cdot \mathbf{H}]$.

The propagator factor for a nucleon of momentum $\mathbf{p}$ after the absorption or the emission of quantum of momentum $\mathbf{k}$ may often be computed assuming $\mathbf{p} = (0, 0, 0, M)$ and $\gamma_i \ll \gamma_4 \approx 1$. Then $(\not{p}_\mathrm{I} \pm \not{k} - M)^{-1} \approx (\pm k_4)^{-1}$, in agreement with the result of second-order nonrelativistic perturbation theory which requires a factor $(E_{\text{initial}} - E_{\text{intermediate}})^{-1}$.

In some problems the nucleons can be considered as infinitely massive and always at rest. If they are combined in a nucleus of zero spin, we consider only the electrostatic effects, and the vertex factor is simply Ze. This approximation can be used in the diagrams of Figs. 6.24-6 and 7 and is developed in 6.26.

[1] In the gage where $\mathbf{A} = 0$.

(ii) *The High Energy Vertex.* In high-energy processes, however, the nucleons must be treated relativistically. In computing their electromagnetic interaction, we must include the anomalous magnetic moment and we must also take into account the form factors.

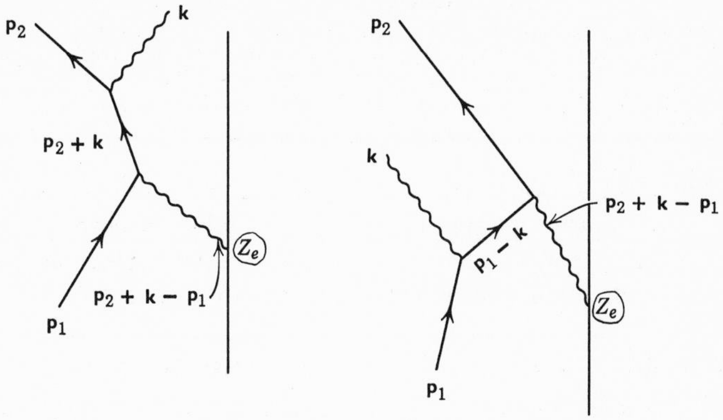

Fig. 6.24-6. Diagrams for emission of bremsstrahlung.

As pointed out in 3.33, there are four nucleon form factors of interest. Relativistically, they are invariant functions of the square of the four momentum transfer $k^2 = |\mathbf{p}_F - \mathbf{p}_I|^2$. The form factors are measured by electron-nucleon scattering and are most conveniently defined in the

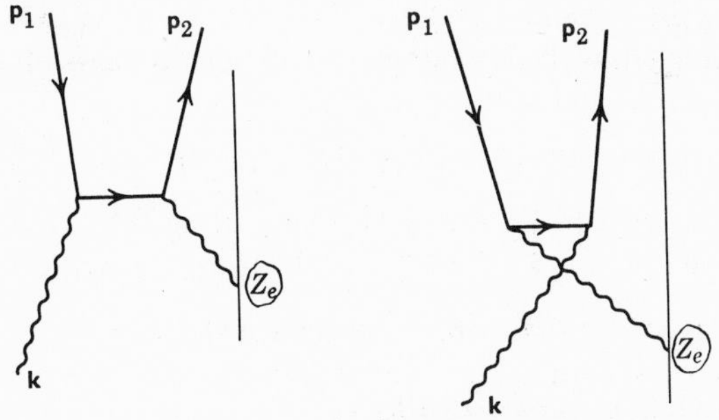

Fig. 6.24-7. Diagrams for pair production in the field of a nucleus.

center-of-mass system of the scattering, where the energy transfer k_4 is zero. If, in this system, $\rho_{N,c}$ and $\rho_{N,\mu}$ are the densities of charge and anomalous magnetic moment, the form factors are introduced as

$$F_{N,c}(k) = \frac{1}{e}\int e^{-i\mathbf{k}\cdot\mathbf{r}}\rho_{N,c}\, d^3\mathbf{r}$$

(7)

$$F_{N,\mu}(k) = \frac{1}{\mu_{a,N}}\int e^{-i\mathbf{k}\cdot\mathbf{r}}\rho_{N,\mu}\, d^3\mathbf{r}.$$

Clearly[1]

(8a) $$F_{p,c}(0) = F_{p,\mu}(0) = F_{n,\mu}(0) = 1,$$

but

(8b) $$F_{n,c}(0) = 0.$$

Taking the form factors into account, the Fourier transform of the current density due to the charge of the nucleons is[2]

(9) $$eF_{N,c}(\mathsf{k})(\bar{w}_{N,\mathrm{F}}\gamma_\mu w_{N,\mathrm{I}}).$$

To this current we must add the current due to the anomalous magnetic moment. Classically, a density of magnetization $\mathbf{m}$ corresponds to a current density $\mathbf{j} = \nabla \times \mathbf{m}$. Relativistically, the anomalous magnetic moment of a free point nucleon corresponds to a current[3]

$$\frac{1}{2} i\mu_{a,N}\partial_\mu[\bar{\psi}_{N,\mathrm{F}}(\gamma_\mu\gamma_\nu - \gamma_\nu\gamma_\mu)\psi_{N,\mathrm{I}}] = \mu_{a,N}\partial_\mu(\bar{\psi}_{N,\mathrm{F}}\sigma_{\mu\nu}\psi_{N,\mathrm{I}})$$

$$= \mu_{a,N}\,(\bar{w}_F\sigma_{\mu\nu}w_{\mathrm{I}})\partial_\mu e^{i(\mathbf{p}_\mathrm{F}-\mathbf{p}_\mathrm{I})\cdot\mathbf{x}} = \pm\, i\mu_{aN}(\bar{w}_\mathrm{F}\sigma_{\mu\nu}w_\mathrm{I})k_\mu e^{\pm i\mathbf{k}\cdot\mathbf{x}},$$

and its Fourier transform, including the form factor, is

(10) $$\pm iF_{N,\mu}(\mathsf{k})\mu_{a,N}(\bar{w}_\mathrm{F}\sigma_{\lambda\nu}w_\mathrm{I})k_\lambda,$$

where k is the four-momentum of the absorbed (+sign) or emitted (−sign) photon.

The factor at a nucleon-photon vertex of a Feynman diagram is obtained by projecting the current operator in the direction of the polatization of the photon $\hat{\boldsymbol{\epsilon}}$; including both charge and magnetic-moment coupling, this vertex factor is

(11a) $$eF_{N,c}(\mathsf{k})\not{\epsilon} \pm i\mu_{a,N}F_{N,\mu}(\mathsf{k})\sigma_{\lambda\nu}k_\lambda\epsilon_\nu.$$

This expression can be transformed by using 6.12(11) and (16d) and considering that k and $\hat{\boldsymbol{\epsilon}}$ are orthogonal. It can be written

(11b) $$eF_{N,c}(\mathsf{k})\not{\epsilon} \mp \mu_{a,N}F_{N,\mu}(\mathsf{k})\not{\epsilon}\not{k}.$$

6.25 Methods of Computation

a. Rationalization and Calculation of the Matrix Element. After the matrix element has been written down according to the rules

[1] Note that the normalization of the magnetic form factors is different from that in 3.33.

[2] We have written $F(\mathsf{k})$ rather than $F(k)$ in order to obtain a formula valid in any system of reference.

[3] Nonrelativistically, for $\nu = 1$ the sum $(i/2)\,\partial_\mu[\bar{\psi}(\gamma_\mu\gamma_\nu - \gamma_\nu\gamma_\mu)\psi]$ has two terms, for the term with $\mu = 1$ vanishes and that with $\mu = 4$ is small. Thus the sum becomes $-\partial_2(\bar{\psi}\sigma_3\psi) + \partial_3(\bar{\psi}\sigma_2\psi)$ which is the first component of $\nabla \times (\bar{\psi}\boldsymbol{\sigma}\psi)$.

stated in the preceding section, we can begin the computation of the transition rates.

The first step consists of the removal of the γ matrices from the denominator of the propagation factor. For this the numerator and denominator of the factor $(\not{p} - m)^{-1}$ are multiplied by $\not{p} + m$ to obtain

$$\frac{1}{\not{p} - m} = \frac{\not{p} + m}{p^2 - m^2}. \tag{1}$$

After the rationalization, the calculation of the matrix element can be carried out directly by using the explicit form of the spinors 6.21(13). This method is used in 6.26b.

In parts b and c of this section we describe how spin averages can be computed by the method of traces [compare with 3.59(8)], a method which often reduces the algebraic labor to a considerable extent.

An example of this type of calculation is reported in 6.26a and c.

b. Spin Averages. In order to obtain transition probabilities, we must compute the square of a matrix element of the form

$$M = (w_F{}^\dagger \mathcal{O} w_I), \tag{2}$$

where $\mathcal{O}$ is an operator which may contain the γ matrices. If we define

$$Q = \gamma_4 \mathcal{O} \qquad Q^\dagger = \mathcal{O}^\dagger \gamma_4, \tag{3}$$

the matrix element assumes the form used in 6.23:

$$M = (\bar{w}_F Q w_I). \tag{2'}$$

Its square can be written

$$\begin{aligned} |M|^2 &= (w_F{}^\dagger \mathcal{O} w_I)(w_F{}^\dagger \mathcal{O} w_I)^* \\ &= (w_F{}^\dagger \mathcal{O} w_I)(w_I{}^\dagger \mathcal{O}^\dagger w_F) \\ &= (\bar{w}_F \gamma_4 \mathcal{O} w_I)(\bar{w}_I \gamma_4 \mathcal{O}^\dagger w_F) \\ &= (\bar{w}_F Q w_I)(\bar{w}_I \gamma_4 Q^\dagger \gamma_4 w_F). \end{aligned} \tag{4}$$

Frequently the transition probability must be averaged over initial spins and summed over final spins. The spin sum S is a sum over two of the four assigned momentum solutions of the Dirac equation. This sum can be extended to all four solutions by using projection operators appropriate to the sign of charge of the particle considered (see 6.21d):

$$\begin{aligned} \mathsf{S} &= \sum_{(s)=1}^{4} \Lambda_e \qquad \text{for electrons,} \\ \mathsf{S} &= -\sum_{(s)=1}^{4} \Lambda_p \quad \text{for positrons.} \end{aligned} \tag{5a}$$

In general,

$$\mathsf{S} = \sum_{(s)=1}^{4} \varepsilon_{(s)}\Lambda, \tag{5b}$$

where $\varepsilon_{(s)} = \varepsilon_{(s)(s)}$ [see 6.21(14)] is $+1$ for $(s) = 1, 2$ (electrons) and -1 for $(s) = 3, 4$ (positrons).

Thus, by making use of 6.21(15) and indicating with Λ_I, Λ_F the projection operators appropriate to the initial and final particles,

$$\begin{aligned}(6)\quad \langle |M| \rangle^2_{\text{spin averaged}} &= \frac{1}{2}\mathsf{S}_\mathrm{I}\,\mathsf{S}_\mathrm{F}\,|M|^2 \\ &= \frac{1}{2}\sum_{(s)}\sum_{(s')}[\bar{w}_{\mathrm{F}(s)}Q\Lambda_\mathrm{I}\varepsilon_{(s')}w_{\mathrm{I}(s')}][\bar{w}_{\mathrm{I}(s')}\gamma_4 Q^\dagger\gamma_4\Lambda_\mathrm{F}\varepsilon_{(s)}w_{\mathrm{F}(s)}] \\ &= \frac{1}{2}\sum_{(s)}(\bar{w}_{\mathrm{F}(s)}Q\Lambda_\mathrm{I}\gamma_4 Q^\dagger\gamma_4\Lambda_\mathrm{F}\varepsilon_{(s)}w_{\mathrm{F}(s)}) \\ &= \tfrac{1}{2}\mathrm{Tr}\,\{Q\Lambda_\mathrm{I}\gamma_4 Q^\dagger\gamma_4\Lambda_\mathrm{F}\}.\end{aligned}$$

If Q does not contain the γ matrices, $\gamma_4 Q^\dagger\gamma_4 = Q^\dagger$; if Q contains the γ matrices, it is useful to recall that $\gamma_4\gamma_\mu{}^\dagger\gamma_4 = \gamma_\mu$.

c. Computation of Traces. It is well known that the factors of a product of matrices can undergo cyclic permutation without changing the value of the trace:

$$\mathrm{Tr}\,ABCD = \mathrm{Tr}\,DABC = \mathrm{Tr}\,CDAB = \mathrm{Tr}\,BCAD. \tag{7}$$

Simple traces containing γ matrices can be computed immediately:

$$(8)\quad \begin{array}{lll}\mathrm{Tr}\,1 = 4 & \mathrm{Tr}\,\gamma_\mu = 0 & (\mu = 1, 2, 3, 4, 5) \\ \mathrm{Tr}\,\gamma_i^2 = -4 & \mathrm{Tr}\,\gamma_4^2 = +4 & \mathrm{Tr}\,\gamma_\mu\gamma_\nu = 0 \quad \text{for } \mu \neq \nu.\end{array}$$

The formulas are often simplified by remembering that

(9) the trace of any product containing an odd power of any of the $\gamma_\mu (\mu = 1, \cdots, 5)$ is zero.

The trace of a slashed vector (6.12c) as well as the trace of the product of an odd number of slashed vectors is zero. The trace of the product of two slashed vectors is easily obtained by using 6.12(16*d*):

$$\mathrm{Tr}\,\not{A}\not{B} = \mathrm{Tr}\,\mathbf{A}\cdot\mathbf{B} = 4\mathbf{A}\cdot\mathbf{B}. \tag{10}$$

Similarly, by repeated application of (7) and 6.12(16), we obtain the useful formula

$$\mathrm{Tr}\,(\not{A}\not{B}\not{C}\not{D}) = 4[(\mathbf{A}\cdot\mathbf{B})(\mathbf{C}\cdot\mathbf{D}) - (\mathbf{A}\cdot\mathbf{C})(\mathbf{B}\cdot\mathbf{D}) + (\mathbf{A}\cdot\mathbf{D})(\mathbf{B}\cdot\mathbf{C})]. \tag{11}$$

d. External Factors. In order to compute transition probabilities, we need to derive the density of states appropriate to our normalization. We generally refer the matrix elements to the spinors w which are the most convenient for the computation; their normalization, $\bar{w}w = \pm 1$, corresponds to spinors u or v normalized to unity in a volume $m/|E|$ (6.21). Thus the density of states for each final free electron must be written

$$\text{(12)} \qquad \frac{m}{E}\frac{p^2\,dp\,d\Omega}{(2\pi)^3\,dE} = \frac{mp\,d\Omega}{(2\pi)^3}\frac{p\,dp}{E\,dE} = \frac{mp\,d\Omega}{(2\pi)^3}.$$

Finally, for the cross section formula, we need to compute the initial flux; since the incident electron density corresponding to w_{I} is $|E|/m$, we must use

$$\text{(13)} \qquad \text{incident flux} = \frac{|E|}{m}v = \frac{|E|}{m}\frac{p}{|E|} = \frac{p}{m}.$$

Expressed in terms of momenta, (12) and (13) are identical to the corresponding nonrelativistic quantities.

6.26 *Two Examples of First-Order Processes*

a. Rutherford Scattering. We shall now apply the theoretical apparatus developed in the preceding sections to the simple and classical problem of the coulomb scattering of an electron by a heavy particle of mass M and of charge Ze. The diagram corresponding to this process is shown in Fig. 6.26-1*a*.

With the help of 6.25(12) and (13), the usual formula for the cross section gives[1]

$$\text{(1)} \qquad \sigma = \frac{2\pi}{\text{flux}}\,\rho(E)\,|\mathsf{M}|^2 = \frac{m^2\,d\Omega}{(2\pi)^2}\,|\mathsf{M}|^2,$$

where the matrix element is 6.23(21) with $P = (0, 0, 0, M)$. Using the indices 1 and 2 in place of I and F, and defining $\mathbf{q} = \mathbf{p}_2 - \mathbf{p}_1$, we have

$$\text{(2)} \qquad \mathsf{M} = -i\,\frac{4\pi Z e^2}{q^2}\,(\bar{w}_2\gamma_4 w_1).$$

The process can also be thought as consisting of the interaction of the electron with a virtual electrostatic (transverse) quantum of momentum $\mathbf{q}$ resulting from the Fourier analysis of the electrostatic field [2]. With this interpretation, the matrix element (2) is obtained (apart from the factor i) according to the usual rules from the diagram of Fig. 6.26-1*a*.

The spin average of the square of the matrix element in (2) can be

[1] Because of coulomb distortion the present treatment is not valid for large Z; in that case the complete theory (Mott, M-32) predicts polarization effects which are not found here.

[2] $q_t = 0$ in elastic scattering.

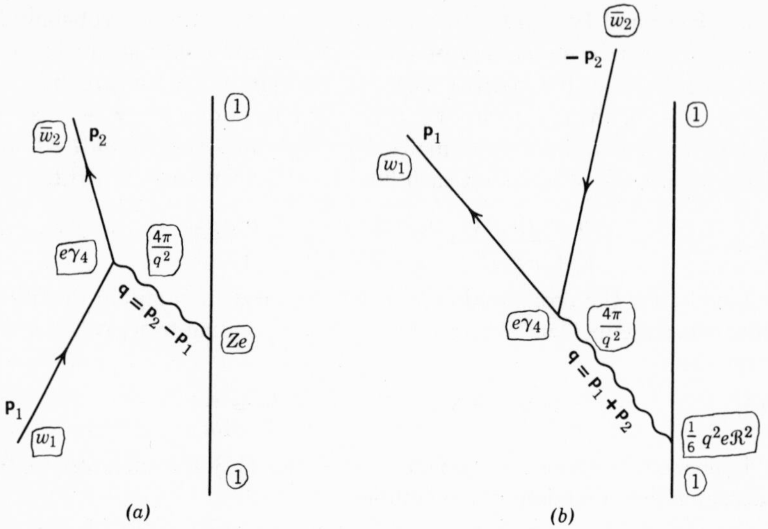

Fig. 6.26-1. (*a*) Scattering of electrons by heavy nuclei. (*b*) Pair production in O^{16}. The wavy lines represent the virtual photons which transmit the electrostatic interaction. The two diagrams show the similarity between two processes.

computed with the method of traces. In what follows the computation is carried out step by step, as an example:

$$(3) \quad \tfrac{1}{2} \underset{1}{\mathsf{S}} \underset{2}{\mathsf{S}} |(\bar{w}_2\gamma_4 w_1)|^2$$

$$= \tfrac{1}{2}\mathrm{Tr}\,(\gamma_4\Lambda_{e1}\gamma_4\Lambda_{e2})$$

$$= \frac{1}{2}\frac{1}{4m^2}\,\mathrm{Tr}\,[\gamma_4(\not{p}_1 + m)\gamma_4(\not{p}_2 + m)]$$

$$= \frac{1}{8m^2}\,\mathrm{Tr}\,(\gamma_4\not{p}_1\gamma_4\not{p}_2 + m^2 + \text{traceless terms})$$

$$= \frac{1}{8m^2}\,\mathrm{Tr}\,(-\not{p}_1\not{p}_2 + 2E_1E_2 + m^2)$$

$$= \frac{1}{8m^2}(-4\mathbf{p}_1 \cdot \mathbf{p}_2 + 8E_1E_2 + 4m^2)$$

$$= \frac{1}{2m^2}(E^2 + \mathbf{p}_1 \cdot \mathbf{p}_2 + m^2) = \frac{E^2}{2m^2}\left(1 + v^2\cos\theta + \frac{m^2}{E^2}\right)$$

$$= \frac{E^2}{2m^2}(1 + v^2\cos\theta + 1 - v^2) = \frac{E^2}{m^2}\left(1 - v^2\sin^2\frac{\theta}{2}\right).$$

If we collect terms and use $q = 2p\sin\tfrac{1}{2}\theta$, the cross section per unit solid angle is

$$\sigma = \frac{Z^2e^4}{4p^2v^2 \sin^4(\theta/2)}[1 - v^2 \sin^2(\theta/2)] \tag{4}$$

The result is the same as that from classical theory apart from the relativistic correction in v^2.

b. Computation without the Use of Traces. The reader who is not familiar with the method of traces may find it, depending on his disposition, either tricky or miraculous. In order to show that there is no magic in this sort of computation, we shall perform the sum (3) in a more direct fashion.

The sum is composed of four terms, corresponding to solutions $(s) = (1)$ and $(s) = (2)$ (see 6.21c) for the initial and final electron state. We assume that the initial momentum is along the z axis (components $0, 0, p$), and the final momentum is in the xz plane (components $p \sin\theta, 0, p\cos\theta$).

We compute only the two terms for the initial electron in state $(s) = (1)$ (nonrelativistically the spin-up state), since it is easily verified that the other two terms give an equal contribution to the sum. The two terms can be written with the help of 6.21(13):

(5*a*) $[\bar{w}_{(1)}(\mathbf{p}_F)\gamma_4\, w_{(1)}(\mathbf{p}_I)]$

$$= \frac{E+m}{2m}\overbrace{\left(1 \quad 0 \quad \frac{-p\cos\theta}{E+m} \quad \frac{-p\sin\theta}{E+m}\right)}\begin{pmatrix} 1 & 0 & 0 & 0 \\ 0 & 1 & 0 & 0 \\ 0 & 0 & -1 & 0 \\ 0 & 0 & 0 & -1 \end{pmatrix}\begin{pmatrix} 1 \\ 0 \\ \dfrac{p}{E+m} \\ 0 \end{pmatrix}$$

$$= \frac{E+m}{2m}\left[1 + \frac{p^2\cos\theta}{(E+m)^2}\right];$$

(5*b*) $[\bar{w}_{(2)}(\mathbf{p}_F)\gamma_4\, w_{(1)}(\mathbf{p}_I)]$

$$= \frac{E+m}{2m}\overbrace{\left(0 \quad 1 \quad \frac{-p\sin\theta}{E+m} \quad \frac{p\cos\theta}{E+m}\right)}\begin{pmatrix} 1 & 0 & 0 & 0 \\ 0 & 1 & 0 & 0 \\ 0 & 0 & -1 & 0 \\ 0 & 0 & 0 & -1 \end{pmatrix}\begin{pmatrix} 1 \\ 0 \\ \dfrac{p}{E+m} \\ 0 \end{pmatrix}$$

$$= \frac{E+m}{2m}\frac{p^2\sin\theta}{(E+m)^2}.$$

When these two terms are squared and added, we will have computed one half the sum. Thus we should get exactly the same result as in (3). This is easily verified, for by squaring (5*a*) and (5*b*) and adding the results we obtain

$$\frac{(E+m)^2}{4m^2}\left[1+\frac{p^4}{(E+m)^4}+\frac{2p^2\cos\theta}{(E+m)^2}\right]$$
$$=\frac{1}{4m^2}\left[(E+m)^2+\frac{(E^2-m^2)^2}{(E+m)^2}+2p^2\cos\theta\right]$$
$$=\frac{1}{4m^2}[(E+m)^2+(E-m)^2+2p^2\cos\theta]$$
$$=\frac{E^2}{2m^2}\left(1+\frac{m^2}{E^2}+v^2\cos\theta\right).$$

c. Emission of Pairs in Zero-Zero Nuclear Transitions. We now discuss the decay of a nucleus in a $0 \to 0$ transition with the emission of electron pairs (O-39, O-41). The classical example is the decay of the 6.06 MeV excited state of O^{16} (Fig. 4.37-2). The diagram is given in Fig. 6.26-1*b*.

This example is particularly interesting as an introduction to the theory of β decay.

In a classical model we could assume that the nucleus would undergo spherically symmetrical oscillations with frequency $\omega = E_0/\hbar = 6$ MeV$/\hbar$. These vibrations produce a pulsating electrostatic potential *within the nucleus*, whose finite radius R must be taken into account. In turn, this potential creates the pairs by first-order scattering of electrons from backward to forward propagation in time.

In writing the matrix element we shall treat the nuclear motion nonrelativistically and make use of the approximation 6.14(19′) for the nuclear four-current. The intermediate photon of Fig. 6.26-1*b* is therefore a purely "electrostatic," or longitudinal, photon of spin 0. This is why only the γ_4 term is written at the electron-photon vertex of the diagram. If we choose, as usual, the gage in which div $\mathbf{A} = 0$, we have $\partial\Phi/\partial t = 0$ in vacuum, and the propagator is $4\pi/q^2$. This factor is the same as that of elastic scattering and corresponds to the form factor of the coulomb field.

The factor at the nucleus-photon vertex involves some consideration of nuclear physics. The electric current interaction in Chapter 4, $(e/M)\mathbf{p}\cdot\mathbf{A}$, must be replaced by the electric charge interaction $e\Phi$ (the operator γ_4 can be omitted because of the nonrelativistic motion of the nucleons).

Since no effect is expected from a point nucleus, the nuclear part of the matrix element must be written to include retardation:

$$\langle\psi_F|\sum_\alpha e_\alpha \exp(-i\mathbf{q}\cdot\mathbf{r}_\alpha)\,|\psi_I\rangle.$$

In this expression the nuclear states ψ_{I} and ψ_{F} are spherically symmetrical and orthogonal to each other. Thus the first and second terms in the development of the exponential, $1 - i\mathbf{q}\cdot\mathbf{r}$, give a vanishing contribution, and the dominant term, averaged over all directions of $\mathbf{q}$, is

$$\tfrac{1}{6}q^2\langle\psi_F|\sum_\alpha e_\alpha r_\alpha{}^2\,|\psi_I\rangle \equiv \tfrac{1}{6}q^2 e\mathfrak{R}^2,$$

where $\mathfrak{R} \approx R$ in the single particle model.

We conclude that the matrix element has the form

$$M = \tfrac{1}{6}q^2 e\mathfrak{R}^2 \frac{4\pi}{q^2}\, e(\bar{w}_2\gamma_4 w_1). \tag{6}$$

This must be squared and *summed* over the spins of the electron and positron with the result

$$\begin{aligned} \mathop{\mathsf{S}}_{p}\mathop{\mathsf{S}}_{e} |M|^2 &= \tfrac{4}{9}\pi^2 e^4\mathfrak{R}^4 \frac{1}{4m^2}\,\mathrm{Tr}\,[\gamma_4(\not{p}_1 + m)\,\gamma_4(\not{p}_2 - m)] \\ &= \tfrac{4}{9}\pi^2 e^4\mathfrak{R}^4 \frac{1}{m^2}\{E_1E_2 + \mathbf{p}_1\cdot\mathbf{p}_2 - m^2\}. \end{aligned} \tag{7}$$

We can now compute the transition probability for an electron momentum between p_1 and $p_1 + dp_1$ and for a positron direction within a solid angle $d\Omega$ relative to the electron. Remembering the normalization factors m/E_1 and m/E_2 from 6.25(12), we obtain

$$w\,dp_1\,d\Omega = 2\pi \frac{4\pi p_1{}^2\,dp_1}{(2\pi)^3E_1}\,d\Omega\,\frac{d}{dE_0}\int_0^{p_{2max}} \tfrac{4}{9}\pi^2e^4\mathfrak{R}^4\{\quad\}\frac{p_2{}^2\,dp_2}{(2\pi)^3E_2}. \tag{8}$$

The integral can be transformed into an integral in dE_2 by using

$$p_2{}^2\,dp_2/E_2 = p_2\,dE_2:$$

then it depends on E_0 only through its upper limit $E_0 - E_1$, and the differentiation is immediately performed. Passing to the energy variable also for the electron, we derive from (8)

$$w\,dE_1\,d\Omega = \frac{1}{18\pi^2}\,e^4\mathfrak{R}^4\{E_1E_2 + \mathbf{p}_1\cdot\mathbf{p}_2 - m^2\}p_1p_2\,dE_1\,d\Omega. \tag{9}$$

This formula describes the spectrum of the emitted electrons and is in excellent agreement with the experiment (R-50, L-63, and Fig. 6.26-2).

In the approximation of high energy m can be neglected, and p_1 and p_2 can be replaced with E_1 and E_2:

$$w\,dE_1\,d\Omega \cong \frac{1}{18\pi^2}\,e^4\mathfrak{R}^4(1 + \cos\theta)E_1{}^2E_2{}^2\,dE_1\,d\Omega.$$

Finally, by integrating over $d\Omega$ and dE_1, we obtain the following expression for the total transition probability:

$$w \cong \frac{4\pi}{18\pi^2} e^4 \mathfrak{R}^4 \int_0^{E_0} E_1^{\,2}(E_0 - E_1)^2\, dE_1 = \frac{1}{135\pi} e^4 \mathfrak{R}^4 E_0^{\,5}.$$

The experimentally measured half-life of the 6.06 MeV excited state of O^{16} is $5.0 \pm 0.5 \times 10^{-11}$ sec (D-54c) in satisfactory agreement with the estimate from this formula.

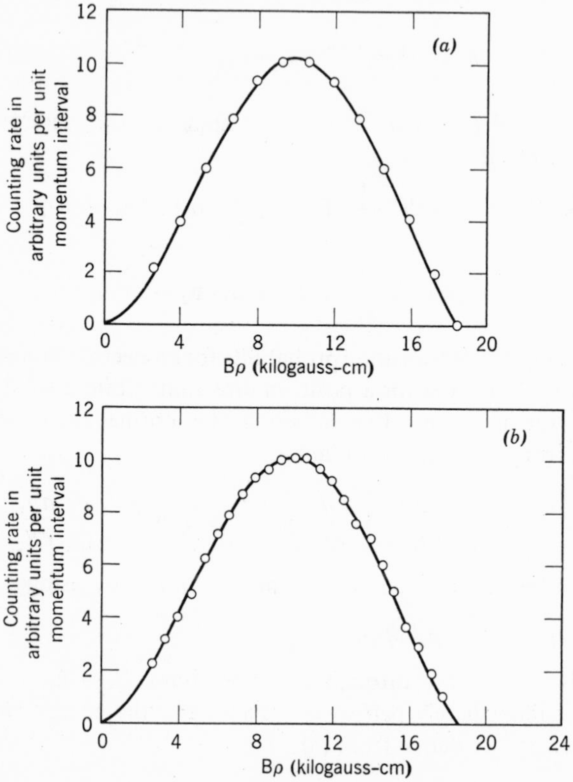

Fig. 6.26-2. (*a*) Momentum spectrum of the positrons from the pairs of O^{16}. (*b*) Momentum spectrum of the electrons from the pairs of O^{16}. The solid curves are the theoretical distributions and the points are experimental. [From Y. K. Lee, L. W. Mo, and C. S. Wu, *Phys. Rev. Letters*, **10**, 258 (1963).]

6.27 Electron-Positron Annihilation at Small Velocity

a. Approximations Used in the Calculation. We shall now compute the annihilation cross section, starting from the amplitude 6.24(3). This example is instructive and particularly simple if we assume that the electron and positron move with small velocity.

The calculation is developed under the following approximation:

(i) We assume $v \ll 1$ for both positron and electron, and only the fourth component of $\mathbf{p}_1$ and $\mathbf{p}_2$ is considered as nonvanishing:

(ii) We assume $v \gg \frac{1}{137}$, so that the electrostatic attraction between electron and positron may be neglected. After computing the matrix element for electron and positron plane waves, the electrostatic effects can be taken into account to extend the validity of the result to smaller velocities.

Using the laws of conservation of energy and momentum in the approximation stated, we write the time and space components of the four-momenta entering into the problem:

(1)
$$\begin{aligned} \mathbf{p}_1 = \mathbf{p}_2 &= \quad 0, \quad m \\ \mathbf{k}_1 &= \quad m\hat{\mathbf{k}}_1, m \\ \mathbf{k}_2 &= -m\hat{\mathbf{k}}_1, m. \end{aligned}$$

where $\hat{\mathbf{k}}_1$ is a unit vector in the direction of propagation of the "first" γ ray.

b. Computation of the Matrix Element. The first step of the computation is the "rationalization" of the matrix element. Following the method outlined in 6.25a we obtain:

(2)
$$-\frac{2\pi e^2}{\sqrt{\omega_1\omega_2}}\left[\left(\bar{w}_2\not{e}_2\,\frac{\not{p}_1 - \not{k}_1 + m}{|\mathbf{p}_1 - \mathbf{k}_1|^2 - m^2}\,\not{e}_1 w_1\right) + \left(\bar{w}_2\not{e}_1\,\frac{\not{p}_1 - \not{k}_2 + m}{|\mathbf{p}_1 - \mathbf{k}_2|^2 - m^2}\,\not{e}_2 w_1\right)\right].$$

If we now introduce the approximations in (1), the matrix element becomes[1]

$$-\frac{2\pi e^2}{m}\left[\left(\bar{w}_2\not{e}_2\,\frac{m\boldsymbol{\gamma}\cdot\hat{\mathbf{k}}_1 + m}{2m^2}\,\not{e}_1 w_1\right) + \left(\bar{w}_2\not{e}_1\,\frac{-m\boldsymbol{\gamma}\cdot\hat{\mathbf{k}}_1 + m}{2m^2}\,\not{e}_2 w_1\right)\right].$$

Since the terms $\not{e}_2 m\not{e}_1 + \not{e}_1 m\not{e}_2 = 2m\hat{\boldsymbol{\epsilon}}_1\cdot\hat{\boldsymbol{\epsilon}}_2$ do not contain γ matrices, they do not induce transitions between electron and positron states and may be left out. The matrix element reduces to

(3)
$$-\frac{\pi e^2}{m^2}\,[\bar{w}_2(\not{e}_2\boldsymbol{\gamma}\cdot\hat{\mathbf{k}}_1\not{e}_1 - \not{e}_1\boldsymbol{\gamma}\cdot\hat{\mathbf{k}}_1\not{e}_2)w_1].$$

At this point it may be well to keep in mind that the transition probability must eventually be summed over all the final states of polarization of the γ rays. Keeping, for the moment, $\hat{\boldsymbol{\epsilon}}_1$ fixed, we see that parallel polarization of the two gammas ($\hat{\boldsymbol{\epsilon}}_1 = \hat{\boldsymbol{\epsilon}}_2$) gives a vanishing contribution, and thus we must consider only the case in which the three unit vectors $\hat{\boldsymbol{\epsilon}}_1$, $\hat{\boldsymbol{\epsilon}}_2$ and $\hat{\mathbf{k}}_1$ are orthogonal.

[1] $|\mathbf{p}_1 - \mathbf{k}_1|^2 = p_1^2 + k_1^2 - 2\mathbf{p}_1\cdot\mathbf{k}_1 = m^2 + 0 - 2m^2 = -m^2$.

From the orthogonality of these vectors it follows that $\not\epsilon_1$, $\boldsymbol{\gamma}\cdot\hat{\mathbf{k}}_1$, and $\not\epsilon_2$ anticommute [6.12(16)] and thus

$$\not\epsilon_2\boldsymbol{\gamma}\cdot\hat{\mathbf{k}}_1\not\epsilon_1 - \not\epsilon_1\boldsymbol{\gamma}\cdot\hat{\mathbf{k}}_1\not\epsilon_2 = 2\not\epsilon_2\boldsymbol{\gamma}\cdot\hat{\mathbf{k}}_1\not\epsilon_1 = 2\sum_{i\neq j\neq k}^{+++}\gamma_i\gamma_j\gamma_k\epsilon_{2i}k_{1j}\epsilon_{1k},$$

since for $i = j$, etc., we can factor out a vanishing dot product. Considering that $\gamma_i\gamma_j\gamma_k = (-1)^p\gamma_x\gamma_y\gamma_z$ (where p is the number of permutations from xyz to ijk), the matrices in (3) can be written with the help of the triple product of the vectors $\hat{\boldsymbol{\epsilon}}_1$, $\hat{\boldsymbol{\epsilon}}_2$, and $\hat{\mathbf{k}}_1$:

$$\not\epsilon_2\boldsymbol{\gamma}\cdot\hat{\mathbf{k}}_1\not\epsilon_1 = \gamma_x\gamma_y\gamma_z\,\hat{\boldsymbol{\epsilon}}_1\times\hat{\boldsymbol{\epsilon}}_2\cdot\hat{\mathbf{k}}_1.$$

Thus (3) becomes

$$-\frac{2\pi e^2}{m^2}\hat{\boldsymbol{\epsilon}}_1\times\hat{\boldsymbol{\epsilon}}_2\cdot\hat{\mathbf{k}}_1(\bar{w}_2\gamma_x\gamma_y\gamma_z w_1). \tag{4}$$

We can now proceed to the final computation of the matrix element. If we choose conveniently the positive directions of $\hat{\boldsymbol{\epsilon}}_1$, $\hat{\boldsymbol{\epsilon}}_2$, and $\hat{\mathbf{k}}_1$, the triple product $\hat{\boldsymbol{\epsilon}}_1\times\hat{\boldsymbol{\epsilon}}_2\cdot\hat{\mathbf{k}}_1$ is 1; the matrix element involving the spinors can be rewritten in the form $-(w_2{}^\dagger\gamma_5 w_1)$, and it is easily seen[1] that the nonvanishing elements are

$$\begin{aligned}(w^\dagger_{(4)}\gamma_5 w_{(1)}) &= 1,\\ (w^\dagger_{(3)}\gamma_5 w_{(2)}) &= -1.\end{aligned} \tag{5}$$

The first of these elements corresponds to the annihilation of a pair $\alpha_-\beta_+$ (nonrelativistic electron with spin up, positron with spin down), and the second annihilates a pair $\alpha_+\beta_-$. Because of the opposite sign of the matrix elements (5), *only singlet pairs*, $(1/\sqrt{2})(\alpha_-\beta_+ - \beta_-\alpha_+)$, *annihilate*, and the spinor matrix elements contribute a factor $\sqrt{2}$.

[1] The matrix γ_5 transforms an electron with spin up into a positron with spin down and vice versa. However, opposite phases are introduced in the two cases [see 6.21(13)].

$$\gamma_5 w_{(1)}(\mathbf{p}=0) = i\begin{pmatrix}0&0&1&0\\0&0&0&1\\1&0&0&0\\0&1&0&0\end{pmatrix}\begin{pmatrix}1\\0\\0\\0\end{pmatrix} = i\begin{pmatrix}0\\0\\1\\0\end{pmatrix} = w_{(4)}(\mathbf{p}=0),$$

$$\gamma_5 w_{(2)}(\mathbf{p}=0) = i\begin{pmatrix}0&0&1&0\\0&0&0&1\\1&0&0&0\\0&1&0&0\end{pmatrix}\begin{pmatrix}0\\1\\0\\0\end{pmatrix} = i\begin{pmatrix}0\\0\\0\\1\end{pmatrix} = -w_{(3)}(\mathbf{p}=0).$$

Thus we conclude

$$|M_s| = \frac{2\sqrt{2\pi}e^2}{m^2}. \tag{6}$$

It is interesting to observe that the two terms in the matrix element, $\hat{\epsilon}_1 \times \hat{\epsilon}_2 \cdot \hat{k}$ and $(w_2^\dagger \gamma_5 w_1)$, are both pseudoscalars. As we shall see in (d), this is in agreement with parity conservation: the intrinsic parity of the pair is odd and so is the parity of the γ rays of annihilation.

c. Transition Probabilities and Cross Sections. In our approximation the density of final states is[1]

$$2\frac{k_1^2\,dk_1}{8\pi^3}\frac{d\Omega_1}{2dk_1} = \frac{d\Omega_1}{8\pi^3}k_1^2 = \frac{d\Omega_1}{8\pi^3}m^2, \tag{7}$$

and the transition probability for unit-density *singlet* electron-positron plane waves can be written[2]

$$w_s = 2\pi\frac{2\pi}{8\pi^3}m^2\left(\frac{2\sqrt{2\pi}}{m^2}e^2\right)^2 = 4\pi\frac{e^4}{m^2}. \tag{8}$$

The singlet annihilation cross section in free collision is

$$\sigma_s = \frac{4\pi}{v}\frac{e^4}{m^2}|\psi(0)|^2, \tag{9}$$

where $|\psi(0)|^2$ is unity if we neglect coulomb attraction and can otherwise be computed from coulomb wave functions.

The triplet annihilation cross section is much smaller so that the average cross section for unpolarized particles is $\frac{1}{4}$ of (9).

Particularly interesting is the case of positronium singlet, in which the density of the positron at the position of the electron $|\psi(0)|^2$ is easily obtained by solving the atomic problem

(10)

$$w_s = \frac{1}{\tau_s} = \frac{4\pi e^4}{m^2}|\psi(0)|^2 = \frac{4\pi e^4}{m^2}\frac{1}{\pi(2/me^2)^3} = \frac{1}{2}e^{10}m = \frac{1}{1.25 \times 10^{-10}}\,\text{sec}^{-1}.$$

Positronium triplet does not annihilate in two quanta. At least three γ rays are needed to satisfy the conservation principles in this case [see (d)], and the transition probability is smaller of the order of a factor e^2 (D-51; D-52; D-54b; D-61).

[1] The factor 2 in the numerator is for the two polarizations; in the denominator we have written $dE_0 = 2dk_1$.

[2] Integration over $d\Omega_1$ gives 2π, since the γ rays are indistinguishable and the contributions of the two diagrams have been added. The annihilation cross section corresponding to (8), including all constants, is $\sigma_s = 4\pi(c/v)(e^2/mc^2)^2$.

d. Selection Rules for Positronium Annihilation. We now show how some of the results of the computation could have been predicted from the conservation principles, and for this purpose we must determine the quantum numbers of positronium.

The value of the total angular momentum J is found, as it is for any other atom, by combining L $(= 0, 1, 2, \cdots)$ and S $(= 0, 1)$. The states can be classified as ${}^1S_0$, ${}^3S_1$, ${}^1P_0$, ${}^3P_0$, ${}^3P_1$, ${}^3P_2$, $\cdots$, etc.

The *orbital parity* is $(-1)^L$ and the *intrinsic parity is odd.* In order to show this, let us assume as usual that nonrelativistically the electron wave function is intrinsically even: according to 6.14(11), this means that in an even orbital state $\psi_e(\mathbf{r})$ becomes $\gamma_4\psi_e(-\mathbf{r}) \approx \psi_e(-\mathbf{r})$ under reflection of axes. But the positron wave function $\psi_p(\mathbf{r}) = S_C\psi_e(\mathbf{r})$ becomes

$$\gamma_4 S_C \psi_e(-\mathbf{r}) = -S_C\gamma_4\psi_e(-\mathbf{r}) \approx -S_C\psi_e(-\mathbf{r}) = -\psi_p(-\mathbf{r}).$$

Thus electrons and positrons have opposite intrinsic parity[1]. We conclude that the *total parity* of positronium is $(-1)^{L+1}$.

The eigenvalues of the *spin exchange* operator $\mathfrak{T}_\sigma$ are, as we well know, $+1$ for triplet and -1 for singlet; in general, $(-1)^{S+1}$.

Another operator which has definite eigenvalues in positronium states is the *charge conjugation operator*. It can be proved (W-52b) that its eigenvalues are $(-1)^{L+S}$; the fact that they have sign opposite to that of the eigenvalues of the operator $\mathfrak{T}_r\mathfrak{T}_\sigma$ is related to the necessity of antisymmetrizing the states of two electrons.

A simple argument, not requiring the quantization of the Dirac field, can be presented. Positronium is the state of two indistinguishable electrons, a and b, of which one is at position $\mathbf{r}$, with spin coordinate $\mathbf{s}$ and sign $-$, whereas the other is at position $\mathbf{r}'$, with spin coordinate $\mathbf{s}'$ and sign $+$. The state of positronium assumes the form

$$\Psi \simeq \psi_a(\mathbf{r}, \mathbf{s}, -)\,\psi_b(\mathbf{r}', \mathbf{s}', +) - \psi_b(\mathbf{r}, \mathbf{s}, -)\,\psi_a(\mathbf{r}', \mathbf{s}', +),$$

from which it is immediately seen that[2]

$$\begin{aligned} S_C\Psi &\simeq \psi_a(\mathbf{r}, \mathbf{s}, +)\,\psi_b(\mathbf{r}', \mathbf{s}', -) - \psi_b(\mathbf{r}, \mathbf{s}, +)\,\psi_a(\mathbf{r}', \mathbf{s}', -) \\ &= -\mathfrak{T}_r\mathfrak{T}_\sigma\Psi = -(-1)^L(-1)^{S+1}\Psi = (-1)^{L+S}\Psi. \end{aligned}$$

Because annihilation in P states is infrequent (radiative $2P \to 1S$, transitions are much more probable that $2P$ annihilations), we shall be concerned only with the quantum numbers of positronium in S states.

[1] The opposite parity of nonrelativistic electrons and positrons is simply proved with the help of 6.14(11), 6.12(13) and 6.21(13). Clearly $S_{P,r} = \gamma_4$ leaves the large components of $w_{(1)}$ and $w_{(2)}$ unchanged and inverts the sign of the large components of $w_{(3)}$ and $w_{(4)}$.

[2] Note that here S_C plays the role that $\mathfrak{T}_r$ has in the n-p system.

These are

State	J	Parity	$\mathcal{P}_r$	$\mathcal{P}_\sigma$	S_C
$^1S_0$	0	-1	1	-1	1
$^3S_1$	1	-1	1	1	-1

Let us now discuss the quantum numbers of the states of the electromagnetic field.

We shall prove that two photons traveling in opposite directions can have total angular momentum $J = 0$ or 2 (or more) but not $J = 1$, a point that is important also in connection with the decay of the π^0 and η^0 mesons.

For the proof (Y-50b) let us take the axis of quantization z along the direction of propagation. Then, if the two γ's are either both right-handed (rr) or both left-handed (ll) they have $M_J = 0$, whereas for opposite helicities (rl or lr) they have $M_J = \pm 2$. Thus for opposite helicities $J = 1$ is excluded. To show that $J = 1$ is excluded also for equal helicities, let us observe that a $J = 1$, $M_J = 0$ state must behave under rotation like the z component of a vector: thus it must invert its sign under a rotation of 180° around an axis perpendicular to z. But the two opposite γ rays with equal helicities are simply interchanged by such rotation: since photons are bosons, the rotated state has the same sign as the original state, which, therefore, cannot be the $M_J = 0$ component of a $J = 1$ state.

Thus ^3S positronium cannot annihilate into two quanta. The same is true more generally for any system with $J = 1$.

Concerning parity, rl and lr are even, but ll and rr are not parity eigenstates. We can, however, build combinations of rr $\pm$ ll which have, respectively, parity ± 1 and which can be shown to correspond to parallel and perpendicular linear polarization.

For zero total angular momentum the two photons have even or odd parity, according to whether they are polarized parallel (scalar, $\hat{\boldsymbol{\epsilon}}_1 \cdot \hat{\boldsymbol{\epsilon}}_2$, in the matrix element) or perpendicular to each other [pseudoscalar, $\hat{\boldsymbol{\epsilon}}_1 \times \hat{\boldsymbol{\epsilon}}_2 \cdot \hat{\mathbf{k}}_1$, as in (4)]. Thus the perpendicular polarization of the annihilation γ's follows from the odd intrinsic parity of positronium.

Selection rules for decay in many quanta are obviously less strict, but we can derive a simple selection rule as a consequence of invariance under charge conjugation.

The electromagnetic field changes sign under charge conjugation, and the eigenvalue of this operator for each photon is -1. This is so because all electromagnetic field vectors change sign under charge conjugation. It follows that $^1S_0$ positronium may decay only in an even and $^3S_1$ only in an odd number of quanta[1].

[1] For a review of the properties of positronium see (D-54a).

References

Books

Fe-61 R. P. Feynman, *Quantum Electrodynamics*, Benjamin, New York, 1961.

Pa-33 W. Pauli, *Die Allgemeinen Prinzipien der Wellenmechanik*, *Handbuch der Physik*, Springer-Verlag, Berlin, 1933; also, Edwards, Ann Arbor, 1947.

Ro-61 M. F. Rose, *Relativistic Electron Theory*, Wiley, New York, 1961.

SB-55 Schweber, Bethe, and DeHoffman, *Mesons and Fields*, Vol. 1, Row, Peterson, New York, 1955.

Articles

D-51 M. Deutsch, *Phys. Rev.*, **83,** 866 (1951).

D-52 S. DeBenedetti and R. Siegel, *Phys. Rev.*, **85,** 371 (1952).

D-54a S. DeBenedetti and H. C. Corben, *Ann. Rev. Nucl. Sci.*, **4,** 191 (1954).

D-54b S. DeBenedetti and R. Siegel, *Phys. Rev.*, **94,** 955 (1954).

D-54c Devons, Goldring, and Lindsey, *Proc. Phys. Soc.* (*London*), **67A,** 134 (1954).

D-61 M. Deutsch and E. Dulit, *Phys. Rev.*, **84,** 601 (1961).

F-49 R. P. Feynman, *Phys. Rev.*, **76,** 749 (1949).

F-52a L. L. Foldy, *Phys. Rev.*, **87,** 688 (1952).

F-52b L. L. Foldy, *Phys. Rev.*, **87,** 693 (1952).

F-56 P. Franken and S. Liebes, *Phys. Rev.*, **104,** 1197 (1956).

G-51 J. H. Gardner, *Phys. Rev.*, **83,** 996 (1951).

K-52 Koenig, Prodell, and Kusch, *Phys. Rev.*, **88,** 191 (1952).

L-63 Lee, Mo, and Wu, *Phys. Rev. Letters*, **10,** 258 (1963).

M-32 N. F. Mott, *Proc. Roy. Soc.*, A**135,** 429 (1932).

O-39 J. R. Oppenheimer and J. S. Schwinger, *Phys. Rev.*, **56,** 1066 (1939).

O-41 J. R. Oppenheimer, *Phys. Rev.*, **60,** 164 (1941).

R-50 Rasmussen, Hornyak, Lauritsen, and Lauritsen, *Phys. Rev.*, **77,** 617 (1950).

S-57 C. M. Sommerfield, *Phys. Rev.*, **107,** 328 (1957).

S-58 C. M. Sommerfield, *Ann. Phys.*, *N.Y.*, **5,** 26 (1958).

W-50 G. C. Wick, *Phys. Rev.*, **80,** 268 (1950).

W-52a Wick, Wightman, and Wigner, *Phys. Rev.*, **88,** 101 (1952).

W-52b L. Wolfenstein and D. G. Ravenhall, *Phys. Rev.*, **88,** 279 (1952).

Y-50a C. N. Yang and J. Tiomno, *Phys. Rev.*, **79,** 495 (1950).

Y-50b C. N. Yang, *Phys. Rev.*, **77,** 242 (1950).

SEVEN

Pion Physics

7.1 Basic Experiments and Theoretical Ideas

7.11 Discovery of the Muon and of the Pion

The idea that the field of nuclear forces should correspond to a particle of mass intermediate between that of the electron and that of the nucleon (*meson*) originated with Yukawa (1935). In its simplest form it can be stated as follows.

The equation

(1) $$\Box^2 A_\mu = 0$$

describes the propagation of the electromagnetic field, which can be quantized and corresponds to particles of mass 0 (photons). In the static case (1) becomes

(2) $$\nabla^2 A_\mu = 0$$

and admits spherically symmetrical solutions of the form

(3) $$A_\mu \simeq \frac{1}{r}.$$

Thus a $1/r$ (infinite range) field corresponds to a zero rest mass particle.

Now we consider a field (which for simplicity we take to have a single component) that satisfies 6.12(2)

(4) $$(\Box^2 + m^2)\phi = 0,$$

where m is a constant of dimensions $1/L$, which can be considered as the inverse Compton wavelength of a massive particle.

It is immediately verified that the static form of (4)

$$(\nabla^2 - m^2)\phi = 0 \tag{5}$$

admits spherically symmetrical solutions of the form

$$\phi \approx \frac{e^{-mr}}{r}, \tag{6}$$

which can be interpreted as a potential of range $1/m$, acting between point sources of ϕ field.

Yukawa observed that if we want (6) to represent the field of nuclear forces whose range is $\approx 10^{-13}$ cm we need $m_e < m < M_N$, with $m \approx 200m_e$. For this reason the particles predicted by Yukawa have been given the name *mesons*.

Yukawa's remark passed relatively unnoticed until particles of $m \approx 200m_e$ were observed in cosmic radiation.

The events that led to the discovery of the meson can be summarized as follows (Th-52). The work of Rossi (1934) showed that cosmic radiation is composed of soft and hard parts. The soft component consists of electrons and γ rays which are absorbed through the mechanism of repeated bremsstrahlung and pair production, generating the characteristic showers. The hard component was supposed to consist of protons, which are expected to radiate much less because of their heavy mass. But Neddermeyer and Anderson observed that isolated particles traversing a bar of 1 cm of platinum in a cloud chamber projected too many high energy knock-on electrons to be as heavy as protons. Street and Stevenson (1937) found that the energy lost by the isolated cosmic-ray particles corresponded to a mass of ≈ 100 electron masses. Finally, Neddermeyer and Anderson (1938) observed a particle that stopped in the cloud chamber after traversing a metallic plate and could determine its mass as being about 240 electron masses.

The new particle discovered in cosmic radiation had another characteristic predicted by Yukawa: it β-decayed with a mean life of $\approx 2 \times 10^{-6}$ sec. Its decay was first detected by the attenuation resulting from decay in flight in the atmosphere and was finally measured at rest (Rasetti, 1941).

Despite all this favorable evidence, it was eventually found that the particle discovered in the hard component of the cosmic radiation was not the quantum of nuclear force field predicted by Yukawa. Thus this particle is not properly a meson; we call it a *muon* (rather than a μ meson).

This important observation was the result of an experiment (Conversi, Pancini, and Piccioni, 1945) which showed that negative cosmic-ray particles after reaching the K shell in an atom of carbon are not captured by the nucleus for a time as long as several 10^{-6} sec. The weakness of the nuclear interaction could not be reconciled with Yukawa's theory. Neither could it be reconciled with the principle of detailed balance, since there is evidence that the hard component of cosmic rays is produced with a large cross section in nuclear collisions in the high atmosphere.

The puzzle was solved with the development of nuclear emulsions of sensitivity sufficient for the detection of fast ionizing particles. It was found (Lattes, Muirhead, Occhialini, and Powell, 1947) that there were two kinds of particles in cosmic radiation, now called the *pion*, or *π meson*, and the muon. The pion had escaped observation in previous experiments because of its short mean life; it promptly disintegrates according to the reaction

(7) $$\pi^{\pm} \to \mu^{\pm} + \nu,$$

whereas the μ meson disintegrates into three particles,

(8) $$\mu^{\pm} \to e^{\pm} + \nu + \bar{\nu}.$$

The π, or primary, meson is identifiable as the Yukawa particle, but the muon is a puzzle: nobody knows why its mass should be different from that of an electron, since muons and electrons are identical in all other ways (see 8.34). Furthermore, at the present state of our knowledge one has the feeling that the world would be essentially the same if the muon did not exist, and thus this particle remains both unexplained and unneeded.

7.12 *Introductory Theoretical Ideas (without Field Quantization)*

a. Equations for Scalar and Vector Mesons in Vacuum. The quantized form of Yukawa's theory explains nuclear forces in terms of the exchange of mesons between the nucleons and requires that the spin of the pion be integral. Thus before the production of artificial mesons by high-energy accelerators it was thought that the meson could be scalar or vector (We-49).

A scalar meson corresponds to a one-component field whose behavior is fully described by the Klein-Gordon equation.

The equation for a vector meson (P-36) can be obtained as an extension of the Maxwell equations. For the electromagnetic field the four-potential A_λ satisfies the wave equation

(1) $$\square^2 A_\lambda = 0$$

and Lorentz' condition

(2) $$\partial_\lambda A_\lambda = 0.$$

The fields in 6.11(13),

$$F_{\lambda\nu} = \partial_\lambda A_\nu - \partial_\nu A_\lambda, \tag{3}$$

satisfy the equations [which follow from (1) and (2)]

$$\partial_\nu F_{\lambda\nu} = \partial_\nu \partial_\lambda A_\nu - \Box^2 A_\nu = 0, \tag{4}$$

which are part of Maxwell's equations in vacuum.

In perfect analogy, if the components of the vector meson field satisfy the wave equation,

$$(\Box^2 + m^2)\phi_\lambda = 0 \tag{5}$$

together with[1]

$$\partial_\lambda \phi_\lambda = 0; \tag{6}$$

the quantities

$$g_{\lambda\nu} = \partial_\lambda \phi_\nu - \partial_\nu \phi_\lambda \tag{7}$$

satisfy the equations [use (6) and (7)]

$$\partial_\nu g_{\lambda\nu} = \partial_\nu \partial_\lambda \phi_\nu - \Box^2 \phi_\lambda = m^2 \phi_\lambda, \tag{8a}$$

which are the appropriate extension of the Maxwell equations.

In three-dimensional notation we can define a mesoelectric field **e** and a mesomagnetic field **h** which satisfy the equations in vacuum (B-40):

$$\begin{aligned} \operatorname{div} \mathbf{e} + m^2 \phi_4 &= 0, \\ \operatorname{curl} \mathbf{h} - \frac{\partial \mathbf{e}}{\partial t} + m^2 \boldsymbol{\phi} &= 0. \end{aligned} \tag{8b}$$

In vacuum pseudoscalar and pseudovector mesons would be described by the same equations as scalar or vector mesons.

b. Sources of Mesons. The sources of mesic fields are obviously the nucleons. We must imagine that these are provided with a mesic charge, which is the source of the pion field, in the same manner as the electric charge is a source of electromagnetic field.

The electromagnetic potential produced by a point source particle of spin $\frac{1}{2}$ and of charge e satisfies the equation

$$\Box^2 A_\lambda = 4\pi e(\bar{\psi}\gamma_\lambda \psi), \tag{9}$$

where ψ is the source wave function.

But we have also seen that if the source possesses an anomalous magnetic

[1] With this restriction, only three of the ϕ_λ are independent, as required by the fact that $J = 1$ states are triplets. Without the restriction (6) the fourth ϕ_λ could be assigned to an extra particle of spin zero; but such a particle would have negative energy and must be discarded (see We-49, Chapter 3).

moment μ_a we must add another source term, as in 6.24c, and write

$$\Box^2 A_\lambda = 4\pi e(\bar{\psi}\gamma_\lambda\psi) + 4\pi\mu_a \frac{i}{2}\,\partial_\nu[\bar{\psi}(\gamma_\nu\gamma_\lambda - \gamma_\lambda\gamma_\nu)\psi]. \tag{10}$$

In field theoretical language we would say that the vector potential is "vector-coupled" or "derivative tensor-coupled" to the source, with "coupling constants" e and μ_a respectively.

These ideas can easily be extended to the meson fields. The rule is simple: the source term must contain the wave function of the source and must have the same tensor properties as the field.

By making use of the hermitian tensors 6.14e, we are led to write the following equations:

Scalar meson wave function:

$$(\Box^2 + m^2)\phi = -\sqrt{4\pi}\, f_{SS}(\bar{\psi}_N\psi_N) + \frac{\sqrt{4\pi}}{m} f_{SV}\,\partial_\nu(\bar{\psi}_N\gamma_\nu\psi_N); \tag{11}$$

Pseudoscalar meson wave function:

$$(\Box^2 + m^2)\phi = -\sqrt{4\pi}\, f_{PP}(\bar{\psi}_N\gamma_5\psi_N) + \frac{i\sqrt{4\pi}}{m} f_{PA}\,\partial_\nu(\bar{\psi}_N\gamma_5\gamma_\nu\psi_N); \tag{12}$$

Vector meson wave function:

$$(\Box^2 + m^2)\phi_\lambda = -\sqrt{4\pi}\, f_{VV}(\bar{\psi}_N\gamma_\lambda\psi_N) + \frac{i\sqrt{4\pi}}{m} f_{VT}\,\partial_\nu[\bar{\psi}_N(\gamma_\lambda\gamma_\nu - \gamma_\nu\gamma_\lambda)\psi_N)]; \tag{13}$$

Pseudovector (or axial vector) meson wave function:

$$(\Box^2 + m^2)\phi_\lambda = -i\sqrt{4\pi}\, f_{AA}(\bar{\psi}_N\gamma_5\gamma_\lambda\psi_N) + \frac{i\sqrt{4\pi}}{m} f_{AD}\,\partial_\nu[\bar{\psi}_N\gamma_5(\gamma_\lambda\gamma_\nu - \gamma_\nu\gamma_\lambda)\psi_N]. \tag{14}$$

In these equations ψ_N is the nucleon wave function and the f's are appropriate coupling constants[1] to be determined from the experiment. For the scalar meson (11) the term in f_{SS} is said to correspond to scalar theory with scalar coupling and that in f_{SV}, to scalar theory with vector coupling, and so on in the other cases.

Since the coupling constants in (11), (12), (13), (14) are multiplied by a factor $\sqrt{4\pi}$, they are termed "nonrationalized." Rationalized coupling constants F_{SS}, F_{SV}, etc., are also used in the literature. The relation

[1] All the f's are dimensionally the same because the factor ∂_ν/m is dimensionless. With appropriate normalization of the wave functions the f's are pure real numbers. It may be useful to recall that, having chosen hermitian tensors in the formulation of the theory, the reality of the coupling constants conforms with the requirements of time reversal invariance.

between rationalized and nonrationalized coupling constants is the same as in electromagnetism:

$$F^2 = 4\pi f^2. \tag{15}$$

c. The Lagrangian Formalism. The wave equations written in (b) can be obtained as equations of motion from appropriate field Lagrangians. Let us recall that if $\mathscr{L}$ is a Lagrangian density, the Lagrange equations for the field components ϕ_n are

$$\frac{\partial \mathscr{L}}{\partial \phi_n} - \sum_{i=1}^{3} \frac{\partial}{\partial x_i} \frac{\partial \mathscr{L}}{\partial \frac{\partial \phi_n}{\partial x_i}} - \frac{\partial}{\partial x_4} \frac{\partial \mathscr{L}}{\partial \left(\frac{\partial \phi_n}{\partial x_4}\right)} = 0. \tag{16}$$

The Lagrangian density of a free scalar field, consisting of several, possibly complex, components[1], is

$$\begin{aligned} \mathscr{L}_{\text{free}} &= \frac{1}{2} \sum_n \{|\Box \phi_n|^2 - m^2 |\phi_n|^2\} \\ &= \frac{1}{2} \sum_n \left\{ \left| \frac{\partial \phi_n}{\partial x_4} \right|^2 - \sum_{i=1}^{3} \left| \frac{\partial \phi_n}{\partial x_i} \right|^2 - m^2 |\phi_n|^2 \right\}, \end{aligned} \tag{17}$$

since it is easily verified that (17), introduced into (16), gives the propagation equation (5) [precisely $(-\Box^2 - m^2)\phi = 0$] for each field component.

The interaction Lagrangians, which, added to (17), lead to the source terms in (11), (12), (13), and (14), are

$$-\sqrt{4\pi}\, f_{SS}(\bar{\psi}_N \psi_N)\phi - \frac{\sqrt{4\pi}}{m} f_{SV}(\bar{\psi}_N \gamma_\nu \psi_N)\, \partial_\nu \phi \tag{18}$$

$$-\sqrt{4\pi}\, f_{PP}(\bar{\psi}_N \gamma_5 \psi_N)\phi - \frac{i\sqrt{4\pi}}{m} f_{PA}(\bar{\psi}_N \gamma_5 \gamma_\nu \psi_N)\, \partial_\nu \phi \tag{19}$$

$$-\sqrt{4\pi}\, f_{VV}(\bar{\psi}_N \gamma_\nu \psi_N)\phi_\nu - \frac{i\sqrt{4\pi}}{m} f_{VT}(\bar{\psi}_N \gamma_\lambda \gamma_\nu \psi_N)(\partial_\lambda \phi_\nu - \partial_\nu \phi_\lambda) \tag{20}$$

$$-i\sqrt{4\pi}\, f_{AA}(\bar{\psi}_N \gamma_5 \gamma_\nu \psi_N)\phi_\nu - \frac{i\sqrt{4\pi}}{m} f_{AD}(\bar{\psi}_N \gamma_5 \gamma_\lambda \gamma_\nu \psi_N)(\partial_\lambda \phi_\nu - \partial_\nu \phi_\lambda). \tag{21}$$

Clearly, the interaction Lagrangians must be scalars formed by saturating the indices of the mesic field components or their derivatives with tensors of equal rank formed from the source spinors.

[1] The different components of a scalar field are used to describe mesons of different charges (see 7.14d). For the Lagrangian of a vector field, consistent with the wave equation (8), consult Wentzel.

The Hamiltonian densities can be obtained by using the relations

$$\mathscr{H} = \sum_n \frac{\partial \mathscr{L}}{\partial \dot{\phi}_n} \dot{\phi}_n - \mathscr{L}, \qquad \dot{\phi}_n = \frac{\partial \phi_n}{\partial x_4}. \tag{22}$$

From (17) and (22) we obtain the Hamiltonian of the free scalar field:

$$\mathscr{H}_{\text{free}} = \frac{1}{2} \sum_n \left\{ \left| \frac{\partial \phi_n}{\partial x_4} \right|^2 + \sum_{i=1}^{3} \left| \frac{\partial \phi_n}{\partial x_i} \right|^2 + m^2 |\phi_n|^2 \right\}. \tag{23}$$

If the interaction Lagrangian does not contain $\dot{\phi}_n$, we can write

$$\mathscr{H}_{\text{int}} = -\mathscr{L}_{\text{int}}; \tag{24}$$

this relation is valid for all the first terms of (18) to (21) that do not involve derivative coupling; for (19), which is of special interest, $\partial\mathscr{L}/\partial\dot{\phi} \approx \langle\gamma_5\gamma_4\rangle$ is small nonrelativistically, and in this approximation (24) is satisfied by both terms of the interaction Lagrangian of pseudoscalar mesons.

7.13 Properties of Pions and Muons

a. Masses of Charged Mesons. Accurate values of the masses of pions and muons are obtained from measurements of $\pi \to \mu$ decay in photographic emulsion combined with results on critical absorption of mesonic x rays.

The photographic measurement of the kinetic energy of μ^+ mesons from π^+ decay at rest determines the $\pi - \mu$ mass difference:

$$m_{\pi^+} - m_{\mu^+} = (66.41 \pm 0.1)m_e. \tag{1}$$

The energy of mesonic x rays in relation to the atomic absorption edges gives an upper and lower limit of the masses of the negative mesons:

$$\begin{aligned} (272.2 \pm 0.03)m_e \leq m_{\pi^-} \leq (273.5 \pm 0.04)m_e, \\ (206.77 \pm 0.04)m_e \leq m_{\mu^-} \leq (208.95 \pm 0.04)m_e. \end{aligned} \tag{2}$$

Assuming $m_{\mu^+} = m_{\mu^-}$ and $m_{\pi^+} = m_{\pi^-}$, the masses of the charged mesons can be obtained. An even more precise determination of the mass of the muon has been derived from the measurement of the overlap between a μ-mesic x ray line ($3d \to 2p$ transition in phosphorus) and the absorption edge of Pb (B-60b, D-60b).

Recent accurate measurements of the gyromagnetic ratio (see 8.34a) and of the magnetic moment (G-60) of the muon provide another determination of its mass. The result is

$$m_\mu = (206.77 \pm 0.01)m_e. \tag{2b}$$

Again, if we assume $m_{\mu^+} = m_{\mu^-}$ and $m_{\pi^+} = m_{\pi^-}$, the masses of all charged mesons can be obtained, with the result (B-60a)

$$m_{\mu^\pm} = (105.655 \pm 0.010) \text{ MeV}, \tag{3}$$
$$m_{\pi^\pm} = (139.59 \pm 0.05) \text{ MeV}. \tag{4}$$

The assumption that the masses do not depend on the sign is verified within 0.2% from photographic work on π mesons.

b. Mean Lives of Charged Mesons. The mean life of the μ^+ is measured electronically. Its value is[1]

$$\tau_{\mu^+} = (2.212 \pm 0.001) \times 10^{-6} \text{ sec}. \tag{5}$$

There are no direct measurements of the mean lives of free μ^-, for these particles form mu-atoms before decaying. However, from the measurements of the mean lives of bound μ^- we can deduce with good accuracy that the free mean lives are the same for the two signs.

A similar situation prevails for pions. The π^+ mean life is measured directly from decay of π^+ at rest with the result (B-60a)

$$\tau_{\pi^+} = (2.55 \pm 0.03) \times 10^{-8} \text{ sec}. \tag{6$^+$}$$

Observations of π^- decay are limited to events of decay in flight. The measured mean life (L-51) is less accurate but agrees with (6$^+$):

$$\tau_{\pi^-} = (2.55 \pm 0.19) \times 10^{-8} \text{ sec}. \tag{6$^-$}$$

The equality of the mean lives of free particles of opposite sign is required under the assumption of invariance under charge conjugation.

c. Spins. There has been for a long time much indirect evidence in favor of a spin $\frac{1}{2}$ for the muon. The mode of decay proves that the spin must be a half integer, and the gyromagnetic ratio agrees with great accuracy with that of a Dirac particle (8.34a). Finally, recent measurements of the hyperfine splitting of the atom of muonium (see 8.34b) definitely establish that

(7) *the spin of the muon is* $\frac{1}{2}$.

The spin of the π meson is obtained from the detailed balance comparison (5.14b) of the reaction (C-51a, c)

$$\text{p} + \text{p} \rightarrow \text{D} + \pi^+$$

with its inverse (C-51b; D-51)

$$\pi^+ + \text{D} \rightarrow \text{p} + \text{p}.$$

The result is that

(8) *the spin of the pion is zero.*

[1] See references in 8.31d.

d. Discovery and Properties of the Neutral π Meson. Since like nucleons cannot exchange charged pions, the observed charge independence of nuclear forces requires the existence of a π^0. Search for this particle was started under the assumption, later verified, that it would rapidly decay into two γ rays, a process forbidden to $\pi^{\pm}$ because of conservation of electric charge. The decay is supposed to occur through the intermediate of a nucleon-antinucleon pair (Fig. 7.13-1).

The photoproduction of π^0 $(\gamma + \mathcal{N} \rightarrow \mathcal{N} + \pi^0)$ was discovered at Berkeley in 1950 (Steinberger and Panofsky) by the observation of the decay γ rays in coincidence.

At about the same time Panofsky studied the γ rays from π^- captured in hydrogen, proving that these consisted of two groups according to the reactions:

(9) $$\pi^- + \text{p} \rightarrow \text{n} + \gamma$$

(10) $$\pi^- + \text{p} \rightarrow \text{n} + \pi^0, \quad \pi^0 \rightarrow 2\gamma$$

emitted with roughly the same intensity ("Panofsky ratio" $R = \pi^0/\gamma = 0.94 \pm 0.2$ from the original experiments; ≈ 1.5 from more recent determinations, see 7.33).

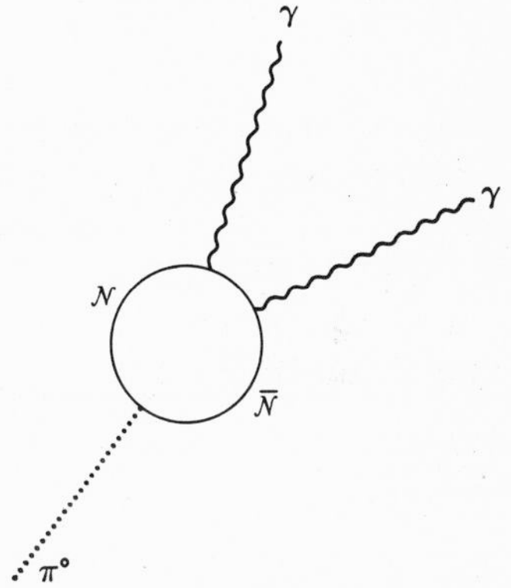

Fig. 7.13-1. The simplest diagram describing the decay of the neutral pion.

The energy of the neutral π meson emitted in reaction (10) depends on the π^-–π^0 mass difference. The kinetic energy of the π^0 in turn produces a Doppler broadening of the γ rays emitted. From a measurement of the Doppler broadening of the γ line Panofsky obtained

$$m_{\pi^-} - m_{\pi^0} = (10.6 \pm 2.0)m_e.$$

Later measurements of angular correlation between the γ rays (C-54d; C-57) (which are emitted in opposite direction in the π^0 rest system) give

$$m_{\pi^-} - m_{\pi^0} = (8.9 \pm 0.14)m_e.$$

The most recent estimate of the π^0 mass (B-60a) is

(11) $$m_{\pi^0} = (135.00 \pm 0.05) \text{ MeV}.$$

The spin of the π^0 cannot be 1 because two γ rays in opposite directions cannot carry one unit of angular momentum (7.27d). It is assumed to be zero like that of the charged pions.

The mean life of the π^0 is expected to be very short. Direct measurements of this quantity have recently been reported (B-60c; G-61b;

S-62b, c), and one of the latest published values is

(12a) $$\tau_{\pi^0} \sim 1.9 \begin{matrix} +0.7 \\ -0.4 \end{matrix} \times 10^{-16} \text{ sec.}$$

The measurement consists of the observation of the path length traveled by the π^0 formed in K-meson decay ($K^+ \rightarrow \pi^0 + \pi^+$) in photographic emulsion (Fig. 7.13-2), when the π^0 decays with the emission of an electron-positron pair and a γ ray.

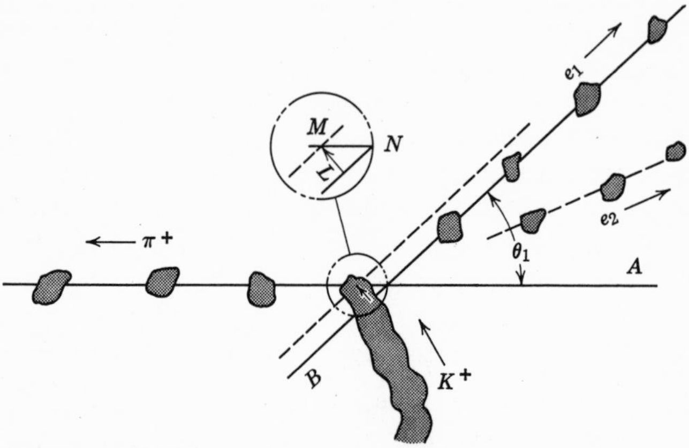

Fig. 7.13-2. From the end of a K^+ track in photographic emulsion (M) a π^+ and a π^0 are emitted in opposite directions. The π^+ trajectory is recognized as the sequence of dark grains to the left. The π^0 travels to the right until it decays emitting a γ and an electron pair (e_1, e_2) whose trajectories are visible and locate the decay point (N). [From Glaser, Seeman, and Stiller, *Phys. Rev.*, **123**, 1015 (1961).]

An indirect measurement of π^0 mean life has also been suggested (G-61a; P-51b). This is based on the study of the inverse reactions of the decay, such as

(13a) $$\gamma + \gamma \rightarrow \pi^0,$$

(13b) $$\gamma + \text{coulomb field of heavy nucleus} \rightarrow \pi^0,$$

or

(13c) $$e^+ + e^- \rightarrow \pi^0,$$

and on the application of detailed balance.

The observation of (13b) has been reported (T-60) with the conclusion

(12b) $$\tau_{\pi 0} \geq 5 \times 10^{-17} \text{ sec}; \qquad \text{possibly} \approx 10^{-16} \text{ sec.}$$

e. The Parity of π Mesons. Panofsky and collaborators extended the measurements of capture of π^- in H to deuterium (P-51a). A group of

γ rays from the reaction $\pi^- + \mathrm{D} \rightarrow \mathrm{n} + \mathrm{n} + \gamma$ was observed, but these did not account for the totality of the π^- captured. These authors conclude that the reaction

$$\pi^- + \mathrm{D} \rightarrow \mathrm{n} + \mathrm{n} \tag{14}$$

occurs with a frequency corresponding to a ratio $(\mathrm{n} + \mathrm{n})/(\mathrm{n} + \mathrm{n} + \gamma) = 2.4 \pm 0.5$. The same reaction was directly observed through the coincidences between neutrons by Chinowsky and Steinberger (C-54c) who find $(\mathrm{n} + \mathrm{n})/(\mathrm{n} + \mathrm{n} + \gamma) = 1.5 \pm 0.8$; more recent results on this ratio are reported in 7.33.

Let us study the balance of spin and parity in (14).

There is both theoretical and experimental evidence that the isolated system $\pi^- + \mathrm{D}$ forms a $1S$ atomic state before capture. The theoretical evidence is based on the calculation of the radiative transition probability between the $2P$ and $1S$ state of the mesic deuterium and of an estimate of direct nuclear capture of the meson in the $2P$ state (B-51). The experimental evidence is the observation of mesic x rays for the $2p \rightarrow 1s$ transition in Be and Li.

In a condensed target the π-D atom—a small neutral body—diffuses through matter like a thermal neutron and interacts with the fields of neighboring atoms. Because of Stark effect, its states of high total quantum number and $l \neq 0$ become mixed with $l = 0$ components in which the pion appreciably overlaps the deuteron: thus the capture may occur in S states with total quantum number larger than one, without previous cascading to the lowest atomic orbit (D-59).

We conclude that both in rarefied and condensed matter *the state from which capture occurs* [left side of (14)] *has spin one*; *its orbital parity is even, and its total parity is equal to the intrinsic parity of the pion.*

For total angular momentum 1 the two nucleons in the right side of (14) could be in ^3S or $^3P_1$ or $^3D_1$ or $^1P_1$ state. But, since they are two neutrons which satisfy the exclusion principle, ^3S, $^3D_1$, and $^1P_1$ are forbidden. Thus the *right side must be* $^3P_1$ *odd.*

We conclude that *the* π^- *has odd intrinsic parity* in relation to the nucleons. If we arbitrarily assign an even parity to the nucleons, they are $\frac{1}{2}^+$, and the negative pion is 0^-. Its wave function in a state of 0-orbital angular momentum is invariant under rotation of axes but changes sign under reflection of axes. It is *pseudoscalar*.

There is no direct determination of the parity of π^+, which is assumed to be odd because of invariance under charge conjugation.

The π^0 is also assumed to be odd, for the three pions must have the same properties to account for charge independence. An experiment for the measurement of π^0 parity was suggested by Yang (Y-50) and consists of a study of the relative polarization of the 2γ of π^0 decay. If the π^0 is even, the two γ rays must be polarized in the same plane, whereas, if the π^0 is odd, the polarization is in perpendicular planes (Fig. 7.13-3), as in the ^1S state of positronium.

This experiment has been considered by many experimentalists but discarded because of the difficulty in building efficient polarimeters for high-energy γ rays. If, however, the π^0 decay emits two electron-positron

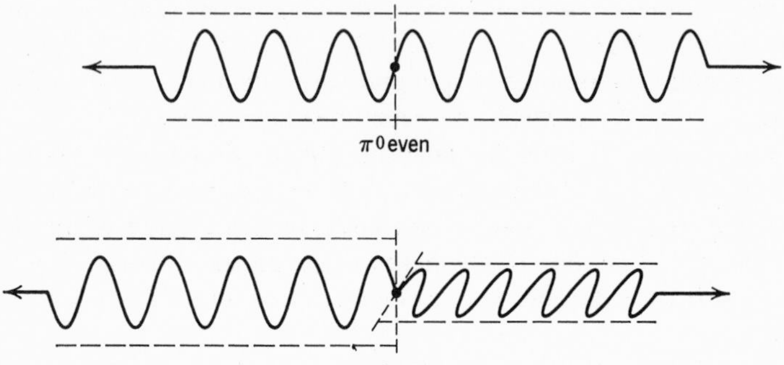

Fig. 7.13-3. Polarization of γ rays from π^0 decay.

pairs ("Dalitz" pairs) instead of two γ rays, they can be observed in a hydrogen bubble chamber at the end of a π^- track. This double internal materialization is an improbable event [its probability is $\approx 1/30{,}000$, $\approx (137)^{-2}$], but the correlation of the planes of the pairs still depends on the π^0 parity (K-55) and can be measured.

Analysis of 112 events (P-59; S-62a) (836,000 pictures were studied!) led to the conclusion that the π^0 is odd as expected.

Observe that the intrinsic parity of π^0 is measured absolutely (or in relation to the vacuum), whereas that of π^- is compared with the parity difference between proton and neutron. There is agreement with the natural assumption that both nucleons have positive parity and all three pions are odd.

7.14 *Nonquantized Pseudoscalar Meson Theory with Nonrelativistic Coupling*

a. Nonrelativistic Pseudoscalar Interaction for Neutral Mesons. In the preceding section we presented evidence of the pseudoscalar character of the pion wave function. This experimental result uniquely determines the form of the interaction between the nucleons and the mesic field, at least in the nonrelativistic approximation.

The interaction is necessarily similar to the coupling of loops of electric current with a pseudoscalar magnetostatic potential Φ_m. A current loop of magnetic moment $\boldsymbol{\mu}$ produces a potential $\Phi_m = -\boldsymbol{\mu} \cdot \nabla(1/r)$; the same loop in an external potential Φ_m has an energy $\boldsymbol{\mu} \cdot \nabla\Phi_m$. As a result, two loops, $\boldsymbol{\mu}_1$ and $\boldsymbol{\mu}_2$, interact with each other with a potential

$$-(\boldsymbol{\mu}_1 \cdot \nabla)(\boldsymbol{\mu}_2 \cdot \nabla)(1/r),$$

which is equivalent to 1.22(9).

Similar expressions are found for the interactions of point nucleons with the mesic field and with one another. The only difference is that the radial function $1/r$ becomes $(1/r) \exp(-mr)$ and that the magnetic moment is replaced with the product of spin and coupling constant.

To proceed more formally, let us start from the pseudovector part of the interaction Lagrangian density 7.12(19) and consider only one kind of meson—the neutral meson—whose wave function is assumed to be real. In the nonrelativistic approximation we retain only the "large" terms of this Lagrangian, with the result

$$(1) \qquad \mathscr{L}_{\text{int}} = -i\frac{\sqrt{4\pi}}{m} f_{PA}(\bar{\psi}\gamma_5\gamma_i\psi)\frac{\partial\phi}{\partial x_i} = -\frac{\sqrt{4\pi}}{m} f_{PA}(\psi^\dagger\sigma_i\psi)\frac{\partial\phi}{\partial x_i}.$$

Since $\partial\phi/\partial t$ no longer appears in the Lagrangian, the corresponding Hamiltonian also has the form $\boldsymbol{\sigma} \cdot \nabla\phi$, which is that of the interaction energy of the analogous electromagnetic case.

For a point nucleus at position $\mathbf{r}$ the matrix element $(\psi^\dagger\sigma_i\psi)$ can be replaced by $\langle\sigma_i\rangle\,\delta(\mathbf{r} - \mathbf{r}')$, where the σ_i are 2×2 Pauli matrices. But we shall find it useful to consider nucleons of finite extent, whose distribution of mesic source is expressed by a function $\rho(r)$, which satisfies $\int \rho(r)\, d\mathbf{r} = 1$. Then, if the nucleus is at $\mathbf{r}$, the Lagrangian and Hamiltonian densities at $\mathbf{r}'$ are given by

$$(2) \qquad \mathscr{L}_{\text{int}}(\mathbf{r}, \mathbf{r}') = -\mathscr{H}_{\text{int}}(\mathbf{r}, \mathbf{r}') = -\frac{\sqrt{4\pi}}{m} f_{PA}\rho(|\mathbf{r}' - \mathbf{r}|)\boldsymbol{\sigma} \cdot \nabla\phi(\mathbf{r}').$$

The corresponding Lagrangians and Hamiltonians are obtained by integrating over the "internal variable" $\mathbf{r}'$. Observe that the expression in (2) is scalar, as required by a parity conserving theory, since $\nabla\phi$ is a pseudovector[1].

We might suspect that (2) is not unique and that we would have obtained a different result by starting from the pseudoscalar part of the interaction Lagrangian 7.12(19). We can show, however, that this is not the case. In effect, it is impossible to construct a scalar expression of a form different

[1] The mesic field, like the magnetostatic potential, must be odd under time reversal in order to ensure that the interaction is time reversible.

from (2) by using the space and spin coordinates of the particles considered; and we may recall [6.14(21′)] that $\bar{\psi}\gamma_5\psi$ reduces nonrelativistically to $\approx \boldsymbol{\sigma} \cdot \mathbf{v}_{\mathcal{N}} \approx (\boldsymbol{\sigma} \cdot \mathbf{p}_\pi)(m_\pi/M_{\mathcal{N}})$, which leads to a form essentially similar to (2). The equivalence between pseudoscalar and pseudovector coupling holds to a certain extent even relativistically and is discussed more precisely in 7.16e.

At this point we introduce two simplifications in our notation:

(i) we drop the subscript from the coupling constant

$$f \equiv f_{PA}; \tag{3}$$

(ii) we use units such that

$$m_\pi \equiv 1. \tag{4}$$

With this notation the nonrelativistic interaction Lagrangian and Hamiltonian densities are, for a nucleon at the origin,

$$\mathscr{L}_{\text{int}}(\mathbf{r}) = -\mathscr{H}_{\text{int}}(\mathbf{r}) = -\sqrt{4\pi} f \rho(r)\boldsymbol{\sigma} \cdot \boldsymbol{\nabla} \phi(\mathbf{r}), \tag{5a}$$

while the integrated Hamiltonian becomes

$$\mathcal{H}_{\text{int}} = \sqrt{4\pi} f \int \rho(r)\, \boldsymbol{\sigma} \cdot \boldsymbol{\nabla}\, \phi(\mathbf{r})\, d\mathbf{r}, \tag{5b}$$

and the wave equation is[1]

$$(\Box^2 + 1)\phi = \sqrt{4\pi} f \boldsymbol{\sigma} \cdot \boldsymbol{\nabla}\rho. \tag{6}$$

b. The Neutral Meson Cloud. For a point source fixed at the origin $\rho(r)$ can be replaced by a δ function and (6) admits a static solution

$$\phi(r) = \frac{f}{\sqrt{4\pi}} \boldsymbol{\sigma} \cdot \boldsymbol{\nabla} \frac{e^{-r}}{r} = -\frac{f}{\sqrt{4\pi}}\left(\frac{1}{r} + \frac{1}{r^2}\right) e^{-r} \boldsymbol{\sigma} \cdot \mathbf{r}, \tag{7}$$

whereas for a general source distribution we have

$$\phi(r) = \frac{f}{\sqrt{4\pi}} \boldsymbol{\sigma} \cdot \boldsymbol{\nabla} \int \rho(r') \frac{e^{-|\mathbf{r}-\mathbf{r}'|}}{|\mathbf{r} - \mathbf{r}'|}\, d\mathbf{r}'. \tag{8}$$

These formulas describe the meson cloud of nonrelativistic pseudoscalar theory in the same way as 7.11(6) represented the meson cloud of scalar theory.

The mesons in the cloud are static; their wave function has no time dependence, and thus their energy is zero. This means that their rest energy is compensated by the binding energy and that a unit of energy ($= m_\pi c^2$) is needed to make the mesons appear as free particles.

The mesic cloud extends about a unit distance ($\hbar/m_\pi c$), a distance which

[1] Note the similarity between $-\boldsymbol{\nabla}\cdot(\rho\boldsymbol{\sigma})$ in the source in (6) and the "magnetic charge density" $-\boldsymbol{\nabla}\cdot\mathbf{m}$ (p. 31).

is somewhat larger but of the same order of magnitude as the "size" of the proton. The wave function (7) has an angular dependence $\cos \widehat{\sigma r}$, characteristic of a P state. The odd angular dependence is obviously needed to compensate for the intrinsic oddness of the meson, since the nucleons, including their meson cloud, must be even.

c. Nuclear Forces. Assume for simplicity that the nucleons 1 and 2 are points. Nucleon 1, assumed to be at the origin, produces, according to (7), a mesic field

$$\phi_1 = \frac{f}{\sqrt{4\pi}} \boldsymbol{\sigma}_1 \cdot \nabla \frac{e^{-r}}{r}.$$

In this field the second point nucleon, at position $\mathbf{r}$, according to (5*b*) has an energy

$$U(r) = \sqrt{4\pi} f \boldsymbol{\sigma}_2 \cdot \nabla \phi_1(r) = f^2(\boldsymbol{\sigma}_2 \cdot \nabla)(\boldsymbol{\sigma}_1 \cdot \nabla) \frac{e^{-r}}{r}. \tag{9}$$

This is the nuclear potential obtained in the simplest form of pseudoscalar meson theory. By computing the gradients[1] we obtain

$$U = f^2\left[\left(\frac{3}{r^2} + \frac{3}{r} + 1\right) S_{12} + \boldsymbol{\sigma}_1 \cdot \boldsymbol{\sigma}_2\right] \frac{e^{-r}}{3r} - \frac{4\pi}{3} f^2 \boldsymbol{\sigma}_1 \cdot \boldsymbol{\sigma}_2 \, \delta(r), \tag{10}$$

where S_{12} is the tensor force operator 1.22(11).

Expression (10) is, to say the least, encouraging. With a very simple

[1] For any function of r, $f(r)$,

$$\begin{aligned}
\nabla(\boldsymbol{\sigma}_2 \cdot \nabla f) &= \nabla\left(\frac{1}{r}\frac{\partial f}{\partial r} \boldsymbol{\sigma}_2 \cdot \mathbf{r}\right) \\
&= \frac{\partial f}{\partial r} (\boldsymbol{\sigma}_2 \cdot \mathbf{r}) \nabla \frac{1}{r} + \frac{1}{r} (\boldsymbol{\sigma}_2 \cdot \mathbf{r}) \nabla \frac{\partial f}{\partial r} + \frac{1}{r}\frac{\partial f}{\partial r} \nabla(\boldsymbol{\sigma}_2 \cdot \mathbf{r}) \\
&= \hat{\mathbf{r}}(\boldsymbol{\sigma}_2 \cdot \hat{\mathbf{r}}) \left[\frac{\partial^2 f}{\partial r^2} - \frac{1}{r}\frac{\partial f}{\partial r}\right] + \boldsymbol{\sigma}_2 \frac{1}{r}\frac{\partial f}{\partial r},
\end{aligned}$$

and thus

$$\begin{aligned}
(\boldsymbol{\sigma}_1 \cdot \nabla)(\boldsymbol{\sigma}_2 \cdot \nabla f) &= 3(\boldsymbol{\sigma}_1 \cdot \hat{\mathbf{r}})(\boldsymbol{\sigma}_2 \cdot \hat{\mathbf{r}}) \frac{1}{3}\left[\quad\right] + (\boldsymbol{\sigma}_1 \cdot \boldsymbol{\sigma}_2) \frac{1}{r}\frac{\partial f}{\partial r} \\
&= (3(\boldsymbol{\sigma}_1 \cdot \hat{\mathbf{r}})(\boldsymbol{\sigma}_2 \cdot \hat{\mathbf{r}}) - \boldsymbol{\sigma}_1 \cdot \boldsymbol{\sigma}_2) \frac{1}{3}\left[\quad\right] + (\boldsymbol{\sigma}_1 \cdot \boldsymbol{\sigma}_2)\left\{\frac{1}{r}\frac{\partial f}{\partial r} + \frac{1}{3}\left[\quad\right]\right\}.
\end{aligned}$$

For $f = e^{-r}/r$ we obtain (10) by carrying on the derivatives and noting that

$$\left\{\quad\right\} = \frac{1}{3r^2}\frac{\partial}{\partial r}\left(r^2 \frac{\partial f}{\partial r}\right) = \frac{1}{3}\nabla^2 f = \frac{1}{3}\nabla^2 \frac{e^{-r}}{r} = \frac{e^{-r}}{3r} - \frac{4\pi}{3}\delta(r).$$

Observe that, for $m = 0$, we can write $e^{-r} = 1$ and $1/r^2 \gg 1/r \gg 1$; thus (10) reduces to 1.22(9).

treatment we have found a potential that includes tensor- and spin-exchange forces and has a range of the proper order of magnitude. If we assume that the nucleons are mesic sources of finite size, the δ-function term becomes an attractive or repulsive core.

d. The Isospin of the Pion and the Charge Symmetrical Hamiltonian. The treatment developed so far involves only neutral mesons and it is obviously charge-independent: all nucleons are assigned the same coupling constant to the mesic field and thus behave exactly alike as far as strong forces are concerned.

But all nucleons cannot behave in the same manner in relation to charged mesons. A neutron, for instance, can emit a negative meson and become a proton or it can emit a neutral meson and remain a neutron, but it cannot emit a positive meson. As we have already observed, no exchange of charged mesons can occur—in the lowest order—between like nucleons.

We must now formulate a theory which takes into account the existence of the three pion charge states, yet is in agreement with charge independence of nuclear forces. In order to formulate this theory, we make use of the isospin formalism.

Let us recall that the isospin operator for the nucleons is a vector $\frac{1}{2}\vec{\tau}$ in isospin space whose components are $\frac{1}{2}$ of the usual Pauli matrices 1.14(7); the eigenvalue of $|\frac{1}{2}\vec{\tau}|^2$ is $\frac{3}{4}$, and those of $\frac{1}{2}\tau_3$ are $\pm\frac{1}{2}$, according to whether the nucleon is in a proton or a neutron charge state. In short, we say that the isospin of the nucleon is $\frac{1}{2}$: *The wave function of a nucleon is a Dirac spinor in physical space and a Pauli spinor in isospin space.*

Since the π meson exists in three charge states, +, 0, −, it is natural to say that *its isospin is* 1. The pion isospin operator is a vector $\vec{t}$ whose components are the matrices 1.14(27) or (28). The eigenvalue of $|\vec{t}|^2$ is 2, and those of t_3 are $+1, 0, -1$, according to whether the meson is in its positive, neutral, or negative charge state. In isospin space the pion wave function must have the rotational behavior characteristic of one unit of angular momentum. Thus *the pion wave function $\vec{\phi}$ is a pseudoscalar in physical space and a vector*[1] *in isospin space.* Its components ϕ_1, ϕ_2, ϕ_3 are taken to be real[2].

The condition of charge independence can be formulated by stating (1.33a) that *the interaction Hamiltonian must be rotationally invariant (scalar) in isospin space.* Thus the $\vec{\phi}$ appearing in the Hamiltonian must be dotted with an isospin vector belonging to the nucleons. For a nucleon at the origin the nonrelativistic interaction Lagrangian density (5) must

[1] Or a pseudovector, but we shall not discuss here the question of isoparity.

[2] In 7.31d this assumption will be shown to be consistent with invariance under charge conjugation.

be modified to read[1]

$$\mathscr{L}_{\text{int}} = -\mathscr{H}_{\text{int}} = -\sqrt{4\pi} f\, \rho(r) \boldsymbol{\sigma} \cdot \nabla(\vec{\tau} \cdot \vec{\phi}) \tag{11}$$
$$= -\sqrt{4\pi} f\, \rho(r)\, \boldsymbol{\sigma} \cdot \nabla(\tau_1\phi_1 + \tau_2\phi_2 + \tau_3\phi_3).$$

From this Lagrangian we obtain the wave equation

$$(\square^2 + 1)\vec{\phi} = \sqrt{4\pi} f \vec{\tau}\, \boldsymbol{\sigma} \cdot \nabla\, \rho(r), \tag{12}$$

which admits a static solution

$$\vec{\phi} = \frac{f}{\sqrt{4\pi}} \vec{\tau}\, \boldsymbol{\sigma} \cdot \nabla \int \rho(r') \frac{e^{-|\mathbf{r}-\mathbf{r}'|}}{|\mathbf{r}-\mathbf{r}'|}\, d\mathbf{r}' \tag{13}$$

and, for point source, leads to a nucleon-nucleon potential of the form

$$U = f^2\, \vec{\tau}_1 \cdot \vec{\tau}_2 \left\{ \left(\frac{3}{r^2} + \frac{3}{r} + 1 \right) S_{12} + \boldsymbol{\sigma}_1 \cdot \boldsymbol{\sigma}_2 \right\} \frac{e^{-r}}{3r} - \frac{4\pi}{3} f^2 (\vec{\tau}_1 \cdot \vec{\tau}_2)(\boldsymbol{\sigma}_1 \cdot \boldsymbol{\sigma}_2)\, \delta(r). \tag{14}$$

The coupling formalism described is called the charge-symmetrical coupling and is originally due to Kemmer (K-38).

It is important to note that the potential (14) has been obtained by assuming only that the interaction between nucleons is transmitted by pseudoscalar pions and that it is charge-independent. The approximations of point, nonrelativistic nucleons and of small coupling were used, but the theory could easily have been made to include finite size or relativistic sources of mesons. The extension to the case of strong coupling ($f^2 > \sim 1$) is instead very difficult, for we would have to consider meson-meson interactions and other high-order effects.

7.15 Comparison with Experiment

a. Comparison with Nuclear Forces in the Singlet *S* State. The potential in 7.14(14) obviously has some of the features needed to account for nuclear forces: it has a range of the proper order of magnitude; it is charge-independent and contains exchange and tensor-force operators. We must now compare it more closely with our knowledge of nuclear interactions, starting with the information available at low energy.

The *S* state of two nucleons can exist as an isosinglet ($\vec{\tau}_1 \cdot \vec{\tau}_2 = 1$) and an isotriplet ($\vec{\tau}_1 \cdot \vec{\tau}_2 = -3$). In the first case we must have spin triplet ($\boldsymbol{\sigma}_1 \cdot \boldsymbol{\sigma}_2 = -3$), and in the second, spin singlet ($\boldsymbol{\sigma}_1 \cdot \boldsymbol{\sigma}_2 = 1$). In either

[1] In the formulae which follow the symbols $\boldsymbol{\sigma}$, $\vec{\tau}$ stand for the matrix elements of the corresponding operators between the nuclear states of interest.

case we can write

$$(\vec{\tau}_1 \cdot \vec{\tau}_2)(\boldsymbol{\sigma}_1 \cdot \boldsymbol{\sigma}_2) = -3. \tag{1}$$

Thus the potential 7.14(14) is attractive, with the exception of the δ-function term, which is repulsive. But a δ-function repulsion added to an attractive potential imposes no new restriction to the solution of the radial wave equation, $u = r\psi$, which is already required to vanish at the origin because of the assumed continuity of ψ; therefore the δ function can be disregarded[1].

If we limit our attention to singlet states, in which the tensor force does not act, the potential 7.14(14) reduces to a simple attractive Yukawa well:

$$U_{\text{singlet}} = -f^2 \frac{e^{-r}}{r}. \tag{2}$$

We can now determine f^2 from the value of the singlet scattering length: we know that this length 3.19(15) is large and corresponds almost to zero binding of the singlet state. For a square well the zero-binding condition is 1.23(13) $V_0 r_0^2 = \pi^2/(4M) \approx (0.4M)^{-1}$; for a Yukawa well we have a similar relation with a different numerical coefficient (BW-52, p. 56, formula 2.17): $f^2 r_0^2 = (0.59M)^{-1}$, where r_0 is the pion Compton wavelength (= 1 in our units) and M is the nucleon mass (≈ 6.7). Thus we obtain

$$f^2 = \frac{1}{0.59 \times 6.7} \approx \frac{1}{4}. \tag{3}$$

We find that the coupling constant of pseudoscalar theory with axial coupling is considerably larger than the elementary electric charge, but not larger than unity.

Considering that $f^2 \approx 1$, the theory is certainly inaccurate without the inclusion of higher order effects in the nuclear potential. Thus the value (3) of the coupling constant cannot be precise. The subject of nuclear forces in nonrelativistic meson theory is discussed again in 7.18 and 7.26, where we shall find that $f^2 = 0.08$ is a better estimate of the nonrelativistic coupling constant.

b. The Triplet State and Necessity of Cutoff. In triplet states, such as in the deuteron, the tensor force must be taken into account. Qualitatively, this force provides an added attraction and may be considered responsible for the binding of the deuteron. It also has the proper sign to account for the sign of the quadrupole moment of the deuteron.

[1] Note that the use of the Born approximation for a δ-function potential is not generally justified.

But if we try to solve the Schrödinger equation for the deuteron by using the potential 7.14(14) we will soon be disappointed. The term $1/r^3$ diverges too strongly at the origin for an acceptable solution: the result is an infinitely small deuteron with infinitely large binding energy. This difficulty is caused by the fact that 7.14(14) is a second-order nonrelativistic formula and cannot be expected to hold at short distances where high momentum transfers and many-meson exchanges become important.

Unfortunately, it has not yet been found possible to treat the many-meson exchanges in a satisfactory relativistic theory. In order to circumvent this difficulty, most theories resort to the device of "cutoff," which is equivalent to the assumption that the source of mesons is spread over a finite volume. The singularities at the origin are then eliminated.

It was first pointed out by Lévy (L-52a, b) that a consistent treatment of the extended source spreads the δ-function repulsion over a finite distance, giving rise to a repulsive core that can no longer be disregarded.

Thus cutoff theories predict a repulsive core, as required for the interpretation of the results of nucleon-nucleon scattering and in agreement with current ideas on nuclear forces.

Meson theories with cutoff have two parameters with which to fit the experimental data:

(i) A coupling constant f, which describes the coupling of mesons at distances not too short and which is not necessarily the same as the point-interaction coupling constant.

(ii) A cutoff parameter, such as a minimum radius r_{min} or a maximum momentum k_{max}, which describes the "size of the source."

The cutoff is frequently introduced by assuming that the meson source of a nucleon at rest has density $\rho(r)$ and that the Fourier transform of this density (form factor)

$$v(k) = \int e^{-i\mathbf{k}\cdot\mathbf{r}}\,\rho(r)\,d\mathbf{r}, \tag{4}$$

is cutoff at $k = k_{\text{max}}$:

$$\begin{aligned} v(k) &= 1 \quad \text{for } k < k_{\text{max}}, \\ v(k) &= 0 \quad \text{for } k > k_{\text{max}}. \end{aligned} \tag{5}$$

All the troublesome effects at short distances and high energies are eliminated in this manner. However, the structure of the extended source remains wrapped in mystery, and, in the words of Feynman, the cutoff theories are equivalent to "hiding the dirt under the rug."

Nevertheless, it cannot be denied that cutoff theories have been successful in interpreting low-energy pion physics, despite the fact that they cannot be applied at high energy. For further discussion and references see 7.25.

c. The Possible Existence of a Second Neutral Pion. We have seen that we can formulate a charge-independent meson theory consistent with the existence of a pion charge triplet. But it is also possible to obtain charge independence with a pion charge singlet: a neutral pion of isospin zero.

Are there two distinct neutral pions, one, the charge zero state of the isospin triplet and the other, the only member of an isospin singlet?

This question can be answered only by experiment, and several authors have looked for a second π^0 on the assumption that it might have a mass not too different from that discovered by Panofsky. The results of these investigations have always been negative (C-59a; S-60).

Recently, however, a pseudoscalar neutral meson with $T = 0$ has been found in high-energy experiments (see 7.37). This particle is more than three times heavier than the pion and is of no interest in the present discussion of low-energy pion physics.

7.16 Quantization of the Meson Field

a. Quantization of the Free Neutral Field. We must now introduce in our formalism the important concept—so far neglected in our theoretical considerations—that the meson field corresponds to particles. The energy of the free-meson field cannot assume an arbitrary value; for each wave of momentum k it can vary only in steps of magnitude $\sqrt{k^2 + 1}$.

Again the situation is perfectly similar to that of the electromagnetic field which had to be quantized in order to take its photon aspect into account (4.12). The quantization of the meson field can be performed by using exactly the same techniques.

First we shall assume that our experiments are to be conducted in a box of a unit volume[1], so that the states of the free mesons are quantized. The possible stationary states of the mesons in the box are denoted by the subscript k, which corresponds to *specified momentum state* ($|k_i| = \pi m_i$, with $i = x, y, z$ and m_i a positive integer).

If we consider for the moment only neutral mesons, the field within the box can be decomposed in a sum of proper modes,

$$\phi = \sum (q_k e^{i\mathbf{k}\cdot\mathbf{r}} + q_k{}^* e^{-i\mathbf{k}\cdot\mathbf{r}}), \tag{1}$$

and the amplitudes q_k must be quantized.

[1] The unit volume here must be larger than the cube of the mesonic Compton wavelength! In order to be consistent with our units, we should speak of a box of volume $L^3 \gg 1$, but since the size of the box never appears in the results we will not write the L^3 in our formulas.

The nonquantized free-field Hamiltonian density 7.12(23) with $m = 1$ is

$$\mathscr{H}_{\text{free}} = \frac{1}{2}\left(\left|\frac{\partial \phi}{\partial x_4}\right|^2 + |\nabla\phi|^2 + |\phi|^2\right); \tag{2}$$

by introducing (1) into (2) and integrating, we obtain the free-field Hamiltonian

$$\begin{aligned} \mathcal{H}_{\text{free}} &= \frac{1}{2}\sum_k [(\dot{q}_k + \dot{q}_k{}^*)^2 + k^2(q_k + q_k{}^*)^2 + (q_k + q_k{}^*)^2] \\ &= \sum_k \left(\frac{1}{2\mathfrak{m}} P_k{}^2 + \frac{1}{2}\mathfrak{m}\omega_k{}^2 Q_k{}^2\right), \end{aligned} \tag{3}$$

where

$$\omega_k = \sqrt{k^2 + 1} \tag{4}$$

is the quantum energy and, as in 4.12, $Q_k = q_k + q_k{}^*$, $P_k = \mathfrak{m}(\dot{q}_k + \dot{q}_k{}^*)$; however, we have here $\mathfrak{m} = 1$ (instead of $\mathfrak{m} = 1/4\pi c^2$).

We note that the Hamiltonian of the free meson field, like that of the electromagnetic radiation field, corresponds to a sum of oscillators, and we need not carry the computation further, since we can make use of the results of 4.12d[1]. The mesic field can be expanded in annihilation and creation operators a_k and $\mathsf{a}_k{}^\dagger$:

$$\phi = \sum_k \sqrt{\frac{1}{2\omega_k}}\,(\mathsf{a}_k e^{i\mathbf{k}\cdot\mathbf{r}} + \mathsf{a}_k{}^\dagger e^{-i\mathbf{k}\cdot\mathbf{r}}). \tag{5}$$

We must now expand in a sum of creation and annihilation operators the Hamiltonian of the interaction between the nucleon and the mesic field.

For this purpose let us consider a nucleon at position $\mathbf{r}$ (for which the nonquantized interaction Hamiltonian is 7.14(5*b*), with $\mathbf{r}$ replaced by $\mathbf{r}' - \mathbf{r}$) and let us introduce in this formula the quantized form of the mesic field (5). In this way we obtain the quantized Hamiltonian

$$\begin{aligned} \mathcal{H}_{\text{int}} &= \sqrt{4\pi} f \sum_k \sqrt{\frac{1}{2\omega_k}} \int \rho(|\mathbf{r}' - \mathbf{r}|)\, \boldsymbol{\sigma}\cdot\nabla(\mathsf{a}_k e^{i\mathbf{k}\cdot\mathbf{r}'} + \mathsf{a}^\dagger e^{-i\mathbf{k}\cdot\mathbf{r}'})\, d\mathbf{r}' \\ &= i\sqrt{4\pi} f \sum_k v(k) \sqrt{\frac{1}{2\omega_k}}\, \boldsymbol{\sigma}\cdot\mathbf{k}\,(\mathsf{a}_k e^{i\mathbf{k}\cdot\mathbf{r}} - \mathsf{a}_k{}^\dagger e^{-i\mathbf{k}\cdot\mathbf{r}}). \end{aligned} \tag{6}$$

where $v(k)$ is defined in 7.15(4).

This Hamiltonian operates over the spin states of the nucleon and over the states of the meson field.

[1] There is a difference of a factor $\sqrt{4\pi}$ because the electromagnetic field Hamiltonian 4.12(8) has a factor $1/8\pi$ whereas the mesic field Hamiltonian (2) has a factor $\frac{1}{2}$.

b. Use of Rotational Axes in Isospace. Before proceeding to the quantization of the charged meson field it will be useful to describe its nonquantized components for +, 0, and − charge.

Let us fix a system of right-handed orthogonal axes in isospace, defined by the unit vectors $\hat{e}_1$, $\hat{e}_2$, $\hat{e}_3$, and let us project all isospin vectors in the direction of the unit vectors[1]

$$\hat{e}_+ = -\frac{1}{\sqrt{2}}(\hat{e}_1 + i\hat{e}_2),$$
$$(7) \qquad \hat{e}_- = \frac{1}{\sqrt{2}}(\hat{e}_1 - i\hat{e}_2),$$
$$\hat{e}_0 = \hat{e}_3.$$

These vectors, as we know, are normalized eigenvectors of isospin 1 for third components equal to +1, −1, and 0, respectively [see 1.14(25)]. The components of the meson field in these directions

$$\phi_+ = -\frac{1}{\sqrt{2}}(\phi_1 + i\phi_2), \qquad \left(\phi_1 = -\frac{1}{\sqrt{2}}(\phi_+ - \phi_-)\right),$$
$$(8) \qquad \phi_- = \frac{1}{\sqrt{2}}(\phi_1 - i\phi_2), \qquad \left(\phi_2 = \frac{i}{\sqrt{2}}(\phi_+ + \phi_-)\right),$$
$$\phi_0 = \phi_3, \qquad (\phi_3 = \phi_0).$$

correspond, respectively, to that part of the meson field whose isospin third component is +1, −1, 0 and thus to positive, negative, and neutral pions.

It is easily seen that expressed in terms of ϕ_+, ϕ_-, and ϕ_0 the Lagrangian density of the free meson field 7.12(17) becomes (for $m = 1$)

$$(9) \quad \mathscr{L}_{\text{free}} = \frac{1}{2}\Bigg\{-|\nabla\phi_+|^2 - |\nabla\phi_-|^2 - (\nabla\phi_0)^2 + \left|\frac{\partial\phi_+}{\partial t}\right|^2 + \left|\frac{\partial\phi_-}{\partial t}\right|^2 + \left(\frac{\partial\phi_0}{\partial t}\right)^2 - |\phi_+|^2 - |\phi_-|^2 - (\phi_0)^2\Bigg\}.$$

The interaction Lagrangian density 7.14(11) can be written by using the rotational components of isospin,

$$\tau_+ = -\frac{1}{\sqrt{2}}(\tau_1 + i\tau_2) = -\sqrt{2}\begin{pmatrix}0 & 1\\ 0 & 0\end{pmatrix},$$
$$(10) \qquad \tau_- = \frac{1}{\sqrt{2}}(\tau_1 - i\tau_2) = \sqrt{2}\begin{pmatrix}0 & 0\\ 1 & 0\end{pmatrix},$$
$$\tau_0 = \tau_3 = \begin{pmatrix}1 & 0\\ 0 & -1\end{pmatrix},$$

[1] Compare with 1.13e.

with the result that

$$(11)\quad -\mathscr{L}_{\text{int}} = \mathscr{H}_{\text{int}} = \sqrt{4\pi}\, f\, \rho(r)\boldsymbol{\sigma}\cdot\nabla(-\tau_+\phi_- - \tau_-\phi_+ + \tau_0\phi_0)$$

$$= \sqrt{4\pi}\, f\, \rho(r)\boldsymbol{\sigma}\cdot\nabla\left[\sqrt{2}\begin{pmatrix}0 & 1\\ 0 & 0\end{pmatrix}\phi_- - \sqrt{2}\begin{pmatrix}0 & 0\\ 1 & 0\end{pmatrix}\phi_+ + \begin{pmatrix}1 & 0\\ 0 & -1\end{pmatrix}\phi_0\right].$$

This formula expresses a formal relation between the charge states of the mesons and of the nucleons; its meaning will become clear after the quantization of the charged field.

c. Quantization of the Charge Symmetrical Field. The three real components of the pion field on the cartesian isospin axes, ϕ_1, ϕ_2, ϕ_3, can be expanded in annihilation and creation operators $\mathsf{a}_{i,k}$, $\mathsf{a}^\dagger_{i,k}$ $(i = 1, 2, 3)$ exactly as we have done for the neutral field.

Thus the expansion of the complex fields ϕ_+ and ϕ_- is

$$(12)\quad \phi_+ = -\frac{1}{\sqrt{2}}\sum_k \sqrt{\frac{1}{2\omega_k}}\,[(\mathsf{a}_{1,k} + i\mathsf{a}_{2,k})e^{i\mathbf{k}\cdot\mathbf{r}} + (\mathsf{a}^\dagger_{1,k} + i\mathsf{a}^\dagger_{2,k})e^{-i\mathbf{k}\cdot\mathbf{r}}],$$

$$\phi_- = \frac{1}{\sqrt{2}}\sum_k \sqrt{\frac{1}{2\omega_k}}\,[(\mathsf{a}_{1,k} - i\mathsf{a}_{2,k})e^{i\mathbf{k}\cdot\mathbf{r}} + (\mathsf{a}^\dagger_{1,k} - i\mathsf{a}^\dagger_{2,k})e^{-i\mathbf{k}\cdot\mathbf{r}}].$$

The interpretation of these formulas requires some comment, since the coefficient of $e^{-i\mathbf{k}\cdot\mathbf{r}}$ in ϕ_+ is the hermitian conjugate of the coefficient of $e^{+i\mathbf{k}\cdot\mathbf{r}}$ in ϕ_-, and not in ϕ_+ itself.

The meaning of the operators in (12) becomes clear when we introduce these expansions in (11), and we see that the operator ϕ_+ is multiplied by $\begin{pmatrix}0 & 0\\ 1 & 0\end{pmatrix}$. Since $\begin{pmatrix}0 & 0\\ 1 & 0\end{pmatrix}$ lowers the charge of the nucleons, in order to conserve electric charge, ϕ_+ must raise the charge of the meson field; similarly ϕ_-, which is multiplied by $\begin{pmatrix}0 & 1\\ 0 & 0\end{pmatrix}$, must lower the charge of the meson field. Thus the operators in (12) must be interpreted as follows:

(13)

$$\frac{1}{\sqrt{2}}(\mathsf{a}_{1,k} + i\mathsf{a}_{2,k}) \equiv \mathsf{a}_{-,k}, \qquad \text{annihilation operator for } \pi^-,$$

$$\frac{1}{\sqrt{2}}(\mathsf{a}_{1,k} - i\mathsf{a}_{2,k}) \equiv \mathsf{a}_{+,k}, \qquad \text{annihilation operator for } \pi^+,$$

$$\frac{1}{\sqrt{2}}(\mathsf{a}^\dagger_{1,k} - i\mathsf{a}^\dagger_{2,k}) \equiv \mathsf{a}^\dagger_{-,k}, \qquad \text{creation operator for } \pi^-,$$

$$\frac{1}{\sqrt{2}}(\mathsf{a}^\dagger_{1,k} + i\mathsf{a}^\dagger_{2,k}) \equiv \mathsf{a}^\dagger_{+,k}, \qquad \text{creation operator for } \pi^+.$$

From (11)[1], (12), (13) we obtain the following expression for the quantized interaction Hamiltonian with cutoff expanded in destruction and creation operators for +, −, 0 charge:

$$(14)\quad \mathcal{H}_{\text{int}} = -\mathcal{L}_{\text{int}} = \sum_k i\sqrt{4\pi}\, f\, v(k)\sqrt{\frac{1}{2\omega_k}}\,\boldsymbol{\sigma}\cdot\mathbf{k}$$

$$\times\left[\sqrt{2}\begin{pmatrix}0 & 1\\0 & 0\end{pmatrix}\mathrm{a}_{+,k} + \sqrt{2}\begin{pmatrix}0 & 0\\1 & 0\end{pmatrix}\mathrm{a}_{-,k} + \begin{pmatrix}1 & 0\\0 & -1\end{pmatrix}\mathrm{a}_{0,k}\right]e^{i\mathbf{k}\cdot\mathbf{r}}$$

$$-\sum_k i\sqrt{4\pi}\, f\, v(k)\sqrt{\frac{1}{2\omega_k}}\,\boldsymbol{\sigma}\cdot\mathbf{k}$$

$$\times\left[\sqrt{2}\begin{pmatrix}0 & 0\\1 & 0\end{pmatrix}\mathrm{a}^{\dagger}_{+,k} + \sqrt{2}\begin{pmatrix}0 & 1\\0 & 0\end{pmatrix}\mathrm{a}^{\dagger}_{-,k} + \begin{pmatrix}1 & 0\\0 & -1\end{pmatrix}\mathrm{a}^{\dagger}_{0,k}\right]e^{-\mathbf{k}\cdot\mathbf{r}}.$$

Though the second sum is the hermitian conjugate of the first, it is written explicitly for the sake of clarity.

The physical meaning of this expression is clear: the transformation of a neutron into a proton $\left[\text{operator }\begin{pmatrix}0 & 1\\0 & 0\end{pmatrix}\right]$ is accompanied either by the absorption of a positive pion (operator $\mathrm{a}_{+,k}$) or, in the hermitian conjugate expression, by the emission of a negative pion (operator $\mathrm{a}^{\dagger}_{-,k}$). All other terms can be similarly interpreted, consistently with conservation of charge.

For the purpose of computation, however, it is sometimes more convenient to use real cartesian axes in isospin space. Then we obtain

$$(15)\quad \mathcal{H}_{\text{int}} = -\mathcal{L}_{\text{int}}$$

$$= \sum_k i\sqrt{4\pi}\, f\, v(k)\sqrt{\frac{1}{2\omega_k}}\,\boldsymbol{\sigma}\cdot\mathbf{k}\sum_{i=1}^{3}\tau_i(\mathrm{a}_{i,k}e^{i\mathbf{k}\cdot\mathbf{r}} - \mathrm{a}^{\dagger}_{i,k}e^{-i\mathbf{k}\cdot\mathbf{r}}),$$

where the operators τ_i have the form of the conventional Pauli spin operators and are hermitian.

d. Matrix Elements for Meson Processes. Under the assumption of a not-too-large coupling constant between pions and nucleons it is possible to compute meson processes by means of perturbation theory, and the transition matrix elements can be obtained with the help of Feynman diagrams.

Meson processes are represented by diagrams similar to those that describe the interaction of electrons with radiation, in which the nucleons, which are fermions, take the place of the electrons, and the pions, which are bosons, replace the photons. In such diagrams we conventionally represent the propagation of a pion with a dashed line.

[1] Equation (11) is written for a nucleon at the origin and must be transformed to a nucleon at position **r**, in order to obtain (14).

From the discussion of this section it appears that in these diagrams we must use

(16) a normalization factor $\sqrt{\dfrac{1}{2\omega_k}}$ with $\omega_k = \sqrt{k^2+1}$

at the entrance or exit of each meson line. Following a procedure similar to that used for photons[1], we obtain

(17) a propagator factor $\dfrac{1}{k^2-1}$

for each meson line propagating between two vertices.

But the physics of the problem is in the factor at the pion-nucleon vertex. This can be written, *relativistically*, for *pseudoscalar coupling*,

$$\sqrt{4\pi}\, f_{PP}\gamma_5\tau_i, \tag{18}$$

and, for *pseudovector coupling*,

$$\pm i\sqrt{4\pi}\, f_{PA}\gamma_5\gamma_\nu k_\nu\tau_i = \pm i\sqrt{4\pi} f_{PA}\gamma_5 \not{k}\tau_i \tag{19}$$

(+ for absorption, − for emission).

In the nonrelativistic pseudovector theory with cutoff the factor at the vertex becomes

$$\pm i\sqrt{4\pi}\, f\, v(k)\, \boldsymbol{\sigma}\cdot\mathbf{k}\tau_i. \tag{20}$$

In all these expressions the factor τ_i is the component of the isospin operator of the nucleon in the direction i of the real isospin polarization (charge state) of the interacting pion. The simplest case, analytically, is that of pions polarized along one of the real isospin axes; then the τ_i are the hermitian Pauli matrices, τ_1, τ_2, τ_3.

But from the experimental point of view the case of interest is that of the pion with +, −, or 0 charge, in which case τ_i is not hermitian and must be replaced by $\tau_i^\dagger$ for emission. Its expression as an operator

[1] Proceeding as in the footnote of 6.23d, we find that the three dimensional form factor of e^{-mr}/r is $4\pi/(k^2+m^2)$.

We can also introduce the meson propagator in four dimensions in a way similar to that used for the electron [6.22(2)] or for the photon (footnote in 6.24a). We start from the equation $(\Box_2{}^2 + m^2)K_\pi(\mathbf{2}, \mathbf{1}) = \delta(\mathbf{2}, \mathbf{1})$, whose solution is

$$K_\pi(\mathbf{2}, \mathbf{1}) = \frac{-1}{(2\pi)^4}\int \frac{e^{-i\mathbf{k}\cdot(\mathbf{x}_2-\mathbf{x}_1)}}{k^2-m^2}\, d^4\mathbf{k}.$$

The ambiguity of the path of integration is solved, as for photons, by accepting only contributions from the past.

The Fourier transform of $K_\pi(\mathbf{2}, \mathbf{1})$, $(k^2-m^2)^{-1}$, is the propagator to be used in the relativistic matrix element.

For more details consult, for instance, Schweber, Bethe, and de Hoffman (SB-55).

and the numerical factor which replaces τ_i in the different processes are obtained from the form (14) of the quantized Hamiltonian and are shown in the following table:

	Vertex	τ_i	$\langle \mathcal{N}' \vert \tau_i \vert \mathcal{N} \rangle$
Absorption	$n + \pi^+ \to p$	$\sqrt{2}\begin{pmatrix} 0 & 1 \\ 0 & 0 \end{pmatrix}$	$\sqrt{2}$
	$p + \pi^- \to n$	$\sqrt{2}\begin{pmatrix} 0 & 0 \\ 1 & 0 \end{pmatrix}$	$\sqrt{2}$
	$\begin{cases} p + \pi_0 \to p \\ n + \pi_0 \to n \end{cases}$	$\begin{pmatrix} 1 & 0 \\ 0 & -1 \end{pmatrix}$	$+1$ -1

	Vertex	$\tau_i^\dagger$	$\langle \mathcal{N}' \vert \tau_i^\dagger \vert \mathcal{N} \rangle$
Emission	$p \to n + \pi^+$	$\sqrt{2}\begin{pmatrix} 0 & 0 \\ 1 & 0 \end{pmatrix}$	$\sqrt{2}$
	$n \to p + \pi^-$	$\sqrt{2}\begin{pmatrix} 0 & 1 \\ 0 & 0 \end{pmatrix}$	$\sqrt{2}$
	$\begin{cases} p \to p + \pi^0 \\ n \to n + \pi^0 \end{cases}$	$\begin{pmatrix} 1 & 0 \\ 0 & -1 \end{pmatrix}$	$+1$ -1

The values $\langle \tau_i \rangle$ of the last column are also shown on the graphs of Fig. 7.16-1.

e. Equivalence between Pseudoscalar and Pseudovector Coupling. We now prove that the first-order matrix elements of pseudoscalar coupling theory (18) are identical with those of pseudovector theory (19), apart from a change in the value of the coupling constant.

We have seen in 7.14a a nonquantized argument for the equivalence of the two couplings. For a more complete proof, and a more precise evaluation of the ratio between the coupling constants, we may start from (19) and, in this equation, replace **k** by $\pm(\mathbf{p}_F - \mathbf{p}_I)$, the nucleon's momentum transfer. Then the matrix element corresponding to the absorption vertex factor (19) can be written as follows:

$$
\begin{aligned}
i\sqrt{4\pi} f_{PA}\, [\bar{w}(\mathbf{p}_F)\, \gamma_5 (\not{p}_F - \not{p}_I) \tau_i\, w(\mathbf{p}_I)] \\
&= i\sqrt{4\pi} f_{PA}\, \bar{w}(\mathbf{p}_F)(-\not{p}_F \gamma_5 - \gamma_5 \not{p}_I) \tau_i\, w(\mathbf{p}_I) \\
&= -i\sqrt{4\pi}\, 2M\, [\bar{w}(\mathbf{p}_F) \gamma_5 \tau_i\, w(\mathbf{p}_I)];
\end{aligned}
$$

in the last step we have made use of the Dirac equation

$$\not{p}_{\mathrm{I}}\, w(\mathbf{p}_{\mathrm{I}}) = M\, w(\mathbf{p}_{\mathrm{I}}) \quad \text{and} \quad \bar{w}(\mathbf{p}_{\mathrm{F}})\not{p}_{\mathrm{F}} = M\, \bar{w}(\mathbf{p}_{\mathrm{F}}),$$

where M is the mass of the nucleon.

We note that apart from the unimportant factor $-i$, the matrix elements of (19) are the same as those of (18), provided

(21) $$2Mf_{PA} = f_{PP}.$$

The question whether the equivalence extends to higher order perturbation terms has been investigated by several authors (D-48; SB-55);

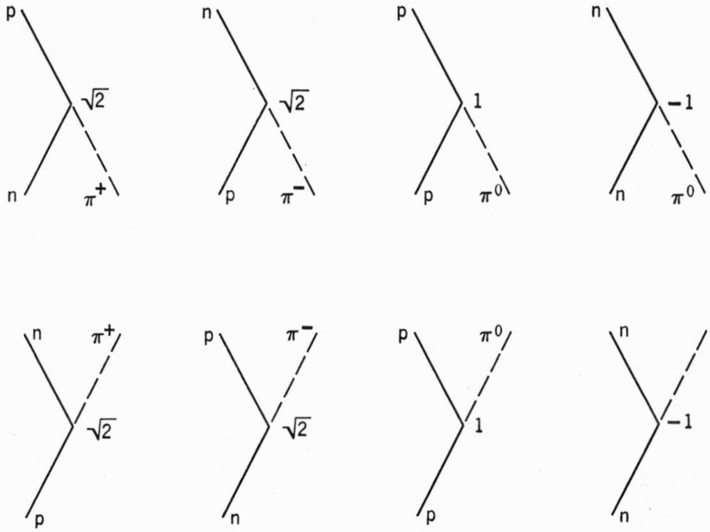

Fig. 7.16-1. Numerical factors $\langle\tau_i\rangle$ or $\langle\tau_i^\dagger\rangle$ in matrix elements for absorption or emission of pions. In order to obtain the complete vertex factors, multiply by $\pm i\sqrt{4\pi}\, fv(k)\, \boldsymbol{\sigma}\cdot\mathbf{k}$ (+ for absorption, − for emission).

without entering into the detail of the discussion, the result is that the difference between pseudoscalar and pseudovector coupling cannot be eliminated in the exact Hamiltonian.

7.17 Difficulties of the Theory of Strong Interactions

a. Pseudovector and Pseudoscalar Coupling Constants. At this point we may get the impression that the Hamiltonians in the preceding section can be used in the same way as the electromagnetic interaction Hamiltonian to obtain accurate results with diagrams in lowest order perturbation theory and possibly including higher order corrections.

This, however, is not the case, and we must make a few sobering comments before we proceed.

We shall see (7.25) that the nonrelativistic, pseudoscalar, charge symmetrical meson theory accounts in an almost quantitative way for several of the observations in pion and nuclear physics at low energy for a coupling constant

$$f^2 \approx 0.08 \tag{1}$$

and a cutoff momentum

$$k_{\max} \approx 6, \qquad (\omega_{\max} \approx 800 \text{ MeV}) \tag{2}$$

The small value of f^2, which (like $e^2 = \frac{1}{137}$ in electromagnetism) is the parameter that determines the ratio of the contributions of successive orders in the perturbation development, allows the use of perturbation theory, with some reservations (see 7.24c) and modifications (7.25). We shall see that the results obtained in this manner agree with experiment as long as we are *below cutoff* and can neglect relativistic effects on the nucleons.

Within the range of validity of this kind of theory, pseudoscalar and pseudovector coupling are perfectly equivalent. Nonrelativistic pseudoscalar coupling introduces the velocity of the nucleon, where, in pseudovector coupling, we have the velocity of the meson: in light of conservation of momentum, the two couplings may be made equal by a suitable choice of the coupling constants. This subject has been discussed quantitatively in 7.16e, and by using 7.16(21) with $M \approx 6.7$ we find that the pseudoscalar coupling constant corresponding to (1) is

$$f_{PP}^2 = (2M)^2 f^2 \approx 15. \tag{3}$$

At high energy, however, the difficulties are great.

Let us consider, for instance, the annihilation of nucleons and antinucleons, where the energy released is of the order of 2 beV. The annihilation occurs with emission of pions and no γ rays, and this in itself proves that the pion-nucleon coupling is much stronger than the coupling between nucleons and photons. Furthermore, we find that the number of pions emitted in the annihilation process is often large, the average being four or more (see Fig. 7.36-1). Considering that the statistical factors favor low multiplicity, if we look at the problem from the point of view of perturbation theory, we must conclude either that the coupling is strong or that other effects—such as pion-pion forces—must be included in the discussion.

But under these conditions the perturbation treatment becomes meaningless, and it is also meaningless to ask whether it is the pseudovector or the pseudoscalar factor that is most appropriate to describe the single-pion nucleon vertex.

Let us mention, in passing, that some theorists have a preference for the pseudoscalar form of coupling because it is possible to eliminate the divergences from this theory with a process of "renormalization".

b. Perturbation Theory and Peripheral Collisions. If we accept pseudoscalar coupling and $f_{PP} \approx 15$, we cannot even think of using perturbation theory. For such a large value of coupling it becomes difficult even to define what we mean with the words "pion" or "nucleon."

In fact, if we try to visualize a pion (Fig. 7.17-1*a*), we must immediately include the nucleon-vacuum polarization that accompanies it and all the

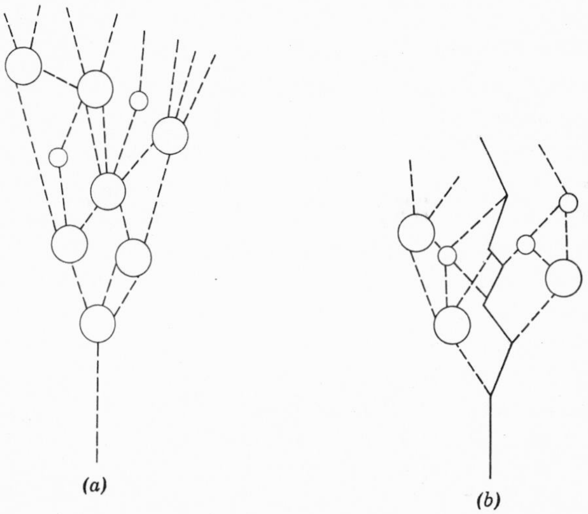

Fig. 7.17-1. As a result of the strength of the coupling, an initially "bare" pion (a) or nucleon (b) immediately acquires a complicated structure.

virtual pions that it generates. If, instead, we imagine a bare nucleon (Fig. 7.17-1*b*), we must consider the meson cloud surrounding it and all the nucleon-antinucleon pairs it creates.

Thus we realize that "bare nucleons" and "bare pions" exist only in our vocabulary and in our imagination; in the real world there are only "physical nucleons" and "physical pions" which have very complicated structures, distinguishable because of their different quantum numbers, but essentially composed of the same stuff. In the language of the daily press it is difficult to distinguish between the nucleons, and the "glue" that covers and permeates them!

We are left with the task of describing the interaction between physical nucleons and physical pions. Obviously this interaction is also a complicated affair (Fig. 7.17-2*a*). However, if we consider only the "peripheral" part of the interaction—distant collisions or low momentum transfer—the situation is greatly simplified (Fig. 7.17-2*b*). With appropriate cutoffs, which, as we have seen, are equivalent to the introduction of form factors of the meson source, all the dirt is hidden and the lowest order diagrams predominate.

We are again justified in using perturbation theory with the understanding that each vertex (such as those of Fig. 7.16-1), should really be drawn as in Fig. 7.17-2*b* to represent the *peripheral coupling of a physical nucleon with a physical meson.*

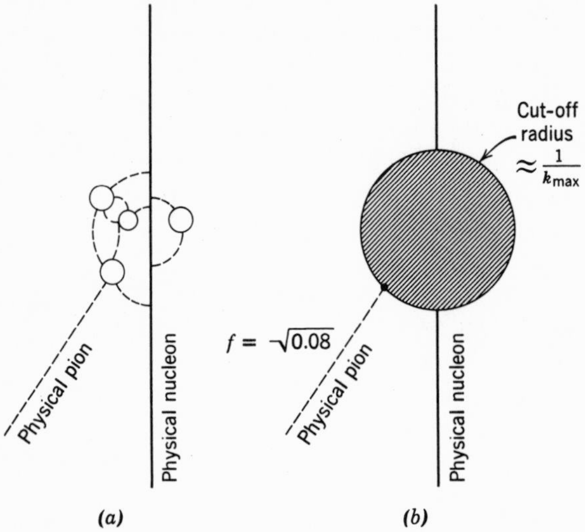

Fig. 7.17-2. As a consequence of strong coupling, the vertex joining the physical pion with the physical nucleon has a complex structure (*a*), but, for distant collisions, it can be replaced by a simple vertex with a relatively small coupling constant (*b*).

For a more complete treatment of strong interactions, new mathematical techniques will have to be devised, and some progress in this direction has been achieved with the development of "dispersion relations." However, we do not intend to cover this new and expanding theoretical subject at this point[1].

We add the remark that even a perfectly consistent and satisfactory theory of pion-nucleon interactions would not provide a complete description of strong interactions, since we know that strange particles, and particularly K mesons, surely play a role in nuclear forces at high energy.

Thus we may just as well start (in 7.2) by limiting our attention to the nonrelativistic theory and disregard all the nonunderstood high energy effects, including many mesons, nucleon-antinucleon pairs, and strange particles.

[1] For a brief, introductory presentation see Section 7.25.

7.18 Perturbation Treatment of Nuclear Forces

We shall now report the main lines of a computation (G-55)—based on the ideas of the preceding section—of the nuclear potential arising from the exchange of virtual mesons between nucleons.

If we limit our interest to the investigation of nuclear forces for not-too-large momentum transfer, the nucleons can be considered as rigid entities interacting with the meson field with a coupling constant considerably smaller than unity. Thus we expect that perturbation theory may have a certain degree of validity, and we can perform the computation by considering only the terms of lowest order, which in the present case are the second and the fourth. We also neglect the nucleon recoil in meson interaction, in comformity with the "static" approximation, in which the nucleons are assumed to be infinitely heavy.

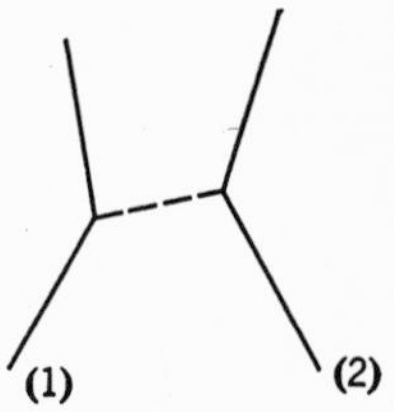

Fig. 7.18-1. Second-order diagram for the nuclear force potential.

We can start from the Hamiltonian 7.16(15) to express the interaction of two nucleons, 1 and 2, with the quantized meson field. Then the second-order contribution to the nuclear potential, $U_2(|\mathbf{r}_2 - \mathbf{r}_1|)$, is obtained from the diagram in Fig. 7.18-1 and assumes the form

$$(1)\quad U_2(|\mathbf{r}_2 - \mathbf{r}_1|) = -\frac{4\pi f^2}{(2\pi)^3}\vec{\tau}_1 \cdot \vec{\tau}_2 \int \frac{v^2(k)}{\omega_k{}^2} e^{i\mathbf{k}\cdot(\mathbf{r}_2 - \mathbf{r}_1)}(\boldsymbol{\sigma}_1 \cdot \mathbf{k})(\boldsymbol{\sigma}_2 \cdot \mathbf{k})\, d^3\mathbf{k}.$$

Note that the Born approximation scattering matrix element of this potential, $\int e^{i\mathbf{k}\cdot\mathbf{r}'} U_2(r')\, d^3\mathbf{r}'$, is equal to that obtained from the diagram of Fig. 7.18-1, according to the rules in 7.16d.

By performing the integration, one can show that U_2 consists of a central and a tensor part. For no cutoff $[v(k) = 1]$, and in even angular momentum states the central part of the potential has a Yukawa-like attractive well [exactly as in 7.15(2)] and a δ-function repulsive core:

$$(2)\qquad U_{2(\text{central})} = -f^2\frac{e^{-r}}{r} + 4\pi f^2\,\delta(\mathbf{r}),$$

with $r = |\mathbf{r}_2 - \mathbf{r}_1|$. For finite values of $k_{\max}$ the attractive well is somewhat distorted, and the repulsive core assumes a finite size, needed for the interpretation of the nucleon-nucleon scattering experiments.

No repulsive core, however, is predicted for odd angular momentum states.

The fourth-order contributions to the potential are computed from diagrams involving two virtual mesons (Fig. 7.18-2*a* to *g*). Diagrams of the type *a* and *b* are neglected because they describe the "inner meson cloud," or the internal structure of the nucleon, already taken into account if we use the empirical values of the nucleon mass, coupling constant, and cutoff parameter. The diagram in (*c*), the so-called ladder diagram with two bare nucleon lines between two virtual meson lines, is also neglected[1].

The contribution of the remaining four diagrams is not difficult to compute. We shall not report the computation here, nor the cumbersome formulas that are finally obtained: the result, including second- and fourth-order contributions, has already been presented in graphical form

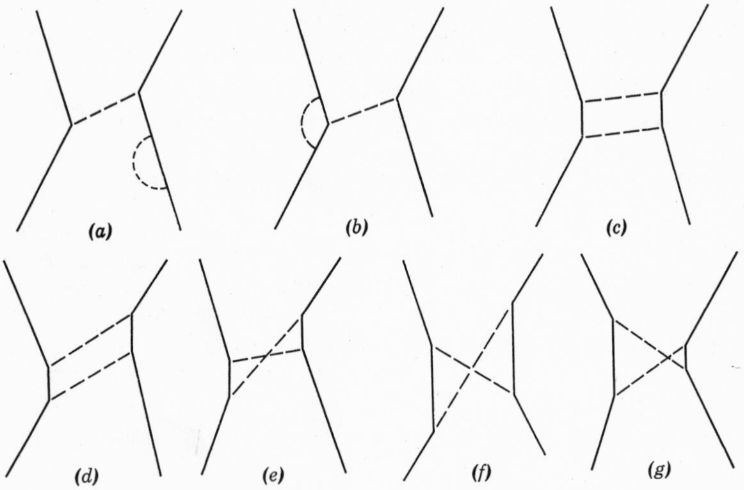

Fig. 7.18-2. Fourth-order diagrams to be considered in the computation of nuclear forces.

in the Figs. 1.25-1 and 3.58-1. The curves in these figures were computed for the numerical values of f^2 and k_{max} close to those of 7.17(1), (2).

The comparison of the potential obtained in this manner with the data on the deuteron and on nucleon-nucleon scattering has also been discussed in 1.25 and 3.58. It may be recalled that the comparison with the low-energy data was satisfactory but that the high-energy experiments were in only partial agreement with the prediction of the present theory. Considering that the theory contains no arbitrary constants, since f and k_{max} are determined from π-N scattering (see 7.25), and that many approximations are involved in the computation, even this partial agreement can be regarded as satisfactory.

[1] This selection of fourth order graphs is due to Brueckner and Watson (B-53). Its validity is still open to discussion.

7.2 Scattering of Pions by Nucleons

7.21 *Total Cross Section for π-p Scattering*

a. Experimental Data. Data on the total cross section for π^+ and π^- in hydrogen are available from transmission measurements extending up to ≈2 beV. The results[1] are shown in Fig. 7.21-1.

The most remarkable feature of the curves of Fig. 7.21-1 is the presence of resonances. As in neutron scattering in low-energy nuclear physics,

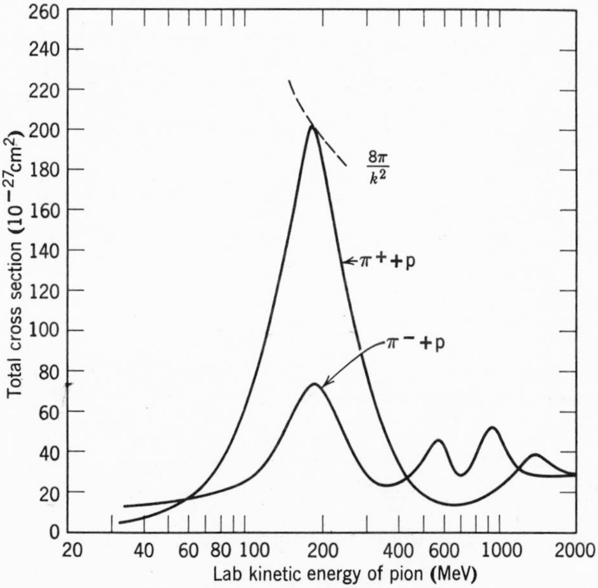

Fig. 7.21-1. π^+p and π^-p total cross section (adapted from J. D. Jackson, *The Physics of Elementary Particles*, Copyright 1958, Princeton University Press).

these resonances can be interpreted as evidence for intermediate states with a mean life that is long compared to transit time.

We are thus faced with *excited states*[2] *of the nucleon.* An energy-level

[1] The low energy data (peak at ≈200 MeV) are due to Fermi and collaborators, Ashkin and collaborators, etc. [see Bethe and de Hoffmann (Be-55) for detailed references]; the first high energy results are due to Piccioni et al. (C-56b); the resolution of the two π^- peaks in the 500–1000 MeV region has been obtained more recently [Burrowes et al. (B-59c); Brisson et al. (Saclay) (B-59b); Devlin et al. (Berkeley), (D-60c)].

Higher energy data have become available in recent years, but are of no relevance for the present discussion.

[2] These excited states are often called *isobars*, but we avoid this nomenclature for which we see no clear reason.

diagram of the nucleon with its first three excited states is shown in Fig. 7.21-2. The quantum numbers assigned to each state are also given. The fourth excited state (at 1.4 beV π scattering energy) is not included because very little information is available.

The energy values are obtained from simple kinematics and the assignment of the quantum numbers are discussed in what follows.

In the beginning of our discussion we concentrate our attention on the scattering around the $\approx$200-MeV peak and thus on the first excited state.

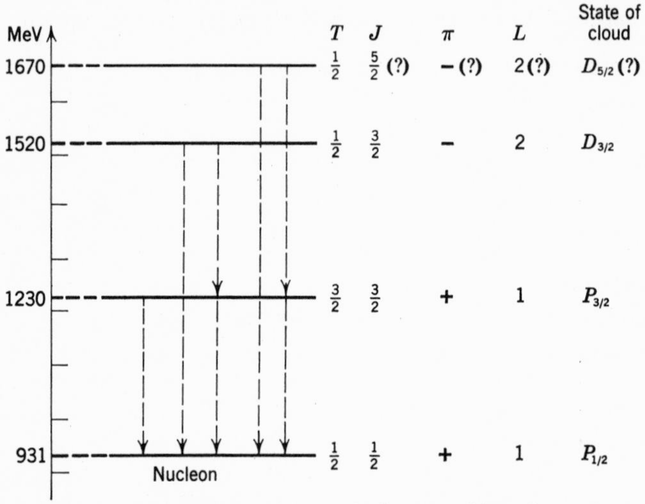

Fig. 7.21-2. The nucleon and its first three excited states with assignment of quantum numbers. The arrows indicate the decay modes with π emission.

At higher energy the scattering is not completely elastic, since the reaction

$$\mathcal{N} + \pi \rightarrow \mathcal{N} + \pi + \pi$$

is already possible for the second excited state.

b. Assignment of Quantum Numbers. The isotopic spin quantum numbers can easily be assigned if we consider that π^+p is necessarily $T = \frac{3}{2}$, whereas π^-p is a mixture of $T = \frac{1}{2}$ and $T = \frac{3}{2}$. By making use of the rule of addition of angular momentum, we can write

$$|\pi^+ \mathrm{p}\rangle = |\tfrac{3}{2}, \tfrac{3}{2}\rangle \tag{1}$$

$$|\pi^- \mathrm{p}\rangle = \sqrt{\tfrac{1}{3}}\, |\tfrac{3}{2}, -\tfrac{1}{2}\rangle - \sqrt{\tfrac{2}{3}}\, |\tfrac{1}{2}, -\tfrac{1}{2}\rangle, \tag{2}$$

where the quantum numbers on the right-hand-side refer to T and T_3.

Thus the $\approx$600- and $\approx$900-MeV resonances, which do not occur for π^+p, must be pure $T = \frac{1}{2}$. The $\approx$200- and $\approx$1400-MeV peaks must be, at least in part, $T = \frac{3}{2}$. The ratio 3/1 in the π^+p and π^-p cross sections at 200 MeV indicates that the first resonance is pure $T = \frac{3}{2}$.

It is interesting to observe that the first excited state of the nucleon occurs in four charge states with the charge going from -1 (π^-n) to $+2$ (π^+p).

Most of the information concerning the assignment of angular momenta comes from the analysis of the differential cross section. However, the fact that the total π^+p cross section at the $\approx$200-MeV maximum is equal to $8\pi/k^2$ is in itself a strong argument in favor of a $J = \frac{3}{2}$ value for the first resonance state [compare with 3.51(13)].

Since most of the $\pi\mathcal{N}$ interaction is expected to occur in a P state, it is natural to think that the "meson cloud" of the first resonance is in a $P_{3/2}$ state and thus has even parity as the nucleon ground state.

The initial increase of the total cross section with energy indicates that the scattering cannot be S scattering: we know that the elastic S-scattering cross section is energy-independent for small momenta. The observed energy dependence of the $\pi\mathcal{N}$ scattering cross section near zero energy corresponds to a $\approx k^3$ dependence of the predominant phase shifts, in agreement with the prediction for short-range P scattering [3.12(13)].

c. Charge Exchange Scattering. Since there are two nucleons and three meson charges, a complete experimental study of $\pi\mathcal{N}$ scattering should involve six different experiments; but the results of these experiments are related by the requirement of charge independence, and all the needed information can be obtained from π^+p and π^-p scattering.

By using available charged meson beams and hydrogen targets we can measure three cross sections, σ_+, σ_-, and σ_0, corresponding to the elastic reactions

$$(3_+)\qquad \pi^+ + \mathrm{p} \rightarrow \pi^+ + \mathrm{p},$$

$$(3_-)\qquad \pi^- + \mathrm{p} \rightarrow \pi^- + \mathrm{p},$$

$$(3_0)\qquad \pi^- + \mathrm{p} \rightarrow \pi^0 + \mathrm{n}.$$

The π^0's of (3_0) are detected by means of their decay gamma's.

The π^-p total cross section of Fig. 7.21-1 (at low energy, where inelastic events are negligible) is the sum of σ_- and σ_0. The two reactions (3_-) and (3_0) are commonly called π^-p scattering *without or with charge exchange*, or π^-p scattering *without or with isospin flip*.

The cross sections σ_- and σ_0 are not independent if T is a good quantum number in the intermediate state. In general, the relation between σ_- and σ_0 can be obtained by using a treatment similar to that of scattering with and without physical spin flip, which was discussed in detail in Chapter 3.

The amplitude for scattering without charge exchange is (from 2)

$$(4)\qquad \langle \pi^-\mathrm{p}\,|a|\,\pi^-\mathrm{p}\rangle = \tfrac{1}{3}a_{T=3/2} + \tfrac{2}{3}a_{T=1/2}.$$

By computing

$$(5)\qquad |\pi^0 n\rangle = \sqrt{\tfrac{2}{3}}\,|\tfrac{3}{2}, -\tfrac{1}{2}\rangle + \sqrt{\tfrac{1}{3}}\,|\tfrac{1}{2}, -\tfrac{1}{2}\rangle,$$

we obtain

$$(6)\qquad \langle \pi^0 n\,|a|\,\pi^- p\rangle = \tfrac{1}{3}\sqrt{2}\,a_{T=3/2} - \tfrac{1}{3}\sqrt{2}\,a_{T=1/2}.$$

Thus the ratio of the cross sections for (3_-) and (3_0) is

$$(7)\qquad \frac{\sigma_-}{\sigma_0} = \frac{|\tfrac{1}{3}a_{T=3/2} + \tfrac{2}{3}a_{T=1/2}|^2}{|\tfrac{1}{3}\sqrt{2}\,a_{T=3/2} - \tfrac{1}{3}\sqrt{2}\,a_{T=1/2}|^2}$$

In particular, if the scattering is pure $T = \frac{3}{2}$ near the 200 MeV resonance, $a_{T=1/2} = 0$ and

$$(8)\qquad \frac{\sigma_-}{\sigma_0} = \frac{1}{2}, \qquad (\approx 200\text{ MeV}).$$

This relation is in good agreement with experiment. Since we have already seen that theory and experiment agree on the ratio $\sigma_+/(\sigma_- + \sigma_0) = 3$, we find that, in accordance with charge independence and with the $T = \frac{3}{2}$ assignment for the first excited state,

$$(9)\qquad \sigma_+ : \sigma_- : \sigma_0 = 9:1:2, \qquad (\approx 200\text{ MeV}).$$

The three cross sections at the maximum are then completely determined by the conservation principles and the assignment of quantum numbers:

$$(10)\quad \sigma_+ = 8\pi/k^2; \qquad \sigma_- = (\tfrac{1}{9})8\pi/k^2; \qquad \sigma_0 = (\tfrac{2}{9})8\pi/k^2, \qquad (\approx 200\text{ MeV}).$$

7.22 *Differential Cross Section and Phase Shift Analysis*

a. Definition of Phase Shifts. For energies of interest for the interpretation of the first resonance the angular distribution of πp scattering can be attributed to S and P waves only. Thus, at each energy, the differential scattering cross sections can be expressed by means of nine coefficients[1]:

$$(1)\qquad \begin{aligned} \frac{d\sigma_+}{d\omega} &= A_+ + B_+ \cos\theta + C_+ \cos^2\theta, \\ \frac{d\sigma_-}{d\omega} &= A_- + B_- \cos\theta + C_- \cos^2\theta, \\ \frac{d\sigma_0}{d\omega} &= A_0 + B_0 \cos\theta + C_0 \cos^2\theta. \end{aligned}$$

The nine coefficients are obtained from the measurement of the differential cross section.

[1] Coulomb scattering is important only at very low energies and small angles.

The quantities conserved during the scattering are J, T, and l (as observed in 3.51c, the orbital angular momentum is a good quantum number because of parity conservation). Thus the scattering amplitudes, and the corresponding phases, must be labeled by the three quantum numbers lJT. It has become customary to use the notation shown below for the amplitudes a_{ij}:

(2)

	$l = 0$ (S wave)	$l = 1$ (P wave)	
	$J = \frac{1}{2}$ ($S_{1/2}$)	$J = \frac{1}{2}$ ($P_{1/2}$)	$J = \frac{3}{2}$ ($P_{3/2}$)
$T = \frac{1}{2}$	a_1	a_{11}	a_{13}
$T = \frac{3}{2}$	a_3	a_{31}	a_{33}

To each amplitude there corresponds a real phase shift δ_{ij}, according to 3.12(6).

If the assumption of charge independence is valid, we should be able to express the nine empirical coefficients appearing in (1) by means of six real phase shifts corresponding to the amplitudes defined in (2); the A's, B's, and C's as well as a_{ij} and δ_{ij} depend on energy but not on angle.

b. Phase Shift Analysis. Let us first perform the separation of the isospin states. For this purpose we define at each scattering angle θ two amplitudes $f_1(\theta)$ and $f_3(\theta)$ for $T = \frac{1}{2}$ and $\frac{3}{2}$, respectively.

Also for each experiment, π^+p, π^-p no exchange, π^-p exchange, we define an amplitude $f_+(\theta), f_-(\theta), f_0(\theta)$. Then we can write [7.21(4) and (6)]

$$f_+(\theta) = f_3(\theta), \tag{3_+}$$

$$f_-(\theta) = \tfrac{1}{3}[f_3(\theta) + 2f_1(\theta)], \tag{3_-}$$

$$f_0(\theta) = \tfrac{1}{3}\sqrt{2}\,[f_3(\theta) - f_1(\theta)]. \tag{3_0}$$

The analysis of (3_+) in S, $P_{1/2}$, $P_{3/2}$ waves is exactly the same as that performed for the scattering of neutrons in He. For the other two equations the same analysis has to be performed separately for the isospin singlet and triplet amplitudes.

By substituting 3.52(6a), we obtain

$$\begin{aligned} f_+ &= [a_3 + (2a_{33} + a_{31}) \cos\theta]\alpha + (a_{31} - a_{33}) \sin\theta e^{i\varphi}\beta, \\ f_- &= \tfrac{1}{3}\big(\{(a_3 + 2a_1) + [2(a_{33} + 2a_{13}) + (a_{31} + 2a_{11})] \cos\theta\}\alpha \\ &\qquad + [(a_{31} + 2a_{11}) - (a_{33} + 2a_{13})] \sin\theta e^{i\varphi}\beta\big), \\ f_0 &= \tfrac{1}{3}\sqrt{2}\,\big(\{(a_3 - a_1) + [2(a_{33} - a_{13}) + (a_{31} - a_{11})] \cos\theta\}\alpha \\ &\qquad + [(a_{31} - a_{11}) - (a_{33} - a_{13})] \sin\theta e^{i\varphi}\beta\big), \end{aligned} \tag{4}$$

and finally

$$\frac{d\sigma_+}{d\omega} = \left|a_3 + (2a_{33} + a_{31})\cos\theta\right|^2 + \left|a_{31} - a_{33}\right|^2 \sin^2\theta,$$

$$(5) \qquad \begin{aligned} \frac{d\sigma_-}{d\omega} &= \tfrac{1}{9}\left|(a_3 + 2a_1) + (2a_{33} + a_{31} + 4a_{13} + 2a_{11})\cos\theta\right|^2 \\ &\quad + \tfrac{1}{9}\left|(a_{31} + 2a_{11} - a_{33} - 2a_{13})\sin\theta\right|^2, \\ \frac{d\sigma_0}{d\omega} &= \tfrac{2}{9}\left|(a_3 - a_1) + [2(a_{33} - a_{13}) + (a_{31} - a_{11})]\cos\theta\right|^2 \\ &\quad + \tfrac{2}{9}\left|[(a_{31} - a_{11}) - (a_{33} - a_{13})]\sin\theta\right|^2. \end{aligned}$$

Comparison with (1) shows the relations between the six complex amplitudes a_{ij} and the nine experimentally determined constants $A_{\substack{\pm \\ 0}}$, $B_{\substack{\pm \\ 0}}$, and $C_{\substack{\pm \\ 0}}$. When the a_{ij} are expressed in terms of the phase shifts, we obtain the desired relations between the six real phases δ_{ij} and the nine experimental constants (Be-55).

c. Ambiguities in the Determination of the Phases. The numerical solution of the equation for the phase shifts is obtained with the help of electronic computers, though a simple graphical method (A-53) may be used if maximum accuracy is not required.

We find not only that it is possible to determine, at each energy, a set of phases which accounts for the experimental measurements within the accuracy of the observations, but we are faced with the choice of several sets. In order to eliminate the ambiguities, new experiments have been performed, and the values of the phases are now known with fair accuracy and with no ambiguity up to the energy at which the inelastic scattering becomes important.

7.23 Other Experiments for the Determination of Pion-Nucleon Phase Shifts

a. π-Mesic x Rays. The interaction between negative mesons and nuclei at small kinetic energy can be studied by observing the spectrum of mesic x rays. In an element of atomic number Z the energies of the mesic atomic states, in the simplest Bohr model of the atom, are given by

$$(1) \qquad \frac{1}{2}\frac{mZ^2}{(137)^2 n^2}\frac{1}{1 + (m/MA)},$$

where n is the total quantum number, MA is the mass of the nucleus, and m is the mass of the muon or pion in the atomic trajectory. We see from (1) that the mesic K lines of hydrogen have an energy of a few keV, which is difficult to study experimentally; for this reason mesic x rays have been measured only in heavier elements.

Deviations from (1) can be expected for several reasons. The most important are the following:

(i) Finite nuclear radius, important for heavy atoms with muons (see 2.21c);
(ii) Relativistic corrections which can be computed with the equations of Dirac (muons) or Klein-Gordon (pions);
(iii) Vacuum polarization effect, calculable from quantum electrodynamics;
(iv) Nucleus-meson interaction, expected only for pions.

After (ii) and (iii) are calculated and the nuclear radii are determined experimentally with muons, it becomes possible to study the interaction of pions with nuclei (iv).

Because of the high capture probability, π-mesic x rays are observed only for relatively low Z. For $Z \approx 10$ the K lines have already become weak because of direct nuclear absorption from the $2P$ state, and for $Z \approx 20$ the L lines also decrease in intensity because of capture from the $3D$ state. If we consider the small overlapping of $2P$ and $3D$ wave functions with the nucleus, we see that pions are indeed captured rapidly by nucleons. To account for the experimental results, the mean life of a pion in nuclear matter must be $\not\sim \hbar/m_\pi c^2 \approx 10^{-24}$ sec.

Thus π-mesic x rays can be observed only in the energy range between $\approx$10 and 100 keV, where they are studied with scintillation spectrometers, proportional counters, and by comparison with the atomic absorption edges (critical absorption) (D-56; S-58b).

The most important experimental result is that the π x-ray lines of the K series are decreased in energy by the nuclear interaction. This corresponds to a *repulsion* between the meson in the $1S$ state and the nucleus and eliminates the ambiguity in sign in the determination of the phase shifts.

The nuclear shifts of the K lines of pions in light elements are shown in Fig. 7.23-1. The data can be interpreted in the simple assumption that the effects of the individual nucleons are additive[1]. According to this view, the nearly constant S-scattering amplitude of a nucleus for a slow π meson is

$$a = Na_{\text{n}} + Za_{\text{p}}, \tag{2}$$

where a_{n} and a_{p} are the neutron- and proton-scattering amplitudes,

[1] Though the assumption of additivity is recognized to be naïve, there is not yet any more satisfactory theoretical discussion of this phenomenon (D-54).

simply expressed in terms of S-scattering phase shifts:

$$
a_n = a_3 \approx \frac{\delta_3}{k}, \qquad (3)
$$
$$
a_p = \tfrac{2}{3}a_1 + \tfrac{1}{3}a_3 \approx \frac{\tfrac{2}{3}\delta_1 + \tfrac{1}{3}\delta_3}{k}.
$$

In the Born approximation the scattering amplitude corresponds to a δ-function potential[1]

$$
V = -2\pi\left(\frac{1}{m_\pi} + \frac{1}{MA}\right) a\,\delta(\mathbf{r}), \qquad (4)
$$

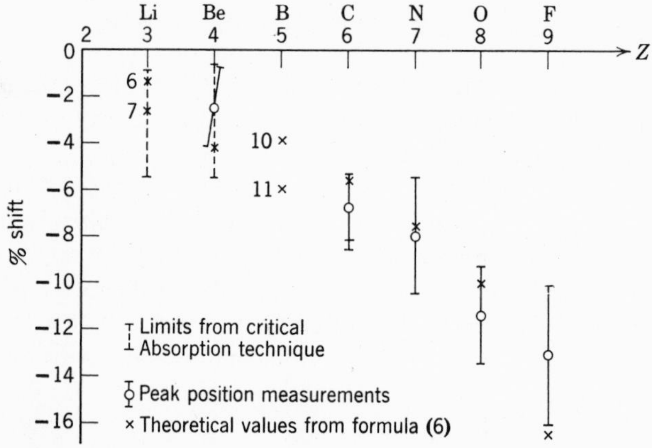

Fig. 7.23-1. Percentage of shift of π^--mesonic K lines [from Stearns, Stearns, DeBenedetti, and Leipuner, *Phys. Rev.*, **97**, 241 (1955)].

which, in turn, produces a shift in the atomic levels:

$$
\Delta E = \int V\psi^*\psi\, d^3\mathbf{r} \approx -|\psi(0)|^2\, 2\pi\left(\frac{1}{m_\pi} + \frac{1}{MA}\right) a \qquad (5)
$$
$$
= -2\frac{Z^3}{r_0^{\,3}}\left(\frac{1}{m_\pi} + \frac{1}{MA}\right) a,
$$

where

$$
r_0 = (137)^2\left(\frac{1}{m_\pi} + \frac{1}{MA}\right)
$$

is the meson's Bohr radius.

Thus, according to this theory, the measurement of ΔE allows the determination of

$$
a = \frac{2\delta_1 + \delta_3}{3k} Z + \frac{\delta_3}{k} N. \qquad (6)
$$

Neither the measurements nor the theory are accurate enough for a detailed

[1] The use of the Born approximation with a δ-function potential is surely justified, at least *for the comparison* of the scattering phases with the atomic level shifts.

comparison of each element. Nevertheless, the general trend of the shifts is satisfactorily explained by the formula for $N = Z = A/2$

$$a \approx \frac{A}{3k}(\delta_1 + 2\delta_3), \tag{7}$$

which agrees in magnitude with the phase shift values obtained from scattering data (8) and determines their sign.

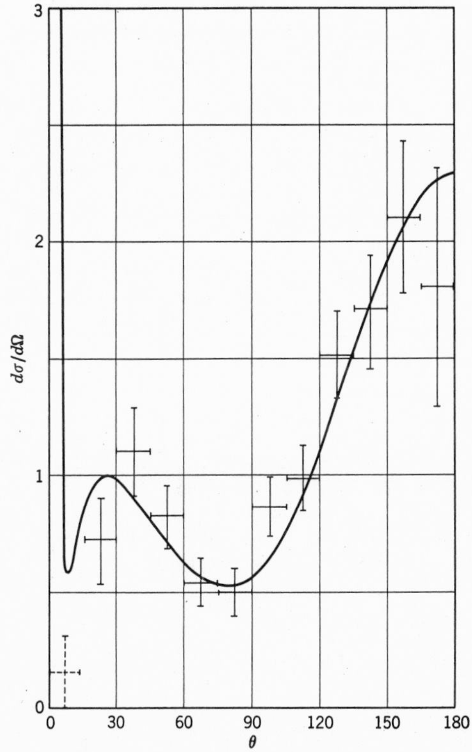

Fig. 7.23-2. Cross section for 125-Mev π^+p scattering showing destructive interference between coulomb and nuclear amplitudes (from G. Puppi, in *Proc. Conf. High En. Phys.*, Rochester, 1955).

b. Interference between Nuclear and Coulomb Scattering. For low energy and small angles it is possible to observe interference effects between nuclear and coulomb scattering which—as in the measurements of mesic x rays—eliminate the ambiguity in sign in the choice of the scattering phase shifts.

Experiments (P-55) have been performed in photographic emulsion, which is more suited than counters to the observation of low-energy small-angle scattering. The result for π^+ of 120 MeV (Fig. 7.23-2) shows that the interference is destructive; thus the nuclear interaction is attractive. Since the phase δ_{33} is the most important one in these experiments, we conclude that $\delta_{33} > 0$. This is consistent with $\delta_1 + 2\delta_3 < 0$ as obtained in (a).

c. Measurements of Polarization. After the elimination of the ambiguity in sign, there still remain other ambiguities in the determination

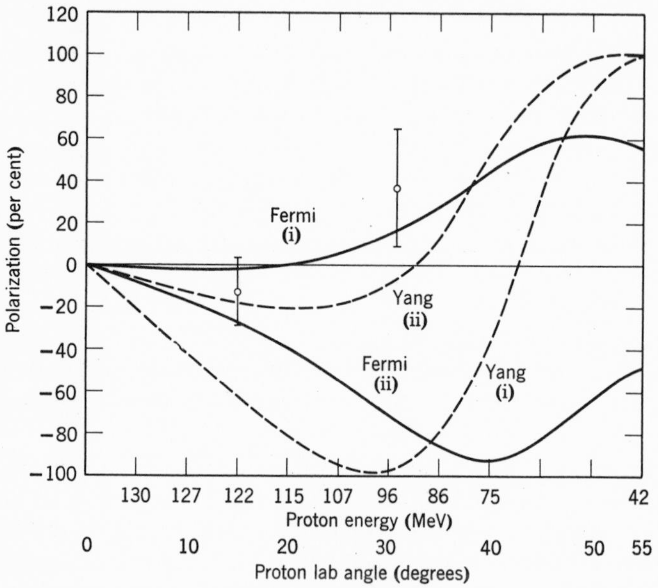

Fig. 7.23-3. Theoretical polarization for the recoil proton in π^--p scattering for four different phase shift sets and the experimental results [from Kunze, Romanowski, Ashkin, and Burger, *Phys. Rev.*, **117**, 859 (1960)].

of the phase shifts. As in n-He scattering, polarization measurements give supplementary data which may be used to choose the correct set of phases.

Figure 7.23-3 shows the polarization of the recoil proton expected at various angles for 220 MeV π^-. The four curves refer to four sets of phase shifts which would account satisfactorily for the unpolarized scattering cross section.

The experimental points (K-60) exclude two sets and favor—as we could have expected—the first set proposed by Fermi.

d. The Values of the Phase Shifts. At low energy we expect the S phase shifts to vary as k and the P phase shifts to vary as k^3. With this in mind, when all experimental evidence and theoretical arguments are taken into account, we conclude that at low energy the phase shifts have the following values (A-59) (in radians, with k in units of $m_\pi c$):

$$\begin{aligned} \delta_1 &= (0.173 \pm 0.011)k, \\ \delta_3 &= (-0.11 \pm 0.004)k, \\ \delta_{33} &= (0.234 \pm 0.019)k^3, \\ \delta_{31} &= (0.044 \pm 0.005)k^3, \\ \delta_{11} &\quad \text{small.} \end{aligned} \tag{8}$$

Particularly important is *the* δ_{33} *phase shift*, which *predominates* at $\approx$100 MeV and accounts for the first resonance in the scattering; the others do not grow above 5° or 10° in the region of the first resonance.

From zero-range theory [3.12(12)] we expect $k^3 \cot \delta_{33} =$ constant, and it is interesting to compare the observed values of δ_{33} with this prediction. It can be shown (Fig. 7.25-1) that there are departures attributable to the finite size of the nucleon source, whose extension (cutoff) can be obtained from the behavior of the 33 phase shift. The theoretical discussion of the phase shifts, and particularly of δ_{33}, is of great fundamental importance and is the subject of the next two sections.

For energies above $\approx$300 MeV (F-61a; M-61b) the angular distribution includes terms in $\cos^3 \theta$ and the phase-shift analysis must include D waves. Moreover, at $\approx$400 MeV inelastic scattering ($\pi + \mathcal{N} \rightarrow \pi + \pi + \mathcal{N}$) becomes appreciable and the phase shifts are complex. Near the second and third maximum ($\approx$500–1000 MeV) a large part of the total cross section is inelastic. At $\approx$900 MeV the π^-p elastic angular distribution becomes peaked backwards, and this "calls for a superimposition of spin flip amplitudes through F waves." At 760 MeV we find the threshold for strange particle production ($\pi + \mathcal{N} \rightarrow \Lambda + K$).

7.24 *Pion Scattering in Pseudoscalar Theory: Lowest Order Perturbation Treatment*

a. Cross Sections for Different Charges. The computation of the phase shifts provides a condensed way of expressing the experimental data; the success of the computation is consistent with the conservation principles but does not represent a detailed verification of any theory.

We shall now attempt a closer comparison of the data with the theoretical results from pseudoscalar theory, and for this purpose we proceed to a computation of the scattering in lowest order perturbation theory (Born approximation, see W-55).

In this order the diagrams for meson scattering (Fig. 7.24-1) are the same as those of Compton scattering. If the nucleon is treated as infinitely heavy, the propagator (6.24c) is simply the inverse of the energy of the absorbed or emitted pion $(E_0 - E_{\text{int}})^{-1} = \pm\omega^{-1}$, as in conventional perturbation theory. In the diagrams the vertex factors have been written in conformity with 7.16(20), with $v(k) = 1$, since we are performing the calculation for energies well below cutoff.

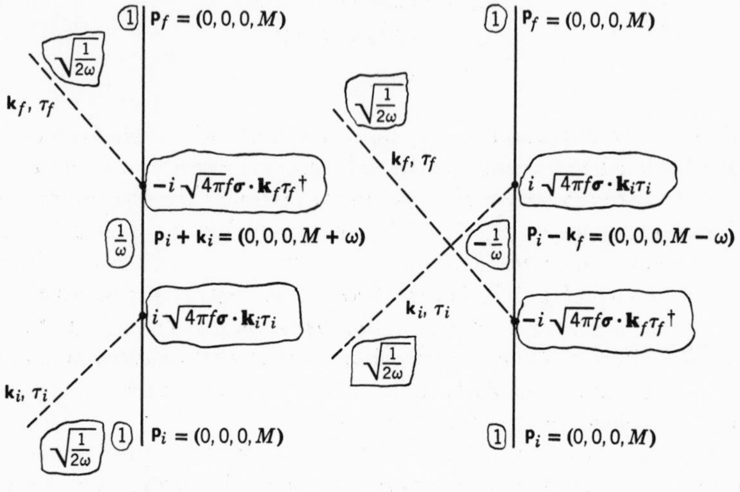

Fig. 7.24-1. Diagrams for pion-nucleon scattering.

With the notation of Fig. 7.24-1 we obtain the matrix element

$$(1)\quad M^{(B)} = M_a + M_b = \frac{4\pi}{2\omega} f^2 \left[\frac{\tau_f^{\dagger}\tau_i(\boldsymbol{\sigma}\cdot\mathbf{k}_f)(\boldsymbol{\sigma}\cdot\mathbf{k}_i)}{\omega} + \frac{\tau_i\tau_f^{\dagger}(\boldsymbol{\sigma}\cdot\mathbf{k}_i)(\boldsymbol{\sigma}\cdot\mathbf{k}_f)}{-\omega} \right].$$

If we want to perform the computation for mesons in definite charge states, we can obtain the expectation value of the products $\tau_i\tau_f^{\dagger}$ and $\tau_f^{\dagger}\tau_i$ from the table in 7.16d or from Fig. 7.16-1[1]. One obtains in this way:

[1] In order to illustrate the procedure, let us compute the case of charge exchange scattering $\pi^- + \mathrm{p} \to \pi^0 + \mathrm{n}$. The factors τ_i and $\tau_f^{\dagger}$ do not commute, and in our case $(i = -, f = 0)$ we obtain, as shown in the diagrams,

$$\tau_f^{\dagger}\tau_i \to \langle \mathrm{n}|\, \tau_0^{\dagger}\, |\mathrm{n}\rangle\langle \mathrm{n}|\, \tau_-\, |\mathrm{p}\rangle = (-1)(\sqrt{2}) = -\sqrt{2},$$

$$\tau_i\tau_f^{\dagger} \to \langle \mathrm{n}|\, \tau_-\, |\mathrm{p}\rangle\langle \mathrm{p}|\, \tau_0^{\dagger}\, |\mathrm{p}\rangle = (\sqrt{2})(1) = \sqrt{2}.$$

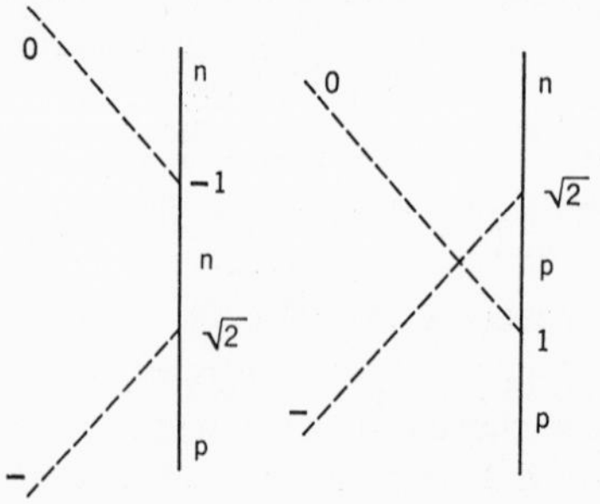

$i \longrightarrow$

$\tau_f{}^\dagger \tau_i$ ($f \downarrow$)	$\pi^+ + p$	$\pi^+ + n$	$\pi^0 + p$	$\pi^0 + n$	$\pi^- + p$	$\pi^- + n$
$\pi^+ + p$	0	0	0	0	0	0
$\pi^+ + n$	0	2	$\sqrt{2}$	0		0
$\pi^0 + p$	0	$\sqrt{2}$	1			0
$\pi^0 + n$	0	0		1	$-\sqrt{2}$	0
$\pi^- + p$	0			$-\sqrt{2}$	2	0
$\pi^- + n$	0	0	0	0	0	0

(2)

$i \longrightarrow$

$\tau_i \tau_f{}^\dagger$ ($f \downarrow$)	$\pi^+ + p$	$\pi^+ + n$	$\pi^0 + p$	$\pi^0 + n$	$\pi^- + p$	$\pi^- + n$
$\pi^+ + p$	2	0	0	0	0	0
$\pi^+ + n$	0	0	$-\sqrt{2}$	0		0
$\pi^0 + p$	0	$-\sqrt{2}$	1			0
$\pi^0 + n$	0	0		1	$\sqrt{2}$	0
$\pi^- + p$	0			$\sqrt{2}$	0	0
$\pi^- + n$	0	0	0	0	0	2

The products of the dot products in the spins can be handled by using

$$(\boldsymbol{\sigma} \cdot \mathbf{k}_f)(\boldsymbol{\sigma} \cdot \mathbf{k}_i) = \mathbf{k}_f \cdot \mathbf{k}_i + i\boldsymbol{\sigma} \cdot \mathbf{k}_f \times \mathbf{k}_i = k^2 \cos\theta - ik^2\boldsymbol{\sigma} \cdot \hat{\mathbf{n}} \sin\theta,$$
$$(\boldsymbol{\sigma} \cdot \mathbf{k}_i)(\boldsymbol{\sigma} \cdot \mathbf{k}_f) = \mathbf{k}_i \cdot \mathbf{k}_f + i\boldsymbol{\sigma} \cdot \mathbf{k}_i \times \mathbf{k}_f = k^2 \cos\theta + ik^2\boldsymbol{\sigma} \cdot \hat{\mathbf{n}} \sin\theta,$$

where $\hat{\mathbf{n}} = (\mathbf{k}_i \times \mathbf{k}_f)/k^2$ is a unit vector normal to the plane of scattering.

Substituting in (1), we find for $\pi^-p \to \pi^-p$:

(3₋) $$M_-^{(B)} = 2\pi \frac{f^2}{\omega^2} k^2[2(\cos\theta - i\hat{\mathbf{n}}\cdot\boldsymbol{\sigma}\sin\theta) + 0(\cos\theta + i\hat{\mathbf{n}}\cdot\boldsymbol{\sigma}\sin\theta)];$$

for $\pi^-p \to \pi^0n$:

(3_0)
$$M_0^{(B)} = -2\pi \frac{f^2}{\omega^2} k^2[\sqrt{2}(\cos\theta - i\hat{\mathbf{n}}\cdot\boldsymbol{\sigma}\sin\theta) + \sqrt{2}(\cos\theta + i\hat{\mathbf{n}}\cdot\boldsymbol{\sigma}\sin\theta)];$$

for $\pi^+p \to \pi^+p$:

(3_+) $$M_+^{(B)} = 2\pi \frac{f^2}{\omega^2} k^2[0(\cos\theta - i\hat{\mathbf{n}}\cdot\boldsymbol{\sigma}\sin\theta) - 2(\cos\theta + i\hat{\mathbf{n}}\cdot\boldsymbol{\sigma}\sin\theta)].$$

Thus for $\boldsymbol{\sigma}\cdot\hat{\mathbf{n}} = \pm 1$ the cross sections, apart from common factors, should go as

(4_-) $$|M_-^{(B)}|^2 \simeq 4\,|\cos\theta - i\hat{\mathbf{n}}\cdot\boldsymbol{\sigma}\sin\theta|^2 = 4,$$

(4_0) $$|M_0^{(B)}|^2 \simeq 8\cos^2\theta,$$

(4_+) $$|M_+^{(B)}|^2 \simeq 4.$$

Unfortunately, these formulas do not agree with the observations; the reason for the disagreement has to be found in the inadequacy of the Born approximation.

b. Amplitudes for Given *T* and *J*. In computing (4) we separated the isospin components according to the sign of the charges and expressed the angular distributions in terms of simple trigonometric functions. This is obviously convenient for a direct comparison with the experimental data.

But we have seen in 7.22 and 7.23 that the experimental results can be expressed in a more condensed and meaningful form by means of six phase shifts, labeled by the good quantum numbers of the scattering process. Thus it seems desirable to express the results of perturbation theory in a form that stresses the quantum numbers $\frac{1}{2}$ and $\frac{3}{2}$ of J and T rather than the charges and the angles.

We start by deriving the scattering amplitudes $a_\alpha^{(B)}$ [$\alpha = 11, 13, 31, 33$; see 7.22(2)] from the matrix elements in the Born approximation. The relation connecting these amplitudes with the plane-wave matrix elements in this approximation is, for spinless particles [see 3.12(5) and 3.53(1)],

(5) $$f(\theta) = \sqrt{4\pi}\sum_l \sqrt{2l+1}\, a_l^{(B)} Y_l^0(\cos\theta) = -\frac{\mu}{2\pi\hbar^2} M^{(B)}.$$

In π-$\mathcal{N}$ scattering we need some modification because of the spin of the nucleon: the matrix elements (3) are operators on the initial spin states and the expansion of $f(\theta)$ is a sum over l and j. Taking the z axis along the direction of incidence, and assuming that the nucleon is initially in the spin state α, we can write [from 3.51(12)].

$$\sqrt{4\pi}\sum_l \sqrt{2l+1}\left[-\sqrt{\frac{l}{2l+1}}\,a_{l,l-\frac12}^{(B)}\mathcal{Y}_{l-\frac12}^{\frac12} + \sqrt{\frac{l+1}{2l+1}}\,a_{l,l+\frac12}^{(B)}\mathcal{Y}_{l+\frac12}^{\frac12}\right] = -\frac{\omega}{2\pi}\mathsf{M}^{(B)}\alpha.$$

In this expression the rest mass μ has been replaced by the total energy ω to conform with relativistic kinematics, and we have used $\hbar = 1$. Considering now that only P states contribute to the scattering, the sum consists of only two terms, and we obtain

$$(6) \qquad -a_{1,\frac12}^{(B)}\mathcal{Y}_{\frac12}^{\frac12} + \sqrt{2}a_{1,\frac32}^{(B)}\mathcal{Y}_{\frac32}^{\frac12} = -\frac{\omega}{2\pi\sqrt{4\pi}}\mathsf{M}^{(B)}\alpha.$$

This equation must be solved for the amplitudes a, using on the right-hand side the matrix elements (3). For π^+p scattering (which is pure $T = 3/2$), $\mathsf{M}^{(B)}$ is $\mathsf{M}_+^{(B)}$, and $a_{1,\frac12}^{(B)}$ and $a_{1,\frac32}^{(B)}$ are the $a_{31}^{(B)}$ and $a_{33}^{(B)}$ of 7.22(2). For scattering to the left in the xz plane ($\hat{\mathbf{n}} = \hat{\mathbf{y}}$, $\varphi = 0$), (6) becomes

$$(7) \quad -a_{31}^{(B)}\mathcal{Y}_{\frac12}^{\frac12}(\varphi = 0) + \sqrt{2}a_{33}^{(B)}\mathcal{Y}_{\frac32}^{\frac12}(\varphi = 0) = \frac{2f^2k^2}{\sqrt{4\pi}\,\omega}(\cos\theta + i\sigma_y\sin\theta)\alpha.$$

This can be solved for $a_{31}^{(B)}$ and $a_{33}^{(B)}$ by making use of the orthonormal properties of the $\mathcal{Y}$'s. We take the hermitian conjugate of (7), multiply to the right by $\mathcal{Y}_{\frac12}^{\frac12}$ and $\mathcal{Y}_{\frac32}^{\frac12}$, respectively, and integrate over the solid angle to obtain[1]

$$a_{31}^{(B)} = -\frac{2f^2k^2}{\sqrt{4\pi}\,\omega}\int \alpha^\dagger(\cos\theta - i\sigma_y\sin\theta)\left(-\frac{1}{\sqrt{4\pi}}\alpha\cos\theta - \frac{1}{\sqrt{4\pi}}\beta\sin\theta\right)d\Omega$$
$$= \frac{2f^2k^2}{\omega}\left(\frac13 - \frac23\right) = -2\frac{f^2k^2}{3\omega},$$

and similarly

$$a_{33}^{(B)} = \frac{2f^2k^2}{\sqrt{2}\sqrt{4\pi}\,\omega}\int \alpha^\dagger(\cos\theta - i\sigma_y\sin\theta)\left(\frac{\sqrt{2}}{\sqrt{4\pi}}\alpha\cos\theta - \frac{1}{\sqrt{2}}\frac{1}{\sqrt{4\pi}}\beta\sin\theta\right)d\Omega$$
$$= \frac{2f^2k^2}{\sqrt{2}\,\omega}\left(\frac{\sqrt{2}}{3} + \frac{2}{3\sqrt{2}}\right) = 4\frac{f^2k^2}{3\omega}.$$

[1] We use

$$\mathcal{Y}_{\frac12}^{\frac12}(\varphi = 0) = -\sqrt{\frac13}\,Y_1^0\alpha + \sqrt{\frac23}\,Y_1^1\beta = -\frac{1}{\sqrt{4\pi}}\alpha\cos\theta - \frac{1}{\sqrt{4\pi}}\beta\sin\theta,$$

$$\mathcal{Y}_{\frac32}^{\frac12}(\varphi = 0) = \sqrt{\frac23}\,Y_1^0\alpha + \sqrt{\frac13}Y_1^1\beta = \frac{\sqrt{2}}{\sqrt{4\pi}}\alpha\cos\theta - \frac{1}{\sqrt{2}}\frac{1}{\sqrt{4\pi}}\beta\sin\theta,$$

and also $\qquad i\sigma_y\alpha = -\beta, \quad i\sigma_y\beta = \alpha.$

The solution for the $T = \frac{1}{2}$ scattering amplitudes is only slightly more complicated. Using 7.22(3), we obtain

$$(8)\qquad f_1 = f_- - \frac{1}{\sqrt{2}} f_0 = -\frac{\omega}{2\pi}\left(\mathsf{M}_-^{(B)}\alpha - \frac{1}{\sqrt{2}}\mathsf{M}_0^{(B)}\alpha\right)$$
$$= \sqrt{4\pi}\,(-a_{11}^{(B)}\mathcal{Y}_{1/2}^{1/2} + \sqrt{2}a_{13}^{(B)}\mathcal{Y}_{3/2}^{1/2}).$$

Thus

$$a_{11}^{(B)} = \frac{\omega}{2\pi\sqrt{4\pi}}\int \alpha^\dagger\left(\mathsf{M}_-^{(B)\dagger} - \frac{1}{\sqrt{2}}\mathsf{M}_0^{(B)\dagger}\right)\mathcal{Y}_{1/2}^{1/2}\,d\Omega = -8\frac{f^2k^2}{3\omega}$$
$$a_{13}^{(B)} = \frac{-\omega}{2\pi\sqrt{4\pi}}\frac{1}{\sqrt{2}}\int \alpha^\dagger\left(\mathsf{M}_-^{(B)\dagger} + \frac{1}{\sqrt{2}}\mathsf{M}_0^{(B)\dagger}\right)\mathcal{Y}_{3/2}^{1/2}\,d\Omega = -2\frac{f^2k^2}{3\omega}.$$

We can briefly write

$$(9)\qquad a_\alpha^{(B)} = \frac{f^2k^2}{3\omega}\lambda_\alpha \quad\text{with}\quad \begin{aligned}\lambda_{11} &= -8\\ \lambda_{13} &= \lambda_{31} = -2\\ \lambda_{33} &= +4.\end{aligned}$$

The expression (9) is still perfectly equivalent to (3) and just as much in disagreement with the experiment.

It is interesting to observe, however, that a_{33} is positive and that the other a's are negative, as if the forces were attractive in the $T = J = 3/2$ state and repulsive in the other cases. We shall see how this feature can be used to explain the existence of a resonance for $\alpha = 33$.

c. Calculation of the Phase Shifts. Importance of Poles. The l-wave scattering amplitudes are related to the phase shifts by the equation 3.12(6)

$$(10)\qquad a_l = \frac{e^{2i\delta_l} - 1}{2ik} = \frac{1}{k\cot\delta_l - ik},$$

so that we can write

$$(11)\qquad k\cot\delta_l = \mathrm{Re}\,\frac{1}{a_l} \qquad \text{(for } k \text{ real).}$$

The foregoing relations (10) and (11) are exact.

As a result of the Born approximation, we have obtained the real amplitudes (9) for π-$\mathcal{N}$ scattering. In general, they are a poor approximation to the exact amplitudes, which are complex; the Born approximation may be meaningful only when the imaginary part of the amplitude is negligible. This happens for k real, provided

$$(12)\qquad \cot\delta_l \gg 1;$$

this condition is satisfied if the phase shifts are small or near π.

Even when the exact amplitudes are real, or almost real, the amplitudes (9) are not necessarily accurate. It is natural to assume, however, that *the Born approximation amplitudes are valid near* $\omega = 0$ $(k \approx i)$, *where they become so large that the other terms of the perturbation development may be neglected.*

This simple argument forms the basis of much of the present-day thinking about strong forces: *perturbation methods may not be justified in general, but they are expected to give correct results near the predicted "resonances" or "poles."* The theory developed along these lines has received the informal name of "polology."

In the same sense that the bound deuteron state, $k = i/R$, $\cot \delta_0 = -1/R$, is a pole of the scattering amplitude which dominates the low-energy n-p scattering, so the $\omega = 0$ $(k = i)$ resonance dominates π-$\mathcal{N}$ scattering, at least for $\alpha = 33$.

By applying the argument to π-$\mathcal{N}$ scattering, we can write

(13*a*) $$a_\alpha^{(B)} = a_\alpha \quad \text{for} \quad \omega \approx 0,$$

or

(13*b*) $$\frac{f^2k^2}{3\omega}\lambda_\alpha = \frac{1}{k \cot \delta_\alpha - ik} \quad \text{for} \quad \omega \approx 0.$$

The term in ik turns out to be negligible compared to $3\omega/f^2k^2\lambda_\alpha$ in all cases of interest, and we obtain the simple result

(14) $$k \cot \delta_\alpha = \frac{3\omega}{f^2k^2}\frac{1}{\lambda_\alpha} \quad \text{for} \quad \omega \approx 0.$$

How closely must the condition $\omega \approx 0$ be satisfied for the validity of (14)? The answer to this question is not evident a priori, but we shall see that in some cases (14) may be used, with some correction, even for real momenta $(\omega \geq 1)$.

7.25 The Effective Range Formula

a. Simplified Discussion of the Phase Shifts. We have seen in 3.12(12) that for *P*-wave scattering due to short-range forces the quantity $k^3 \cot \delta$ is independent of energy. The theory developed in the preceding section leads indeed to a very similar result. We have from 7.24(14)

(1) $$\frac{k^3 \cot \delta_\alpha}{\omega} = \frac{3}{\lambda_\alpha}\frac{1}{f^2} = \text{constant}.$$

Since this formula was derived without introducing form factors or high-energy cutoff, it must be interpreted as a zero-range approximation to π-$\mathcal{N}$ scattering. The slowly varying factor $1/\omega$ in the left-hand side reduces, nonrelativistically, to the constant rest mass and must be attributed to kinematical relativistic effects rather than to a finite range of the forces.

In simple words (1) means that, as expected for zero range, $k^3 \cot \delta_\alpha/\omega$ does not vary with energy and can be determined from the first order pole at $\omega = 0$, which corresponds to pions bound in the mesic cloud around a nucleon.

In particular, for $\alpha = 33$, the zero-range approximation (1) gives

(2) $$\frac{k^3 \cot \delta_{33}}{\omega} = \frac{3}{4}\frac{1}{f^2}.$$

When this formula is compared with the low-energy data in 7.23(8), we obtain $f^2 \approx \frac{3}{4}\,0.235 = 0.17$. This is not too different from the estimate in 7.15(3), which was obtained from the low-energy neutron-proton interaction.

But, if we consider the experimental data at somewhat higher energy, we find that $k^3 \cot \delta_{33}/\omega$ is not independent of energy, in disagreement with the zero-range approximation. This is not surprising since (2) cannot be expected to be valid near a resonance for real k (see comment at the end of 3.12c).

For the discussion of the energy dependence, it is convenient to replace ω with a new total-energy variable ω_t which includes the kinetic energy of the nucleon in the center-of-mass system:

(3) $$\omega_t = \omega + \frac{k^2}{2M}.$$

When the experimental values of $k^3 \cot \delta_{33}/\omega_t$ are plotted against ω_t (Fig. 7.25-1), they are found to decrease linearly, passing through zero at the peak of the 33 resonance and approximately following the numerical equation

(4) $$\frac{k^3 \cot \delta_{33}}{\omega_t} \approx 9 - 4.1\omega_t.$$

We shall interpret the constant term on the right-hand side of this equation as the contribution (1) *of zero-range scattering and the term in* ω_t *as an effective range correction.*

This interpretation is consistent with an actual theoretical computation of effective range corrections [see (d) and (e)], from which we derive an equation of the form

(5) $$\frac{k^3 \cot \delta_{33}}{\omega_t} = \frac{3}{4f^2} - R_{33}\omega_t.$$

By comparing (4) and (5) we obtain a two-parameter fit to the scattering

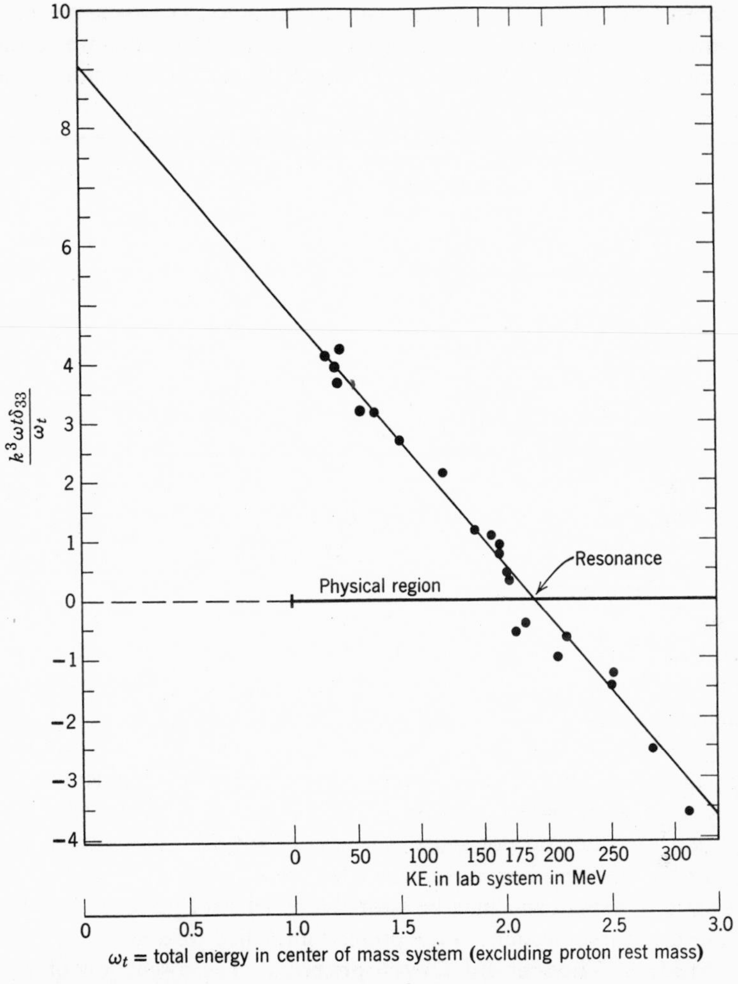

Fig. 7.25-1. Experimental values of $(k^3 \cot \delta_{33})/\omega_t$ plotted versus ω_t [(adapted from S. Lindenbaum and L. C. Yuan, *Phys. Rev.*, **100**, 322 (1955) and from Barnes, Rose, Giacomelli, Ring, Miyake, and Kinsey, *Phys. Rev.*, **117**, 235 (1960)].

in the $\alpha = 33$ state for the numerical values[1]

(6*a*) $$f^2 = 0.08, \qquad R_{33} = 4.1.$$

The effective range parameter R_{33} has the dimension of a momentum, and it can be proved that its numerical value corresponds to a cutoff momentum,

(6*b*) $$k_{\max} = 6.$$

[1] A better fit to the data of Fig. 7.25-1 is obtained for $f^2 = 0.085$. A recent experimental paper (B-60d) quotes $f^2 = 0.087 \pm 0.01$.

Thus the low-energy 33 scattering can be described by two parameters very much in the spirit of a cutoff theory (7.15). From the data we obtain the numerical values of coupling constant and cutoff momentum. The full significance of this result can be appreciated only after we prove that the same numerical values account quantitatively for many other effects in low-energy meson and nuclear physics; this is shown in the following sections.

We are now tempted to extend the effective range treatment to $\alpha \neq 33$ and to write in general

$$(7a) \qquad \frac{k^3 \cot \delta_\alpha}{\omega_t} = \frac{3}{\lambda_\alpha f^2} - R_\alpha \omega_t$$

or

$$(7b) \qquad \frac{k^3 \cot \delta_\alpha}{\omega_t} = \frac{3}{\lambda_\alpha f^2}(1 - r_\alpha \omega_t), \qquad r_\alpha = \frac{\lambda_\alpha f^2}{3} R_\alpha.$$

This equation, which we have presented here as almost empirically derived, was actually found theoretically by Chew and Low. Not only does it account quantitatively for the $\alpha = 33$ scattering, but it is qualitatively meaningful for the other α's.

Its success is connected with the observation that the constants R_α must be positive. Thus *resonances* ($\cot \delta_\alpha = 0$ for $\omega > 1$) *are possible only if* $\lambda_\alpha > 0$; and a glance at 7.24(9) convinces us that we cannot expect resonances for $\alpha \neq 33$.

This observation was the first success of pseudoscalar meson scattering theory and was of great importance in all subsequent developments.

If we were to analyze the phase shifts for $\alpha \neq 33$ in more detail, we would find that they do not satisfy (7) with $f^2 = 0.08$. This discrepancy must not be considered as a significant failure of the theory, since these phase shifts are small and may be strongly influenced by effects that have not been taken into account in the present simplified treatment.

b. Modern Theoretical Developments. The discussion of π-N scattering presented in this section is a simplified intuitive version of theoretical results, originally obtained after considerable study.

As we have mentioned, the effective range equation (7) was first derived by Chew and Low (C-54a; C-56a) from an analysis of the relative importance of perturbation diagrams of various orders and a consistent interpretation of the significance of cutoff. The method employed by these authors has been presented and clarified in a review article by Wick (W-55).

Some of the ideas involved have already been discussed in 7.15b and 7.17. We discard the idea that perturbation theory may provide a complete description of the true relativistic interaction between a "bare" point nucleon and the mesic field. This interaction probably involves a large coupling constant [$f_{PP}^2 \approx 15$; see 7.17(3)] that would require consideration of complicated diagrams, with multiple meson emissions and absorptions, virtual nucleon pairs, etc.

We are satisfied instead with the interaction of low-energy mesons with a "physical" nucleon at rest ("static approximation"), already surrounded by some "inner cloud" of finite extent. The coupling constant $f^2 = 0.08$ ("renormalized coupling constant") expresses the strength of the coupling of low-energy mesons with the physical nucleon, and the cut-off momentum $k_{\text{max}} = 6$ limits the validity of the theory to interactions with low-momentum transfer or with a relatively large impact parameter (peripheral collisions), hiding what happens at high energy and short range.

A justification of the effective range formula from conventional effective range theory was reported by Jackson (Ja-58) [see (e)], and a derivation based on the calculation of logarithmic derivatives was given by Weisskopf (W-59).

In the meantime new theoretical approaches to strong interaction were introduced. Starting from the principle of "causality" (according to which an event at a space-time point $\mathbf{x}_1$, t_1, cannot produce an effect at the space-time point $\mathbf{x}_2$, t_2 if $|\mathbf{x}_2 - \mathbf{x}_1| > c\,|t_2 - t_1|$), Goldberger and Gell-Mann derived some useful equations, called "dispersion relations," which have received wide attention and numerous applications.

The same dispersion relations were subsequently obtained by assuming that the scattering amplitudes and the scattering matrix could be treated, with some restrictions, as analytical functions of their complex kinematical parameters (Mandelstam conjecture); when the poles of the amplitudes are known, either from perturbation theory or from the experimental information concerning resonances, and the other singularities are determined, it becomes possible to obtain the functional dependence of the cross sections by using Cauchy's theorem.

In what follows (c) we introduce this method and apply it to the derivation of the equation of Chew and Low (d).

c. Introduction to Analyticity. Nonrelativistically, the kinematics of the scattering is described by the kinetic energy and the scattering angle. The corresponding relativistically invariant quantities are the *square of the center-of-mass energy s* and the *square of the four-momentum transfer t*. These quantities can be defined with reference to the graph of Fig. 7.25-2:

$$\begin{aligned} s &= |\mathsf{p}_1 + \mathsf{p}_2|^2 = |\mathsf{p}_3 + \mathsf{p}_4|^2 \\ t &= |\mathsf{p}_1 + \mathsf{p}_3|^2 = |\mathsf{p}_2 + \mathsf{p}_4|^2 \end{aligned} \tag{8}$$

As shown by the arrows in the diagram, the center of mass momenta must be taken as positive for incoming particles (initial momenta for any of the reaction $1 + 2 \rightarrow 3 + 4$, $1 + 3 \rightarrow 2 + 4$, $1 + 4 \rightarrow 2 + 3$) and negative for outgoing particles. The sum in the definition of t is actually a difference between initial and final momenta for the channel $1 + 2 \rightarrow 3 + 4$, as appropriate to a momentum transfer.

For π-$\mathcal{N}$ scattering, a little algebra[1] shows that s and t, as defined by (8) have the meaning stated:

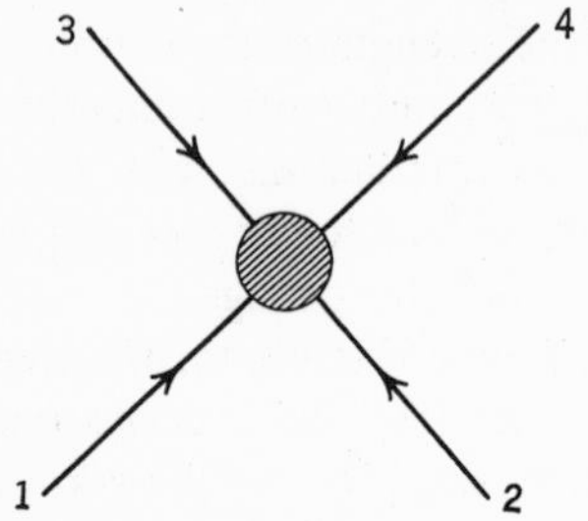

Fig. 7.25-2. Defining the notation for the kinematics of reactions involving two initial and two final particles.

(9)
$$s = (E_{\mathcal{N}} + E_\pi)^2$$
$$t = -2p^2(1 - \cos\theta) = -4p^2 \sin^2 \tfrac{1}{2}\theta.$$

We can also introduce a third variable, the square of the *exchange four momentum transfer* t^{ex}, by the relation

$$(10) \quad t^{ex} = |\mathbf{p}_1 + \mathbf{p}_4|^2 = |\mathbf{p}_2 + \mathbf{p}_3|^2,$$

but this is not independent of the other two, since we easily find that

$$(11) \quad s + t + t^{ex} = 2(M^2 + 1).$$

In the "physical" region s and t must be real and $\cos\theta \leq 1$. But we shall consider both "physical" and "unphysical" values of these variables: s and t are allowed to take any value in the complex plane. The scattering amplitudes $f(s, t)$ are then functions of these complex variables and, in the assumption of analyticity, can be computed by making use of Cauchy's formula. For instance, for fixed t

$$(12) \qquad f(s, t) = \frac{1}{2\pi i} \oint \frac{f(s', t)}{s' - s} \, ds',$$

where the integral extends to an anticlockwise close contour surrounding the point s, but not enclosing any pole or discontinuity of the function $f(s, t)$.

Equation (12) can be considered the simplest dispersion relation.

It is often convenient to extend the path of integration to infinite circles in the complex plane. When the integral in (12) does not converge fast enough for this purpose, it is useful to use a subtraction procedure in

[1] By making use of the fact that in the center of mass system of nucleon and pion $\mathbf{p}_{\mathcal{N}} = -\mathbf{p}_\pi$, we obtain

$$|\mathbf{p}_1 + \mathbf{p}_2|^2 = (E_{\mathcal{N}} + E_\pi)^2$$
$$|\mathbf{p}_1 + \mathbf{p}_3|^2 = |\mathbf{p}_{\mathcal{N}} - \mathbf{p}_{\mathcal{N}}'|^2 = \mathbf{p}_{\mathcal{N}}^2 + \mathbf{p}_{\mathcal{N}}'^2 - 2E_{\mathcal{N}}E_{\mathcal{N}}' + 2p_{\mathcal{N}}^2 \cos\theta$$
$$= 2M_{\mathcal{N}}^2 - 2E_{\mathcal{N}}^2 + 2p_{\mathcal{N}}^2 \cos\theta = 2p_{\mathcal{N}}^2(-1 + \cos\theta).$$

order to eliminate or reduce the divergence. By applying this procedure and focusing our attention on the dependence on the variable s, we obtain the dispersion relation

$$f(s_1) - f(s_2) = \frac{1}{2\pi i}\oint f(s')\left(\frac{1}{s' - s_1} - \frac{1}{s' - s_2}\right) ds' = \frac{s_1 - s_2}{2\pi i}\oint \frac{f(s')}{(s' - s_1)(s' - s_2)}\, ds', \tag{13}$$

which contains an extra power of s' in the denominator of the integral.

For the computation of the integrals we must know the analytical properties of the amplitude. In (d) of this section we show how this is done in the particular example of π-$\mathcal{N}$ scattering in the P wave. The same method, applied to nonrelativistic S scattering would lead to the effective range relation for n-p scattering 3.15(10), but we leave the verification of this point to the reader.

d. Derivation of the Chew-Low Equation from Analyticity. In the case of π-$\mathcal{N}$ scattering the interaction is, at least theoretically, only in the P state. Thus the angular dependence (dependence on t) is contained in the spin-angle functions, and we are concerned only with the energy dependence of the P-wave amplitudes $a_\alpha(s)$. The function $a_\alpha(s)$ is supposedly known at $s = M^2$ ($\omega = 0$), where it has a pole obtained from the Born approximation; we want to compute its value for values of s in the physical region. To do this without worrying about the divergence at $s = M^2$, we apply the dispersion relation (13) to the ratio $a_\alpha^{(B)}/a_\alpha$ and obtain

$$\frac{a_\alpha^{(B)}(s)}{a_\alpha(s)} - \frac{a_\alpha^{(B)}(M^2)}{a_\alpha(M^2)} = \frac{s - M^2}{2\pi i}\oint \frac{a_\alpha^{(B)}(s')}{a_\alpha(s')}\frac{ds'}{(s' - s)(s' - M^2)}. \tag{14}$$

In this equation we can introduce

$$\frac{a_\alpha^{(B)}(M^2)}{a_\alpha(M^2)} = 1, \tag{15}$$

$$s - M^2 = (E_\mathcal{N} + \omega)^2 - M^2 = k^2 + \omega^2 + 2E_\mathcal{N}\omega \approx 2M\omega_t.$$

On the other hand, by making use of 7.24(10), we can write

$$\frac{a_\alpha^{(B)}}{a_\alpha} = a_\alpha^{(B)}(k \cot \delta_\alpha - ik). \tag{16}$$

We are interested in the analytical continuation of $\cot \delta_\alpha$ in the physical region, in which this quantity is real because of unitarity. For this purpose we must investigate the discontinuities of the ratio $a_\alpha^{(B)}/a_\alpha$ in the complex s plane.

The most important of these discontinuities, and the only one that we shall consider, is a branch cut along the physical region for our scattering reaction:

$$s \text{ real} > (M + 1)^2.$$

In this region the momentum is real and can be expressed in the form

$$k = \pm|k(s)| = \pm \frac{1}{2}\sqrt{\frac{1}{s}[s - (M + 1)^2][s - (M - 1)^2]}, \tag{17}$$

with the plus (minus) sign holding for s just above (below) the real axis.

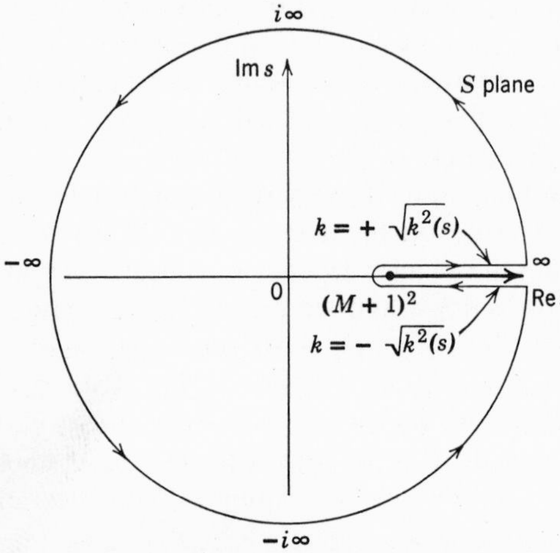

Fig. 7.25-3. Path of integration in the complex S plane for the calculation of the formula of Chew and Low. The path avoids the branch cut in the physical region of the scattering.

If we limit our attention to the region of not-too-large momenta, which is dominated by the $J = T = \frac{3}{2}$ resonance, we are justified in neglecting all other poles and discontinuities. Such discontinuities, corresponding to the virtual formation of excited states of the nucleon or to resonant states between mesons, could be taken into account in a more refined form of the theory[1].

It is reasonable to perform the integration in (14) along the contour of Fig. 7.25-3, for the contribution of the infinite circle vanishes since $a_\alpha^{(B)}/a_\alpha$ is presumably well behaved at infinity. Thus the integral in (14) becomes the sum of integrals performed along the real axis; considering

[1] The branch cut for s real, $0 < s < (M - 1)^2$, where, as seen from (17), k is real and has an ambiguity in sign, is also disregarded, since it is along the physical region for pion anti-nucleon scattering.

(16) and (17), we can write for $\alpha = 33$

$$\oint = -2i \int_{(M+1)^2}^{\infty} \frac{a_{33}^{(B)}(s')\,|k(s')|}{(s'-s)(s'-M^2)}\, ds'.$$

By introducing this equation into (14) and making use of (15), we obtain

$$\text{(18)} \qquad \operatorname{Re} \frac{a_{33}^{(B)}(s)}{a_{33}(s)} = \frac{f^2 k^2 \lambda_{33}}{3\omega}\, k \cot \delta_{33}$$

$$= 1 - \omega_t \frac{M}{\pi} \int_{(M+1)^2}^{\infty} \frac{a_{33}^{(B)}(s')\,|k(s')|}{(s'-s)(s'-M^2)}\, ds'.$$

The integral diverges and must be cut off by replacing the upper limit by some finite $s_{\max}$. Then, for $s \ll s_{\max}$, it becomes a slowly varying function of s and may be considered as a positive constant.

Thus it is recognized that (18) is equivalent to (5).

A numerical evaluation of the integral for $\alpha = 33$ shows that the value of $s_{\max}$ required for agreement with the experiment corresponds to the cutoff momentum (6).

e. The Chew-Low Equation from Effective Range Theory. We now present proof of the equation by Chew and Low, making use of effective range theory in its conventional form (3.15). However, in order to apply the effective range treatment to the scattering of pseudoscalar mesons, we must extend the formalism of 3.15 to the case of P waves.

Let us start by defining our function v_n in a way similar to 3.15(1): in the present case v_n is a P-wave solution for $V = 0$, with a phase shift δ_n relative to the asymptotic P-wave solution that behaves regularly at the origin. By definition

$$\text{(19)} \qquad v_n(r \to \infty) \cong \frac{\sin(k_n r - \frac{1}{2}\pi + \delta_n)}{\sin \delta_n}$$

$$= \sin(kr - \tfrac{1}{2}\pi) \cot \delta_n + \cos(kr - \tfrac{1}{2}\pi)$$

and thus [1.13(17)]

$$\text{(20)} \qquad v_n(r) = k_n r[j_1(k_n r) \cot \delta_n + n_1(k_n r)]$$

$$= \left(\frac{\sin k_n r}{k_n r} - \cos k_n r\right) \cot \delta_n + \sin k_n r + \frac{\cos k_n r}{k_n r}.$$

To proceed as in 3.15, we need now to compute v_n and v_n' at the origin; but this is impossible since the term $(\cos k_n r)/k_n r$ diverges for $r = 0$.

Let us be satisfied with computing v_n and v_n' near the origin for a small $r = \varepsilon$. For this we need to expand (20) in powers of r. We find that the formulas 1.13(18) are not sufficient and that we must go a step farther.

By writing

$$\text{(21)}\qquad \begin{aligned} \sin k_n\varepsilon &= k_n\varepsilon - \frac{(k_n\varepsilon)^3}{6}, \\ \cos k_n\varepsilon &= 1 - \frac{(k_n\varepsilon)^2}{2}, \end{aligned}$$

in (20) we obtain, keeping terms up to $(k\varepsilon)^2$,

$$\text{(22)}\qquad \begin{aligned} v(\varepsilon) &= \frac{(k_n\varepsilon)^2}{3}\cot\delta_n + \frac{1}{k_n\varepsilon} + \frac{k_n\varepsilon}{2}, \\ v'(\varepsilon) &= k_n\left[\frac{2}{3}(k_n\varepsilon)\cot\delta_n - \frac{1}{(k_n\varepsilon)^2} + \frac{1}{2}\right]. \end{aligned}$$

We can now continue as in 3.15. The only difference is that the wave equation includes an angular momentum term $2/r^2$. This term cancels in the subtractions, and an equation exactly like 3.15(7) is obtained. Considering that $u_n(0) = u_m(0) = 0$, we write

$$\text{(23)}\qquad (v_nv_m' - v_mv_n')_{r=\varepsilon} = (k_n^2 - k_m^2)\int_\varepsilon^\infty (u_nu_m - v_nv_m)\,dr.$$

Let us substitute (22) in the left-hand side of this equation. In the products, since ε is small, we must keep all the negative powers of $k\varepsilon$ (continuing the expansion (22) will not give any higher negative power of $k\varepsilon$), but we are allowed to discard all the positive powers. The result is

$$\text{(24)}\qquad \frac{1}{k_nk_m}\left[k_m^3\cot\delta_m - k_n^3\cot\delta_n + (k_m^2 - k_n^2)\frac{1}{\varepsilon}\right] = (k_n^2 - k_m^2)\int_\varepsilon^\infty (u_nu_m - v_nv_m)\,dr.$$

Of course, the divergence at the origin ($\varepsilon = 0$) remains. But such divergence exists also on the right-hand side, where the product v_nv_m goes as $1/k_nk_mr^2$. We use the formal relation

$$\frac{1}{\varepsilon} = \int_\varepsilon^\infty \frac{dr}{r^2}$$

and transfer the terms $1/\varepsilon$ inside the integral:

(25)

$$k_m^3\cot\delta_m - k_n^3\cot\delta_n = (k_n^2 - k_m^2)\int_\varepsilon^\infty \left[k_nk_m(u_nu_m - v_nv_m) + \frac{1}{r^2}\right]dr.$$

Let us assume that the integral appearing in (25) is a slowly varying function of energy and that it has a finite limit for $k_n = k_m = 0$. Then we can define an effective P-wave momentum:

(26) $$k_e = \lim_{\substack{k_n \to 0 \\ k_m \to 0}} \int_0^\infty \left[k_m k_n (u_n u_m - v_n v_m) + \frac{1}{r^2} \right] dr.$$

Finally, the corrections to the zero-range theory—according to which $k^3 \cot \delta$ is energy-independent—are expressed by

(27) $$k_m{}^3 \cot \delta_m - k_n{}^3 \cot \delta_n = (k_n{}^2 - k_m{}^2) k_e.$$

If this formula is used to compare $k^3 \cot \delta$ at $k = i\ (\omega \approx 0)$ and at any real $k\ (\omega > 1)$ we obtain

(28) $$k^3 \cot \delta - (k^3 \cot \delta)_{\omega=0} = (-1 - k^2) k_e = -\omega^2 k_e\,,$$

and this justifies the form of (5) and (7).

7.26 Nuclear Forces and Anomalous Moments

a. Nuclear Forces. It is obviously of the greatest interest to see if the two parameters of nonrelativistic pseudoscalar theory, f^2 and $k_{\max}$, as determined from π-$\mathcal{N}$ scattering, lead to sensible results when used in other problems.

Let us start by considering once again the problem of nucleon-nucleon interaction in the S state.

We have seen in 7.15 that in order to obtain agreement between the ^1S scattering length and the potential of 7.14(14) (OPEP[1] with no cutoff) we need $f^2 = 0.25$, a value significantly different from that found in the preceding section. This disagreement is not surprising because OPEP with no cutoff is obviously incorrect at short distance, to the point that it leads to nonconvergent results for the ^3S binding.

We shall now briefly describe how the short-range effects can be taken into account in a semiempirical manner, without making any assumptions on cutoff values or on a specific form of MPEP (I-56). In order to understand the method, let us classify the S state properties into "inner" and "outer," according to their dependence on the behavior of the wave function at short or long range. More specifically, for ^3S we are interested in the quadrupole moment of the deuteron and in the triplet effective range. The quadrupole moment Q [1.24(16)] is typically an "outer" quantity, since it is the radial integral of the nuclear wave function squared, multiplied by r^2; the triplet effective range ^3r_e [3.15(9)] is, instead, a typical "inner" quantity, since it is the radial integral of the difference between the asymptotic and the true value of the wave functions squared.

[1] See 3.56c.

Thus the effective range conveys information on the inner behavior of the deuteron wave function; it can be shown that this information, together with the OPEP interaction, is sufficient to determine the outer part of the wave function without any further knowledge on the short-range potential. Following this procedure numerically, we can compute the quadrupole moment of the deuteron in terms of two parameters: the triplet effective range ${}^3r_e$, which is experimentally known, and the coupling constant f, which enters in OPEP.

The value of f^2 which leads to agreement with the experimental data on the nuclear ${}^3S$ and ${}^1S$ states is

$$0.07 < f^2 < 0.09.$$

Thus the coupling constant obtained from the effective range treatment of pion scattering can be successfully used in an effective range treatment of the nuclear S state at low energy.

For higher energy the OPEP is expected to be adequate only for distant collisions and thus for high values of angular momentum. We have seen in 3.56c that it does account for the high angular momentum phase shifts of p-p scattering, with a coupling constant close to 0.08.

In order to develop a theory applicable to closer collisions and to other short-range effects, several authors have attempted to compute the effect of two-meson exchange, but the predictions of the theory for exchanges of more than one meson are not entirely unambiguous. We have seen, however, that a reasonable calculation (Gartenhaus, see 7.18) with addition of spin-orbit coupling (Signell and Marshak, see 3.58d) accounts for many features of $\mathcal{N}$-$\mathcal{N}$ scattering by using f^2 and $k_{\max}$ determined from π-$\mathcal{N}$ scattering.

Our knowledge of the interaction between nucleons is still very limited, but it seems that any advance in the understanding of mesons can be used to make a better theory of nuclear forces. For instance, the exchanges of two and three pions in the form of ρ and ω vector mesons (see 7.35 and 7.36) can be considered with some advantage. One has the impression that the original idea of Yukawa, according to which nuclear forces are due to meson exchanges, is fully justified and that a satisfactory meson theory would lead to a satisfactory understanding of nuclear forces.

To the limited extent to which the present theory is able to explain the scattering of pions, it is also capable of accounting for the interaction between nucleons.

b. Anomalous Magnetic Moments. It is tempting to attribute the anomalous part of the nucleons' magnetic moment to electric currents in the meson cloud. If it is assumed that the anomalous moments are produced mostly by pions in the outer part of the cloud (virtual pions of low momentum), it should be possible to account almost quantitatively for their values with the constant f^2 and $k_{\max}$ obtained from low energy π-N scattering.

This point of view has been developed by Miyazawa (M-55) with a quantized form of meson theory (graphs of Fig. 7.38-2). Since we have not yet discussed the electromagnetic interaction of the quantized pion field (7.31), we now compute the anomalous magnetic moments arising from a classical meson cloud (Ja-58).

The charged part of the cloud is obtained by solving for ϕ_+ and ϕ_- the wave equation derived from the free Lagrangian 7.16(9) with a source term from 7.16(11). We obtain in this manner

$$(1) \qquad \phi_\pm = \frac{1}{\sqrt{4\pi}} f\tau_\pm \boldsymbol{\sigma} \cdot \nabla\, Y(r)$$

with

$$(2) \qquad Y(r) = \int \rho(r') \frac{e^{-|\mathbf{r}-\mathbf{r}'|}}{|r-r'|}\, d^3\mathbf{r}' \quad \text{and} \quad \rho = \int_0^{k_{\max}} e^{i\mathbf{k}\cdot\mathbf{r}}\, d^3\mathbf{k}.$$

The cloud (1) corresponds to a density of electric current

$$(3) \qquad \mathbf{j}_e = -\frac{ie}{2}(\phi_+{}^*\nabla\phi_+ - \phi_+\nabla\phi_+{}^* - \phi_-{}^*\nabla\phi_- + \phi_-\nabla\phi_-{}^*)$$
$$= -ie(-\phi_-\nabla\phi_+ + \phi_+\nabla\phi_-).$$

Note that as long as the fields ϕ_+ and ϕ_- are commutative functions, the first term of the current can be written indifferently either $\phi_-\nabla\phi_+$ or $(\nabla\phi_+)\phi_-$; but, as soon as the substitution (1) is made, the order of the factors becomes important, since τ_+ and τ_- do not commute. The ambiguity arises from the fact that the nonquantized theory of a static cloud does not distinguish between absorption and emission processes. If the ambiguity is solved to agree with quantized theory, we obtain

$$\mathbf{j}_e = \frac{ie}{4\pi} f^2[(\tau_+\boldsymbol{\sigma}\cdot\nabla Y)\tau_-\nabla(\boldsymbol{\sigma}\cdot\nabla Y) - \tau_-(\boldsymbol{\sigma}\cdot\nabla Y)\tau_+\nabla(\boldsymbol{\sigma}\cdot\nabla Y)]$$
$$= -\frac{ie}{4\pi} f^2\, 2\tau_3(\boldsymbol{\sigma}\cdot\nabla Y)\,\nabla(\boldsymbol{\sigma}\cdot\nabla Y);$$

and thus the anomalous moment operator is

$$(4) \qquad \boldsymbol{\mu}_a = \tfrac{1}{2}\int (\mathbf{r}\times\mathbf{j}_e)\, d^3\mathbf{r}$$
$$= -ie\frac{f^2}{4\pi}\tau_3 \int (\boldsymbol{\sigma}\cdot\nabla Y)(\mathbf{r}\times\nabla)(\boldsymbol{\sigma}\cdot\nabla Y)\, d^3\mathbf{r}$$
$$= -ie\frac{f^2}{4\pi}\tau_3 \int \frac{dY}{dr}(\boldsymbol{\sigma}\cdot\hat{\mathbf{r}})(\mathbf{r}\times\nabla)\frac{dY}{dr}(\boldsymbol{\sigma}\cdot\hat{\mathbf{r}})\, d^3\mathbf{r}$$
$$= -ie\frac{f^2}{4\pi}\tau_3 \int \frac{1}{r^2}\left(\frac{dY}{dr}\right)^2 (\boldsymbol{\sigma}\cdot\mathbf{r})(\mathbf{r}\times\boldsymbol{\sigma})\, d^3\mathbf{r}.$$

For the z component the integral contains a factor $(x\sigma_x + y\sigma_y + z\sigma_z) \times (x\sigma_y - y\sigma_x)$, of which only the terms $x^2\sigma_x\sigma_y - y^2\sigma_y\sigma_x = i\sigma_z(x^2 + y^2) = i\sigma_z r^2 \sin^2\theta$ give a nonvanishing contribution. Thus the value of $(\mu_a)_z$ in the "spin up" state is

$$\text{(5)} \qquad \langle\mu_a\rangle = e\tau_3 \frac{f^2}{4\pi} \int \left(\frac{dY}{dr}\right)^2 \sin^2\theta \, d^3\mathbf{r} = e\tau_3 \frac{f^2}{4\pi} \frac{2}{3} \int \left(\frac{dY}{dr}\right)^2 d^3\mathbf{r}.$$

For $f^2 = 0.08$ and square cutoff Jackson reports the numerical value $\mu_a = 1.76\tau_3$, to be compared with the measured anomalous moments: $+1.79$ for the proton and -1.91 for the neutron. The agreement seems indeed satisfactory.

But the classical meson cloud contributes only an "isovector" (proportional to τ_3, see 4.37) anomalous moment. From the quantized form of the theory an "isoscalar" part and a contribution from the nucleon's core are also obtained. Unfortunately, these refinements of the theory make the agreement with the measured values less favorable and the problem of the anomalous magnetic moments is still unsolved.

c. Conclusions. From the discussion of the last three sections we can conclude that the static pseudoscalar meson theory with charge-symmetrical, nonrelativistic pseudovector coupling and cutoff accounts consistently for several effects in low-energy meson-nucleon and nucleon-nucleon interactions.

Some of the successes and limitations of the theory are summarized as follows:

(i) The theory predicts that the π-N interaction is exclusively in the P wave, and the experiment shows that π-N scattering is predominantly P-wave scattering.

(ii) The theory predicts, in agreement with the experiment, that a resonance should occur in the $\frac{3}{2}\frac{3}{2}$ state.

(iii) The theory allows the determination of the constants f^2 and $k_{\max}$: the values are found from the analysis of the scattering account for several other observations, including nuclear forces and—at least in a naïve way—anomalous magnetic moments.

(iv) The theory does not account directly for the fact that the S phase shifts of π-N scattering are different from zero.

(v) The theory does not explain what happens beyond the first maximum in the π-N scattering cross section.

(vi) The theory does not—and cannot because of the static approximation—predict spin-orbit coupling in N-N interaction.

7.3 Pion Production

7.31 General Introduction to Photoproduction

a. Qualitative Description of the Effect. Pi mesons are produced by bombarding targets of different substances with high-energy beams emerging from accelerators. As usual, we limit our interest to "elementary" targets, such as protons and neutrons, and we start the discussion with an analysis of the photoproduction experiments. These are in a way the

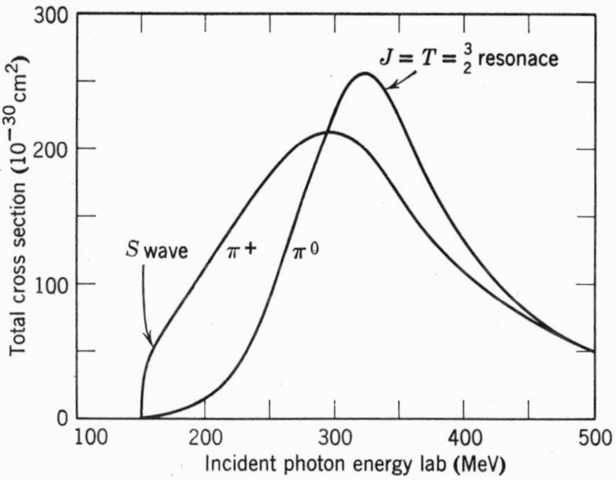

Fig. 7.31-1. Photoproduction cross section (from J. D. Jackson, *The Physics of Elementary Particles*, Copyright 1958, Princeton University Press).

easiest to interpret, since the coupling to the electromagnetic field is known better than the strong nuclear interaction.

Experiments on the production of π mesons by the interaction of γ rays on free nucleons are limited to measurement on the two reactions

(1) $$\gamma + \mathrm{p} \rightarrow \pi^+ + \mathrm{n}$$

(2) $$\gamma + \mathrm{p} \rightarrow \pi^0 + \mathrm{p}.$$

However, in the assumption of charge independence the reactions with neutron targets would not give any fundamentally different information.

The total cross sections for reactions (1) and (2) are shown in Fig. 7.31-1. The π^0 photoproduction has a maximum at the resonant energy for the intermediate formation of the first excited state of the nucleon $T = J = \frac{3}{2}$, ($\mathcal{N}_{33}$*). The angular distribution is $1 + \frac{3}{2}\sin^2\theta$, as discussed in 5.16d.

The charged meson photoproduction cross section is less easy to interpret and results from the sum of several distinct amplitudes. Near threshold S-wave photoproduction predominates, as shown by the energy dependence of the cross section; at higher energy P-wave final states are important, as for the production of neutral pions.

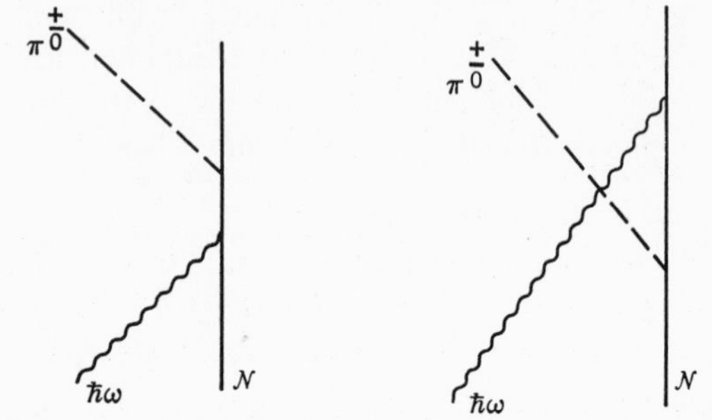

Fig. 7.31-2. Diagrams for "shake-off" photoproduction.

From the theoretical point of view at least three different ways of computing the matrix elements must be distinguished. These are intuitively described by the diagrams in Figs. 7.31-2, 3, and 4.

The diagrams in Fig. 7.31-2 correspond to the so-called "shake-off"

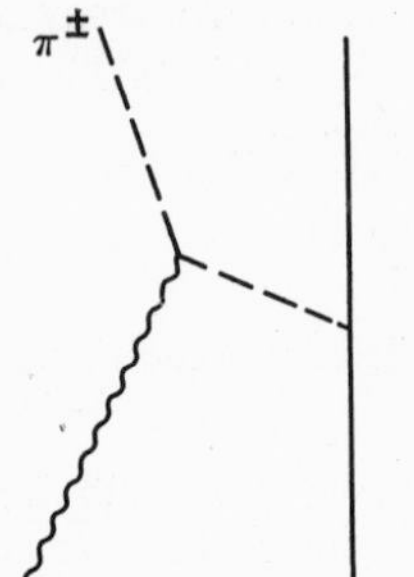

Fig. 7.31-3. Diagram for photoproduction through photo-effect.

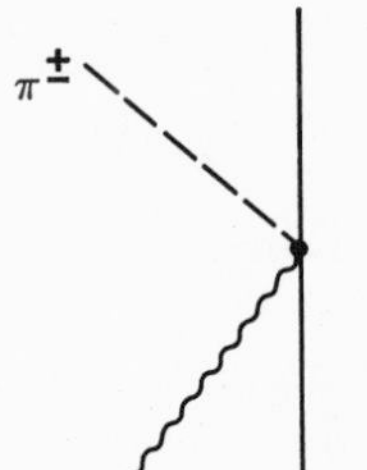

Fig. 7.31-4. Catastrophic photomeson production.

process, similar to π-$\mathcal{N}$ scattering. This process is enhanced by the intermediate formation of the $\mathcal{N}_{33}{}^*$ resonant state, which is reached through a $\mathcal{M}1$ transition induced by magnetic moment coupling ($\mu_{\mathcal{N}}\boldsymbol{\sigma} \cdot \mathbf{curl\, A}$). The electric dipole interaction of the γ ray with the current of the proton ($e\mathbf{p} \cdot \mathbf{A}$) is negligible because the mass of the nucleons is large (infinite in the static approximation).

Note that "shake-off" is about equally important for neutron and proton; it is the only mechanism of photoproduction of π^0, since it does not involve direct meson-photon interaction.

Figure 7.31-3 illustrates another mechanism of photo production in which the γ ray ejects a meson from the "cloud" surrounding the target nucleon. This process is similar to the atomic photoelectric effect. The interaction is a $\mathbf{p} \cdot \mathbf{A}$ interaction between the electric field of the γ ray and the electric current of the meson. It vanishes for π^0.

Finally, Fig. 7.31-4 describes a first order or "catastrophic" process which occurs only for $\pi^{\pm}$, because of a term in the interaction Hamiltonian whose origin and form are made clear in (b).

b. Interaction Lagrangian and Hamiltonian. In the presence of the electromagnetic potential $\mathbf{A}$ the Lagrangian density of the nucleon-meson system can be decomposed in the following terms:

(3) $$\mathscr{L} = \mathscr{L}_N + \mathscr{L}_\pi + \mathscr{L}_A + \mathscr{L}_{N\pi} + \mathscr{L}_{\pi A} + \mathscr{L}_{NA} + \mathscr{L}_{N\pi A}.$$

The notation is self-explanatory: the first three terms are the free-field Lagrangians; the next three are interaction Lagrangians, and the last is the one responsible for first-order photoproduction (Fig. 7.31-4).

The nonrelativistic nucleons, the free electromagnetic field, and their interaction have already been treated in 4.1, and we need not discuss the terms $\mathscr{L}_N$, $\mathscr{L}_A$, and $\mathscr{L}_{NA}$ here.

Because of the importance of electric charge in electromagnetic coupling, it is convenient to use $\mathscr{L}_\pi$ expressed in terms of "rotational components." Considering that $\phi_+{}^* = -\phi_-$, 7.16(9) can be written

(4) $$\mathscr{L}_\pi = \nabla\phi_+ \cdot \nabla\phi_- - \frac{\partial\phi_+}{\partial t}\frac{\partial\phi_-}{\partial t} - \frac{1}{2}(\nabla\phi_0)^2 + \frac{1}{2}\left(\frac{\partial\phi_0}{\partial t}\right)^2 - \frac{1}{2}(-2\phi_+\phi_- + \phi_0{}^2).$$

For $\mathscr{L}_{N\pi}$ we write, from 7.14(11) and 7.16(11), for a nucleon fixed at the origin,

(5) $$\mathscr{L}_{N\pi} = -\mathscr{H}_{N\pi} = \sqrt{4\pi}f\,\rho(r)\boldsymbol{\sigma} \cdot \nabla(\tau_+\phi_- + \tau_-\phi_+ - \tau_0\phi_0).$$

Clearly, the interaction of the pions with the vector potential field is obtained by the replacements

(6) $$\nabla\phi_\pm \rightarrow (\nabla \mp ie\mathbf{A})\phi_\pm$$

in (4) and (5). When (6) is introduced in (4), the new terms

(7) $$\mathscr{L}_{\pi A} = -\mathscr{H}_{\pi A} = ie(\phi_-\mathbf{A} \cdot \nabla\phi_+ - \phi_+\mathbf{A} \cdot \nabla\phi_-) + e^2A^2\phi_+\phi_-$$

are obtained; and from (5) we have the "catastrophic" term

(8) $$\mathscr{L}_{N\pi A} = -\mathscr{H}_{N\pi A} = ie\sqrt{4\pi}f\,\rho(r)(\tau_+\phi_- - \tau_-\phi_+)\boldsymbol{\sigma} \cdot \mathbf{A}.$$

c. Matrix Elements and Vertex Factors. The Hamiltonian density (7) expresses the classical interaction between the electric current of the mesons [compare with 7.26(3)] and the electromagnetic field. In a quantized form it allows us to compute the vertex factor for Feynman diagrams involving the interaction between pions and photons.

Let us compute the classical Hamiltonian, neglecting, as usual, the term in e^2A^2 and integrating (7) over all space

$$\mathcal{H}_{\pi A} = -ie\int(\phi_-\mathbf{A}\cdot\nabla\phi_+ - \phi_+\mathbf{A}\cdot\nabla\phi_-)\,d^3\mathbf{r};$$

This can be written in quantized form by expanding the fields ϕ_-, ϕ_+, $\mathbf{A}$ in a sum of creation and annihilation operators, as in 7.16(12), (13).

As an example, let us consider the term of interest in the diagram in Fig. 7.31-3, which corresponds to the absorption of a photon of momentum $\mathbf{k}_\gamma$ by a positive meson which changes its momentum from $\mathbf{k}_\pi$ to $\mathbf{k}_\pi'$. The matrix element of the interaction is the coefficient of $\mathsf{a}_{+,k_\pi}\mathsf{a}_{k_\gamma}\mathsf{a}^\dagger_{+,k_\pi'}$ [1]:

$$\begin{aligned} M(\pi^+ + \gamma \to \pi^+) &= ie\sqrt{\frac{1}{2\omega_\pi}}\sqrt{\frac{1}{2\omega_\pi'}}\sqrt{\frac{2\pi}{\omega_\gamma}}\int\Big(e^{i\mathbf{k}_\pi\cdot\mathbf{r}}e^{i\mathbf{k}_\gamma\cdot\mathbf{r}}\hat{\boldsymbol{\epsilon}}_\gamma\cdot\nabla e^{-i\mathbf{k}_\pi'\cdot\mathbf{r}} \\ &\qquad - e^{-i\mathbf{k}'\cdot\mathbf{r}}e^{i\mathbf{k}_\gamma\cdot\mathbf{r}}\hat{\boldsymbol{\epsilon}}_\gamma\cdot\nabla e^{i\mathbf{k}_\pi\cdot\mathbf{r}}\Big)\,d^3\mathbf{r} \\ &= e\sqrt{\frac{1}{2\omega_\pi}}\sqrt{\frac{1}{2\omega_\pi'}}\sqrt{\frac{2\pi}{\omega_\gamma}}(2\pi)^3\,\delta(\mathbf{k}_\pi + \mathbf{k}_\gamma - \mathbf{k}_\pi')\hat{\boldsymbol{\epsilon}}_\gamma\cdot(\mathbf{k}_\pi + \mathbf{k}_\pi'). \end{aligned}$$

This must still be integrated over all intermediate momenta $[(2\pi)^{-3}\int d^3\mathbf{k}_\pi]$; considering that $\hat{\boldsymbol{\epsilon}}_\gamma\cdot\mathbf{k}_\pi = \hat{\boldsymbol{\epsilon}}_\gamma\cdot(\mathbf{k}_\pi' - \mathbf{k}_\gamma) = \hat{\boldsymbol{\epsilon}}_\gamma\cdot\mathbf{k}_\pi'$ we obtain

$$\text{(10)}\qquad M(\pi^+ + \gamma \to \pi^+) = 2e\sqrt{\frac{1}{2\omega_\pi}}\sqrt{\frac{1}{2\omega_\pi'}}\sqrt{\frac{2\pi}{\omega_\gamma}}\,\hat{\boldsymbol{\epsilon}}_\gamma\cdot\mathbf{k}_\pi'.$$

where $\mathbf{k}_\pi'$ is the momentum of the emitted pion.

Since the normalization factors are written next to the lines entering the diagram, the vertex factor is simply

$$\text{(11)}\qquad 2e\hat{\boldsymbol{\epsilon}}_\gamma\cdot\mathbf{k}_\pi'.$$

Naturally, the sign would be inverted for a negative meson.

The matrix element for catastrophic π^+ photoproduction is obtained by integrating the interesting term of (8) over $\mathbf{r}$,

$$\text{(12)}\qquad \mathcal{H}(\gamma + \mathrm{p} \to \mathrm{n} + \pi^+) = ie\sqrt{4\pi}\,f\tau_-\int\rho(r)\phi_+\boldsymbol{\sigma}\cdot\mathbf{A}\,d^3\mathbf{r},$$

[1] It is assumed that absorption occurs from a state containing a single quantum and that no quantum is present before emission.

and replacing ϕ_+ by the coefficient of the π^+ production operator and $\mathbf{A}$ by the coefficient of the photon annihilation operator in the quantized expression of the fields. The result is

$$M(\gamma + \mathrm{p} \to \mathrm{n} + \pi^+) = -ie\sqrt{4\pi}\, f v(|\mathbf{k}_\pi - \mathbf{k}_\gamma|)\sqrt{\frac{1}{\omega}}\sqrt{\frac{2\pi}{\omega}}\, \boldsymbol{\sigma}\cdot\hat{\boldsymbol{\epsilon}}_\gamma \tau_-, \tag{13}$$

with $\omega = \omega_\gamma = \omega_\pi$. Near threshold, where the momentum transfer is small, the vertex factor for the catastrophic π^+ photoproduction is

$$-ie\sqrt{4\pi}\, f\boldsymbol{\sigma}\cdot\hat{\boldsymbol{\epsilon}}_\gamma\tau_-. \tag{14}$$

This factor transforms the proton into a neutron and contains both the coupling constants e and f.

d. Behavior of Pions under Charge Conjugation and Time Reversal. Before closing this section on the electromagnetic interaction of the π meson it is appropriate to introduce a brief comment on the behavior of the mesic field under charge conjugation.

The Klein-Gordon equation with electromagnetic coupling

$$(\partial_\mu + ieA_\mu)(\partial_\mu + ieA_\mu)\phi + m^2\phi = 0 \tag{15}$$

contains the electric charge multiplied by the imaginary unit. Thus the operator of charge conjugation C is identical with the operator of complex conjugation $\pm K$. This justifies our choice of complex conjugate states for π^+ and π^-.

The choice of sign must be made to account for the allowed decay of π^0 into two γ, under the assumption of invariance under charge conjugation. Thus we must write $C\phi = K\phi = \phi^*$.

The transformations of the mesons of the three signs under charge conjugation are immediately obtained:

$$\begin{aligned} C\,|\pi^+\rangle &= K\Big[-\frac{1}{\sqrt{2}}(\phi_1 + i\phi_2)\Big] = -\frac{1}{\sqrt{2}}(\phi_1 - i\phi_2) = -|\pi^-\rangle, \\ C\,|\pi^-\rangle &= K\Big[\frac{1}{\sqrt{2}}(\phi_1 - i\phi_2)\Big] = \frac{1}{\sqrt{2}}(\phi_1 + i\phi_2) = -|\pi^+\rangle, \\ C\,|\pi^0\rangle &= K\phi_3 = \phi_3 = |\pi^0\rangle. \end{aligned} \tag{16}$$

In the quantized form of the theory the meson field is expanded in creation and annihilation operators. The operation of complex (not hermitian) conjugation transforms the creation operator for π^+ into a creation operator for π^-, etc., as shown by 7.16(13).

Let us now study the behavior under charge conjugation of the coupling of the pions with the nucleons. The requirement of invariance under charge conjugation is satisfied if the transformation $\mathrm{a}_+ \to \mathrm{a}_-$, etc., is accompanied by $\tau_- \to -\tau_+$, etc., as can be seen from the interaction

Lagrangian 7.16(14). Thus the operator $\tau_- a_+^\dagger$ corresponding to the reaction $p \rightarrow n + \pi^+$ is transformed into $-\tau_+ a_-^\dagger$ which must be interpreted as describing the charge conjugate reaction[1] $\bar{p} \rightarrow \bar{n} + \pi^-$.

For internal consistentency we must assign isospin $-\frac{1}{2}$ to the antiproton and isospin $\frac{1}{2}$ to the antineutron. The nucleon's charge is $\frac{1}{2}(A + \tau_3)$, where $A = 1$ for a nucleon and $A = -1$ for an antinucleon.

Let us close with a brief comment about time reversal. We remarked in a footnote on p. 435 that the neutral pion field must invert its sign under time reversal, just like a magnetostatic potential. To study the behavior of the charged components under time reversal, let us go back to (15). In this equation time reversal inverts the sign of ∂_4 and A_i; thus it is effectively equivalent to complex conjugation. We conclude that the operator of time reversal applied to the pion field is the product of sign inversion and charge conjugation: $T\phi = -K\phi = -\phi^*$.

7.32 *Photoproduction Cross Sections*

a. Outline of the Calculation. The photoproduction cross section can be written

$$\sigma = \frac{1}{(2\pi)^2} k_\pi \omega \, d\Omega_\pi \, |M_1 + M_2 + M_3|^2, \tag{1}$$

where M_1, M_2, and M_3 are the matrix elements for the three processes described in the preceding section and $\omega = \omega_\pi = \omega_\gamma$.

Let us start computing the *catastrophic* process from the diagram in Figure 7.31-4. Since the Hamiltonian contains a factor e, it is small and perturbation theory can safely be used. From 7.31(14) we obtain

$$M_1 = -ie\sqrt{\frac{2\pi}{\omega}}\sqrt{\frac{1}{2\omega}}\sqrt{4\pi}f\boldsymbol{\sigma}\cdot\hat{\boldsymbol{\epsilon}}_\gamma\sqrt{2}. \tag{2}$$

Next we shall discuss the matrix element for the *photoeffect* diagram in Fig. 7.32-1. The use of perturbation theory in lowest order can also be justified here, and by using 7.31(11) and following the usual rules we can write

$$M_2 = \sqrt{\frac{2\pi}{\omega}}\sqrt{\frac{1}{2\omega}}(2e\hat{\boldsymbol{\epsilon}}_\gamma\cdot\mathbf{k}_\pi)\frac{1}{(\mathbf{k}_\pi - \mathbf{k}_\gamma)^2 - 1}[-i\sqrt{4\pi}f\boldsymbol{\sigma}\cdot(\mathbf{k}_\pi - \mathbf{k}_\gamma)\sqrt{2}]. \tag{3}$$

The process of *shake-off* photoproduction is more complicated, for the diagrams (Fig. 7.32-2*a*) are similar to those of pion-nucleon scattering (Fig. 7.35-2*b*), to which the lowest order perturbation treatment is not applicable. But, as in scattering, we could compute the γ–$\mathcal{N}$ interaction

[1] $\bar{p}$ and $\bar{n}$ stand for antiproton and antineutron.

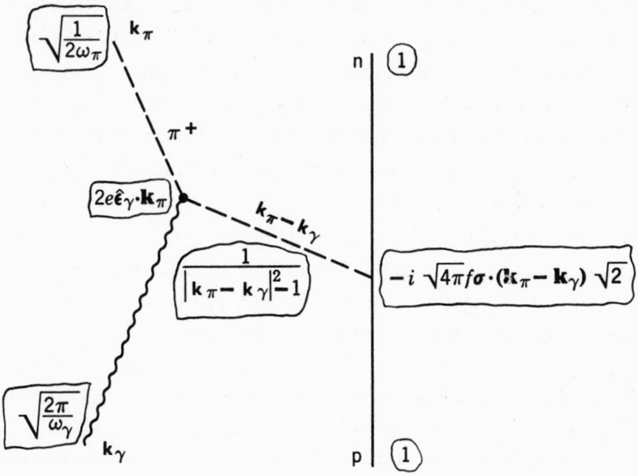

Fig. 7.32-1. Diagram of photo-effect photoproduction with the factors entering in the matrix element.

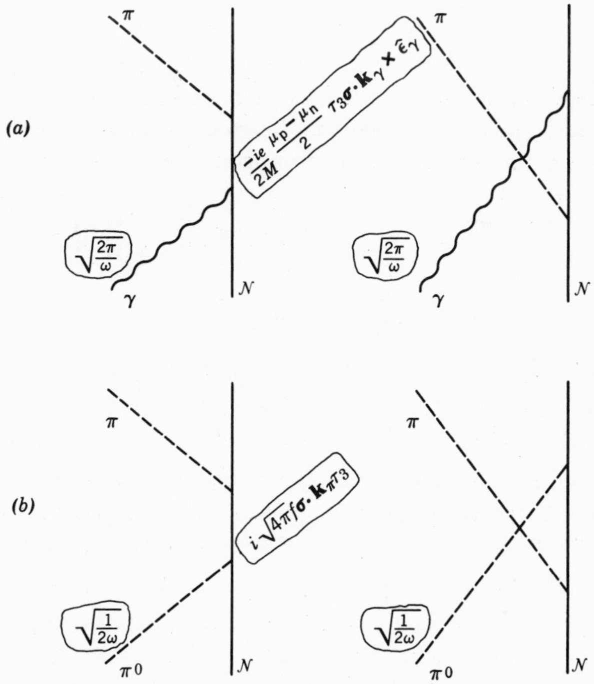

Fig. 7.32-2. Comparison of shake-off photoproduction (*a*) and π^0 scattering (*b*) diagrams showing the factors that are different in the two cases.

amplitude at $\omega \approx 0$ in lowest order and then pass to the physically interesting values of ω ($\omega > 1$), proceeding as in 7.25.

This method should be as successful as the treatment of scattering and should therefore properly describe shake-off photoproduction *near the* $J = T = \frac{3}{2}$ *resonance.*

If the diagrams in Fig. 7.32-2 cannot be used for computation, they can at least be used to compare scattering and photoproduction amplitudes. We shall therefore write, near resonance,

$$(4) \qquad M_3 = \frac{\sqrt{2\pi/\omega}\ (\gamma\text{-}\mathcal{N}\ \text{vertex factor})}{\sqrt{1/2\omega}\ (\pi^0\text{-}\mathcal{N}\ \text{vertex factor})} M(\pi^0 + \mathrm{p} \rightarrow \pi + \mathcal{N})$$

where $M(\pi^0 + \mathrm{p} \rightarrow \pi^0 + \mathrm{p})$ and $M(\pi^0 + \mathrm{p} \rightarrow \pi^+ + \mathrm{n})$ can be computed from the scattering phase shifts.

The γ-$\mathcal{N}$ vertex factor is obtained from 6.24c. However, only the part corresponding to the formation of the first excited state of the nucleon will give appreciable contribution in the region in which the present procedure is justified. The transition of the nucleon to the $T = J = \frac{3}{2}$ state is characterized by

$$\Delta J = 1, \qquad \Delta\pi = 0, \qquad \Delta T = 1,$$

and therefore only the part of the γ-$\mathcal{N}$ coupling contributing to a magnetic dipole transition with isospin change needs to be considered. Since the nonrelativistic magnetic coupling is $-(e/2M)\mu_{\mathcal{N}}\boldsymbol{\sigma} \cdot \mathbf{curl\,A}$, if we take only the isovector part of the nucleon's magnetic moment [from 1.32(8)], we can write

$$\gamma\text{-}\mathcal{N}\ \text{vertex factor} = -i\frac{e}{2M}\frac{\mu_{\mathrm{p}} - \mu_{\mathrm{n}}}{2}\tau_3\boldsymbol{\sigma} \cdot \mathbf{k}_\gamma \times \hat{\boldsymbol{\epsilon}}_\gamma,$$

as shown in Fig. 7.32-2. Thus (4) becomes

$$(5) \qquad |M_3| = \frac{e}{2Mf}\frac{\mu_{\mathrm{p}} - \mu_{\mathrm{n}}}{2}|M(\pi_0 + \mathrm{p} \rightarrow \pi + \mathcal{N})|.$$

b. Comparison with Experiment. Let us first discuss the photoproduction of neutral pions to which only the matrix element M_3 contributes. If the appropriate "external" factors are taken into account, (5) yields the following relation between the cross sections of π^0 photoproduction and π^0 scattering:

$$(6) \quad \sigma(\gamma + \mathrm{p} \rightarrow \mathrm{p} + \pi^0) = \frac{k}{\omega}\left(\frac{e}{2Mf}\right)^2\left(\frac{\mu_{\mathrm{p}} - \mu_{\mathrm{n}}}{2}\right)^2\sigma(\pi^0 + \mathrm{p} \rightarrow \pi^0 + \mathrm{p}),$$

where, as already mentioned, the π^0 scattering cross section can be computed from the phase shifts 7.23d. When this is done, we find that (6) accounts satisfactorily for the data on π^0 photoproduction (Fig. 7.32-3), for the value of f^2 obtained from the scattering.

Another aspect of photoproduction which allows a simple comparison between theory and experiment is the behavior of the charged π cross section for small k_π (near threshold). In this case it is expected that the catastrophic cross section will predominate and will result in the production of S-wave photomesons.

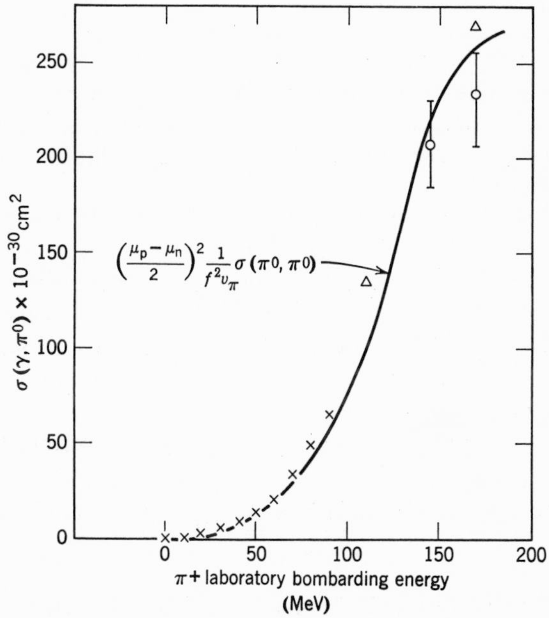

Fig. 7.32-3. Comparison between experiment and theory (formula (6)) of π^0 photoproduction [from L. J. Koester and F. E. Mills, *Phys. Rev.*, **105,** 1900 (1957)].

The theoretical cross section is easily obtained by substituting in (1) the expression of M_1 given by (2):

$$\sigma = 8\pi \frac{k_\pi}{\omega} e^2 f^2 \qquad \omega \approx 1. \tag{7}$$

Also this prediction is in satisfactory agreement with the experiment for $f^2 = 0.08$. Thus an independent confirmation of the value of f^2 is obtained from an experiment that can be analyzed in first-order perturbation.

7.33 *Capture of Pions by Nucleons*

a. Capture of π^- at Rest in Hydrogen and Deuterium. As we have seen in 7.13d and e, the capture of negative pions from an atomic K shell in hydrogen and deuterium occurs with comparable rates, with and without the emission of radiation. At first sight this observation may appear to be surprising because the electromagnetic interaction does not usually compete in reactions induced by strong forces. This state of affairs finds a simple explanation if we consider that the π^- is captured from an atomic S state; in this state the nuclear interactions are weak because of the pseudovector nature of the coupling and may be of the same order as the catastrophic interaction responsible for radiative capture.

It should be possible to compute with good accuracy the radiative capture rates by using the catastrophic interaction matrix element 7.31(14); but the present theory, which is limited to mesons interacting with nucleons in the P state, does not enable us to calculate directly the S-state radiationless capture.

Because of this difficulty the results of the capture experiments are not compared with theory but with other experimental results, to which they are related by the generally accepted principles of detailed balance and charge independence. The logical scheme that connects the experimental results of low-energy pion physics is reported in Fig. 7.33-1 from a paper by Cassels (C-59b). In the figure the measured quantities are circled and the connecting theoretical links are indicated by arrows.

For the Panofsky ratio we have a fairly accurate experimental value (D-60a; R-62),

$$P = \frac{\pi^- + \mathrm{p} \to \pi^0 + \mathrm{n}}{\pi^- + \mathrm{p} \to \gamma + \mathrm{n}} = 1.51 \pm 0.04, \tag{1}$$

which can be compared with the S-wave part of the π-$\mathcal{N}$ exchange scattering cross section and with the S-wave photoproduction cross section.

The corresponding ratio in deuterium, S, is also known (R-62):

$$S = \frac{\pi^- + \mathrm{D} \to 2\mathrm{n}}{\pi^- + \mathrm{D} \to 2\mathrm{n} + \gamma} = 3.16 \pm 0.10. \tag{2}$$

In this ratio the numerator is related to the S-wave part of the cross section of the reaction $\mathrm{p} + \mathrm{p} \to \pi^+ + \mathrm{D}$, and the denominator can be connected to the photoproduction cross section.

One of the connecting links is the value of the deuterium/hydrogen radiative capture ratio, T, which can be computed from the formula

$$T = \frac{\pi^- + \mathrm{D} \to 2\mathrm{n} + \gamma}{\pi^- + \mathrm{p} \to \mathrm{n} + \gamma} = \frac{|\langle 2\mathrm{n}| \sum_{N=1,2} \boldsymbol{\sigma}^{(N)} \cdot \hat{\boldsymbol{\epsilon}}_\gamma^* (\tau_-^{(N)}/\sqrt{2})\, |\mathrm{D}, \pi^-\rangle|^2}{|\langle \mathrm{n}|\, \boldsymbol{\sigma} \cdot \hat{\boldsymbol{\epsilon}}_\gamma^* (\tau_-/\sqrt{2})\, |\mathrm{p}, \pi^-\rangle|^2}, \tag{3}$$

where the density of final states has been assumed to be the same in numerator and denominator, for the nucleons are much heavier than the photon. The ratio of the squares of the π^- wave functions, which must be

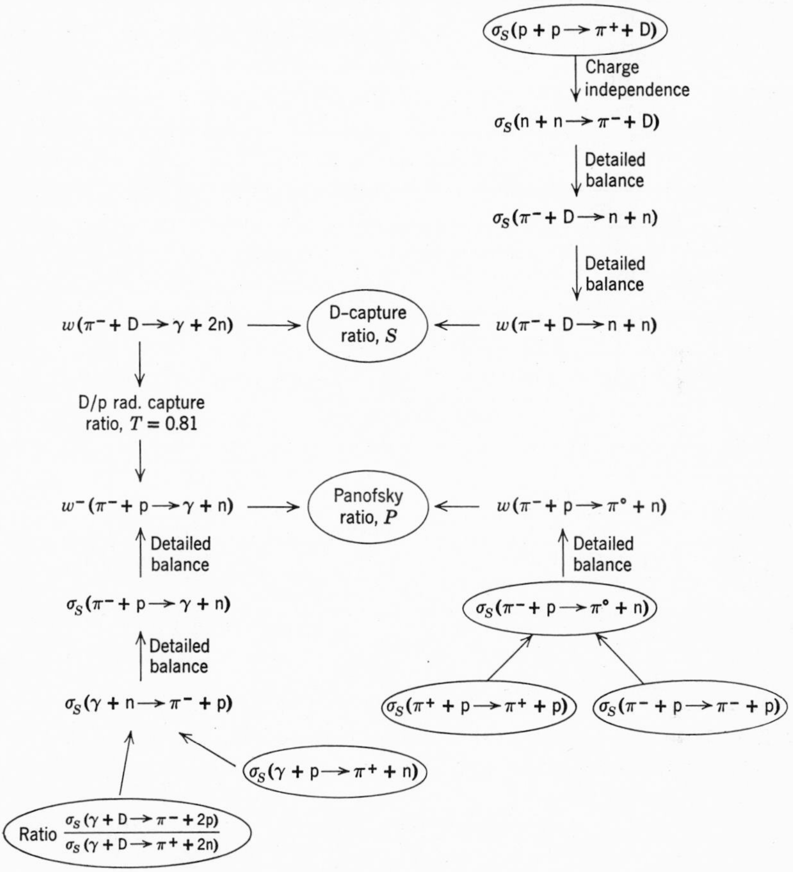

Fig. 7.33-1. Connecting links between low-energy pion experiments. Index S means S-wave process. Encircled quantities are experimentally measured.

computed at the nucleus of the mesic atom, contributes a factor $(r_0^{\rm H}/r_0^{\rm D})^3$, where $r_0^{\rm H}$ and $r_0^{\rm D}$ are the Bohr radii for mesic hydrogen and deuterium. If we now take the γ polarization along the z axis, we find, as in 4.22d, that the deuteron disintegrates only if it is in the $M_J = 0$ state, transforming into ^1S neutrons. Thus the average over the initial spins gives a factor $\frac{1}{3}$. Finally, the ratio of the matrix elements is $\sqrt{2}$ [1] and we can conclude that

$$(4) \qquad T = \frac{2}{3}\left(\frac{r_0^{\mathrm{H}}}{r_0^{\mathrm{D}}}\right)^3 = 0.81.$$

b. Comparison of Data of Low-Energy Pion Physics. It is obviously of great interest to verify that the theoretical relations indicated by the diagram in Fig. 7.33-1 are indeed satisfied. A disagreement could be due to a failure of charge independence or could indicate that some important fact, such as the existence of a $\pi_0{}^0$ with $T = 0$, has been neglected.

The detailed balance extrapolation of the cross sections in order to obtain the capture probabilities at low energy is not, however, so simple as we may imagine. The main difficulty is that only the *S*-wave part of the cross section is needed, whereas the experiment measures contributions from all angular momenta.

Particularly difficult is the separation of the "catastrophic" *S* part of the photoproduction cross section. Even very near threshold some contribution of "photoelectric" photoproduction may be expected and must be subtracted.

These subtractions and extrapolation procedures have been widely discussed (B-58; C-58b), and after a thorough analysis of the data the values reported in the last column of the following table have been obtained:

Ratio	From zero energy measurements of *P* and *S* (Cassels 1959)	(Ryan 1962)	From positive energy cross sections (Cassels)
$P = \dfrac{\pi^- + \mathrm{p} \to \pi^0 + \mathrm{n}}{\pi^- + \mathrm{p} \to \gamma + \mathrm{n}}$	1.74	1.51	1.53
$ST = \dfrac{\pi^- + \mathrm{D} \to 2\mathrm{n}}{\pi^- + \mathrm{p} \to \mathrm{n} + \gamma}$	1.88	2.56	1.63
$\dfrac{ST}{P} = \dfrac{\pi^- + \mathrm{D} \to 2\mathrm{n}}{\pi^- + \mathrm{p} \to \pi^0 + \mathrm{n}}$	1.08	1.7	1.06

[1] In the denominator $(\tau_-/\sqrt{2})\mathrm{p} = \mathrm{n}$. In the numerator we must compute, for $M_J = 0$,

$$\left(\sigma_z^{(1)}\frac{\tau_-^{(1)}}{\sqrt{2}} + \sigma_z^{(2)}\frac{\tau_-^{(2)}}{\sqrt{2}}\right)\frac{1}{\sqrt{2}}(\mathrm{p}^{(1)}\mathrm{n}^{(2)} - \mathrm{n}^{(1)}\mathrm{p}^{(2)})\frac{1}{\sqrt{2}}(\alpha^{(1)}\beta^{(2)} + \alpha^{(2)}\beta^{(1)})$$

$$= \sqrt{2}(\mathrm{n}^{(1)}\mathrm{n}^{(2)})\frac{1}{\sqrt{2}}(\alpha^{(1)}\beta^{(2)} - \alpha^{(2)}\beta^{(1)}) = \sqrt{2}\,|\text{two singlet neutrons}\rangle.$$

The comparison of the zero-energy measurements with the results of the extrapolation shows an excellent agreement for the Panofsky ratio, if we accept the last experimental results corroborated by independent measurements of two groups; but the new experimental data lead to considerable disagreement for the other two ratios. Clearly more experimental and theoretical work is needed; for the time being, considering the good agreement for the Panofsky ratio and the many difficulties in the experiments and in the extrapolation procedures, we may be justified in saying that there is no definite evidence of contradiction between theory and experiment.

7.34 *Production of Pions in Nucleon-Nucleon Collisions*

a. Isospin and Angular Momentum Analysis at Low Energy. The production of pions in nucleon-nucleon collision is, from the theoretical point of view, a more complex problem than photoproduction

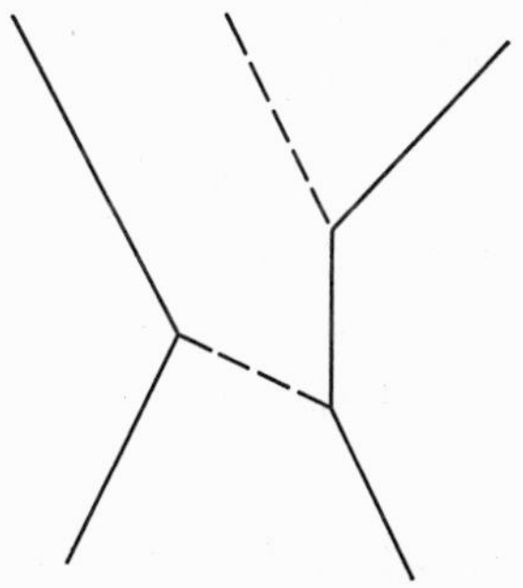

Fig. 7.34-1. One of the simplest diagrams describing the production of pions by nucleons in the lowest order.

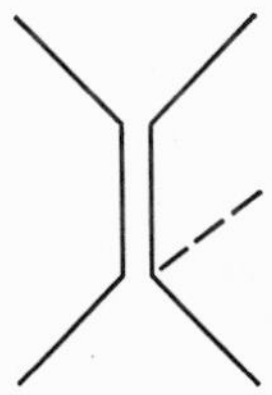

Fig. 7.34-2. Pion production in nucleon-nucleon collision with final state interaction between the nucleons.

because of the many strong-coupled vertices that appear even in the simplest diagram (Fig. 7.34-1). The presence of three particles in the final state also creates some experimental and theoretical difficulties.

We therefore start the discussion by considering the consequences of the conservation principles and particularly of charge independence. The initial states of the two nucleons can be divided into isosinglets and isotriplets. In the final state the total isospin is best discussed in terms of some simplifying coupling scheme.

The coupling scheme appropriate to the isospin analysis near threshold (293 MeV) corresponds to the diagram in Fig. 7.34-2, in which the effect of the strong S state nucleon-nucleon interaction in the final state is considered.

The importance of this interaction is corroborated by the fact that the two nucleons often emerge bound as a deuteron (Fig. 7.34-3).

The reaction cross sections can be expressed in terms of three amplitudes that correspond to the different initial isospins T and to final isospin of the two nucleons T':

$$\begin{aligned} A_{11} &= \langle T' = 1 |\, A \,| T = 1 \rangle \\ A_{01} &= \langle T' = 0 |\, A \,| T = 1 \rangle \\ A_{10} &= \langle T' = 1 |\, A \,| T = 0 \rangle. \end{aligned} \tag{1}$$

The $(T = 0) \to (T' = 0)$ amplitude is zero because the process is not compatible with the production of a meson of isospin 1.

When the rules of vector addition are taken into account, it is found that the total cross sections of the possible reactions are related as follows to the amplitudes:

$$\begin{aligned} \mathrm{p} + \mathrm{p} &\to \mathrm{p} + \mathrm{p} + \pi^0 & \sigma &= \sigma_{11} \\ &\to \mathrm{p} + \mathrm{n} + \pi^+ & \sigma &= \sigma_{01} + \sigma_{11} \\ &\to \mathrm{D} + \pi^+ & \sigma &= x\sigma_{01} \\ \mathrm{n} + \mathrm{p} &\to \mathrm{p} + \mathrm{p} + \pi^- & \sigma &= \tfrac{1}{2}(\sigma_{10} + \sigma_{11}) \\ &\to \mathrm{n} + \mathrm{n} + \pi^+ & \sigma &= \tfrac{1}{2}(\sigma_{10} + \sigma_{11}) \\ &\to \mathrm{p} + \mathrm{n} + \pi^0 & \sigma &= \tfrac{1}{2}(\sigma_{10} + \sigma_{01}) \\ &\to \mathrm{D} + \pi^0 & \sigma &= \tfrac{1}{2}x\sigma_{01} \end{aligned} \tag{2}$$

with[1]

$$\sigma_{11} = \tfrac{1}{2}\int |A_{11}|^2, \qquad \sigma_{01} = \int |A_{01}|^2,$$

$$\sigma_{10} = \tfrac{1}{3}\int |A_{10}|^2,$$

where the integration extends over angles, energy, etc.

The foregoing expressions imply relations between the cross sections which are verified by the experiment, and the factor x may be determined from the frequency of observed deuterons which is $\approx 50\%$. The experimental total cross sections for π production in p-p collisions near threshold (under 340 MeV) can be expressed as follows (R-54) as a function of the momentum of the produced pion:

$$\begin{aligned} \sigma_{11} &= \sigma(\mathrm{p} + \mathrm{p} \to \pi^0) && \approx 0.2k^8 \\ \sigma_{01} &= \sigma(\mathrm{p} + \mathrm{p} \to \pi^+) - \sigma_{11} && \approx 1.5k^4 \\ \sigma_{10} &= 2\sigma(\mathrm{n} + \mathrm{p} \to \pi^\pm) - \sigma_{11} && \lesssim 0.3k^4 \\ \sigma_{\mathrm{D}} &= \sigma(\mathrm{p} + \mathrm{p} \to \pi^+ + \mathrm{D}) && \approx 0.14k + 1.0k^3. \end{aligned} \tag{3}$$

[1] For the details of the derivation see F-55.

The energy dependence of these cross sections can be explained with statistical considerations. The speed of the incoming beam is constant near threshold, the density of final states for n final nonrelativistic particles goes as $k^{3(n-1)-2}$, and the matrix element varies as k^g if g is the number of outgoing particles in the P state. Thus for σ_D ($n = 2, g = 0$, or 1) the

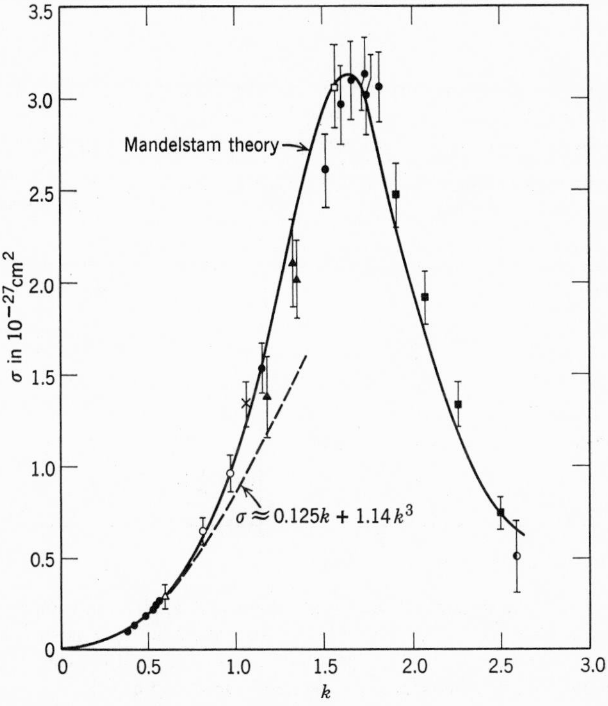

Fig. 7.34-3. Cross section of the reaction $p + p \rightarrow D + \pi^+$ (from Naganov and Parfenov, *Proc. Int. Conf. High En. Phys.*, Rochester, 1958).

energy dependence is k or k^3; for the three body reactions ($n = 3, g = 0$, 1, or 2) the expected dependence is k^4, k^6, or k^8.

From this analysis it appears that emission in P state occurs in many cases.

At higher energies the nucleon-nucleon final state interaction becomes less important, as is dramatically indicated by the decrease of the cross section for deuteron production (Fig. 7.34-3), and an entirely different method of analysis is required.

b. Kinematical and Isospin Analysis at Intermediate Energy. We shall consider a range of energy that is too high for final state nucleon-nucleon interaction but not high enough for frequent multiple pion or strange-particle emission. This energy range extends from $\approx$ 500 MeV to 1 or 2 beV.

In this range the nucleon-pion interaction plays a dominant role and results in the formation of the excited states of the nucleons as intermediate states.[1] Thus the reaction can be described as a two-step process:

$$\mathcal{N} + \mathcal{N} \longrightarrow \mathcal{N}_r + \mathcal{N}^* \quad \text{(4)}$$
$$\mathcal{N}^* \longrightarrow \mathcal{N}_d + \pi.$$

In writing (4) we have made a distinction between the "recoil" nucleon $\mathcal{N}_r$ and the "decay" nucleon $\mathcal{N}_d$ (Fig. 7.32-5), which have recognizable spectra.

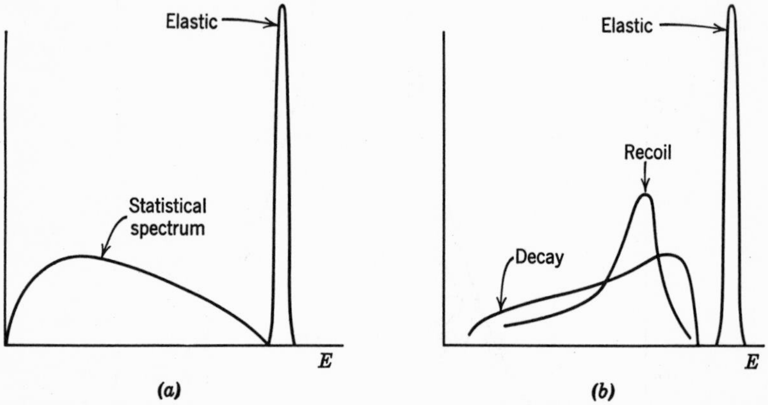

Fig. 7.34-4. Qualitative spectra of scattered protons at a given lab angle. (*a*) The inelastically scattered protons are statistically distributed if there is no interaction between the final particles. (*b*) The inelastically scattered protons can be resolved into a decay and a recoil spectrum if the reaction is described by (4).

In the absence of interaction between the three particles in the final state, their energy spectrum should be described by the statistical factors. But, if the reaction occurs in two steps, as indicated in (4) the energy of the recoil nucleon is determined by two-body kinematics: the recoil nucleon has a definite energy in the center-of-mass system (and at each angle in the lab system), apart from the intrinsic width of $\mathcal{N}^*$.

Thus the validity of (4) can be tested by the study of the kinematics of the nucleon-nucleon inelastic scattering which accompanies the production of pions. The spectrum of the nucleons scattered at a given angle can be resolved in components, as indicated in Fig. 7.34-4.

The peaks corresponding to the formation of nucleon excited states have been observed in a counter experiment (C-62c) on inelastic p-p scattering

[1] "Isobaric model" (L-57; S-58c).

($p + p \rightarrow p + p + \pi^0$) and in diffusion and bubble chamber work for $p + p \rightarrow p + n + \pi^+$ (B-59a). Thus the mechanism of (4) is confirmed.

The relative probabilities of the different meson production reactions through the intermediate of $\mathcal{N}_{33}{}^*$ can be computed by isospin analysis:

$p + p \rightarrow$	$n + \mathcal{N}_{33}^{*(++)} \rightarrow$	$p + \pi^+$	3/4
	$p + \mathcal{N}_{33}^{*(+)} \rightarrow$	$p + \pi^0$	1/6
		$n + \pi^+$	1/12
$p + n \rightarrow$	$n + \mathcal{N}_{33}^{*(+)} \rightarrow$	$n + \pi^+$	1/6
		$p + \pi^0$	1/3
	$p + \mathcal{N}_{33}^{*(0)} \rightarrow$	$n + \pi^0$	1/3
		$p + \pi^-$	1/6

A similar table could be made for the other excited states of the nucleon.

c. The Theory of Peripheral Collisions. The simple diagram of Fig. 7.34-1, with the addition of some expressions suggesting a possibility for the computation, is reproduced in Fig. 7.34-5.

In this lowest order diagram the nuclear forces are treated in the OPEP (one-pion-exchange-potential) approximation, which we know has a limited range of validity. However, if the momentum transfer k' is small, the single-pion exchange should give the main contribution to the matrix element. Since a low-momentum transfer corresponds to a large impact parameter, diagrams such as that in Fig. 7.34-5 are said to represent "peripheral collisions."

In the computation of the diagram in Fig. 7.34-5 the vertex on the left side can be treated according to the rules of nonrelativistic pseudoscalar coupling (7.16) with $f^2 = 0.08$. Then we can observe that the right-hand side of the diagram is an $\mathcal{N}$-π scattering diagram. Accordingly, we make use on the right-hand side of the matrix element of the scattering problem M_{sc}, either theoretically computed or obtained from the empirical scattering cross section.

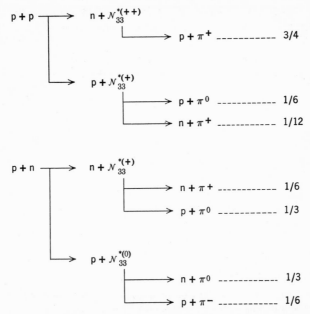

Thus we write tentatively

$$(5)\quad \sigma(\mathcal{N}+\mathcal{N}\to\mathcal{N}+\mathcal{N}+\pi) = 2\pi\frac{\omega_{\mathcal{N}}}{k_{\mathcal{N}}}\rho_{\mathrm{F}}\frac{4\pi\langle\tau_i\rangle^2 f^2 k'^2}{|\mathrm{k}'^2-1|^2}\frac{\sigma_{\mathrm{sc}}(\omega'')}{2\pi\rho_{\mathrm{F}}''}\frac{k'}{\omega'}.$$

In this expression $\omega_{\mathcal{N}}/k_{\mathcal{N}} \approx M/k_{\mathcal{N}}$ is the inverse incoming flux, ρ_{F}, the density of final states, $4\pi\langle\tau_i\rangle^2 f^2 k'^2$, the contribution of the vertex on the left side, and $(\mathrm{k}'^2 - 1)^{-1}$, the propagator of the exchanged pion; the other factors are the square of the scattering matrix elements obtained from the cross section after taking into account the appropriate kinematical factors.

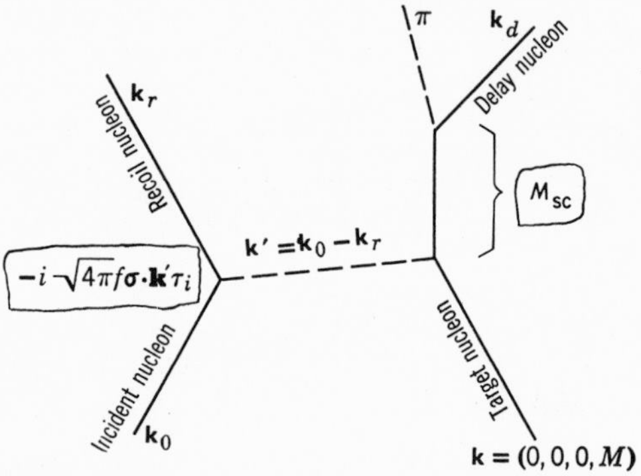

Fig. 7.34-5. The right side of the pion production diagram is similar to a scattering diagram. The scattering matrix element is used for its computation.

There are several comments and corrections that must be made in connection with this formula.

First of all, because of the indistinguishability of the protons we must consider another diagram in which the role of the two initial protons is inverted and construct an antisymmetrical combination. This is easily done, but it is not important for forward angles, since in this second diagram the momentum transfer is much larger and the propagator much smaller.

Second, and more important, we must recognize that so far we have been loose in introducing the scattering cross section and associated kinematical factors into (5) without specifying the energy at which they should be taken. It seems reasonable to use the scattering cross section at the energy ω'' of the final pion and decay nucleon in their own center-of-mass system: but we realize that this is not the same as the incident energy $\omega' = \omega_0 - \omega_r$ of our "scattering"; this is because the "incident" meson is virtual and its four-momentum does not satisfy the relation $\mathrm{k}^2 = m_\pi^2 = 1$ (it is not on the mass shell).

Are we justified in using for the "scattering" of a virtual particle the cross section measured with real particles?

The answer to this question is that this procedure, though not exact, may be justified in an approximate manner, chiefly if the virtual particle is not too far from the mass shell ($k'^2 \approx m^2$); and it is just such virtual particles that contribute most to the cross section (5) because of their large propagator factor.

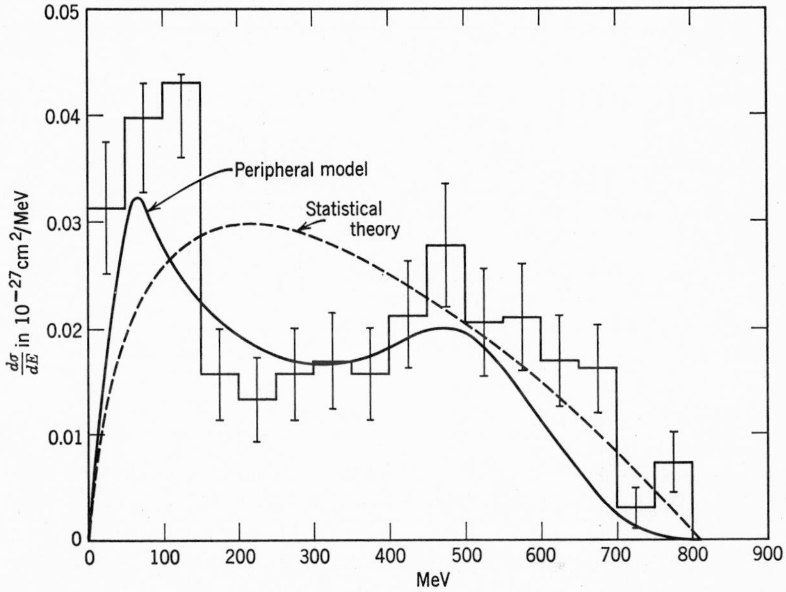

Fig. 7.34-6. The energy spectrum of the recoil neutrons from $p + p \to p + n + \pi^+$ (at 970 Mev), compared with statistical and peripheral theory [from F. Selleri, *Phys. Rev. Letters*, **6**, 65 (1961)].

Formulas similar to (5), including some analytical detail, have been used in the literature. For instance, Chew and Low (C-59c) write a formula[2] similar to (5) as a limit for $k'^2 \to m^2$:

$$\lim_{k'^2 \to m^2} \frac{\partial^2 \sigma}{\partial k'^2 \, d\omega^2} = \frac{f^2}{2\pi k_0^{\,2}} \frac{k'^2/m^2}{|k'^2 - m^2|} \, \omega \sqrt{\tfrac{1}{4}\omega^2 - m^2} \; \sigma_{sc} \tag{6}$$

Despite its approximate validity, this formalism has been applied to the problem of pion production with considerable success. Selleri[1] (Fig. 7.34-6) has compared the peripheral model to the data on π^+ production

[1] See this paper for the antisymmetrization required when the initial particles are equal fermions (S-61a).

[2] The kinematical factors in (6) are for pion production by pion (7.35). Consult the original paper for a precise definition of the notation.

by p + p and Chadwick et al. (C-62c) to the results on π production in p + p.

It is first of all remarkable that the cross section is given by the theory without any arbitrary factor and that the coupling constant $f^2 = 0.08$

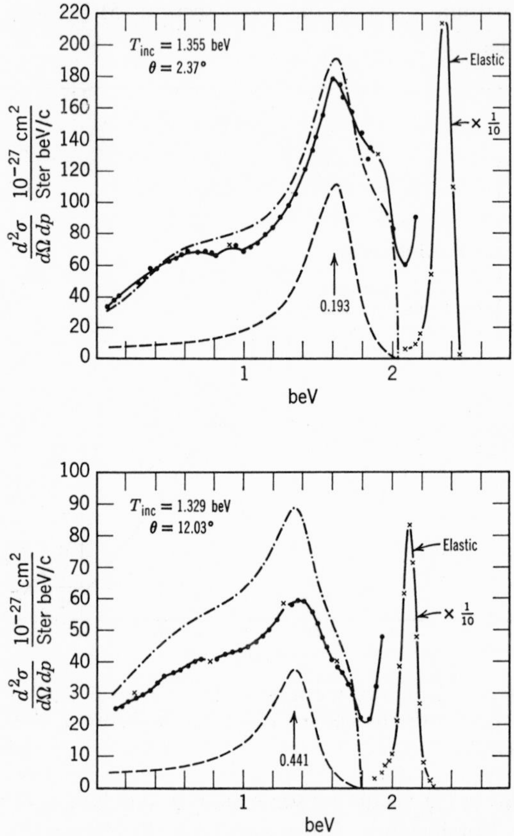

Fig. 7.34-7. Experimental spectrum of inelastic scattered protons near the forward direction (full line). Theoretical spectrum for recoil proton (dashed line) and theoretical spectrum of recoil + decay proton (dashed-dotted line) [from Chadwick, Collins, Duke, Fujii, Hien, Kemp, and Turkot, *Phys. Rev.*, **128**, 1828 (1962)].

gives the correct magnitude of the transition probability. It can also be seen that the differential cross section is in fairly good agreement with the measured inelastic scattering spectra. In the counter experiment on p + p → π^0, in which the statistical accuracy is good, it is seen that the agreement is better at small proton scattering angles where the momentum transfer is smaller (Fig. 7.34-7).

7.35 Pion Production by Pions and the ρ particle

a. Kinematical Analysis of Pion Production by Pions. The energy spectrum of the particles emitted in the reaction

(1) $$\pi + N \rightarrow \pi + \pi + N$$

can be studied from bubble-chamber pictures in magnetic field. Monoenergetic mesons of around 1 beV enter the chamber and are observed to interact with the protons of the liquid hydrogen.

In the analysis a search is made for evidence of intermediate formation of resonant states. If two of the final particles form such a state, the third, or recoil particle, has a definite energy in the center-of-mass system, as we have seen for pion production by nucleons.

Evidence of two possibilities has been sought,

(2) $$\pi + N \longrightarrow \pi + \underbrace{(\pi + N)}_{\to\ \pi + N}$$

(3) $$\pi + N \longrightarrow \underbrace{(\pi + \pi)}_{\to\ \pi + \pi} + N$$

and *both have been found.* The existence of N-π excited states has already been discussed, but the discovery of a π-π resonance is an important new fact, and we present some of the relevant experimental evidence.

Typical results for incident π^+ are reported in Fig. 7.35-1 and for incident π^- in Fig. 7.35-2; in these figures the number of observed events is plotted against the kinetic energy Q of the two pions in their mutual center-of-mass system. If the distribution is peaked at $Q = Q_{res}$, we can say that the two pions form an intermediate compound state whose mass is $2m_\pi + Q_{res}$ and whose mean life can be found from the width of the peak.

b. The ρ Particle. The 2π resonance described above has been named ρ particle. Its properties are

$$\text{mass} \approx 775 \pm 10 \text{ MeV}$$
$$T = 1$$
$$J = 1$$
parity: negative

decay is to $\pi + \pi$ with width $\approx$ 100 MeV.

[1] See P-61b for an extensive list of references.

The value of isospin follows from the fact that neutral and singly charged ρ are observed, but not the doubly charged (see Figs. 7.35-1 and 2). The determination $J = 1$ is made by analyzing the angular distribution of the decay products of ρ particles emitted parallel or antiparallel to the

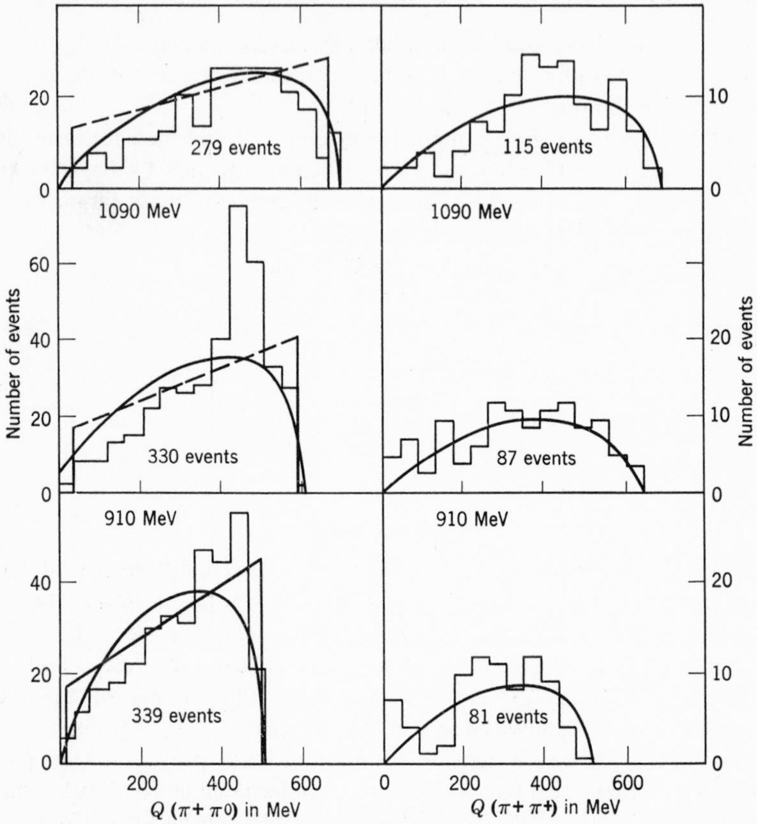

Fig. 7.35-1. Evidence for formation of ρ^+ (but no ρ^{++}) in the reaction $\pi^+ + p \rightarrow \mathcal{N} + \pi^+ + \pi$. Full line: statistical theory; dotted line computed for $\pi^+ + p \rightarrow \mathcal{N}_{33}{}^* + \pi$ [from Stonehill, Baltay, Courant, Fickinger, Fowler, Kraybill, Sandweiss, Sanford, and Taft, *Phys. Rev. Letters*, **6**, 625 (1961)].

direction of the incident pion (A-55). In these directions, where there is no orbital angular momentum, the decay should be spherically symmetrical for $J = 0$; instead, a distribution characteristic of $J = 1$ is observed. The negative parity follows from $J = 1$, considering that two decay pions have zero intrinsic spin and even intrinsic parity.

c. Pion-Pion Scattering Cross Section. The simplest diagrams for the computation of pion production by pions are shown in Fig. 7.35-3.

The first suggests a double shake off mechanism, and the second is similar to a meson-induced photoeffect or to the diagram for pion production by nucleon.

If there is a strong pion-pion interaction, the second diagram should predominate, particularly if the exchanged meson is almost real (four-

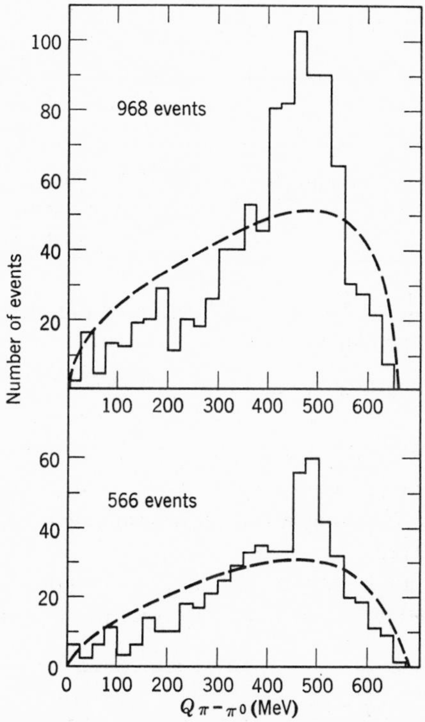

Fig. 7.35-2. Evidence for the formation of ρ^0 and ρ^- in the reaction $\pi^- + p \rightarrow \mathcal{N} + \pi^- + \pi$ [from Pickup, Robinson, and Salant, *Phys. Rev. Letters*, **7**, 193 (1961)].

momentum transfer close to 1, large propagator). However, unlike preceding cases, we do not know what interaction to write for the four-pion vertex.

From basic pseudoscalar theory a pion-pion interaction[1] is predicted through the intermediate of nucleon-antinucleon pairs (Fig. 7.35-4). But this idea cannot be carried out quantitatively because nucleon pair production occurs at energies far above the cutoff energy of the Chew and Low theory.

[1] Observe that there can be no interaction between three pion lines because $2\pi \rightarrow \pi$ is forbidden by conservation of angular momentum and parity.

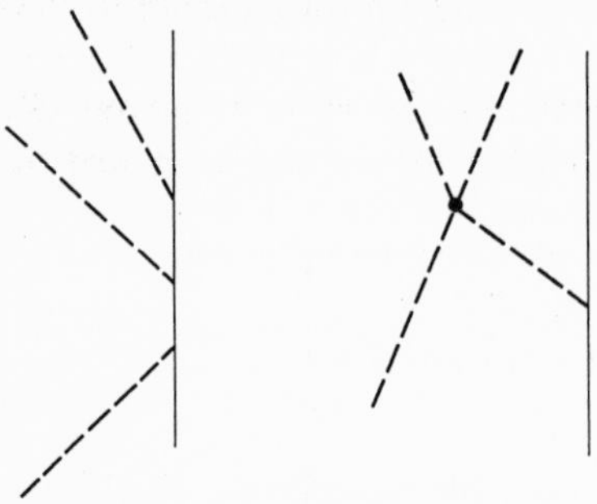

Fig. 7.35-3. Diagrams for the production of pions by pions.

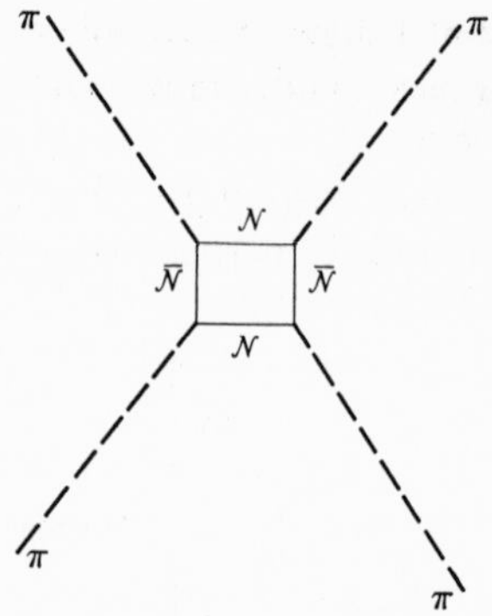

Fig. 7.35-4. Mechanism of pion-pion interaction through the creation of virtual nucleon pairs.

Therefore, we shall use the second diagram of Fig. 7.35-3 backward. By writing a formula similar to 7.34(5):

$$(4) \qquad \sigma(\pi + \mathcal{N} \to \pi + \pi + \mathcal{N}) = 2\pi \frac{\omega_0}{k_0} \rho_F \frac{4\pi N^2 f^2 k'^2}{|\mathrm{k}'^2 - 1|^2} \frac{\sigma_{\pi\pi}}{2\pi \rho_F''} \frac{k''}{\omega''},$$

we shall use the experimental pion production cross section to obtain the pion-pion scattering cross section (A-61; A-62a; C-62b). The results are shown in Fig. 7.35-5. Naturally a peak corresponding to the excitation of the ρ particle is observed.

The fact that (4) holds only at the limit $\mathrm{k}'^2 \to 1$ can be taken into account in the processing of the data. The experimental cross section is a

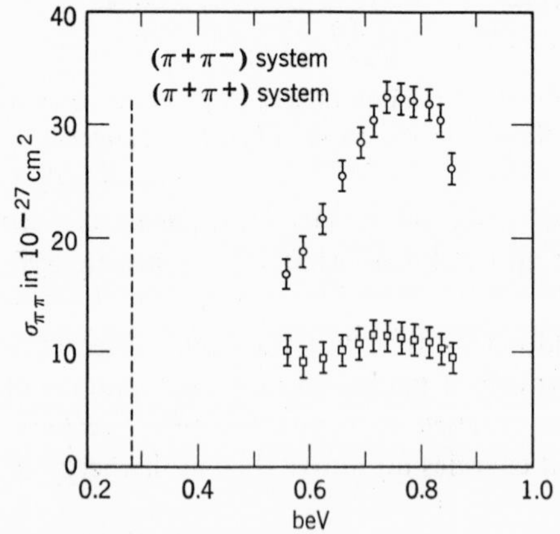

Fig. 7.35-5. Total cross section for scattering of pions by pions [from Auerbach, Eliott, Johnson, Lach, Wiegand, and Ypsilantis, *Phys. Rev. Letters*, **9**, 175 (1962)].

function of k'^2, which can be measured from the recoil nucleon, and of $\omega_{\pi\pi}^2$, the energy of the final pions in their center-of-mass system. For each value of $\omega_{\pi\pi}^2$ we can plot the data as a function of k'^2: then we extrapolate (either by eye or by using theoretical recipes) to $k'^2 \to 1$ to obtain the scattering cross section of real pions. However, though several authors have attempted to apply the extrapolation procedure to the experimental data, no clean-cut result has yet been obtained with this method.

7.36 Pion Production in Antinucleon Annihilation and the ω particle

a. Some Features of Nucleon Annihilation. Nucleon-antinucleon pairs annihilate with the emission of π (and possibly K) mesons (S-58a). Although in electron-positron annihilation the minimum number of quanta compatible with the conservation principles is emitted, the annihilation of antinucleons occurs with the emission of many particles (Fig. 7.36-1). This is evidence of the strength of the nucleon-meson coupling, as distinct from their peripheral interaction.

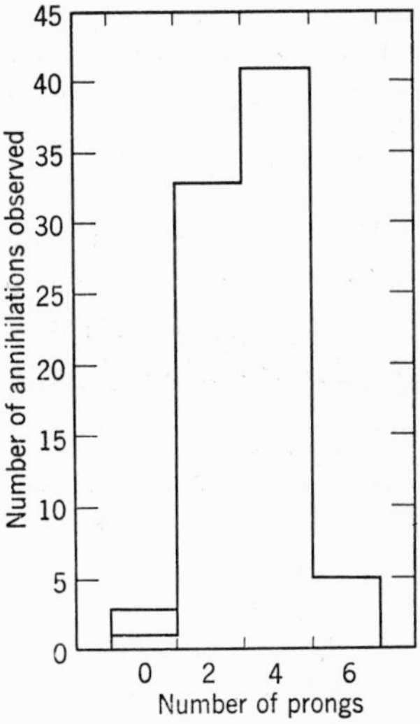

Fig. 7.36-1. Charged pion multiplicity distribution for antiproton annihilation in hydrogen [from Horwitz, Miller, Murray, and Tripp, *Phys. Rev.*, **115,** 474 (1959)].

Owing to the great strength of the π nucleon coupling, the annihilation is not necessarily limited to initial S states. We have already seen that the π^- mesons of mesic atoms may be captured from states with $l = 1, 2, \cdots$, etc., despite the small overlapping of the meson wave function with the nucleus. Similarly, we expect that the atom of free protonium may annihilate from P states with a nonnegligible probability.

The annihilation of protonium into pions (K mesons must be emitted in pairs for conservation of strangeness and are infrequent[1]) is restricted by selection rules similar, but more complex, to those acting in the annihilation of positronium. The complexity arises from the necessity of considering various angular momentum states in the initial system and various charge states in the final system.

[1] An experiment on the annihilation of antiproton beams (in flight) in propane has shown that K-meson pairs are emitted in $\approx 4\%$ of the cases (G-61c).

In order to derive these selection rules (Ro-60), the parity and charge conjugation quantum numbers of the states of interest must be found. The quantum numbers of protonium are the same as those of positronium [see 6.27d]: the total parity is $(-1)^{L+1}$ and the charge conjugation eigenvalue is $(-1)^{L+S}$. A two-pion system is intrinsically even, and thus has parity $(-1)^{L_\pi}$; the charge conjugation quantum number for $\pi^0\pi^0$ is 1 and for $\pi^+\pi^-$ it is $(-1)^{L_\pi}$.

The situation is more involved for three final pions. In this case it is convenient to consider the relative orbital angular momentum L_π of two of the mesons and the orbital angular momentum l_π of the third in relation to the center of mass of the other two. The following table is obtained without difficulty.

	Protonium	$\pi^0\pi^0$	$\pi^+\pi^-$	$\pi^0\pi^0\pi^0$	$\pi^+\pi^-\pi^0$
Angular momentum	$\mathbf{J} = \mathbf{L} + \mathbf{S}$	$\mathbf{L}_\pi$ (even)	$\mathbf{L}_\pi$	$\mathbf{J} = \mathbf{L}_\pi \text{ (even)} + \mathbf{l}_\pi$	$\mathbf{J}_\pi = \mathbf{L}_\pi + \mathbf{l}_\pi$
Parity	$(-1)^{L+1}$	$+1$	$(-1)^{L_\pi}$	$(-1)^{1+l_\pi}$	$(-1)^{1+L_\pi+l_\pi}$
Charge conjugation	$(-1)^{L+S}$	$+1$	$(-1)^{L_\pi}$	$+1$	$(-1)^{L_\pi}$

The selection rules are obtained from conservation of angular momentum and parity and invariance under charge conjugation. The allowed decays are listed in tabular form: the L_π quantum numbers are indicated by S, P, and D, the l_π states, by s, p, and d.

Protonium	$\pi^0\pi^0$	$\pi^+\pi^-$	$\pi^0\pi^0\pi^0$	$\pi^+\pi^-\pi^0$
$^1S_0$	—	—	$Ss_0, Dd_0, \cdots$	$Ss_0, Dd_0, \cdots$
$^3S_1$	—	P_1	—	$Pp_1, Ff_1, \cdots$
$^1P_1$	—	—	—	$Ps_1, Pd_1, \cdots$
$^3P_0$	S_0	S_0	—	—
$^3P_1$	—	—	$Sp_1, Dp_1, \cdots$	$Sp_1, Dp_1, \cdots$
$^3P_2$	D_2	D_2	$Dp_2, Df_2, \cdots$	$Dp_2, Df_2, \cdots$

For decays into more than three pions the situation becomes quite complicated, and the selection rules are less strict because of the many possible quantum numbers in the final state.

The two-pion selection rules can be applied to the determination of the relative probability of protonium annihilation from the S and P states, since $2\pi^0$ annihilation may occur only from the P state of the atom. Unfortunately, neutral pions are difficult to observe in a hydrogen bubble chamber, and the experiment is not easy to perform. But the same selection rules hold for the annihilation into two $K_1{}^0$ mesons and these though rare are easier to observe because they may decay in two charged particles within the chamber. Failure to observe such decay (A-62b) can be interpreted as evidence that in most cases protonium is in an S state before annihilating. In liquid hydrogen the protonium atom probably annihilates from S states of large total quantum number due to Stark collision admixture (D-60d; see also the discussion of π^--D capture in 7.13e).

A detailed study of the different modes of protonium annihilation is presently being performed using bubble chamber pictures taken at CERN.

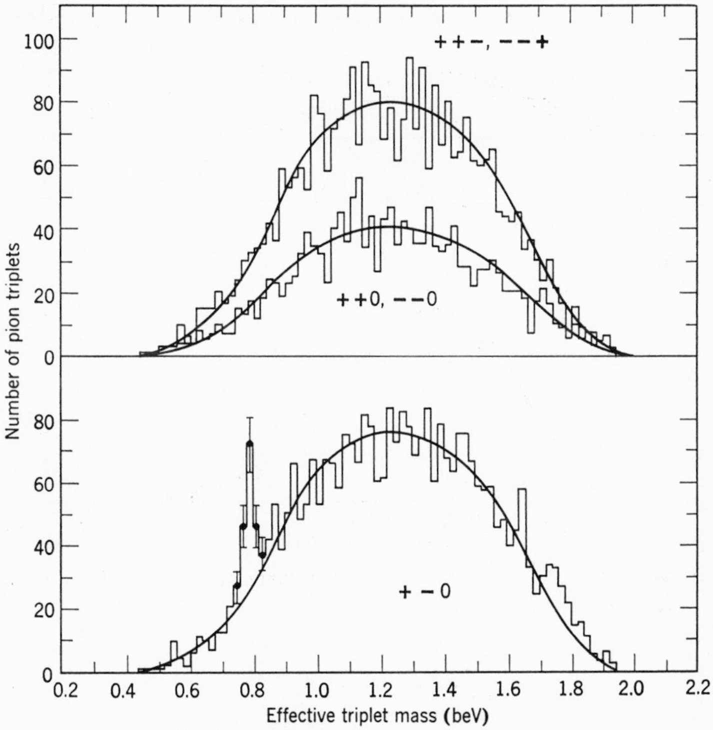

Fig. 7.36-2. Evidence for ω^0 formation (and no charged ω) from the analysis of triplets in 5-meson proton-antiproton annihilation [from Stevenson, Alvarez, Maglic, and Rosenfeld, *Phys. Rev.*, **125**, 687 (1962)].

b. Discovery of the ω particle. The presence of interactions between the pions produced in antiproton annihilation can be revealed in studies on the kinematics of their emission. It has been possible to determine in this manner that the ρ particle is formed in the annihilation process.

Since certain theories of the nuclear form factor (see 7.38) required the existence of a neutral meson with $T = 0$ and $J = 1^-$ (ω particle), a search has been made for such particles among the annihilation products of the antiproton.

A particle with the quantum numbers specified above cannot decay into 2π, since two pions in the $T = 0$ state must have even parity because of Bose statistics. Thus the search for the ω particle was undertaken under

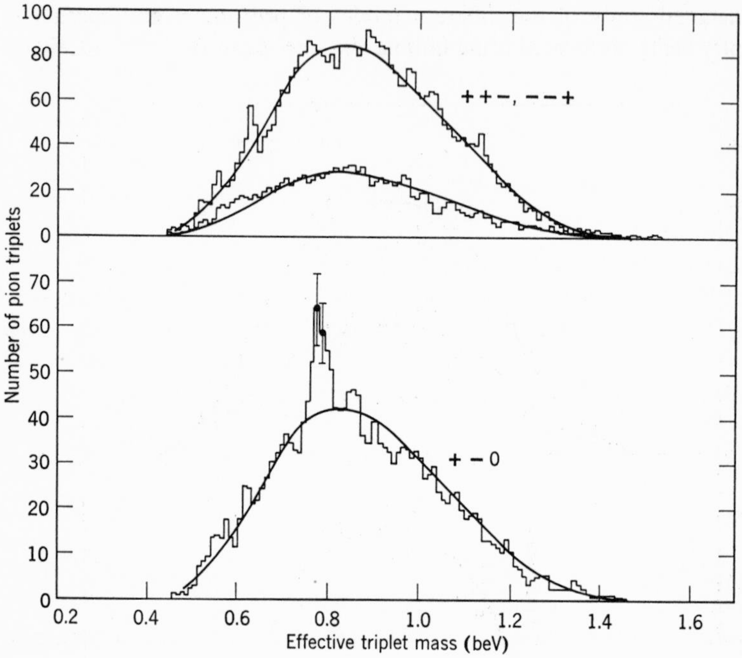

Fig. 7.36-3. Same as Fig. 7.36-2, but from 7-meson annihilation events [from Xuong and Lynch, *Phys. Rev. Letters*, **7**, 327 (1961)].

the assumption that it would decay into three pions:

$$\omega \rightarrow \pi^+ + \pi^- + \pi^0,$$

$$\omega \rightarrow \pi^0 + \pi^0 + \pi^0.$$

Annihilation events with four and six visible prongs were selected for this investigation. In many cases the balance of energy and momentum (protonium annihilates at rest) ensures that the visible prongs are accompanied by a single neutral pion according to the reactions

$$\bar{p} + p = 2\pi^+ + 2\pi^- + \pi^0 \qquad \text{(four visible prongs)}$$

$$\bar{p} + p = 3\pi^+ + 3\pi^- + \pi^0 \qquad \text{(six visible prongs).}$$

In these cases the kinematics of each pion is determined, and it is possible to obtain the effective mass of each pion triplet. The distribution of these masses (M-61a; S-62d; X-62) (Figs. 7.36-2 and 3) shows prominent peaks for neutral triplets but not for charged ones.

These experiments can be regarded as definite evidence for the existence of a 3π resonance, or ω particle, to which the following properties can be assigned:

mass[1] 784.0 $\pm$ 0.9 MeV
$T = 0$
$J = 1$
parity: negative
decay into 3π with width[1] 9.5 $\pm$ 2.1 MeV.

The assignment 1^- is confirmed by the angular distribution of the decay (Dalitz plot).

7.37 The η Particle

a. Discovery and Properties of the η Particles. Evidence of the existence of a neutral particle of mass $\approx$ 550 MeV disintegrating into 3π mesons was first reported by Pevsner and collaborators (P-61a). The particle was observed in a deuteron bubble chamber exposed to a 1.23 beV/c π^+ beam and was named η. The reaction used for its production and detection is

(1)
$$\pi^+ + D \longrightarrow p + p + \eta^0$$
$$\eta^0 \longrightarrow \pi^+ + \pi^- + \pi^0.$$

The effective mass of the 3π system shows two prominent peaks: one, at $\approx$ 770 MeV, attributed to ω^0, and the other to η^0.

No evidence of charged η's has been reported, and it can be assumed that the η particles have $T = 0$ [2].

The formation of η's has been confirmed at Berkeley (B-62a) where this particle has been observed in the bombardment of protons by K^- mesons:

(2)
$$K^- + p \longrightarrow \Lambda + \eta$$
$$\eta \longrightarrow \pi^+ + \pi^- + \pi^0.$$

The Berkeley group finds that the width of the η is very narrow, as narrow as the instrumental resolution, and gives an upper limit of 7 MeV.

The η particles often decay into neutral products, according to the branching ratio

(3)
$$\frac{\eta \to \pi^+ + \pi^- + \pi^0}{\eta \to \text{neutral}} = 0.31 \pm 0.11.$$

Recent observations in a methyl iodide bubble chamber (C-62d) have revealed that the η decays in two γ rays. For roughly half of the neutral

[1] See G-63; the width corresponds to a lifetime of $(0.69 \pm 0.15) \times 10^{-22}$ sec.
[2] For a discussion on this point see C-62a.

decays

$$\eta \rightarrow \gamma + \gamma; \qquad \frac{\eta \rightarrow \gamma + \gamma}{\eta \rightarrow \text{all modes}} \approx 40\%; \tag{4}$$

the other 60% of neutral decays presumably is $\eta \rightarrow 3\pi^0$ (events with six and five visible γ rays were observed).

Thus the η necessarily has spin 0, 2 or larger. Spin 2 or larger is excluded because it would result in marked anisotropies in the decay, which are not observed. Therefore we can safely assign $J = 0$ to the η particle.

Its parity can be determined from the absence of decay into two pions. As we have already remarked, the parity of two pions in a $T = 0$ state is necessarily even, and thus the η particle must have odd parity.

The properties of the η particle are

mass 550 MeV
width < 7 MeV
$T = 0$
$J = 0$
parity: negative
decay into $\pi^+ + \pi^- + \pi^0$, $\gamma + \gamma$ and possibly $\pi^0 + \pi^0 + \pi^0$.

According to 6.27(7), the density of final states for 2γ decay goes as m^2. Thus η should have a γ width about 20 times larger than that of π^0 [7.13(12)]. Considering that the γ decay mode contributes roughly one half of the width, the mean life of the η, obtained by comparison with that of π^0, should be $\approx 5 \times 10^{-18}$ sec[1]. This corresponds to a width of less than 1 keV.

b. *G* Selection Rule and the Decay of the η Particle. By using the conservation laws discussed so far we have assigned to the η particle quantum numbers that account for its decay modes. But we must still explain another important observation: why does the "electromagnetic" 2γ decay compete with the "strong" 3π decay"?

The answer to this question comes from the so-called G selection rule (P-52).

This selection rule does not imply any new conservation law. The G operator is defined as the product of charge symmetry (1.33a) and charge conjugation. It can be written formally as

$$G = CR_\eta(\pi), \tag{5}$$

where $R_\eta(\pi)$ is a rotation of 180° around the η isospin axis. All interactions that are invariant under charge conjugation and under rotation in isospace must necessarily be invariant under G.

[1] An estimate of $\approx 3 \times 10^{-18}$ sec is obtained by Brown and Singer (B-62b).

However, the operator G is convenient because pions of all signs are eigenstates of G, whereas they are not generally eigenstates of rotations in isospace and of charge conjugation taken separately.

The eigenvalues of G for pions are easily obtained (see 7.31d):

$$
\begin{aligned}
G\,|\pi^+\rangle &= KR_\eta(\pi)\left[-\frac{1}{\sqrt{2}}(\phi_\xi + i\phi_\eta)\right] = K\left[-\frac{1}{\sqrt{2}}(-\phi_\xi + i\phi_\eta)\right] \\
&= -\frac{1}{\sqrt{2}}(-\phi_\xi - i\phi_\eta) = -|\pi^+\rangle, \\
G\,|\pi^-\rangle &= KR_\eta(\pi)\left[\frac{1}{\sqrt{2}}(\phi_\xi - i\phi_\eta)\right] = K\left[\frac{1}{\sqrt{2}}(-\phi_\xi - i\phi_\eta)\right] \\
&= -\frac{1}{\sqrt{2}}(\phi_\xi - i\phi_\eta) = -|\pi^-\rangle. \\
G\,|\pi^0\rangle &= KR_\zeta(\pi)\phi_\zeta = K(-\phi_\zeta) = -\phi_\zeta = -|\pi^0\rangle.
\end{aligned} \tag{6}
$$

Thus the three pions are odd under G, or, as is sometimes said, they have odd G parity.

If we now assume that the η particle is even under G (or under C, since rotations in isospace do not affect a $T = 0$ particle),

$$G\,|\eta\rangle = |\eta\rangle, \tag{7}$$

we immediately obtain an approximate selection rule that accounts for the slow decay of η into 3π.

Thus we shall say that η is a 0^{-+} particle, where the quantum numbers refer, in the order written, to J, parity, and G (F-62a).

The decay of η into three pions occurs with violation of conservation of G. Since C must be strictly conserved, it is the conservation of T that is violated. This is not surprising, since we know that T selection rules are not strict because electromagnetic interactions violate charge independence.

The three-pion decay must then occur in a virtual electromagnetic transition.

Much theoretical speculation concerning the relative probability of the different decay modes of the η can be found in the present literature, but it may be better to postpone further discussions until more data have been collected.

c. Quantum Numbers of Mesons and of Nucleon Pairs. At the present writing we can consider as established the existence of four kinds of nonstrange mesons whose quantum numbers are reported in Table 7.37-1.

The G parities of ρ and ω are assigned by assuming allowed decay into 2π and 3π, respectively.

It is of interest to observe that the quantum numbers of the four mesons are the same as those of the nucleon-antinucleon system in an S state, as indicated in the more detailed Table 7.37-2.

The equivalence of the mesons with the corresponding $N\overline{N}$ systems is obviously clear for the electric charge and for the quantum numbers J

Table 7.37-1

Mesons	J	P_r	T	G
π	0	-1	$+1$	-1
η	0	-1	0	$+1$
ρ	$+1$	-1	$+1$	$+1$
ω	$+1$	-1	0	-1

and P_r. For the isospin the equivalence is easily verified if we recall (from 7.31d) that antinucleons have τ_ζ opposite to nucleons, so that $p\bar{n}$ and $n\bar{p}$ are pure $T = 1$, whereas $p\bar{p}$ and $n\bar{n}$ are in a mixed $T = 0$ and $T = 1$ state.

We now show that the charged nucleon-antinucleon states have the same G eigenvalues as the corresponding mesons. For this purpose we

Table 7.37-2

Meson	J	P_r	T	G	C	Equivalent $N\overline{N}$ System			
π^+	0	-1	$+1$	-1	—	$p\bar{n}$	in ^1S	$T = 1$	state
π^-					—	$n\bar{p}$	in ^1S	$T = 1$	state
π^0					$+1$	$p\bar{p}$ or $n\bar{n}$	in ^1S	$T = 1$	state
η^0	0	-1	0	$+1$	$+1$	$p\bar{p}$ or $n\bar{n}$	in ^1S	$T = 0$	state
ρ^+	$+1$	-1	$+1$	$+1$	—	$p\bar{n}$	in ^3S	$T = 1$	state
ρ^-					—	$n\bar{p}$	in ^3S	$T = 1$	state
ρ^0					-1	$p\bar{p}$ or $n\bar{n}$	in ^3S	$T = 1$	state
ω^0	$+1$	-1	0	-1	-1	$p\bar{p}$ or $n\bar{n}$	in ^3S	$T = 0$	state

start by studying the transformation properties of nucleons and antinucleons under charge symmetry. Keeping in mind the rotational properties of Pauli spinors, we have

$$(8a) \qquad \begin{aligned} R_\eta(\pi)\,|p\rangle &= |n\rangle \\ R_\eta(\pi)\,|n\rangle &= R_\eta(2\pi)\,|p\rangle = -|p\rangle, \end{aligned}$$

and, similarly (since C and $R_\eta(\pi)$ operate on different coordinates and commute),

$$(8b) \qquad \begin{aligned} R_\eta(\pi)\,|\bar{p}\rangle &= |\bar{n}\rangle \\ R_\eta(\pi)\,|\bar{n}\rangle &= -|\bar{p}\rangle. \end{aligned}$$

From (8) one immediately obtains

$$
\begin{aligned}
&G\,|\mathrm{p}\rangle = S_C R_\eta(\pi)\,|\mathrm{p}\rangle = S_C\,|\mathrm{n}\rangle = |\bar{\mathrm{n}}\rangle,\\
(9)\qquad &G\,|\mathrm{n}\rangle = S_C R_\eta(\pi)\,|\mathrm{n}\rangle = -S_C\,|\mathrm{p}\rangle = -|\bar{\mathrm{p}}\rangle,\\
&G\,|\bar{\mathrm{p}}\rangle = |\mathrm{n}\rangle, \qquad G\,|\bar{\mathrm{n}}\rangle = -|\mathrm{p}\rangle.
\end{aligned}
$$

Using this result, we can proceed as in 6.27(11) to find the G quantum numbers of the charged nucleon-antinucleon pairs. For instance,

$$
\begin{aligned}
G\,|\mathrm{p}\bar{\mathrm{n}}\rangle &= G[\psi_a(\mathbf{r}, \mathbf{s}, \mathrm{p})\,\psi_b(\mathbf{r}', \mathbf{s}', \bar{\mathrm{n}}) - \psi_b(\mathbf{r}, \mathbf{s}, \mathrm{p})\,\psi_a(\mathbf{r}', \mathbf{s}', \bar{\mathrm{n}})]\\
&= -\psi_a(\mathbf{r}, \mathbf{s}, \bar{\mathrm{n}})\,\psi_b(\mathbf{r}', \mathbf{s}', \mathrm{p}) + \psi_b(\mathbf{r}, \mathbf{s}, \bar{\mathrm{n}})\,\psi_a(\mathbf{r}', \mathbf{s}', \mathrm{p})\\
&= \mathcal{S}_r\mathcal{S}_\sigma\,|\mathrm{p}\bar{\mathrm{n}}\rangle = (-1)^L(-1)^{S+1}\,|\mathrm{p}\bar{\mathrm{n}}\rangle.
\end{aligned}
$$

In particular, for $L = 0$ the charged nucleon-antinucleon systems have $G = (-1)^{J+1}$. Thus the ^1S state of $\mathrm{p}\bar{\mathrm{n}}$ and $\mathrm{n}\bar{\mathrm{p}}$ have $G = -1$ like π^+ and π^-, and the ^3S states have $G = +1$ like ρ^+ and ρ^-.

Next, let us consider the neutral states. The neutral systems $\mathrm{p}\bar{\mathrm{p}}$ and $\mathrm{n}\bar{\mathrm{n}}$ are not in general eigenstates of G but of C, with eigenvalues $(-1)^{L+S}$ [6.27(11)]; for $L = 0$ the C eigenvalues are $(-1)^J$. But the $T = 0$ part of a neutral system is even under $R_\eta(\pi)$, and the $T = 1$ part is odd under the same operation. It follows that the G value of $\mathrm{p}\bar{\mathrm{p}}$ or $\mathrm{n}\bar{\mathrm{n}}$ in the S state is $(-1)^{J+T}$. This remark completes the proof of the correctness of Table 7.37-2.

The quantum numbers in Table 7.37-2, which can easily be extended to states with $L \neq 0$, result in selection rules for the annihilation of charged nucleon-antinucleon pairs with the emission of mesons (L-56) of different kind. More generally, they must be kept in mind in the prediction and in the interpretation of all reactions—real or virtual—involving production and absorption of mesons and of nucleon pairs.

7.38 *Electromagnetic Structure of the Nucleons*

a. Isoscalar and Isovector Form Factors. The experimental values of the form factors of the nucleons are obtained by comparing the high-energy nucleon-electron scattering cross sections (3.33) with the results of computations based on the Dirac equation with finite-size source terms. The definition of the form factors, 6.24(7), involves the four densities of charge and magnetic moment $\rho_{\mathrm{p},e}(r)$, $\rho_{\mathrm{n},e}(r)$, $\rho_{\mathrm{p},\mu}(r)$, $\rho_{\mathrm{n},\mu}(r)$, where r is measured in the center-of-mass system of the e-$\mathcal{N}$ scattering.

It will be recalled that the experiments indicate that the size of the nucleons corresponds to a radius smaller than the pion Compton wavelength. In order to explain this observation, we must resort to particles heavier than the pion. Following this idea, the existence of the ρ meson was predicted from a discussion of the anomalous magnetic moment form factor, which is essentially a pure isovector quantity.

From the point of view of meson theory, it is convenient to decompose the charge and magnetic moment densities into their isoscalar and isovector part $\rho_{S,c}(r)$, $\rho_{V,c}(r)$, $\rho_{S,\mu}(r)$, $\rho_{V,\mu}(r)$:

$$(1)\quad \begin{aligned} \rho_{N,c}(r) &= \tfrac{1}{2}[\rho_{S,c}(r) + (\tau_3)_N\, \rho_{V,c}(r)], \\ \rho_{N,\mu}(r) &= \tfrac{1}{2}[\rho_{S,\mu}(r) + (\tau_3)_N\, \rho_{V,\mu}(r)]. \end{aligned}$$

The form factors corresponding to these newly introduced densities are defined as usual:

$$(2a)\quad F_{S,c}(q) = \tfrac{1}{2}\int e^{-i\mathbf{q}\cdot\mathbf{r}}\, \rho_{S,c}(r)\, d^3\mathbf{r}, \quad \text{with} \quad F_{S,c}(0) = \frac{e}{2},$$

$$(2b)\quad F_{V,c}(q) = \tfrac{1}{2}\int e^{-i\mathbf{q}\cdot\mathbf{r}}\, \rho_{V,c}(r)\, d^3\mathbf{r}, \quad \text{with} \quad F_{V,c}(0) = \frac{e}{2},$$

$$(2c)\quad F_{S,\mu}(q) = \tfrac{1}{2}\int e^{-i\mathbf{q}\cdot\mathbf{r}}\, \rho_{S,\mu}(r)\, d^3\mathbf{r}, \quad \text{with} \quad F_{S,\mu}(0) = \frac{\mu_{a\text{p}} + \mu_{a\text{n}}}{2} = -0.06\,\frac{e}{2M},$$

$$(2d)\quad F_{V,\mu}(q) = \tfrac{1}{2}\int e^{-i\mathbf{q}\cdot\mathbf{r}}\, \rho_{V,\mu}(r)\, d^3\mathbf{r}, \quad \text{with} \quad F_{V,\mu}(0) = \frac{\mu_{a\text{p}} - \mu_{a\text{n}}}{2} = 1.83\,\frac{e}{2M}.$$

The relation between the new form factors and those of 6.24(7), (8) is simply

$$(3)\quad \begin{aligned} F_{N,c}(q) &= \frac{1}{e}\,[F_{S,c}(q) + (\tau_3)_N\, F_{V,c}(q)], \\ F_{N,\mu}(q) &= \frac{1}{\mu_{a,N}}\,[F_{S,\mu}(q) + (\tau_3)_N\, F_{V,\mu}(q)]. \end{aligned}$$

The isoscalar and isovector form factors are obtained from the data on electron nucleon scattering reported in 3.33. The result is semiquantitatively shown in Fig. 7.38-1.

From this figure it is immediately apparent that the anomalous magnetic moment and its distribution are almost entirely due to the isovector part of the form factor. The charge and its distribution correspond instead to isoscalar and isovector form factors of the same order of magnitude.

b. Isoscalar and Isovector Electromagnetic Interaction of the Nucleon. We have already seen in 4.37 that the electromagnetic field may be coupled to the isoscalar and to the isovector part of the nucleon's charge and magnetic moment; in order to make a theory of the isoscalar and the isovector part of the form factors, we consider separately the interaction of the electromagnetic field with isoscalar and isovector combinations of the virtual mesons surrounding the nucleon.

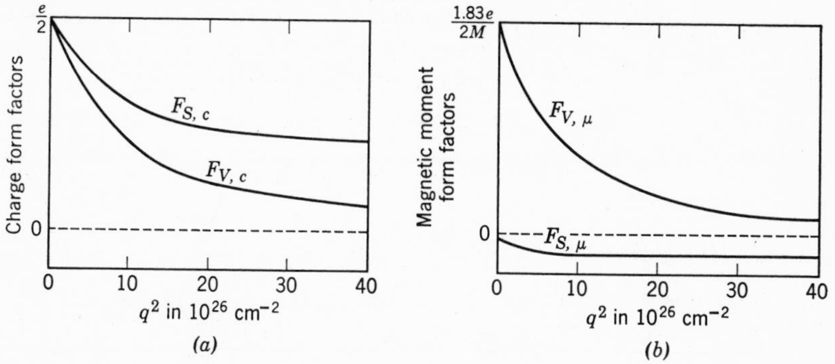

Fig. 7.38-1. Isoscalar and isovector form factors for charge (*a*) and anomalous moment (*b*) [Adapted from Littauer, Schopper, and Wilson, *Phys. Rev. Letters*, **7**, 145 (1961)].

To fix the ideas, let us consider the vector electromagnetic interaction corresponding to the diagrams of Fig. 7.38-2.

Diagram (*a*) represents a direct interaction with a point nucleon; diagram (*b*) does not contribute because it violates the law of invariance

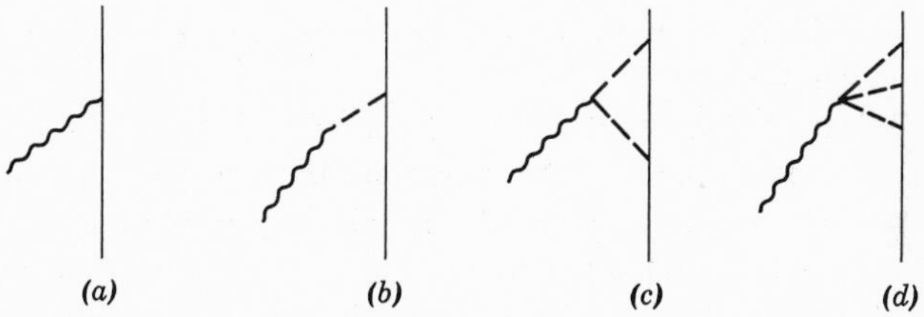

Fig. 7.38-2. Electromagnetic interaction of the nucleon. (*a*) Direct; (*b*) through one pion: forbidden; (*c*) through two pions: isovector; (*d*) through three pions; isoscalar, etc.

under charge conjugation (remember that π^0 is even and γ is odd under C); diagram (*c*) represents the coupling of the electromagnetic field to the meson current. This diagram corresponds to the quantized form of the Lagrangian 7.31(7) and accounts for the anomalous magnetic moment in the naïve approximation 7.26b. As seen from the form of 7.26(5), it results in isovector coupling. Diagram (*d*) indicates the possibility of a three-pion interaction, and conceivably other graphs can be drawn in which the electromagnetic coupling is transmitted by any number of intermediate pions.

We now prove quite in general that *all diagrams with an even number of pions contribute to isovector coupling, whereas all diagrams with an odd number of pions contribute to isoscalar coupling.*

For the proof we begin by observing that *the photon is odd under charge conjugation,* whereas a system of n pions has G parity $(-1)^n$. Because a neutral isovector state is odd under $R_\eta(\pi)$ and an isoscalar is even under the same isospace rotation, it follows that an *even number of pions with* $T = 1$ *and an odd number of pions with* $T = 0$ *are odd under charge*

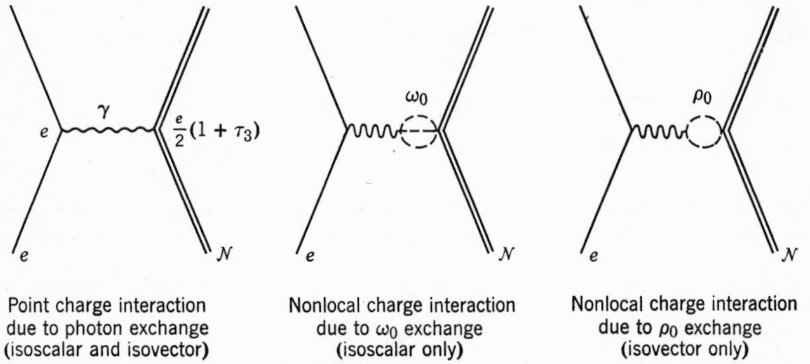

Fig. 7.38-3. Vector electromagnetic coupling between electron and nucleon due to the exchange of photons and of neutral vector mesons.

conjugation. The proof is then complete if we assume invariance under charge conjugation[1].

It is important to note that when the contributions of the diagrams of Fig. 7.38-2 are added together, the charge of the nucleon remains the same as that given by the first diagram alone. This is a consequence of charge conservation, which is respected by our gage invariant formalism. Thus diagrams (c) and (d) may spread out the charge but will not change its total value.

The situation is different for the magnetic moment in which we obtain not only a finite size distribution but also a contribution to the integrated value.

c. Effect of the New Mesons. In the diagrams in Fig. 7.38-2 we disregarded the possible existence of pion-pion forces; but we know that there are resonances in the two-pion and three-pion systems, and we can expect that such resonances may have some effect on the electromagnetic structure of the nucleons.

[1] We could also have assigned G values to the photon. It is easily seen that the isoscalar part of a photon is G-odd (like an odd number of pions), and the isovector part of a photon is G-even (like an even number of pions).

Figures 7.38-3 and 4 show in symbolic graphical form the main contributions to electron nucleon scattering, assuming that the corrections to point particle electrodynamics are dominated by the intermediate formation of neutral ω and ρ mesons.

These intermediate states contribute new propagators which can be identified as form factors. The propagators of the three diagrams in

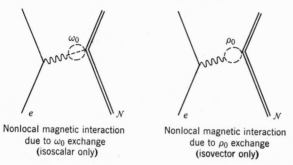

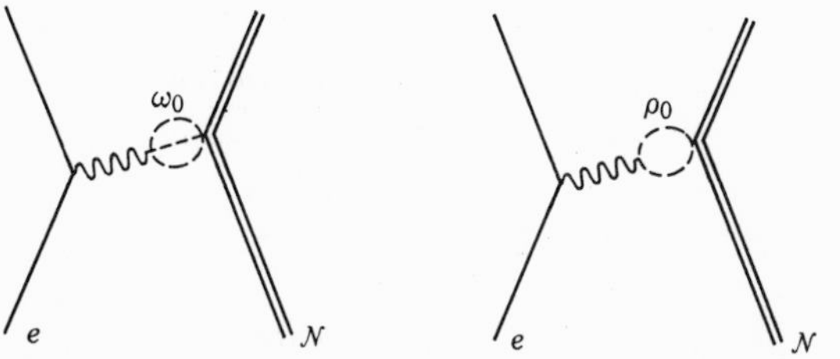

Fig. 7.38-4. "Anomalous" magnetic interaction between electron and nucleon, due to the exchange of neutral vector mesons.

Fig. 7.38-3 have poles at $m^2 = \infty$, m_ω^2 and m_ρ^2, respectively. The total charge form factors are obtained by adding together the contributions of the three diagrams, with weighting factors which must satisfy the restriction $F_{S,c}(0) = F_{V,c}(0) = e/2$, but remain otherwise to be determined from the experiment. Hence we can write[1]

$$(4a) \qquad F_{S,c}(q) = \frac{e}{2}\left[(1 + a_{S,c}) + \frac{m_\omega^2 a_{S,c}}{q^2 - m_\omega^2}\right] = \frac{e}{2} + f_{S,c}\frac{q^2}{q^2 - m_\omega^2}$$

$$(4b) \qquad F_{V,c}(q) = \frac{e}{2}\left[(1 + a_{V,c}) + \frac{m_\rho^2 a_{V,c}}{q^2 - m_\rho^2}\right] = \frac{e}{2} + f_{V,c}\frac{q^2}{q^2 - m_\rho^2},$$

where the a's and the f's are appropriate constants whose ratio is $e/2$.

Similarly, the form factors for the interaction with the anomalous magnetic moment may be written, from Fig. 7.38-4:

$$(4c) \qquad F_{S,\mu}(q) = f_{S,\mu}\frac{1}{q^2 - m_\omega^2},$$

$$(4d) \qquad F_{V,\mu}(q) = f_{V,\mu}\frac{1}{q^2 - m_\rho^2},$$

where $f_{S,\mu}/m_\omega^2 = -0.06e/2M$, and $f_{V,\mu}/m_\rho^2 = 1.83e/2M$.

[1] For comparison with the form factors (2) (which are defined in the center-of-mass system of scattering, where $q_4 = 0$) q^2 should be replaced with $-q^2$ in (4) and (5).

Formula (4) can be generalized to take into account the width of the ρ and ω resonances and to include other contributions possibly arising from the presence of other pion-pion interactions. Then the constants f become functions of the mass (*spectral functions*), and we must integrate over the mass with the result that

$$F_{S,c}(q) = \frac{e}{2} + q^2 \int_{3m_\pi}^{\infty} \frac{f_{S,c}(m^2)\, dm^2}{q^2 - m^2}, \tag{5a}$$

$$F_{V,c}(q) = \frac{e}{2} + q^2 \int_{2m_\pi}^{\infty} \frac{f_{V,c}(m^2)\, dm^2}{q^2 - m^2}, \tag{5b}$$

$$F_{S,\mu}(q) = \int_{3m_\pi}^{\infty} \frac{f_{S,\mu}(m^2)\, dm^2}{q^2 - m^2}, \tag{5c}$$

$$F_{V,\mu}(q) = \int_{2m_\pi}^{\infty} \frac{f_{V,\mu}(m^2)\, dm^2}{q^2 - m^2}. \tag{5d}$$

These equations were originally derived by Chew et al. (C-58a; G-58). In an analysis of the data on anomalous moment form factors by means of (5), Frazer and Fulco (F-59) found that $f_{V,\mu}$ needed to be peaked at $m^2 \approx 20m_\pi^2$, and suggested the existence of a pion-pion scattering resonance which was subsequently found (ρ meson).

However, if the spectral functions are peaked only at m_ω and m_ρ, the agreement with the experimental form factors at high momentum transfer is poor. Higher mass contributions—possibly new resonances—seem to be required.

d. Some Related Questions. The structure of elementary particles is a question of the most fundamental interest, whose experimental investigation is not limited to the study of electron-nucleon scattering.

Electron-nucleon scattering is dominated by a first-order electromagnetic interaction with the nucleon and yields the form factor of the nucleons, considered as having a rigid shape. On the other hand, the Compton effect on nucleons involves two nucleon-photon vertices in its lowest order description and is influenced by the intermediate formation of nucleon excited states. Measurements of Compton effect at and above ≈ 1 beV (S-63) give some information on the contribution of these states which, in classical terms, corresponds to the polarizability of the nucleons.

The nucleons are not the only particles whose structure is of interest. Pions should have form factors comparable to those of nucleons. Unfortunately, electron-pion scattering is not easy to study because of the unavailability of pion targets; the possibility of bombarding electrons with pions is being considered, but there are difficulties because the electron targets contain unwanted nucleons; furthermore the small electron rest mass reduces the center-of-mass energy. Structural effects which could also influence the 2γ decay of π^0, have been sought in the angular distribution of Dalitz pairs (see 7.13*e*), but they have not been detected because of their small size.

References

Books

Be-55 H. Bethe and F. deHoffman, *Mesons and Fields*, Vol. II, Row, Peterson, New York, 1955.

BW-52 J. M. Blatt and V. F. Weisskopf, *Theoretical Nuclear Physics*, Wiley, New York, 1952.

Ja-58 J. D. Jackson, *Elementary Particles*, Princeton University Press, 1958.

Ro-60 P. Roman, *Theory of Elementary Particles*, North Holland, Amsterdam, 1960.

SB-55 Schweber, Bethe, and deHoffmann, *Mesons and Fields*, Vol. I, p. 405, Row, Peterson, New York, 1955.

Th-52 A. M. Thorndike, *Mesons, A Summary of Experimental Facts*, McGraw-Hill, New York, 1952.

We-49 G. Wentzel, *Quantum Theory of Fields*, Interscience, New York, 1949. (Original edition, 1943.)

Articles

A-53 J. Ashkin and S. H. Vosko, *Phys. Rev.*, **91**, 1248 (1953).

A-55 R. K. Adair, *Phys. Rev.*, **100**, 1540 (1955).

A-59 J. Ashkin, *Nuovo Cimento Suppl.*, **14**, 221 (1959).

A-61 Anderson, Bang, Burke, Carmony, and Schmitz, *Phys. Rev. Letters*, **6**, 365 (1961).

A-62a Auerbach, Elioff, Johnson, Lach, Wiegand, and Ypsilantis, *Phys. Rev. Letters*, **9**, 173 (1962).

A-62b Armenteros, Montanet, Morrison, Nilsson, Shapira, Vandermeulen, d'Andlay, Astier, Ballam, Ghesquiere, Gregory, Rahm and Rivet, *Proc. Int. Conf. High En. Phys.* CERN, 1962, p. 351.

B-40 H. Bethe, *Phys. Rev.*, **57**, 260 (1940).

B-51 Brueckner, Serber, and Watson, *Phys. Rev.*, **81**, 575 (1951).

B-53 K. A. Brueckner and K. M. Watson, *Phys. Rev.*, **92**, 1023 (1953).

B-58 Beneventano, Bernardini, Stoppini, and Tau, *Nuovo Cimento*, **10**, 1109 (1958).

B-59a Batson, Culwick, Hill, and Reddiford, *Proc. Roy. Soc.* (*London*), **251**, 219 (1959).

B-59b Brisson, Detolf, Falk-Variant, van Rossum, Valladas, and Yuan (Saclay), *Phys. Rev. Letters*, **3**, 561 (1959).

B-59c Burrowes, Caldwell, Frisch, Hill, Ritson, Schluter, and Wahlig, *Phys. Rev. Letters*, **2**, 119 (1959).

B-60a W. H. Barkas and A. H. Rosenfeld, in 1960 Rochester Conference Report, p. 878, Interscience, New York, (1960).

B-60b A. J. Bearden, *Phys. Rev. Letters*, **4**, 240 (1960).

B-60c Blackie, Engler, and Mulvey, *Phys. Rev. Letters*, **5**, 384 (1960).

B-60d Barnes, Rose, Giacomelli, Ring, Miyake, and Kinsey, *Phys. Rev.*, **117**, 235 (1960).

B-62a Bastien, Berge, Dahl, Ferro-Luzzi, Miller, Murray, Rosenfeld, and Watson, *Phys. Rev. Letters*, **8**, 114 (1962).

B-62b Brown and Singer, *Phys. Rev. Letters*, **8**, 460 (1962).

C-51a Cartwright, Richman, Whitehead, and Wilcox, *Phys. Rev.*, **81**, 652 (1951).

C-51b Clark, Roberts, and Wilson, *Phys. Rev.*, **83**, 649 (1951).

C-51c Crawford, Crowe, and Stevenson, *Phys. Rev.*, **82**, 97 (1951).

C-54a G. F. Chew, *Phys. Rev.*, **94**, 1748, 1755 (1954).

C-54b G. F. Chew, *Phys. Rev.*, **95**, 1669 (1954).

C-54c W. C. Chinowsky and J. Steinberger, *Phys. Rev.*, **95**, 1561 (1954).

C-54d W. C. Chinowsky and J. Steinberger, *Phys. Rev.*, **93**, 586 (1954).

C-56a G. F. Chew and F. Low, *Phys. Rev.*, **101**, 1570 (1956).

C-56b Cool, Piccioni, and Clark, *Phys. Rev.*, **103**, 1082 (1956).

C-57 Cassels, Fidecaro, Wetherell, and Wormold, *Proc. Phys. Soc.* (*London*), **A70**, 405 (1957).

C-58a Chew, Karplus, Gasiorowicz, and Zachariasen, *Phys. Rev.*, **110**, 265 (1958).

C-58b Cini, Gatto, Goldwasser, and Ruderman, *Nuovo Cimento*, **10**, 243 (1958).

C-59a Cassels, Jones, Murphy, and O'Neill, *Proc. Phys. Soc.* (*London*), **74**, 92 (1959).

C-59b J. M. Cassels, *Nuovo Cimento Suppl.*, **14**, 259 (1959).

C-59c G. F. Chew and F. E. Low, *Phys. Rev.*, **113**, 1640 (1959).

C-62a Carmony, Rosenfeld, and Van de Walle, *Phys. Rev. Letters*, **8**, 73, 117 (1962).

C-62b Carmony and R. T. Van de Walle, *Phys. Rev. Letters*, **8**, 73 (1962).

C-62c Chadwick, Collins, Duke, Fujii, Hien, Kemp, and Turkot, *Phys. Rev.*, **128**, 1823, 1836 (1962).

C-62d Chretien, Bulos, Crouch, Lanou, Massimo, Shapiro, Averell, Bordner, Brenner, Firth, Law, Roust, Strauch, Street, Szymanski, Weinberg, Nelson, Pless, Rosenson, Salandin, Yamamoto, Guerriero, Waldner, *Phys. Rev. Letters*, **9**, 127 (1962).

D-48 F. J. Dyson, *Phys. Rev.*, **73**, (1948).

D-51 Durbin, Loar, and Steinberger, *Phys. Rev.*, **83**, 646 (1951).

D-54 Deser, Goldberger, Baumann, and Thirring, *Phys. Rev.*, **96**, 774 (1954).

D-56 S. DeBenedetti, *Nuovo Cimento Suppl.*, **4**, 1209 (1956).

D-59 Day, Snow, and Sucher, *Phys. Rev. Letters*, **3**, 61 (1959).

D-60a Derrick, Fetkovitch, Fields, and Deahl, *Phys. Rev.*, **120**, 1022 (1960).

D-60b Devons, Gidal, Lederman, and Shapiro, *Phys. Rev. Letters*, **5**, 330 (1960).

D-60c Devlin, Barish, Hess, Perez-Mendez, and Solomon, *Phys. Rev. Letters*, **4**, 242 (1960).

D-60d B. R. Desai, *Phys. Rev.*, **114**, 1385 (1960).

F-55 E. Fermi, *Nuovo Cimento Suppl.*, **2**, 17 (1955).

F-59 W. R. Frazer and J. R. Fulco, *Phys. Rev. Letters*, **2**, 365 (1959).

F-61a P. Falk-Variant and G. Valladas, *Rev. Mod. Phys.*, **33**, 362 (1961).

F-62a Foelsche, Fowler, Kraybill, Sanford, and Stonehill, *Phys. Rev. Letters*, **9**, 223 (1962).

G-55 S. Gartenhaus, *Phys. Rev.*, **100**, 900 (1955).

G-58 M. Gell-Mann, *Proc. Int. Conf. High En. Phys.*, CERN, 33 (1958).

G-60 Garwin, Hutchinson, Penman, and Shapiro, *Phys. Rev.*, **118**, 271 (1960).

G-61a V. Glasser and R. A. Ferrell, *Phys. Rev.*, **121**, 886 (1961).

G-61b Glaser, Seeman, and Stiller, *Phys. Rev.*, **123**, 1014 (1961).

G-61c Goldhaber, Goldhaber, Powell, and Silberberg, *Phys. Rev.*, **121**, 1525 (1961).

G-63 Gelfand, Miller, Nussbaum, Ratau, Schultz, Steinberger, Tan, Kirsch, and Plano, *Phys. Rev. Letters*, **11**, 436 (1963).

I-56 Iwadare, Otsuki, Tamagaki, and Watari, *Progr. Theor. Phys.*, **16**, 455 (1956).

K-38 N. Kemmer, *Proc. Cambridge Phil. Soc.*, **34**, 354 (1938).

K-55 N. Kroll and W. Wada, *Phys. Rev.*, **98**, 1355 (1955).

K-60 Kunze, Romanowski, Ashkin, and Burger, *Phys. Rev.*, **117**, 859 (1960).

L-51 Loar, Durbin, and Havens, *Bull. Am. Phys. Soc.*, **26**, 23 (1951).

L-52a M. M. Levy, *Phys. Rev.*, **86**, 806 (1952).

L-52b M. M. Levy, *Phys. Rev.*, **88**, 72, 725 (1952).

L-56 T. D. Lee and C. N. Yang, *Nuovo Cimento*, **3**, 749 (1956).

L-57 S. J. Lindenbaum and R. M. Sternheimer, *Phys. Rev.*, **105**, 1874 (1957).

M-55 H. Miyazawa, *Phys. Rev.*, **101**, 1564 (1955).

M-61a Maglic, Alvarez, Rosenfeld, and Stevenson, *Phys. Rev. Letters*, **7**, 178 (1961).

M-61b B. J. Moyer, *Rev. Mod. Phys.*, **33**, 367 (1961).

P-36 Proca, *J. Phys.*, **7**, 347 (1936).

P-51a Panofsky, Aamodt, and Hadley, *Phys. Rev.*, **81**, 565 (1951).

P-51b H. Primakoff, *Phys. Rev.*, **81**, 899 (1951).

P-52 A. Pais and R. Jost, *Phys. Rev.*, **87**, 871 (1952).

P-55 G. Puppi, *Proc. Conf. High En. Phys.*, Rochester, Interscience, New York, 1955, p. 9.

P-59 Plano, Prodell, Samios, Schwartz, and Steinberger, *Phys. Rev. Letters*, **3**, 525 (1959).

P-61a Pevsner, Krammer, Nussbaum, Richardson, Schlein, Strand, Toohig, Block, Engler, Gessoroli, and Meltzer, *Phys. Rev. Letters*, **7**, 421 (1961).

P-61b Pickup, Robinson, and Salant, *Phys. Rev. Letters*, **7**, 192 (1961).

R-54 A. H. Rosenfeld, *Phys. Rev.*, **96**, 139 (1954).

R-62 J. W. Ryan, *Bull. Am. Phys. Soc.*, **7**, 468 (1962).

S-58a E. Segre, *Ann. Rev. Nucl. Sci.*, **8**, 127 (1958).

S-58b M. B. Stearns, *Progr. Nucl. Phys.*, **6**, 108 (1958).

S-58c R. M. Sternheimer and S. J. Lindenbaum, *Phys. Rev.*, **109**, 1723 (1958).
S-60 W. Selove and M. Gettner, *Phys. Rev.*, **120**, 593 (1960).
S-61a F. Selleri, *Phys. Rev. Letters*, **6**, 64 (1961).
S-61b Stonehill, Baltay, Courant, Fickinger, Fowler, Kraybill, Sandweiss, Sanford, and Taft, *Phys. Rev. Letters*, **6**, 624 (1961).
S-62a Samios, Plano, Prodell, Schwartz, and Steinberger, *Phys. Rev.*, **126**, 1844 (1962).
S-62b Shwe, Smith, and Barkas, *Phys. Rev.*, **125**, 1024 (1962).
S-62c H. Shwe, *Bull. Am. Phys. Soc.*, **7**, 468 (1962).
S-62d Stevenson, Alvarez, Maglic, and Rosenfeld, *Phys. Rev.*, **125**, 687 (1962).
S-63 Steining, Loh, and Deutsch, *Phys. Rev. Letters*, **10**, 536 (1963).
T-60 Tollestrup, Berman, Gon ez, and Ruderman, *Proc. Int. Conf. High En. Phys.*, Rochester, Interscience, New York, 1960.
W-55 G. C. Wick, *Rev. Mod. Phys.*, **27**, 339 (1955).
W-59 V. F. Weisskopf, *Phys. Rev.*, **116**, 1615 (1959).
X-61 N. H. Xuong and G. R. Lynch, *Phys. Rev. Letters*, **7**, 327 (1961).
X-62 N. H. Xuong and G. R. Lynch, *Phys. Rev.*, **128**, 1948 (1962).
Y-50 C. N. Yang, *Phys. Rev.*, **77**, 242 (1950).

EIGHT

Weak Interactions

8.1 Nuclear β-Decay (Parity-Conserving Theories)

8.11 Introduction

a. General Description of Nuclear β Decay. It has been known since the early days of radioactivity that certain nuclei emit electrons, and the first artificial radioactive nuclei to be discovered were found to emit positrons: the process is traditionally called β decay.

The identity of the β^- particles with the atomic electrons is proved by the fact that the radioactive electrons satisfy the exclusion principle[1]; on the other hand, the radioactive positrons (β^+ particles) annihilate with the electrons of matter, and an alternate process to β^+ emission is the capture of one of the atomic electrons (K or L capture). Thus the β particles are identical with the other electrons of matter and with their antiparticles and have spin $\frac{1}{2}$,

It is observed, however, that the change in spin of the source is an integer, in apparent violation of the law of conservation of angular momentum. Moreover, the spectrum of the emitted β particles is continuous, extending from zero energy to a maximum energy E_0, whereas the states of the initial and final nuclei are sharp in apparent contradiction with conservation of energy.

In order to save the conservation principles, a new particle, the neutrino, was postulated (Pauli, 1927). This was supposed to have zero charge,

[1] Otherwise, after losing their kinetic energy, they would fall into the atomic K shell, with emission of characteristic x rays.

small mass, and spin $\frac{1}{2}$ and could carry away the missing energy and angular momentum in a way that would escape observation.

The fundamental process of β decay is the decay of the neutron[1]

$$\text{n} \rightarrow \text{p} + e^- + \bar{\nu} \qquad \begin{aligned} E_0 &= 0.78 \text{ MeV} \\ T_{1/2} &= 12 \text{ min} \end{aligned} \tag{1}$$

into an electron and a neutral particle which we call the *antineutrino*. Though this name is perfectly arbitrary, it is consistent with a principle of *conservation of leptons*, which, as we shall see, has some physical meaning. This principle can be stated as follows: leptons, or light particles of spin $\frac{1}{2}$ (including electrons, neutrinos, and muons), cannot be produced or annihilated individually (like bosons), but only in pairs; the number of leptons minus the number of antileptons always remains constant.

The long life of the neutron shows that the β interaction is weak: a gamma decay of comparable energy would have a mean life of $\approx 10^{-12}$ sec!

The free proton is a stable particle, but, if sufficient energy is available, reaction (1) can proceed in the opposite direction. This occurs, in effect, if the proton is bound to a nucleus in which the energy needed for the decay may be provided by a change in nuclear binding. In nuclear physics the β process can take the well-known three forms:

$$\beta^- : N(Z, N) \rightarrow N'(Z + 1, N - 1) + e^- + \bar{\nu}, \tag{2a}$$

$$\beta^+ : N(Z, N) \rightarrow N'(Z - 1, N + 1) + e^+ + \nu, \tag{2b}$$

$$e\text{-capture} : N(Z, N) + e \rightarrow N'(Z - 1, N + 1) + \nu. \tag{2c}$$

The energy available for the kinetic energy of the leptons (assuming zero neutrino mass) is

$$E_0 = M(Z, N) - M(Z + 1, N - 1), \tag{3a}$$

$$E_0 = M(Z, N) - M(Z - 1, N + 1) - 2m, \tag{3b}$$

$$E_0 = M(Z, N) - M(Z - 1, N + 1) - E_B, \tag{3c}$$

where E_B is the atomic binding energy of the captured electrons and M is the *atomic* mass (neglecting the difference in binding energies of the atomic electrons). Equation (3) shows that the atom Z, N is β stable only if it is lighter than both its neighboring isobars and precludes the existence of pairs of stable neighboring isobars.

b. Neutrino Experiments. The history of the experiments performed in order to prove the existence of the neutrino is a long one.

A first class of experiments consists of attempts to measure the neutrino recoil; such experiments aim to prove that the neutrino is not only needed

[1] We shall use the symbol e or e^- for the negative electron and $\bar{e}$ or e^+ for the positron; similarly, ν for neutrino and $\bar{\nu}$ for antineutrino.

to account for conservation of energy and angular momentum but also to re-establish the balance of linear momenta. In recent years these experiments have been successful in establishing the existence of neutrino recoil and also in measuring the distribution—in magnitude and direction—of the momentum of emitted neutrino (see 8.15b).

Finally Cowan and Reines (C-57a; C-59a) have been able to detect the effects of neutrinos away from their source by observing the reaction of neutrino capture:

$$\bar{\nu} + \mathrm{p} \rightarrow n + e^{+} \tag{4}$$

in proximity to a nuclear reactor, in a 370-gallon liquid scintillation

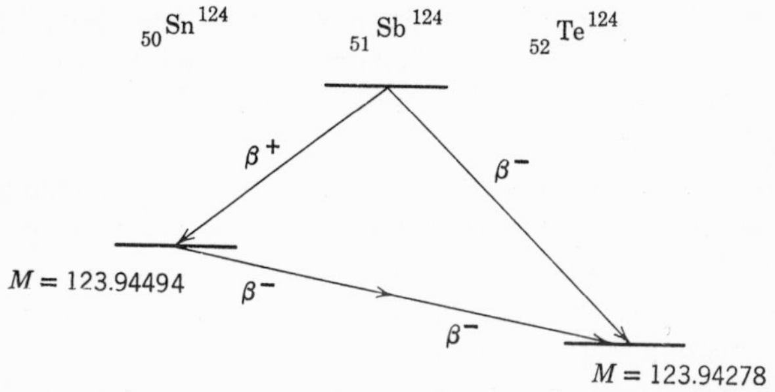

Fig. 8.11-1. Level scheme, illustrating the possibility of double β decay in Sn^{124}. From the atomic masses (*Amer. Inst. Phys. Handbook*, McGraw-Hill, 1957) one sees that about 2 MeV are available for the kinetic energy of double β decay. The mass of Sb^{124} is 2.9 MeV above that of Te^{124}.

counter. The process was revealed by the time relation of the γ ray of positron decay and the delayed γ rays of neutron capture.

It is interesting to report that Davies (D-55; D-59) failed to observe the reaction

$$\bar{\nu} + {}_{17}\mathrm{Cl}^{37} \not\rightarrow {}_{18}\mathrm{A}^{37} + e^{-} \tag{5}$$

$$(\bar{\nu} + \mathrm{n} \not\rightarrow \mathrm{p} + e^{-}) \tag{6}$$

which he tried to find—again near a reactor—by the chemical separation of the gaseous reaction products. The reason for this failure can be attributed to the conservation of leptons: the neutrinos from the reactor—mostly originating from neutron-abundant radio isotopes—are antiparticles and can give rise only to antielectrons.

Other evidence in favor of conservation of leptons is the absence of double β decay. Let us consider, for example, the three isobars Sn^{124}, Sb^{124}, Te^{124}, whose masses are in the order indicated in Fig. 8.11-1. Energetically Sn^{124} could transform into Te^{124} with the emission of two negative electrons. According to conservation of leptons, they must be accompained by two antineutrinos, whereas, if leptons need not be conserved, the two electrons could emerge without neutrinos (or accompanied by a self-annihilating pair ν, $\bar{\nu}$).

The expected mean life is longer in the case of lepton conservation because the process is of higher order, and thus the failure to observe the double β decay of Sn^{124} is indirect evidence in favor of the existence of distinguishable neutrinos and antineutrinos and of lepton conservation.

We shall see later that neutrinos and antineutrinos differ in an essential way, having opposite "helicity."

c. Coulomb Correction Factors. In order to write an expression for the decay transition probability, we may make use of perturbation theory because the coupling is extremely small. The statistical factors entering in β decay and K capture have already been discussed [5.11(20), (21), and (6)]; the matrix element must be appropriate to the creation of lepton pairs in the nucleus.

Since the nucleus has an electric charge, the wave function of the electron resulting from β decay is a coulomb wave function rather than a plane wave. The result is that the matrix elements split into two factors, one corresponding to the creation of free electron neutrino pairs and a coulomb correction factor.

If the nucleus is taken to be a point, the correction factor is

$$F(\pm Z, E) = \frac{|\psi_{\pm}(0)|^2_{\text{coulomb}}}{|\psi(0)|^2_{\text{free}}}, \tag{7}$$

and, nonrelativistically,

$$F(\pm Z, E) = \frac{2\pi\eta}{1 - \exp(-2\pi\eta)}$$

where $\eta = \pm Ze^2/v$ for $\beta^{\mp}$ (v is the electron's speed in units of c).

Relativistic expressions for $F(\pm Z, E)$ have been computed and tabulated (R-55).

In electron capture the Coulomb factor is the density at the nucleus of the electrons to be captured. For capture of K electrons we have

$$F(K) = |\psi(0)|^2_{\text{atomics}} / |\psi(0)|^2_{\text{free}} \approx \frac{2}{\pi}(me^2Z)^3. \tag{8}$$

d. Experimental Spectral Shape. Most observed spectra of β electrons agree with the distribution expected from the product of the statistical factor 5.11(20) and of the coulomb correction factor (7). This last factor increases the probability of finding high-energy positrons and low-energy electrons as expected from simple electrostatic considerations (Fig. 8.11-2).

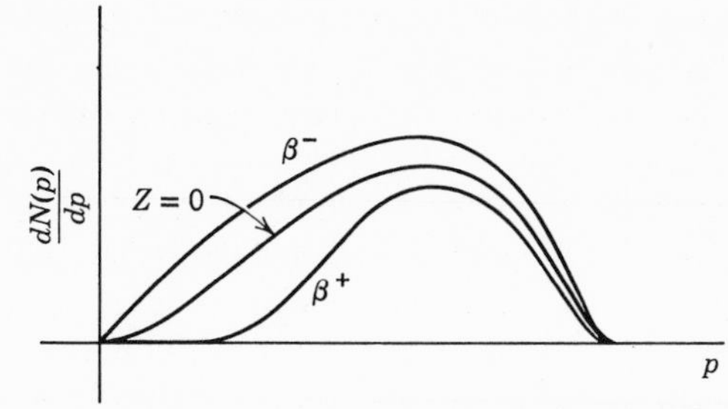

Fig. 8.11-2. Schematic picture of the Coulomb corrections in β decay (from J. M. Blatt and V. F. Weisskopf, Reprinted with permission from *Theoretical Nuclear Physics*, Wiley, New York, 1952).

The comparison between theory and experiment is done by means of the "Fermi plot" (sometimes called Kurie plot). The experimental data, usually obtained with a magnetic β spectrograph which yields the momentum spectrum dN/dp, are used to compute $[(dN/dp)/p^2F(\pm Z, E)]^{1/2}$. The result is plotted as a function of energy (Fig. 8.11-3).

In most cases one obtains a straight line that intersects the energy axis at $E = E_0$. This shows that *the matrix element is energy independent*. There are exceptions, such as RaE, which was the first isotope to be investigated with care because of its availability from natural radioactivity. There are also experimental difficulties caused by electron scattering and absorption in the source, which must be very thin and on light support.

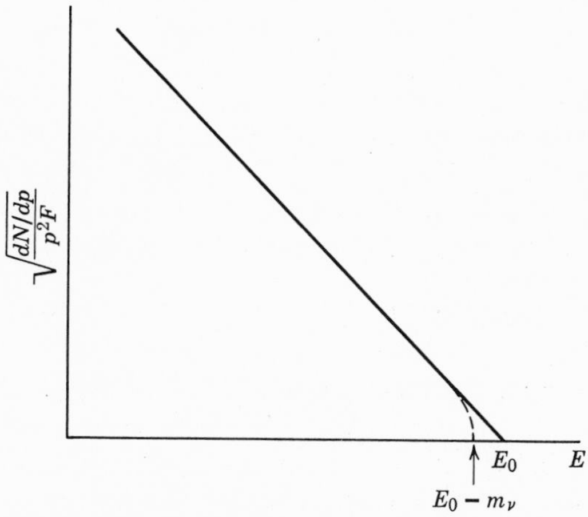

Fig. 8.11-3. Fermi plots for β spectra. Full line for zero neutrino mass; dashed line for finite neutrino mass.

But it is now ascertained that most Fermi plots are linear, including that of H^3, which has $E_0 = 18$ keV.

The study of the Fermi plot near E_0 gives information on the neutrino mass. The effect of a finite neutrino mass, according to 5.11(19), is shown by the dotted line in Fig. 8.11-3. From the linearity of the Fermi plot of H^3 an upper limit for the mass of the neutrinos (H-53; S-58a) is deduced:

$$m_\nu < \sim 200 \text{ eV}.$$

8.12 "ft" Products and Selection Rules

a. Definition of *ft*. Let us denote, by $|M|^2_{\text{av}}$, the square of the matrix element of a β transition averaged over initial spins, summed over final spins, and appropriately averaged also over the momenta of the electron and of the neutrino. Then, if $\rho_F(E)$ is the statistical factor already computed in 5.11, the β-decay *half*-life, $t_{1/2}$, is given by the expression

$$\frac{\ln 2}{t_{1/2}} = 2\pi\, |M|^2_{\text{av}} \int_0^{E_0} \rho_F(E)\, F(\overset{\pm}{K}\, ZE_0)\, dE \int d\Omega_e \int d\Omega_\nu$$

$$(1) \qquad = \begin{cases} \dfrac{1}{2\pi^3}\, |M|^2_{\text{av}} \displaystyle\int_0^{p_0} F(\pm Z, E)\, p^2 (E_0 - E)^2\, dp & \text{for } \beta^\pm, \\[2ex] \dfrac{1}{2\pi^3}\, |M|^2_{\text{av}}\, 4\pi (Ze^2 m)^3 E_0^2 & \text{for } K \text{ capture.} \end{cases}$$

It is usual to introduce the dimensionless functions

$$(2) \qquad \begin{aligned} f_\pm &= \frac{1}{m^5} \int_0^{p_0} F(\pm Z, E)\, p^2 (E_0 - E)^2\, dp, \\ f_K &\approx \frac{4\pi}{m^5} (Ze^2 m)^3\, E_0^2, \end{aligned}$$

and then it is found that in all cases the product $f^{\pm}_{K} t_{1/2}$, or, in short form, ft:

$$(3) \qquad ft = \frac{2\pi^3 \ln 2}{m^5\, |M|^2_{\text{av}}} \qquad (t \text{ in seconds})$$

is inversely proportional to the transition probability of β decay divided by the external (statistical and Coulomb) factors[1].

[1] For numerical calculation it is useful to write (3) more completely:

$$ft = \frac{2\pi^3 \hbar^7 \ln 2}{m^5 c^4\, |M|^2_{\text{av}}} = \frac{1.13 \times 10^{-94}}{|M|^2_{\text{av}}}\ \text{g}^2\, \text{cm}^{10}\, \text{sec}^{-3}.$$

In this formula f is a pure number (E and p are in units of mc² and mc) and t is the half-life in seconds. M is of the order of 10^{-49} erg cm³ for allowed transitions ($ft \approx 1000$).

b. Values of *ft* and Selection Rules. The values of ft for the various β transitions are obtained by applying (2) to the measurements of energy and mean life. The results are given in Table 8.12-1 for some typical cases.

It is seen that the mirror nuclei all have $ft \approx 3000$ but that there are cases in which ft is much larger.

Values of $\log_{10} ft$ vary from 3 to 18. Transitions with $\log_{10} ft \approx 3$—which include the neutron, all mirror nuclei, He^6, O^{14}—are called allowed[1].

Table 8.12-1 Examples of *ft* Values

Mirror Nuclei		$\log_{10} ft$	Other Examples		$\log_{10} ft$
$n \to p$	$(\frac{1}{2}^+ \to \frac{1}{2}^+)$	3.075	O^{14}	$(0^+ \to 0^+)$	3.49
$H^3 \to He^3$	$(\frac{1}{2}^+ \to \frac{1}{2}^+)$	3.06	He^6	$(0^+ \to 1^+)$	2.91
$Be^7 \to Li^7$	$(\frac{3}{2}^- \to \frac{3}{2}^-)$	3.36	Na^{22}		13.82
$Be^7 \to Li^{7*}$	$(\frac{3}{2}^- \to \frac{1}{2}^-)$	3.50			
N^{13}		3.67	C^{14}		9.05
O^{15}		3.65	Co^{60}		7.51
Ne^{19}		3.28	K^{40}		18.05
Mg^{23}		3.65	Rb^{87}		16.52
. . .					
Cl^{33}		3.78	RaE		8.05
. . .					
Ce^{39}		3.49			

Considerably larger ft values are classified as belonging to "forbidden" transitions; these usually occur when the change in spin is large, and one suspects the existence of selection rules similar to those found for γ rays. As in γ rays the distinction between the different orders of forbiddenness is not very evident from the data (Table 8.12-1 and Fig. 8.12-1).

In what follows we discuss almost exclusively the allowed transitions, aiming toward the discovery of the nature of the weak interaction coupling.

From an inspection of Table 8.12-1, we see that

allowed transitions have either

(4*a*) $\Delta J = 0 \quad \Delta\pi = 0$ (Fermi, or nonrelativistic-scalar selection rule)

(4*b*) $\Delta J = 1, 0 \quad \Delta\pi = 0$ (no $0 \to 0$) (Gamow Teller, or nonrelativistic-pseudovector selection rule)

[1] In the literature of nuclear physics these transitions are called super-allowed. Other allowed transitions have $\log_{10} ft$ up to ≈ 5.

The most typical pure Fermi transition is the decay of O^{14}, whereas He^6 is the classical example of an allowed disintegration following Gamow-Teller selection rules.

We can assume that in a Fermi (F) allowed transition electron and neutrino are emitted in an S state with opposite spin, whereas in a Gamow-Teller (GT) transition the orbital angular momentum is also zero but the spins of the leptons are parallel. This idea is developed nonrelativistically

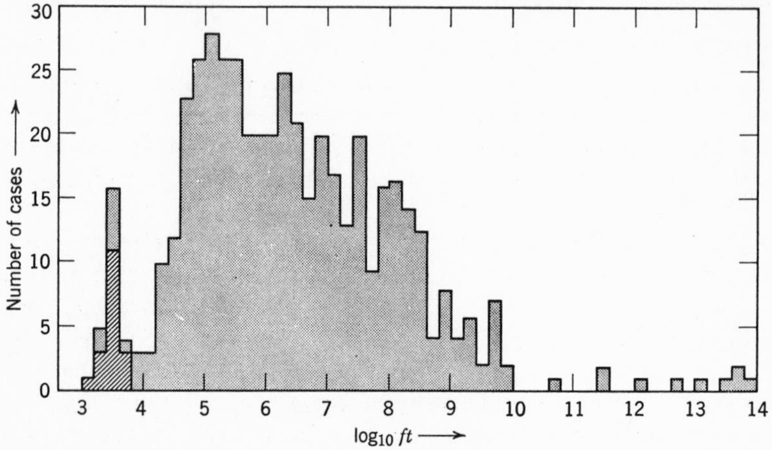

Fig. 8.12-1. Histogram of $\log_{10} ft$ values. Cross-hatched area, mirror transitions (Reprinted with permission from M. Deutsch and O. Kofoed-Hansen, in *Experimental Nuclear Physics*, E. Segrè, editor, Wiley, 1959).

by Blatt and Weisskopf (BW-52). In what follows we proceed directly to the relativistic treatment which is essential considering the high velocity of the particles concerned.

8.13 Fermi's Theory

a. Formulation of the Theory. Until 1957 it was assumed that parity was conserved in weak interactions such as β decay. This idea, which was proved erroneous by experiments performed at the suggestion of Yang and Lee, has effectively hindered progress toward an understanding of the β process; great strides were made only after the principle of parity conservation was discarded.

In our discussion, however, we follow the historical approach. First of all it is easier to understand the concepts entering in the more modern treatment if their evolution is traced from the origin; and second but not less important, it is instructive to follow the alternations of success and failure, of experimenting and theorizing, of trial and error, which are so characteristic of contemporary physics. Weak interaction is one of the most successful examples of modern methods of research and may be taken as a model for other subjects in which progress has not been so rapid.

The story starts with Fermi, who was the first to develop a theory of β decay involving the simultaneous emission of an electron and a neutrino. In Fermi's theory the β interaction is obtained as an analogy to the electromagnetic interaction of nucleons,

$$(1) \qquad \tfrac{1}{2}(1 + \tau_3)e(\bar{\psi}_F \gamma_\mu \psi_I)A_\mu,$$

which describes the emission of a photon (quantum of field A_μ) while the source undergoes a transition from an initial state ψ_I to a final state ψ_F. In (1) the electromagnetic potential vector is dotted with the source current vector to give a scalar interaction, as required for conservation of angular momentum and parity.

A theory of β decay must describe the emission of an electron and a neutrino. Thus the vector **A**, appearing in (1), must be replaced by a vector containing the wave functions of both electron and neutrino. We know how to form vectors with either electron or neutrino states by writing [6.14(19)] expressions such as $\bar{\psi}_e \gamma_\mu \psi_e$ or $\bar{\psi}_\nu \gamma_\mu \psi_\nu$, but we can also form vectors including both fields by writing $\bar{\psi}_e \gamma_\mu \psi_\nu$ or $\bar{\psi}_\nu \gamma_\mu \psi_e$: these are the vectors that may be used (in place of A_μ) to describe the process of β emission.

The interpretation of these mixed electron-neutrino vectors is best obtained in terms of a quantized field theory, in which the states ψ_e and ψ_ν are expanded in annihilation and creation operators. However, they can also be understood by comparison with the matrix elements $\bar{\psi}_F \gamma_4 \psi_I$ which enter into the computation of coulomb scattering and of pair production (6.26). The matrix element for coulomb scattering has been interpreted as describing the transition produced by an electrostatic potential (contributing a γ_4 because it is the fourth component of a vector) between two states of an electron; but we could equally well have said that the matrix element $\bar{\psi}_F \gamma_4 \psi_I$ described the annihilation of an electron in state I and the creation of an electron in state F. Similarly, the matrix element for pair production can be interpreted either as destroying an electron in a negative energy state and creating one with positive energy, or as creating two electrons of positive energy but opposite sense of time propagation.

In the same manner we have two alternative interpretations of the matrix element $\bar{\psi}_{e,F} \gamma_\mu \psi_{\nu,I}$. We may say that it annihilates a negative-energy neutrino in state I and creates an electron in positive energy state F (Fig. 8.13-1) or that it creates an electron and an antineutrino (Fig. 8.13-2). We shall take this second point of view in carrying out our computations,

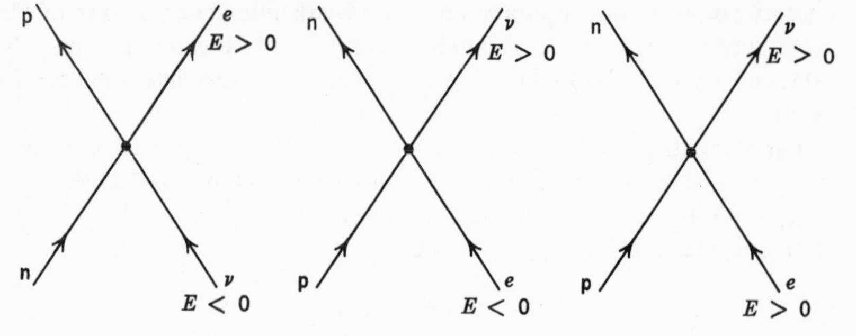

Fig. 8.13-1. Diagrams represents β decay as transitions of leptons from negative to positive energy states.

since we have developed a theoretical apparatus [positive energy spinors $w_{(i)}$, particle and antiparticle projection operators $(\not{p} \pm m)/2\mathring{m}$] appropriate to it.

With either interpretation, the theory automatically satisfies the principle of conservation of leptons.

As in (1), the vector describing the emitted particles must be dotted with another vector describing the source and its transitions if we want a theory respecting conservation of angular momentum and parity. In the present case the source undergoes transitions from neutron state to proton state, or vice versa, and the source vector must be written $\bar{\psi}_p \gamma_\mu \psi_n$ or $\bar{\psi}_n \gamma_\mu \psi_p$.

The coupling to the electromagnetic charge $\frac{1}{2}(1 + \tau_3)e$ appearing in (1) is to be replaced by a new coupling whose magnitude is expressed by a

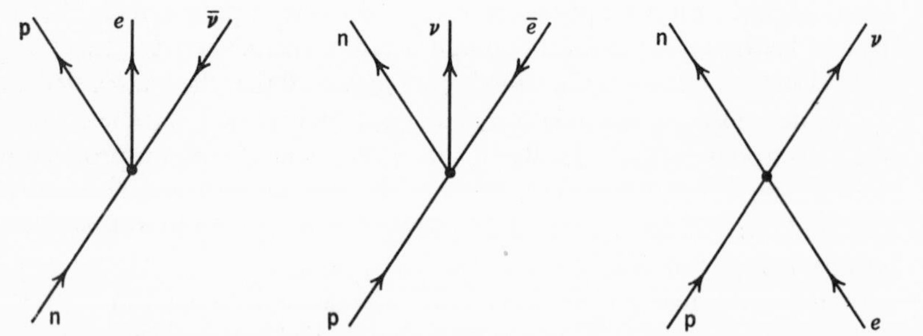

Fig. 8.13-2. Diagrams representing β decay as production of a lepton (propagating forward in time) and an antilepton (propagating backward in time).

coupling constant, g, and whose isospin character is $-\sqrt{\frac{1}{2}}\tau_+ = \tau^+ = \begin{pmatrix} 0 & 1 \\ 0 & 0 \end{pmatrix}$ or $\sqrt{\frac{1}{2}}\tau_- = \tau^- = \begin{pmatrix} 0 & 0 \\ 1 & 0 \end{pmatrix}$ to account for the change in charge of the nucleon undergoing β decay.

The Fermi matrix element for the elementary β-decay process can be written as a hermitian operator consisting of two terms, of which the first corresponds to β^- decay and the second (which is the conjugate of the first) to β^+. If, for compactness of notation, we omit the sign of integration over the space coordinates, it can be written as

$$g[(\bar{\psi}_{N,\mathrm{F}}\tau^+\gamma_\mu\psi_{N,\mathrm{I}})(\bar{\psi}_e\gamma_\mu\psi_\nu) + (\bar{\psi}_{N,\mathrm{F}}\tau^-\gamma_\mu\psi_{N,\mathrm{I}})(\bar{\psi}_\nu\gamma_\mu\psi_e)], \tag{2}$$

where the coupling constant g is to be found from the experiment.

Diagrams representing this matrix element are shown in Figs. 8.13-1 and 2.

For the decay of a nucleus containing A nucleons (labeled with α) the matrix element is[1]

$$g\left[\bar{\psi}_\mathrm{F}(1, \cdots, A) \sum_{\alpha=1}^{A} (\tau^+\gamma_\mu)_\alpha \psi_\mathrm{I}(1, \cdots, A)\right](\bar{\psi}_e\gamma_\mu\psi_\nu) + \text{h.c.}, \tag{3}$$

where ψ_I and ψ_F are the initial and final states of the nucleus.

This expression is an exact formulation of Fermi's theory, if the wave functions were known, it would predict all the details of the decay, including the polarization of the leptons and their angular distribution.

b. The Allowed Approximation. Each term of the matrix element (2) or (3) is composed of two factors which we call the *nuclear factor* and the *leptic factor*. For the computation it is usual to make the following approximations, which are said to correspond to *allowed transitions*:

(i) Since the nucleons move in the nucleus with $v \ll c$, the space components of γ_μ are neglected compared to the fourth component;

(ii) Since the wavelengths $1/p$ and $1/q$ of electron and neutrino are much larger than the nuclear radius in all cases of interest, the quantities $\mathbf{p}\cdot\mathbf{r}$ and $\mathbf{q}\cdot\mathbf{r}$ are neglected compared to unity.

Thus in the discussion of allowed transitions only the fourth term of the sums in (2) and (3) is retained and we may write 1 instead of γ_4 in the nuclear factor. In the leptic factor the exponentials in $\psi_e = w_e \exp(i\mathbf{p}\cdot\mathbf{r})$ and in $\psi_\nu = w_\nu \exp(i\mathbf{q}\cdot\mathbf{r})$ are omitted.

Then (3) becomes

$$M = g[\psi_\mathrm{F}^\dagger(1, \cdots, A)(\sum_\alpha \tau_\alpha^+)\psi_\mathrm{I}(1, \cdots, A)](\bar{w}_e\gamma_4 w_\nu) + \text{h.c.} \tag{4}$$

[1] In (3) 1 stands for $\mathbf{x}_1$, $\boldsymbol{\sigma}_1$, $\vec{\tau}_1$; h.c. means hermitian conjugate.

It has become customary to abbreviate the nuclear integral appearing in (4) as follows

$$\int 1 = \int \psi_F^\dagger(1, \cdots, A)(\sum_\alpha \tau_\alpha^+)\psi_I(1, \cdots, A)\, d^3\mathbf{x}_1 \cdots d^3\mathbf{x}_A. \tag{5}$$

c. The Transition Probability. In order to obtain the transition probability the matrix element (4) must be squared, averaged over initial spin states, and summed over final states.

Let us consider first the leptic factor. In order to use the density of final states normalized to unit lab volume, as in 5.11(20), we must introduce a factor $(m_e/|E_e|)(m_\nu/|E_\nu|)$ in the matrix element squared; this is to compensate for the factors E/m in the normalization (6.21) of the w's (before the end of the computation we shall pass to the limit $m_\nu \to 0$). In the spin averaging both the electron and the neutrino must be considered as final particles, and there is no factor $\frac{1}{2}$ in front of the spin sum. Thus, if p is the electron's momentum and q the momentum of the antineutrino, the properly averaged square of the leptic factor for β^- (see 6.25b) is

$$\begin{aligned} |M_l|^2_{\text{av}} &= \frac{m}{|E_e|}\frac{m_\nu}{|E_\nu|} \mathop{S}_e \mathop{\dot{S}}_\nu |\bar{w}_e\gamma_4 w_\nu|^2 \\ &= \frac{mm_\nu}{|E_e|\,|E_\nu|} \operatorname{Tr}\left(\gamma_4 \frac{\not{q} - m_\nu}{2m_\nu} \gamma_4 \frac{\not{p} + m}{2m}\right). \end{aligned} \tag{6}$$

We can now pass to the limit for $m_\nu \to 0$ and obtain

$$\begin{aligned} |M_l|^2_{\text{av}} &= \frac{1}{4\,|E_e|\,|E_\nu|} \operatorname{Tr}\,[\gamma_4\not{q}\gamma_4(\not{p} + m)] \\ &= \frac{1}{4Eq} \operatorname{Tr}\,(\gamma_4\not{q}\gamma_4\not{p}) = \frac{1}{4Eq} \operatorname{Tr}\,(-\not{q}\not{p} + 2Eq) \\ &= \frac{1}{4Eq}(8Eq - 4\mathbf{p}\cdot\mathbf{q}) = \frac{1}{4Eq}(8Eq - 4Eq + 4\mathbf{p}\cdot\mathbf{q}) \\ &= 1 + \frac{\mathbf{p}\cdot\mathbf{q}}{Eq} = 1 + v\cos\theta_{e\nu}, \end{aligned} \tag{7}$$

where $v = p/E$ is the electron's speed.

We have thus found the theoretical electron-neutrino angular correlation, with the result that small angles between neutrino and electron are favored[1].

If we average over $\theta_{e\nu}$, the square of the leptic factor contributes a factor unity, and (4) squared gives us

$$|M|^2_{\text{av}} = g^2\,|(\psi_F^\dagger \sum_\alpha \tau_\alpha^+ \psi_I)|^2. \tag{8}$$

[1] The same result holds for β^+, since the sign of m in $\not{p} \pm m$ does not affect the angular correlation.

As we could have guessed Fermi theory gives Fermi selection rules, $\Delta J = \Delta\pi = 0$, for the nuclear transition.

In order to proceed with the computation of the nuclear factor, we must perform the integral over the nuclear wave functions. This may be approximated in particular cases with sufficient accuracy. For light nuclear states T is a good quantum number, and when the transition occurs between two nuclei belonging to the same T multiplet the integral can be evaluated[1].

In the decay of mirror nuclei T is $\frac{1}{2}$ and T_3 changes from $\pm\frac{1}{2}$ to $\mp\frac{1}{2}$. Thus, from 1.13(27), $\sum_\alpha \tau_\alpha{}^+ = \sum_\alpha 2T_\alpha{}^+ = 1$; and for all mirror nuclei, including the neutron-proton decay, we can write

(9) $$|M|^2_{\text{av(Fermi)}} = g^2.$$

This result is easily understood in the independent-particle model: mirror nuclei have single nucleons which can β-decay because of the exclusion principle. The wave function of the daughter particle is the same (as far as spin and spatial dependence is concerned) as the wave function of the parent particle and $\int \psi_F{}^\dagger \psi_I = 1$.

d. Determination of the Fermi Coupling Constant. The value of the Fermi coupling constant cannot be obtained from the analysis of the decay of mirror nuclei since they are $\frac{1}{2} \to \frac{1}{2}$ transitions, with no parity change, allowed for both Fermi and Gamow-Teller selection rules. The decay of O^{14}, instead, is easier to interpret. This isotope decays to the first excited state of N^{14} (see Fig. 2.14-2 for the level diagram), and the initial and final quantum numbers are well known: from $J = 0^+$ to $J = 0^+$; from $T = 1$, $T_3 = 1$ to $T = 1$, $T_3 = 0$. The transition is allowed according to Fermi selection rules and forbidden for Gamow-Teller selection rules.

By using the single-particle model, we would expect in this case $|\psi_F{}^\dagger(\sum_\alpha \tau_\alpha{}^-)\psi_I|^2 = 2$, since there are two protons that may decay compatibly with the exclusion principle. The same result is obtained more formally if we use the angular momentum step-down operator; recalling that $\sum_\alpha \tau_\alpha{}^- = \sqrt{2}\mathrm{T}_-$ and [1.13(27)]

$$\langle \mathrm{T} = 1, \mathrm{T}_3 = 0 |\, \mathrm{T}_- \,| \mathrm{T} = 1, \mathrm{T}_3 = 1 \rangle = \sqrt{\tfrac{1}{2}(1+1)(1-1+1)} = 1$$

we obtain from (8), for O^{14},

(10) $$|M|^2_{\text{av(Fermi)}} = 2g^2.$$

[1] Remember that the total isospin is defined [1.32(10)] as $\vec{T} = \sum_\alpha \frac{1}{2}\vec{\tau}_\alpha$. Its $\pm$ components are $T_\pm = \sum_\alpha \frac{1}{2}\tau_{\pm,\alpha} = \mp\sqrt{\frac{1}{2}}\sum_\alpha \tau_\alpha{}^\pm$ and can be evaluated by using the angular momentum formalism.

The mean life and the disintegration energy of O^{14} are well known (H-61), and thus the coupling constant for Fermi coupling can be accurately determined. The main error is the result of difficulties in computing two small theoretical corrections. The first of these corresponds to a difference in the wave functions of O^{14} and N^{14} due to electrostatic effects and the second is a radiative correction (see 8.17).

The values of the Fermi (vector) coupling constant reported by Hendrie and Gerhart are

$$g_V = (1.420 \pm 0.003) \times 10^{-49} \text{ erg cm}^3, \tag{11}$$

including Coulomb (M-58), but not radiative corrections and

$$g_V = \begin{pmatrix} 1.407 \\ & \pm 0.003 \\ 1.427 \end{pmatrix} \times 10^{-49} \text{ erg cm}^3, \tag{12}$$

with two different estimates of radiative corrections (D-60; K-59a).

8.14 Other Parity-Conserving Theories

a. The Five Parity-Conserving Theories. Clearly Fermi's theory of β decay does not explain the fact that the decay of He^6 ($\Delta J = 1$, $\Delta\pi = 0$) is allowed, and we must look for a different form of interaction in order to account for Gamow-Teller transitions.

If we want to limit ourselves to theories respecting the conservation of parity and of angular momentum, the matrix element must still be scalar: such a scalar can be obtained by saturating the indices of any tensor (not necessarily a vector) formed from the nuclear state with a tensor of the same rank formed from the electron-neutrino field. As we have seen in 6.14 there are five tensors that may be constructed from Dirac spinors: thus (without introducing derivative coupling) we may formulate five different theories of β decay consistent with the principles of conservation and with relativistic invariance.

Let us introduce the five tensor operators Q_X ($X = S, V, T, A, P$ for scalar, vector, tensor, axial-vector, pseudoscalar) as written below[1], together with their nonrelativistic limits (6.14e, f):

$$\begin{aligned}
Q_S &= 1 && \approx 1 \\
Q_V &= \gamma_\mu && \approx \gamma_4 \approx 1 \\
Q_T &= \frac{i}{2}(\gamma_\mu\gamma_\nu - \gamma_\nu\gamma_\mu) && \approx \sigma_i \\
Q_A &= -\gamma_\mu\gamma_\nu\gamma_\lambda = -\gamma_5\gamma_\rho && \approx i\gamma_4\sigma_i \approx i\sigma_i \\
Q_P &= \gamma_5 && \approx i\boldsymbol{\sigma}\cdot\boldsymbol{\gamma} \ll 1
\end{aligned} \tag{1}$$

[1] The operators (1) are chosen so that $\psi^\dagger\gamma_4 Q_X\psi$ is hermitian, with the exception of $\psi^\dagger\gamma_4 Q_A\psi$, which is antihermitian. This is done in order to have a positive sign in the allowed matrix element M_A of (3).

Then the matrix element for any one of these theories can be written[1]

$$(2)\quad M_X = g_X\Big[\bar{\psi}_F(1, \cdots, A) \sum_\alpha (\tau^+ Q_X)_\alpha \psi_I(1, \cdots, A)\Big] \cdot (\bar{\psi}_e Q_X \psi_\nu) + \text{h.c.}$$

It is seen that Fermi's theory is the particular case $X = V$.

In the allowed approximation (nonrelativistic nucleons, pR and $qR \ll 1$) the matrix element becomes

$$(3)\quad \begin{aligned} M_S &= g_S\left(\int 1\right)(\bar{w}_e 1 w_\nu) + \text{h.c.},\\ M_V &= g_V\left(\int 1\right)(\bar{w}_e \gamma_4 w_\nu) + \text{h.c.},\\ M_T &= g_T\left(\int \boldsymbol{\sigma}\right) \cdot (\bar{w}_e \boldsymbol{\sigma} w_\nu) + \text{h.c.},\\ M_A &= g_A\left(\int \boldsymbol{\sigma}\right) \cdot (\bar{w}_e \gamma_4 \boldsymbol{\sigma} w_\nu) + \text{h.c.},\\ M_P &= g_P\Big[\psi_F^\dagger(1, \cdots, A) \sum_\alpha (\tau^+ i\gamma_4 \boldsymbol{\sigma} \cdot \boldsymbol{\gamma})_\alpha \psi_I(1, \cdots, A)\Big](\bar{w}_e \gamma_5 w_\nu) + \text{h.c.}, \end{aligned}$$

where $\int 1$ has the meaning defined in 8.13(6) and

$$(4)\quad \int \boldsymbol{\sigma} = \int \psi_F^\dagger(1, \cdots, A) \sum_\alpha (\tau^+ \boldsymbol{\sigma})_\alpha \psi_I(1, \cdots, A)\, d^3\mathbf{x}_1 \cdots d^3\mathbf{x}_A.$$

Clearly, S and V give Fermi selection rules (zero-pole); T and A give Gamow-Teller selection rules (magnetic dipole); P gives zero in the static case, since the matrix element contains the velocity $\gamma_4\gamma_i$, and would lead to a selection rule $\Delta J = 0$, $\pi_F \neq \pi_I$, in contradiction with the experiment. Thus we can discard this form of the theory at least for the discussion of allowed β decay.

b. Angular Correlations. Proceeding as we did for Fermi's theory, we can compute the leptic factors squared and summed over spins. We obtain the following results which describe the electron-neutrino angular correlations predicted by the different theories:

$$(5)\quad \frac{m}{E}\frac{m_\nu}{q} \mathop{\mathsf{S}}_{e} \mathop{\mathsf{S}}_{\nu} |\text{leptic factor}|^2 = 1 + \lambda_X v \cos\theta_{e\nu} \quad \text{with} \quad \begin{aligned} \lambda_S &= -1\\ \lambda_V &= +1\\ \lambda_T &= +\tfrac{1}{3}\\ \lambda_A &= -\tfrac{1}{3} \end{aligned}$$

It is worthwhile to develop the details for one of the spin-coupled Gamow-Teller interactions, and we shall treat the axial-vector case.

If the initial nuclear spin J does not vanish, we shall take the z axis in the direction of J and we shall write the dot product of nuclear and leptic

[1] The dot stands for sum over repeated tensor indices, as defined in 6-11 (5), (8).

factors in the notation of 1.13e:

$$(6)\quad \langle \boldsymbol{\sigma} \rangle_N \cdot \langle i\gamma_5 \boldsymbol{\gamma} \rangle_l = -\langle \sigma_+ \rangle_N \langle i\gamma_5\gamma_- \rangle_l - \langle \sigma_- \rangle_N \langle i\gamma_5\gamma_+ \rangle_l + \langle \sigma_z \rangle_N \langle i\gamma_5\gamma_z \rangle_l.$$

The first and second terms correspond to $\Delta M_J = \pm 1$ and the last term to $\Delta M_J = 0$ for the nuclear state. For this last case the spin averaged leptic factor squared is

$$(7_0)\quad \begin{aligned} &\frac{m}{E}\frac{m_\nu}{q} \mathop{S}_{e} \mathop{S}_{\nu} |\bar{w}_e(i\gamma_5\gamma_z)w_\nu|^2 \\ &\quad = \frac{1}{4Eq} \operatorname{Tr} [(i\gamma_5\gamma_z)\not{q}(-i\gamma_z\gamma_5)\not{p}] \\ &\quad = \frac{1}{4Eq} \operatorname{Tr} [\gamma_z\not{q}\gamma_z\not{p}] = \frac{1}{4Eq} \operatorname{Tr} [-\gamma_z\gamma_z\not{q}\not{p} + 2p_zq_z] \\ &\quad = \frac{4}{4Eq}(Eq - \mathbf{p}\cdot\mathbf{q} + 2p_zq_z) = 1 - v\cos\theta_{e\nu} + 2v\cos\theta_{eJ}\cos\theta_{\nu J}. \end{aligned}$$

In this manner we have obtained the angular distribution of electrons and neutrinos around the nuclear spin[1]; we must now average over the orientations of the spin axis in order to obtain the electron-neutrino angular distribution:

$$\begin{aligned} \langle \cos\theta_{eJ}\cos\theta_{\nu J} \rangle_{\text{av}} &= \langle \cos\theta_{eJ}(\cos\theta_{eJ}\cos\theta_{e\nu} + \text{terms with } \cos\varphi) \rangle_{\text{av}} \\ &= \langle \cos^2\theta_{eJ}\cos\theta_{e\nu} \rangle_{\text{av}} = \tfrac{1}{3}\cos\theta_{e\nu}. \end{aligned}$$

This average, substituted in (7_0), gives the result reported in (5).

The computation for $\Delta M_J = \pm 1$ is a little more involved. Instead of (7_0), we obtain

$$(7_\pm)\quad \frac{m}{E}\frac{m_\nu}{q} \mathop{S}_{e} \mathop{S}_{\nu} |\bar{w}_e(i\gamma_5\gamma_\pm)w_\nu|^2 = 1 - v\cos\theta_{eJ}\cos\theta_{\nu J},$$

but the average result still agrees with (5).

c. The Nuclear Matrix Element. Since all the expressions (5) average to 1 over the angle of neutrino emission, we have

$$(8)\quad \begin{aligned} |M_S|^2_{\text{av}} &= g_S^{\,2}\left|\int 1\right|^2 \\ |M_V|^2_{\text{av}} &= g_V^{\,2}\left|\int 1\right|^2 \\ |M_T|^2_{\text{av}} &= g_T^{\,2}\left|\int \boldsymbol{\sigma}\right|^2 \\ |M_A|^2_{\text{av}} &= g_A^{\,2}\left|\int \boldsymbol{\sigma}\right|^2 \end{aligned}$$

[1] Observe that $\mathbf{p}\cdot\mathbf{q}$ is scalar; $p_z \approx \mathbf{p}\cdot\mathbf{J}$ and $q_z \approx \mathbf{q}\cdot\mathbf{J}$ are pseudoscalars, but their product is again scalar, as it must be in a parity-conserving theory.

The computation of $|\int\boldsymbol{\sigma}|^2$ is complicated even for mirror nuclei. It requires the knowledge not only of the spin but also of the configuration (ratio $L = J + \frac{1}{2}$ to $L = J - \frac{1}{2}$) of the nuclear states (T-57).

Only one case can be computed easily and accurately: the decay of the free neutron for which $|\int\boldsymbol{\sigma}|^2 = \sigma_x{}^2 + \sigma_y{}^2 + \sigma_z{}^2 = 3$. Thus we have two examples in which all the matrix elements are rather accurately computed from simple considerations:

the decay of the *free neutron*, for which

(9) $|M_S|^2{}_{\text{av}} = g_S{}^2;\quad |M_V|^2{}_{\text{av}} = g_V{}^2;\quad |M_T|^2{}_{\text{av}} = 3g_T{}^2;\quad |M_A|^2{}_{\text{av}} = 3g_A{}^2;$

the decay of O^{14}, for which

(10) $|M_S|^2{}_{\text{av}} = 2g_S{}^2;\quad |M_V|^2{}_{\text{av}} = 2g_V{}^2;\quad |M_T|^2{}_{\text{av}} = 0;\quad |M_A|^2{}_{\text{av}} = 0.$

We obviously cannot obtain the four coupling constants from the *ft* values of the neutron and O^{14} unless we take into account other factors, which are discussed in the next section.

d. Derivative-Coupled Theories. The five theories mentioned above are not the only possible ones, since, as we have seen for the electromagnetic and mesic fields, derivative couplings consistent with the required invariances may be introduced. Such couplings were incorporated in β decay theory by Konopinski and Uhlenbeck; for instance, the derivative coupled vector theory corresponds to a matrix element of the form

(11) $$g_V{}'\left[\bar{\psi}_F\gamma_\mu\left(\sum_\alpha \tau_\alpha{}^+\right)\psi_I\right]\partial_\mu(\bar{\psi}_e\psi_\nu).$$

Derivative-coupled matrix elements involve the momentum of the electron-neutrino field and predict a distorted spectrum. They were seriously considered before accurate data on the spectral shape were available but can now be discarded because they do not agree with the experiment.

8.15 Analysis of the Experimental Data

a. Selection Rules and Spectral Shape. In the most general form of the theory the matrix element is the sum of 10 terms including 10 arbitrary coupling constants: five g_X [from theories without derivative coupling, 8.14(3)] and five $g_X{}'$ [from theories with derivative coupling, 8.14(11)]:

(1) $$M = M_S + M_V + M_T + M_A + \cdots.$$

The 10 g's must be determined from the experiment. We have already mentioned that we are justified in writing

$$(2) \qquad g_{X}' = 0; \qquad g_P = 0.$$

We are thus left with only four possible nonvanishing coupling constants, and in the allowed approximation (1) takes the form

$$(3) \quad M = \left(\int 1\right)[\bar{w}_e(g_S + g_V\gamma_4)w_\nu] + \left(\int \boldsymbol{\sigma}\right)\cdot[\bar{w}_e(g_A\gamma_4 + g_T)\boldsymbol{\sigma}w_\nu] + \text{h.c.}$$

The selection rules require that the coefficients of $\int 1$ and $\int \boldsymbol{\sigma}$ must not vanish. Thus g_S and g_V (and g_A and g_T) cannot vanish simultaneously.

We shall now prove that if the allowed spectrum is undistorted (matrix element independent of energy) only one of g_S and g_V and only one of g_T and g_A can be different from zero.

Let us assume, for example, that both g_S and g_V are different from zero. Then the average square of the Fermi leptic factor is

$$\frac{m}{E}\frac{m_\nu}{q}\mathop{\mathsf{S}}_{e}\mathop{\mathsf{S}}_{\nu}|\bar{w}_e(g_S + g_V\gamma_4)w_\nu|^2 = \frac{1}{4Eq}\operatorname{Tr}[(g_S + g_V\gamma_4)\not{q}(g_S + g_V\gamma_4)(\not{p} + m)]$$

$$= \text{scalar part in } g_S^2 + \text{vector part in } g_V^2 + \frac{1}{4Eq}g_Sg_V\operatorname{Tr}(\gamma_4\not{q}m + \not{q}\gamma_4 m).$$

The interference term (Fierz) in g_Sg_V yields $(2m/E)g_Sg_V$ and is energy-dependent. Hence within the limit of accuracy with which the undistorted spectral shape is experimentally verified[1] we have

$$(4) \qquad g_Sg_V = 0,$$

and, similarly, for Gamow-Teller transitions

$$(5) \qquad g_Tg_A = 0.$$

In what follows we shall assume that (4) and (5) are exactly valid and we shall see that the experimental results never contradict this simplyfying view.

b. Experiments on Electron-Neutrino Angular Correlation. Since the neutrinos cannot be detected, the electron-neutrino angular correlations are obtained indirectly from the measurement of nuclear recoil, in the assumption of conservation of energy and momentum. But nuclei are much heavier than leptons, and the recoil energy is small; thus the binding of the atoms in a solid source may lead to erroneous results.

[1] According to C. S. Wu (W-55), we can conclude from the experimental data that $2g_Sg_V/(g_S^2 + g_V^2) \lesssim \sim 0.2$ and $2g_Tg_A/(g_T^2 + g_A^2) < \sim 0.08$.

In practice, the only sources that may be used are the rare gases. The technique of recoil measurement has been developed mostly by Allen (A-59a) over a number of years and has finally been successful in the determination of the angular correlation. The instrument in Fig. 8.15-1 (A-59a) measures the energy of the recoil (detected by an electron multiplier) from a gaseous source, by means of a double electrostatic spectrometer. Naturally, the recoil energy is larger if the leptons are emitted parallel rather than antiparallel to one another.

For He^6 (Fig. 8.15-2) the best fit to the data is obtained for $\lambda = -0.39 \pm 0.05$, showing that the Gamow-Teller interaction is mostly axial ($\lambda_A = -\frac{1}{3}$); similar results are obtained for Ne^{23} and Ne^{19} (also Gamow-Teller decays). The disintegration of A^{35} (mostly Fermi) gives $\lambda = +0.97 \pm 0.04$ (Fig. 8.15-3), corresponding to vector interaction ($\lambda_V = 1$).

From these results we feel justified in writing

$$(6) \qquad g_V \neq 0; \qquad g_A \neq 0; \qquad \text{all other } g \text{ and } g' \text{ vanish,}$$

and in concluding that Fermi decays are pure vector, Gamow-Teller decays pure pseudovector.

c. Determination of g_A. Since g_V is known [8.13 (11) and (12)], the value of g_A can be obtained from the decay of the neutron [see 8.14(9)]. We find (G-58a)

$$(7) \qquad \left|\frac{g_A}{g_V}\right| = 1.19 \pm 0.04.$$

Thus g_A is almost, but not quite, equal to g_V. For the time being we shall not comment on this observation (see 8.35b for a discussion of this point).

Since the mean life of the neutron is difficult to measure, it is interesting to obtain the value of g_A from other data. If we use[1]

$$(8) \qquad |M|^2_{\text{av}} = g_V^2\left|\int 1\right|^2 + g_A^2\left|\int \boldsymbol{\sigma}\right|^2,$$

the value of g_A^2 can be obtained from any decay for which $\int 1$ and $\int \boldsymbol{\sigma}$ are computable with good accuracy. This is true for several light nuclei, whose structures are fairly well understood. From the experimental ft values and the theoretical $\int 1$ and $\int \boldsymbol{\sigma}$, we can plot the quantity

$$(9) \qquad A = \frac{ft}{g_V^2}|M|^2_{\text{av}} = ft\left(\left|\int 1\right|^2 + \left|\frac{g_A}{g_V}\right|^2\left|\int \boldsymbol{\sigma}\right|^2\right)$$

(which should be the same for all nuclei, since ft is inversely proportional to

[1] The mixed term, in the first power of σ_i vanishes upon spin averaging.

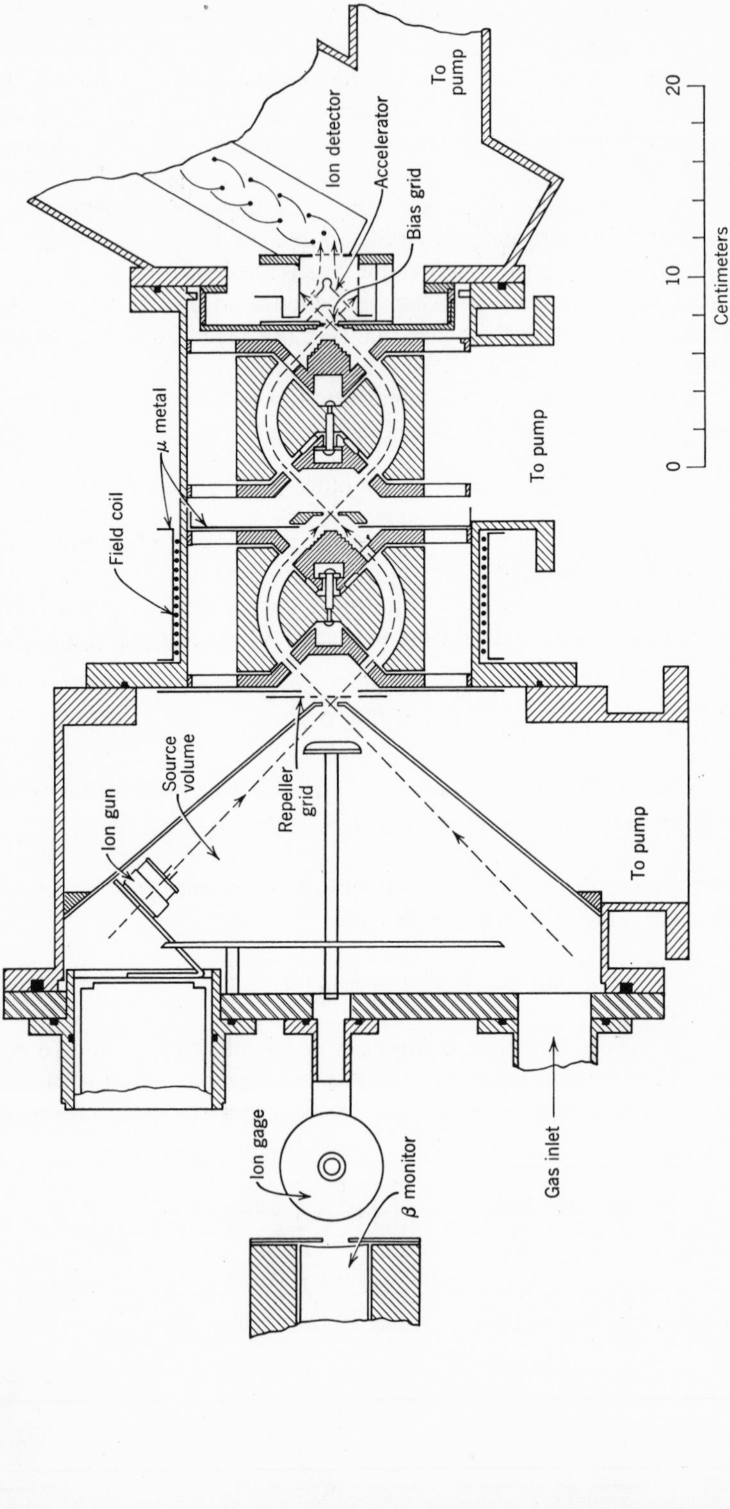

Fig. 8.15-1. Schematic of the double spectrometer used in the study of β recoil spectra. The effective source volume is inside the cone at the left of the diagram [from J. S. Allen, *Rev. Mod. Phys.*, **31**, 795 (1959)].

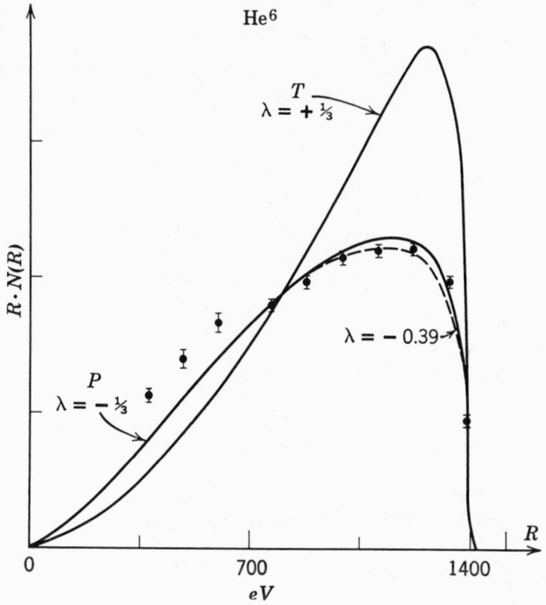

Fig. 8.15-2. Recoil spectrum of He^6, corresponding to pseudovector interaction [from J. S. Allen, *Rev. Mod. Phys.*, **31,** 796 (1959)].

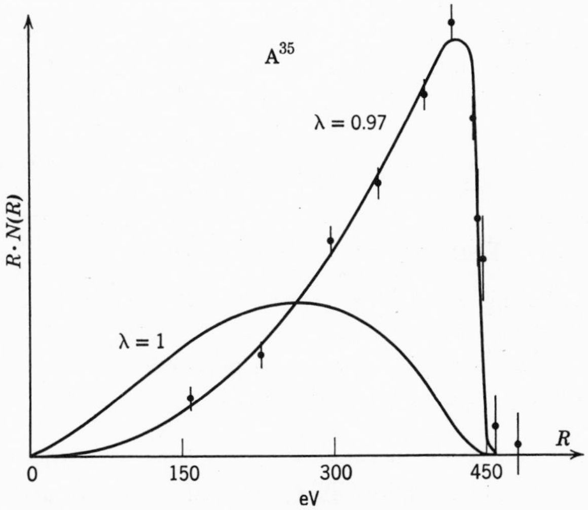

Fig. 8.15-3. Recoil spectrum of A^{35} corresponding to vector interaction [from J. S. Allen, *Rev. Mod. Phys.*, **31,** 795 (1959)].

$|M|^2_{av}$) as a function of $|g_A/g_V|^2$ (Fig. 8.15-4). If there were no errors, the straight lines obtained for the different isotopes would intersect at a point corresponding to the common value of $|g_A/g_V|^2$; in Fig. 8.15-4 we can see that the intersections gather around the value

$$\left|\frac{g_A}{g_V}\right| = 1.11 \pm 0.05 \tag{10}$$

in agreement with (7). The fact that $|g_A| > |g_V|$ seems well established.

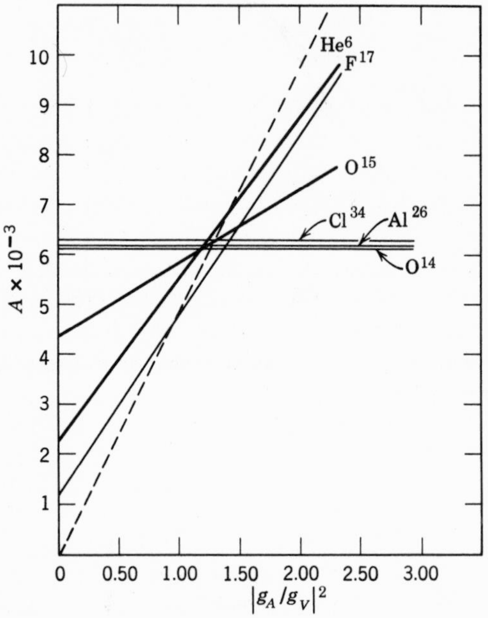

Fig. 8.15-4. Plot for the determination of $|g_A/g_V|$ from the decay of some superallowed transitions [from L. Michel, *Rev. Mod. Phys.*, **29**, 227 (1957)].

8.16 Forbidden Transitions

If two neighboring isobars have levels for which the matrix elements $\int 1$ and $\int \boldsymbol{\sigma}$ vanish, we say that β decay is forbidden between the two levels. This does not mean that the β transition probability between two such states is necessarily zero but only that the mean life is long and the ft product large.

In order to explain forbidden transitions, we must reconsider the terms that were left out in the "allowed approximation" [8.13b and 8.14(3)]. Two approximations were made.

First, the small components of the Dirac matrices were neglected in the nuclear part of the matrix element; second, the exponentials $\exp(i\mathbf{p}\cdot\mathbf{r})$, $\exp(i\mathbf{q}\cdot\mathbf{r})$ in the leptic wave functions were replaced by unity neglecting "retardation effects."

The terms contributed by the small components are smaller by a factor of $\approx v_\alpha \approx \omega_\alpha R \approx E_0 R$ in relation to the allowed matrix element.

The retardation effects are taken into account by writing the wave functions of the electron emitted and of the neutrino absorbed by the αth nucleon as

$$\bar{\psi}_e = \bar{w}_e e^{i\mathbf{p}\cdot\mathbf{r}_\alpha}, \qquad \psi_\nu = w_\nu e^{i\mathbf{q}\cdot\mathbf{r}_\alpha}, \tag{1}$$

where $\mathbf{p}$ is the four-momentum of the electron and $-\mathbf{q}$ that of the absorbed neutrino ($+\mathbf{q}$ is then the momentum of the emitted antineutrino).

But the r_α's in the exponentials of (1) operate on the nuclear wave function[1]. When expanded in series, the successive powers of r_α contribute to the successively forbidden transitions. Each extra power of r_α contributes a factor $\approx (p+q)R \approx E_0 R$ in the matrix element; this is of the same order as the factor contributed by the small Dirac components.

Thus it is customary to call *first forbidden* the transitions induced *either* by the first power of r_α *or* by the relativistic small components in the nuclear matrix element. Using a condensed notation[2], we obtain the following matrix elements and selection rules:

First Order Forbidden Transitions for Vector Interaction

Nuclear Matrix Element	Three Dimensional Tensor Character	Nuclear Selection Rule
$\int \boldsymbol{\gamma} \approx \int \mathbf{v}$ (small relativistic term)	Vector	$\Delta J = 0, 1$; no $0 \to 0$; $\pi_F \neq \pi_I$
$\int \mathbf{r}$ (first term from exponential)	Vector	Same

[1] This might not be evident in the notation in which the nuclear and leptic matrix elements are written as separate factors, but it becomes clear if, for instance, 8.13(3) is rewritten in the form

$$g\bar{\psi}_F(1\cdots A)\bar{\psi}_e \sum_{\alpha=1}^{A} (\tau^+\gamma_\mu)_\alpha(\gamma_\mu)_{\text{leptons}}\, \psi_\nu\psi_I(1\cdots A).$$

[2] For instance $\int \boldsymbol{\gamma}$ stands for $\int \psi_F^\dagger(1\cdots A)\sum_\alpha (\tau^+\boldsymbol{\gamma})_\alpha\, \psi_I(1\cdots A)\, d^3\mathbf{x}_1\cdots d^3\mathbf{x}_A$.

First Order Forbidden Transitions for Axial Vector Interaction

Nuclear Matrix Element	Three Dimensional Tensor Character	Nuclear Selection Rule
$\int \boldsymbol{\sigma} \times \mathbf{r}$	Vector	$\Delta J = 0, 1$; no $0 \to 0$; $\pi_F \neq \pi_I$
$\int B_{ij}$	Symmetrical traceless tensor*	$\Delta J = 0, 1, 2$; no $0 \to 0$; no $\frac{1}{2} \to \frac{1}{2}$; no $0 \leftrightarrow 1$; $\pi_F \neq \pi_I$
$\int \boldsymbol{\sigma} \cdot \mathbf{r}$	Pseudoscalar	$\Delta J = 0, \quad \pi_F \neq \pi_I$
$\int \gamma_5 \gamma_4$ (small relativistic term)	Pseudoscalar	Same

* $B_{ij} = \sigma_i x_j + \sigma_j x_i - \frac{2}{3}\delta_{ij}\boldsymbol{\sigma} \cdot \mathbf{r}$.

Similarly, for the second order we include transitions induced by matrix elements which are of second order in r (such as $r_i r_j$) or which are both relativistically small and of first order in r (such as $\boldsymbol{\gamma} \cdot \mathbf{r}$).

Since each $\mathbf{r}_\alpha$ from the development of the exponentials in (1) is accompanied by a factor $\mathbf{p} + \mathbf{q}$, forbidden transitions may have distorted spectra.

In some cases the shape of the spectrum can be predicted without ambiguity. For instance, a first forbidden transition with $\Delta J = 2$ necessarily has a $\int B_{ij}$ matrix element. Thus the factor that distorts the

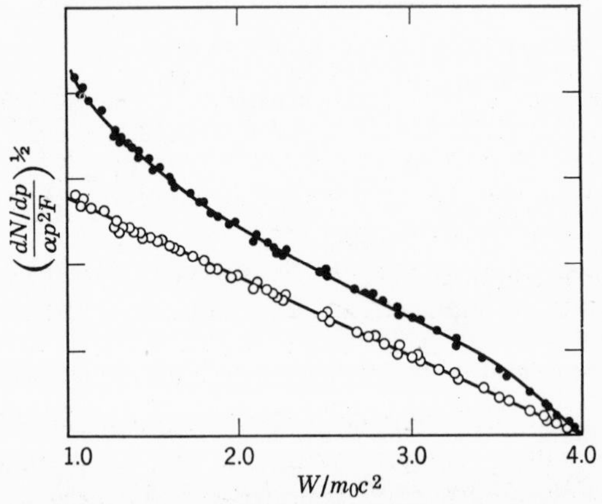

Fig. 8.16-1. Fermi plot of the Y^{91} spectrum. Solid circles, usual plot, α = constant; open-circle plot corrected to account for distortion according to formula (2): $\alpha = a_1$ (Reprinted with permission from M. Deutsch and O. Kofoed-Hansen, in *Experimental Nuclear Physics*, E. Segrè, editor, John Wiley, 1959, p. 531.)

spectrum is $\langle|\mathbf{p} + \mathbf{q}|^2\rangle$ and, this, when averaged over all neutrino directions, reduces to,

$$a_1 = p^2 + q^2 = (E^2 - m^2) + (E_0 - E)^2. \tag{2}$$

Fig. 8.16-1 shows a spectrum with a distortion of this kind.

In the discussion of forbidden transitions we must also keep in mind the possible contribution of interactions other than V and A. We have seen that S, T, P, and derivative coupling are negligible in allowed transitions; but they could be present with coupling constants smaller than g_V and g_A and become more important when the decay according to the predominant V and A interaction is forbidden.

For more detail on forbidden transitions the reader is referred to the literature (D-53; K-55; W-61b).

8.17 Radiative Corrections

a. Description of the Effect. We now discuss the electromagnetic radiation which sometimes accompanies the process of β decay and which consists of x rays produced in the coulomb field of the radioactive atom (*internal bremsstrahlung*): the quanta have a continuous energy spectrum from 0 to the maximum available energy E_0. Theoretically, their emission can be computed as a radiative correction to β decay by using the methods discussed in 6.2.

The emission of internal bremsstrahlung increases the decay probability and must be taken into account for the accurate determination of the coupling constants. In electron capture the energy available for the transition, which is usually carried by the neutrino, can be measured by studying the maximum energy of the internal bremsstrahlung.

The effect is of importance also for the decay of elementary particles (for instance, in π and μ decay, in which it is more frequent because of the larger energy available). Its computation is interesting as an example of an electromagnetic process of higher order.

We can start as usual by writing the diagrams, shown in Fig. 8.17-1. Only one diagram is important in each case, since the neutrino does not radiate and the nucleons radiate weakly because of their heavy mass.

In what follows we shall compute in detail the probability of emission of internal bremsstrahlung for electron capture. This is a particularly simple problem because the electron to be captured can be treated nonrelativistically.

b. Calculation of Bremsstrahlung from Electron Capture. Figure 8.17-2 shows the diagram of K capture with and without radiative

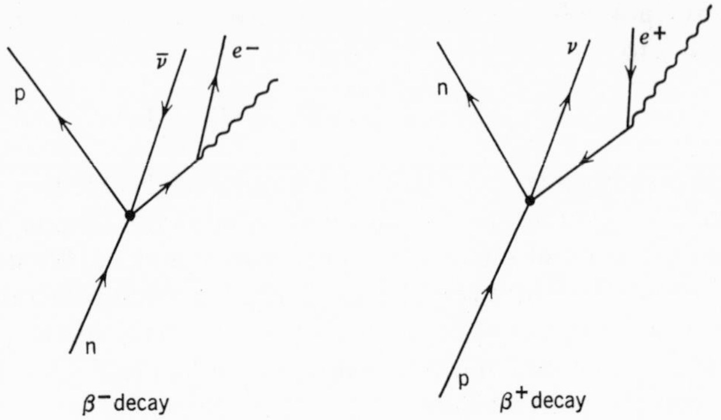

Fig. 8.17-1. Diagrams for radiative correction for β^- and β^+ decay.

corrections and defines the symbols used in the calculation. We shall discuss for simplicity only the case of an allowed Fermi transition[1].

The purpose of this calculation is to compute the spectrum and the relative frequency of the bremsstrahlung emitted in K capture $w_{K,\gamma}\, dk/w_K$; in the calculation of this quantity the nuclear matrix elements are the same in numerator and denominator and cancel.

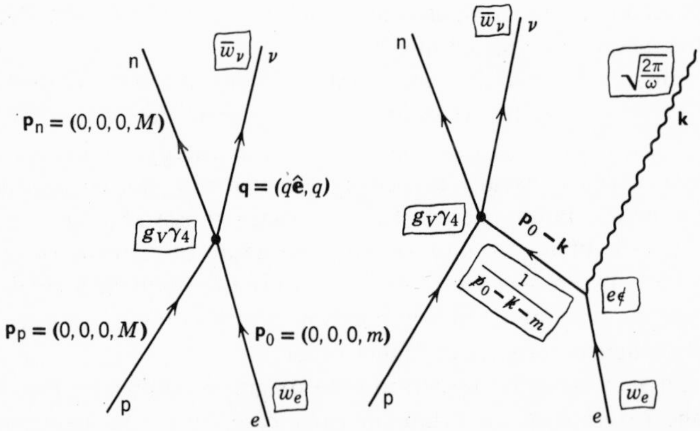

Fig. 8.17-2. Diagrams for K capture without and with radiative corrections, showing the symbols used in the computation and some of the factors to be written in the matrix element.

[1] In parity violating theory the $g\gamma_4$ factor at the β interaction vertex should be replaced by $g\gamma_4\sqrt{\tfrac{1}{2}}(1 - \Gamma_5)$. The internal bremsstrahlung would then be 100% circularly polarized left-handed.

With self-explanatory notation, we can write

$$\frac{w_{K,\gamma}\,dk}{w_K} = \frac{\rho_{K,\gamma}\,dk}{\rho_K}\frac{|M_{K,\gamma}|^2_{\text{av}}}{|M_K|^2_{\text{av}}}, \tag{1}$$

where (with normalization in unit lab volume)[1]

$$\rho_{K,\gamma}\,dk\,d\Omega_k = \frac{2}{(2\pi)^6}\,k^2\,dk\,\frac{d}{dE_0}\int_0^{E_0-k} q^2\,dq\,d\Omega_q\,d\Omega_k \tag{2a}$$

$$= 2\,\frac{(E_0-k)^2k^2\,dk}{(2\pi)^6}\,d\Omega_q\,d\Omega_k,$$

$$\rho_K = \frac{q^2\,dq\,d\Omega_q}{(2\pi)^3\,dq} = \frac{E_0^{\,2}}{(2\pi)^3}\,d\Omega_q, \tag{2b}$$

and

$$M_{K,\gamma} = eg_V\sqrt{\frac{2\pi}{k}}\sqrt{\frac{m_\nu}{q}}\left(\bar{w}_\nu\gamma_4\frac{1}{\not{p}-\not{k}-m}\not{\epsilon}w_e\right) \tag{3a}$$

$$M_K = g_V\sqrt{\frac{m_\nu}{q}}\,(\bar{w}_\nu\gamma_4 w_e). \tag{3b}$$

The matrix element (3*b*) is easily squared and summed over the two *K* electrons and the neutrino's spin by using the method of traces and remembering $\not{p} = m\gamma_4$;

$$\mathop{\mathsf{S}}_{e}\mathop{\mathsf{S}}_{\nu}|M_K|^2 = g_V^{\,2}\,\mathrm{Tr}\,\frac{m_\nu}{q}\left(\gamma_4\frac{\not{p}+m}{2m}\gamma_4\frac{\not{q}}{2m_\nu}\right) = g_V^{\,2}. \tag{4}$$

The parenthesis in (3b) must be rationalized and simplified before squaring. It is easily found that it can be written[2]

$$\left(\bar{w}_\nu\gamma_4\frac{\not{p}-\not{k}+m}{|\mathbf{p}-\mathbf{k}|^2-m^2}\not{\epsilon}w_e\right) = \frac{1}{2mk}\,(w_\nu\gamma_4\not{k}\not{\epsilon}w_e). \tag{5}$$

[1] The factor 2 in (2*a*) is for the two possible γ-ray polarizations, consistent with (3*a*), which is computed for specified polarization $\hat{\boldsymbol{\epsilon}}$. The factor $(m_\nu/q)^{1/2}$ in (3*a*) and (3*b*) is to reduce the neutrino wave normalization to a unit lab volume.

[2] In order to simplify the numerator of the propagator, observe that $\not{p} = m\gamma_4$ anti-commutes with $\not{\epsilon} = -\epsilon_1\gamma_1 - \epsilon_2\gamma_2 - \epsilon_3\gamma_3$; thus $(\not{p}+m)\epsilon w_e = \not{\epsilon}(-\not{p}+m)w_e = 0$, since w_e satisfies the Dirac equation. By developing the square in the denominator we obtain

$$|\mathbf{p}-\mathbf{k}|^2 = p^2 - k^2 - 2\mathbf{p}\cdot\mathbf{k} = m^2 - 0 - 2mk.$$

We can now sum and square (5) with the method of traces[1]:

$$\frac{1}{4m^2k^2} \mathop{S}_{e} \mathop{S}_{\nu} |(\bar{w}_\nu \gamma_4 \not{k} \not{e} w_e)|^2$$

(6)
$$= \frac{1}{4m^2k^2} \mathrm{Tr}\left(\gamma_4 \not{k} \not{e} \frac{m\gamma_4 + m}{2m} \not{e} \not{k} \gamma_4 \frac{\not{q}}{2m_\nu}\right)$$
$$= \frac{1}{4m^2k^2} \frac{2k}{4m_\nu} \mathrm{Tr}\,(\gamma_4 \not{k} \gamma_4 \not{q}) = \frac{1}{2} \frac{q}{m^2 m_\nu} (1 + \cos\theta_{\gamma\nu}).$$

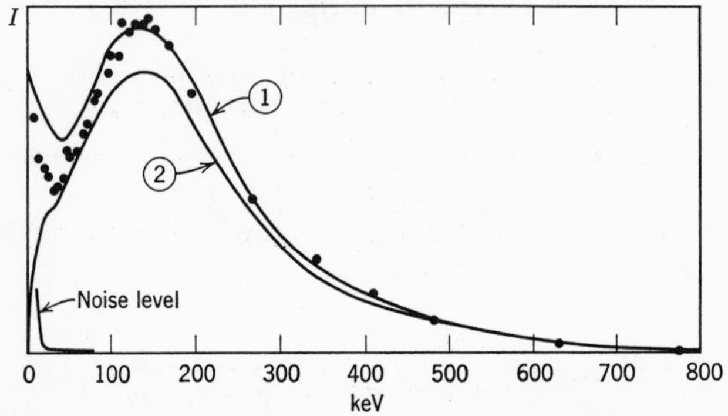

Fig. 8.17-3. Internal bremsstrahlung from A^{37}; points from experiments; curve (2), from the theory of Morrison and Schiff, which is essentially the same as reported in the text [from Lindquist and Wu, *Phys. Rev.*, **100**, 149 (1955)].

Thus the angular correlation between gammas and neutrinos is found. Collecting terms, we conclude

(7)
$$\frac{w_{K,\gamma}\, dk\, d\Omega_k}{w_K} = \frac{2(E_0 - k)^2 k^2\, dk\, d\Omega_k}{(2\pi)^3 E_0^2} e^2 \frac{2\pi}{k} \frac{m_\nu}{q} \frac{q}{2m^2 m_\nu} (1 + \cos\theta_{\gamma\nu})$$
$$= \frac{e^2}{(2\pi)^2} \frac{(E_0 - k)^2}{E_0^2} \frac{k\, dk}{m^2} (1 + \cos\theta_{\gamma\nu})\, d\Omega_k.$$

And, finally, integrating over $d\Omega_k$,

(8)
$$\frac{w_{K,\gamma}\, dk}{w_K} = \frac{e^2}{\pi} \frac{(E_0 - k)^2}{E_0^2} \frac{k\, dk}{m^2}.$$

Comparison of this formula with experiment is shown in Fig. 8.17-3.

[1] In (6) we may leave out as usual the m in the numerator of Λ_e. Considering that $\not{e}\gamma_4\not{e} = -\not{e}\not{e}\gamma_4 = \hat{e}\hat{e}\gamma_4 = \gamma_4$, the trace in the second line of (6) is

$$\mathrm{Tr}\, \frac{1}{4m_\nu} (\gamma_4 \not{k} \gamma_4 \not{k} \gamma_4 \not{q}).$$

But $\not{k}\gamma_4\not{k} = \not{k}(-\not{k}\gamma_4 + 2k) = 2k\not{k}$, since $\not{k}\not{k} = k^2 = 0$. Thus the trace becomes

$$\mathrm{Tr}\, \frac{2k}{4m_\nu} (\gamma_4 \not{k} \gamma_4 \not{q}) = \frac{2k}{4m_\nu} \mathrm{Tr}\,(-\not{k}\not{q} + 2kq) = \frac{2k}{m_\nu} (kq + \mathbf{k} \cdot \mathbf{q}).$$

8.2 Parity Violation in Nuclear β Decay

8.21 Evidence of Violation of Parity

a. Observation of Nonconservation of Parity in *K*-Meson Decay. In the late 1940's and early 1950's physicists had discovered a number of new particles and were busily engaged in determining their properties. One of these particles, originally called θ, decayed into two π mesons, and another, named τ, disintegrated into three π's. A study of the angular distribution of the decay products strongly indicated that these had 0 angular momentum, and (considering the negative intrinsic parity of the π meson) it was natural to assign spin and parity 0^+ and 0^- to the θ and τ particles respectively.

Measurements of mass and mean life were initially inaccurate, but by 1957 they had given the following results:

	θ^+	τ^+	
Mass	966.7 ± 2.0	966.3 ± 2.1	(in electron masses)
Lifetime	1.21 ± 0.02	1.19 ± 0.05	(in 10^{-8} sec)

Struck by the similarity of these data, Yang and Lee discussed the possibility that θ and τ were, in effect, the same particle (today called the K meson) with alternate decay modes. But, if this were the case, parity would not be a good quantum number: *parity would not be conserved.*

This observation led Yang and Lee to examine the experimental evidence for parity conservation: *they concluded that there is abundant evidence that parity is conserved in strong and electromagnetic interactions, but they could not find any evidence that it was conserved in weak interactions, including β decay.*

Since the θ and τ decay is weak, they suspected that parity may not be conserved in any weak interaction; they predicted theoretically several measurable consequences of parity violation in β decay, and they suggested definite experiments to test the validity of the parity conservation principle.

b. Experimental Evidence for Correlation between Nuclear Spin and β-Electron Momentum. According to our discussion in 1.15, parity conservation requires that all terms of an equation must have the same behavior under reflection. Thus a transition probability (number of events per unit time) must be scalar and cannot contain pseudoscalar terms[1]. This law, as we have seen, is respected for electromagnetic and strong interactions.

If parity is not conserved in nuclear β decay, we can possibly have a transition probability containing both scalar and pseudoscalar terms such as

$$w = A\left(1 + \alpha \frac{\mathbf{J} \cdot \mathbf{p}}{Jp}\right) = A(1 + \alpha \cos \theta_{Jp}), \tag{1}$$

where A and α are scalars, $\mathbf{J}$ is the spin of the nucleus, and $\mathbf{p}$, the momentum of the emitted electron. In other words, the number of electrons emitted

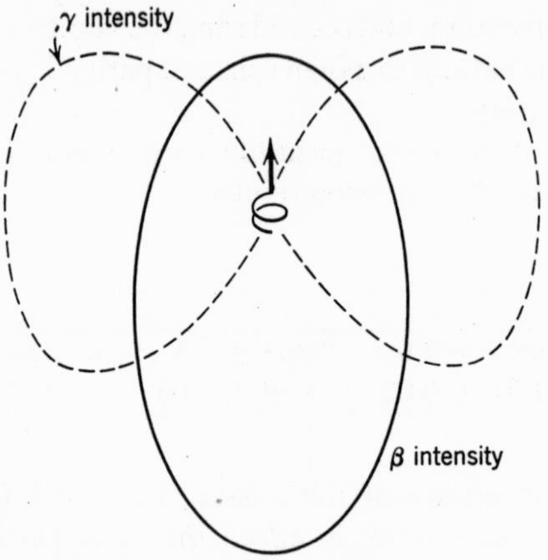

Fig. 8.21-1. β asymmetry (full line) and γ anisotropy (dashed line) $|X_2^2|^2$ (see Fig. 4.15-1) in the decay of Co^{60} polarized with spin up.

parallel and antiparallel to the spin of the source could be different (Fig. 8.21-1).

At the suggestion of Yang and Lee, this possibility was explored experimentally, and a large amount of *asymmetry* was found in the emitted electrons.

The experiments (Fig. 8.21-2) were performed with sources of Co^{60} (W-57) and Co^{58} (A-57), since, as we have seen in 4.32a, it is possible to prepare polarized samples of these isotopes by applying a magnetic field at

[1] A transition amplitude (matrix element) can contain pseudoscalar operators without violating parity conservation. For instance the matrix element for pion-nucleon interaction contains the operator $\boldsymbol{\sigma} \cdot \mathbf{p}$ whose odd parity is compensated by the opposite parity of the pion and nucleon wave functions. In this case the transition probability contains $|\boldsymbol{\sigma} \cdot \mathbf{p}|^2$, which is a perfectly acceptable scalar.

However, *conservation of parity prevents the mixing of even and odd operators* in the amplitude because such mixing would result in odd interference terms in the amplitude squared.

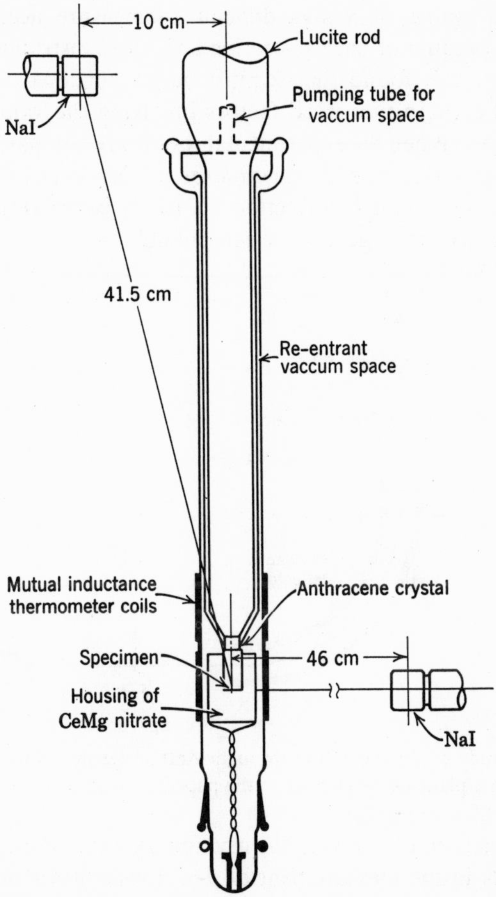

Fig. 8.21-2. Apparatus used to establish violation of parity in the β decay of Co. The NaI counter measures the γ anisotropy (and thus the polarization of the source) and the anthracene crystal the β asymmetry [from Wu, Ambler, Hayward, Hopper, and Hudson, *Phys. Rev.*, **105,** 1413 (1957)].

low temperature. The amount of source polarization was determined by measuring the anisotropy of the γ rays emerging from the cryostat, and, simultaneously, the asymmetry of the β rays was studied with an electron counter inside the cryostat itself. A clear correlation was found corresponding to an "*asymmetry coefficient*:"

$$\begin{aligned} &\alpha < 0 \quad \text{for} \quad \beta^- \, (\mathrm{Co}^{60}) \\ &\alpha > 0 \quad \text{for} \quad \beta^+ \, (\mathrm{Co}^{58}) \end{aligned} \tag{2}$$

This corresponds to electrons being emitted preferentially opposite to the spin and vice versa for positrons.

The actual value of α was difficult to measure accurately in these experiments because of back scattering and other instrumental difficulties. Theoretically, it is found that α must be proportional to the electron's velocity and contain numerical factors involving the values of the initial and final spins. When the experimental results are compared to the theory, they all indicate that α *is always as large as theoretically possible.* Parity violation is not a small correction to parity-conserving theories: the effects are always as large as they can possibly be.

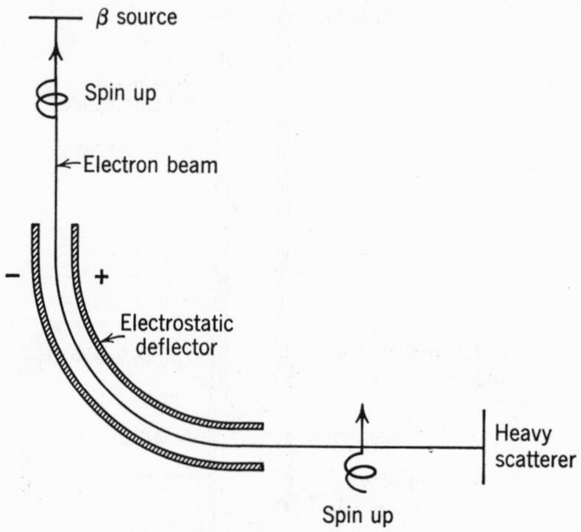

Fig. 8.21-3. Study of β polarization through Mott scattering. The scattered electrons are detected in a plane perpendicular to the paper.

Another method of studying the asymmetry without using low temperatures consists in the measurement of *β-γ circular polarization correlation.* In this method the β source is unpolarized, and the polarization of the nucleus after β emission is revealed by the circular polarization of subsequent γ rays.

c. Helicity of Electrons. Another possible consequence of parity violation is the polarization of the β particles in the direction of their motion (helicity). Polarization effects of β decay electrons had been observed as early as 1928 (C-28), but the experiments had not received the attention they deserved.

Following the papers of Lee and Yang and the experiment of Wu and Ambler, many investigators studied the polarization of the electrons of β decay. For this purpose the β rays are first deflected electrostatically—in order to transform the longitudinal polarization into a transverse one—and then scattered in the electrostatic field of a nucleus (Mott scattering) (Fig. 8.21-3). The polarization is measured from the asymmetry of the scattering (K-59b).

We can also study the longitudinal polarization directly by scattering from a target of electrons (K-59b) polarized along the direction of incidence (Moeller scattering from magnetized iron).

Another experimental method consists of the measurement of the circular polarization of the γ rays of internal bremsstrahlung (G-57) (see 8.17), which depends on the direction of the spin of the radiating electron (Fig. 8.21-4).

The helicity of the positrons can also be studied by means of observations on their annihilation (H-57a, b; H-58; P-57a). It is seen, for instance,

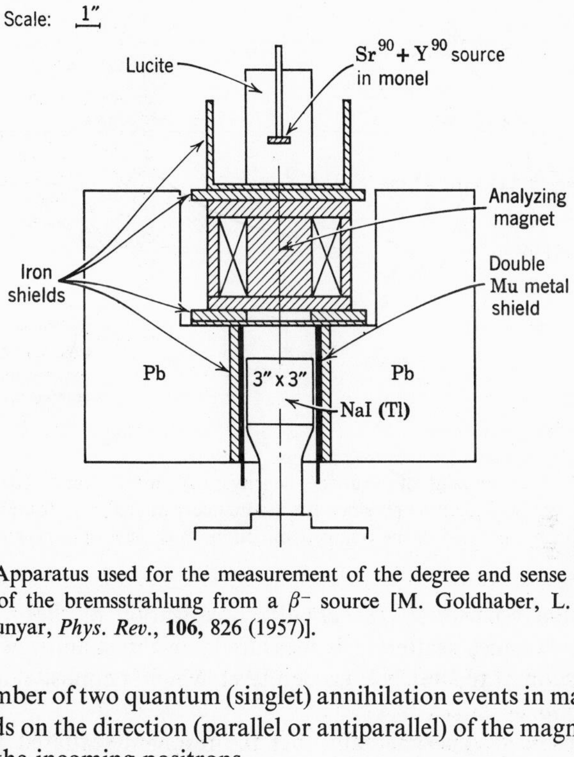

Fig. 8.21-4. Apparatus used for the measurement of the degree and sense of circular polarization of the bremsstrahlung from a β^- source [M. Goldhaber, L. Grodzins, and A. W. Sunyar, *Phys. Rev.*, **106**, 826 (1957)].

that the number of two quantum (singlet) annihilation events in magnetized iron depends on the direction (parallel or antiparallel) of the magnetization relative to the incoming positrons.

For K capture the violation of parity is revealed by the circular polarization of internal bremsstrahlung (B-58a).

All of these experiments concur in showing that β electrons and positrons are partially polarized and that the polarization is

$$(3) \qquad P_e = \mp v \quad \begin{cases} - \text{ (left-handed, } \mathbf{p} \text{ and } \boldsymbol{\sigma} \text{ antiparallel) for electrons} \\ + \text{ (right-handed, } \mathbf{p} \text{ and } \boldsymbol{\sigma} \text{ parallel) for positrons} \end{cases}$$

within the limit of accuracy.

d. Helicity of Neutrinos. The helicity of the neutrinos has been measured in an ingenious experiment by Goldhaber, Grodzins, and Sunyar (G-58d). These authors used a source of Eu^{152}, whose *K*-capture decay into Sm^{152} is followed by a $\mathcal{E}1$ γ ray of 961 keV (Fig. 8.21-5*a*). The 961 keV transition is so fast [$\tau = (3 \pm 1) \times 10^{-14}$ sec] that *resonance scattering is observable* at room temperature if the neutrino is *emitted opposite to the* γ *ray*, compensating for the γ-recoil energy. By means of a

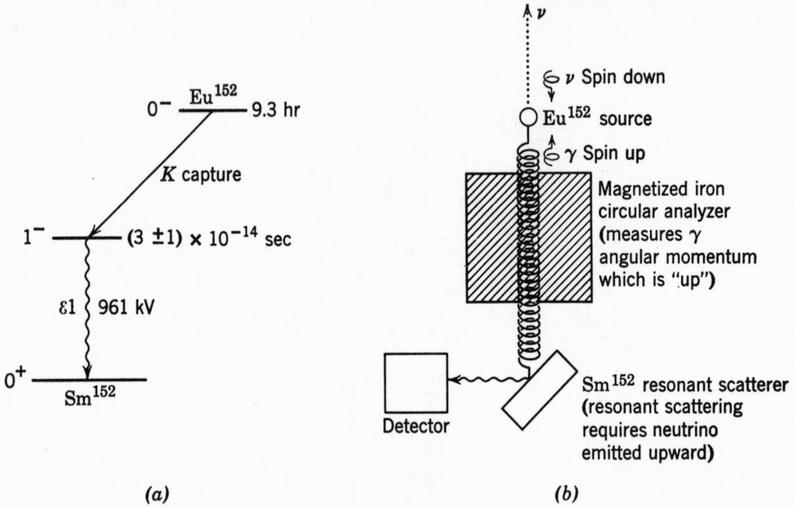

Fig. 8.21-5. Measurement of Neutrino helicity. (*a*) partial decay scheme of Eu^{152}, (*b*) scheme of the experiment: since the resonance-scattered γ is found to have spin up, the neutrino, emitted in the opposite direction, must have spin down.

transmission polarimeter the circular polarization of the γ rays which produce resonance scattering is measured; in this manner we know the spin direction of the 961 keV excited level, which is opposite to the spin of the neutrino.

It is observed experimentally that the resonant scattered γ rays have negative helicity (spin up in the scheme of Fig. 8.21-5*b*). Thus the 961 keV excited state giving rise to the resonant scattered γ had spin up. Considering that Eu^{152} (9.3 hr) has spin zero, it is concluded that the *K*-capture process has produced in the source an upward change in angular momentum of one unit. Since the spin-parity values indicate an allowed Gamow-Teller transition and the electron captured was in an *S* state, there is no orbital angular momentum to be considered. The electron captured must have had spin up, and the neutrino emitted spin down.

Finally, since we know that the neutrino[1] went up, we deduce that it has *negative* helicity.

The results of the experiment are consistent with 100% polarization of the neutrinos. Thus, in agreement with the simplest theoretical formulation and with all experimental data, we assume in what follows that

$$P_\nu = \mp 1 \quad \begin{cases} - \text{ for neutrinos,} \\ + \text{ for antineutrinos.} \end{cases} \tag{4}$$

e. Connection between Helicity and Angular Correlation. It is of interest to observe that the helicity measurements are consistent with

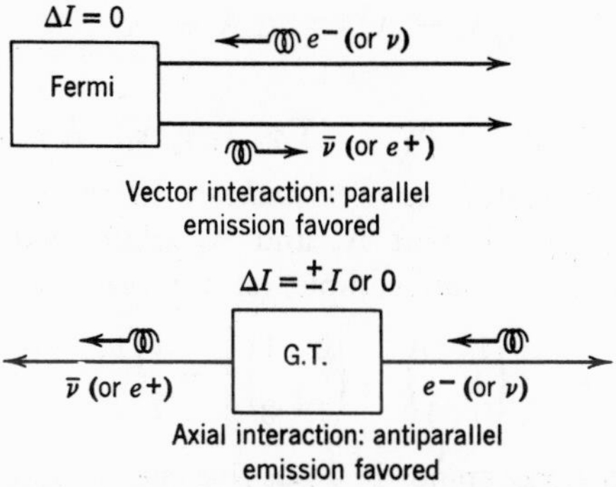

Fig. 8.21-6. Pictorial explanation of the connection between helicity and angular correlation. Note that scalar or tensor interaction would lead to contradiction between helicity and correlation.

the experiments on electron-neutrino angular correlation. For an allowed Fermi transition electron and neutrino must be polarized with antiparallel spins in order to account for $\Delta J = 0$; in a Gamow-Teller decay the two leptons must have parallel spins to allow for the possibility $\Delta J = 1$ (Fig. 8.21-6).

Thus the selection of the vector and axial-vector coupling could have been made as a result of helicity measurements. (This is indeed what happened, for the determination of helicity preceded the correct angular distribution measurements.)

8.22 Theory of β Decay with Parity Violation

a. Helicity Projection Operators. In order to formulate the theory of weak interactions with parity violation, we shall make use of the

[1] Neutrinos emitted in *K* capture must be particles (not antiparticles) for conservation of leptons!

relativistic pseudoscalar operator γ_5 or, to conform with usual signs and nomenclature of the equivalent Hermitian operator[1]

$$\Gamma_5 = -i\gamma_5 = \begin{pmatrix} 0 & 1 \\ 1 & 0 \end{pmatrix}. \tag{1}$$

Let us introduce the parity-mixing operators

$$\Lambda_r = \tfrac{1}{2}(1 + \Gamma_5), \qquad \Lambda_l = \tfrac{1}{2}(1 - \Gamma_5), \tag{2}$$

which satisfy the relations appropriate to projection operators

$$\begin{gathered} \Lambda_r + \Lambda_l = 1, \qquad \Lambda_r\Lambda_l = \Lambda_l\Lambda_r = 0, \\ \Lambda_r\Lambda_r = \Lambda_r, \qquad \Lambda_l\Lambda_l = \Lambda_l, \end{gathered} \tag{3}$$

and

$$\Lambda_r^{\dagger} = \Lambda_r, \quad \Lambda_l^{\dagger} = \Lambda_l; \qquad \Lambda_r\gamma_\mu = \gamma_\mu\Lambda_l, \quad \Lambda_l\gamma_\mu = \gamma_\mu\Lambda_r. \tag{4}$$

These operators are called the *right and left helicity projection operators*, since it is easily proven that Λ_r and Λ_l select right- and left-handed neutrinos, respectively. For example, let us write Λ_l in matrix form

$$\Lambda_l = \frac{1}{2}\left[\begin{pmatrix} 1 & 0 \\ 0 & 1 \end{pmatrix} - \begin{pmatrix} 0 & 1 \\ 1 & 0 \end{pmatrix}\right] = \frac{1}{2}\begin{pmatrix} 1 & -1 \\ -1 & 1 \end{pmatrix}, \tag{5}$$

and apply it to a Dirac spinor in a positive energy state:

$$\Lambda_l\psi = \frac{1}{2}\begin{pmatrix} 1 & -1 \\ -1 & 1 \end{pmatrix}\begin{pmatrix} \zeta \\ \dfrac{\boldsymbol{\sigma}\cdot\mathbf{p}}{|E| + m}\zeta \end{pmatrix} = \frac{1}{2}\begin{pmatrix} \zeta - \dfrac{\boldsymbol{\sigma}\cdot\mathbf{p}}{|E| + m}\zeta \\ -\zeta + \dfrac{\boldsymbol{\sigma}\cdot\mathbf{p}}{|E| + m}\zeta \end{pmatrix}. \tag{6}$$

For neutrinos ($m = 0$) (6) becomes

$$\Lambda_l\psi_\nu = \frac{1}{2}\begin{pmatrix} \zeta_\nu - \dfrac{\boldsymbol{\sigma}\cdot\mathbf{q}}{q}\zeta_\nu \\ -\zeta_\nu + \dfrac{\boldsymbol{\sigma}\cdot\mathbf{q}}{q}\zeta_\nu \end{pmatrix} = \begin{cases} \begin{pmatrix} \zeta_\nu \\ -\zeta_\nu \end{pmatrix} & \text{if } \dfrac{\boldsymbol{\sigma}\cdot\mathbf{q}}{q} = -1 \text{ (left helicity)} \\ 0 & \text{if } \dfrac{\boldsymbol{\sigma}\cdot\mathbf{q}}{q} = +1 \text{ (right helicity)} \end{cases} \tag{7}$$

This proves that Λ_l selects left-handed neutrinos. We can also see that it selects right-handed antineutrinos: this can be argued from the theory of "holes," or, more formally, it can be proved by considering that Γ_5 anticommutes with the charge exchange operator S_C.

When applied to electrons whose mass does not vanish, the helicity operators select partially polarized beams. The relative probabilities, P_r and

[1] The representation 6.12(13) of the γ matrices is used in the present treatment.

P_l for right- and left-handed polarization ($\boldsymbol{\sigma} \cdot \mathbf{p} = \pm p$) in the state $\Lambda_l \psi_e$ are from (6)

(8)
$$P_r = \left| 1 - \frac{p}{|E| + m} \right|^2,$$
$$P_l = \left| 1 + \frac{p}{|E| + m} \right|^2;$$

and thus the (left-handed) polarization of the selected electron beam is

(9) $$-P = \frac{P_l - P_r}{P_r + P_l} = \frac{4[p/(|E| + m)]}{2 + 2[p/(|E| + m)]^2} = \frac{p(|E| + m)}{E^2 + m\,|E|} = \frac{p}{|E|} = v.$$

If (7) and (9) are compared with 8.21(3) and (4), we see that we obtain agreement with the observed helicities if the lepton wave functions ψ in the weak interaction Hamiltonian are replaced by their left-handed components $\Lambda_l \psi$.

The asymmetries, such as those observed in the Wu and Ambler experiment, can be deduced from the helicities, as already observed in 8.21e. For a formal computation of the asymmetries see part c of this section.

b. The Parity-Violating Matrix Element. Since the helicities can be obtained in agreement with the experiment if the lepton wave functions ψ are replaced by their left-handed components, we shall write the matrix element of parity-violating theory by inserting a factor Λ_l to the left of all lepton states. If we introduce a special symbol for the left-handed components

(10) $$\Lambda_l \psi \equiv \chi$$

the leptic part of the matrix element for β^- decay must be written

(11)
$$\bar{\chi}_e \gamma_\mu \chi_\nu \quad \text{for vector coupling,}$$
$$\bar{\chi}_e \gamma_5 \gamma_\mu \chi_\nu \quad \text{for axial vector coupling.}$$

It is interesting to observe that the helicity of one of the leptons is a consequence of the helicity of the other. This must be so because of conservation of angular momentum and can be proved formally as follows[1]:

(12)
$$\begin{aligned} \bar{\psi}_e \gamma_\mu \chi_\nu &= \bar{\psi}_e \gamma_\mu \Lambda_l \psi_\nu = \bar{\psi}_e \gamma_\mu \Lambda_l \Lambda_l \psi_\nu \\ &= \bar{\psi}_e \Lambda_r \gamma_\mu \Lambda_l \psi_\nu = \overline{\Lambda_l \psi_e} \gamma_\mu \Lambda_l \psi_\nu = \bar{\chi}_e \gamma_\mu \chi_\nu . \end{aligned}$$

[1] If the matrix element contained an even number of γ's, as for scalar or tensor interaction, we would find that left-handed neutrinos are accompanied by right-handed electrons.

Since the insertion of Λ_l does not change the predictions of electron-neutrino angular distribution, the nuclear factor must contain only vector and axial terms with[1]

$$(13)\qquad \begin{aligned} &\text{Vector coupling constant} = \sqrt{2}g \\ &\text{Axial coupling constant} \ = \sqrt{2}Rg \qquad (|R| \approx 1.15), \end{aligned}$$

where $g = 1.4 \times 10^{-49}$ erg cm³ is the vector coupling constant of parity-conserving theory [8.13(11), (12)]. Thus we can write from 8.14(2)

$$(14)\quad M = \sqrt{2}g\Big[\bar{\psi}_{\mathrm{F}}(1, \cdots, A)\sum_{\alpha}(\tau^{+}\gamma_{\mu})_{\alpha}\psi_{\mathrm{I}}(1, \cdots, A)\Big](\bar{\chi}_{e}\gamma_{\mu}\chi_{\nu})$$
$$-\sqrt{2}Rg\Big[\bar{\psi}_{\mathrm{F}}(1, \cdots, A)\sum_{\alpha}(\tau^{+}\Gamma_{5}\gamma_{\mu})_{\alpha}\psi_{\mathrm{I}}(1, \cdots, A)\Big](\bar{\chi}_{e}\Gamma_{5}\gamma_{\mu}\chi_{\nu}) + \text{h.c.}$$

But the leptic factors turn out to be identical[2]:

$$(15)\qquad \bar{\chi}_{e}\gamma_{\mu}\chi_{\nu} = \bar{\chi}_{e}\Gamma_{5}\gamma_{\mu}\chi_{\nu},$$

and (14) can be rewritten more simply as

$$(16)\quad M = \sqrt{2}g\Big\{\bar{\psi}_{\mathrm{F}}(1, \cdots, A)\sum_{\alpha}[\tau^{+}(1 - R\Gamma_{5})\gamma_{\mu}]_{\alpha}\psi_{\mathrm{I}}(1, \cdots, A)\Big\}(\bar{\chi}_{e}\gamma_{\mu}\chi_{\nu}) + \text{h.c.}$$

Nonrelativistically in the nucleons this becomes

$$(17)\quad \begin{aligned} M &= \sqrt{2}g\Big(\int 1\Big)(\bar{\chi}_{e}\gamma_{4}\chi_{\nu}) + \sqrt{2}Rg\Big(\int \boldsymbol{\sigma}\Big)\cdot(\bar{\chi}_{e}\gamma_{4}\boldsymbol{\sigma}\chi_{\nu}) + \text{h.c.} \\ &= \sqrt{2}g\Big(\int 1\Big)(\bar{\chi}_{e}\gamma_{4}\chi_{\nu}) \\ &\quad - \sqrt{2}Rg\Big(\int \sigma_{+}\Big)(\bar{\chi}_{e}\gamma_{4}\sigma_{-}\chi_{\nu}) - \sqrt{2}Rg\Big(\int \sigma_{-}\Big)(\bar{\chi}_{e}\gamma_{4}\sigma_{+}\chi_{\nu}) \\ &\quad + \sqrt{2}Rg\Big(\int \sigma_{z}\Big)(\bar{\chi}_{e}\gamma_{4}\sigma_{z}\chi_{\nu}) + \text{h.c.} \end{aligned}$$

For allowed transitions $\psi_{\nu,e}$ is replaced by $w_{\nu,e}$ and $\chi_{\nu,e}$ by $\frac{1}{2}(1 - \Gamma_5)w_{\nu,e}$.

c. Transition Rates and Asymmetries. In order to compute the asymmetries, we must calculate the average square of the matrix element for polarized nuclei in the new form of the theory. For this we must proceed as in 8.13(7) and 8.14(7), but inserting a projection operator $\Lambda_l = \frac{1}{2}(1 - \Gamma_5)$ to select left-handed neutrinos: as proved in (12), this automatically selects left-handed electrons also.

When the new matrix element is squared and averaged by the method of traces, it is sufficient to write the left-hand projection operator only

[1] The factor $\sqrt{2}$ is needed because we want the same transition probability for the same value of g, despite the fact that we accept only one half of the neutrino states.

[2] $\Gamma_5\gamma_\mu\chi_\nu = -\gamma_\mu\Gamma_5\frac{1}{2}(1 - \Gamma_5)\psi_\nu = -\gamma_\mu\frac{1}{2}(\Gamma_5 - 1)\psi_\nu = \gamma_\mu\chi_\nu$.

once[1]. Thus the new transition probability consists of separate parity-conserving and parity-violating parts[2]. The parity-conserving part has been computed in 8.13(7) and 8.14(7). For the parity-violating part the calculation of the trace must be repeated after inserting a factor $-\Gamma_5$ to the left of the neutrino projection operator $\not{q}$.

It can be seen immediately (by counting the number of the various γ_μ) that the contributions of parity violation vanish for the nonrelativistic vector interaction (γ_4) and for the axial vector terms without spin flip ($\gamma_4\sigma_z$ or $-\Gamma_5\gamma_3$):

$$\text{(18)} \qquad \mathrm{Tr}\,[\gamma_4(-\Gamma_5)\not{q}\gamma_4(\not{p} + m)] = 0,$$

$$\text{(19)} \qquad \mathrm{Tr}\,[\Gamma_5\gamma_3(-\Gamma_5)\not{q}\Gamma_5\gamma_3(\not{p} + m)] = 0.$$

For spin flip ($\gamma_4\sigma_\pm = -\Gamma_5\gamma_\pm$) the parity-violating trace does not vanish and its contribution describes the asymmetries. We obtain[3]

$$\text{(20)} \qquad \frac{1}{4Eq}\,\mathrm{Tr}\,[\Gamma_5\gamma_\pm(-\Gamma_5)\not{q}\gamma_\mp\Gamma_5(\not{p} + m)] = \mp v\cos\theta_{eJ} \pm \cos\theta_{\nu J}.$$

By making a comparison with (17) we see that for a nuclear transition with $\Delta M = -1$ (nuclear term in $\int \sigma_-$, leptic term in σ_+) we must use the upper signs in (20). Thus we obtain that the electrons of Co^{60} go predominantly backward with asymmetry coefficient v and that the neutrinos go predominantly forward with asymmetry coefficient 1, in agreement with the experiment.

The formulas developed apply to β^- emission. The results for β^+ are derived in the same manner and are also in agreement with experiment.

d. General Formulation of Parity-Violating Theories. The general form of the matrix element for a parity-nonconserving theory (without derivative coupling) can be obtained as a modification of 8.14(2). The

[1] For instance,

$$\begin{aligned}\mathrm{Tr}\, Q\Lambda_l\not{q}\gamma_4(Q\Lambda_l)^\dagger\gamma_4(\not{p} + m) &= \mathrm{Tr}\, Q\Lambda_l\not{q}\gamma_4\Lambda_l Q^\dagger\gamma_4(\not{p} + m)\\ &= \mathrm{Tr}\, Q\Lambda_l\Lambda_l\not{q}\gamma_4 Q^\dagger\gamma_4(\not{p} + m)\\ &= \mathrm{Tr}\, Q\Lambda_l\not{q}\gamma_4 Q^\dagger\gamma_4(\not{p} + m).\end{aligned}$$

[2] Taking (13) into account, one sees that the g^2 of the old theory is replaced by $(\sqrt{2}g)^2\,\frac{1}{2} = g^2$ in the parity-conserving part and by $-(\sqrt{2}g)^2\,\frac{1}{2}\Gamma_5 = -g^2\Gamma_5$ in the parity-violating part of the new transition probability.

[3] First, it is readily verified that $\gamma_4(\Gamma_5\gamma_\pm)^\dagger\gamma_4 = \gamma_\mp\Gamma_5$. For the computation we observe that the term in m vanishes as usual, and we may use $\Gamma_5 q\gamma_i\Gamma_5 = q\gamma_i$. Then the trace (20) becomes

$$\begin{aligned}-\mathrm{Tr}\,[\Gamma_5\gamma_\pm\not{q}\gamma_\mp\not{p}] &= -\tfrac{1}{2}\mathrm{Tr}\,[i\gamma_1\gamma_2\gamma_3\gamma_4(\gamma_1 \pm i\gamma_2)\not{q}(\gamma_1 \mp i\gamma_2)\not{p}]\\ &= \tfrac{1}{2}\mathrm{Tr}\,[i\gamma_1\gamma_2\gamma_3\gamma_4(\gamma_1 \pm i\gamma_2)(\gamma_1 \mp i\gamma_2)\not{q}\not{p} + \text{traceless terms}]\\ &= \tfrac{1}{2}\mathrm{Tr}\,[i\gamma_1\gamma_2\gamma_3\gamma_4(\mp 2i\gamma_1\gamma_2)\not{q}\not{p} + \text{traceless terms}]\\ &= \mp\mathrm{Tr}\,\gamma_3\gamma_4\not{q}\not{p} = 4(\mp q p_3 \pm E q_3).\end{aligned}$$

general matrix element will be the sum of five terms (for different $X = S, V, T, A, P$), but now each term can contain an even and an odd part in the leptic factor. For this 8.14(2) is written by substituting each g_X with $(1/\sqrt{2})(g_X + \Gamma_5 g_X')$, where Γ_5 operates on the leptons:

$$(21)\quad M_X = \left[\bar{\psi}_F(1, \cdots, A) \sum_\alpha (\tau^+ Q_X)_\alpha \psi_I(1, \cdots, A)\right] \cdot [\bar{\psi}_e Q_X \sqrt{\tfrac{1}{2}}(g_X + \Gamma_5 g_X')\psi_\nu] + \text{h.c.}$$

The theory now has 10 arbitrary constants g_X and g_X'. If we also want to take into account the possibility of time-reversal violation, each g_X and g_X' is complex and one is faced with 20 real constants.

Formulas describing the parity-violating and time-nonreversible effects (asymmetries, helicities, etc.) in terms of these 20 constants have been computed and are available in the literature (J-57). The parity-violating effects thus obtained are smaller than those derived from (9) and (20) unless $|g_X| = |g_X'|$.

8.23 Two-Component Relativistic Spinor Equations

a. Two-Component Neutrino Theory. It can be seen from 8.22(6) that the operator Λ_l (and Λ_r) transforms a four-component spinor into one whose upper and lower components differ only in sign. Thus effectively $\chi = \Lambda_l \psi$ is a two-component wave function.

For neutrinos ($m = 0$) χ_ν satisfies the Dirac equation. This is easily shown by multiplying to the left by $\Lambda_r = \frac{1}{2}(1 + \Gamma_5)$ the neutrino's Dirac equation $i\not{\partial}\psi_\nu = 0$; recalling that $\Lambda_r \not{\partial} = \not{\partial}\Lambda_l$, we can write

$$(1)\qquad i\not{\partial}\chi_\nu = 0$$

or

$$(2)\qquad i\gamma_4 \partial_4 \chi_\nu = -i\boldsymbol{\gamma} \cdot \nabla \chi_\nu,$$

which is a zero mass Dirac equation for χ_ν.

In order to see the meaning of this equation, let us multiply (2) to the left by $\Gamma_5 \gamma_4$; considering that $\Gamma_5 \chi_\nu = -\chi_\nu$ and $\Gamma_5 \gamma_4 \gamma_i = \sigma_i$ [see 6.12(12)], we obtain

$$(3)\qquad i\partial_4 \chi_\nu = i\boldsymbol{\sigma} \cdot \nabla \chi_\nu.$$

For definite momentum $\mathbf{q}$ and energy E (3), becomes

$$(4)\qquad E\chi_\nu = -\boldsymbol{\sigma} \cdot \mathbf{q}\chi_\nu.$$

In this last form the equation for χ_ν shows clearly that if $\boldsymbol{\sigma} \cdot \mathbf{q} = -q$ (left-handed neutrinos) $E = q$, whereas for $\boldsymbol{\sigma} \cdot \mathbf{q} = q$ (right-handed neutrinos) $E = -q$: thus all positive-energy neutrinos are left-handed and all negative-energy neutrinos are right-handed.

It is immediately apparent that (4) splits into two 2-component equations. Making a distinction between upper and lower components and using 8.22(7), (4) can be written

$$E\begin{pmatrix} \chi_{U,\nu} \\ -\chi_{U,\nu} \end{pmatrix} = -\begin{pmatrix} \boldsymbol{\sigma}\cdot\mathbf{q} & 0 \\ 0 & \boldsymbol{\sigma}\cdot\mathbf{q} \end{pmatrix}\begin{pmatrix} \chi_{U,\nu} \\ -\chi_{U,\nu} \end{pmatrix}, \tag{5}$$

which is clearly equivalent to two identical 2-component equations.

The possibility of formulating a relativistic theory of neutrinos involving only two components was recognized long ago (P-33). This possibility arises from the fact that for $m = 0$ the relation 6.12(4), $(\gamma_\mu p_\mu)(\gamma_\nu p_\nu) = 0$, reduces to 6.12(1), $E^2 = p^2$, if the γ's are the 2×2 matrices $\gamma_i = \sigma_i$, $\gamma_4 = \pm 1$. Thus the first-order wave equation for massless particles of spin $\frac{1}{2}$ can be written

$$\boldsymbol{\sigma}\cdot\nabla\zeta \pm \frac{\partial}{\partial t}\zeta = 0, \tag{6}$$

where ζ is a two-component Pauli spinor; (6) reduces to (3) if ζ is identified with upper or lower components of χ_ν and if the minus sign is chosen.

Equation (6) was discarded because it does not conserve parity, but it is quite appropriate to describe the neutrinos of parity-violating β theory.

b. A Two-Component Equation for the Electron. The concept of helicity for the electron is basically different from that of the neutrino, and the difference can be explained in simple physical terms.

Since the neutrino always travels at the speed of light, its helicity is the same in all systems of reference. The helicity of the electron, instead, is not invariant: an electron that appears to be left-handed in the laboratory system, looks right-handed to an observer that is traveling faster than the electron itself because he will see the same spin direction but an opposite direction of momentum.

This behavior is reflected in differences in the formalism. The function $\chi_e = \Lambda_l \psi_e$ does not satisfy the Dirac equation with mass $m \neq 0$ (since $\Lambda_r \not{\partial} = \not{\partial}\Lambda_l$, but $\Lambda_r m = m\Lambda_r$).

It is interesting to observe that the equation for spinors of finite mass can also be written as a two-component equation. In this case, however, it is a second-order differential equation in the time variable: thus the specification of the initial state requires the knowledge of the two-component wave function and of its derivative, in all four different functions, as in the original equation of Dirac.

In order to find the two component equations for the electron, let us multiply the Dirac equation 6.15(3)

$$(i\not{\partial} - e\not{A} - m)\psi_e = 0,$$

by $\frac{1}{2}(1 + \Gamma_5)$ to the left. Remembering that $\Gamma_5 \not\partial = -\not\partial \Gamma_5$, $\Gamma_5 \not A = -\not A \Gamma_5$, $\Gamma_5 m = m\Gamma_5$, we obtain

$$(i\not\partial - e\not A)\tfrac{1}{2}(1 - \Gamma_5)\psi_e = m\tfrac{1}{2}(1 + \Gamma_5)\psi_e$$
$$= m\psi_e + m\tfrac{1}{2}(-1 + \Gamma_5)\psi_e.$$

Using $\frac{1}{2}(1 - \Gamma_5)\psi_e = \chi_e$, we can write

$$\psi_e = \frac{1}{m}(i\not\partial - e\not A + m)\chi_e.$$

Finally, considering that ψ_e satisfies 6.15(3), we find the following second order equation for χ_e:

$$(i\not\partial - e\not A - m)\frac{1}{m}(i\not\partial - e\not A + m)\chi_e = 0.$$

This equation can be written in the form

(7) $$(i\not\partial - e\not A)^2\chi_e = m^2\chi_e,$$

and by developing the square, it becomes

(8) $$[(i\partial_\mu - eA_\mu)(i\partial_\mu - eA_\mu) - \tfrac{1}{2}e\sigma_{\mu\nu}F_{\mu\nu}]\chi_e = m^2\chi_e,$$

which is a Klein-Gordon equation with an added spin term.

Let us now distinguish between the upper and lower components of χ. If we make use of the fact that, from 8.22(6), $\chi_L = -\chi_U$ and express the product $\sigma_{\mu\nu}F_{\mu\nu}$ as in 6.15(6), (8) splits into two identical equations for χ_U and χ_L

(9) $$[(i\partial_\mu - eA_\mu)^2 + e\boldsymbol{\sigma}\cdot(\mathbf{H} + i\mathbf{E})]\chi_U = m^2\chi_U,$$

which are clearly two-component equations.

c. Two-Component Formulation of Left-Handed Interactions. The leptic part of the matrix element 8.22(11) is conveniently expressed in two-component theory as follows:

(10)
$$(\bar\chi\gamma_4\chi) = \begin{pmatrix}\chi_U^\dagger & -\chi_U^\dagger\end{pmatrix}\begin{pmatrix}\chi_U \\ -\chi_U\end{pmatrix} = 2(\chi_U^\dagger\chi_U)$$
$$(\bar\chi\gamma_i\chi) = \begin{pmatrix}\chi_U^\dagger & -\chi_U^\dagger\end{pmatrix}\begin{pmatrix}0 & \sigma_i \\ \sigma_i & 0\end{pmatrix}\begin{pmatrix}\chi_U \\ -\chi_U\end{pmatrix} = 2(\chi_U^\dagger\sigma_i\chi_U).$$

This formalism is particularly useful in relativistic calculations involving four left-handed weakly interacting particles, such as in the decay of the muon. In this case one obtains

(11) $$(\bar\chi_\nu\gamma_\lambda\chi_\mu)(\bar\chi_e\gamma_\lambda\chi_{\nu'}) = 4(\chi_{U,\nu}^\dagger\chi_{U,\mu})(\chi_{U,e}^\dagger\chi_{U,\nu'}) - 4(\chi_{U,\nu}^\dagger\boldsymbol{\sigma}\chi_{U,\mu})\cdot(\chi_{U,e}^\dagger\boldsymbol{\sigma}\chi_{U,\nu'})$$

The two-component form of the theory simplifies the relativistic computation, since the Pauli matrices are more easily handled than the four-component Dirac matrices.

8.24 *Relative Sign of Vector and Axial Coupling from the Decay of Polarized Neutrons*

a. Calculation of Asymmetries for the Decay of Polarized Neutrons. In the preceding sections we have written the leptic part of the parity-violating matrix element by choosing the sign Γ_5 to account for the observed helicities of electrons and neutrinos. We must now concern ourselves with the nuclear part of the interaction and in particular with the relative sign of the vector and axial terms. A positive ratio R of axial-to-vector coupling is said to correspond to the "*vector-plus-axial*," or $V + A$, form of the theory, whereas the theory for $R < 0$ is called "*vector minus axial*," or $V - A$.

It can be observed that if R turned out to be negative ($V - A$) the nuclear and leptic factors would have almost identical form, since the nuclear factor in the relativistic formula [8.22(16)] would become, for each nucleon,

$$(1) \qquad \sqrt{2}g\{\bar{\psi}_F\tau^+(1 + |R|\,\Gamma_5)\gamma_\mu\psi_I\} = \sqrt{2}g\{\bar{\psi}_F\tau^+\gamma_\mu(1 - |R|\,\Gamma_5)\psi_I\} \approx 2\sqrt{2}g(\bar{\chi}_F\tau^+\gamma_\mu\chi_I).$$

Apart from the small difference between $|R|$ and 1, a satisfying simplicity would be achieved with nucleons and leptons all interacting in left-handed states[1].

But these aesthetic arguments are not a proof, and it is necessary to submit the choice of sign in the nuclear factor to an experimental test.

An experiment to test this point must involve a decay in which both the vector (Fermi) and axial (Gamow-Teller) interactions contribute and interfere: the decay of the neutron 8.14(9) is typical. Therefore we start with a computation of the asymmetries expected in the decay of polarized neutrons for arbitrary values of R, positive or negative.

If the spin of the neutron is initially in the $+z$ direction, the matrix element is 8.22(17) with $(\int 1) = 1$, $(\int \sigma_+) = 0$, $(\int \sigma_-) = \sqrt{2}$, and $(\int \sigma_z) = 1$; the nuclear matrix elements $(\int 1)$ and $(\int \sigma_z)$ contribute to transitions without spin flips, whereas $(\int \sigma_-)$ induces decay accompanied by spin flip. Thus we can write

$$(2) \qquad \begin{aligned} M_{\text{flip}} &= -2Rg(\bar{\chi}_e\gamma_4\sigma_+\chi_\nu), \\ M_{\text{no flip}} &= \sqrt{2}g(\bar{\chi}_e\gamma_4\chi_\nu) + \sqrt{2}Rg(\bar{\chi}_e\gamma_4\sigma_z\chi_\nu). \end{aligned}$$

[1] Left-handed interaction for all particles could be reconciled with $V + A$ theory only if the electrons were particles and the nucleons antiparticles or vice-versa.

We now square and sum over the states of the leptons by using the method of traces. For spin flip the result is obtained directly from 8.14($7_{\pm}$) and 8.22(20)[1]:

$$(3a)\quad \frac{m}{E}\frac{m_\nu}{q}\underset{e}{S}\,\underset{\nu}{S}\,|M_{\text{flip}}|^2$$
$$= 4R^2g^2(1 - v\cos\theta_{eJ}\cos\theta_{\nu J} - v\cos\theta_{eJ} + \cos\theta_{\nu J}).$$

The decay with no spin flip is a little more complicated. Though we can read the contribution of the square of the vector term directly in 8.13(7), 8.22(18) and that of the axial term in 8.14(7_0), the mixed product remains to be computed. The computation can also be performed with the method of traces[2], and the result is

$$(3b)\quad \frac{m}{E}\frac{m_\nu}{q}\underset{e}{S}\,\underset{\nu}{S}\,|M_{\text{no flip}}|^2 = 2g^2[\underset{\text{vector part}}{(1 + v\cos\theta_{e\nu})}$$
$$+ \underset{\text{axial part}}{R^2(1 - v\cos\theta_{e\nu} + 2v\cos\theta_{eJ}\cos\theta_{\nu J})} \underset{\text{mixed term}}{- 2R(v\cos\theta_{eJ} + \cos\theta_{\nu J})}].$$

We must now sum over the final spin states of the nucleon. This is easily accomplished by adding together the last two expressions:

$$(4)\quad \frac{m}{E}\frac{m_\nu}{q}\underset{e}{S}\,\underset{\nu}{S}\,(|M_{\text{no flip}}|^2 + |M_{\text{flip}}|^2)$$
$$= 2g^2[1 + 3R^2 + (1 - R^2)v\cos\theta_{e\nu}$$
$$- 2(R^2 + R)v\cos\theta_{eJ} + 2(R^2 - R)\cos\theta_{\nu J}].$$

This formula is proportional to the transition probability and expresses its dependence on the directions of the electron and neutrino.

In particular, for $R = \pm 1$, $R^2 = 1$, which is approximately the case of interest, we have

$$(5)\qquad 8g^2\left(1 - \frac{1 \pm 1}{2}v\cos\theta_{eJ} + \frac{1 \mp 1}{2}\cos\theta_{\nu J}\right).$$

[1] Remember that $\gamma_4\sigma_i = i\gamma_5\gamma_i = -\Gamma_5\gamma_i$.

[2] Following the procedure of 6.25b, we obtain for the matrix elements M_1 and M_2 of two operators Q_1 and Q_2:

$$\underset{I}{S}\,\underset{F}{S}(M_1{}^*M_2) = \text{Tr}\,(Q_2\Lambda_I\gamma_4Q_1{}^\dagger\gamma_4\Lambda_F).$$

In our case, for the parity-conserving part, $Q_1 = \gamma_4\sigma_z = -\Gamma_5\gamma_3$, $Q_2 = \gamma_4$, and there are two terms in the mixed product $M_1{}^*M_2 + M_2{}^*M_1$; thus the parity-conserving part gives

$$\text{Tr}\,[\gamma_4\not{q}(-\Gamma_5\gamma_3)\not{p} + (-\Gamma_5\gamma_3)\not{q}\gamma_4\not{p}] = 0.$$

The parity-violating part is obtained by inserting Γ_5 to the left of q:

$$\text{Tr}\,[\gamma_4(-\Gamma_5)\not{q}(-\Gamma_5\gamma_3)\not{p} + (-\Gamma_5\gamma_3)(-\Gamma_5)\not{q}\gamma_4\not{p}]$$
$$= \text{Tr}\,(-\gamma_4\not{q}\gamma_3\not{p} - \gamma_3\not{q}\gamma_4\not{p}) = -4(2qp_3 + 2q_3E).$$

We see that the $V + A$ theory predicts almost spherically symmetrical neutrinos and backward electrons, whereas from the $V - A$ theory almost spherically symmetrical electrons and neutrinos in the direction of the spin are expected.

b. Measurement of the Asymmetries in the Decay of Polarized Neutrons. The measurement of the asymmetry in the emission of electrons and neutrinos from a beam of polarized neutron has been performed at the Argonne National Laboratory. From (4) the result expected for the two relative signs of the vector and axial term can easily be computed. For J along the polar axis these are

$$(6)\quad \begin{array}{lll} 1 - 0.07v \cos\theta_e + \cos\theta_\nu & \text{for } V - A \text{ theory;} & |R| = 1.15, \\ 1 - v\cos\theta_e + 0.07\cos\theta_\nu & \text{for } V + A \text{ theory;} & |R| = 1.15. \end{array}$$

The polarized neutrons were obtained by reflection on magnetized mirrors (3.31c), and the electrons were counted in coincidence with the recoil protons. In a first experiment (B-57) no attempt was made to define the directions of the recoil protons, and the result obtained was

$$1 - (0.37 \pm 0.11)v\cos\theta_e.$$

This result did not agree with either theory, though it seemed to favor the $V + A$ form. But it was realized that the possibility of an asymmetry in the emission of the neutrinos could affect the experimental results, since the recoil protons would be anisotropic.

In a second experiment (B-58c) both the directions of the electrons and of the recoil protons were selected, to measure the asymmetries of both electrons and neutrinos. The experimental result was

$$1 - 0.09v\cos\theta_e + 0.88\cos\theta_\nu,$$

in good agreement with $V - A$ theory and with aesthetical predictions.

The validity of $V - A$ theory is now universally accepted.

c. Evidence Concerning Time-Reversal Invariance. In order to discuss the possibility of violations of time-reversal invariance we should develop the theory of weak interactions with complex coupling constants. But to avoid complications in the formalism, we shall discuss time reversal in a more direct physical manner.

It is intuitively clear, under the assumption of time-reversal invariance, that the transition probability must not include terms that change sign when the direction of the time axis is inverted[1]. Thus scalar expressions,

[1] This argument is correct if the interaction being tested for time-reversal invariance creates or absorbs particles in a state of definite linear momentum. Coulomb distortions of the final waves introduce corrections of the order of Ze^2.

such as

$$\mathbf{J} \cdot \mathbf{p} \times \mathbf{q} \tag{7}$$

in simple β decay, (**J** is the nuclear spin), or pseudoscalars such as

$$\mathbf{J} \cdot (\mathbf{p} \times \mathbf{k})(\mathbf{J} \cdot \mathbf{k}) \tag{8}$$

in β-γ correlation (**k** is the γ-ray momentum), should not enter into the formula of the transition probability, since they contain an odd number of factors which change sign under time reversal.

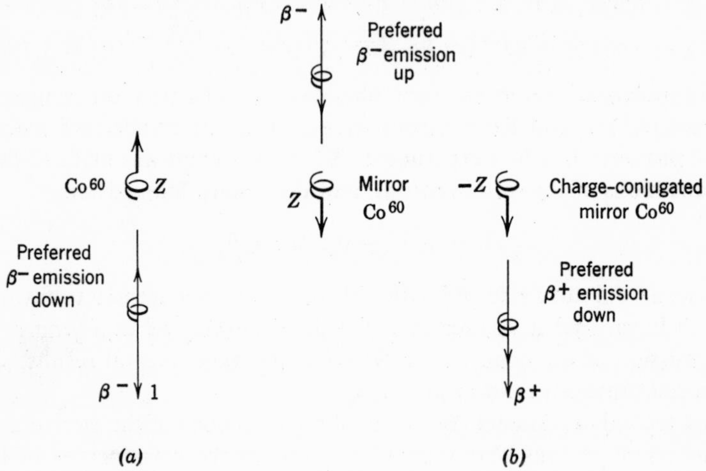

Fig. 8.24-1. The decay of mirror Co^{60} *is not* the mirror image of Co^{60} decay; but the decay of mirror-anti-Co^{60} *is* the mirror image of Co^{60} decay. (The "mirror" is perpendicular to the direction →)

A term like (7) predicts that in the decay of neutrons polarized along the z axis the transition probability should be different for electrons in the x direction and neutrinos in the y direction and for interchanged electron and neutrino momenta. This and other predictions have been tested experimentally and no evidence contrary to time-reversal invariance has been found in neutron decay (B-58d; C-58) or in any other experiment.

It is therefore assumed that weak interactions are invariant under time reversal.

Because of a general field theoretical theorem[1] (L-57b), according to which any Lorentz invariant theory of interacting fields must be invariant under the product of the three operations PTC (parity, time reversal, and

[1] This theorem (Lüders-Pauli theorem) is valid for local interactions.

charge conjugation), the present view is that weak interactions are

(9) invariant under PTC
invariant under T
invariant under PC

but

(10) not invariant under P and C separately.

Stated in intuitive terms, PC invariance means that although the β decay of Co^{60} is not invariant under reflection (Fig. 8.24-1*a*) the decay of charge conjugated Co^{60} is the mirror image of Co^{60} decay (Fig. 8-24-1*b*). Thus, if the electrons from Co^{60} decay are left-handed, the positrons from anti-Co^{60} must be right-handed, and the β^+ decay is predominantly in the spin direction.

8.3 Weak Interactions of Muons and Pions

8.31 *The Decay of the Muon and the Idea of Universal Fermi Interaction*

a. Similarity between the β Decay of Muons and Nucleons. From the mean life of the muon [7.13(5)] and the statistical analysis of its three-particle decay [5.11(26)] it is possible to obtain a first estimate of the coupling constant for μ decay:

$$(1) \qquad g_\mu \approx \mathsf{M}_\mu = \left(\frac{\hbar}{2\pi}\,\frac{96 \times 160}{7}\,\frac{\pi^4 \hbar^6}{c^4 {m_\mu}^5}\,\frac{1}{\tau_\mu}\right)^{1/2} \approx 3 \times 10^{-49}\ \text{erg cm}^3.$$

One is immediately impressed by the fact that the result—within a factor 2—is the same as the coupling constants for nuclear β decay g_V and g_A [8.13(11), (12); 8.15(10)].

It becomes tempting to assume that weak interaction is a general property of all fermions and that the coupling constants, as well as all the other laws of the coupling, are the same in all cases. This is the idea of a *universal Fermi interaction*, whose successes and limitations are discussed in what follows.

We start with a more detailed analysis of the decay of the muon in order to make a more accurate comparison with the decay of nucleons.

b. Parity Conserving Theories of μ Decay. In developing a theory of μ decay we are faced with choices similar to those that we met in the case of nuclear β decay. We can introduce any linear combination of the five possible couplings, S, V, T, A, P, if we want a parity-conserving theory; and we can mix terms of different parities if parity violation is allowed.

There are, however, other ambiguities. One concerns the distinguishability or indistinguishability of the neutrinos, and another the order in which the different fermions enter the coupling. These possibilities—six in all—are best illustrated by the diagrams of Fig. 8.31-1.

If we choose one of the six interactions and specify the form of Q_X, we can compute the matrix element in a way similar to that used for β decay.

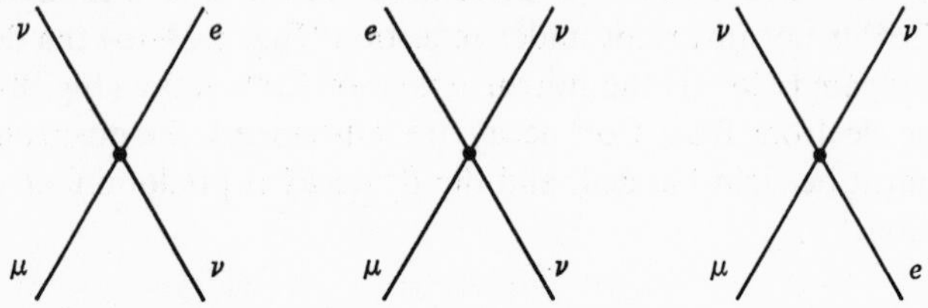

Fig. 8.31-1. Various ways of coupling the muon to the electron-neutrino field. Each of these diagrams leads to two different results, according to whether or not one assumes that the neutrino are distinguishable.

The main difference in the computation is that we cannot use the non-relativistic approximation in the muon factor as we did for the nuclear factor.

The matrix element depends on the energy of the muon daughter particles, and the differential transition probability is given by an expression of the form

$$dw = \text{constant}\,\frac{4\pi p_e^{\,2}\,dp_e}{(2\pi)^3}\,\frac{d}{dE_0}\int |M|^2\,\frac{d^3\mathbf{p}_\nu}{(2\pi)^3}\,. \tag{2}$$

If the electron's mass is neglected, p_e varies between the limits:

$$0 \leq p_e \leq p_0 = \frac{m_\mu}{2}\,. \tag{3}$$

For the parity-conserving case the computations have been carried out by Tiomno and Wheeler (T-49) and extended by Michel (M-53).

The result is that the electron spectrum has the shape

$$w\left(\frac{p_e}{p_0}\right)d\left(\frac{p_e}{p_0}\right) \approx \left[\left(1-\frac{p_e}{p_0}\right)-\frac{2}{9}\rho\left(3-4\frac{p_e}{p_0}\right)\right]\left(\frac{p_e}{p_0}\right)^2 d\left(\frac{p_e}{p_0}\right), \tag{4}$$

where ρ (the so-called Michel parameter) has different values for the different forms of the theory. Figure 8.31-2 shows the spectral shape for different values of ρ.

c. The $V - A$ Theory. We know that the nucleon decay violates parity, and it is natural to assume that the same happens in the decay of the muon. More specifically, according to the idea of universal Fermi interaction, we assume that the weak coupling of the muon is described by the $V - A$ interaction, with left-handed helicity operators for all fermions [compare with 8.22(16) and 8.24(1)], and $|R| = 1$.

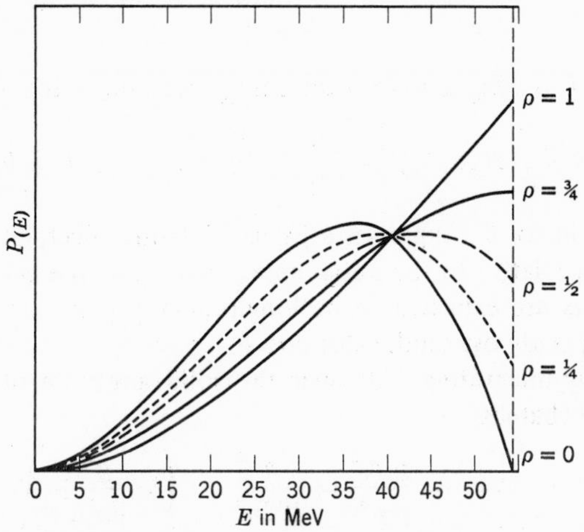

Fig. 8.31-2. Electron spectrum from μ-meson decay (from L. Michel, *Rev. Mod. Phys.*, **29**, 227 (1957)].

Assuming that the neutrinos emitted are antiparticles of one another, the matrix element for μ decay can be written

(5) $$2\sqrt{2}g(\bar{\chi}_\nu\gamma_\lambda\chi_\mu)(\bar{\chi}_e\gamma_\lambda\chi_\nu) + \text{h.c.},$$

with

(6) $$g = g_\mu = g_V.$$

Since there is, in effect, experimental evidence [see (d) and 8.33e] that the two neutrinos are distinguishable, there is no need to antisymmetrize (5) for the neutrinos, and all particles are treated in the same manner. It follows that the order of the factors in (5) is indifferent, and the $V - A$ theory can be formulated without ambiguity. The resulting decay rate (K-59b), which we report without derivation, is

(7) $$w\left(\frac{p_e}{p_0}, \theta_{e\sigma}\right) d\left(\frac{p_e}{p_0}\right) d(\cos\theta_{e\sigma})$$
$$= \frac{g^2 p_0^5}{6\pi^3}\left[\left(3 - 2\frac{p_e}{p_0}\right) \pm \left(2\frac{p_e}{p_0} - 1\right)\cos\theta_{e\sigma}\right]\left(\frac{p_e}{p_0}\right)^2 d\left(\frac{p_e}{p_0}\right) d(\cos\theta_{e\sigma}),$$

where $\theta_{e\sigma}$ is the angle between the meson's spin and the electron's momentum, and the signs $\pm$ apply to $\mu^{\pm}$ decay, respectively.

When (7) is integrated over the solid angle, we obtain the spectrum

$$w\left(\frac{p_e}{p_0}\right) d\left(\frac{p_e}{p_0}\right) = \frac{g^2 p_0^{\ 5}}{3\pi^3} \left(3 - 2\frac{p_e}{p_0}\right)\left(\frac{p_e}{p_0}\right)^2 d\left(\frac{p_e}{p_0}\right), \tag{8}$$

which corresponds to

$$\rho = \tfrac{3}{4}. \tag{9}$$

If, instead, (7) is integrated over the energy, we get the angular distribution

$$w(\theta_{e\sigma})\, d(\cos\theta_{e\sigma}) = \frac{g^2 p_0^{\ 5}}{12\pi^2} (1 \pm \tfrac{1}{3}\cos\theta_{e\sigma})\, d(\cos\theta_{e\sigma}). \tag{10}$$

The term in $\cos\theta_{e\sigma}$ expresses a parity-violating effect, an asymmetry of the emission relative to the initial spin. Naturally, the emitted neutrinos and electrons are expected to be longitudinally polarized: the electron polarization is almost total, since $v \approx c$.

Finally, by integrating (10) over the solid angle we obtain the total transition probability

$$w = \frac{1}{\tau} = \frac{g^2 p_0^{\ 5}}{6\pi^3} = \frac{g^2 m_\mu^{\ 5}}{192\pi^3} \qquad \left(= \frac{g^2 p_0^{\ 5}}{6\pi^3 \hbar^7 c^6}\right). \tag{11}$$

d. Comparison with Experiment. Let us start by presenting experimental evidence for the fact that the two neutrinos of μ decay are distinguishable one from the other. If the two neutrinos were identical particles, they would obey the exclusion principle and could not be emitted in the same state of motion: the decay mode of Fig. 8.31-3 (electron emerging with half the available energy and two equal neutrinos emitted in the opposite direction) could not occur. More generally it can be proved that for identical neutrinos the electron can never be emitted with half the available energy.

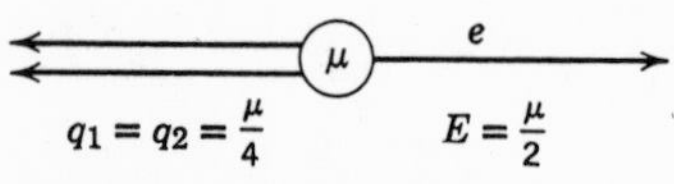

Fig. 8.31-3. A mode of μ decay which is forbidden for identical neutrinos.

Since electrons of energy $\mu/2$ are found frequently in μ decay, we conclude that the two neutrinos are different.

The first possibility that comes to mind is that one is a neutrino and the other an antineutrino, according to the following decay:

$$\mu^{\pm} \rightarrow e^{\pm} + \nu + \bar{\nu}. \tag{12}$$

Thus the two neutrinos would have opposite helicity, and the spin of the electron in the high-energy part of the spectrum would be in the same direction as the spin of the muon. Assuming lepton conservation, it would follow from (12) that μ^- is a lepton like e^-, and μ^+ an antilepton like e^+.

Though the experiment shows that the two neutrinos actually have opposite helicities[1], (12) and the arguments that follow from it are meaningless: it is now established (see 8.33e) that the two neutrinos are different without being each other's antiparticle.

Let us pass to the determination of the coupling constant, which can now be made more accurately than by means of the statistical theory. Since the factor containing ρ in (4) vanishes on integration, the relation between coupling constant and μ-decay time does not depend on the form of the spectrum. From (11) and from recent experimental data we can obtain (R-60), without radiative corrections,

(13*a*) $$g = (1.428 \pm 0.002) \times 10^{-49} \text{ erg cm}^3,$$

and, if radiative corrections (K-59a) are applied,

(13*b*) $$g = (1.431 \pm 0.002) \times 10^{-49} \text{ erg cm}^3.$$

It can be seen that the assumption (5) is in good agreement with the experiment. The difference between (13*b*) and one of the values of g_V reported in 8.13(12) is about 1%. Though the stated experimental error is smaller than 1%, it is not excluded that the difference may be due entirely to errors of omission or commission in the theoretical corrections[2].

The shape of the spectrum of μ-decay electrons has been the object of many investigations. The experimental value of ρ is difficult to determine and different results have been reported through the years. We quote only the most recent and apparently most reliable data, which are (C-57b; P-59a; R-58; S-59a)

$$\rho = 0.65 \pm 0.05,$$

$$\rho = 0.79 \pm 0.03.$$

It is seen also that the shape of the decay spectrum agrees well with $V - A$ theory, which predicts $\rho = \frac{3}{4}$.

The electron's asymmetry can be measured by taking advantage of the fact that π decay provides longitudinally polarized μ beams (see Fig. 8.31-4). It appears from recent and quite difficult experiments that μ^+ from π^+ decay at rest are left-handed and μ^- for π^- decay are right-handed[3]. In proper circumstances this polarization is maintained when the μ mesons are stopped, making available a polarized source of μ mesons

[1] This follows from the measurement of the helicity of the muons from π decay (8.36a) and from the studies of asymmetry and polarization of the electrons from μ decay.
[2] See 8.31c, 8.35e for a discussion of form factor effects.
[3] See Section 8.36 for the description of this work.

at rest. The asymmetry about the spin direction can then be measured by moving the electron counters around the source or, more simply and elegantly, by rotating the spin of the muon by means of an externally applied magnetic field (G-59a). We find that the positrons from μ^+ decay are preferentially emitted opposite to the muon beam direction and thus

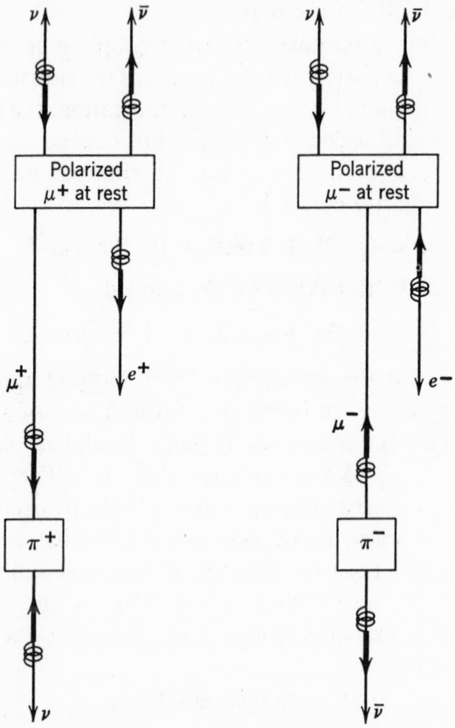

Fig. 8.31-4. Spins and asymmetries in the decays of pions and muons. Only one kind of neutrinos, together with their anti-particles, is assumed in this figure, but helicities and asymmetries are in agreement with those actually observed.

parallel to the muon spin, as predicted by $V - A$ theory. For negative charge the electrons are also preferentially opposite to the muon beam, but this now corresponds to emission antiparallel to the spin, as it should be.

More quantitatively, we find that the absolute value of the parameter λ is also near to $\frac{1}{3}$, as predicted by $V - A$ theory (B-59a; L-58c).

The left-handed helicity of the electron and the right-handed helicity of the positron from μ decay have also been verified with observations on the transmission of their bremsstrahlung in magnetized iron (C-59b).

In conclusion one can say that the idea of universal Fermi interaction is very successful in the comparison of the main features of the β decay of nucleons and muons. We shall see in what follows some of the difficulties and limitations of this idea.

8.32 *Capture of Muons by Nuclei*

a. Formulation of Simplified Universal Fermi Interaction. In conformity with the idea of universal Fermi interaction, there should be a weak coupling between the nucleons and the μ–ν field. The neutron-proton mass difference is too small to allow the μ decay of the nucleons, but the phenomenon of μ^- capture, analogous to K-electron capture, is energetically possible and experimentally observed. In its elementary form it can be written

$$\mu^- + \mathrm{p} \to \mathrm{n} + \nu. \quad (1)$$

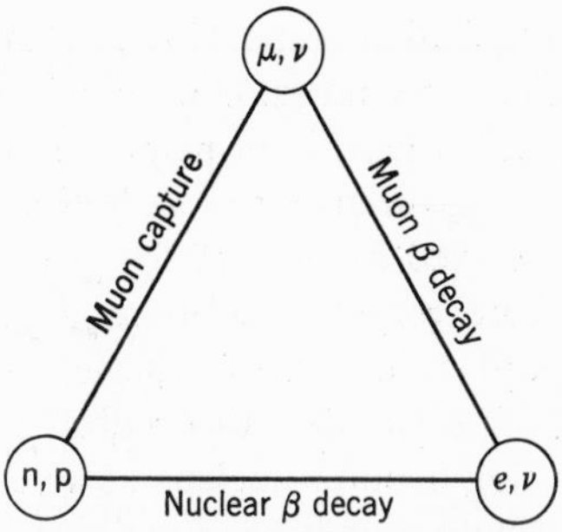

Fig. 8.32-1. The Puppi triangle for weak interactions between nucleons and leptons.

The weak interaction between nucleons and leptons can be graphically represented by means of the "Puppi triangle" of Fig. 8.32-1. For the sake of simplicity, we shall neglect in this preliminary discussion the fact that $|R| \neq 1$ in the nuclear β decay, and, according to the principle of universal Fermi interaction, we shall assume that the μ-capture interaction has the same form $(V-A)$ and the same coupling constant as muon β decay.

The consequences of this assumption are compared with the experiment in what follows.

b. Muon Capture in Complex Nuclei. The elementary reaction (1) is difficult to observe because the overwhelming majority of the muons falling in hydrogenic K orbits decay instead of being captured. For the moment, our discussion is limited to the capture of muons in complex nuclei; the capture in hydrogen is considered in part e of this section.

After a negative muon has reached an atomic K shell, it either decays or it is captured. Its mean life τ_K is given by

$$\frac{1}{\tau_K} = w_d + w_c, \quad (2)$$

where w_d and w_c are the decay and capture rates. On the other hand, the number of decay electrons per muon is

$$\frac{N_e}{N_\mu} = \frac{w_d}{w_d + w_c}. \tag{3}$$

Thus both w_d and w_c can be obtained if τ_K and N_e/N_μ are measured.

The decay rate w_d is different from the decay rate of a free muon. The difference has several causes: the available energy (the binding energy of a muon in Pb is of the order of 10 MeV, and the decay rate varies with the fifth power of the available energy), the presence of a coulomb field, and relativistic corrections arising from the orbital speed of the muon. We shall not report in detail the measurements of w_d (L-58b; Y-60; B-59b), since the interpretation of the results involves well-known interactions and, at least in principle, should present no difficulty (G-60b).

Measurements of w_c for many elements ranging from Be to U have been reported by Sens (S-53; see this paper for references to previous work); more recently, accurate data have been obtained at Liverpool (A-58; A-61) and at the Carnegie Institute of Technology.

The simplest theoretical estimate of the capture rate is obtained by using a point-nucleus atomic model and assuming that all protons contribute equally to muon capture. In this case we expect $w_c \approx Z^4$, since the muon density at the nucleus varies as Z^3, and the number of nuclear protons is Z.

However we know (2.21c) that the nuclear size cannot be neglected in comparison with the first Bohr orbit of the muon; a better estimate of the μ-capture rate is obtained by taking into account the finite nuclear radius in the computation of the muon wave function and of the probability that the muon is within the nucleus (W-49).

A satisfactory theory of μ capture requires a precise knowledge of the matrix element for the nuclear transition. First of all it is clear from conservation of energy and momentum that the neutrino takes most of the available energy. Stars with visible prongs are seldom seen at the end of μ^- tracks: the energy left to the capturing nucleus is often insufficient for its disintegration, or at most it may cause the emission of a few neutrons.

For such small excitation energies the exclusion principle plays an important role, and only the protons sufficiently close to the "Fermi surface" can participate in the capture.

A discussion of the data for heavy elements necessarily involves the use of approximate nuclear models. As a result of such an analysis, Leite-Lopez (L-58a) finds that the experimental results are in agreement with a capture coupling constant $g = 1.5 \times 10^{-49}$ erg cm^3. When compared with the coupling constants for nucleon and muon decay, this result strongly supports the idea of universal Fermi interaction.

Similar conclusions are reached (S-59b; T-62) by comparing the experimental results with a theoretical formula due to Primakoff (P-59c).

c. Universal Fermi Interaction and Strong Forces[1]. The nuclei resulting from the capture of muons in heavy elements are formed in various excited states and may disintegrate with the emission of heavy particles. Because of the many quantum numbers in the final state, it is difficult to draw detailed conclusions on the nature of the interaction.

New experiments on capture in light elements select the final nuclear state and the results can be interpreted more precisely. In order to discuss these results, it is no longer sufficient to assume a simple $V-A$ coupling, but the effects of the complex structure of the nucleons must be taken into account.

Since the nucleons are not point particles but are surrounded by pions, which in turn decay weakly into leptons, we must expect that their weak coupling constants depend on the momentum transfer $\mathbf{q}$. Because of the low energy of nuclear β decay, the previously determined quantities g_V and g_A must be considered as values appropriate only for $q^2 = 0$; they should be decreased a few percent for μ capture.

If we suppose, in accord with the idea of weak current conservation (8.35), that the form factor of g_V is the same as the charge form factor of the nucleon (3.33), we obtain[2]

$$g_V^{(\mu)} = 0.97 g_V^{(\beta)}. \tag{4}$$

The comparison of the axial coupling constants is not so straight forward, though one expects that $g_A^{(\mu)}$ and $g_A^{(\beta)}$ are very close to each other; the relation $g_A^{(\mu)} = 0.999 g_A^{(\beta)}$ is found in the literature.

In writing the matrix element, the exponential $\exp(-i\mathbf{p}_\nu \cdot \mathbf{r})$ cannot be replaced by unity because the wavelength of the neutrino emitted in muon capture is of the order of the pion's Compton wavelength.

Furthermore the speed of the recoil neutron is not entirely negligible and, to take into account corrections in first order in the velocity, the vector coupling constant must be replaced by an effective constant (p. 597)

$$G_V = g_V^{(\mu)}\left(1 + \frac{p_\nu}{2M}\right). \tag{5}$$

It can be seen from 8.16 that there are no first-order recoil contributions to axial coupling. However, we must include the effects of weak magnetism (8.35c), which are of the same order. If μ_p and μ_n are the (total) magnetic moments of the nucleons, we obtain an effective axial constant

$$G_A = g_A^{(\mu)} - g_V^{(\mu)}(\mu_\text{p} - \mu_\text{n})\frac{p_\nu}{2M}. \tag{6}$$

[1] Parts c and d of this section may be omitted in a first reading.

[2] For the details of the derivation of formulas (4) to (8) the reader is referred to F-59b.

In the same order of approximation we must also consider the pseudoscalar terms that arise for three reasons: small relativistic terms from the axial vector interaction (see 8.16), weak magnetism (see 8.35c), and "direct" pseudoscalar coupling. The effective pseudoscalar constant is

$$G_P = [g_A^{(\mu)} - g_V^{(\mu)}(\mu_p - \mu_n) + g_P^{(\mu)}] \frac{p_\nu}{2M}. \tag{7}$$

The "direct" pseudoscalar constant $g_P^{(\mu)}$ results from the weak interaction of the pion cloud around the nucleon and is computed in part (d) of this section.

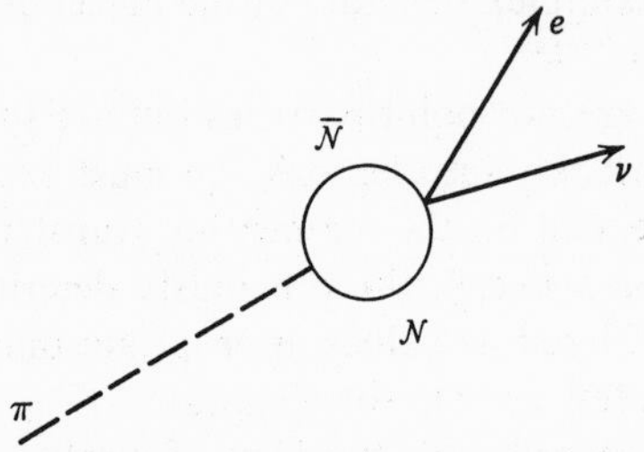

Fig. 8.32-2. Decay of π meson through the intermediate of a nucleon antinucleon pair.

Making use of these effective constants, the nuclear part of the matrix element for μ capture by a proton at rest assumes the form

$$M = G_V + G_A\langle \boldsymbol{\sigma}_\mu \cdot \boldsymbol{\sigma}_P \rangle - G_P\langle (\boldsymbol{\sigma}_\mu \cdot \hat{\mathbf{p}}_\nu)(\boldsymbol{\sigma}_P \cdot \hat{\mathbf{p}}_\nu)\rangle. \tag{8}$$

d. The Pseudoscalar Interaction. We want to show how the strong interaction of the nucleons with pions results in a pseudoscalar weak interaction of the nucleons which is negligible in β decay but can affect μ capture (L-58a).

Let us start by analyzing the process of π^- decay (7.13b) which occurs through the intermediate production of nucleon-antinucleon pairs (Fig. 8.32-2). At the vertex describing this process—replaced, for simplicity, by a point interaction in Fig. 8.32-3—the vector index of the usual leptic factor is saturated with the vector index of the pion's momentum. After a moment's reflection we conclude that there is no other possible form of interaction.

If we introduce a suitable coupling constant $g_{\pi\mu}$ the vertex factor is[1]

$$i\frac{g_{\pi\mu}}{m_\pi} p_{\pi,\lambda}(\bar{\chi}_\mu \gamma_5 \gamma_\lambda \chi_\nu) = ig_{\pi\mu}\left(\bar{\chi}_\mu \gamma_5 \frac{\not{p}_\pi}{m_\pi} \chi_\nu\right), \tag{9}$$

which, for pions at rest, becomes simply $g_{\pi\mu}(\bar{\chi}_\mu \gamma_5 \gamma_4 \chi_\nu)$.

[1] Since $\Gamma_5 \Lambda_l = -\Lambda_l$, the operator γ_5 may be omitted without changing the results.

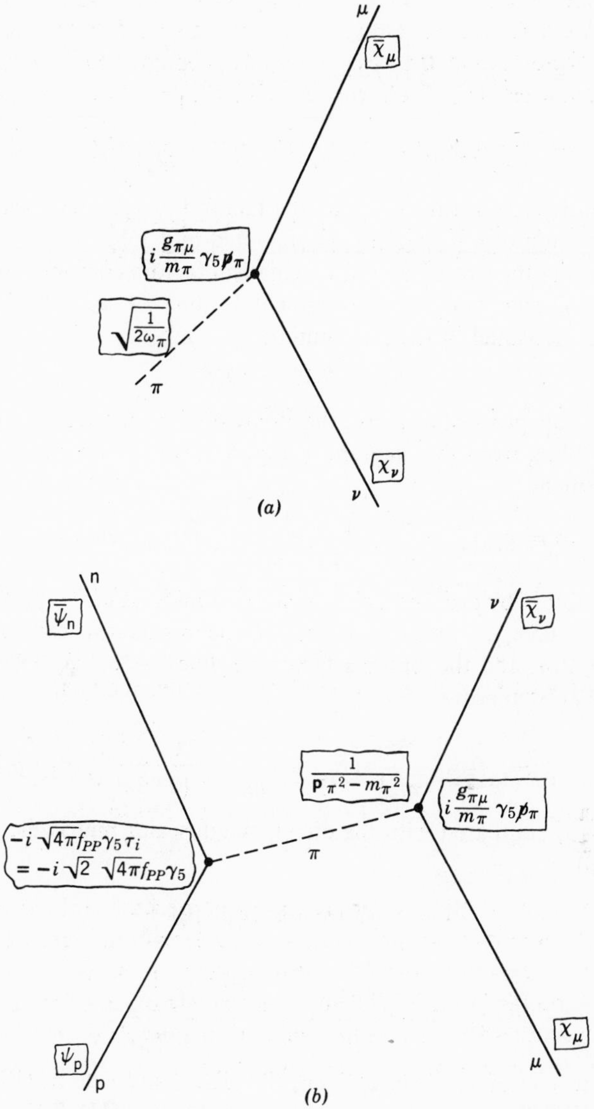

Fig. 8.32-3. Feynman diagrams for π-μ decay (*a*) and for pion-induced pseudoscalar μ capture (*b*). In this diagram $g_{\pi\mu} = 2.1 \times 10^{-7}$ [see (11)] and $f_{PP}^2 = 15$ [see 7.17(3)].

The transition probability can be computed with the usual rules, and we obtain

$$(10)\quad \begin{aligned} \frac{w_{\pi\mu}}{m_\pi} &= \frac{2\pi}{m_\pi}\rho_\mu \mathop{S}_\mu \mathop{S}_\nu \left| \sqrt{\frac{1}{2m_\pi}}\, g_{\pi\mu}(\bar{\chi}_\mu \gamma_5 \gamma_4 \chi_\nu) \right|^2 \\ &= \frac{\pi}{m_\pi^2}\rho_\mu g_{\pi\mu}^2[1 + v_\mu \cos(180°)] = \pi \frac{\rho_\mu}{m_\pi^2} g_{\pi\mu}^2(1 - v_\mu). \end{aligned}$$

An intuitive argument to explain the factor $1 - v_\mu$, which accounts for the suppression of $\pi \to e$ decay, is presented in 8.36b.

Introducing the statistical and kinematical factors computed in 5.11(16) and 8.36(1), and using the experimental value of $w_{\pi\mu}$ (7.13b) we can determine the value[1] of the pure number

$$(11)\quad g_{\pi\mu} = 2.10 \times 10^{-7}.$$

We can now proceed to derive the strength of the induced weak pseudoscalar coupling from the diagram in Fig. 8.32-3b. We readily obtain the matrix element

$$(12)\quad \mathsf{M} = g_{\pi\mu}\left(\bar{\chi}_\nu \gamma_5 \frac{p_\pi}{m_\pi} \chi_\mu\right) \frac{1}{\mathsf{p}_\pi^{\,2} - m_\pi^{\,2}} \sqrt{4\pi} f_{PP} \sqrt{2}(\bar{w}_{\mathrm{n}} \gamma_5 w_{\mathrm{p}}).$$

For μ capture by protons the momentum transfer is $\mathsf{p}_\pi \approx (\mathbf{p}_\nu, 0.05m_\pi) \approx (0.95m_\mu \hat{\mathbf{p}}_\nu, 0.05m_\mu)$. From 7.16e the nucleon's factor can be written $\langle \boldsymbol{\sigma}_{\mathrm{p}} \cdot \hat{\mathbf{p}}_\nu \rangle p_\nu / 2M$, and the lepton's factor becomes $-\langle \boldsymbol{\sigma}_\mu \cdot \hat{\mathbf{p}}_\nu \rangle 0.95 m_\mu / m_\pi$. Thus (12) becomes

$$\mathsf{M} = \sqrt{8\pi} g_{\pi\mu} f_{PP} \frac{0.95m_\mu}{m_\pi} (\boldsymbol{\sigma}_\mu \cdot \hat{\mathbf{p}}_\nu) \frac{1}{m_\pi^{\,2} + (0.95m_\mu)^2} (\boldsymbol{\sigma}_{\mathrm{p}} \cdot \hat{\mathbf{p}}_\nu) \frac{p_\nu}{2M}$$

When this is compared with the direct pseudoscalar matrix element from (7) and (8)

$$\mathsf{M} = -g_P^{(\mu)} (\boldsymbol{\sigma}_\mu \cdot \hat{\mathbf{p}}_\nu)(\boldsymbol{\sigma}_{\mathrm{p}} \cdot \hat{\mathbf{p}}_\nu) \frac{p_\nu}{2M}$$

we obtain

$$(13)\quad g_P^{(\mu)} = -\frac{0.95m_\mu}{m_\pi} \frac{\sqrt{8\pi} g_{\pi\mu} f_{PP}}{m_\pi^{\,2} + (0.95m_\mu)^2}.$$

In order to compute $g_P^{(\mu)}$ in erg cm^3, the right-hand side of (13) must be multiplied by $\hbar^3/c$. Then, using the numerical values (11), 7.17(3), 8.13(11) and 8.22(13), we have

$$(14)\quad \begin{aligned} g_P^{(\mu)} &= -12.5 \times 10^{-49}\ \text{erg cm}^3 \\ &= -8.8 g_V = 7.7 g_A. \end{aligned}$$

[1] The ambiguity in sign is solved considering that π decay occurs through the intermediate of a nucleon-antinucleon pair (W-58).

This result is often quoted as

$$g_P^{(\mu)} = 8g_A.$$

The induced pseudoscalar coupling is negligible in β decay because of the small value of the electron's mass.

e. Comparison with Experiment. We now discuss the results of the measurements of μ capture rates between definite initial and final nuclear states.

Among these experiments, the simplest, at least in principle, is the capture by protons according to (1).

The rate of muon capture in liquid hydrogen has been measured in bubble chamber (H-62; B-62b) and with counters (B-62c; R-63b); in both cases the method consists in the observation of the 5.2 MeV recoil neutron in coincidence with the stopping meson.

The experiment must be carried out in extremely pure hydrogen because the hydrogen-muonic atom, which is a small neutral body diffusing through matter like a neutron, may easily lose its muon and transfer it to impurity nuclei. But matters are not simple even in pure hydrogen, in which a muonic H_2 molecule (p, p, μ, e) is formed. Without entering into detailed discussion of these effects, the experimental results are

$$w = (435 \pm 100)\ \text{sec}^{-1} \qquad \text{(H-62)}$$

$$w = (450 \pm 50)\ \text{sec}^{-1} \qquad \text{(R-63a)}$$

$$w = (464 \pm 42)\ \text{sec}^{-1} \qquad \text{(R-63b)}$$

where w is the capture rate from ppμe molecules in liquid hydrogen.

These results must be compared with the theoretical value from (8) and (14):

$$w = (562 \pm 60)\ \text{sec}^{-1} \qquad \text{(B-62c)}.$$

Among the experiments performed with complex nuclei, the simplest to interpret are those of the capture in He^3 and in C^{12}, leading to the ground state of H^3 and B^{12}. The interpretation is simplified because H^3 and B^{12} decay back to He^3 and C^{12}, with a β transition that involves the same nuclear states as the μ capture; the comparison between the β- and μ-transition rates is theoretically a much simpler problem than the calculation of any one of them.

The experimental data on He^3 are quite accurate. After experiments in a diffusion chamber containing He^3 (Z-61, F-63), measurements with He^3 scintillation counters were performed (A-63, Berkeley; E-63, Carnegie). In these experiments the recoil energy of the final tritium nucleus is measured, to make sure that it was produced in its bound (ground) state.

The results are

$$w = (1410 \pm 140)\ \text{sec}^{-1} \qquad \text{(F-63)}$$
$$w = (1520 \pm 50)\ \text{sec}^{-1} \qquad \text{(A-63)}$$
$$w = (1440 \pm 90)\ \text{sec}^{-1} \qquad \text{(E-63)}$$

and are in agreement with the theoretical prediction

$$w = (1540 \pm 80)\ \text{sec}^{-1} \qquad \text{(W-61a)}.$$

Concerning C^{12}, the results of various groups are not in complete agreement. A recent result for the transition rate $C^{12} + \mu \rightarrow B^{12}(\text{ground}) + \nu$ is

$$w = (6.31 \pm 0.24) \times 10^3\ \text{sec}^{-1} \qquad \text{(M-61)}$$

and is consistent with $g_P^{(\mu)} = 8g_A$.

Finally, data have been obtained on the capture rate in O^{16} with the production of definite states of N^{16}, which are identified by the detection of nuclear γ rays following muon capture. But the discussion of this work seems premature at the present writing.

Experimental studies of the asymmetry of the neutrons emitted after the capture of polarized muons are also interesting in this connection.

The simple $V - A$ form of interaction in the allowed approximation predicts that no asymmetry should be observed. The transition matrix element from 8.22(17) with $R = -1$ contains the operator $1 - \boldsymbol{\sigma}_p \cdot \boldsymbol{\sigma}_\mu$ applied to the nonrelativistic state of the muon and proton. Recalling that the eigenvalues of the operators $\boldsymbol{\sigma}_p \cdot \boldsymbol{\sigma}_\mu$ are 1 and -3 for triplet and singlet states, respectively [1.14(36)], we see that the capture occurs only from the singlet state of mesic hydrogen.

Since the capture by free protons occurs in a spherically symmetrical ^1S state, the emission of the neutrino and of the recoil neutron should be isotropic even when the captured muons are polarized.

Though the complete theory predicts some asymmetry, experiments on capture in sulfur and magnesium (A-59b, T-60a) reveal that the asymmetry is larger than expected; in order to explain the observations the amount of pseudoscalar coupling should be larger than $8g_A$.

As a result of the spin-dependence of the capture probability in hydrogen, we expect that, for heavier elements, the different hyperfine structure levels should have different capture probabilities and thus different mean lives. These effects have also been investigated theoretically and experimentally (B-58b; T-60b).

We must conclude that the weak interaction between nucleons and muons is still an open subject. Though the experiments of capture in He^3—which are the most accurate—agree with theory, the capture rate in hydrogen and the asymmetry of the neutrons emitted from heavy elements require a pseudoscalar coupling larger than theoretically predicted.

8.33 *Selection Rules for μ Decay and Capture. Discovery of Two Kinds of Neutrinos*

a. Conservation Laws for Universal Fermi Interaction. The law of universal Fermi interaction is limited by selection rules that prevent its action in many cases. Some of these rules correspond to conservation principles that we have already encountered, such as usual rotational and translational invariance, invariance under T and PC, and conservation of charge; but some new ones must be introduced, and a great deal of speculation about their meaning can be found in the recent literature.

If the weak interactions did couple in the same manner all pairs of fermions to all other fermion pairs, the proton could decay into a positron and two neutrinos, the neutron into an electron pair and a neutrino, and the muon into three electrons—all events that are known not to occur.

The first new selection rule is given by the law of *conservation of nucleons* which is a particular case of the *conservation of baryons.* Defining as baryons strongly interacting fermions, of which the nucleons are the lightest example, the law of conservation of baryons states that *the total number of baryons minus the total number of antibaryons must be a constant.*

We are tempted to associate the conservation of baryons with the conservation of mesic charge in the same manner as the stability of the electron may be connected with the conservation of electric charge. This, however, is not possible since a continuity equation, such as the conservation of electric charge, $\partial_\mu j_\mu = 0$, can be written only for sources of massless vector fields. Thus the conservation of baryon must be accepted as a (fortunate) empirical fact[1].

Another limitation in the number of possible weak couplings is given by the postulated law of *conservation of leptons*, formulated in 8.11a.

b. Two Forbidden Weak Reactions. A new and independent selection rule is needed to prevent the decay of the muon into three electrons,

$$\mu^\pm \rightarrow e^\pm + e^+ + e^-, \tag{1}$$

or the neutrinoless conversion of μ^- into e^- in the proximity of nuclei

$$\mu^- + \mathcal{N} \rightarrow e^- + \mathcal{N}, \tag{2}$$

[1] A conservation law can be written (S-62) for a source of vector mesons of zero "bare" mass even if their "physical" mass is finite. Thus conservation of baryon may be related to the existence of ρ and ω mesons.

which could occur without violating any of the conservation laws stated above.

The three-electron decay of the muon has been sought experimentally in a bubble chamber (L-59) in which the event is easily recognizable. Care must be taken, however, about the possibility of misinterpreting a radiative correction of normal μ decay as direct three-electron decay: in a magnetic field, the three electrons produced through the intermediate of a virtual γ

$$\mu^+ - e^+ + \nu + \bar{\nu} + (\gamma) \qquad (\gamma) \longrightarrow e^- + e^+ \tag{3}$$

can be distinguished from the direct three-electron emission (1) because they do not share the full μ energy and do not carry zero momentum.

From a total sample of 2.2×10^5 μ^+'s ending in the chamber, three 3-electron prongs were observed, but none belonged to reaction (1). Thus we can conclude (P-62)

$$\text{ratio}\, \frac{\mu^+ \to e^+ + e^- + e^+}{\mu^+ \to e^+ + \nu + \bar{\nu}} < \approx 5 \times 10^{-7}. \tag{4}$$

The possible conversion of muons into electrons according to reaction (2) has also been investigated recently in a spark-chamber experiment (C-62b). The result is that in Cu

$$\text{ratio}\, \frac{\mu^- + N \to e^- + N}{\text{total } \mu} < \approx 3 \times 10^{-7}. \tag{5}$$

We conclude that both reactions (1) and (2) are, to say the least, improbable, and we are tempted to associate this fact with some new selection rule.

c. The Hypothesis of the Weakon. It has been observed (F-58c; S-58b; S-58c) that the absence of the two reactions (1) and (2) could be explained if the weak interactions were transmitted by a *charged particle*. This hypothetical particle has been named intermediate boson, or *weakon*. If the weakon existed, the weak interaction coupling of fermions would become similar to their electromagnetic coupling (Fig. 8.33-1), and this makes the idea of an intermediate field particularly attractive.

The hypothetical weakon should have the following properties:

(i) Spin 1 and nondefined parity to account for the $V - A$ form of interaction.

(ii) Positive or negative, but not zero, electric charge.

(iii) Mass larger than the mass of the K meson ($\approx$500 MeV) to account for the stability of this particle against $K^\pm \to W^\pm + \gamma$.

With the condition that $m_W > m_K$, the two diagrams of Fig. 8.33-1 give similar results for all the reactions in which we are interested. The matrix element from diagram (*b*) contains an extra propagator factor $(k_W{}^2 - m_W{}^2)^{-1}$, in which $\mathbf{k}_W$ is the four-momentum transfer between the two fermion pairs. Thus, as long as $k_W{}^2 \ll m_W{}^2$, this factor is practically constant and the effects of the "nonlocality" of the interaction are negligible. In nuclear β decay $k_W \approx$ MeV and the propagator is almost constant. Somewhat larger effects can be expected in μ decay, where $k_W \sim 100$ MeV. For instance, we find (L-57a; L-60) that the Michel

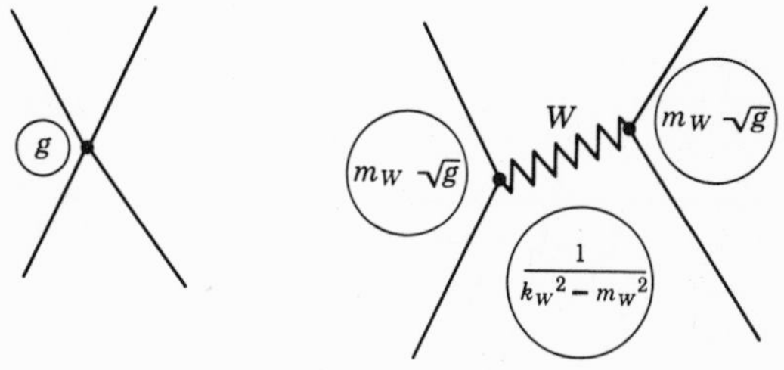

(*a*) (*b*)

Fig. 8.33-1. (*a*) Direct weak coupling; (*b*) weak coupling transmitted by a weakon *W*.

spectrum parameter ρ would become $\frac{3}{4} + \frac{1}{3}(m_\mu/m_W)^2$: the difference from the value $\frac{3}{4}$ is still too small to be observable with the present experimental techniques.

d. Search for the Weakon. Since the weakon is assumed to be charged, it interacts with the electromagnetic field, and its radiative properties may be used to investigate its possible existence. It is found in effect (F-58b) that the existence of the intermediate boson would result in a radiative decay of the muon

(6) $$\mu^\pm \rightarrow e^\pm + \gamma,$$

according to the diagrams of Fig. 8.33-2 (F-59a).

Our ignorance of the properties of the weakon does not enable us to compute the probability of reaction (6)[1]. The rate could even be made to vanish for certain choices of magnetic and quadrupole moments; but it is not unreasonable to expect that (6) should account for 10^{-3} to 10^{-6} of the total μ decays.

The question has been investigated experimentally by several groups (B-62a) and with different techniques. The result has always been negative,

[1] Reaction (6) cannot proceed through simple electromagnetic interaction. See (F-59a).

and we can say from the latest data that

$$\text{(7)} \qquad \text{ratio} \frac{\mu^+ \to e^+ + \gamma}{\mu^+ + e^+ + \nu + \bar{\nu}} < \approx 10^{-7}.$$

Thus it appears that either the weakon does not exist, or it is very heavy, or there is some unlucky cancellation in its radiative properties[1].

e. The Discovery of Two Different Neutrinos. The absence of reactions (1) and (2) can be explained if we assume that there are two

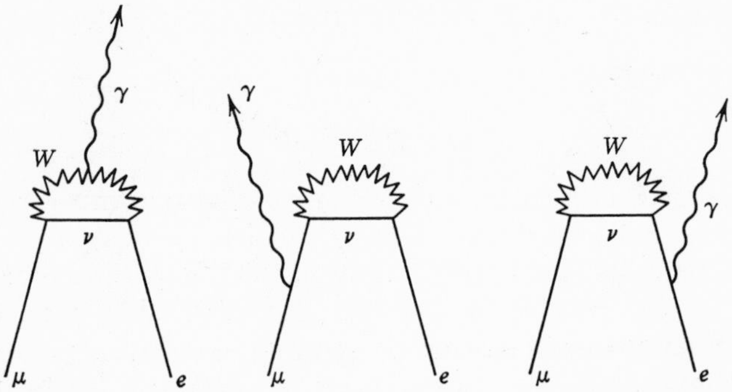

Fig. 8.33-2. Diagrams describing the reaction $\mu \to e + \gamma$ with intermediate weakon and neutrino.

different kinds of neutrinos (K-53) ν_e and ν_μ (each with its own anti-particle) and that

(8) conservation of muonlike leptons, or *meptons*, consisting of *muon* and *mutrino* (μ and ν_μ),
conservation of electronlike leptons, or *eptons*, consisting of *electron* and *electrino* (e and ν_e)

are two laws that must be separately satisfied. We have a conservation principle at each of the vertices of the Puppi triangle.

The electrino and mutrino differ from each other because of some internal coordinate, possibly the same which describes the difference between electron and muon.

The suggestion of two neutrinos accounts for all the facts and is consistent with the existence of an intermediate boson, because it would prevent the radiative decay of the muon according to the diagrams in

[1] A preliminary report on the possible observation of the weakon has appeared in the daily press (S-63).

Fig. 8.33-2. However, it could not be finally accepted so long as the differences in the two neutrinos had not been experimentally and independently established.

An experimental test (L-60; P-59b; S-60a) of the two-neutrino idea has been recently performed at the high-energy (30 beV) accelerator at Brookhaven. The experiment makes use of high-energy (several beV) neutrinos from π decay. If (8) holds, they must be μ-like neutrinos. When they interact with matter (at very high energy the cross section increases) we can expect to observe the production of muons

$$\nu_\mu + \mathcal{N} \rightarrow \mu + \mathcal{N} \tag{9a}$$

but *not* of electrons

$$\nu_\mu + \mathcal{N} \nrightarrow e + \mathcal{N}. \tag{9b}$$

If, instead, (8) does not hold, both electrons and muons may be produced, the electrons being favored by statistical factors.

The experimental results (D-62) show that only muons are produced by neutrinos from pion decay and thus that electronlike and muonlike neutrinos are essentially different.

In the experiment the neutrino beam was generated by the decay in flight of pions which were in turn produced by 15 beV protons striking a beryllium target. After the other particles had been filtered out of the beam by an iron shield 13.5-m thick[1], the interactions of the neutrinos were observed in a 10-ton aluminum spark chamber; 29 single-track events satisfying preset geometrical and energetical requirements could be identified as muons, as expected from the interaction of μ-like neutrinos. Appropriate tests were made to prove that the remaining events could not be neutrino-produced electrons.

8.34 On the Differences between Eptons and Meptons

a. The Magnetic Moment and the Gyromagnetic Ratio of the Muon. Does the difference between eptons and meptons correspond to some tangible difference in structure or in interaction to account for the selection rules and for the electron-muon mass difference?

In order to answer this question, it is interesting to determine whether the muon has any anomalous moment.

[1] 1.35×10^3 cm $\times$ 7.8 g/cm^3 $\approx 10^4$ g/cm^2. For comparison, the side of the base of Cheops' pyramid, built by 100,000 et al., laboring several decades, is 2.3×10^4 cm $\times$ 3 g/cm^3 $\approx 7 \times 10^4$ g/cm^2. The agreement in the order of magnitude is significant, though it would be inappropriate to draw quantitative conclusions.

If the muon is a Dirac particle with no anomaly, its gyromagnetic ratio, g, including quantum electro-dynamical corrections[1] is expected to be

$$(1) \qquad g(\text{theor}) = 2\left(1 + \frac{\alpha}{2\pi} + \frac{3}{4}\frac{\alpha^2}{\pi^2} + \cdots\right) = 2 \times 1.00116.$$

An accurate measurement of the muon's precession frequency in a magnetic field (G-60a) gave a result consistent with (1) and with the previously measured value of the muon's mass.

On the other hand, the value of g has been measured with a method that does not depend on the mass of the muon, which can be computed from the comparison of the results of these experiments.

It is easy to see that if g were exactly 2 the frequency of rotation of a muon trajectory in a magnetic field would be equal to the frequency of precession of the spin. Thus, if a beam of muons entered a magnetic field longitudinally polarized in the direction of motion, it would emerge longitudinally polarized in the same way no matter how long and complicated its trajectory. Any deviation from this law can be used to measure the difference $g - 2$.

In an experiment at CERN (C-61, C-62a) the muons were "stored" in a magnet for more than 1500 turns. From the measurement of the difference in longitudinal polarization at the entrance and exit of the magnet (studied through the asymmetry of the decay) one obtains

$$(2) \qquad g(\text{expt}) = 2 \times (1.001145 \pm 0.000022).$$

The agreement with straightforward Dirac theory is impressive. No "tangible" difference between muons and electrons is revealed by this experiment.

b. Discovery and Hyperfine Splitting of Muonium. Muonium is a neutral atomic system consisting of an electron and a muon, usually

[1] It may seem surprising that the theoretical gyromagnetic ratio of the muon should differ at all from that of the electron. The difference (in the term α^2, which is a fifth-order term in the magnetic moment) arises from the comparison of the fifth-order diagrams (*a*) and (*b*). The effect of electron-vacuum polarization in the electromagnetic interaction of electrons (*a*) and the effect of muon-vacuum polarization in the electromagnetic interaction of muons give identical corrections to the gyromagnetic ratio of the two particles. For the muon there is also a contribution of the electron-vacuum polarization (P-57b; S-57) whereas the polarization of the muon vacuum is negligible for electrons.

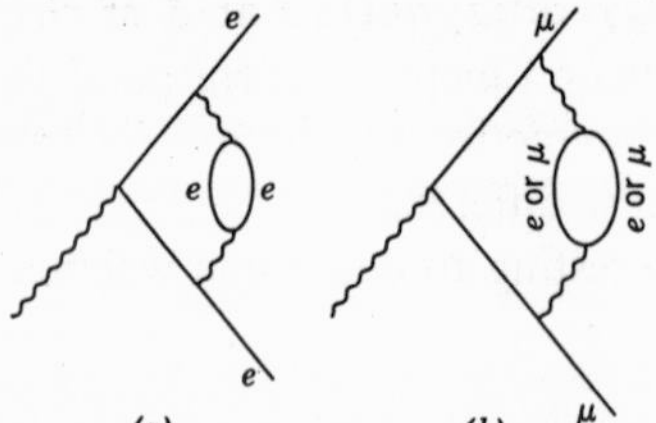

(*a*) (*b*)

one of the negative electrons of matter bound to a positive muon. Its ground state can exist with two different values of J, 0 and 1.

The expectation value of the magnetic moment of muonium for the triplet state can be computed: it is contributed mostly by the electron and it is much larger than that of the free muon. Thus the presence of muonium can be detected by its characteristic precession frequency in a magnetic field, which is quite different from that of the free muon. The precession of muonium is, in turn, revealed through the precession of the asymmetric pattern of emission of μ-decay electrons.

It is in this manner that Hughes and collaborators were able to show first that polarized muonium could be formed in high pressure Argon gas and then to measure accurately the precession frequency of muonium (H-60; Z-62). From the experimental results they obtain that the hyperfine splitting of its ground state is

$$\Delta\nu(\text{expt}) = 4461.3 \pm 2.2 \text{ Mc/sec}, \tag{3}$$

to be compared with the theoretical value

$$\Delta\nu(\text{theor}) = 4463.13 \pm 0.10 \text{ Mc/sec}. \tag{4}$$

Thus the muon behaves quite normally in its binding to electrons.

c. Possible Annihilation of Muonium. Obviously the muon in muonium can decay into an electron and two neutrinos with its characteristic mean life. But we may ask whether muonium can annihilate into two γ rays as positronium does.

Let us observe that the electromagnetic annihilation of muonium does not violate any of the conventional conservation principles, but it is forbidden by the separate conservation of eptons and meptons.

It has been found experimentally that the two-quantum annihilation of electrons and muons does not occur. A measurement of coincidences at 180° from a target of Cu where positive muons were brought to rest (Y-59) gave the following lower limit for the annihilation mean life:

$$\tau(\mu^+ + e^- \rightarrow \gamma - \gamma) > \tfrac{1}{4} \text{ sec}; \tag{5}$$

this must be compared with the mean life of positrons in Cu, which is $\approx 10^{-9}$ sec!

The absence of muonium annihilation, despite the fact that both muons and electrons behave separately as simple Dirac particles, furnishes further evidence for the basic difference between electrons and muons.

8.35 Weak Current and Its Conservation

a. Weak Current and Weak Interactions. The weak interactions of nucleons and leptons can be expressed in a simple way as the interaction of a parity-violating weak current with itself (F-58c).

If we take into account the existence of two different neutrinos, the weak current $\mathfrak{J}$ can be written as the sum of three terms for nucleons, eptons and meptons, respectively:

$$\mathfrak{J}_\lambda = \mathfrak{J}_\lambda^{(N)} + \mathfrak{J}_\lambda^{(e)} + \mathfrak{J}_\lambda^{(m)}, \tag{1}$$

with

$$\begin{aligned} \mathfrak{J}_\lambda^{(N)} &= \sqrt{\tfrac{1}{2}}\,\bar{\psi}_{\mathrm{p}}\gamma_\lambda(1-|R|\,\Gamma_5)\psi_{\mathrm{n}} \approx \sqrt{2}\,\bar{\chi}_{\mathrm{p}}\gamma_\lambda\chi_{\mathrm{n}}, \\ \mathfrak{J}_\lambda^{(e)} &= \sqrt{\tfrac{1}{2}}\,\bar{\psi}_{\nu_e}\gamma_\lambda(1-\Gamma_5)\psi_e = \sqrt{2}\,\bar{\chi}_{\nu_e}\gamma_\lambda\chi_e, \\ \mathfrak{J}_\lambda^{(m)} &= \sqrt{\tfrac{1}{2}}\,\bar{\psi}_{\nu_\mu}\gamma_\lambda(1-\Gamma_5)\psi_\mu = \sqrt{2}\,\bar{\chi}_{\nu_\mu}\gamma_\lambda\chi_\mu \end{aligned} \tag{2}$$

(the particles e and μ have negative sign and the three terms of (1) are all charge raising). If the weak interaction Hamiltonian is postulated to be

$$\mathcal{H} = \sqrt{2}g\mathfrak{J}_\lambda{}^\dagger\mathfrak{J}_\lambda, \tag{3}$$

we obtain the same interaction as in 8.31(4), 8.22(16) with $R = -1$.

Clearly, the term $g\mathfrak{J}_\lambda^{(N)\dagger}\mathfrak{J}_\lambda^{(e)}$ corresponds to nuclear β^+ decay; the term $g\mathfrak{J}_\lambda^{(e)\dagger}\mathfrak{J}_\lambda^{(N)}$, to nuclear β^- decay, etc., whereas terms such as $g\mathfrak{J}_\lambda^{(e)\dagger}\mathfrak{J}_\lambda^{(e)}$ express weak scattering of electrons by electrinos, etc.

Thus (3) accounts in a simple condensed manner for all the interactions of the Puppi triangle, which (in the approximation $|R| = 1$) are symmetrically expressed, as appropriate to the idea of universal Fermi interaction. The forbidden reactions of 8.33b are automatically excluded by (3).

b. Conservation of Weak Vector Current. In writing (3), we have assumed that the *vector* coupling of the three weak interacting fermions pairs is identical. This assumption is justified by the almost perfect equality of the values of the constants g_V and g_μ, determined from the experiment.

At first sight the equality of these two constants seems to be in the most satisfactory and straightforward agreement with the idea of universal Fermi interaction. A little more thought, however, makes one suspect that this first impression may be somewhat naïve.

In effect, it would be natural to assume that the idea of universal Fermi interaction applies to "bare" fermions, those that, like the muon and the electron, satisfy the point-charge, no-anomalous-magnetic-moment Dirac equation or, in other words, that are not surrounded by complicated "clouds" of strongly coupled fields.

It should be the bare nucleons, and not the physical nucleons, that are vector-coupled with a constant equal to g_μ. The observed coupling of the neutron should be smaller, since this particle is "part time" decomposed into $\mathrm{p} + \pi^-$, and the proton cannot emit β^-.

But it is found experimentally that it is the physical nucleon and not the bare nucleon that is vector-coupled like the muon. This is a new and significant fact, not necessarily included in the idea of universal Fermi interaction.

We can observe in this connection that the vector coupling of the physical proton and muon are identical also for the electromagnetic field: this is because charge is conserved in the virtual reaction $p \rightleftharpoons n + \pi^+$, and the pion carries the charge that the nucleon has lost[1]. However, the tensor (anomalous magnetic-moment) coupling of the physical proton to the electromagnetic field is different for proton and muon: the difference, we know, is due to the meson cloud that surrounds the nucleus.

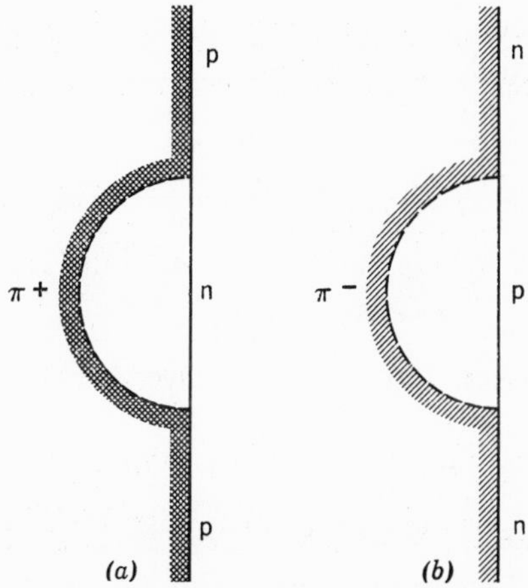

Fig. 8.35-1. (*a*) The electric charge (cross shading) remains constant in the virtual decomposition of the proton: the vector coupling constant to photons does not depend on the presence of the nucleon cloud; (*b*) the weak interaction vector coupling (diagonal shading) also remains the same despite the virtual decomposition of the neutron.

Thus the behavior of the electromagnetic field and of the weak field in this respect is also similar: in both there is a *vector-current conservation*; but the conservation does not extend to the other modes of coupling; presumably, the interaction with mesons which produces an anomalous tensor electromagnetic coupling ($\mu_N \neq 1$) also accounts for an anomalous axial weak coupling ($|R| \neq 1$).

In the same manner as the pion "replaces" the nucleon in its vector interaction with the electromagnetic field, so the pion also "replaces" the nucleon in its interaction with the weak field (Fig. 8.35-1). It follows that the pions must be a source of vector weak field and must β-decay. This point is discussed more fully in 8.36.

[1] The equality of the vector (charge) coupling of p and μ to the electro-magnetic field holds only at low energy, where the nucleon's form factor can be replaced by unity. Also the form factor finds its equivalent in the weak coupling of the nucleons [see (e)].

These ideas take the following analytical form. In isotopic spin notation the electric current associated to a bare nucleon (bN) is

$$j_\lambda^{(bN)} = e\bar{\psi}_N\gamma_\lambda\tfrac{1}{2}(1 + \tau_3)\psi_N; \tag{4}$$

this current is not conserved when τ_3 changes (p $\rightleftharpoons$ n, as, for instance, in π^+ photoproduction). Thus

$$\partial_\lambda j_\lambda^{(bN)} \neq 0. \tag{5}$$

The electric current due to both nucleons and pions is

$$j_\lambda = e[\bar{\psi}_N\gamma_\lambda\tfrac{1}{2}(1 + \tau_3)\psi_N] + ie\vec{\phi}\,\partial_\lambda t_3\vec{\phi}, \tag{6}$$

where t_3 is the third component of the pion isospin operator[1]; this current is conserved[2] and satisfies the equation

$$\partial_\lambda j_\lambda = 0. \tag{7}$$

If we now assume that this argument applies to all isospin components of the current, we can proceed in exactly the same manner for the weak-vector interaction. The bare nucleon current in this case is

$$\mathfrak{J}_\lambda^{(bN),V} = \sqrt{\tfrac{1}{2}}\bar{\psi}'_{N'}\gamma_\lambda\tau^+\psi_N \tag{8}$$

and is not divergenceless. But we obtain a divergenceless vector in analogy to (6) if we write

$$\mathfrak{J}_\lambda^{(N),V} = \sqrt{\tfrac{1}{2}}\bar{\psi}_N\gamma_\lambda\tau^+\psi_N + \sqrt{2}i\vec{\phi}\,\partial_\lambda t^+\vec{\phi}, \tag{9}$$

where $t^+ = \frac{1}{2}(t_1 + it_2)$ is the operator that raises the meson charge by one unit.

Expression (9) gives definite predictions on the β decay of the pion, which is discussed in the next section. In what follows immediately we are concerned with the effects of weak-vector current conservation in nuclear β decay.

c. Weak Magnetism. It can now be observed that the vector part of the nuclear current $\sqrt{\frac{1}{2}}\bar{\psi}_N\gamma_\lambda\tau^+\psi_N$ is coupled to the parity-violating weak current $\sqrt{2}\bar{\chi}_e\gamma_\lambda\chi_\nu$ (only the electron term is written for simplicity) in exactly the same manner that the electric nucleon current $\frac{1}{2}(1 + \tau_3)\bar{\psi}_N\gamma_\lambda\psi_N$ is coupled to the electromagnetic potential A_λ.

Thus the allowed Fermi term in γ_4, which expresses a coupling between fourth vector-components, can be called *weak electrostatics*, and the small Fermi terms in γ_i contribute to *weak magnetism*.

But the analogy goes further. The pion "cloud," which produces the

[1] The matrices t_i, with t_3 diagonal, have the form of the matrices S_i of 1.14(28). Then we see that

$$-ie\vec{\phi}\cdot\nabla t_3\vec{\phi} = ie\phi_+\nabla t_3\phi_- + ie\phi_-\nabla t_3\phi_+ - ie\phi_0\nabla t_3\phi_0 = -ie\phi_+\nabla\phi_- + ie\phi_-\nabla\phi_+$$

is the meson electric current in conformity with 7.26(3) and 7.31(7).

[2] Strange particles are neglected.

anomalous magnetic moment of the nucleon, is also coupled to the weak field in the assumption of a conserved vector current. If the pion cloud contributes an isovector (7.26b) tensor [6.15(6)] coupling to the electromagnetic field, it must produce also an isovector tensor coupling to the weak field. The same argument extends to the exchange pion currents responsible for nuclear binding: if these currents contribute to the magnetic moment, they must contribute proportionally also to weak magnetism.

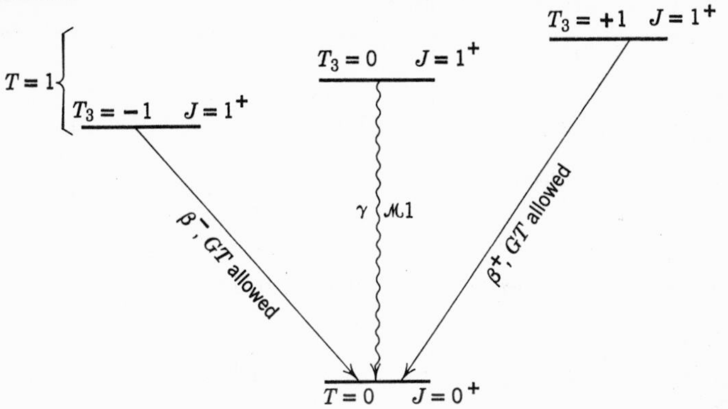

Fig. 8.35-2. Example of β transitions in which the effects of weak magnetism can be estimated by comparison with an $\mathcal{M}1$ electromagnetic transition.

The isovector magnetic coupling constant of a nucleon at rest is $\frac{1}{2}(\mu_p - \mu_n)\tau_3\, e/(2M)$ [1.32(8)]. The corresponding coupling constant for weak magnetism is $\frac{1}{2}(\mu_p - \mu_n)(-\sqrt{2}\tau^+)g_V/(2M)$ for nuclear charge raising and $\frac{1}{2}(\mu_p - \mu_n)(\sqrt{2}\tau^-)g_V/(2M)$ for nuclear charge lowering. This last constant enters in the computation of muon capture [8.32(6)]. For weak interactions the magnetic field is replaced by the **curl** of the weak lepton current.

As an example of the prediction of weak magnetism in β decay, let us consider, following Gell-Mann (G-58a), the transition between the terms of an isotopic spin triplet with $J = 1^+$ to an isotopic spin singlet with $J = 0^+$ (Fig. 8.35-2).

The states of equal T_3 are connected by a $\mathcal{M}1$ γ transition. Since $\Delta T = -1$, only the isovector part of the electromagnetic Hamiltonian contributes to the transition probability. Then the effective Hamiltonian is, nonrelativistically,

(10) $$-\frac{e}{2M}\,\boldsymbol{\mu}\cdot(\nabla\times\mathbf{A}),$$

where $\boldsymbol{\mu}$ is the (isovector) transition magnetic moment in units of nuclear magnetons.

The states of different T_3 are connected by an allowed GT β transition, which, in conventional β theory, is due to the axial-vector part of the interaction. But if the idea of weak-vector-current conservation is accepted, the states connected by the $\mathcal{M}1$ radiative transition are coupled in the same manner to the β-decay field. The added term in the β-decay Hamiltonian is, nonrelativistically,

$$-\frac{g}{\sqrt{2}M}\,\boldsymbol{\mu}\cdot[\boldsymbol{\nabla}\times\mathbf{J}^{(e)}_{\text{weak}}], \tag{11}$$

where μ has the same value as in (10).

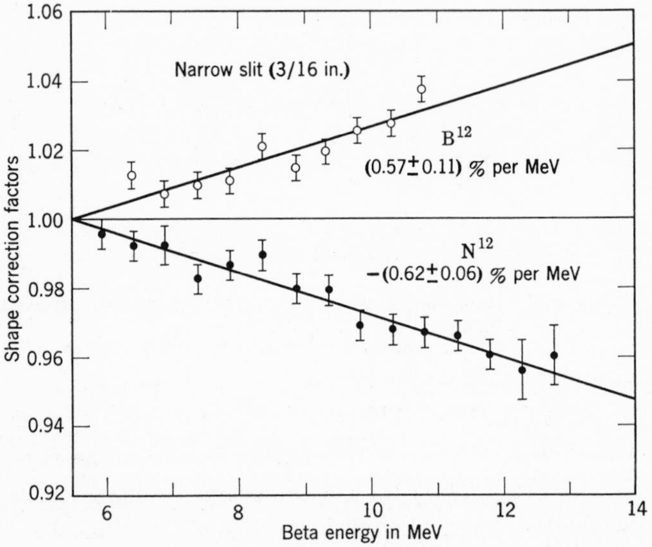

Fig. 8.35-3. Shape correction factors in the β decay of B^{12} and N^{12} [Y. K. Lee, L. W. Mo, and C. S. Wu, *Phys. Rev. Letters*, **10**, 253 (1963)].

This term is the nonrelativistic part of a derivative-coupled tensor interaction (8.14d). If sufficiently large, it will produce an observable distortion in the spectral shape due to the interference with the predominant-axial vector contribution.

It is important to note that the matrix element (10), and thus (11), can be obtained from a measurement of the γ-transition probability. In this case the predictions of weak magnetism are, at least in principle, complete and unambiguous.

d. Experimental Evidence for Weak Magnetism. After some preliminary work to detect the effects of weak magnetism in β decay (N-60; W-60) the results of a conclusive experiment were recently reported (L-63). Sources of B^{12} (0.02 sec) and N^{12} (0.012 sec) were produced directly in a β spectrometer by bombarding with a pulsating beam from a Van de Graaff accelerator: the reactions used were B^{11}(d, p) B^{12} and B^{10} (He^3, n) N^{12}, and the β spectra were measured between pulses. The spectrometer was carefully studied to make sure that there were no distortions, and the Fermi plots of the two isotopes were obtained. As predicted from the theory of weak magnetism, slight departures from linearity, corresponding to the correction factors of Fig. 8.35-3, were found.

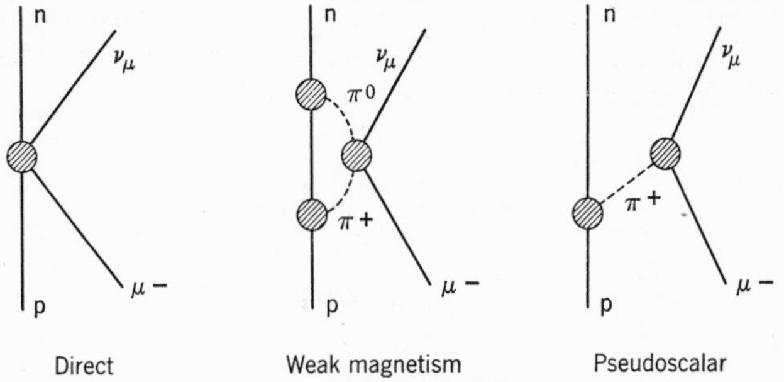

Fig. 8.35-4. Diagrams describing the capture of μ^- by protons.

The correction term changes sign as we go from β^- to β^+, in agreement with theory, and the magnitude of the observed effect agrees with the calculated value within the limit of errors.

e. Form Factors for Weak Interactions. Since the "meson cloud" plays a role in weak interactions, it can be expected that the effect of its finite size will be felt at sufficiently high momentum transfer. Though the nucleons can be considered as points for β decay, the effect of a form factor may be of some importance in their interaction with muons.

When all the possibilities are taken into account, the nucleon part of the parity-violating weak current (2) can be written (G-58c; G-59b; W-59)

(12)
$$\mathfrak{J}_\lambda^{(N)} = \sqrt{\tfrac{1}{2}}\bar{w}_p[F_1(q)\gamma_\lambda + RF_2(q)\gamma_\lambda\Gamma_5 + AF_3(q)\sigma_{\lambda\kappa}q_\kappa + BF_4(q)\Gamma_5 q_\lambda]w_n,$$

where **q** is the nucleon's four momentum transfer.

In this expression the F_i are four form factors which satisfy $F_i(0) = 1$; A and B are two constants to be determined. The first and second terms are the usual vector and axial coupling, the third corresponds to anomalous weak magnetism [compare with 6.24(10)], and the last to pseudoscalar coupling. Under the assumption of a conserved current, the constant A can be predicted from the anomalous moments, and the form factors F_1 and F_3 can be calculated from the electromagnetic form factors of the nucleons; BF_4 can be computed as in 8.32d.

Figure 8.35-4 illustrates with diagrams the origin of the different terms of (12). Weak magnetism is due to $\pi \to \pi^0 + \mu + \nu_\mu$, whereas pseudoscalar coupling is associated with $\pi^+ \to \mu + \nu_\mu$.

Some experimental evidence for these effects is found in recent work on μ capture (8.32e).

8.36 *The Decays of the π Meson*

a. π → μ Decay. The "usual" decay of the pion [7.11(7)] results in the production of a muon and a neutrino. It follows from conservation of linear and angular momentum that these two particles must be emitted with *opposite spin* and *equal helicity* (Fig. 8.36-1).

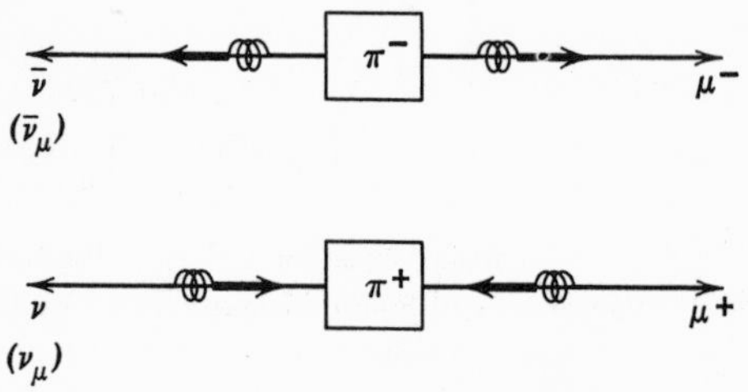

Fig. 8.36-1. Pion decay with spin assignments according to left-handed neutrinos.

Let us start the discussion of π decay with the old assumption of a single kind of neutrinos: as for nuclear β decay, we expect that the neutrino emitted must be left-handed and the antineutrinos right-handed. Furthermore, since the pion has leptic number zero, the leptic numbers of the decay muon and neutrino must be opposite.

We know from our analysis of μ decay that, in the hypothesis of a single neutrino, the negative muon is a lepton. Conservation of leptons thus requires that it be accompanied by a right-handed antineutrino. Thus the spins of the products of π decay are unambiguously predicted from the assumptions of a single neutrino and of lepton conservations, as indicated in Fig. 8.36-1. Note that the sign of the muon's helicity is that unfavored by its leptic number.

It is clearly a matter of considerable interest to measure the helicity of the muons from π decay, especially after the discovery that μ neutrinos are different from e neutrinos. Unfortunately, the direct measurements are difficult, since spin effects are relativistic, and the meson beams available around conventional synchrocyclotrons have nonrelativistic velocities.

However, three different groups of experimenters have recently reported results in agreement with Fig. 8.36-1. The first experiment was performed in the Soviet Union, with the predominantly positive muons of cosmic radiation (A-60a). The second is a study of Moeller scattering of a 8 beV/c μ^- beam from polarized electrons in magnetized iron, at CERN (B-61a). The third is a measurement of asymmetry of Mott scattering of a high-energy μ^- beam, also at CERN (B-61b). Though the errors are large, all of these experiments are in agreement with the helicities of Fig. 8.36-1, which we regard as established.

It is therefore convenient to continue to call the negative muon a particle, like the negative electron. Then it follows from the helicity measurement that all particles are identically coupled in weak interactions, interacting through their left-handed components.

The contradiction between the helicity of the muons from π decay and the left-handed interaction of μ^- is only apparent: the muon emerges with small kinetic energy in the rest system of the pion ($E_\mu - m_\mu = 4.2$ MeV $\ll m_\mu$), and the amount of left-handed polarization required by the $1 - \Gamma_5$ operator is very small [8.22(9)]. The muon may compromise on its left-handedness, and the extremely relativistic neutrino may not.

b. $\pi \to e$ Decay. The fact that the two products of π decay must carry opposite angular momentum while propagating in opposite directions (and thus have the same helicity) favors the emission of a slow massive muon rather than a fast, light electron. *This is why the μ decay mode predominates despite the statistical factors.*

This consideration can be made quantitative and leads to the correct prediction of the ratio $(\pi \to e + \nu)/(\pi \to \mu + \nu)$.

The probability of right-handed emission for the negative muon interacting through its left-handed component [compare with 8.22(9) and see 5.11(14) for the algebra] is[1]

$$(1) \qquad 1 - v_\mu = 1 - \frac{p_\mu}{E_\mu} = \frac{2m_\mu^2}{m_\pi^2 + m_\mu^2};$$

then, considering the statistical factors ρ already computed in 5.11(16), we obtain

$$(2) \qquad \text{ratio}\,\frac{\pi \to e + \nu}{\pi \to \mu + \nu} = \frac{\rho_e}{\rho_\mu}\frac{1 - v_e}{1 - v_\mu} = \frac{m_e^2(m_\pi^2 - m_e^2)^2}{m_\mu^2(m_\pi^2 - m_\mu^2)^2} \simeq 1.3 \times 10^4.$$

After some unsuccessful attempts, the electron decay of the pion has been observed with counters and in bubble chambers (F-58a; I-58). Finally, it was quantitatively studied with a magnetic spectrometer

[1] See 8.32(10) for a more formal derivation of the factor $1 - v_\mu$.

(Fig. 8.36-2) (A-60b). The experimental value of the e/μ branching ratio is

$$(1.21 \pm 0.07) \times 10^{-4}$$

in good agreement with (2).

c. Further Considerations on the Decay of Pions in Two Leptons. After having reported the success of the theory of weak interactions in predicting the e/μ branching ratio in π decay, we must point out that there are many points that remain to be elucidated.

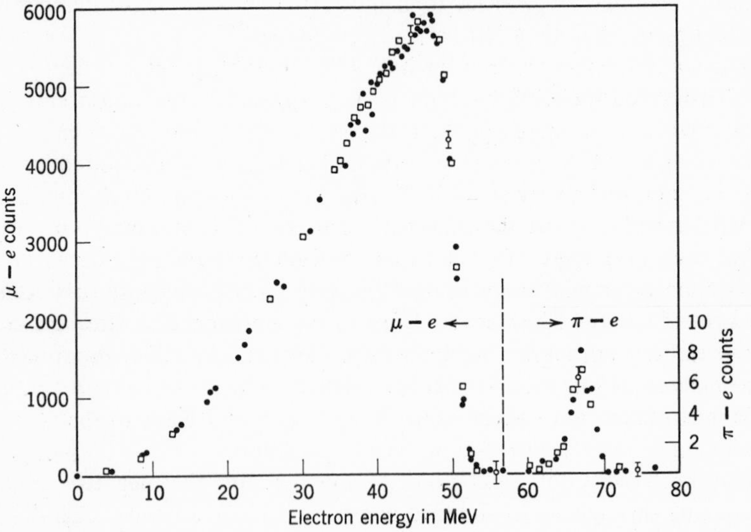

Fig. 8.36-2. Plot of π-e and μ-e data. Note the change in scale above 55 MeV. Errors are indicated at selected points [from Anderson, Fujii, Miller, and Tau, *Phys. Rev.*, **119**, 2060 (1960)].

We must, for instance, explain the value of the mean life of the π meson. This is a difficult theoretical problem because, presumably, the pion is coupled to the muon-neutrino field through the intermediary of nucleon-anti-nucleon pairs. The simplest diagram describing π-decay is shown in Fig. 8.32-2.

Even if we assume that weak interactions are well known, the coupling of the pion to the nucleons presents all the uncertainties inherent in the strong forces. The relativistic coupling of pions and nucleons is poorly known, and many more complex diagrams should be considered with that of Fig. 8.32-2.

It is possible to circumvent these difficulties with dispersion relation techniques. Using this method, and a strong coupling constant $f_{PP}^2 = 15$

[see 7.17(3)], Goldberger and Trieman (G-58b) succeeded in accounting with fair accuracy for the observed π mean life.

d. Three-Particle Decay of Charged Pions. Since the charged pions are heavier than the neutral ones, the reaction

$$\pi^{\pm} \rightarrow \pi^0 + e^{\pm} + \nu \tag{3}$$

is energetically possible. Its rate can be unambiguously predicted from the idea of weak-vector-current conservation discussed in 8.35. From 8.35(2), (3), and (9), the coupling responsible for reaction (3) is

$$i2\sqrt{2}g(\vec{\phi} \cdot \partial_\lambda t^+ \vec{\phi})(\bar{\chi}_e \gamma_\lambda \chi_\nu) + \text{h.c.}$$

From this we predict a partial decay rate of $(0.37 \pm 0.07)\ \text{sec}^{-1}$, corresponding to a branching ratio

$$\frac{\pi^+ \rightarrow \pi^0 + e^+ + \nu}{\pi^+ \rightarrow \mu^+ + \nu} = (1.0 \pm 0.2) \times 10^{-8}. \tag{4}$$

More simply the probability of $\pi^{\pm} \rightarrow \pi^0 + e^{\pm} + \nu$ decay can be computed, assuming the same ft as for allowed nucleon β decay.

The three-particle decay of the charged pion is difficult to observe because of its rarity, but recent advances in experimental techniques, such as the advent of spark chambers have made possible the experimental investigation of this most fundamental effect. The result of recent measurements of the ratio (4) is

$$(1.15 \pm 0.22) \times 10^{-8} \qquad \text{(D-63)}$$
$$(1.0 \pm 0.3) \times 10^{-8} \qquad \text{(B-64)}$$

in accord with the theory of conserved vector current.

References

Books

BW-52 J. M. Blatt and V. F. Weisskopf, *Theoretical Nuclear Physics*, Wiley, New York, 1952.

Articles

A-57 Ambler, Hayward, Hoppes, Hudson, and Wu, *Phys. Rev.*, **106**, 1361 (1957).

A-58 Astbury, Kemp, Lipman, Muirhead, Voss, Zangler, and Kirk, *Proc. Phys. Soc. (London)*, **72**, 494 (1958).

A-59a J. S. Allen, *Rev. Mod. Phys.*, **31**, 791 (1959).

A-59b Astbury, Blair, Hussain, Kemp, Muirhead, and Voss, *Phys. Rev. Letters*, **3**, 476 (1959).

A-60a Alichanov, Galaktionov, Gorodkov, Eliseev, and Lyubimov, *J. Exptl. Theor. Phys.* (*USSR*), **38,** 1918 (1960) *transl. Soviet Physics JEPT*, **11,** 1380 (1960).

A-60b Anderson, Fujii, Miller, and Tau, *Phys. Rev.*, **119,** 2050 (1960).

A-61 Astbury, Kemp, Muirhead, Voss, and Woodhead, *Proc. Phys. Soc.* (*London*), **78,** 1151 (1961).

A-63 Auerbach, Esterling, Hill, Jenkins, Lach and Lipman, *Phys. Rev. Letters*, **11,** 23 (1963).

B-57 Burgy, Epstein, Krohn, Novey, Ringo, and Telegdi, *Phys. Rev.*, **107,** 1731 (1957).

B-58a Bernardini, Brovetto, DeBenedetti, and Ferroni, *Nuovo Cimento*, **7,** 419 (1958).

B-58b Bernstein, Lee, Yang, and Primakoff, *Phys. Rev.*, **111,** 313 (1958).

B-58c Burgy, Krohn, Novey, Ringo, and Telegdi, *Phys. Rev.*, **110,** 1214 (1958).

B-58d Burgy, Krohn, Novey, Ringo, and Telegdi, *Phys. Rev. Letters*, **1,** 324 (1958).

B-59a Bardon, Berley, and Lederman, *Phys. Rev. Letters*, **2,** 56 (1959).

B-59b Barrett, Holmstrom, and Keuffel, *Phys. Rev.*, **113,** 661 (1959).

B-61a Backenstoss, Hyams, Knop, Marin, and Stierlin, *Phys. Rev. Letters*, **6,** 415 (1961).

B-61b Bardon, Franzini, and Lee, *Phys. Rev. Letters*, **7,** 23 (1961).

B-62a Bartlett, Devons, and Sachs, *Phys. Rev. Letters*, **8,** 120 (1962).

B-62b Bertolini, Citron, Gianlanella, Focardi, Mukhin, Rubbia, and Saporetti, *Proc. Int. Conf. High En. Phys.*, Geneva (1962).

B-62c Bleser, Lederman, Rosen, Rothberg, and Zavattini, *Phys. Rev. Letters*, **8,** 288 (1962).

B-64 Bartlett, Devons, Meyer, and Rosen, *Bull. Am. Phys. Soc.*, **9,** 71 (1964).

C-28 Cox, McIlwraith, and Kurrelmeyer, *Proc. Nat. Acad. Sci.*, **14,** 544 (1928).

C-57a C. L. Cowan and F. Reines, *Phys. Rev.*, **107,** 528 (1957).

C-57b K. L. Crowe, *Bull. Am. Phys. Soc.*, **2,** 206 (1957).

C-58 Clark, Robson, and Nathans, *Phys. Rev. Letters*, **1,** 100 (1958).

C-59a C. L. Cowan and F. Reines, *Nature* **178,** 466 (1959).

C-59b G. Culligan, S. G. F. Frank, and J. R. Holt, *Bull. Am. Phys. Soc.*, **4,** 81 (1959).

C-61 Charpack, Farley, Garwin, Muller, Sens, Telegdi, and Zichichi, *Phys. Rev. Letters*, **6,** 128 (1961).

C-62a Charpack, Farley, Garwin, Muller, Sens, and Zichichi, *Phys. Letters*, **1,** 16 (1962).

C-62b Conversi, di Lella, Penso, Toller, and Rubbia, *Phys. Rev. Letters*, **8,** 125 (1962).

D-53 M. Deutsch and O. Kofoed-Hansen, *Experimental Nuclear Physics*, (E. Segre, editor), Wiley, New York, 1953.

D-55 R. Davies, *Phys. Rev.*, **97,** 766 (1955).

D-59 R. Davies and D. S. Harmer, *Bull. Am. Phys. Soc.*, **4,** 217 (1959).

D-60 Durand, Landovitz, and Marr, *Phys. Rev. Letters*, **4,** 620 (1960).

D-62 Danby, Gaillard, Goulianos, Lederman, Mistry, Schwartz, and Steinberger, *Phys. Rev. Letters*, **9**, 36 (1962).
D-63 Dupommier, Heintz, Rubbia, and Soergel, *Phys. Letters*, **5**, 61 (1963).
E-63 Edelstein, Keuffel, Wagner, and Clay, Report at the Brookhaven Conference on Weak Interactions, 1963.
F-58a Fazzini, Fidecaro, Merrison, Paul, and Tollestrup, *Phys. Rev. Letters*, **1**, 247 (1958).
F-58b G. Feinberg, *Phys. Rev.*, **110**, 1482 (1958).
F-58c R. P. Feynman and M. Gell-Mann, *Phys. Rev.*, **109**, 193 (1958).
F-59a Feinberg, Kabir, and Weinberg, *Phys. Rev. Letters*, **3**, 527 (1959).
F-59b A. Fujii and H. Primakoff, *Nuovo Cimento*, **12**, 327 (1959).
F-62 Frankel, Halpern, Holloway, Wales, Yearian, Chamberlain, Lemonick, and Pipkin, *Phys. Rev. Letters*, **8**, 123 (1962).
F-63 Falomkin, Filippov, Kulijukin, Pontecorvo, Scherbakov, Sulysev, Tsupko-Sitnikov, and Zaimdoroga, *Phys. Lett.* **3**, 229 (1963).
G-57 Goldhaber, Grodzins, and Sunyar, *Phys. Rev.*, **106**, 826 (1957).
G-58a M. Gell-Mann, *Phys. Rev.*, **111**, 362 (1958).
G-58b M. L. Goldberger and S. B. Trieman, *Phys. Rev.*, **110**, 1178 (1958).
G-58c M. L. Goldberger and S. B. Trieman, *Phys. Rev.*, **111**, 354 (1958).
G-58d Goldhaber, Grodzins, and Sunyar, *Phys. Rev.*, **109**, 1015 (1958).
G-59a Garwin, Lederman, and Weinrich, *Phys. Rev.*, **105**, 1415 (1959).
G-59b M. Gell-Mann, *Rev. Mod. Phys.*, **31**, 834 (1959).
G-60a Garwin, Hutchinson, Penman, and Shapiro, *Phys. Rev.*, **118**, 271 (1960).
G-60b V. Gilinsky and J. Mathews, *Phys. Rev.*, **120**, 1450 (1960).
H-53 Hamilton, Alford, and Gross, *Phys. Rev.*, **92**, 1521 (1953).
H-57a S. S. Hanna and R. S. Preston, *Phys. Rev.*, **106**, 1363 (1957).
H-57b S. S. Hanna and R. S. Preston, *Phys. Rev.*, **108**, 160 (1957).
H-58 S. S. Hanna and R. S. Preston, *Phys. Rev.*, **108**, 1460 (1958).
H-60 Hughes, McCohn, Ziock, and Prepost, *Phys. Rev. Letters*, **5**, 63 (1960).
H-61 D. L. Hendrie and J. B. Gerhard, *Phys. Rev.*, **121**, 846 (1961).
H-62 R. H. Hildebrand and J. H. Doede, *Proc. Int. Conf. High En. Phys.*, Geneva (1962).
I-58 Impeduglia, Plano, Prodell, Samios, Schwartz, and Steinberger, *Phys. Rev. Letters*, **1**, 249 (1958).
J-57 Jackson, Treiman, and Wyld, *Phys. Rev.*, **106**, 517 (1957).
K-53 E. Konopinski and H. Mahmoud, *Phys. Rev.*, **92**, 1045 (1953).
K-55 E. Konopinski, in *β and γ Spectroscopy* (edited by K. Siegbahn), North Holland, Amsterdam, 1955, p. 292.
K-59a T. Kinoshita and A. Sirlin, *Phys. Rev.*, **113**, 1652 (1959).
K-59b E. Konopinski, *Ann. Rev. Nucl. Sci.*, **9**, 99 (1959).
L-57a T. D. Lee and C. N. Yang, *Phys. Rev.*, **108**, 1611 (1957).
L-57b G. Luders, *Ann. Phys.*, **2**, 1 (1957).
L-58a J. Leite Lopez, *Phys. Rev.*, **109**, 509 (1958).
L-58b Lundy, Sens, Swanson, Telegdi, and Yovanovitch, *Phys. Rev. Letters*, **1**, 102 (1958).
L-58c Lynch, Orear, and Rosendorff, *Phys. Rev. Letters*, **1**, 471 (1958).

L-59 J. Lee and N. P. Samios, *Phys. Rev. Letters*, **3**, 55 (1959).
L-60 T. D. Lee and C. N. Yang, *Phys. Rev. Letters*, **4**, 307 (1960).
L-63 Lee, Mo, and Wu, *Phys. Rev. Letters*, **10**, 253 (1963).
M-50 L. Michel, *Proc. Roy. Soc.* (*London*), **A63**, 514 (1950).
M-53 L. Michel, Thesis, University of Paris, 1953.
M-58 W. M. MacDonald, *Phys. Rev.*, **100**, 1420 (1958).
M-61 Maier, Bloch, Edelstein, and Siegel, *Phys. Rev. Letters*, **6**, 417 (1961).
N-60 Nordberg, Povh, and Barnes, *Phys. Rev. Letters*, **4**, 23 (1960).
P-33 W. Pauli, in *Handbuch der Physik* (1933 edition) Vol. 24, Part 1, p. 226, Springer-Verlag, Berlin.
P-57a Page and Heinberg, *Phys. Rev.*, **106**, 1220 (1957).
P-57b A. Petermann, *Phys. Rev.*, **105**, 1931 (1957).
P-59a R. J. Plano and A. Le Curtois, *Bull. Am. Phys. Soc.*, **4**, 82 (1959).
P-59b B. Pontecorvo, *J. Expl. Theor. Phys.* (*USSR*), **37**, 1759 (1959); transl. *Soviet Physics, JETP*, **10**, 1236 (1960).
P-59c H. Primakoff, *Rev. Mod. Phys.*, **31**, 802 (1959).
P-62 S. Parker and S. Penman, *Nuovo Cimento*, **23**, 485 (1962).
R-55 M. E. Rose, Appendices II and III in *β and γ Spectroscopy* (edited by K. Siegbahn), North Holland, Amsterdam, 1955.
R-58 L. Rosenson, *Phys. Rev.*, **109**, 958 (1958).
R-60 Reiter, Romanowski, Sutton, and Chidley, *Phys. Rev. Letters*, **5**, 22 (1960).
R-63a C. Rubbia, Report at the Brookhaven conference on weak interactions, 1963.
R-63b J. E. Rothberg, Columbia University Thesis (1963).
S-53 J. C. Sens, *Phys. Rev.*, **113**, 679 (1953).
S-57 C. M. Sommerfield, *Phys. Rev.*, **107**, 328 (1957).
S-58a J. J. Sakurai, *Phys. Rev. Letters*, **1**, 40 (1958).
S-58b J. J. Sakurai, *Nuovo Cimento*, **8**, 649 (1958).
S-58c E. C. G. Sudershan and R. E. Marshak, *Phys. Rev.*, **109**, 1860 (1958).
S-59a Sargent, Rinehart, Lederman, and Roger, *Phys. Rev.*, **99**, 885 (1959).
S-59b J. C. Sens, *Phys. Rev.*, **113**, 679 (1959).
S-60a M. Schwartz, *Phys. Rev. Letters*, **4**, 306 (1960).
S-60b F. Russell Stannard, *Phys. Rev. Letters*, **4**, 523 (1960).
S-62 J. Schwinger, *Phys. Rev.*, **125**, 397 (1962).
S-63 W. Sullivan, *The New York Times*, **113**, Oct. 13, 1963.
T-49 J. Tiomno and J. Wheeler, *Rev. Mod. Phys.*, **21**, 144 (1949).
T-57 G. L. Trigg, *Phys. Rev.*, **86**, 506 (1952).
T-60a V. L. Telegdi, *Proc. Int. Conf. High Eng. Phys.*, Rochester, Interscience, New York, 1960, p. 718.
T-60b V. L. Telegdi, *Proc. Int. Conf. High Eng. Phys.*, Rochester, Interscience, New York, 1960, p. 715.
T-62 V. L. Telegdi, *Phys. Rev. Letters*, **8**, 327 (1962).
W-49 J. Wheeler, *Rev. Mod. Phys.*, **21**, 133 (1949).
W-55 C. S. Wu, in *β and γ Spectroscopy* (edited by K. Siegbahn), North Holland, Amsterdam, 1955.

W-57 Wu, Ambler, Hayward, Hoppes, and Hudson, *Phys. Rev.*, **105**, 1413 (1957).

W-58 L. Wolfenstein, *Nuovo Cimento*, **8**, 882 (1958).

W-59 L. Wolfenstein, *Nuovo Cimento*, **13**, 319 (1959).

W-60 H. A. Weidenmuller, *Phys. Rev. Letters*, **4**, 299 (1960).

W-61a L. Wolfenstein, *Bull. Am. Phys. Soc.*, **6**, 33 (1961).

W-61b H. A. Weidenmuller, *Rev. Mod. Phys.*, **33**, 574 (1961).

Y-59 York, Kim, and Kernan, *Phys. Rev. Letters*, **3**, 288 (1959).

Y-60 D. D. Yovanovitch, *Phys. Rev.*, **117**, 1580 (1960).

Z-61 Zaimidorogo, Kulyukin, Pontecorvo, Sulajev, Filipov, Tsupko-Sitnikov, and Shcherbakov, *J. Expt. Theor. Phys.*, **41**, 1804 (1961).

Z-62 Ziock, Hughes, Prepost, Bailey, and Cleland, *Phys. Rev. Letters*, **8**, 103 (1962).

Appendix: Some Useful Numbers

$$
\begin{aligned}
1\ \text{Mev} &= 1.6021 \times 10^{-6}\ \text{erg} \\
\hbar &= 1.054 \times 10^{-27}\ \text{erg sec} = 6.5817 \times 10^{-22}\ \text{MeV sec} \\
c &= 2.99793 \times 10^{10}\ \text{cm/sec} \\
\hbar c &= 1.973 \times 10^{-11}\ \text{MeV cm} \\
e &= 4.803 \times 10^{-10}\ \text{esu} = 1.6021 \times 10^{-19}\ \text{coulombs} \\
e^2 &= 1.44 \times 10^{-13}\ \text{MeV cm} \\
e^2/\hbar c &= 1/137.037
\end{aligned}
$$

	Electron	Charged pion	Proton
mass, m	9.109×10^{-28} g	2.489×10^{-25} g	1.6724×10^{-24} g
mc^2	0.5110 MeV	139.6 MeV	938.2 MeV
$\hbar/mc$	3.861×10^{-11} cm	1.413×10^{-13} cm	2.103×10^{-14} cm
$\hbar/mc^2$	1.288×10^{-21} sec	4.713×10^{-24} sec	7.014×10^{-25} sec
$e\hbar/2mc$	0.9273×10^{-20} erg/gauss		5.050×10^{-24} erg/gauss
$e\hbar/2mc$	5.788×10^{-15} MeV/gauss		3.152×10^{-18} MeV-gauss
e^2/mc^2	2.818×10^{-13} cm		1.535×10^{-16} cm

Mass Ratios	m_e	m_π	m_p
m_e	1	273.26	1836.12
m_π	3.660×10^{-3}	1	6.719
m_p	5.4462×10^{-4}	0.1488	1

Author Index

Symbols in parentheses refer to references at the end of each chapter.

Subject Index

Italic numbers are used to indicate the pages containing the most important information. Bold numbers in parenthesis refer to sections listed in the table of contents which may be consulted for further detail.